W9-CUK-328

NUCLEAR CHEMISTRY

AND ITS

APPLICATIONS

ADIWES INTERNATIONAL SERIES IN CHEMISTRY

This book is in the
ADDISON-WESLEY SERIES IN CHEMISTRY

Consulting Editor
Francis T. Bonner

NUCLEAR CHEMISTRY
AND ITS
APPLICATIONS

by

M. HAÏSSINSKY

Institut du Radium, Paris

TRANSLATED FROM THE FRENCH

by

D. G. TUCK

University of Nottingham, England

ADDISON-WESLEY PUBLISHING COMPANY, INC.

READING, MASSACHUSETTS · PALO ALTO · LONDON

Printed in the United States of America

Library of Congress Catalog Card No. 62–14060

This volume is an English translation of *La Chimie Nucléaire et ses Applications* by M. Haïssinsky, published and sold by permission of Masson et Cie. Éditeurs, the owner of all rights to publish and sell the same.

FOREWORD TO THE ENGLISH EDITION

Nuclear chemistry has played an important role in nuclear physics since its very inception, and the great developments of nuclear science have provided research materials and techniques that have opened many new areas of chemistry and that have enriched every conventional field of pure and applied chemistry. Thus the subject "Nuclear Chemistry and Its Applications" requires a treatment in depth of a broad front of modern chemical science. Until now, no adequate treatment on such a scale has been available in the English language. The comprehensive and scholarly book presented here under this title could only be written by a nuclear chemist of distinction, a good organizer and writer who has had decades of experience in pure and applied nuclear chemistry.

Dr. Moïse Haïssinsky is indeed a nuclear chemist of distinction, with a commanding position in nuclear chemistry in its traditional and modern areas of activity which comes from his catholicity of chemical interests, his technical imaginativeness, his productive scholarship, and his world-wide scientific ties. His early work involved collaboration with Marie Curie, Enrico Fermi, and Irène and Fréderic Joliot-Curie. He has been for thirty years a leader in the French school of nuclear science at the Institut du Radium, where the techniques of nuclear chemistry and physics developed jointly, and where physical chemistry and chemical physics influenced greatly the flow of research.

Dr. Haïssinsky was the first person to present in a monograph the detailed coverage of nuclear chemistry over its broad front, in his now classic 1957 book *La Chimie Nucléaire et ses Applications* (Masson et Cie., Paris). The present monograph, ably translated by Dr. Dennis G. Tuck of Nottingham University, is based on a completely reworked manuscript carried out in the same bold spirit. In addition, a number of problems for the student are included in an appendix to facilitate the use of the book in course work of the American style.

The present writer holds the same philosophy that Dr. Haïssinsky does, that there are sound historic, educational, and scientific reasons for presenting nuclear chemistry in its broadest form, including nuclear reactions, radioelements, radiochemistry, isotope chemistry, radiation chemistry, and tracer applications. This form gives the student much broader nuclear perspectives, it emphasizes the variety of nuclear techniques that can be used in chemistry, it presents a solid chemical framework for the appreciation of the new developments, and it helps continue the "ésprit de corps" of nuclear chemistry that exists among the professionals and is reflected in the activities of most large research centers. This outstanding book is a very important and timely contribution to research and to teaching in modern chemistry.

Charles D. Coryell

CONTENTS

CHAPTER 1. THE DEVELOPMENT OF RADIOACTIVITY, NUCLEAR PHYSICS, AND NUCLEAR CHEMISTRY

CHAPTER 2. THE FUNDAMENTAL PARTICLES

CHAPTER 3. THE NUCLEUS

CHAPTER 4. SPONTANEOUS RADIOACTIVE TRANSFORMATIONS

CHAPTER 1

THE DEVELOPMENT OF RADIOACTIVITY, NUCLEAR PHYSICS, AND NUCLEAR CHEMISTRY

1-1 Radioactivity and the first radioelements. The progress of science is the result of separate discoveries and inventions, large and small, which form part of a continuous chain of observation, deduction and argument, based in general on experiment and directed either intuitively or by common sense. The majority of such discoveries are the collective result of the endeavors of numerous individuals, working simultaneously or successively, so that it is often difficult and sometimes impossible to identify the origins of a given scientific discovery with certainty. Occasionally, however, there emerges, more or less unexpectedly, a discovery which marks a decisive fresh advance in our knowledge of nature and, in such cases, the origins can be sufficiently clearly identified as to be beyond dispute. Nevertheless, even such singular developments cannot be completely divorced from the development of science as a whole. Sometimes they are dependent upon other fundamental discoveries and are, in any case, only possible when the evolution of science has reached a sufficient level of knowledge and maturity.

The discovery of radioactivity by Henri Becquerel and of radium by Pierre and Marie Curie provide examples which are in many ways typical of such circumstances. The former arose almost accidentally and followed the slightly earlier discovery of x-rays by Roentgen. The subsequent amazing developments in radioactivity were made possible, on the physical side, by the discovery of the electron, itself the result of work first undertaken by Hittorf (1864) and further developed by Hertz, Lenard, Crookes, Lorentz, Zeeman, J. J. Thomson, Perrin, Wilson, Millikan, and a number of others in the period 1897 to 1917. The success of the periodic system (1867) and the resultant discovery of the new elements predicted by Mendeleev were equally important for a proper understanding of the chemical aspects of radioactivity.

It was in 1895 that Roentgen observed that a penetrating radiation was emitted at the anticathode of a Crooke's tube and that this radiation was capable of exciting fluorescence and of affecting photographic plates. On January 20, 1896, Henri Poincaré exhibited one of the plates obtained by Roentgen to the Academy of Sciences in Paris and suggested that it might be interesting to see whether certain bodies emitted x-rays on being made to fluoresce. This remark drew the attention of his colleague, Henri Becquerel, to the salts of uranium, which have a remarkably harmonic series of bands in their absorption and fluorescent spectra. Becquerel [1]* was able to prove that these salts undoubtedly emit radiations

* Bracketed numerals are keyed to the References at the end of the chapter.

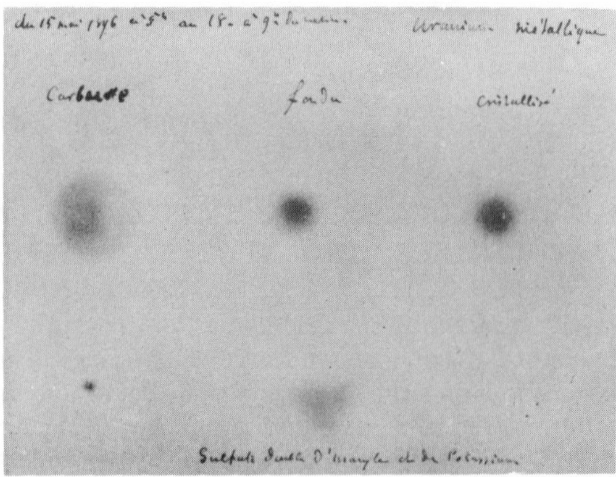

FIG. 1–1. Becquerel's first observation of the effect of uranium and its compounds on a photographic plate.

which affect photographic plates (Fig. 1–1) even through a layer of black paper or various screens of metal and thin glass, and he quickly realized that the emission was unaffected by any of the known modes of excitation, whether electrical, thermal, or actinic. He observed, moreover, that the radiation discharged electrically charged bodies some distance from the uranium, an effect which was used to obtain quantitative information on the intensity of the radiations. Eventually he realized that these effects were due to the element uranium itself, irrespective of its chemical form, and were quite unrelated to the optical properties of the salts.

A short time later, in the early part of 1898, Marie Curie in France and Schmidt in Germany found that thorium possessed similar properties [2]. Furthermore, Marie Curie showed that of the materials in normal laboratory use, only the compounds of uranium and thorium emitted appreciable quantities of Becquerel rays, or, to use the nomenclature which she introduced, are *radioactive*. The atomic origin of radioactivity, suggested by Becquerel, was fully confirmed. Madame Curie proceeded to make the extremely important observation that certain minerals were more radioactive than would have been expected from their uranium and thorium content, and that synthetic chalcolite was less active than the natural material. She suggested in fact that these minerals contained unknown radioactive chemical elements and, in collaboration with her husband, Pierre Curie, she set out to isolate and identify these elements.

The history of these researches can be followed from the daily laboratory notes kept by Pierre and Marie Curie in three small notebooks, now in the keeping of the Laboratoire Curie, Paris (Fig. 1–2). Much has been related of the courage and tenacity of the Curies, and of the miserable conditions under which this work was carried out, in a small shed with neither associates nor material help. What is perhaps even more striking from an examination of these notebooks is the certainty with which they advanced toward the goal which they had set themselves, in a field at that time completely unexplored. The first notebook begins on Decem-

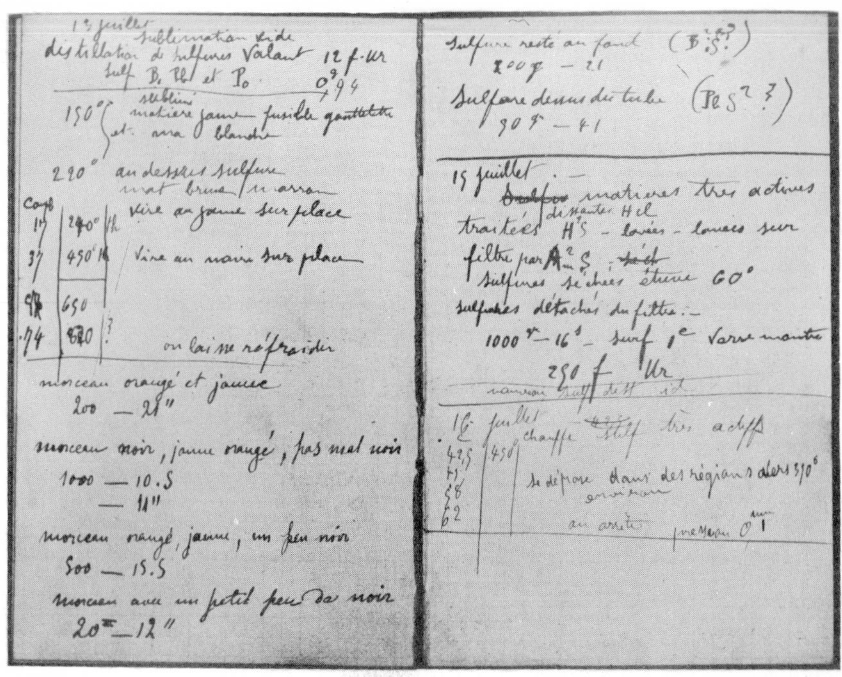

FIG. 1-2. Pages from the laboratory notebooks of Pierre and Marie Curie, with the first mention of the element polonium (July 13, 1898).

ber 16, 1897, and by July 18, 1898, the name of the first new radioactive element, polonium, had already been written alongside bismuth and lead. Some months later the fractionation of barium and radium was suggested, and a polonium source 19,000 times more active than uranium oxide is mentioned. In the course of this work, the Curies had introduced uranium as a standard of radioactivity and initiated the use of the quadrant electrometer with piezoelectric quartz as a precise tool for the measurement of radioactivity; equally, they had noted that radioactivity was unaffected by electrical and magnetic fields, or by x-rays. The techniques of volatilization and of fractionation were applied in concentrating active materials, and an attempt was made to determine the atomic weight of barium containing radium. Toward the end of 1899, the colorizing and chemical action of the radiations was observed, marking the beginnings of radiation chemistry (Section 1-9).

The discovery of polonium was announced by Pierre and Marie Curie to the Academy of Sciences on July 18, 1898. On December 26 of the same year, almost exactly two years after the discovery of x-rays, the discovery of radium (in collaboration with Bémont) was announced. The quantity of this new element present in a barium chloride preparation was sufficient to allow Demarçay to identify a new spectral line at 3818.8 A. Actinium was discovered independently by Debierne in 1899 and by Giesel in 1901. At the beginning of 1900, Rutherford, in Montreal, took up the experiments begun by Owens on the loss of activity in thorium compounds and

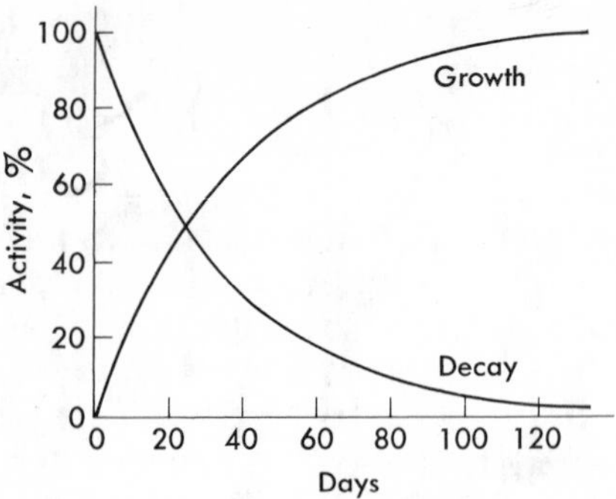

FIG. 1–3. The exponential growth and decay of radioactivity.

identified the first *emanation*, thoron. At almost the same time, radon was discovered by Dorn and actinon by Debierne and Giesel. The discovery of these gases and the proof that the activity of the vessels containing them decayed with time according to an exponential law (Fig. 1–3) resulted in a fuller understanding of the nature of the activity induced in solids adjacent to radium salts (Pierre and Marie Curie, 1899); Rutherford showed that in fact this effect arose from an *active deposit* of short half-life produced by the emanation.

1–2 The radiations and the theory of atomic disintegration. By studying the effect of interposed thin aluminum sheets on the rate of discharge of an electroscope by radiations from uranium, Rutherford showed that the radiation consisted of two components, one much less penetrating than the other. The first of these he named "alpha" and the second "beta." In 1900, Villard and Becquerel detected the existence of a yet more penetrating third component, the so-called "gamma" radiation. Giesel showed that beta rays, like the cathode rays, are deflected in a magnetic field and carry a negative charge. The e/m ratio of these rays was measured by Becquerel, who in this way confirmed their identity with cathode rays, so that the β-rays are fast-moving electrons. Rutherford's experiments established that α-rays are particles carrying a positive charge and having an e/m ratio of $\frac{1}{2}$, where m is the mass of the hydrogen atom. This result confirmed that the α-rays are atomic particles, as had been proposed by Pierre and Marie Curie in 1900. It also appeared to confirm the suggestion made by Rutherford and Soddy that the α-particles are doubly charged helium atoms. This conclusion was completely substantiated by a number of different experiments. First, Ramsay and Travers demonstrated the presence of helium in minerals containing uranium and thorium, and Ramsay and Soddy followed this by detecting the accumulation of the gas in a 30-mg radium source which had been sealed up for some months. Debierne showed that helium is also produced by actinium. Rutherford and Royds detected helium spectroscopically in an airtight vessel containing radium in a thin-walled glass ampoule through which the α-rays could pass.

Later (1908 to 1910) Rutherford and Geiger constructed a counter for α-particles, similar in principle to the Geiger-Müller counter (Section 12–6), and in this way established that the number of α-particles emitted per second by one gram of radium is 3.4×10^{10}, a value close to that currently accepted. The same result was obtained by counting the scintillations produced when the rays strike a screen of fluorescent zinc sulfide, a phenomenon discovered independently by Elster and Geitel, by Crookes, and by Giesel in 1903. From the total charge carried by a known flux of α-particles, they were able to deduce that each particle was in fact doubly charged and consequently had a mass of four. Finally, in 1908, Dewar measured the rate of helium generation in a radium source and showed that this rate is in good agreement with the known rate of α-emission only if the α-particle and the helium atom are in fact identical.

During this same period, Crookes had achieved the chemical separation of a β-active substance from a sample of uranium and succeeded in concentrating it free from uranium. He found that in time the substance lost its activity, which had fallen by half after 24 days (the *half-life* for the decay) while the uranium regained its original activity at exactly the same rate. Analogous experiments were carried out by Rutherford and Soddy in their discovery and isolation of thorium-X; in this case, the half-life for decay and recovery was four days. Furthermore, as the emanating power of the thorium-X decreased, that of thorium grew with the same half-life.

Finally, Pierre Curie and Laborde showed that radioactive sources continually generate heat, to the extent of about 100 calories per hour for a gram of radium. This release of heat is virtually constant over a period of years and is equivalent to the deposition of a considerable amount of energy, in apparent contradiction to the principle of the conservation of energy.

A review of these experimental facts led Rutherford and Soddy to formulate the theory of *radioactive transformation*, which had already been suggested in a less precise fashion by the Curies [3]. This extremely important theory has been completely verified by every subsequent experiment. According to Rutherford and Soddy, radioactive bodies are gradually changing at a rate which is constant for each species; the products are atoms which are chemically different from the parent material due to the emission of radiations which are either atoms (α-particles) or electrons. Changes in the activity of a given source are therefore associated with the partial or total disappearance of one atomic species and an increase in the quantity of another. An atom of uranium (or thorium) gives rise to a series of atoms of lower and lower mass, since in these cases the daughter elements are themselves radioactive. The loss of weight of the source cannot be detected, either because the changes are extremely slow, as in the case of uranium or radium, or because the quantities involved are unweighably small (radon, polonium). The energy release, which is related to the change of mass, was more easily understood at a later date on the basis of the Einstein theory (Sections 1–4 and 2–3). The statistical nature of the radioactive disintegration process was established by Schweidler in 1905.

The disintegration theory led to an understanding of the relationships between almost all the radioelements then known, and it became possible to arrange them in three *radioactive series* or families, starting with uranium, actinium, and thorium, although the detailed completion of these series came later (Chapter 7). Only potassium and rubidium, the β-activity of which had been detected in 1906 by Campbell, remained unequivocally outside these series.

The extreme boldness of the theory of radioactive disintegrations can be fully realized only if it is remembered that at the time many chemists, including some of the most influential, regarded the atomic structure of matter as a rather fanciful idea, while others failed to distinguish clearly between atoms and molecules.

1–3 Isotopes. The disintegration theory put forward by Rutherford and Soddy was dependent on the fact that the "new" elements, radium, polonium, and actinium, are not molecular combinations of other atoms with helium, but are as chemically well defined as uranium, thorium, or the stable elements. The arrangement of these elements in the periodic system consequently presented no difficulties. Polonium, initially thought to be chemically similar to bismuth, was subsequently shown to be identical with the radiotellurium which Marckwald had obtained by spontaneous deposition upon bismuth. The existence of this higher homologue of tellurium had been predicted in 1891 by Mendeleev, who named it eka-tellurium and allotted it an atomic weight of 212 (cf., the value of 210 later found). Radium was immediately recognized as homologous with barium, and actinium with lanthanum. Finally, the discovery of argon by Ramsay and Strutt (Lord Rayleigh) in 1894, of helium by Ramsay and by Cleve in 1895, and of the other inert gases, neon, krypton, and xenon, by Ramsay and Travers in 1898 led to the classification of the emanations as members of this group of elements.

The arrangement in the periodic system of other radioelements which had been discovered was by no means as obvious. Among these were uranium-X, mentioned above, radiothorium, identified by Ramsay and Hahn, and ionium, discovered independently by Boltwood, and by Marckwald and Keetman. These three radioactive species showed the same chemical and (nonradioactive) physical properties as thorium, and every attempt to separate them from the latter failed; particularly careful experiments were carried out by Hahn and by McCoy and Ross with radiothorium in 1906 to 1907. In 1910, Marckwald and Soddy showed that the chemical properties of mesothorium-1 are identical with those of radium, and in 1912, Fleck demonstrated the inseparability of thorium-B (and actinium-B) and lead, of radium-E and bismuth, of mesothorium-2 and actinium, of radioactinium and thorium, and of radium-A and polonium. Some time earlier, Herschfinkel had failed in attempts to separate radium-D from lead; this negative result was confirmed by Hevesy and Paneth, who tried some 20 different chemical methods and at the same time were able to establish the identical electrochemical behavior of these species. Here, then, was an extremely difficult and confusing problem: was the product of each of the 30 or more radioactive transformations to be regarded as a distinct chemical element despite the fact that the number of places between lead and uranium in the periodic table is strictly limited?

The idea that these inseparable elements might in fact be identical began to gain ground. Stromholm and Svedberg, having shown that thorium-X formed mixed crystals with barium salts, suggested that the identity of behavior found with certain radioactive substances might also apply to the stable elements of the periodic system, so that each would be in fact a mixture of several elements. The measured atomic weight would then represent the mean of the weights of the components, and in this way the three anomalous pairs of elements then known in the periodic table (A-K, Co-Ni, Te-I) could be explained. In 1912, Soddy developed a coherent and definitive theory of the nonhomogeneity of chemical elements, based upon the atomic model proposed the year before by Rutherford, in which a clear distinction was made between the chemical and the radioactive or nuclear properties of the atom. The latter originate from the center of the atom, the positively charged nucleus, and are the result of irreversible changes; the former are connected with the orbital electrons which can undergo reversible transformations such as changes of valency. The nuclear charge was identified as the algebraic sum of the positive and negative charges and, according to Soddy, atoms which have the same overall charge but which differ in the number of charges of each sign are chemically identical, and the elements are then *isotopic;* that is to say they occupy the same place in the periodic table. We shall see throughout this book that the concept of isotopy has been absolutely fundamental to much of the subsequent development of chemistry, even though later research has shown that isotopes do not in fact have absolutely identical chemical properties (Chapter 9). The relation established by Moseley in 1913 between the atomic numbers of the elements and their characteristic x-ray frequencies placed a definitive limit on the number of existing chemical elements and provided excellent confirmation of Soddy's theory.

The *laws of radioactive displacement,* which were stated independently by Soddy and by Fajans, and in a less definite form by Russell and Hevesy, depended closely on these developments (Fig. 1-4). According to these laws, the α-disintegration of an atom A results in an atom B which is two places to the left of A in the periodic table; the product of β-emission is removed one place to the right. As a result of these new ideas, all the known radioelements could be placed in the periodic system, each place in the table being occupied by a number of isotopes. It was also possible to work out the details of the three radioactive series and the existence of new radioelements could be predicted in those cases where the transformation apparently did not obey the laws. For example, uranium-II had been regarded as the product of the β-decay of uranium-X, a thorium isotope, despite the fact that according to the displacement law this transformation should have resulted in an isotope of ekatantalum. Fajans and Göhring showed that in fact the so-called uranium-X was a mixture of two radioelements, uranium-X_1, a thorium isotope, and uranium-X_2, the first known isotope of protactinium, which itself decayed with a very short half-life (1.13 min), emitting a β-particle and forming uranium-II. A similar gap was found between uranium-Y, another thorium isotope, and

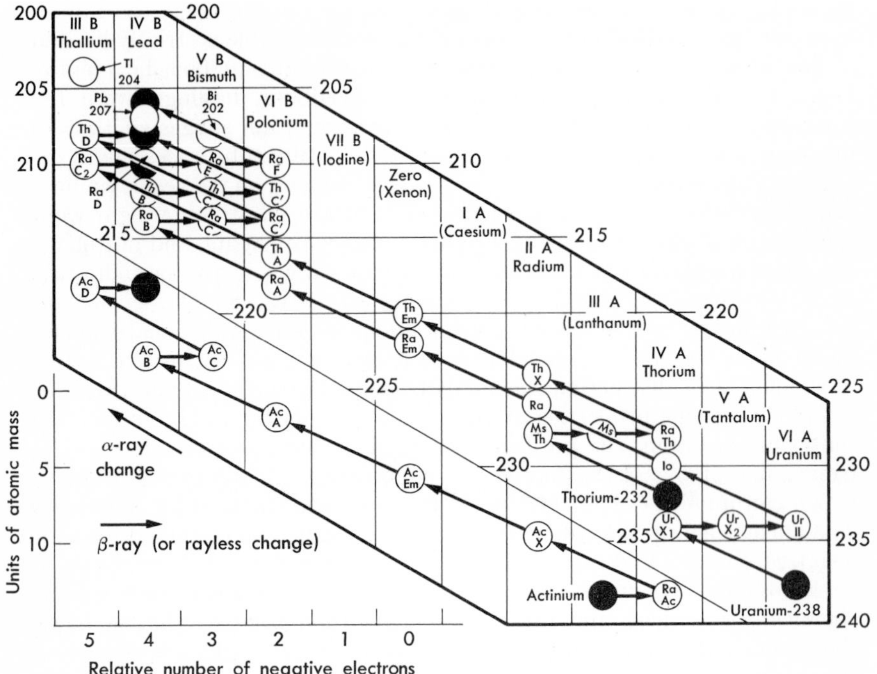

FIG. 1–4. The radioactive displacement laws (after F. Soddy). "All elements in the same place in the periodic table are chemically nonseparable and (probably) spectroscopically indistinguishable."

actinium; this was filled in 1918 when Hahn and Meitner and (independently) Soddy and Cranston discovered protactinium-231. A little later, in 1921, Hahn identified uranium-Z, a new isotope of protactinium resulting from the γ-decay of uranium-X_2, which is the excited state of the nucleus of uranium-Z. This was the first recognition of the phenomenon of *nuclear isomerism,* which occurs frequently among the artificial radioelements (Section 4–9).

The work of Richards, Fajans, and Honigschmid (and others) on the atomic weight of lead obtained from various radioactive minerals showed that the concept of isotopy could be extended to the stable elements. It was found that the atomic weight of lead varied according to its origin, although the chemical properties and the spectra were constant. Since the atomic weights of the three lead isotopes which are the end-members of the radioactive series (RaG, ThD, AcD) are 206, 208, and 207, the atomic weight of the lead depends on the uranium and thorium contents of the minerals.

A new and important aspect of this subject opened in 1912. While studying the mass:charge ratio of the positive ions produced in neon at low pressure by an intense electric field, J. J. Thomson obtained two parabolas (Section 9–10), apparently corresponding to masses of 20 and 22. The suggestion that neon is a mixture of two components was confirmed by Aston. In his first experiments the gas was fractionated by diffusion through a series of clay pipes, and after several months two fractions were obtained with a difference of 0.7% in the atomic weights. Aston subsequently constructed the first *mass spectrograph*, in which Thomson's parabolas were replaced by beams of ions, and confirmed unambiguously the complexity of neon, chlorine, argon, xenon, and other elements. This work has since been extended by Dempster, Mattauch, Bainbridge, Nier, and others (Section 9–10).

Aston's work had, moreover, demonstrated the important fact that the atomic weights of individual isotopes are very close to integral numbers. It was therefore possible to refute the most substantial argument against Prout's hypothesis (1815) that there is a single fundamental unit of matter. Opponents of this hypothesis had been quick to point out that it was in contradiction to the nonintegral atomic weights of a large number of elements (taking the mass of hydrogen as unity).

The spectroscopic identification by Urey in 1932 of the heavy isotope of hydrogen of mass 2 (named deuterium) was an important development in the study of isotopes. We shall later see the fundamental part which the deuterium atom and ion have played in both chemical and physical research.

1–4 The structure of the atom, and the quantum theory. The elementary kinetic theory of gases treats the atom as an elastic sphere which obeys the normal laws of mechanics, and from this simple assumption it is possible to deduce values for the mass and radii of atoms and molecules and for Avogadro's number. The shortcomings of this approach were, however, quite obvious, since the complex nature of the atom could be shown by such phenomena as electrolytic dissociation, cathode rays, positive rays, and radioactivity, all of which suggested that the components of the atom carry electrical charges of opposite sign. In 1897, J. J. Thomson put forward a model of the atom as a sphere of positive electricity inside which the electrons are kept in equilibrium by quasi-elastic forces.

In experiments on the passage of α-particles through thin metal foils, Rutherford and Marsden found that in addition to the normal slight deviations which occur, particles were occasionally deflected through angles as large as 150°. These results implied the existence of an intense electrical field, more powerful than that deduced from Thomson's model, and Rutherford suggested that the positive charge is concentrated in a very small volume at the center of the atom, forming a *nucleus* whose dimensions are of the order of 10^{-13} cm (Fig. 1–5). The electrons, then, are distributed around the nucleus in a comparatively large space corresponding to the volume of the atom itself, whose radius is of the order of 10^{-8} cm. The positive charge of the nucleus is equal to the total charge of the orbital electrons and is also equal, as had been suggested by Van den Broek, to the atomic number of the element in the periodic system, as defined by Moseley's law. It was not possible, however, to explain the stability of the atom from Rutherford's model on the basis of classical mechanics. In order to understand the emission spectra of atoms, it was necessary to assume that the electrons revolve in circular or elliptical orbits around

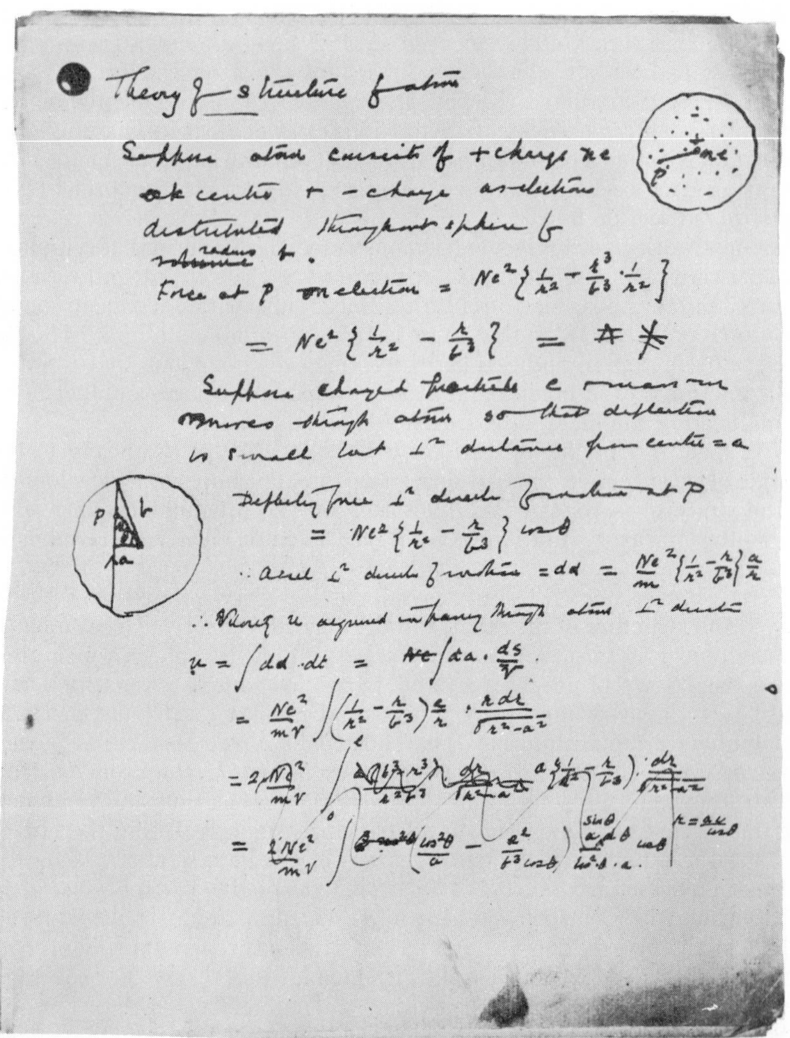

Theory of structure of atom

Suppose atom consists of + charge Ne at centre & − charge as electrons distributed throughout sphere of radius b.

Force at P on electron $= Ne^2\left\{\frac{1}{r^2} - \frac{r^3}{b^3}\cdot\frac{1}{r^2}\right\}$

$= Ne^2\left\{\frac{1}{r^2} - \frac{r}{b^3}\right\}$

Suppose charged particle e mass m moves through atom so that deflection is small but ⊥ distance from centre = a

Deflecting force ⊥ direction of motion at P

$= Ne^2\left\{\frac{1}{r^2} - \frac{r}{b^3}\right\}\cos\theta$

∴ accel ⊥ direction of motion $= d\alpha = \frac{Ne^2}{m}\left\{\frac{1}{r^2} - \frac{r}{b^3}\right\}\frac{a}{r}$

∴ Velocity u acquired in passing through atom ⊥ direction

$u = \int d\alpha \cdot dt = \int d\alpha \cdot \frac{ds}{V}$

$= \frac{Ne^2}{mV}\int\left(\frac{1}{r^2} - \frac{r}{b^3}\right)\frac{a}{r}\cdot\frac{r\,dr}{\sqrt{r^2-a^2}}$

$= \frac{2Ne^2}{mV}\int a\left\{\frac{1}{r^2} - \frac{r}{b^3}\right\}\cdot\frac{dr}{\sqrt{r^2-a^2}}$

$= \frac{2Ne^2}{mV}\int\left(\frac{\cos^2\theta}{a} - \frac{a^2}{b^3\cos\theta}\right)$

Fig. 1–5. Lord Rutherford's preliminary notes on the structure of the atom (early in 1911). [D. J. Price, *Notes and Records Roy. Soc.*, (*London*), **10,** 139 (1953)]

the nucleus (Maxwell), but if this is the case, the kinetic energy of the electrons should be continually decreasing, resulting in the orbits becoming smaller and smaller so that the electrons, attracted by the positive nucleus, should finally fall into the latter.

These difficulties were overcome by Bohr, who saw in the quantum theory a means of establishing the laws which govern the movements of electrons in their orbits. While studying the relation between the energy and the entropy of a radiating oscillator, Planck (1889) had introduced two universal constants into the laws of radiation; one is known as the

Boltzmann constant ($k = R/N$) and the other as Planck's constant, h, which expresses the elementary quantum of action, the product of energy and time. This was the starting point of the quantum theory, which was to overthrow the classical view of the continuous variation of energy. The fundamental significance of the new theory was illustrated in 1905 when Einstein put forward the quantum interpretation of the photoelectric effect. Einstein boldly revived the idea of the discontinuous nature of light, which had been abandoned since the work of Huygens, and assumed that each particle of light (or photon) striking the surface of the metal with sufficient energy releases an electron which carries away the excess energy. The quantum theory has also proved extremely useful in understanding the specific heat of solids and gases (Einstein, Born and Karman, Debye and Nernst), and has led to the interpretation and calculation of the chemical constants, and hence the absolute entropies, introduced by Nernst in his third law of thermodynamics (Sackur, Tetrode).

While accepting Rutherford's model, Bohr rejected the classical laws for the movement of electrons in the atom and suggested that the emission of a quantum of light occurs only when an electron passes from one orbit to another. The number of orbits and the energy levels to which they correspond, and consequently the energies of the radiation related to the electronic transitions, are limited and defined by the quantum theory. The three postulates set out by Bohr to sum up his ideas, completely revolutionary at that point, led to the correct calculation of the distribution of the spectral lines in the hydrogen spectrum, and from the charge and mass of the electron, Rydberg's constant was calculated from Planck's constant to within 1%. The theory was confirmed by the elegant experiments of Franck and Hertz on the collisions between atoms and electrons, which may result either in the emission of light or in ionization. Sommerfeld made further progress in considering the elliptical movement of electrons and by using two *quantum numbers.* To these were added two others when Goudsmit and Uhlenbeck introduced the hypothesis of the rotation of the electron around itself, setting up a mechanical moment (spin) and a magnetic moment. These developments were later to have profound repercussions on theories of the nucleus which are largely founded, formally at least, on similar concepts.

The same is also true of the later extension of the quantum theory, which led to the development of wave mechanics. We shall note here only the most important steps. These include Pauli's exclusion principle (1924); the dualistic nature of matter-particles and associated waves (de Broglie, 1925); the establishment of the fundamental equation of wave mechanics by Schrödinger and the introduction of wave functions (1926); the new matrix mechanics of Born and Heisenberg, and Heisenberg's uncertainty principle; the Heitler-London theory of quantized exchange forces in the formation of homopolar chemical bonds (1927); the discovery by G. P. Thomson and by Davisson and Germer of the diffraction of electrons by crystals (1927) analogous to the diffraction of x-rays, which had been first observed by Laue in 1912; Bose-Einstein statistics and Fermi-Dirac statistics for fundamental particles (Section 2–3). To these must be added the relation between mass and energy, deduced by Einstein from his theory of relativity; this relationship is fundamental to the theory of nuclear transformations (Section 2–2). The development of the various theories on the structure of the nucleus will be described in Chapter 3.

1–5 Alpha, beta, and gamma spectra. The historical development of knowledge of the properties of α-particles is much simpler than is the case for β- and γ-rays. Within the limits of the experimental techniques available in the early days of radioactivity, the α-particles from any given substance appeared as a homogeneous group which could be characterized by the energy or velocity and hence by the range in various substances. This latter quantity can be obtained by measuring the ionizing power at various points along the path of a collimated beam of particles (Bragg, 1904). It was not until 1916 that Rutherford and Wood found that thorium-C + C′ emits a small group of α-particles with a range greater than the mean. Similar long-range particles were later also found in radium-C + C′. This emission is always of a much lower intensity than the main group of α-particles, so that the Geiger-Nuttall relationship can still be applied; this states that the logarithm of the range of the α-particles is a linear function of the logarithm of the decay constant of the emitting element.

By studying the effect of a magnetic field on the path of the α-particles from thorium-C, Rosenblum (1929) showed that the α-spectrum of this element possessed considerable fine structure and contained a number of groups of particles, differing in energy by as much as several hundred kev. This effect was later investigated in more detail by Rosenblum himself, by Rutherford, and others for both natural and artificial α-emitters; the correct wave-mechanical explanation was given independently in 1928 by Gamow, and by Gurney and Condon (Section 4–6). This theory correctly explained the whole of the process of α-emission to a satisfactory accuracy and related the fine structure to the associated γ-ray emission.

The β-spectra, on the other hand, are much more complex, and the study of β-emission has been a slow and arduous one, both from the theoretical and the experimental point of view. One difficulty lay in the nonlinear path of the β-rays, since they are easily deviated by nuclei or even by periphery electrons, especially if they are of low energy. Magnetic measurements, moreover, showed that for a given substance, there is a continuous energy spectrum of β-particles; superimposed on this are groups of monoenergetic rays. The electrons which give rise to the continuous spectrum are now known to be emitted directly from the nucleus as a result of disintegration, while the others are secondary in origin, arising from the *internal conversion* of the γ-rays which are also emitted (Section 4–8). This conclusion was reached only after considerable research and controversy (Ellis, Meitner and others). The most difficult and puzzling feature, however, was the spectrum of the primary electrons, since this appeared to be in contradiction to the principle of conservation of energy. One of the first explanations put forward was that the primary electrons are all emitted with an energy equal to the upper limit of the spectrum, and that part of this energy is dissipated in secondary processes, but the calorimetric work of Ellis and Wooster (1928) and of Meitner and Orthmann (1930) demonstrated the fallacy of this hypothesis. Bohr even went so far as to suggest that the conservation principle might not apply to nuclear phenomena but this rather defeatist idea was rejected, and finally Pauli (1933) proposed that the emission of each electron is accompanied by the simultaneous emission of an uncharged particle, of very small mass, which carries away the excess energy. In 1934, Fermi put forward a theory of β-emission based on the existence of this hypothetical particle, the *neutrino* (Sections 2–6 and 4–2).

In addition to the authors already mentioned, de Broglie, Compton, Chadwick, Geiger, Bothe, Skobelzyne, Thibaud, and a number of others made important contributions to the study of the β-spectra of the natural radioelements. This work was often closely connected with studies of the γ-ray spectra, and as with α-emission, the γ-rays associated with β-decay yielded information on the energy level differences in nuclei; such studies form part of what is now called *nuclear spectroscopy*.

The recoil of atoms as a result of radioactive disintegration was observed by Rutherford in 1905 and was later studied by Hahn, Debierne, Russ and Makower (1909), and (especially) Wertenstein. Fajans and others made use of the recoil effect in the separation of a disintegration product from its mother substance.

Research on all the radiations was considerably facilitated by Wilson's invention of the *cloud chamber*. In this apparatus, the paths of the particles or rays are made visible by the condensation of water vapor on the ions which are formed. The use of Geiger-Müller counters and more recently of scintillation counters has, of course, now become widespread, especially since the discovery of artificial radioactivity.

Cosmic radiation was discovered by Hess and Kolhoerster in the period 1911 to 1914. With the aid of meteorological balloons, these authors observed that with increasing altitude the weak spontaneous ionization of the atmospheric air first of all diminished, reached a minimum some hundreds of meters above the ground and then began to rise again; at 6000 meters the ionization is about 40 times stronger than at sea level. Kolhoerster attributed this effect to a highly penetrating radiation originating outside our planet. The strong penetration was confirmed by Millikan and Cameron when this work was taken up again in 1925; at this stage, the radiation was thought to be uniquely electromagnetic. In 1927, Skobelzyne initiated the use of the Wilson cloud chamber in cosmic ray research and Bothe and Kolhoerster introduced Geiger counters. Since that time there has been rapid and almost unceasing progress, due to the use of techniques such as counting and registering equipment (Regener, 1928), simple coincidence circuits (Bothe and Kolhoerster), multiple coincidence circuits (Rossi, 1932), cloud chambers controlled by the discharge of two counters in coincidence (Blackett and Occhialini, 1933), and nuclear photographic plates of extremely high sensitivity (Powell and Occhialini, 1946). Research at high altitudes and below sea level in various parts of the world has led to the discovery of new fundamental effects such as the effect of latitude and of direction, and the existence of showers and multiple showers (Auger). The very complex nature of the cosmic radiation in terms of both composition and energy has been realized, and among other results have been the identification of new elementary particles such as the positron and the mesons. These recent developments are closely connected with those in the field of nuclear physics and will be discussed in detail later (Section 2–8).

1–6 The transmutation of atoms, and artificial radioactivity. It was shown by Marsden in 1914 that when the α-particles from radium-C strike hydrogen, or some hydrogeneous material, hydrogen atoms are knocked out of the target; in accordance with the laws of the conservation of energy, these "natural" H atoms have high kinetic energy, and their range can be determined by using a fluorescent screen of zinc sulfide. Using similar techniques, Rutherford bombarded nitrogen gas with the same α-particles and observed scintillations corresponding to H atoms with a much greater range than seemed possible for "natural" H atoms. Rutherford suggested that when an α-particle strikes the nucleus of a nitrogen atom, it knocks out a hydrogen atom and in this way forms a new nucleus. Later work by Blackett, using a Wilson cloud chamber, showed that the new species formed is an oxygen atom, by the reaction

$$_7N^{14} + {}_2He^4 \rightarrow {}_8O^{17} + {}_1H^1. \tag{1–1}$$

This first artificial transmutation of the so-called modern alchemy was carried out in the extremely simple apparatus shown in Fig. 1–6. Rutherford and his collaborators subsequently extended this work using targets of boron, fluorine, sodium, aluminum, and phosphorus, while beryllium, magnesium, and silicon were studied by Kirsch and Petterson.

Since the energies of the natural α-particles are always less than 10 Mev, such investigations were limited to the light elements, and at the same time, the α-particle remained the only available bombarding particle. On the basis of Gamow's theory of α-particle emission, Cockroft suggested that if protons could be accelerated to a few hundred kev, they would then be able to penetrate into nuclei such as lithium and boron and bring about

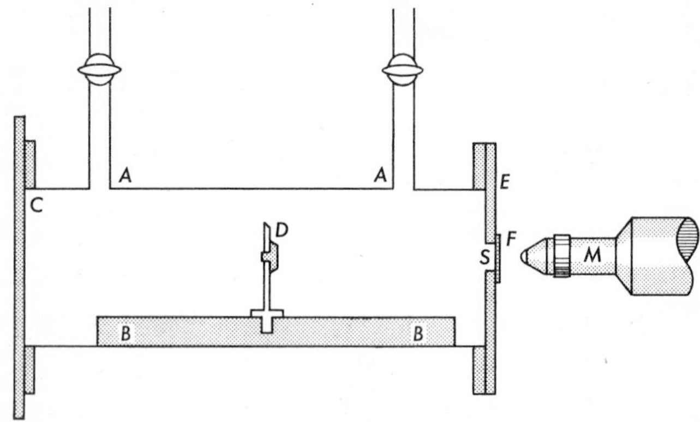

FIG. 1–6. The apparatus used by Rutherford for studying the disintegration of nitrogen; D, α-particle source; S, a screen of ZnS immediately opposite an aperture in the metal plate E; the vessel $ACBE$ contains nitrogen gas. [*Phil. Mag.*, **37,** 543 (1919)]

their disintegration. In 1932, Cockroft and Walton constructed an accelerator for positive ions by applying a voltage of 500 kv across a small discharge tube. Lithium targets were bombarded with the protons produced in this apparatus, and scintillations corresponding to α-particles with energies of 125 kev were observed:

$$_3\text{Li}^7 + {}_1\text{H}^1 \rightarrow 2\ {}_2\text{He}^4. \tag{1-2}$$

The measurement of the energy of the two particles emitted led to the first direct confirmation of the Einstein equation relating mass and energy (Section 5–1). Positive results were also obtained in the bombardment of boron and fluorine. In the same year, Urey had discovered deuterium, and Rutherford and Oliphant bombarded this element with its own accelerated ions.

About the same time that these major advances were being made, there occurred a startling series of discoveries which were to change completely the orientation of chemistry and physics. Not least in importance are the political and economic consequences which continue to follow these scientific developments. In 1930, Bothe and Becker bombarded a number of light elements, notably beryllium, with α-particles from polonium and noticed the emission of a low intensity radiation whose penetrating power was greater than that of the strongest natural γ-rays. This radiation was initially believed to be itself electromagnetic. These experiments were taken up by Irène Curie and Frederic Joliot, who found that the effect of this radiation on paraffin was to produce high-energy protons, a phenomenon which could hardly be attributed to γ-rays. Chadwick confirmed this result and found similar effects when lithium, beryllium, or boron were substituted for paraffin. Furthermore, it was shown that this secondary radiation consisted of uncharged recoil atoms whose mass was very close to that of the hydrogen atom. Chadwick explained these results in terms of a hypothesis which Rutherford had proposed in 1920; in this, the existence of a neutral elementary particle, the *neutron*, believed to be the extremely stable combination of a proton and an electron, had been postulated. The nature and properties of the neutron will be discussed in Chapters 2, 5, and 11.

A short time later, while investigating cosmic radiation with a cloud chamber situated in an intense magnetic field, Anderson identified the track of positively charged high-energy particles whose specific ionization was practically equal to that of the electron. These particles were identified as the positive electrons or *positrons*, which Dirac had already predicted on theoretical grounds. According to this author, the interaction of a photon of energy greater than 1 Mev with a nucleus produces a negative-positive electron pair, and conversely a collision between an electron and a positron results in the disappearance of these two particles with the appearance of two photons each with an energy of 500 kev. A number of workers, including Blackett and Occhialini, Anderson, I. Curie and Joliot, and Chadwick, confirmed the pair production, while the converse phenomenon, called *annihilation*, was identified by Joliot and by Thibaud (Section 2–4).

In the course of work on the transmutations brought about by the bombardment of light elements with α-particles from a very strong polo-

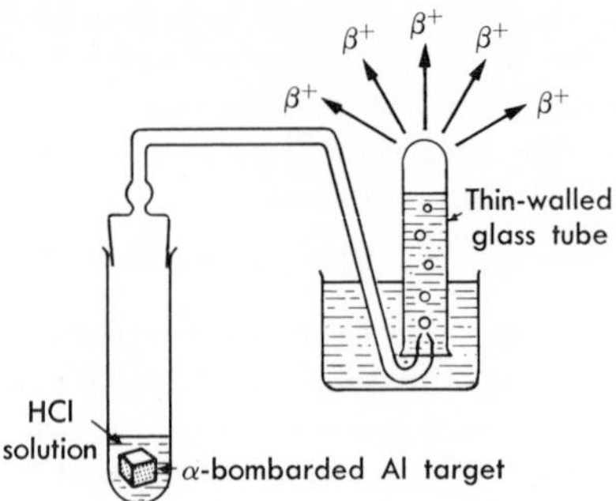

FIG. 1–7. Chemical proof of the transmutation of aluminum into radiophosphorus by bombardment. [I. Curie and F. Joliot, Nobel Prize Lecture, 1935]

nium source, I. Curie and Joliot found themselves faced with a number of apparently irreconcilable results. The bombardment of aluminum (mass 27), for example, resulted in the emission of a neutron and a positron and, since the mass of the latter is negligible, this seemed to imply the formation of a hitherto unknown phosphorus isotope of mass 30 ($27 + 4 = 30 + 1$). It was quickly realized that the positron emission was in fact delayed, continuing after the removal of the polonium and subsequently decreasing with a half-life of three minutes. The Joliot-Curies concluded that the phosphorus formed was not a stable atom as in the transmutations studied earlier, but was in fact a radioactive isotope which decayed by positron emission. This suggestion was confirmed by a very simple and elegant chemical experiment; the irradiated aluminum target was dissolved in hydrochloric acid and the radioactive element thus converted into phosphine, which was swept out in a stream of gas (Fig. 1–7). In this way radiophosphorus was separated and identified, and artificial radioactivity established beyond doubt. Similar results were obtained with boron, which yields radionitrogen, and with magnesium, which gives radioaluminum.

These authors suggested that bombardments with other particles such as protons, deuterons, or neutrons might well also give rise to artificial radioactive isotopes. This was confirmed by experiments carried out in other laboratories and there was a resultant rapid increase in the number of artificial radioelements known. In particular, immediately after the pioneering work of the Joliot-Curies, Fermi and his collaborators (Amaldi, d'Agostino, Rasetti, and Segrè) began a series of systematic experiments in which all the readily available elements were bombarded with neutrons from a radon-beryllium source. After some early setbacks with the lightest elements, they succeeded in producing 37 active species from the 63 elements examined and in chemically identifying most of these. The anomalies which were observed in some cases, and which apparently depended on the nature of the surrounding material, led them to the discovery of the peculiar properties of slow neutrons, which was to result in the development of a new and important chapter in nuclear physics (Sections 2–5 and 11–10). It was only in 1939 that the extraordinary reaction of these neutrons with uranium-235, which undergoes splitting or fission of the nucleus into two parts, was discovered.

1–7 Fission and the transuranium elements. In the Nobel Prize lecture delivered in Stockholm in 1935, Frederic Joliot expressed his faith "in believing that scientists will eventually be able to build up or break down the elements quite freely, and that as a result, transmutations of an explosive nature, resulting from nuclear chain reactions, will be possible." This prediction was first substantiated in 1942 with the construction of a nuclear pile or reactor in which a controlled nuclear chain reaction takes place. Against the immense potential good that has been made available to the world must be set the tragedy implicit in the explosion of atomic bombs over the Japanese cities of Hiroshima and Nagasaki some three years later. The scientific developments which resulted in these events are closely connected with the discovery of the transuranium elements.

Fermi and his collaborators found that the bombardment of uranium with slow neutrons gives rise to several β-active products with half-lives of 10 seconds, 40 seconds, 13 minutes, 90 minutes, and one longer-lived species. An appreciable fraction of the 13- and 90-minute activities could be coprecipitated with manganese dioxide in conditions under which the natural radioelements related to uranium do not appear to be carried down. This was taken as evidence of the formation of a new element, of atomic number 93, the higher homologue of manganese; this ekarhenium, which was named ausonium (Ao), should give element 94 (ekaosmium or hesperium, Hs) by β-emission. This conclusion was criticized by Noddack [4], who pointed out that many elements of medium atomic weight are carried down by MnO_2 and that before the formation of element 93 could be said to be established, all the known elements should be systematically eliminated. Although this criticism was later shown to be a very valid one, it was not then considered to be a serious objection in the light of the views then held on the stability of nuclei. Grosse and Agruss [5] criticized Fermi's conclusion for other reasons, since protactinium also coprecipitates with manganese dioxide, and with rhenium sulfide. Further experiments by d'Agostino and Segrè [6] showed, however, that the 13-min activity could be separated from zirconium by phosphate precipitation in conditions under which protactinium is coprecipitated.

A systematic study of the "transuranics" was then undertaken by Hahn, Meitner, and Strassman [7, 8, 9, 10, 11]; the half-lives of the various activities were measured, a number of new activities identified, and from the chemical evidence their initial conclusion was that Fermi's hypothesis was correct. The following disintegration schemes, which extend at least to element 97, were proposed:

$$_{92}\text{U} + \text{n} \rightarrow {}_{92}\text{U} \xrightarrow[\text{10 sec}]{\beta} {}_{93}\text{Ao} \xrightarrow[\text{2.2 min}]{\beta} {}_{94}\text{Hs} \xrightarrow[\text{59 min}]{\beta}$$

$$_{95}\text{Eka-Ir} \xrightarrow[\text{66 hr}]{\beta} {}_{96}\text{Eka-Pt} \xrightarrow[\text{2.5 hr}]{\beta} {}_{97}\text{Eka-Au(?)}, \qquad (1\text{–}3)$$

$$_{92}\text{U} + \text{n} \rightarrow {}_{92}\text{U} \xrightarrow[\text{40 sec}]{\beta} {}_{93}\text{Ao} \xrightarrow[\text{16 min}]{\beta} {}_{94}\text{Hs} \xrightarrow[\text{5.7 hr}]{\beta} {}_{95}\text{Eka-Ir(?)}, \qquad (1\text{–}4)$$

$$_{92}\text{U} + \text{n} \rightarrow {}_{92}\text{U} \xrightarrow[\text{23 min}]{\beta} {}_{93}\text{Ao(?)}. \qquad (1\text{–}5)$$

These series, however, already seemed rather unlikely, for a number of reasons. They implied, for example, the formation of a number of isomers of uranium and its daughter products, since in view of the low abundances of U^{234} and U^{235} [12] it seemed reasonable to attribute the neutron capture process to U^{238} alone. On the basis of what was then known about the physics of the nucleus, it was not easy to understand why the capture of a neutron should result in five successive β-disintegrations. The chemical characterization of the active products, the number of which continued to increase, left much to be desired and was hedged about with considerable uncertainty [13]. The irradiation of thorium with fast neutrons also produced several β-emitters, the identification of which was not easily accomplished; since natural thorium has effectively only one isotope, of mass 232, it was again necessary to assume that several isomers had been formed.

At this stage, I. Curie and Savitch [14, 15, 16] isolated a strong β-emitter, with a half-life of 3.5 hours, from the products of the neutron irradiation of uranium. This activity could be separated from those which had been ascribed to the "transuranics," and many of the properties corresponded to those of the rare earth elements; coprecipitation with lanthanum oxalate, for example, carried down the active material completely. These authors showed that the activity was not due to actinium, the higher homologue of lanthanum, since it could be separated from actinium by fractional precipitation, nor was it lanthanum itself since the activity of fractions containing equal quantities of lanthanum was not always the same. Faced with this situation, Hahn and Strassmann [17] repeated their earlier experiments and detected a radioactive alkaline earth element, which although initially regarded as a radium isotope was in fact eventually shown to be separable from radium but not from barium. Here then, was chemical proof that an element of atomic number less than 36 is formed as the result of the neutron irradiation of uranium.

Directly after the announcement of this startling result, Meitner and Frisch [18] gave the correct explanation of the experimental data, namely that the uranium nucleus undergoes *fission* into two fragments whose total nuclear charge is equal to 92. This interpretation was based on Bohr's liquid-drop theory of the nucleus (Section 3–10), and shortly afterwards Bohr and Wheeler further developed this theory of the fission process and showed that it is the isotope U^{235} which undergoes fission as a result of the capture of a slow neutron. Experimental confirmation of these ideas was soon forthcoming. Physical proof of the phenomenon, involving the measurement of the considerable ionization produced by the fission fragments, was given by Frisch [19] and by Joliot [20]. Meitner and Frisch found that the so-called transuranics were also isotopes of elements of medium atomic weight. The 3.5-hour β-activity studied by Curie and Savitch was shown in fact to be a lanthanum isotope; its removal from solution with lanthanum carrier appeared to be incomplete because of the presence of an active yttrium isotope, a fission product with almost exactly the same half-life.

The fission of thorium by fast neutrons was also established [21, 22], and as a result of the work of a large number of authors, the fission of both uranium and thorium was shown to give rise to several dozen isotopes, extending from zinc to the rare earths (Section 6-1). At the same time, some elegant experiments by Joliot and his collaborators, by Fermi, and by Szilard showed that the slow neutron fission of uranium results, on the average, in the emission of 2 to 3 neutrons per fission. In principal, therefore, the capture of a neutron by a mass of U^{235} should lead to a nuclear chain reaction analogous to a chemical reaction, such as explosive combustion, in which one of the reactants used up in the initiation process is regenerated in a subsequent step. In practice, however, the abundance of the fissile isotope U^{235} in natural uranium is only 1/140, and the greater fraction of the neutrons produced are captured by U^{238} without causing fission; these are then lost as far as the propagation of the chain is concerned, as are those which escape from the reacting mass.

The conditions under which a nuclear chain reaction is possible were quickly understood by a number of physicists, who saw that it was necessary either to introduce a moderator into natural uranium so that the neutrons are slowed down to velocities at which capture by U^{235} is favored (Chapter 6) or to increase the concentration of this isotope by the appropriate physical methods (Chapter 9). Joliot and his co-workers envisaged the use of heavy water as moderator, and Perrin was able to calculate the critical mass of uranium necessary for the chain reaction to be self-sustaining (or *divergent*). The invasion of France in 1940 prevented the realization of the proposed experiments, for which 165 liters of heavy water had been acquired from Norway. At the time, this constituted practically the whole of the world's supply, and in June, 1940, Halban and Kowarski transported this stock to England, where in December of the same year the theoretical calculations were confirmed experimentally [23]. In the United States, Fermi and Szilard selected graphite as a moderator. The work of Fermi and his group was crowned with success on December 2, 1942, when the first nuclear pile became critical with a power of 0.5 watt, which was increased 10 days later to 200 watts.

In such piles, the chain reaction is controlled, as we shall see later (Sections 6-5 and 6-6), by a suitable choice of dimensions and by the use of moderators and neutron absorbers. Explosive chain reactions were achieved with pure U^{235} and with plutonium formed by the action of slow neutrons on U^{238}. The first atomic bomb was tested on July 16, 1945, in New Mexico [24]. The second uranium bomb was dropped (against the advice of a committee of American scientists headed by Franck) on Hiroshima on August 6, 1945, and two days later Nagasaki was devastated by a plutonium bomb.

The preparation of this element, atomic number 94, followed that of element 93, neptunium, by McMillan and Abelson [25] in 1940. These authors bombarded thin layers of uranyl nitrate with slow neutrons from the Berkeley cyclotron and, having got rid of the fission products by utilizing their recoil energy, they found the 23-minute β-activity which Hahn, Meitner, and Strassmann had (correctly) attributed to U^{239} (Eq. 1-5). It was shown that the new element produced by the β-disintegration of this isotope was not a homologue of rhenium, but in fact possessed chemical properties close to those of uranium, and they suggested that the two elements formed the first members of a *uranide* series, chemically analogous to the lanthanide series in the sixth period of the periodic system. The lanthanides are characterized by their trivalent state, while the uranides could have several oxidation states with a maximum valency of +VI. Subsequent research has provided at least partial confirmation of this hypothesis.

The first plutonium isotope was prepared by Seaborg, McMillan, Kennedy, and Wahl [26] by the bombardment of uranium with deuterons:

$$\begin{aligned} U^{238} + D^2 &\rightarrow Np^{238} + 2n; \\ Np^{238} &\xrightarrow{\beta} Pu^{238} \qquad (t_{1/2} = 90 \text{ yr}). \end{aligned} \tag{1–6}$$

Seaborg and his co-workers have also been responsible for the preparation of the other transuranium elements from americium (95) to mendelevium (101), using the techniques described in Chapters 5 and 8. Like uranium and neptunium, plutonium and americium have the oxidation states III, IV, V, and VI, but the maximum stability gradually passes from the hexavalent to the trivalent state as one goes from uranium to americium. It will be seen later that the chemical properties of the transuranium elements are much more complex than those of the lanthanides, and we shall examine the various proposals which have been made for their classification in the periodic system. The preparation of elements 102 (nobelium) and 103 (lawrencium) are discussed in Section 8–1.

1–8 Accelerators. One way in which it is possible to learn something about the constitution of the nucleus and the nature of nuclear forces is by breaking down nuclei to produce others. The disintegration of nuclei by neutrons can be carried out with a very simple setup requiring only a source of α- or γ-rays such as radium, polonium, radon, etc., which is mixed with a suitable element of low atomic weight, especially beryllium. The applicability of such natural sources is, however, limited, in terms of both energy and intensity. Since the construction of the first high-voltage apparatus for the acceleration of charged particles by Cockcroft and Walton in 1930, there has been a continual search for methods of accelerating such particles to higher and higher energies.

In the arrangement used by Cockcroft and Walton, positive ions are generated in a discharge tube and accelerated by a voltage multiplication based on a series of rectifiers and condensers arranged in cascade (Fig. 1–8). The generator constructed by van de Graaff in the following year was a large scale electrostatic machine in which the charges are produced by a potential of several kilovolts applied to a series of "spray points" at the base of the apparatus. The charges are collected by a motor-driven insulated moving belt which carries them towards a metallic spherical electrode (Fig. 1–9). The sphere collects charge from the belt, with the result that its potential rises to a limiting value governed only by the onset of corona discharge. As with the Cockcroft-Walton type of generator, the maximum voltage obtainable can be increased by working the apparatus in an atmosphere which reduces the opportunity of discharge (e.g., nitrogen or a mixture of nitrogen and freon under pressure). Energies up to 5 or 6 Mev are available from modern van de Graaff machines.

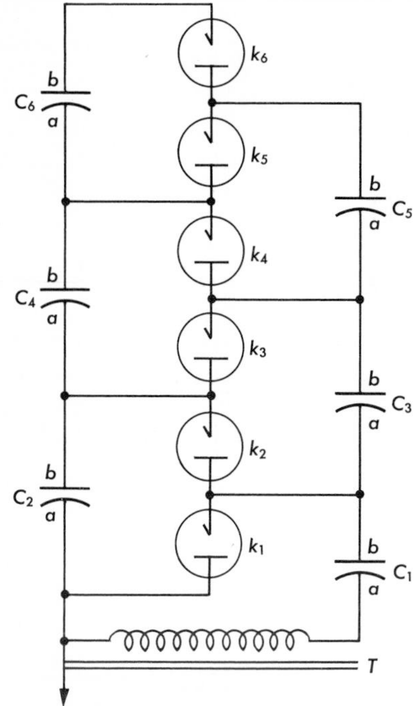

Fig. 1–8. The principle of the Cockcroft-Walton accelerator.

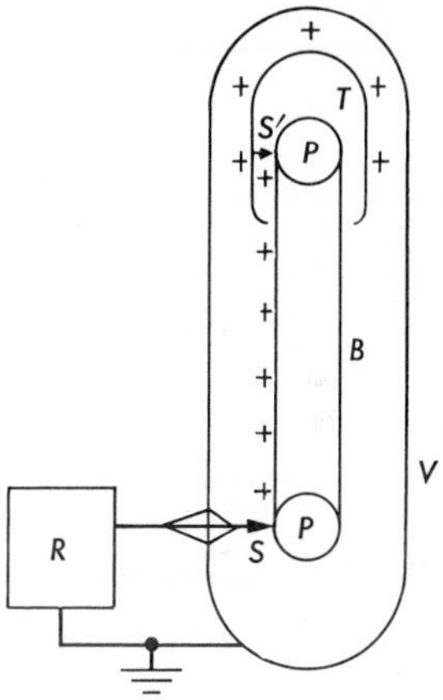

Fig. 1–9. Schematic diagram of a van de Graaff machine.

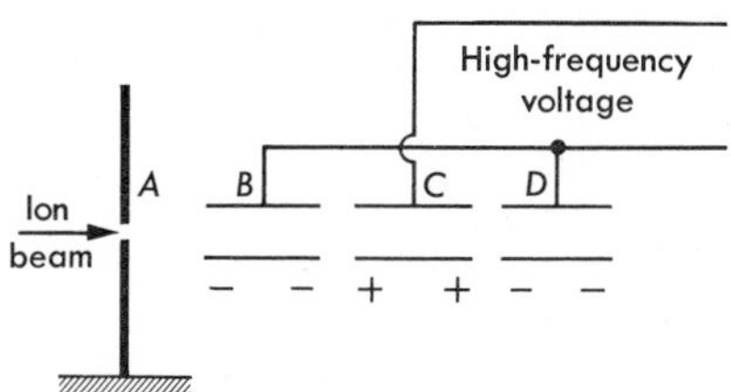

Fig. 1–10. Schematic diagram of a linear accelerator.

In a linear accelerator, a beam of electrons or ions passes along the central axis of a series of cylinders to which a high-frequency alternating voltage is applied in such a way that the alternating sign of each cylinder is always opposed to that of its neighbors (Fig. 1–10). By appropriate choice of frequency and of cylinder length, the electric field continually accelerates the particle as it passes from one cylinder to the next. With this sort of apparatus, it is possible to produce 500-Mev electrons, and protons of more than 30 Mev. One great advantage is that high beam currents are available, at least in the 1- to 10-Mev region. A further advantage is that higher energies can be achieved by the addition of further units to an existing apparatus.

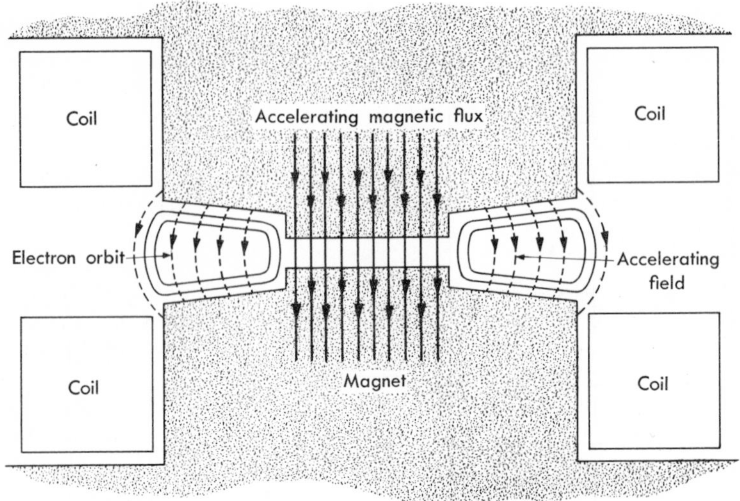

FIG. 1–11. The principle of the betatron.

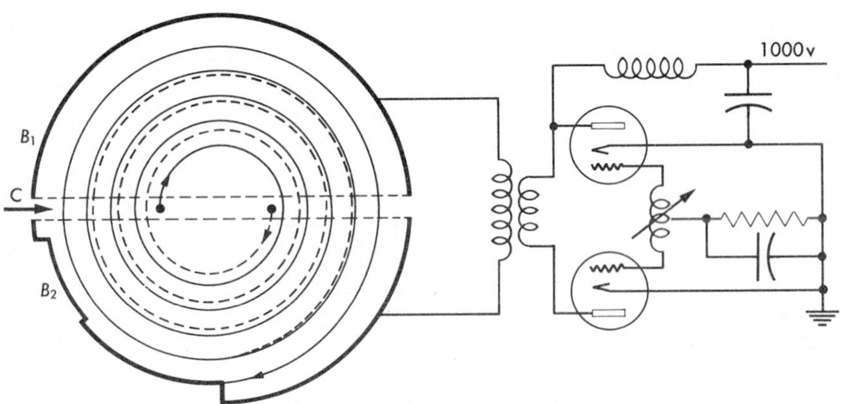

FIG. 1–12. The principle of the cyclotron.

In the induction accelerator or betatron, restricted to electrons, an alternating magnetic field is used to maintain a constant radius for the orbit of the particles accelerated by the induced electric field (Fig. 1–11). Most of the betatrons currently in use give electrons or x-rays with energies in the 25- to 50-Mev region.

In the cyclotron, invented by Lawrence in 1930, a suitable source supplies ions which are accelerated in a resonating magnetic field. In the air gap of a large electromagnet are placed the two hollow semicylindrical electrode boxes, known as the "dees" because of their shape (Fig. 1–12). The pressure inside the dees is reduced to about 10^{-6} mm, and a very high-frequency alternating voltage is applied; the half period of oscillation of this voltage is equal to the time taken by the ions to move around one of the half-cylinders (given by $t = Mc/zeH$, where c is the velocity of light, H is the intensity of the magnetic field, and ze is the charge on the ions of mass M). The ions consequently move in a spiral, undergoing an acceleration each time they pass across the gap between the dees. The maximum energy of the particles does not depend on the voltage across the electrodes but upon the magnetic field and the diameter of the pole face of the magnet; because of this, this diameter is often quoted as a measure of the size of a cyclotron. The first cyclotron built by Lawrence at Berkeley had a diameter of 2.5 inches and accelerated protons to 80 kev. Subsequent models have been of 9, 11, 27, 37, 60, and 72 inches; the 60-inch cyclotron will produce 10-Mev protons, 20-Mev deuterons, or 40-Mev helium ions.

Bethe was the first to point out that as particles are accelerated to still higher energies, the high velocity causes a relativistic increase in the mass; the conditions which make the time of transit independent of the radius of the orbit then no longer hold, and a number of difficulties are encountered. The ways in which these can be overcome were described independently by Veksler and McMillan, who showed that the energy of the particles can be increased either by lowering the frequency of the electric field, or by gradually increasing the intensity of the magnetic field. Accelerators based on the first principle of frequency modulation are known as synchrocyclotrons. One of the largest, that at the Academy of Sciences in Moscow, accelerates protons to energies of 680 Mev. Machines with a variable magnetic field and fixed oscillator frequency are called synchrotrons. In the proton-synchrotron, both conditions can be varied. In contrast to the above accelerators, in this machine the particles move throughout in a circular path of constant diameter. The construction of these immense machines involves enormous amounts of materials, and during their operation several megawatts of power are consumed. An auxiliary accelerator, such as a Van de Graaff or a linear accelerator, serves to inject a stream of protons with an initial energy of several Mev. The proton synchrotron at Berkeley, the bevatron, produces particles of more than 6 Bev (or 6 Gev); its electromagnet alone weighs more than 10,000 tons. A similar 10-Bev machine situated near Moscow has an electromagnet weighing 36,000 tons, made up of four quadrants with a radius of about 90 feet. Figure 1–13 shows part of the so-called "cosmotron" at the Brookhaven National Laboratory; this machine accelerates protons to 3 Bev [27].

The contrast between this machine and the simple apparatus used by Rutherford for the first transmutations (Fig. 1–6) well illustrates the changes which have occurred in the field of nuclear physics in less than 40 years. The efforts made during this period have, however, to a large extent been rewarded. The radioactive sources available to the early workers rarely exceeded a curie, whereas today nuclear reactors provide sources whose strength is measured in *kilocuries*. To the 40 or so natural radioactive isotopes known in 1930 over 1000 new nuclides have been added, more than 100 of which are the isotopes of elements not found in nature. The proton and the electron were the only elementary particles known to the early workers. Following the identification of the neutron and the positron, a large number of unstable particles, the *mesons*, were discovered in

FIG. 1–13. The 3-Bev cosmotron at the Brookhaven National Laboratory. At the lower left can be seen the van de Graaff machine which injects 3-Mev protons into the "doughnut"; next to it is one of the 12 vacuum pumps associated with the accelerator.

cosmic rays and subsequently produced in high-energy accelerators. Intermediate in mass between the electron and the proton, these particles may have positive, negative, or zero charge. More recently, *hyperons*, particles with a mass greater than that of the proton, and the *antiproton* and *antineutron* have been identified (Sections 2–7 and 5–9). We shall see (Section 3–8) that the existence of charged particles with masses between the electron and the proton had been predicted on theoretical grounds by Yukawa in 1935 in order to account for the forces which bind together the particles of the nucleus.

1–9 The development of radiochemistry. In the early days of radioactivity, the word "radiochemistry" was used in connection with the chemical effects produced by ionizing radiations, by analogy with photochemistry. In recent times, however, it has become more and more restricted to describe the study of the chemical properties of the natural and artificial radioelements and, in a more general sense, of the chemical phenomena associated with nuclear transformations. The subject formerly known as radiochemistry is now described as *radiation chemistry*. Throughout this book we shall keep to this nomenclature, at the same time using the adjective "radiochemical" in the most general sense. *Nuclear chemistry* will be taken to be the study of the transmutations and transformations of nuclei, in the same way as molecular chemistry is concerned with the analogous changes in molecules.

In the years between the discovery of polonium and the preparation of lawrencium, radiochemistry has made a tremendous number of useful contributions in all the various fields of chemistry. Apart from the discovery of isotopy and of some 20 new elements, there are several aspects of physical chemistry which could never have been investigated without the use of radiochemical methods. These include (a) the study of the chemical behavior of unweighable amounts of material and of extremely dilute solutions, and the analytical applications which have resulted from such work; (b) applications in geochemistry, including the determination of the ages of minerals and rocks, of the earth's crust, and of carboniferous materials of animal or vegetable origin; (c) radiation chemistry, and the related subjects radiobiology and radiotherapy; (d) stable and radioactive isotopic indicators. The development of these aspects of radiochemistry will be discussed in the appropriate parts of this book, and we shall restrict ourselves here to the early stages of (c) and (d).

Radiation chemistry and radiobiology. The production of ozone by materials containing radium was first observed by the Curies, and in 1901 Pierre Curie and Debierne showed that solutions of radium salts continually give off hydrogen and oxygen [28]. Ramsay and Soddy analyzed these gases and found an excess of hydrogen; this anomaly was later explained by Kernbaum, who detected in the solutions quantities of hydrogen peroxide equivalent to the oxygen deficiency. The reverse process, the radiochemical formation of water from its constituent gases, was achieved by Cameron and Ramsay. Among the early pioneers of radiation chemistry were Duane and Scheuer, Usher, Kailan, Wourtzel, Lind, and Mund.

It is also convenient to consider the chemical phenomena which occur in the region of a molecule containing a radioactive atom at the instant of its radioactive disintegration as part of radiation chemistry (*hot-atom chemistry*). Effects of this sort had been noted with the natural radioactive elements, but the real potential importance was revealed by Szilard and Chalmers who succeeded in 1934 in separating radioiodine from neutron-irradiated ethyl iodide. The capture process $I^{127} + n \rightarrow I^{128}$ results in the emission of a γ-ray, the recoil energy of which splits the organic molecule and liberates the active atom. We shall see later the wide applicability of this elegant technique (Chapter 17).

Radiobiology and radiotherapy arose out of observations of the actions of the radiations on living organisms [29]. Some months after the discovery of x-rays, Daniel noted that as the result of a one-hour exposure of the scalp three weeks previously, one of his collaborators suffered a loss of hair. Soon afterward a number of workers noticed the peculiar rashes and burns caused by the radiations. J. J. Thomson found that irradiating the little finger of his left hand produced a crop of red blotches a week later and this was followed by blistering. The first skin cancer caused by radiation was observed in 1902 in a workman engaged in handling radioactive ampoules in Hamburg. Similar injuries cropped up frequently among people working with radium. Henri Becquerel, having carried a small tube containing a radium salt in the pocket of his waistcoat, was attacked by an ulceration of the abdominal skin, which was slow to heal (radiodermatitis). Pierre Curie confirmed this by exposing his own arm to radium; the ulceration produced took four months to heal.

The therapeutic use of x-rays had, however, already been introduced by Freund in Vienna in 1897, with the successful removal of hair from a hairy birthmark on a four-year old child (roentgentherapy). In 1907 Stenbeck in Stockholm effected the first cure of a skin cancer by radiation. In Paris, Danlos (1901) made use of the radium given by the Curies to one of the hospitals to treat erythematic lupus (Curie-therapy). Radium from the same source was used by Danysz at the Institut Pasteur in studying the actions of the radiations on microorganisms, and Bohr studied their effect on the growth of ova and on unicellular organisms (1903). The bacteriocidal effect of α-particles had been previously investigated by Aschkinass and Caspari in 1901, who later injected a suspension of radium sulfate into tubercular ganglia in guinea pigs, and under the skin of an anthrocoid rabbit. Bohr's work suggested that the part most affected by radiation is the chromatine, and that tissues in the process of growth or of active alteration are the most sensitive to radiation. In 1906, Bergonié and Tribondeau collected the radiobiological data then available into a rule which they called "a correlation between the reproductive activity of cells and their instability to radiation." Others who investigated the action of the rays on different organs of the human body and of mammals up to the turn of the century included Perthes, Exner, Dominici, Béclère, Albers-Schönberg, Pfahler, Halberstädter, Forssell, and Regaud. An important new radiotherapeutic technique was introduced by Lacassagne and Lattès in 1924, who used the photographic method for the localization of polonium in organisms (autohistoradiography or autoradiography); this technique has since found wide application in other branches of radiochemistry.

Radioactive indicators. We have already mentioned (Section 1–3) the unsuccessful attempts made by Hevesy and Paneth to separate radium-D from lead. Although the existence of isotopes was not at that time clearly established, these authors hit upon the idea of using this identity in the behavior of the two species to study the properties and reactions of lead compounds under conditions where normal chemical methods are for some reason inapplicable. In principle, the method consists in labeling an inactive element or compound with its active isotope and following the course of the latter in, say, a chemical reaction by the appropriate radiometric techniques. The first application (1912) was in the determination of the solubilities of lead chromate and sulfide, using radium-D or thorium-B as indicator, and in work on the electrolytic deposition of lead and bismuth. Hevesy subsequently made use of radioactive indicators in work on isotopic exchange reactions, diffusion and self-diffusion in metals, and in the localization of lead in certain plants, while Paneth used the technique in measuring the surface areas of crystals and in various analytical problems. The number of elements for which active isotopes were available was, however, comparatively small and the possible applications of the method were in consequence strictly limited.

The discovery of deuterium and the heavy isotopes of carbon, nitrogen, and oxygen lead to the use of these isotopes in labeling organic compounds and the application of isotopic indicators in biochemistry and biology. Schoenheimer and Rittenberg pioneered the use of such techniques in fundamental work on metabolism. Subsequently, upon the discovery of artificial radioactivity and the preparation of useful radioactive isotopes of almost every element, the tracer method has been widely applied and is now a vital tool in the most varied types of research. As early as 1935 Hevesy and Chievitz used radiophosphorus in studying the metabolism of this element in organisms. Ruben and Kamen's discovery that the deuteron bombardment of carbon results in the formation of a long-lived active carbon isotope (C^{14}, half-life 5570 years) was of the utmost importance for biochemists and biologists. The developments and applications of the tracer technique in physical chemistry, biology, and other fields will be discussed at length in the final chapters of this book.

References

1. H. Becquerel, *Compt. rend.*, **122,** 420, 501, 559, 762, 1086, (1896).
2. For a bibliography of radioactivity up to 1925, see St. Meyer and E. Schweidler, *Radioaktivität,* Leipzig, 1927. Other documents used in the preparation of this chapter include the Nobel Prize lectures given by the various Nobel laureates in this field.
3. M. Curie, *Rev. Scient.*, **14,** 65 (1900).
4. I. Noddack, *Z. angew. Chem.*, **47,** 653 (1934).
5. A. V. Grosse and M. S. Agruss, *J. Am. Chem. Soc.*, **57,** 438 (1935).
6. O. D'Agostino and E. Segrè, *Gazz. Chim. Ital.*, **65,** 1088 (1935).
7. O. Hahn and L. Meitner, *Naturwiss.*, **23,** 37, 230, 320 (1935); **24,** 158 (1936).
8. O. Hahn, L. Meitner, and F. Strassmann, *Naturwiss.*, **23,** 544 (1935).
9. O. Hahn, L. Meitner, and F. Strassmann, *Chem. Ber.*, **69,** 905 (1936); **70,** 1374 (1937).
10. O. Hahn, L. Meitner, and F. Strassmann, *Z. Physik,* **106,** 249 (1937).
11. L. Meitner, *Ann. Physik,* **29,** 246 (1937).
12. L. A. Turner, *Revs. Modern Phys.*, **12,** 1 (1940).
13. P. Savitch, private communication.
14. I. Curie and P. Savitch, *J. phys. radium,* **8,** 385 (1937); **9,** 355 (1938).
15. I. Curie and P. Savitch, *Compt. rend.*, **206,** 906, 1643 (1938).
16. I. Curie, P. Savitch, and A. M. da Silva, *J. phys. radium,* **9,** 440 (1938).
17. O. Hahn and F. Strassmann, *Naturwiss.*, **26,** 755 (1938); **27,** 89 (1939).
18. L. Meitner and O. R. Frisch, *Nature,* **143,** 239, 471 (1939).
19. O. R. Frisch, *Nature,* **143,** 276 (1939).
20. F. Joliot, *Compt. rend.*, **208,** 341, 647 (1939).
21. E. Bretscher and L. G. Cook, *Nature,* **143,** 559 (1939).
22. L. Meitner, *Nature,* **143,** 637 (1939).
23. *British White Paper on Atomic Energy,* H.M.S.O., London, 1945.
24. For details see H. D. Smyth, *Atomic Energy for Military Purposes,* Princeton University Press, Princeton, 1945.
25. E. M. McMillan and P. H. Abelson, *Phys. Rev.*, **57,** 1185 (1940).

26. G. T. SEABORG, E. M. MCMILLAN, J. W. KENNEDY, and A. C. WAHL, *Phys. Rev.*, **69,** 366 (1946).

27. For details of the construction and operation of accelerators see M. S. LIVINGSTON, *High Energy Accelerators,* Interscience Publishing Corp., New York, 1954.

28. For a bibliography see S. C. LIND, *The Chemical Effects of α-Particles,* Chemical Catalog Co., New York, 1938.

29. For a bibliography see A. LACASSAGNE, *Les Cancers produits par les rayonnements electromagnetiques,* and *Les Cancers produits par les rayonnements corpusculaires,* Hermann, Paris, 1945.

CHAPTER 2

THE FUNDAMENTAL PARTICLES

2–1 The elementary structure of matter. Early theories about the ultimate structure of matter assumed that atoms were indivisible particles, incapable of transmutation into other atoms. Chemically homogeneous bodies consisting of a unique atomic species were then supposed to be the principles, or *elements*, of matter. When this view of the atomic theory was shown to be untenable, it was thought that all that was required was a shift of scale; in place of atoms with relative masses between 1 and about 250, the new "elements" should be the proton, the neutron, the positive and negative electrons, and the mesons, which are particles of intermediate mass. It will become clear, however, that recent developments in nuclear physics have changed our ideas about the structure of matter even more radically. Thus, although it is currently believed that atomic nuclei are built up from protons and neutrons, these particles themselves may well correspond to different states of one and the same thing. The two species would thus be capable of transformation from one to the other under the action of a mesonic field by the absorption or emission of a meson, in the same way that an atom passes from one energy level to another under the action of an electromagnetic field with the emission or absorption of a photon. Not only is the nature of these extremely unstable mesons far from clear, but the number of different types of mesons and their respective masses is as yet uncertain. Equally, there seems to be no reason for being certain that some future experimental technique will not reveal the electron as a complex structure rather than as the elementary structureless particle of current theory.

So as not to prejudge the conclusions which may be reached by future developments in this subnuclear physics, we consider it preferable to refer to the so-called elementary particles as *fundamental particles*, in this way giving them a significance on the nuclear scale similar to that of atoms in molecular studies; in other words, they are the corpuscular species from which matter is built up. Such a definition can then extend to include certain nuclei, such as the heavy isotopes of hydrogen and the α-particle, which are clearly made up of simpler particles. The distinction between particles and nuclei has become less significant, since atoms such as oxygen, neon, carbon, etc., have been accelerated to energies at which their orbital electrons are completely or partially removed and the atoms then used as bombarding particles in the production of new nuclei.

In this chapter we shall be concerned with negative and positive electrons, the proton, the neutron, the neutrino, various mesons, and the corresponding antiparticles. The characteristic properties of the deuteron, the triton ($H^{3(+)}$), and the isotopes of helium are noted briefly in Chapter 5.

2–2 Energy and mass. In the free state, fundamental particles are characterized by their mass, electric charge, and intrinsic angular momentum, or spin. The mass is generally quoted in terms of the rest mass of the electron. It is most essential in nuclear physics to distinguish between the mass m_0 of a particle at rest and the relativistic mass m of the same particle moving with a velocity v which is not negligible with respect to the velocity of light *in vacuo* (c). The relativistic mass is always greater than the rest mass, according to the Lorentz equation

$$m = \frac{m_0}{\sqrt{1 - v^2/c^2}} = \frac{m_0}{\sqrt{1 - \beta^2}}. \tag{2–1}$$

For an electron with a velocity corresponding to as little as 100 kv, the ratio m/m_0 is 1.195, increasing to 3 for an energy 10 times larger; in contrast, β^2 for a proton of 1000 kv is 0.0022, and the ratio m/m_0 is practically unity. The relativistic increase in the mass of the proton cannot be neglected, however, in powerful accelerators, where particles may reach energies of the order of 10^{10} ev. A proton accelerated to 200 Mev has a velocity of 1.70×10^{10} cm·sec^{-1}, or 0.568 c, and the mass is then 1.21 times greater than the rest mass; for an energy of 2 Bev (or 2 Gev = 2×10^9 ev), the velocity is 2.85×10^{10} cm·sec^{-1}, or 0.95 c, and the mass 3.15 m_0.

When a material system undergoes an energy change, as for example, when its potential energy decreases as the result of a radioactive transformation involving the emission of a particle with a kinetic energy E, the rest mass changes according to the well-known Einstein equation

$$E = \Delta mc^2. \tag{2–2}$$

The total relativistic mass is conserved, however, since Δm reappears as the increase in the relativistic mass of the particle or other constituents of the system which absorb the emitted energy. The relativistic mass of a completely isolated system which loses no energy to any outside body remains constant, irrespective of any nuclear transformations which occur, in the same way that the energy of an adiabatic system undergoing chemical change remains constant.

The fundamental importance of Eq. (2–2) in nuclear chemistry will be fully illustrated later, but it should be noted here that just as the exothermicity of a chemical reaction characterizes the stability of the products, so nuclear stability is associated with a decrease of the rest mass, since this corresponds to an exoergic change. Such reasons explain why the α-particle, consisting of two protons and two neutrons and having a mass of 4.00377, is stable with respect to dissociation into its constituent particles, whose total mass is $2 \times 1.00759 + 2 \times 1.00898 = 4.03314$.

The fundamental particles are normally divided into three groups according to their masses: (a) *the light particles or leptons*, consisting of the electron e^-, the positron or positively charged electron e^+, and the neutrino of zero charge ν; (b) the *nucleons*, the proton p, and the neutron n; and (c) the mesons, particles having masses between that of the electron and that of the proton, and the *hyperons* with masses lying between those of the proton and the deuteron.

2-3 Spin, statistics, and parity. The spin of a particle gives it an angular momentum about its own central axis. The length of this vector is characterized by a quantum number s, and its projection along any given axis s_z has the values $s\hbar$, $(s - 1)\hbar$, $\ldots$, $-s\hbar$, where $\hbar = h/2\pi$, h being Planck's constant. The spin quantum number determines the number of possible orientations of the particle relative to a given direction, the number of these orientations being $2s + 1$. For light particles and nucleons, $s = \frac{1}{2}$, so that $s_z = \pm\hbar/2$; for certain mesons $s = 0$ or 1.

The spin gives rise to a magnetic moment, which for a particle of mass m and charge e is given by the theoretical equation

$$\mu = \frac{eh}{4\pi m_0 c}\cdot \tag{2-3}$$

For an electron, μ is the Bohr magneton, equal to

$$9.273 \times 10^{-21}\ \text{erg}\cdot\text{gauss}^{-1}.$$

The unit of magnetic moment for nucleons is the nuclear magneton, μ_0, which is 1836 times smaller than the Bohr magneton, this factor arising from the ratio of the masses of the electron and the proton.

There is a close connection between the spin and the statistics which govern the distribution of energy in an assembly of particles. Particles are said to obey Fermi-Dirac statistics when the Pauli exclusion principle is obeyed; that is, two identical particles cannot be in the same quantum state. Such particles are known as *fermions.* In this case, the state of the two identical particles is described by an antisymmetrical wave function, since the sign of the wave function changes when the particles exchange their coordinates,

$$\psi(1, 2) = -\psi(2, 1).$$

The indices 1 and 2 represent the total space and spin coordinates of the two particles. Particles which do not conform to the Pauli principle and whose wave function is symmetrical,

$$\psi(1, 2) = \psi(2, 1),$$

obey Bose-Einstein statistics and are referred to as *bosons.* Light particles and nucleons which have spin $\frac{1}{2}$ are fermions. This is in fact a general rule: particles or nuclei whose spin is an odd multiple of $\frac{1}{2}$ obey Fermi statistics, while those with a spin of 0 or a multiple of a whole number follow Bose-Einstein statistics. It should be noted that the photon, with a spin of 1, falls into this latter category. To some extent, the photon can be regarded as behaving like a particle, as in such phenomena as radiation pressure, relativistic mass, and the like. It is not yet clear whether the photon should be thought of as having a finite rest mass, although this will, in any case, be close to zero.

The particles possess a further important property, that of *parity,* which is also encountered in atomic physics. The state of a particle can be described by a wave function ψ which depends upon the spatial coordinates

TABLE 2–1

THE FUNDAMENTAL PHYSICAL CONSTANTS [3]

Quantity	Symbol	Value
Velocity of light *in vacuo*	c	2.99793×10^{10} cm·sec^{-1}
Planck's constant	h	6.62517×10^{-27} erg·sec
		$= 4.135 \times 10^{-15}$ ev·sec
$h/2\pi$	$\hbar$	1.0544×10^{-27} erg·sec^{-1}
Electronic charge	e	4.80286×10^{-10} esu
		$= 1.60206 \times 10^{-20}$ emu
Bohr magneton	μ	9.273×10^{-21} erg·gauss^{-1}
Rest mass of the electron	m_0	9.1085×10^{-28} gm
		$= 0.00054876$ amu
		$= 0.510976$ Mev
Rest mass of the proton	m_p	1.67239×10^{-24} gm
		$= 1.007593$ amu
		$= 938.211$ Mev
Rest mass of the neutron	m_n	1.67470×10^{-24} gm
		$= 1.008982$ amu
		$= 939.505$ Mev
Avogadro's number	N	6.02486×10^{23} mole^{-1}
Gas constant	R	8.31696×10^{7} erg·mole^{-1}·deg^{-1}
Boltzmann constant	k	1.38044×10^{-16} erg·deg^{-1}
		$= 8.6164 \times 10^{-5}$ ev·deg^{-1}

and upon the spin; more precisely, the function $|\psi|^2$ expresses the probability of finding the particle in a given state indicated by the coordinates (x, y, z, s). Now the state of the particle is obviously independent of the choice of system of coordinates, and it follows that if one replaces (x, y, z) by $(-x, -y, -z)$, an inversion equivalent to the reflection of the particle with respect to the origin of the axes of the coordinates, the state of the particle should be unchanged. The result of this inversion may be either that the wave function retains its sign, or that it must be multiplied by -1. In both cases, the squared function $|\psi|^2$ remains unchanged. The first case, the conservation of the sign of the wave function, corresponds to the particle having even parity and the opposite case to an odd parity of the particle. Particles with zero spin and odd parity are said to be *pseudoscalar*.

For many years it was thought that the parity of an isolated system never changed, so that in nuclear transformations in which particles disappear and others are formed the overall parity remains unchanged. This law implies an intrinsically symmetrical structure for particles and a symmetry in their interactions, as indeed does the idea of parity itself. More recently [1] it has been suggested and proved experimentally (Section 4–2) that this law of the conservation of parity is not in fact universally valid and is not obeyed in the case of radioactive β-decay and in the disintegration reactions of mesons and hyperons. It remains valid, however, for electromagnetic interactions and for interactions between nucleons [2].

Table 2-1 lists the numerical values of some of the characteristic properties of the fundamental particles important in nuclear chemistry. The unit of energy is the electron volt, the energy acquired by an electron initially at rest when it moves under the influence of an electric field produced by a potential difference of one volt. An electron volt is equivalent to 1.602×10^{-12} erg; multiplying 1 ev by Avogadro's number gives the equivalent energy of 23.053 kcal·mole^{-1}. Other energy equivalents are given later in Table 11-10. The mass unit used in nuclear physics (amu) is defined as $\frac{1}{16}$ of the mass of the atom O^{16} (mass 16.00000 units). This is slightly lower than the chemical mass unit, which is based on the mean atomic weight of natural oxygen, a mixture of the three isotopes O^{16}, O^{17} (0.037%), and O^{18} (0.2%). The chemical mass unit is therefore larger than the physical unit by 1.000275. By putting the amu values into Eq. (2-2), we can show that a change of mass of 1 gm corresponds to an energy change of 8.988×10^{20} ergs; a mass change of 1 amu is equal to 1.492×10^{-3} erg, or 931.14 Mev.

2-4 The electron, the positron, and positronium. The electron* is the unit of elementary negative charge, the value of which is given in Table 2-1, together with its mass and magnetic moment; the spin of the electron is $\hbar/2$. The positron has identical properties, except for its charge and magnetic moment, but is extremely unstable in the presence of electrons. It is formed in certain radioactive disintegrations, or as the result of the interaction between matter and a photon of energy equal to or greater than 1.02 Mev, since a photon of this energy can bring about the production of an electron pair, by which we mean an electron plus a positron, whose combined rest masses are exactly equivalent to 1.02 Mev. The inverse process, the interaction of a positron with an electron, gives rise to two photons, each of at least 0.51 Mev, which are emitted in opposite directions. Less frequently, three photons are emitted or, very exceptionally, a single photon in a nuclear field. This phenomenon, the apparent disappearance of an electron and a positron, is known as *annihilation*.

Because of its high reactivity, the positron has a very short average life which is dependent upon the nature of the surrounding medium and in particular upon the local electron concentration; in metals, ionic compounds, and similar solids, it is of the order of 1 to 3×10^{-10} sec. In gases, the average life should be inversely proportional to the pressure, since the pressure determines the probability of encountering an electron. Deutsch [4, 5, 6, 7] has shown experimentally that in certain gases this is valid for only a certain fraction of the positrons, namely those having a life of the order of 10^{-10} sec, while the remainder have a mean life of approximately 10^{-7} sec, independent of the pressure.

These results, which have been confirmed by Benedetti and others [8, 9], are attributed to the formation of extremely short-lived "atomic" combinations of an electron and a positron, called *positronium*. The existence of

---

* Translator's note: We shall use electron and positron throughout this book to indicate the negative and positive electrons, respectively, in order to avoid using the term "negatron."

this had been predicted theoretically and, apart from the stability, its properties are similar to those of the H_2 molecule. As with the hydrogen molecule, two species can be identified: orthopositronium with the spins of the two particles in parallel (the triplet state) and parapositronium with the spins antiparallel (singlet state). For the positrons emitted in the decay of Na^{22}, for example, a fraction of the order of 25 to 30% forms positronium in He, A, N_2, CO_2, CCl_2F_2 (freon), and SF_6, with the ortho-para ratio 3:1. Orthopositronium has an average life of 1.5×10^{-7} sec and decays by the emission of three photons; parapositronium, which has a mean life of 10^{-10} sec, yields two photons on disintegration. The ortho-para conversion is catalyzed by the presence of molecules with an odd number of valence electrons, such as NO or NO_2, since under these conditions the electron of the positronium can exchange with the uncoupled electron of the molecule. The addition of oxygen has a similar effect, arising in this case from the magnetic field of the molecule. The addition of chlorine or bromine depresses the formation of positronium, and to explain this the process

$$Cl_2 + e^+e^- \rightarrow Cl + Cl^-e^+$$

has been postulated, but Deutsch has discounted this explanation because of the unfavorable free-energy change in this reaction. It is, in any case, clear that the stability of positronium depends markedly on the chemical composition of the surrounding medium. An electric field is found to promote the formation of positronium. The electron affinity of the positron, that is to say the bond energy in (e^+—e^-), has been calculated to be 6.8 ev, so that in a gas whose ionization potential is I, only those positrons with a kinetic energy greater than $(I - 6.8)$ ev are able to combine with electrons. The effect of the electric field is to accelerate slow positrons and so increase the probability of combination.

Measurements of the average life of the positron in certain insulators (quartz, polystyrene, teflon, etc.) seem to conform with the suggestion that the particle is not completely free in these materials either [10]. It has been shown theoretically that combinations such as two positrons plus an electron, two electrons plus a positron, a proton plus an electron plus a positron, and the like, should also have a certain stability, but this would be much smaller than for positronium, and there is as yet no experimental evidence for the existence of such complexes.

2–5 Nucleons. The proton is the stable unit of elementary positive charge, 1836.13 times greater in mass than the electron. It has spin $\frac{1}{2}$ and a magnetic moment of +2.793 nuclear magnetons instead of the value of 1 calculated from Eq. (2–3); this anomaly is presumably one manifestation of the nonelementary nature of the proton.

At rest, the proton is the well-known ionized hydrogen atom of molecular chemistry, but when the particle is given sufficient kinetic energy, as for example, in some high-voltage accelerating apparatus, it is capable of bringing about numerous nuclear reactions. According to the de Broglie theory, a moving proton has an associated wave whose length λ (in angstroms) is given by the relation

$$\lambda = \frac{h}{mv} = \frac{3964}{v} = \frac{0.286}{E^{1/2}}, \tag{2-4}$$

where v is the velocity of the particle in m·sec^{-1} and E its energy in ev. At appropriate velocities, protons are diffracted by solid bodies in much the same way as x-rays; this property is utilized in proton microscopy.

In spite of its lack of charge, the neutron has a magnetic moment of −1.91 nuclear magnetons, probably because of reasons similar to those for the anomalous magnetic moment of the proton. The negative sign implies an orientation opposed to that of the spin, which for the neutron is $\hbar/2$. The mass of the neutron (1.00898) is appreciably greater than the sum of the rest masses of the proton (1.00759) and the electron (0.00055), so that the neutron is unstable with respect to dissociation into these two particles. The spontaneous disintegration of the neutron has been demonstrated experimentally [11, 12] and the half-life for the process $\mathrm{n} \rightarrow \mathrm{p} + \beta^-$ found to be approximately 12 minutes. The energy spectrum of the emitted electrons is similar to that found in β-decay, and corresponds to a maximum energy of 0.78 Mev. This value is exactly equivalent to the mass difference $\mathrm{n} - (\mathrm{p} + \mathrm{e})$ calculated from Eq. (2–2).

In addition to this intrinsic instability, the neutron reacts very readily with many nuclei, and especially with the proton in the reaction $\mathrm{n} + \mathrm{p} \rightarrow \mathrm{d}$, so that the average life of the neutron in paraffin, for example, in which there is a high concentration of hydrogen atoms, is only 2×10^{-4} sec. Unlike protons and the other chemical elements, a source of neutrons cannot be kept "on tap" because of their intrinsic instability. Nuclear reactors are the most powerful neutron sources, but it is also possible to produce neutrons in a simpler fashion by utilizing nuclear reactions involving either natural or accelerated high-energy particles (Table 11–11). Neutrons emitted as the result of such nuclear reactions have a high kinetic energy which is dependent upon the nature of the reaction and the energy of the incident particles.

We shall see in Section 5–2 that several nuclear reactions take place much more readily with very slow neutrons than with fast neutrons. The thermalizing of the latter, that is to say the lowering of their kinetic energy until it corresponds to thermal agitation (0.025 ev at ordinary temperatures), can be carried out by making the particles undergo a large number of collisions with hydrogen or other light atoms; the result of each collision is the loss of a significant fraction of the energy, as would be expected from the laws of conservation of momentum (Section 11–10).

The wave properties of neutrons are analogous to those of protons, and the de Broglie wavelength is given by an equation identical with Eq. (2–4). For thermal neutrons ($E = 0.025$ ev), λ is 1.8×10^{-8} cm, which is comparable to the interatomic distances in crystals. Neutrons are diffracted by crystals in a manner analogous to the diffraction of x-rays. (Section 11–10).

2–6 Antinucleons and neutrinos. In the theoretical discussion in which the existence of the positron was postulated, Dirac treated this particle as the negative energy state of the electron. On the basis of this theory, the existence of antinucleons should also be possible; these would be the antiproton, with a negative charge, and the antineutron, in which the magnetic moment and the spin would have the same sign. Investigations of cosmic rays at very high altitudes using photographic emulsions suggested [13, 14, 15] that the antiproton might have a very short existence as a component of cosmic radiation. This particle can be detected by its interaction with a normal proton, analogous to the annihilation of an electron-positron pair, resulting, in this case, in the production of very high-energy γ-radiation. The recent artificial production of the antiproton and the antineutron in the Berkeley bevatron is discussed later (Section 5–3).

As we shall also see in Chapter 4, the study of radioactive disintegrations has led to the postulate of the *neutrino*, a particle of zero charge and a mass close to zero. The properties of this particle have made its direct detection extremely difficult, but despite this its existence has been confirmed by some delicate experiments whose description can be more conveniently left to Section 4–3. Neutrinos and electrons are emitted simultaneously in the course of radioactive transformations, and are also found in the disintegration products of mesons; both have spin $\hbar/2$.

The symmetrical nature of Dirac's theory also requires the existence of an antineutrino $\bar{\nu}$, which would be associated with the ejection of an electron from a nucleus, whereas positron emission would be accompanied by a neutrino:

$$\mathrm{n} \rightarrow \mathrm{p} + \mathrm{e}^- + \bar{\nu}, \tag{2–5}$$

$$\mathrm{p} \rightarrow \mathrm{n} + \mathrm{e}^+ + \nu. \tag{2–6}$$

According to Dirac, these two neutrinos should be physically distinguishable, but Majorana believes that it is impossible to differentiate between them. Reaching an experimental decision would clearly be extremely difficult if not impossible. In particular, if the antineutrino is emitted according to Eq. (2–5) and the neutrino by Eq. (2–6), reactions such as

$$\mathrm{n} + \bar{\nu} \rightarrow \mathrm{p} + \mathrm{e}^-, \tag{2–5a}$$

or

$$\mathrm{p} + \nu \rightarrow \mathrm{n} + \mathrm{e}^+ \tag{2–6a}$$

would not be possible, and only $\mathrm{n} + \nu$ and $\mathrm{p} + \bar{\nu}$ could occur. We shall review in Section 4–3 the various experiments which have been carried out in an effort to choose between these two theories.

The search for the *bineutron*, a neutral particle with a mass of approximately 2, has so far been unsuccessful (Section 5–4). There is equally no experimental proof of the existence of the *neutretto*, a particle postulated by certain authors as having a rest mass equal to that of the electron but with zero charge.

2–7 Mesons. Meson particles were first postulated by Yukawa [16] in 1935 in his theory of nuclear forces (Section 3–8). A short time later an unstable particle with a mass about 200 times greater than that of the electron was discovered in cosmic radiation by Anderson [17], and this was tentatively identified as the meson required by Yukawa's theory. Conversi, Pancini, and Piccioni [18] showed experimentally, however, that the interactions of this new particle, known as the μ-meson or muon, are too weak to satisfy the required properties, and it is currently believed that it is the π-meson or pion, discovered later by Occhialini and Powell [19], which is responsible for the forces of the nucleus.

Mesons were first produced artificially by Gardner and Lattès [20], who bombarded graphite with 400-Mev α-particles and were able to detect the mesons photographically. Other reactions now used involve the interaction of various nuclei with very high-energy protons or γ-rays. The number of meson species which have been discovered in cosmic radiation or prepared artificially with the aid of accelerated particles has multiplied astonishingly as the energy of the bombarding particles has been increased. The properties of these mesons have been studied by means of cloud chambers, photographic emulsions, or specially designed counters. The considerable progress made recently in these techniques has led to information, of differing degrees of reliability, on the characteristic properties of these particles, that is, their mass, charge, average life, and the energy and products of their disintegration.

There has been a good deal of confusion in the past over the nomenclature used to designate the various mesons; in order to remedy this situation, the following recommendations were made by the International Congress on Cosmic Rays held in the Pyrennees in July, 1953 [21, 22]:

(1) The particles should be divided into three groups according to their mass: (a) *L*-mesons, comprising the light particles μ and π; (b) *K*-mesons, intermediate in mass between the pion and the proton; (c) *H*-mesons or hyperons, with masses between those of the proton and the deuteron, designated by the letter *Y*.

(2) The lower-case Greek letters (π, τ, χ, etc.) should be used for mesons and the capitals (Λ, Θ) for hyperons.

(3) The mode of disintegration should be indicated by the letters *V* and *S*, the first for those events which are interpreted as being the disintegration of a heavy meson or a hyperon in flight ($V^{\pm}$, V^0, according to the charge) and *S* for the decay of these particles at rest or for their interaction with a nucleus.

Using this nomenclature, our present knowledge of mesons can be summarized as follows [23], although we must always bear in mind that this information may well undergo revision in the future.

L-mesons. π-mesons with positive, negative, or zero charge are known. The charged species decay to a μ-meson of the same charge plus a neutrino:

$$\pi^{\pm} \rightarrow \mu^{\pm} + \nu + 34 \text{ Mev.} \tag{2-7}$$

The mass is 273 m_0 and the average life 2.5×10^{-8} sec. Uncharged pions decay with the formation of two photons:

$$\pi^0 \rightarrow 2\gamma + 135 \text{ Mev} \tag{2-8}$$

or, more rarely, disintegrate to an electron, a positron, and a photon. The

TABLE 2–2

THE PROPERTIES OF K-MESONS

Particle	Mass, relative to m_0	Half-life, sec	Spin	Modes of disintegration
K^+	966.3	1.2×10^{-8}	0	$2\pi^+ + \pi^-(\tau^+, 6.1\%)$ $\pi^+ + 2\pi^0$ (2.2%) $\pi^+ + \pi^0$ (θ^+, 27%) $\mu^+ + \pi^0$ (1.9%) $\mu^+ + \nu(59\%)$ $e^+ + \pi^0 + \nu(3\%)$
K^-	966.5	1.2×10^{-8}	0	$2\pi^- + \pi^+(\tau^-)$ $\pi^- + \pi^0$ (θ^-) $\mu^- + \nu$ $e^- + \pi^0 + \nu$
K_1^0	965	9.5×10^{-11}	0	$\pi^+ + \pi^-(\theta^0, \sim 85\%)$ $2\pi^0$ ($\sim$15%)
K_2^0	965	$3 \times 10^{-8} - 10^{-7}$	0	$\pi^+ + \pi^- + \pi^0$ (τ^0) $3\pi^0$ $\mu^\pm + \pi^\mp + \nu$ $e^\pm + \pi^\mp + \nu$

mass is 264 m_0 and the mean life is 1.9×10^{-16} sec. All pions have zero spin, and are pseudoscalar particles.

The μ-mesons have either a positive or a negative charge, a mass of 207 m_0, and spin $\frac{1}{2}$. They decay to an electron of the same charge and two neutrinos:

$$\mu^\pm \rightarrow e^\pm + 2\nu + 105 \text{ Mev}, \tag{2–9}$$

with a mean life of 2.1×10^{-6} sec. Muons have so far only been observed as the disintegration products of π-mesons. At sea level and below ground they are the principal component of cosmic radiation. Figure (2–1) shows the successive paths in a photographic emulsion of a π-meson, a μ-meson resulting from the disintegration of the pion, and an electron formed from the subsequent disintegration of the muon. A very small number (0.01%) of pions decay directly to an electron and a neutrino [24, 25].

Heavy mesons, K-mesons. For each type of heavy meson, positive, negative, or neutral, several modes of disintegration are known; these are shown

FIG. 2–1. The successive disintegration of a pion and a muon. (All the illustrations in this chapter are from plates kindly provided by M. Leprince-Ringuet.)

TABLE 2–3

THE PROPERTIES OF HYPERONS

Particle		Mass	Half-life, sec (average)
Λ^0	$\begin{cases} n + \pi^0 + 40.5 \text{ Mev} \\ p + \pi^- + 37 \text{ Mev} \end{cases}$	$2182\, m_0$	2.8×10^{-10}
Σ^+	$\begin{cases} p + \pi^0 + 116 \text{ Mev} \\ n + \pi^+ + 110 \text{ Mev} \end{cases}$	$2325\, m_0$	7.8×10^{-11}
$\Sigma^- \rightarrow$	$n + \pi^- + 117.3$ Mev	$2341\, m_0$	1.6×10^{-10}
$\Sigma^0 \rightarrow \Lambda^0 + \gamma + 73$ Mev		$2324\, m_0$	10^{-11}
$\Xi^- \rightarrow \Lambda^0 + \pi^- + 66$ Mev		$2585\, m_0$	$\sim 10^{-9}$
$\Xi^0 \rightarrow \Lambda^0 + \pi^0$		$2590\, m_0$	

in Table 2–2, where some of the other characteristics of these particles are also given. (See Ref. 26.)

Some years ago, several K-mesons, differing in their mode of disintegration, were believed to exist for each given charge, and these were allotted the Greek letters τ^+, θ^-, etc. (Fig. 2–2). Table 2–2 shows that the number of K-mesons is currently restricted to four.

Hyperons, Y. At the present time, six unstable particles with masses greater than the proton are known. These are described in Table 2–3. In addition, an observation by Prowsne and Coelin [27] of an event in a photographic emulsion exposed to 4.6-Bev π^--mesons has been attributed to the disintegration in flight of an antihyperon $\bar{\Lambda}^0$.

As a result of their behavior in nuclear reactions (Section 5–9), and because of some of their other properties, the heavy K-mesons and hyperons have been named "strange particles." The nucleons and hyperons form a group of "baryons."

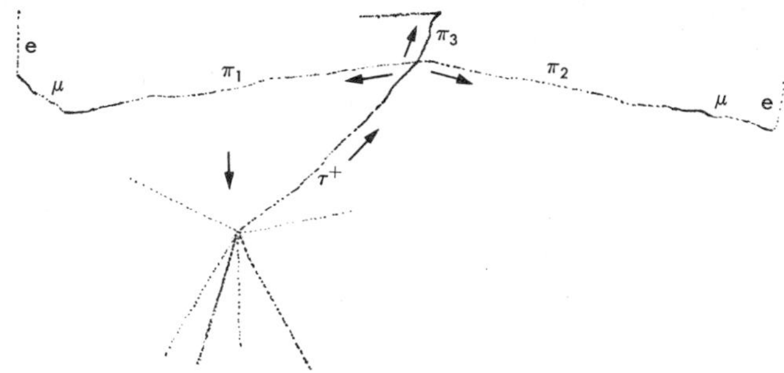

FIG. 2–2. The disintegration of a τ^+-meson, followed by the successive disintegrations of its daughters; π_1 and π_2 are positive pions and π_3 is a negative pion which undergoes capture in the emulsion, causing disintegration of the capturing nucleus.

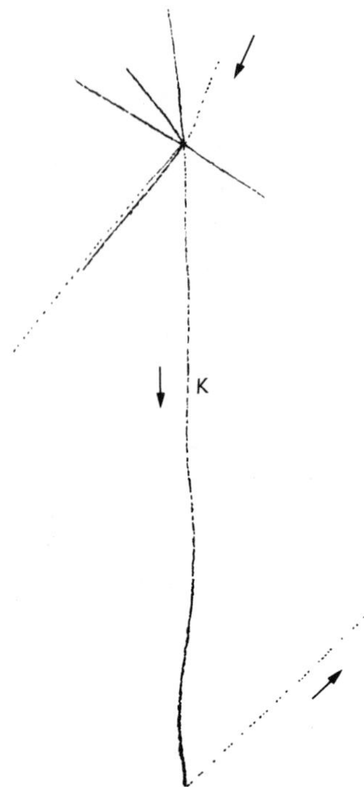

FIG. 2-3. Nuclear disintegration caused by a cosmic-ray particle, with the production of a K-meson. The arrows show the direction of the incident particle and the K-meson.

2-8 Cosmic radiation. It appears that, in addition to the mesons, all the fundamental particles and a certain number of heavy nuclei are to be found in cosmic radiation. Before entering the earth's atmosphere, the primary radiation consists almost entirely of very high-energy protons and α-particles. Certain heavy nuclei with atomic numbers below about 50, including C, N, O, Ne, Mg, and Fe, have been identified, and recent measurements also seem to confirm the presence of Li, B, and Be, about which there had previously been some dispute [28, 29]. The ratio protons : α-particles : heavy nuclei has been shown to be 1000 : 85 : 6. From tracks produced in photographic plates recovered from high-altitude rocket flights [30], the relative abundance in the heavy fraction at a geomagnetic latitude of 41°N is C + N + O 58%, F + Ne 20%, Na — K low, Ca — Fe 11%. A slightly different composition was given earlier by Noon *et al.* [31] from measurements on plates from balloon flights at the same latitude; according to these authors, for every 100 ±20 α-particles there are 3.8 ±0.5 atoms of Li + Be + B, 5.5 ±0.6 atoms of C + N + O, and 2.6 ±0.4 atoms with $Z > 10$.

The energy spectrum of the protons is given approximately [32] by empirical equations of the type

$$N(E) = \frac{k}{(E + 5.3)^{1.75}}, \tag{2-10}$$

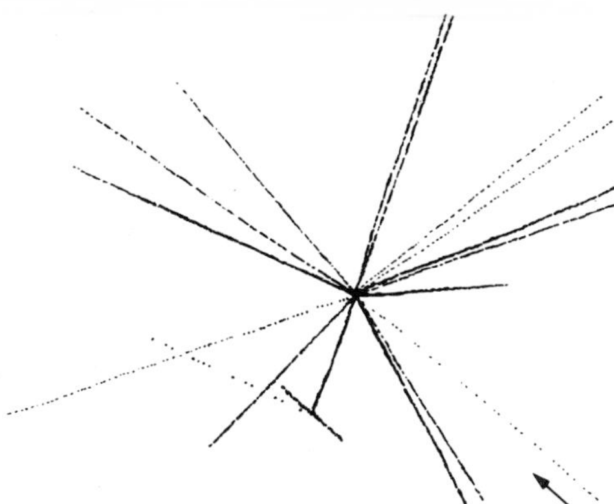

FIG. 2-4. A "star" resulting from the disintegration of a nucleus in the emulsion by a cosmic-ray particle. The original direction of the particle is shown by the arrow. The hammerlike track at the lower left corresponds to the disintegration of an unstable $Li^8 \rightarrow e^- + Be^8 \rightarrow 2\ He^4$.

where $N(E)$ is the number of protons with an energy greater than E (in Bev) and k is some constant. The energy distribution of the α-particles and of the other nuclei is probably very similar to that of the protons. Electrons comprise less than 1% of the primary radiation, and the γ-component is negligible.

As the result of collisions with nuclei in the atmosphere or in some detecting device, the particles of the primary radiation disintegrate into lighter nuclei, protons, neutrons, and mesons. If the particle is a heavy nucleus, it decomposes into simpler particles, so that on a photographic plate an event of this type is seen as a "star" (Figs. 2-3 and 2-4). For a given nucleus, the number and length of the branches of the star, their density and angular distribution, and the distribution of the secondary electrons (δ-rays) depends on the incident energy of the particle, and this energy can be calculated by measuring these parameters. For a particle with an especially high energy, a collision may result in a chain of reactions, leading to the formation of tens of thousands or even millions of *secondary* particles distributed over hundreds of meters or more. This phenomenon of large showers, or showers in cascade, discovered by Auger and his co-workers [33], is triggered by a highly penetrating secondary electron or photon. The mesons produced in the nuclear disintegrations caused by the primaries decompose spontaneously to photons and muons, which themselves decay to electrons and photons. These produce several successive generations of electrons and photons, with progressively lower energies, by the production and the annihilation of electron-positron pairs, or by the Compton effect (Section 11-5). By examining the distribution of the secondary radiation and the number of rays in a shower, it is possible to work out the energy of the particle which initiated the whole process, and this may be as high as 10^{16} or 10^{17} ev. The velocity of a proton of this energy is very close to that of light, and the relativistic mass is 10^6 times its rest mass. By way of comparison, it is worth noting that the most powerful modern accelerators produce particles with energies of the order of 3×10^{10} ev.

The *intensity* of cosmic radiation, on the other hand, is generally very low. Measurements with particle counters [34, 35] installed in artificial earth satellites show that the average number of particles in interplanetary space is of the order of 2 $\text{cm}^{-2} \cdot \text{sec}^{-1}$. Such techniques [34] have, however, also revealed the existence of two much more intense "belts" of cosmic radiation around the earth. Up to 640 km above the geomagnetic equator of the earth, the counting rate is low, but beyond this height it doubles for every 100 km increase in altitude, reaching a maximum at about 3400 km; at this point, a Geiger counter gives about 10^4 counts/sec. The intensity subsequently decreases, up to 8000 km, and then rises again to another maximum at about 18,000 km. The counting rate at a distance from the earth equal to 17 terrestrial radii is only 2 counts/sec. The existence of these two high-intensity zones seems to be the greatest danger at present known to interplanetary travel.

Earlier estimates of the total energy flux reaching the earth's surface gave a value of 2.5×10^{16} $\text{ergs} \cdot \text{sec}^{-1}$. Feynman [36] has calculated that the total charge deposition over the whole surface of the earth amounts to only 1 ampere.

One result of the nature of the successive chain of reactions which follow the nuclear explosion initiated by a primary proton is that the relative intensity of the various components of cosmic radiation varies considerably with altitude. It is usual to distinguish between the *soft* and *hard* components in the secondary radiation, on the basis of their penetrating power; the former consists of electrons and photons, and the latter of the various mesons. In the upper atmosphere, the number of protons and other primary particles falls off rapidly with decreasing altitude, while the number of photons and electrons increases initially and then also falls as a result of the various absorption phenomena discussed in Chapter 11. Since the μ-mesons are less reactive in nuclear interactions, the decrease in the μ-meson flux is slower. The average density of pions is very small throughout because of their short average life. At sea level, the ratio of the vertical intensity of the hard to soft components is 3.3; the ratio becomes equal to unity at an altitude of 3.6 km, and reaches its minimum value, 0.25, at about 12 km.

The origins of cosmic rays, and the nature of the phenomena which give rise to them, have been the subject of speculation since the beginnings of cosmic-ray research. Innumerable experiments have been performed to study the variations of intensity with time and space, but in spite of the great ingenuity and perseverance which has characterized both experiment and theory, no satisfactory answers have yet been given to the questions raised.

By the use of meteorological balloons, an east-west asymmetry has been established, the measured intensity at high altitudes being greater west of the zenith; moreover, this effect increases with the geomagnetic latitude. These results have led to the conclusion that the primary particles are positively charged and that the earth's magnetic field affects the distribution of the components of the radiation. Very small daily fluctuations of intensity have also been observed, but it seems that these are simply caused by the periodic variations in the composition of the atmosphere. On the other hand, intensity variations with a period of 27 days, related to "solar time," have been found, as well as more abrupt variations which coincide with outbreaks of sunspots. From this, it has been suggested that the cosmic radiation originates in the nuclear processes which are continually taking place in the sun (Section 5–8). These arguments, however, are not decisive, since even if the radiation was coming from interstellar or intergalactic space, it would be influenced by conditions on the sun, either as it crossed the electric field set up by the ionic solar currents, or as it approached the terrestrial magnetic field, which itself depends upon the condition of the sun. Furthermore, it seems that the energies of the nuclear processes involved are insufficient to account for the extremely high energies of the primary particles. This argument also weighs against Klein's hypothesis [37] in which the origin of the cosmic radiation is ascribed to the antinucleons which may make up some of the galaxies; interaction between these antiparticles and normal nuclei in intergalactic space would result in phenomena analogous to the transformation $e^+ + e^- \rightleftharpoons$ photons.

Without rejecting finally the concept of the solar origin of cosmic radiation, it is currently believed that the intensity of the primary particles in celestial space is essentially isotropic and that the radiations do in fact arise in cosmic space. Certain theories hold that the radiation has its origin in violent cosmic events such as the explosion of a supernova, although it is not clear how the primary particles would survive such a catastrophe without dissociating into their components [38]. For such reasons, it is believed that the particles may have a low initial energy and are gradually accelerated by a hypothetical electromagnetic field existing in the universe.

Fermi [39], in particular, has put forward the idea that the acceleration of the protons could be due to exchange of momentum with the ionized constituents of the interstellar spaces. It is known that in these spaces are to be found enormous clouds of gas, principally hydrogen, with a mean density of the order of only one atom per cubic centimeter, but with a total mass which may be almost the same as the mass of the stars. A very weak and irregular magnetic field would be associated with the movement of charged particles, and because of this, collisions in which there is a gain of kinetic energy would outnumber those in which there is a loss. A large fraction of the very fast protons would, however, be captured inside the Milky Way in various nuclear reactions; Fermi has calculated that the mean free path for this process is extremely large, 7×10^{25} cm, so that a proton moving with the speed of light will take 6×10^7 years to cover this distance. Protons which succeed in escaping nuclear reaction and which reach our planet should, therefore, on the average have this sort of age. The exact distribution of the particles according to age would be an exponential function, and since the energy of the protons would vary with age, Fermi was able to calculate the energy spectrum of these particles and to show that this is compatible with experimental observations such as Eq. (2–10).

This theory breaks down, however, for primary particles heavier than the proton, since for these the energy losses ought to be greater than the gains from collisions with lighter particles, especially interstellar hydrogen. It may be possible to overcome this difficulty by assuming [40, 41, 42] that the probability of escape from the galaxy is sufficiently great for this to be the process which determines the average life of the particles rather than the probability of collisions. The average life of all the particles would then be independent of their mass, and they would all have these same energy distributions.

Teller [38] has suggested a possible mechanism of escape by which the primary particles originate in those stars which emit radio waves with a wavelength of several meters. These stars are characterized by an intense magnetic activity similar to that of our own sun. The violent expulsion of clouds of gas is observed from time to time in the neighborhood of sunspots, which are related to the magnetic activity, and if the same phenomenon occurs at the surface of radiostars, these masses of gas, traveling at enormous speeds, would carry their magnetic field and the cosmic particles with them. The magnetic energy could be transformed into kinetic energy and the particles would continue their movement in interstellar space.

References

1. T. D. Lee and C. N. Yang, *Phys. Rev.*, **104,** 254 (1956); **108,** 1611 (1957); **108,** 1645 (1957); **109,** 1755 (1958).

2. For reviews of this topic, see O. R. Frisch and T. H. R. Skyrme, *Progress in Nuclear Physics*, Pergamon Press, London, **6,** 267 (1957); and I. S. Shapiro, *Progress Phys. Sci. U.S.S.R.*, **61,** 313 (1957).

3. Based on E. R. Cohen, J. W. M. DuMond, T. W. Layton, and J. S. Rollet, *Revs. Modern Phys.*, **27,** 363 (1955).

4. J. W. Shearer and M. Deutsch, *Phys. Rev.*, **76,** 462 (1949).

5. M. Deutsch, *Phys. Rev.*, **82,** 455 (1951); **83,** 866 (1951).

6. M. Deutsch, *Progress in Nuclear Physics*, Pergamon Press, London, **3,** 131 (1955).

7. M. Deutsch, *β- and γ-Ray Spectroscopy*, K. Siegbahn, ed. North-Holland Publishing Co., Amsterdam, 1955, p. 689.

8. S. DeBenedetti and R. Siegel, *Phys. Rev.*, **85,** 371 (1952); **87,** 235 (1952).

9. S. DeBenedetti and H. Corben, *Ann. Rev. Nuclear Sci.*, **4,** 191 (1954); this review gives a good bibliography of this topic.

10. R. Bell, *β- and γ-Ray Spectroscopy*, op. cit. p. 680; see also Ref. 9.

11. A. H. Snell and L. C. Miller, *Phys. Rev.*, **74,** 1217 (1948).

12. J. M. Robson, *Phys. Rev.*, **78,** 311 (1950); **83,** 349 (1951).

13. M. Schein, D. M. Haskin, and R. G. Glasser, *Phys. Rev.*, **96,** 829 (1954).

14. H. S. Bridge, H. Courant, H. de Staebler, and B. Rossi, *Phys. Rev.*, **95,** 1101 (1954).

15. E. Amaldi, C. Castagnoli, G. Cortini, C. Franzinetti, and A. Manfredini, *Nuovo cimento*, **1,** 492 (1955).

16. H. Yukawa, *Proc. Phys.-Math. Soc. Japan*, **17,** 48 (1935).

17. S. H. Neddermeyer and C. D. Anderson, *Phys. Rev.*, **51,** 884 (1937).

18. M. Conversi, E. Pancini, and O. Piccioni, *Phys. Rev.*, **71,** 209 (1947).

19. G. P. S. Occhialini and C. F. Powell, *Nature,* **162,** 168 (1948).

20. E. Gardner and C. M. G. Lattès, *Science,* **107,** 270 (1948).

21. L. Leprince-Ringuet, *Compt. rend.*, **238,** 25 (1954).

22. L. Leprince-Ringuet, *Ann. Rev. Nuclear Sci.*, **3,** 39 (1953).

23. See the report on the Padua International Congress on Heavy Unstable Particles in *Nuovo cimento,* Suppl. **12,** 163 (1953).

24. T. Fazzini, G. Fidccaro, A. W. Merrison, H. Paul, and A. V. Tollestrup, *Phys. Rev. Letters,* **1,** 247 (1958).

25. G. Impeduglia, R. Plano, A. Prodell, N. Samios, M. Schwartz, and J. Steinberger, *Phys. Rev. Letters,* **1,** 249 (1958).

26. C. Franzinetti and C. Morpurgo, *Nuovo cimento,* Suppl. **6,** 469 (1957).

27. D. Prowsne and B. Coelin, *Nuovo cimento,* **10,** 635 (1958).

28. A. D. Dainton, P. H. Fowler, and D. W. Kent, *Phil. Mag.*, **42,** 317 (1951); **43,** 729 (1952).

29. M. F. Kaplon, J. H. Noon, and G. W. Racette, *Phys. Rev.*, **96,** 1408 (1954).

30. H. Yagoda, quoted by C. A. Tobias, *Federation Proc.*, **18,** 1242 (1959).

31. J. H. Noon, A. J. Herz, and A. J. O'Brian, *Nature,* **179,** 91 (1957).

32. B. Rossi, *High-Energy Particles,* Prentice-Hall, New York, 1952.

33. P. Auger, R. Maze, P. Ehrenfest, and A. Freon, *J. phys. radium,* **10,** 39 (1939).

34. J. A. Van Allen and L. A. Frank, *Nature,* **183,** 430 (1959).

35. S. N. Vernov, A. Y. Tchoudakov, P. V. Vakoulov, and Y. I. Logatchev, *Doklady Akad. Nauk S.S.S.R.*, **125,** 304 (1959).

36. R. Feynman, quoted in D. Halliday, *Introductory Nuclear Physics,* Wiley and Sons, New York, 1950.

37. O. Klein, *Arkiv Mat. Astron. Fysik,* **33 A,** No. 14 (1945).

38. E. Teller, *Reports on Progress in Physics,* **17,** 154 (1954).

39. E. Fermi, *Phys. Rev.*, **75,** 1169 (1949).

40. P. Morrison, S. Olbert, and B. Rossi, *Phys. Rev.*, **94,** 440 (1954).

41. B. Rossi, *Atomes,* **9,** 119 (1954).

42. B. Rossi, *Nuovo cimento,* Suppl. **2,** 275 (1955).

CHAPTER 3

THE NUCLEUS

3–1 Mass and charge. Each nuclear species, or nuclide, is an assemblage of protons and neutrons characterized most simply by its mass and charge. The positive charge Z is given by the *number of protons*, which also defines the atomic number of the atomic species made up of the nucleus plus its peripheral electrons. The *number of neutrons* is denoted by N, so that the sum $(N + Z)$ gives the *mass number* A, a whole number which is in general slightly different from the exact mass M. The difference $(A - M)$ is known as the *mass defect* and is a measure of the stability of the nuclide. The *isotopic number* I $(= N - Z)$ indicates the excess of neutrons over protons.

Two nuclides are *isotopes* if they have the same number of protons but different masses, so that they have different numbers of neutrons. Two nuclides having the same number of neutrons but different Z are *isotones*. Two nuclides with the same mass number and different number of protons are *isobars*. If the atomic numbers differ by one unit, the number of protons in one nuclide may be equal to the number of neutrons in the other, as for example, in the isobars of mass 11 [B $(Z = 5)$ and C $(Z = 6)$] and of mass 27 [Al $(Z = 13)$ and Si $(Z = 14)$]. Such pairs are *mirror nuclides*, and one of them is always radioactive. A nuclide with Z protons is *shielded* if it has two stable isobars with $(Z + 1)$ and $(Z - 1)$; Br^{82}, Sb^{120}, I^{128}, and La^{138} are examples of shielded nuclides. In principle, at least, such nuclides can disintegrate by β-emission to $(Z + 1)$ and by positron emission to $(Z - 1)$ but the disintegration is usually only of a single type. The only exception to this rule is provided by ${}_{23}V^{50}$, isobaric with ${}_{22}Ti^{50}$ and ${}_{24}Cr^{50}$. The β-activity of V^{50} has not yet been detected, although it would be predicted for reasons other than the above. The half-life is probably very long; the spin of this nuclide is unusually large $(I = 6)$, and as we shall see (Section 4–2), the greater the difference in spin between the active nuclide and the product,* the longer the half-lives for β-transitions.

A nuclide may be excited relative to its ground state. If the transformation to the ground state occurs in a measurable time, the excited state is said to be *metastable* and is an *isomer* of the ground state. A nuclide may have two, or, more rarely, three or four isomers, as well as a large number of excited states with average lives of the order of 10^{-13} sec. The study of such excited states constitutes *nuclear spectroscopy*, which is in many respects analogous to atomic spectroscopy.

The mass number of the nuclide will be indicated by a superscript at the upper right of the chemical symbol and the atomic number by a subscript

* Recent experiments by Glover and Watt, [*Phil. Mag.*, **2**, 697 (1957)] indicate that V^{50} is in fact unstable to electron capture, with a half-life of 4×10^{14} years.

at the lower left, as in $_Z\mathrm{S}^A$. The metastable state will be designated by m, as in Br^{80m}. The atomic number Z can be frequently omitted, since it is already indicated without any uncertainty by the chemical symbol.

3–2 Nuclear moments. Each nucleon in the nucleus possesses, in addition to its spin, an angular momentum $\mathbf{l}$ arising from its orbital movement. The quantum number for this is written l, and the length of the angular momentum is $\sqrt{l(l+1)}\hbar$. For the nucleus as a whole, the total angular momentum $\mathbf{I}$ is defined as the vectorial sum of the orbital angular momentum and the spin angular momentum of all the nucleons which make up the nucleus

$$\mathbf{I} = \mathbf{L} + \mathbf{S}.$$

The quantum number I, which is always positive, is an exact number of half-integrals: $0, \frac{1}{2}, 1, \frac{3}{2} \ldots$; the length of the total angular momentum is $\sqrt{I(I+1)}\hbar$. The angular momentum is normally called nuclear *spin;* in general, there is a difference in spin between the ground state and the excited state of a nucleus.

As with the fundamental particles, the different states of a nucleus have odd or even parity. It is usual to write "parity change–yes" to indicate a nuclear system which undergoes a transformation with change of parity and "parity change–no" for the opposite case.

Each nucleon has a spin of $\frac{1}{2}$ and, since the orbital angular momentum is characterized by a whole number, it follows that for nuclei with even mass numbers, I is a whole number, and for odd A it is half-integral. It can be shown that for even A and even Z, I for the ground state is zero. This rule is one of a number of reasons for rejecting the early model, in which the nucleus was considered to be built up from protons and electrons. On this basis, the nuclide $_7\mathrm{N}^{14}$, for example, would have 21 particles (14 protons and 7 electrons), resulting in a value of I which is an odd multiple of $\frac{1}{2}$, because of the law of conservation of spin. In fact, I for this nucleus is a whole number ($I = 1$), as would be expected for a system containing an even number of particles (7 protons and 7 neutrons). We shall see later that the dimensions of the nucleus are also incompatible with the old model.

Nuclei with zero spin have a magnetic moment which is given by

$$\mu = \gamma\mu_0\sqrt{I(I+1)}\hbar, \tag{3–1}$$

where μ_0 is the nuclear magneton and the coefficient γ is the gyromagnetic ratio, analogous to the Lande factor of atomic spectroscopy. Unlike the latter, γ cannot as yet be calculated satisfactorily, although it has been measured with high precision for a large number of nuclei by various experimental methods, in particular by paramagnetic resonance and by analyzing the hyperfine structure of microwave spectra.

If both the magnetic moment and the spin of odd nuclei arise entirely from the unpaired nucleon, then a plot of one as a function of the other should place all the values on two lines. These are the so-called Schmidt lines [1], one of which corresponds to the spin and orbital momentum of

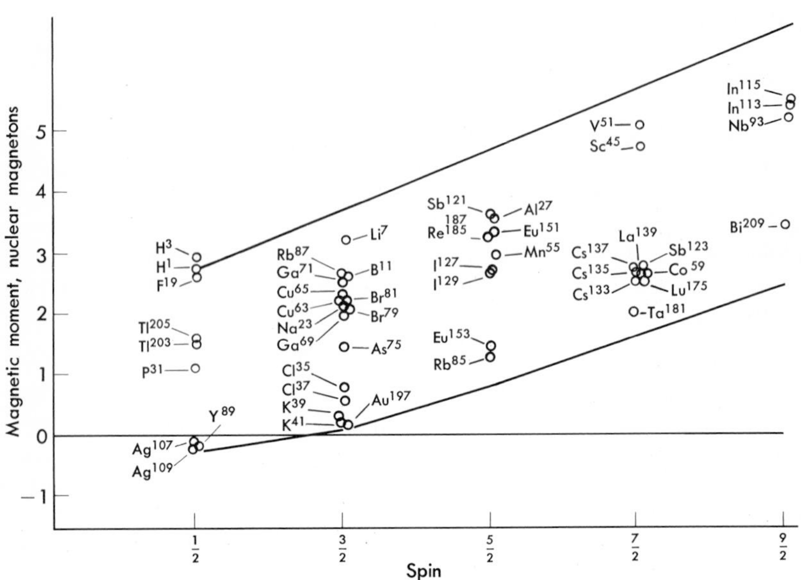

Fig. 3–1. Schmidt lines for odd-even nuclides.

the odd nucleon oriented in parallel and the other to the antiparallel state. Figure 3–1 shows that for nuclei with odd Z and even N, the values are spread out, but lie between the two theoretical lines (Section 3–9).

A nucleus in which there is a spherical distribution of the electric charge has no electric moment. It can be shown that the charged distribution is such that a nucleus must always possess no permanent electric dipole, but if the spin is equal to or greater than 1, the nucleus has a quadrupole moment. For a charge ϵ uniformly distributed over an ellipsoid of revolution, the quadrupole moment q is

$$q = 0.4(c^2 - a^2)\epsilon, \tag{3–2}$$

where a and c are the length of the two half-axes of the ellipsoid. The sign of q is positive for a prolate ellipsoid (i.e., egg-shaped or cigar-shaped) and negative for an oblate ellipsoid. The dimensions of the quadrupole moment are conventionally those of a surface and are expressed in multiples of 10^{-24} cm^2. The values are normally very small for light nuclei and often much higher for the heavy nuclei. Typical values are [2] $D^2 + 0.002738$, $N^{14} + 0.02$, $O^{17} - 0.005$, $Al^{27} + 0.156$, $Lu^{175} + 5.9$, $Re^{187} + 2.6$, $Bi^{209} - 0.4$, etc.; q is zero for He^4, C^{12}, O^{16} ($I = 0$), N^{15}, Cd^{113}, and Pb^{207} ($I = \frac{1}{2}$). There is an overall periodic variation of q with Z, the significance of which will be discussed later.

The connection between spin and statistics which was described for the fundamental particles also applies to assemblies of nucleons. A nucleus with integral spin follows the Bose-Einstein statistics, and those with half-integral spin obey Fermi statistics.

TABLE 3–1

NUCLEAR RADII

Nucleus	Radius, $\times 10^{-13}$ cm	Nucleus	Radius, $\times 10^{-13}$ cm
H^1	1.15	Ni^{62}	6.0
D^2	1.36	Br	6.11
Li^7	2.50	Ag	6.45
Be^9	2.90	Ba	6.83
B^{11}	3.2	Tl^{210}	7.0
C^{13}	3.4	Pb^{208}	7.8
N^{15}	3.5	Bi^{211}	8.1
O^{17}	3.6	Po^{216}	8.5
Na^{23}	4.1	Ra^{223}	8.3
Mg	4.5	Th^{224}	8.4
Al^{27}	4.6	Pu^{236}	9.10
S^{35}	4.88	Cm^{242}	9.14
Cl	5.07		

3–3 The radius of the nucleus. To a reasonable approximation, the nucleus can be treated as a sphere, since the deviations from spherical symmetry are small. With this assumption, several methods can be used for determining the radii of nuclei. As with measurements of atomic radii, different methods give slightly different values, which is perhaps not unexpected since the different results do not necessarily have the same significance.

One important conclusion which can be drawn from these determinations is that the nuclear density is approximately constant for all nuclides. To a first approximation one can write for the radius R of a nucleus of mass A

$$R = r_0 A^{1/3}, \tag{3–3}$$

where r_0 is the elementary nuclear radius. It follows that the nuclear volume is proportional to the mass number, which implies that the forces acting between the nucleons in a nucleus are saturated and do not extend appreciably beyond nearest neighbors. In much the same way the volume of a liquid is proportional to the mass as a result of the short range of the van der Waals' forces. Several methods of determining nuclear radii give values between 1.4 and 1.5×10^{-13} cm for the constant r_0. Experiments on the scattering of very high-energy charged particles (protons, deuterons, α-particles) by nuclei lead to significantly higher values (1.6 to 1.68×10^{-13} cm) [3, 4], while the most recent results (Section 5–10) give rather smaller radii with $r_0 \approx 1.2 \times 10^{-13}$ cm.

The variation of R with A is sometimes written as an equation containing an additional term:

$$R = r_0 A^{1/3} + b. \tag{3–4}$$

With this way of defining r_0, different authors find values which vary between 1.22 and 1.52×10^{-13} cm; b is then between 1.7 and 0.7×10^{-13} cm.

Table 3–1 gives experimental values for the radii of some nuclei. The absence of a mass number implies that the experiment was carried out with the natural mixture of isotopes.

3–4 Stability and binding energy. A nucleus is assumed to be stable when no radioactivity can be detected with the measuring equipment currently available, so that it appears to be in its ground state and does not change to another nuclide by the emission of a particle, the capture of a peripheral electron, or any other process. This is a rather uncertain definition of stability, depending as it does on the sensitivity of the detecting instruments used. A more precise criterion, mentioned briefly in Section 2–2, is based on the Einstein equation relating mass and energy (Eq. 2–2). A nuclear system is stable relative to another if their energy difference calculated from the Einstein equation is negative, or in other words, if the rest mass of the first is smaller than that of the other. The mass difference is a measure of the instability of the second system with respect to the first. On this basis, for example, it can be shown that the neutron is less stable than the system (proton + electron), and that the nuclide He^4 is more stable than its four uncombined constituents.

More generally speaking, the stability of an atom Z^A of mass M with respect to its constituent nucleons is given by

$$[ZM_{\mathrm{H}} + (A - Z)M_{\mathrm{n}} - M]\ 931\ \mathrm{Mev},$$

where M_{H} is the mass of the hydrogen atom and M_{n} that of the neutron. The average binding energy E per nucleon is given by the relation

$$\begin{aligned} E &= \left[\frac{ZM_{\mathrm{H}} + (A - Z)M_{\mathrm{n}} - M}{A}\right] 931 \\ &= \left[1.00898 - 0.00084\frac{Z}{A} - \frac{M}{A}\right] 931\ \mathrm{Mev}. \end{aligned} \tag{3–5}$$

In mass spectrometry, frequent reference is made to the *packing fraction* f, which is the mass defect per nucleon:

$$f = \frac{M - A}{A}, \tag{3–6}$$

where M is expressed in amu. By definition, $f = 0$ for O^{16}; for other nuclides, f may be positive or negative. The binding energy per nucleon can be expressed as a function of the packing fraction:

$$E = 931\left(0.00898 - 0.00084\frac{Z}{A} - f\right). \tag{3–7}$$

If E is plotted as a function of mass for the stable and very long-lived nuclei, the curve in Fig. 3–2 is obtained. It is clear that the binding energy

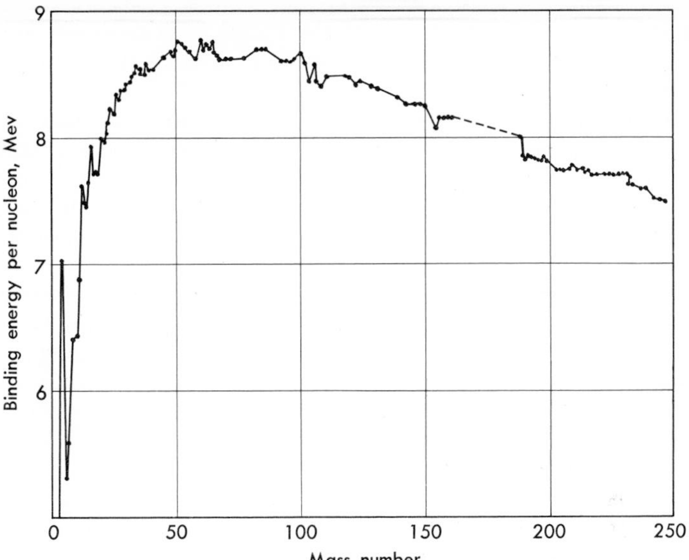

FIG. 3–2. The variation of binding energy per nucleon with the mass number.

increases rapidly for the very light nuclides, reaches a maximum of 8.5 to 8.8 Mev for the nuclides of medium atomic weight, and then falls very slowly to about 7.5 Mev. Each nucleon in the nucleus also possesses kinetic energy, which has been estimated at between 20 and 25 Mev, so that the average potential energy per nucleon is of the order of 30 Mev.

The small variation of average binding energy with increasing mass is further evidence of the saturation of nuclear forces, one effect of which has already been noted in connection with the dimensions of nuclei. These short-range forces act only between neighboring nucleons and are almost unaffected by the addition of further particles. This behavior may be contrasted with that of the coulombic forces which act over a distance and increase with the increasing charge of the system.

Consider now an atom containing Z protons and N $(= A - Z)$ neutrons and with atomic mass ${}_ZM^A$; let ${}_{Z+1}M^A$ be the mass of an isobar containing $(Z + 1)$ protons and $(N - 1)$ neutrons. The first atom will be unstable in terms of β^- decay to the second if

$$ {}_ZM^A > {}_{Z+1}M^A. \tag{3–8}$$

The second atom is unstable relative to the first by positron emission if

$$ {}_{Z+1}M^A - 2m_0 > {}_ZM^A. \tag{3–9}$$

In β^--emission, the total number of electrons does not change as a result of the transformation, but in the second case, two have been lost, a nuclear positron resulting from the proton $\rightarrow$ neutron transition, and the periphery electron lost as a result of the decrease in Z. If the nuclear masses are considered, instead of the masses of the atoms, it is necessary to add m_0 to the right-hand side of the condition (3–8) and to substitute $-m_0$ for $-2m_0$ in Eq. (3–9).

The lack of balance in the proton : neutron ratio, implicit in β^-- or β^+-emission, is particularly important in the study of nuclear forces. The instability which is relieved by the emission of an α-particle is found only among the heavier nuclei and is the result of the increase in the electrostatic repulsion between the protons. This latter factor is small in relation to the specifically nuclear forces.

3–5 The semiempirical mass equation. The semiempirical Bethe-Weizsäcker equation relates the mass of a nucleus containing Z protons and N neutrons [5, 6, 7]:

$$ {}_ZM^A = ZM_\text{p} + (A - Z)M_\text{n} - \alpha A + \beta A^{2/3} + \frac{\gamma}{A}\left(\frac{A}{2} - Z\right)^2 + \frac{3}{5}\frac{e^2Z^2}{r_0A^{1/3}} \pm \delta. \tag{3–10} $$

This equation can in fact be deduced from the statistical model of the nucleus discussed in Section 3–8. The first two terms of this equation represent the masses of the protons and the neutrons in the free state, and the third gives the binding energy of the nucleons, analogous to the cohesive energy of a liquid or a solid (volume energy). The fourth term is a correction for the unsaturated nuclear forces at the surface and is proportional to the surface area and hence to $A^{2/3}$. The fifth term, which takes account of the effect of symmetry on the stability, arises from the experimental observation that each value of A has a value of Z for which there is maximum stability; for light nuclei this occurs when $Z = A/2$. It is assumed, empirically, that a deviation from this neutron-proton symmetry introduces an instability which is represented by a repulsive term proportional to the square of the neutron excess $(A/2 - Z)^2$ and inversely proportional to A. The sixth term arises from the electrostatic repulsion between the protons. The final *pairing* or spin term is due to the fact [8, 9] that nuclei with both N and Z odd are less stable than those in which only one of these numbers is odd, and these are less stable than nuclei with both Z and N even. It was previously believed that the effect of an unpaired proton and neutron was the same, so that if $\delta = 0$ for even-odd and odd-even nuclides (A odd), δ has the same value for odd-odd and even-even nuclides, but is positive in the first case and negative in the second. It has been recently shown, however [8, 9, 10], that the coupling energy is higher for a proton than for a neutron, so that the δ-term cannot be zero, even for nuclides of even A. This energy excess (given the symbol ϵ by Kohman [10]) is negative for even Z-odd N and positive for odd Z-even N. The value of ϵ may be as high as 0.7 Mev, but for the moment we shall neglect this factor (Section 4–3).

From Eq. (3–10), it is possible to calculate the atomic number Z_A of the nuclide which is the most stable isobar of mass number A; that is, to find the value of Z_A which corresponds to the condition $\delta M/\delta Z = 0$.

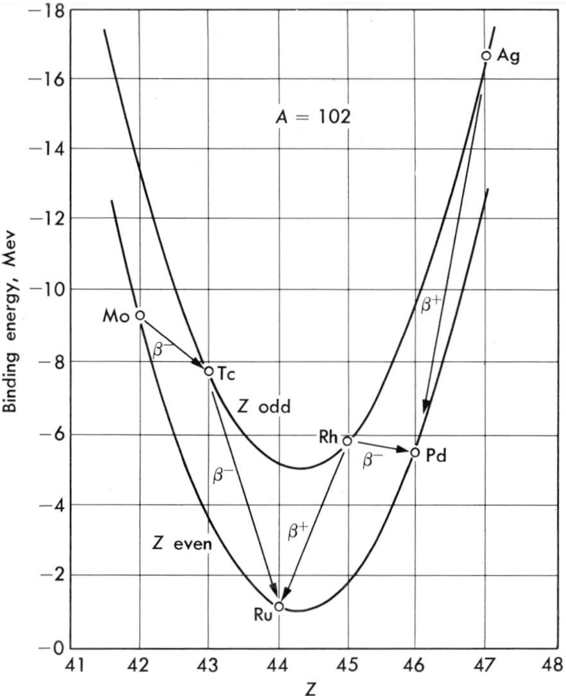

FIG. 3–3. Nuclear stability parabolas for $A = 102$.

Replacing $(M_n - M_p)$ by m' and $\frac{3}{5}(e^2/r_0)$ by k, we have

$$\frac{\delta M}{\delta Z} = -m' + 2kZ_A A^{-1/3} - \frac{2}{A}\gamma\left(\frac{A}{2} - Z_A\right) = 0, \qquad (3\text{–}11)$$

from which

$$Z_A = \frac{m' + \gamma}{2kA^{-1/3} + 2\gamma A^{-1}} = \frac{A}{2} \cdot \frac{m' + \gamma}{2kA^{2/3} + \gamma}. \qquad (3\text{–}12)$$

By combining this with Eq. (3–10), we obtain

$${}_Z M^A = {}_{Z_A} M^A + \frac{B_A}{2}(Z_A - Z)^2 \pm \delta, \qquad (3\text{–}13)$$

where $B_A = (m' + \gamma)/Z_A$. It follows from this second-order equation that for odd A the masses of the isobars lie on a parabola whose peak is at Z_A; it should be noted that this theoretical value is not necessarily a whole number. Those isobars on the parabola corresponding to other values of Z tend to change to Z_A by the emission of electrons or positrons. For even mass numbers, there are two separate parabolas corresponding to even Z and odd Z; such a pair of parabolas are shown schematically in Fig. 3–3 for $A = 102$.

The numerical values of the coefficients in Eq. (3–10) are calculated by fitting them to the exactly known masses of stable nuclides with medium A.

TABLE 3–2*

Nuclide	Volume term	Surface term	Electrostatic term	γ-term	δ
$_{23}V^{50}$	−750	190	90	6.6	+1.91
$_{42}Mo^{100}$	−1500	302	238	53.3	−1.13
$_{75}Re^{187}$	−2805	458	617	151	0
$_{92}U^{238}$	−3570	537	856	255	−0.59

* Values in 10^{-3} amu.

The coefficient of the electrostatic term (in $Z^2/A^{1/3}$) can be calculated from the mass differences of mirror nuclides; different authors have obtained varying results, depending in particular on the value chosen for r_0. With $r_0 = 1.48 \times 10^{-13}$ cm and $k = 6.27 \times 10^{-4}$ amu, one finds (in amu)

$$\alpha = 0.015, \quad \beta = 0.014, \quad \gamma = 0.083, \quad \delta = 0.036A^{-3/4} \quad (\text{even } A).$$

Taking r_0 as 1.216×10^{-13}, Green [11] finds

$$k = 7.628 \times 10^{-4}, \quad \alpha = 0.01692, \quad \beta = 0.01912, \quad \gamma = 0.1018.$$

Similarly, if values are available for all but one of the coefficients of the equation, the missing value can be calculated, and this gives one method of determining nuclear radii.

The relative contributions of the various terms changes with increasing mass. For light nuclei, for which Eq. (3–11) does not in any case hold very well, the surface term β is much more important than the coulombic term, but for heavy nuclei the reverse is true. For nuclides with masses in the region of 100, these two contributions are almost equal. Some examples of the various terms, calculated on the basis of the first set of coefficients quoted above, are given in Table 3–2.

Significant disagreement is found between the calculated and experimental values for certain nuclei with particular structures, and we shall return to this point later.

3–6 The abundance of nuclei. Stability rules. Up to the present time, nearly 1500 nuclides have been identified, and of these more than 1000 are radioactive. This number is continually on the increase as methods of detection become more sensitive and as increasingly powerful means of disintegrating nuclei are developed. There is, however, an upper limit to this increase, since even in a very unstable nucleus the neutron : proton ratio cannot exceed certain limits. The genetic relations between the natural radioelements will be discussed in Chapter 7.

Table 3–3 gives the mass numbers of the stable or very long-lived radioactive isotopes of each naturally occurring element, with the relative

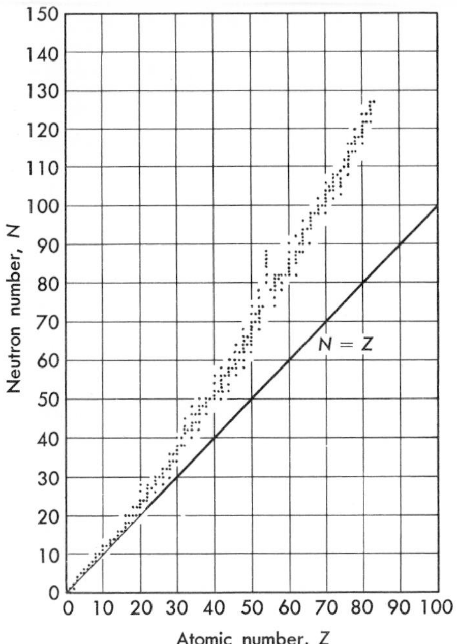

FIG. 3–4. Variation of the proton : neutron ratio with Z.

(percentage) abundance of each isotope. These values should not be confused with the abundances of the elements themselves, which are related to the composition of the terrestrial crust or of cosmic matter (Chapter 10). The table shows that the proportions of the isotopes can vary between very wide limits for a given value of Z, and this is equally true for isobars and isotones. From the values in Table 3–3, it is possible to deduce certain rules which are fundamental to any understanding of nuclear structure and the origin of the elements.

(1) When the number of neutrons N is plotted as a function of Z for each known nuclide, the results shown in Fig. 3–4 are obtained. If this is treated as a smooth curve, the slope at the origin is close to unity, implying that for light nuclei the number of protons is exactly or virtually equal to the number of neutrons. Beyond about $Z = 20$, there are appreciable deviations from the straight line drawn for $N = Z$, and the neutron excess increases with Z, although the ratio $N : Z$ barely exceeds 1.5 even for the heaviest nuclei. The nucleus has therefore an approximately symmetrical composition as far as the ratio of its components is concerned (*symmetry rule*). The degree of symmetry can be expressed as the quotient

$$\alpha = (N - Z)/2 = A/2 - Z;$$

for light nuclei, α has the values 0, 0.5, or 1.

(2) At least one stable nuclide exists for each atomic number from 1 to 82, with the exceptions of $Z = 43$ and $Z = 61$ (Section 7–4).

TABLE 3–3

THE MASSES AND ABUNDANCES OF THE STABLE AND LONG-LIVED ISOTOPES

Element	Z	Mass and percentage abundance
H	1	1 (99.98); 2 (0.015)
He	2	3 ($1.3 \cdot 10^{-4}$); 4 (100)
Li	3	6 (7.5); 7 (92.5)
Be	4	9 (100)
B	5	10 (18.8); 11 (81.2)
C	6	12 (98.892); 13 (1.108)
N	7	14 (99.635); 15 (0.365)
O	8	16 (99.759); 17 (0.037); 18 (0.204)
F	9	19 (100)
Ne	10	20 (90.92); 21 (0.257); 22 (8.82)
Na	11	23 (100)
Mg	12	24 (78.60); 25 (10.11); 26 (11.29)
Al	13	27 (100)
Si	14	28 (92.27); 29 (4.68); 30 (3.05)
P	15	31 (100)
S	16	32 (95.1); 33 (0.74); 34 (4.2); 36 (0.016)
Cl	17	35 (75.4); 37 (24.6)
Ar	18	36 (0.337); 38 (0.063); 40 (99.60)
K	19	39 (93.08); 40 (0.0119); 41 (6.91)
Ca	20	40 (96.97); 42 (0.64); 43 (0.145); 44 (2.06); 46 (0.0033); 48 (0.185)
Sc	21	45 (100)
Ti	22	46 (7.95); 47 (7.75); 48 (73.45); 49 (5.51); 50 (5.34)
V	23	50 (0.24); 51 (99.76)
Cr	24	50 (4.31); 52 (83.76); 53 (9.55); 54 (2.38)
Mn	25	55 (100)
Fe	26	54 (5.84); 56 (91.68); 57 (2.17); 58 (0.31)
Co	27	59 (100)
Ni	28	58 (67.76); 60 (26.16); 61 (1.25); 62 (3.66); 64 (1.16)
Cu	29	63 (69.1); 65 (30.9)
Zn	30	64 (48.89); 66 (27.81); 67 (4.11); 68 (18.56); 70 (0.62)
Ga	31	69 (60.5); 71 (39.5)
Ge	32	70 (20.55); 72 (27.37); 73 (7.67); 74 (36.74); 76 (7.67)
As	33	75 (100)
Se	34	74 (0.87); 76 (9.02); 77 (7.58); 78 (23.52); 80 (49.82); 82 (9.19)
Br	35	79 (50.52); 81 (49.48)
Kr	36	78 (0.354); 80 (2.27); 82 (11.56); 83 (11.55); 84 (56.90); 86 (17.37)

TABLE 3–3 (*Continued*)

Element	Z	Mass and percentage abundance
Rb	37	85 (72.15); 87 (27.85)
Sr	38	84 (0.56); 86 (9.86); 87 (7.02); 88 (82.56)
Y	39	89 (100)
Zr	40	90 (51.46); 91 (11.23); 92 (17.11); 94 (17.40); 96 (2.8)
Nb	41	93 (100)
Mo	42	92 (15.86); 94 (9.12); 95 (15.70); 96 (16.50); 97 (9.45); 98 (23.75); 100 (9.62)
Tc	43	
Ru	44	96 (5.46); 98 (1.86); 99 (12.63); 100 (12.53); 101 (17.02); 102 (31.63); 104 (18.87)
Rh	45	103 (100)
Pd	46	102 (0.8); 104 (9.3); 105 (22.6); 106 (27.2); 108 (26.8); 110 (13.5)
Ag	47	107 (51.35); 109 (48.65)
Cd	48	106 (1.215); 108 (0.875); 110 (12.39); 111 (12.75); 112 (24.07); 113 (12.26); 114 (28.86); 116 (7.58)
In	49	113 (4.23); 115 (95.77)
Sn	50	112 (0.95); 114 (0.65); 115 (0.34); 116 (14.24); 117 (7.57); 118 (24.01); 119 (8.58); 120 (32.97); 122 (4.71); 124 (5.98)
Sb	51	121 (57.25); 123 (42.75)
Te	52	120 (0.089); 122 (2.46); 123 (0.87); 124 (4.61); 125 (6.99); 126 (18.7); 128 (31.79); 130 (34.49)
I	53	127 (100)
Xe	54	124 (0.096); 126 (0.09); 128 (1.92); 129 (26.44); 130 (4.08); 131 (21.18); 132 (26.89); 134 (10.44); 136 (8.87)
Cs	55	133 (100)
Ba	56	130 (0.101); 132 (0.097); 134 (2.42); 135 (6.59); 136 (7.81); 137 (11.32); 138 (71.66)
La	57	138 (0.089); 139 (99.911)
Ce	58	136 (0.193); 138 (0.250); 140 (88.48); 142 (11.07)
Pr	59	141 (100)
Nd	60	142 (27.13); 143 (12.20); 144 (23.87); 145 (8.30); 146 (17.18); 148 (5.72); 150 (5.60)
Pm	61	
Sm	62	144 (3.16); 147 (15.07); 148 (11.27); 149 (13.84); 150 (7.47); 152 (26.63); 154 (22.53)
Eu	63	151 (47.77); 153 (52.23)
Gd	64	152 (0.20); 154 (2.15); 155 (14.73); 156 (20.47); 157 (15.68); 158 (24.87); 160 (21.90)

(*Continued*)

TABLE 3–3 (*Continued*)

Element	Z	Mass and percentage abundance
Tb	65	159 (100)
Dy	66	156 (0.052); 158 (0.090); 160 (2.29); 161 (18.88); 162 (25.53); 163 (24.97); 164 (28.18)
Ho	67	165 (100)
Er	68	162 (0.136); 164 (1.56); 166 (33.41); 167 (22.94); 168 (27.07); 170 (14.88)
Tm	69	169 (100)
Yb	70	168 (0.140); 170 (3.03); 171 (14.31); 172 (21.82); 173 (16.13); 174 (31.84); 176 (12.73)
Lu	71	175 (97.4); 176 (2.6)
Hf	72	174 (0.2); 176 (5.23); 177 (18.55); 178 (27.23); 179 (13.73); 180 (35.07)
Ta	73	181 (100); 180 (0.01)
W	74	180 (0.135); 182 (26.4); 183 (14.4); 184 (30.6); 186 (28.4)
Re	75	185 (37.07); 187 (62.93)
Os	76	184 (0.018); 186 (1.59); 187 (1.64); 188 (13.3); 189 (16.1); 190 (26.4); 192 (41.0)
Ir	77	191 (38.5); 193 (61.5)
Pt	78	190 (0.012); 192 (0.78); 194 (32.8); 195 (33.7); 196 (25.4); 198 (7.23)
Au	79	197 (100)
Hg	80	196 (0.146); 198 (10.02); 199 (16.84); 200 (23.13); 201 (13.22); 202 (29.80); 204 (6.85)
Tl	81	203 (29.50); 205 (70.50)
Pb	82	204 (1.48); 206 (23.6); 207 (22.6); 208 (52.3)
Bi	83	209 (100)
Th	90	232 (100)
U	92	234 (0.006); 235 (0.712); 238 (99.28)

(3) No stable nuclides are known with $N = 19, 21, 35, 39, 45, 61, 115, 123$; for each of these N is odd [12].

(4) The nuclides can be divided into four groups according to the numbers of protons and neutrons they possess; (a) even-even (e.g., ${}_{16}S^{32}$); (b) odd-odd (${}_{7}N^{14}$); (c) even-odd (${}_{6}C^{13}$); (d) odd-even (${}_{9}F^{19}$). More than half of the stable nuclides belong to group (a), but there are only four in group (b) with $Z \leq 7$ (${}_{1}D^{2}$, ${}_{3}Li^{6}$, ${}_{5}B^{10}$, ${}_{7}N^{14}$). Also in group (b) are the unstable isotopes ${}_{19}K^{40}$ and ${}_{71}Lu^{176}$, plus ${}_{23}V^{50}$, which is probably radioactive (Section 3–1). Twenty percent of the stable nuclides are in group (c) and about 16% in group (d). It should also be noted that all the four stable odd-odd nuclides have $Z = N$.

(5) Among the isotopes of even atomic number, even-even nuclides are more abundant than odd-even; among the odd-odd nuclides, only ${}_{7}N^{14}$ is more abundant than its isotope ${}_{7}N^{15}$.

(6) For Z odd and >7, there is normally only one stable nuclear species; for the 13 cases where there are two species, the mass difference between them never exceeds 2. On the other hand, for the 38 elements between $Z = 7$ and $Z = 83$ with even Z, at least 3 stable isotopes are known, and there are often many more than this (10 for $_{50}$Sn, 9 for $_{54}$Xe, 8 for $_{48}$Cd and $_{52}$Te); in fact, the average number of isotopes for elements with even Z is 5.7. For each of these, the heaviest and lightest isotopes have N even [12].

(7) For N odd and >7, there is only one stable nuclide of even Z, with the exceptions of $_{42}Mo^{97}$ and $_{44}Ru^{99}$ ($N = 55$), and $_{48}Cd^{113}$ and $_{50}Sn^{115}$ ($N = 65$), although it is always possible that each of these pairs contains a very long-lived active nuclide.

(8) As a general rule, all the nuclides of even mass number have one or two stable isobars, while those with odd A have none at all (Mattauch's rule). In the three isobaric pairs, Rb^{87}-Sr^{87}, In^{115}-Sn^{115}, and Re^{187}-Os^{187}, the first isotope is radioactive, with a very long half-life. The isobaric pairs Cd^{113}-In^{113} and Te^{123}-Sb^{123} are the only exceptions to this rule, but it is possible that each of these pairs contains a radioactive isotope.

(9) All isobars with $\Delta Z > 1$ belong without exception to group (a) (i.e., even-even).

3–7 Magic numbers. It will be evident from the rules just set out that even numbers of neutrons and protons have a particular importance in the constitution of nuclei. It seems reasonable to assume that the most abundant nuclides are those which have a greater stability than their isotopes or isobars. When Table 3–3 is examined more closely with this in mind, one can see that 2 is not the only number of special significance in the stability of nuclei, but that stability is often associated with certain other numbers, which also crop up when other properties of the nucleus are considered. Before their exact significance was understood, these values were named the "magic numbers"; in spite of this title, it was tempting to compare them with the numbers 2, 8, 18, and 32 which govern the filling of the electron shells of atoms by the Pauli exclusion principle and are consequently fundamental to the periodic system of the elements. It was immediately suggested that the nucleus also has a shell structure [13, 14, 15, 16], but in fact the situation is much more complicated than for atomic orbitals.

The principal observations which support the reality of the magic numbers are the following [17, 18, 19, 20, 21]:

(1) The large number of isotopes with $Z = 50$ (Sn) and their neighbors with even Z, namely 48 (Cd), 52 (Te), and 54 (Xe), has already been noted. There is also a relatively large number (6) of isotones for $N = 50$, and a fairly large number of stable isotopes and isotones with Z or $N = 20$ (6 and 5 respectively), 28 (5 and 5), and 82 (4 and 7).

(2) For Z odd and larger than 7, there is only one nuclear species with even N, save for three exceptions which occur at $N = 20$ ($_{17}Cl^{37}$, $_{19}K^{39}$), 50 ($_{37}Rb^{87}$, $_{39}Y^{89}$), and 82 ($_{57}La^{139}$, $_{59}Pr^{141}$). For Z even and greater than 36, the abundance of the most abundant isotope is less than 35%, with the exception of $_{38}Sr^{88}$ with $N = 50$ (82.14%), and $_{56}Ba^{138}$ (71.66%)

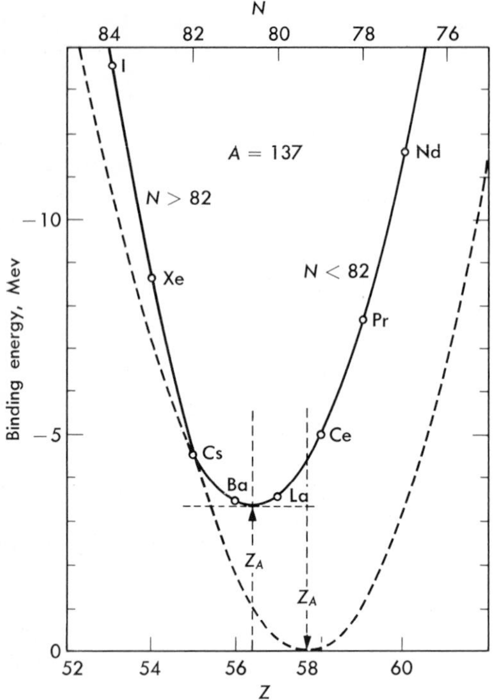

FIG. 3–5. Nuclear stability parabolas for $A = 137$. (From C. D. Coryell, M.I.T. Report, May 1951.)

and ${}_{58}\text{Ce}^{140}$ (88.49%), for which $N = 82$. On the other hand, for Z even and >32, the abundance of the lightest isotope is less than 2%, with five exceptions: ${}_{40}\text{Zr}^{90}$ (51.46%) and ${}_{42}\text{Mo}^{92}$ (15.86%) for which $N = 50$, ${}_{44}\text{Ru}^{96}$ (5.68%) with $N = 52$, and ${}_{60}\text{Nd}^{152}$ (27.13%) and ${}_{62}\text{Sm}^{144}$ (3.16%), for which $N = 82$.

(3) In addition to the number of isotopes which exist for a given element, one can consider the difference in neutron number between the heaviest and the lightest isotopes as a criterion of stability; the greater this difference, the greater the importance of this value of Z in nuclear structure. Thus the first case of $\Delta N = 2$ occurs at $Z = 8$; for the light elements, $\Delta N = 6$ is found at $Z = 28$, and $\Delta N = 8$ at $Z = 20$, for which the heaviest isotope is ${}_{20}\text{Ca}^{48}$ with $N = 28$. Other examples of $\Delta N = 8$ are Kr and Mo, where ${}_{36}\text{Kr}^{86}$ and ${}_{42}\text{Mo}^{92}$ have $N = 50$, and Ba and Nd, where ${}_{56}\text{Ba}^{138}$ and ${}_{60}\text{Nd}^{142}$ have $N = 82$. Finally, the two elements for which $\Delta N = 12$ are Sn, with $Z = 50$, and Xe, with $Z = 54$; the heaviest isotope of the latter, with $A = 136$, has 82 neutrons.

(4) There are fluctuations in the mass-defect curve (Fig. 3–2) for odd-even A; the δ-term in Eq. (3–10) takes account of this, but there are additional discontinuities corresponding to the magic numbers. Close to these numbers, the parabolic isobaric diagrams, based on the Weizsäcker equation, are no longer valid. For a given value of A, nuclei having a neutron

number less than a magic number are found on one parabola and those with N greater than this number on another. This splitting is shown in Fig. 3–5 for $A = 137$, for which the magic number for N is 82.

For the light elements, the breaks in the mass-defect curve are particularly striking when the mass number is a multiple of 4, as in C^{12}, O^{16}, Ne^{20}, Mg^{24}, Si^{28}, and S^{32}. This observation is one of the arguments in favor of the old nuclear model, in which the α-particle is assumed to be at least a short-lived component of the nucleus. There is still some support for this theory [22, 23].

(5) A plot of the distribution of the elements in nature shows fairly pronounced maxima at Z or $N = 8$, 20, 28, 50, 82, and 126; there are secondary maxima at Z or $N = 14$, 30, 40, and 74 (Section 10–11).

(6) When the nuclear magnetic moment is expressed as a function of Z or A, and parameters related to the spin are used, graphs are obtained which show discontinuities or anomalies for the numbers 8, 20, 28, 40, and 82 [24, 25, 26].

(7) The quadrupole electric moments of nuclei are zero (or very small) for the magic numbers (Z or N) 2, 8, 20, 50, 82, and 126. The maximum values are found for those nuclei with Z or N halfway between two successive magic numbers [27].

(8) The study of α- and β-transformations, of nuclear isomerism, and of certain nuclear reactions, especially neutron capture and fission, reveals discontinuities involving the numbers 20, 50, 82, and 126; these are discussed in subsequent chapters.

There are, then, many observations implying without much doubt that special properties are conferred upon nuclei by the proton or neutron numbers 2, 8, 20, 28, 50, 82, and 126, which occur for nearly all the discontinuities just noted. Others appear only in certain cases, the most obvious of these being 14, 40, 58, 74, and numbers which are 2 greater than a magic number (e.g., 30, 52). Before discussing the nuclear model which sets out to explain these facts, we shall consider the most important theories of the nature of the forces that give the nucleus its stability.

3–8 Nuclear forces. Our knowledge of nuclear forces is still very inexact. For the most part, such information as we have comes from (a) experiments on the scattering of nucleons or very light nuclei by other particles or nuclei, especially proton-proton and proton-neutron collisions; (b) mass-spectrometric measurements on the exact masses of nuclei and hence their energies; (c) the study of the nuclear properties of very simple nuclei, such as the deuteron, the triton (the nucleus of H^3), and the α-particle, and on the heaviest nuclei; (d) nuclear spectroscopy and the study of nuclear reactions.

The experimental study of "nuclear chemistry," which should provide the foundation for any theoretical advances, has only been possible in the last few years, when the development of very powerful accelerators and reactors has made feasible the synthesis and decomposition of nuclei, analogous to the reactions which have been part of molecular chemistry for many years. Nuclear theories, on the other hand, necessarily drew their inspiration from the methods and laws already established in atomic and molecular physics, but these turned out to be quite insufficient for a quantitative interpretation of nuclear phenomena. Furthermore, there are very considerable mathematical difficulties in any theoretical treatment of nuclear forces, so that approximations are often necessary, not because they correspond to the experimental facts, but because a simpler mathematical approach is then possible.

Following Heisenberg and Ivanenko, it is currently assumed that the components of the nucleus are the proton and the neutron. Such a model implies the existence not only of repulsive electrostatic forces between the protons, but also of specific attractive forces between the nucleons to give the nucleus its stability. It has already been seen from study of the variation of binding energy and nuclear radius with mass number that these are short-range forces which are quickly saturated. The same conclusion is reached from scattering experiments which give a value of 2 to 3×10^{-13} cm for the range of the proton-proton interaction. These experiments, and others, also show that when allowance is made for the coulombic repulsion, which is only of the order of 0.7 Mev for a proton-proton pair, nuclear forces are for the most part independent of charge; that is to say, the specifically nuclear forces are essentially the same in the proton-proton, proton-neutron, and neutron-neutron interactions, provided that the particles do not have high kinetic energy. In particular, if this charge independence is applied in the calculation of the masses ${}_ZM^A$ and ${}_{Z+1}M^A$ of mirror nuclei, from Eq. (3–10), the difference between these turns out to be due entirely to the difference $M_\text{n} - M_\text{p}$ and to the electrostatic term. This conclusion can be checked by measuring the disintegration energies of mirror nuclei from the lightest pair (H^3-He^3) to the heaviest (Sc^{41}-Ca^{41}). Further evidence comes from energy-level measurements on light nuclei [28].

One result of the hypothesis of charge independence is that the proton and the neutron can be regarded as two quantum states of the same particle, namely the nucleon, which is characterized by an isotopic or isobaric spin, with quantum number T having the value $\frac{1}{2}$. Isotopic spin is conserved in all nuclear transitions, and the total isotopic spin of a nucleus is obtained by vectorial addition of the spins of all its nucleons. The nucleus can therefore be regarded as an assembly of identical particles and treated in the same way as the electron cloud around the atom. If the state of the nucleon, proton ($T_z = +\frac{1}{2}$), or neutron ($T_z = -\frac{1}{2}$) is specified, the isotopic spin introduces a further degree of freedom (or coordinate); this formalism has been found most useful in nuclear physics. It has also been applied to the pions π^+, π^-, π^0, which can be regarded as being three quantum states of the same particle [29], $I_z = +1$ for π^+, -1 for π^-, and zero for π^0. In addition to the *doublet* of nucleons and *triplet* of pions, the heavy mesons and hyperons are also grouped into multiplets characterized by an isotopic spin or *isospin;* examples include the doublet $K^+(I_z = +\frac{1}{2})$ and K^0 $(I_z = -\frac{1}{2})$, the triplet $\Sigma^+(+1)$, $\Sigma^-(-1)$, and $\Sigma^0(0)$, and the singlet $\Lambda^0(0)$.

The isospin of nucleons and pions is related to the charge q (in units of e) by

$$q = I_z + B/2\,, \tag{3–13a}$$

in which B is the number of baryons in the particle, being 1 for nucleons and 0 for pions. We shall see later (Section 5-9) that this formula does not apply to the strange particles (K-mesons and hyperons), for which a correction factor must be introduced (the "strangeness number"). The number of baryons remains constant throughout a nuclear transformation (the *law of conservation of baryon number*).

It follows, of course, from the saturation of nuclear forces that these are not always attractive forces. If this were not the case, the nucleons would tend to cling together with the result that nuclear density, and the binding energy per nucleon, would both increase more rapidly with mass number than is actually the case. For $A \approx 200$, for example, it can be shown that the binding energy would be 1650 Mev instead of the experimentally determined value of 8 Mev. In order to get over this difficulty, some theories assume that the force acting between two nucleons is attractive beyond the distance which separates neighboring nucleons in a nucleus, and repulsive at smaller distances. This behavior would be analogous to intermolecular forces; the attraction due to chemical forces at quite small distances gives way to repulsion when the electron clouds of the atoms overlap. It is, however, more generally believed (Heisenberg and Majorana) that there are nuclear exchange forces which govern the stability of the nucleus in the same way as do the chemical exchange forces in, say, the hydrogen molecule. As in the quantum theory of covalency, it is assumed that two hydrogen atoms can exchange their electrons to give either an attractive or a repulsive state according to the symmetry of their wave functions. Thus the forces between two nucleons can be repulsive or attractive depending on whether the change of coordinates results in a change of the sign of the wave function (antisymmetrical pair) or not (symmetrical pair).

This purely formal and rather unsatisfactory description of nuclear forces was proposed by Yukawa [30] in 1935, who specified that corresponding to the exchange of an electron in molecular chemistry there should be an exchange of a particle of greater mass, the meson. The gist of Yukawa's theory is that nucleons can exchange energy by emission or absorption of "quanta" which have a rest mass greater than the electron, in the same way as atoms or molecules pass from one quantum state to another by the emission or absorption of photons. These nuclear forces will then have a range of action a, which should be related to the mass of the meson m_m by the relation

$$a = \frac{h}{2\pi m_m c} \qquad (3\text{–}14)$$

The variation of energy in a two-nucleon system with distance r is determined by a rapidly decreasing mesonic potential V:

$$V = -\frac{g}{r} e^{-r/a}, \qquad (3\text{–}15)$$

where g is a constant. For $a \approx 10^{-13}$ cm, one finds $m_m \approx 300\, m_0$. Current meson theories assume that nuclear interactions are effected by way

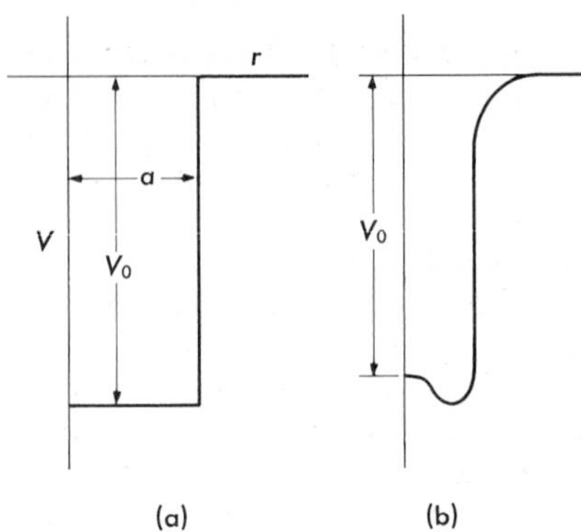

FIG. 3-6. (a) Square-well potential, and (b) wine-bottle (base) potential.

of the π-mesons, whose mass is close to the value just given. It is not known whether or not the heavier mesons play any part in nuclear forces.

Other nuclear models are based on a square-well potential which is constant for $r < a$ ($V_2 = -V_0$) and which falls off sharply for $r > a$ [Fig. 3-6(a)]. The depth of the well, V_0, is of the order of 30 Mev. Certain authors have made corrections for the effect of the protons in the heavy nuclei, by taking the electrostatic repulsion into account; this results in a slight elevation of the center of the well, increasing with Z [the shape of this potential has been likened to that of the bottom of a wine bottle, as shown in Fig. 3-6(b)]. Mention should also be made of the harmonic oscillator or parabolic potential

$$V = -\frac{1}{2V_0r^2}, \tag{3-16}$$

the Gaussian potential

$$V = -V_0e^{-r^2/a^2}, \tag{3-17}$$

and the exponential potential

$$V = -V_0e^{-2r/a}. \tag{3-18}$$

All these potentials correspond to *central* nuclear forces for which the potential energy depends only on the distance between the nucleons. A modification of this is necessitated by the fact that the deuteron has an electrical quadrupole moment, indicating an elongated form for the charge distribution. This implies in effect that the potential energy for the proton-neutron interaction is weaker in the direction parallel to the spins of the particles than in the perpendicular direction. Therefore, tensor forces, as well as central forces, must also act between nucleons.

3-9 The shell model of the nucleus. Although nuclear forces are but imprecisely understood and cannot be calculated, it is possible to construct a model from the empirical data and to see to what extent the essential properties of the nucleus can be deduced from it. These attempts have principally been in two apparently opposite directions: construction of the statistical model and of the independent particle model.

We have already noted the marked relation between the magic numbers and the discontinuities in nuclear properties. By analogy with atomic structure, it seems reasonable to suppose that these correspond to particularly stable configurations due to the formation of complete shells in the nucleus. Various attempts have been made to explain the origin of this structure theoretically and to derive the order in which the shells are filled in a way which would allow the magic numbers to be predicted from the model [17–21, 31, 32]. All are based on the independent particle model and differ in the form chosen for the potential. The results obtained, however, do not differ very widely, and the following discussion is based on the model proposed by Maria Goeppert-Mayer [17] and by Haxel, Jensen, and Suess [18].

Using the analogy of electrons in an atom, nucleons in adjoining energy levels are assumed to form a shell. The nucleons move independently of each other under the influence of a common potential derived from the integrated action of the other particles. The form of this potential has little influence on the order in which the shells are filled; in the model under discussion, it is assumed to be intermediate in form between the harmonic oscillator (Eq. 3–16) and the square-well potential. The state of nucleons (of each species) in the nucleus can therefore be characterized by four quantum numbers; for example, n, the principal quantum number, 1, 2, 3 . . . ; the orbital quantum number l which, as in atomic spectroscopy, is designated by the letters s $= 0$, p $= 1$, d $= 2$, f $= 3$, etc.; m, the orbital magnetic quantum number; and m_s the spin magnetic quantum number. If we apply the Pauli principle, then for a given value of n the number of protons or of neutrons with quantum number l is $2(2l + 1)$, and the number of nucleons of each species in the n-shell is $2n^2$. The principal magic numbers would therefore have the values 2, $2 + 8 = 10$, $10 + 18 = 28$, $28 + 30 = 60$, etc., and not 2, 8, 20, 50, 82, and 128. To overcome this difficulty, a supplementary hypothesis is introduced, to the effect that when the spin of a nucleon with a quantum number l is parallel with the direction of the orbital angular momentum, its energy is not the same as when the spin is opposed to the direction of the orbital angular momentum. To explain this, a strong interaction is postulated between the orbital momentum and the spin, resulting in the levels $l > 0$ being split into two sublevels. The total angular momentum of one is $j = l + \frac{1}{2}$ and that of the other is $j = l - \frac{1}{2}$, the former being appreciably the more stable. The difference between the two sublevels increases as l increases, and may be as much as 2 Mev. The maximum level of sublevels with $j = l + \frac{1}{2}$ is $2l + 2$, and of sublevels with $j = l - \frac{1}{2}$ the maximum level is $2l$.

Even for $l = 2$, the energy difference between $d_{5/2}$ and $d_{3/2}$ is such that the six nucleons in the first sublevel are able to constitute a separate subshell, and the same is true for $l = 3$ for the terms $f_{5/2}$ and $f_{7/2}$. For $l = 4$ and $l = 5$, the difference between the sublevels is so large that they separate into two distinct shells, the nucleons with the higher spin going into the lower shell. The way in which the nucleons of each species in their

TABLE 3–4

THE DISTRIBUTION OF NUCLEONS IN THE SHELLS

Shell	Levels	Number in the shell	Total number
I	$1s_{1/2}$ (2)	2	2
II	$2p_{3/2}$ (4); $2p_{1/2}$ (2)	6	8
II′	$3d_{5/2}$ (6)	6	14
III	$3d_{3/2}$ (4); $2s_{1/2}$ (2)	6	20
III′	$4f_{7/2}$ (8)	8	28
IV	$4f_{5/2}$ (6); $3p_{3/2}$ (4); $3p_{1/2}$ (2); $5g_{9/2}$ (10);	22	50
V	$5g_{7/2}$ (8); $4d_{5/2}$ (6); $4d_{3/2}$ (4); $3s_{1/2}$ (2); $6h_{11/2}$ (12)	32	82
VI	$6h_{9/2}$ (10); $5f_{7/2}$ (8); $5f_{5/2}$ (6); $4p_{3/2}$ (4); $4p_{1/2}$ (2); $7i_{13/2}$ (14)	44	126

ground state fill the successive shells is shown in Table 3–4. The numbers in parentheses are the number of nucleons in the appropriate level. The principal magic numbers 2, 8, 20, 50, 82, and 126 follow immediately from this distribution; the numbers 14 and 28 correspond to the existence of subshells. (For other subshells, see Section 4–6.)

Despite its rather artificial derivation from the atomic model, the shell model is undoubtedly successful in explaining and correlating an increasing number of nuclear properties. There are, however, certain essential differences between the periodicity of nuclear structure and atomic structure. In the atomic model, the Pauli principle is applied to the electrons; in the nucleus there are two kinds of particles to be considered. It must also be emphasized that the nature of nuclear forces and the laws governing them are far from understood, whereas we possess a satisfactory knowledge of the forces which govern the stability of the atom, resulting as they do from an electrostatic equilibrium between the electrons and the nucleus. From this knowledge, a rational foundation can be given to the periodic system of the elements, and the irregularities and apparent anomalies in the filling of the electronic shells and subshells can generally be explained. On the other hand, a number of important inferences which can be drawn from the shell model of the nucleus are not confirmed experimentally, and the reasons for this are not at all obvious at present. One such disagreement is that the various single particle models predict that the magnetic moments of nuclei with zero spin ought to lie on the Schmidt lines (Section 3–2) and not between them. The quadrupole moments are also often anomalous, being higher than the calculated values. Other failures occur in the application of this model to the nuclear transformations associated with β- and γ-emission, and to the distribution of nuclear energy levels.

Some of the difficulties can be eliminated if, instead of dealing with a single independent unpaired particle, we consider the interactions of all the

TABLE 3–5

Nuclide	Z	N
He^4	2	2
O^{16}	8	8
Ca^{40}	20	20
Ca^{48}	20	28
Ni^{62}	28	34
Sr^{88}	38	50
(or Zr^{90}	40	50)
Sn^{120}	50	70
Ce^{140}	58	82
Pb^{208}	82	126

particles outside the completed shells; these particles move in the central field created by the closed shells. In particular, the anomalies of the Schmidt lines and of the quadrupole moments can then be explained [33]. At the end of the chapter, we shall discuss the collective models which have produced successful modification of the shell model. It should be noted here, however, that Kravtzov [34] suggests that the neutron shells may not be independent of the proton shells. From a close examination of the change in the binding energy with the mass number, this author concludes that the discontinuities noted earlier are most pronounced for those nuclei for which Z and N are both magic numbers. The especially stable nuclei would then be those listed in Table 3–5. The numbers 38 (or 40), 58, and 70 would thus correspond to subshells. According to this author, only among the light elements are very stable nuclides found in isolation; for the medium or high mass numbers, there is a small group of very stable nuclides around each magic number. For example, the four isotopes Sn^{116}, Sn^{118}, Sn^{120}, and Sn^{124} with $Z = 50$ are all very stable, but of this group Sn^{120} has the maximum stability. Similarly, for $N = 82$ there is a group of very stable nuclides, ${}_{56}Ba^{138}$, ${}_{57}La^{139}$, ${}_{58}Ce^{140}$, and ${}_{59}Pr^{141}$, with Ce^{140} the most stable.

3–10 Statistical models. In the *uniform model*, developed by Wigner [35, 36], it is assumed that the movement of the nucleons in the nucleus is so complex and their interactions so strong that there is nothing to be gained by discussing details of nuclear structure, and statistical methods therefore offer the best approach to this problem. The exchange forces are supposed to be independent of charge and spin, so that the energy of interaction is a continuous function of the mass, independent of the other properties of the nucleus. This theory then brings together the premises of the Weizsäcker equation (Eq. 3–10), and provides a theoretical justification for this equation, but it is consequently incapable of explaining the periodic variations in certain nuclear parameters noted earlier. Furthermore, it is not applicable to light nuclei, in which the individual properties are especially evident, nor to the very heavy nuclei for which it is difficult to neglect charge effects. For these reasons, despite its initial success, this model now seems to be neglected, at least as far as the interpretation of the properties of nuclei in their ground state is concerned. Weinberg and Blatt, after an elaborate analysis of this model, suggest that it should be retained as a description of the excited states of nuclei [37].

The *liquid-drop model* is equally unconcerned with the fine structure of the nucleus. It is based on certain similarities in the behavior of a nucleus and a drop of liquid. For example, (a) the saturation of cohesive forces for liquids is like that of the nuclear forces for the nucleus; (b) the density is in both cases independent of dimensions, since the radius is proportional to the cube root of the number of molecules or nucleons; and (c) the surface energy [which enters into Eq. (3–11)] is analogous to the surface tension of liquids.

These analogies, and other considerations which provide the Bethe-Weizsäcker equation with a theoretical basis, led Bohr [38] and Frenkel [39, 40] independently to liken the nucleus to an incompressible liquid drop. The nucleons move inside the nucleus with a certain kinetic energy in the same way as the molecules in a drop undergo thermal agitation. The evaporation of molecules due to an increase in temperature is analogous to the "evaporation" of nucleons which results from a sufficient excitation of the nucleus.

Frenkel and Weisskopf [41] have applied statistical methods to the excited states of nuclei, allotting to each state a "temperature" θ defined by the relation

$$\theta = \left(\frac{E}{a}\right)^{1/2}, \tag{3–19}$$

where E is the excitation energy of the nucleus, and a is a constant for a given mass A. The entropy is related to the temperature by the classical thermodynamic equation

$$\frac{\partial S}{\partial E} = \frac{1}{\theta},$$

and can be defined as a quantity proportional to the logarithm of the density w of nuclear levels with energies between 0 and E,

$$S = k \log w, \tag{3–20}$$

just as in molecular thermodynamics the entropy is proportional to the logarithm of the probability of a given state.

The liquid-drop model has found its greatest application in the interpretation of nuclear reactions. Much of the development of this theory is due to Bohr and Wheeler [7]. The capture of a particle by the nucleus is assumed to lead initially to the formation of a compound nucleus, similar to the activated complex of chemical kinetics. This compound nucleus would be highly excited and would return to its normal state by emitting either a particle or electromagnetic radiation after an average life of the order of 10^{-14} sec; these processes would be independent of the way in which the compound nucleus was formed. For example, the processes

$Z^A + n$, $(Z - 1)^A + p$, $(Z - 1)^{A-1} + d$, and $(Z - 2)^{A-3} + \alpha$ would all result in the same compound nucleus Z^{A+1}. This hypothesis implies that the energy brought in by the incident particle is very rapidly distributed among all the nucleons. The probability that a nucleon will be able to acquire sufficient energy to be able to escape from the nucleus will then depend on the concentration of excess energy at this nucleon as the result of local fluctuations. Particularly intense fluctuations may bring about a large distortion of the drop, and this in its turn can cause a disequilibrium in the initially uniform charge distribution, and hence an increase in the electrostatic repulsion between the protons. The final result could be an accentuation of the deformation to the point at which the compound nucleus breaks into two fragments, the process which is known as *fission* (Chapter 6). The probability of this rupture can be calculated for various excited heavy nuclei as a function of their energy, as can the probabilities of de-excitation by other nuclear processes which lead to an energy release.

It may appear that the liquid-drop model is entirely different in concept from the shell model and even that the two are mutually exclusive. The first implies a strong interaction between nucleons which have no individual behavior, while in the second it is assumed that the movement of each nucleon is independent of all the others. It should be noted, however, that the essential properties at the base of the two models are not exactly the same. The shell model sets out to interpret the statistical properties of nuclei and their stability in the ground state, whereas the liquid-drop model is concerned principally with nuclear reactions which occur via a compound nucleus in a highly excited state. It is worthwhile quoting the remark of Salisbury [42] that the two different models allow the same room to be seen by looking in through different windows. A number of attempts have been made to reconcile the liquid-drop and the shell models or to produce a single theory by combining them. Weisskopf [43, 44] has pointed out that the two theories are not necessarily contradictory. The interaction forces, which act in excited nuclei and in the collisions between free nucleons, could possibly be prevented from being effective in the ground state or at low excitation energies by the Pauli principle. If all the low energy levels are occupied, there can be no energy exchange between the nucleons, so that the behavior corresponds to the single particle model. It is only when the nucleus is given some excitation energy that new levels become available, and as a result the transfer of energy becomes more efficient.

Important results have been obtained from *collective models* which treat the movement of the nucleus as a whole, as well as the movements of the nucleons outside the closed shells. In the case of the atom, the nucleus exerts a stabilizing action on the electron shells by virtue of its large mass and attractive force. On the other hand, as Rainwater has pointed out [45], in a nucleus in which there are nucleons outside the shells, a centrifugal pressure which deforms the surface is exerted by those nucleons outside the closed shells. A. Bohr and Mottelson [46, 47, 48, 49] have developed the theory of this model and have shown that a nucleus which has lost its spherical symmetry as the result of deformation executes vibrational and rotational motion like a polyatomic molecule. The importance of these movements increases as the nucleus gets further away from a very stable closed configuration and is seen, not only in the considerable quadrupole moments, but also in the spectra of the levels which correspond to the transitions between discreet rotational states. The energy of these levels will be given by a relation analogous to that found for the rotations of molecules, so that for an even-even nucleus

$$E_{\text{rot}} = \frac{\hbar^2}{2J} I(I + 1), \tag{3–21}$$

where J is the moment of inertia and I the total angular momentum of the nucleus. In the ground state of such nuclei, $I = 0$. The values of I in the excited states derived from the theory for the rotational spectra are 2, 4, 6, etc. For nuclei with odd A

$$E_{\text{rot}} = \frac{\hbar^2}{2J}\left[I(I + 1) - I_0(I_0 + 1)\right], \tag{3–22}$$

where I_0 is the spin in the ground state and the values of I are I_0, $I_0 + 1$, $I_0 + 2$, etc. As the deformation of the nucleus decreases, that is, as a closed shell is approached, the density of the levels and the rotational frequency increase, and interaction occurs with the vibrational movement, which introduces a correction term into Eqs. (3–21) and (3–22). According to this model, the magnetic moment should arise from the deformation of the nucleus as well as from the nucleons outside the closed shells.

Hill and Wheeler [50] have suggested that the relations between the vibrational-rotational states of the nucleus and the excitation of nucleons might be governed by some rule analogous to the Franck-Condon principle in molecules. When a nucleon in a nucleus is excited by the absorption of energy, the other constituents do not immediately pass in their entirety into the equilibrium condition corresponding to the potential energy acquired, because of the large mass involved. Their relative positions and velocities remain temporarily unchanged, and part of the energy is consumed in oscillations of the whole nucleus before it returns to the ground state, or goes to some other stable state.

The predictions of the Bohr and Mottelson theory have been confirmed in a remarkable manner by measurements of α-spectra (Section 4–6) and by experiments on the coulombic excitation of nuclei (Section 5–3), from which the rotational levels of many nuclei have been determined.

To sum up, the collective model has the advantage that while keeping the essential properties of the liquid-drop model, it conserves, as does the shell model, the importance both of the quantum numbers for the nucleons in the uncompleted shell, and of the movement of the nucleus as a whole. In molecular chemistry, a significant understanding of the nature of the forces involved in bond formation and of the structure of molecules was reached only as a result of our advances in our knowledge of atoms; it seems probable that a better knowledge of the fundamental particles is a necessary prerequisite for a completely satisfactory theory of the nucleus.

References

1. T. Schmidt, *Z. Physik,* **106,** 358 (1937).

2. N. Ramsay, *Experimental Nuclear Physics,* E. Segrè, ed. Wiley and Sons, New York, 1953, p. 358.

3. G. P. Millburn, W. Birnbaum, W. E. Crandall, and L. Schecter, *Phys. Rev.,* **95,** 1268 (1954).

4. W. Hecknotte, *Phys. Rev.,* **95,** 1279 (1954).

5. H. Bethe and R. F. Bacher, *Revs. Modern Phys.,* **8,** 82 (1936).

6. C. F. Weizsäcker, *Z. Physik,* **96,** 431 (1935).

7. N. Bohr and J. A. Wheeler, *Phys. Rev.,* **56,** 426 (1939).

8. E. Glueckauf, *Proc. Phys. Soc. (London),* **61,** 25 (1948).

9. H. E. Suess, *Phys. Rev.,* **81,** 1071 (1951).

10. T. P. Kohman, *Phys. Rev.,* **85,** 530 (1952).

11. A. E. S. Green, *Phys. Rev.,* **95,** 1006 (1954).

12. N. Feather, *Nuclear Stability Rules,* Cambridge University Press, 1952.

13. J. H. Bartlett, *Phys. Rev.,* **41,** 370 (1932); **42,** 145 (1932).

14. E. Gapon and D. Ivanenko, *Naturwiss.,* **20,** 792 (1932).

15. W. M. Elsasser, *J. phys. radium,* **4,** 549 (1933); **5,** 389, 635 (1934).

16. K. Guggenheimer, *J. phys. radium,* **4,** 253 (1933).

17. M. Goeppert-Mayer, *Phys. Rev.,* **74,** 235 (1948); **78,** 16 (1950).

18. O. Haxel, J. H. D. Jensen, and H. E. Suess, *Naturwiss.,* **35,** 376 (1948).

19. O. Haxel, J. H. D. Jensen, and H. E. Suess, *Phys. Rev.,* **75,** 1766 (1949).

20. O. Haxel, J. H. D. Jensen, and H. E. Suess, *Ergeb. exakt. Naturwiss.,* **26,** 244 (1952).

21. M. Goeppert-Mayer and J. H. D. Jensen, *Elementary Theory of Nuclear Shell Structure,* Wiley and Sons, New York, 1955.

22. L. Rosenfeld, *Nuclear Forces,* North-Holland Publishing Co., Amsterdam, 1948.

23. A. Herzenberg, *Nuovo cimento,* **1,** 986, 1008 (1955).

24. O. Riedel, *Z. Naturforsch.,* **5a,** 654 (1950).

25. F. Bloch, *Phys. Rev.,* **83,** 839 (1951).

26. G. Béné, *J. phys. radium,* **13,** 161 (1952).

27. W. Gordy, *Phys. Rev.,* **76,** 139 (1949).

28. R. E. Marschak, *J. phys. radium,* **16,** 325 (1955).

29. W. E. Burcham, *Progress in Nuclear Physics,* Pergamon Press, London, **4,** 171 (1955).

30. H. Yukawa, *Proc. Phys.-Math. Soc. Japan,* **17,** 48 (1935).

31. L. W. Nordheim, *Phys. Rev.,* **75,** 1894 (1949).

32. E. Feenberg and K. C. Hammack, *Phys. Rev.,* **75,** 1877 (1949).

33. B. H. Flowers, *Phil. Mag.,* **43,** 1330 (1952).

34. V. Kravtzov, *Bull. Acad. Sci. U.S.S.R.,* **18,** 5 (1954).

35. E. P. Wigner, *Phys. Rev.,* **51,** 106 (1937); **56,** 519 (1939).

36. H. Margenau and E. P. Wigner, *Phys. Rev.,* **58,** 103 (1940).

37. I. G. Weinberg and J. M. Blatt, *Am. J. Phys.,* **21,** 124 (1953).

38. N. Bohr and F. Kalckar, *Danske Videnskab. Mat. Fys.,* **14,** 18 (1937).

39. J. Frenkel, *J. Phys. (U.S.S.R.),* **9,** 641 (1939).

40. J. Frenkel, *Phys. Rev.,* **55,** 987 (1939).

41. V. Weisskopf, *Phys. Rev.,* **52,** 295 (1937).

42. E. SALISBURY, quoted by J. A. WHEELER, *Proc. Glasgow Conference on Nuclear and Meson Physics,* Pergamon Press, London, 1955, p. 38.
43. V. F. WEISSKOPF, *Science,* **113,** 101 (1951).
44. V. F. WEISSKOPF, *Physics,* **18,** 1083 (1952).
45. J. RAINWATER, *Phys. Rev.,* **79,** 432 (1950).
46. A. BOHR, *Phys. Rev.,* **81,** 134 (1951).
47. A. BOHR and B. R. MOTTELSON, *Physica,* **18,** 1066 (1952).
48. A. BOHR and B. R. MOTTELSON, *β- and γ-Ray Spectroscopy,* K. Siegbahn, ed., North-Holland Publishing Co., Amsterdam, 1955, p. 468.
49. A. BOHR, *Thesis,* Copenhagen, 1954.
50. D. L. HILL and J. A. WHEELER, *Phys. Rev.,* **89,** 1102 (1953).

CHAPTER 4

SPONTANEOUS RADIOACTIVE TRANSFORMATIONS

4–1 Radioactive processes. A nucleus which is unstable in the sense defined in Section 3–4 tends to change exoergically into some other nucleus, which will in general be of comparable mass and charge. Similarly, an excited nucleus tends to stabilize itself by decaying to its ground state, in which case the excess energy is either emitted as photons or degraded in a temporary disorganization of the peripheral electrons. Different radioactive decay processes have very different probabilities, in much the same way that thermodynamically unstable chemical systems change at widely differing rates; thus the average lives of the known unstable nuclei vary between 10^{-10} sec and 10^{15} or 10^{17} years, although these values merely represent the present limits of sensitivity of radiometric methods. Both from the isobaric rules, and by putting the known exact masses into the Weizsäcker equation, it can be shown that certain nuclei normally regarded as stable are in fact probably radioactive, with extremely long half-lives. Experiments based on such arguments have resulted in the discovery of the β-activity of In^{115} (isobaric with Cd^{115}) and Re^{187} (isobar of Os^{187}); it is also possible that Sb^{123} (isobar of Te^{123}) is radioactive with a half-life of about 10^{14} years [1]. There appear to be two exceptions to the isobaric rules in the seeming stability of the pair In^{113}-Cd^{113} and in the case mentioned earlier (Section 3–1) of the shielded nuclide V^{50}; mass-spectrometric measurements suggest that this is unstable by 2.3 Mev with respect to Ti^{50} and by 1.2 Mev relative to Cr^{50}. (See footnote in Section 3–1.)

From the data available for the 682 radioactive nuclides known in 1949, Trofimov [2] has plotted the number of unstable nuclides as a function of the logarithm of the half-life. When the half-lives are arranged in tenfold intervals over the range 10^{-8} to 10^{20} sec, an assymmetric Gaussian distribution is obtained, with a maximum in the region of 10^3 to 10^4 sec (Fig. 4–1a). If only the heavy elements are considered (i.e., those above Rb), the maximum shifts slightly toward half-lives about 10 times higher, and the curve becomes more symmetrical (Fig. 4–1b).

Compared with reactions involving molecules, spontaneous radioactive changes are very much simpler to deal with for two reasons; first, there is only one kinetic law and, second, the number of modes of transformation is limited.

1. The rate of radioactive disintegration is always proportional to the amount N of the disintegrating nuclide present, so that a first-order kinetic law is followed:

$$-\frac{dN}{dt} = \lambda N, \tag{4–1}$$

where λ is the disintegration constant. Integration of Eq. (4–1) gives the well-known exponential law

$$N_t = N_0 e^{-\lambda t}, \tag{4–2}$$

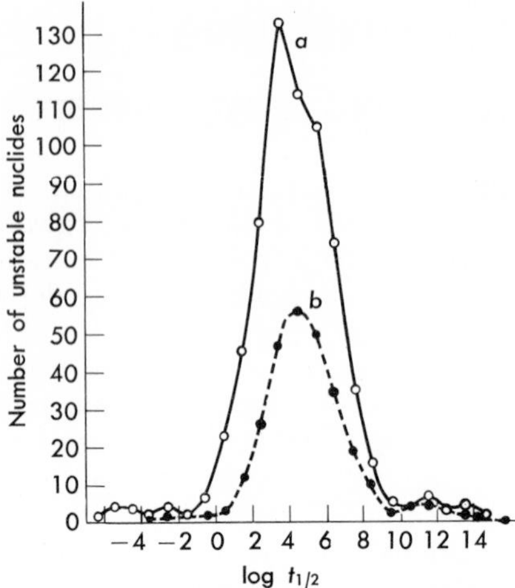

FIG. 4–1. The distribution of the half-lives of the radioactive nuclides (Ref. 2).

where the value of λ is characteristic of a given radioactive decay process. Derived from this are the half-life $t_{1/2} = (1/\lambda) \log 2 = 0.693/\lambda$, and τ, the average life, which is the inverse of λ, so that $t_{1/2} = 0.693\tau$.

2. Since the instability of a nucleus results from an unbalanced neutron : proton ratio, the transformation of the nucleus to its equilibrium state might be expected to occur by the expulsion of a proton or a neutron. Experiment shows that this is not in fact the case. Very few examples are known of delayed neutron emission which apparently obey the exponential law; those that are known occur in fission processes and with the excited states of Li^9 and of O^{17}. This neutron emission is related to β-disintegration, and the rate of this prior β-decay governs the neutron emission

$$\mathrm{Li}^9 \xrightarrow[\text{0.17 sec}]{\beta^-} \mathrm{Be}^{9*}\ (\textit{excited state}) \rightarrow \mathrm{Be}^8 + \mathrm{n},$$

$$\mathrm{N}^{17} \xrightarrow[\text{4.1 sec}]{\beta^-} \mathrm{O}^{17*}\ (\textit{excited state}) \rightarrow \mathrm{O}^{16} + \mathrm{n}.$$

The processes by which an unstable nucleus Z^A passes to a more stable configuration can be summarized as follows:

$$\left.\begin{array}{ll}\text{(a) } Z^A \rightarrow (Z+1)^A, & \text{or n} \rightarrow \text{p} + \text{e}^- \\ \text{(b) } Z^A \rightarrow (Z-1)^A, & \text{or p} \rightarrow \text{n} + \text{e}^+\end{array}\right\} \quad (\beta\textit{-transformations}).$$

The capture of one of the orbital electrons by the unstable nucleus often replaces process (b); the electron is generally from the K-shell, or, more rarely, from the L-shell:

$$\text{(c) } Z^A + \text{e}^- \rightarrow (Z-1)^A, \quad \text{or p} + \text{e}^- \rightarrow \text{n} \quad (\textit{electron capture}).$$

In these three transformations, the mass number is unchanged. Although as the mass of the nucleus increases the number of neutrons increases more rapidly than Z, the electrostatic repulsion which the protons exert

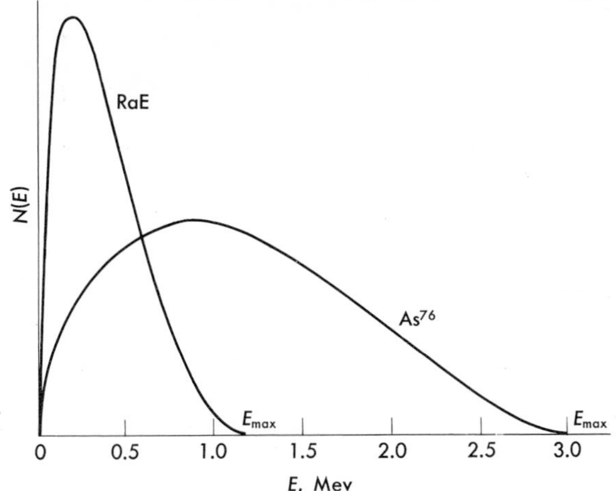

Fig. 4–2. The β-spectra of RaE [C. Wu, F. Boehm, and E. Nagel, *Phys. Rev.*, **91,** 319 (1953)] and of As^{76} [N. Marty-Wollman, *Thesis*, Paris, 1950].

on each other eventually causes a further type of nuclear instability, which results in the *emission of an α-particle:*

(d) $Z^A \rightarrow (Z-2)^{A-4} + {}_2He^4$.

To these four principal processes must be added *isomeric transitions:*

(e) Z^{A*} (excited state) $\rightarrow Z^A +$ energy.

(f) *Spontaneous fission:* the splitting of a heavy nucleus ($Z \geq 92$) into two fragments of roughly equal mass, plus a small number of neutrons. This type of disintegration is discussed in Chapter 6.

4–2 Beta disintegration. The number of β-emitting isotopes known is very large. Since the instability arises from an excess of neutrons in the nucleus, these nuclides lie above the stability line in a plot showing the neutron:proton ratio (Fig. 3–4). Positron emission, on the other hand, is the result of a neutron deficiency, so that β^+-active nuclei are below this curve.

The energy relationships in these reactions can be expressed by the inequalities (3–8) and (3–9); relating these to the neutral *atoms,* we find that the energy release is given by

$$({}_ZM^A - {}_{Z+1}M^A)\ 931 \text{ Mev} \qquad \text{for } \beta^-\text{-emission,} \qquad (4\text{–}3)$$

$$({}_ZM^A - {}_{Z-1}M^A - 2m_e)\ 931 \text{ Mev} \qquad \text{for } \beta^+\text{-emission.} \qquad (4\text{–}4)$$

In either type of disintegration, the energy ΔE should appear as the kinetic energy of the emitted electron if the very low recoil energy of the residual atom is neglected. In fact, one finds that the electrons have a continuous energy distribution extending from zero to a maximum value $E_{\max}$ equal to ΔE. Figure 4–2 shows two typical examples of such spectra. The exact

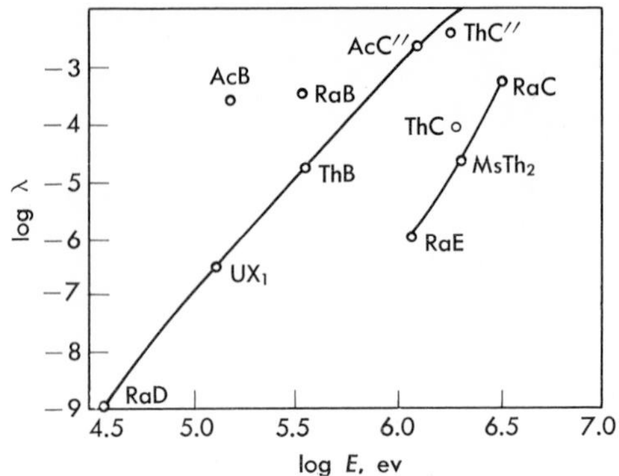

FIG. 4–3. Sargent lines for the β-active natural radioelements.

form of the curve, and in particular the maximum height, which gives the most probable energy, vary from system to system. This maximum depends on Z and on the selection rules (see below) and occurs at slightly less than $0.3E_{\max}$. The average energy $\overline{E}$ falls between 0.2 and $0.4E_{\max}$; for RaE, $\overline{E} = 0.28E_{\max}$.

If the logarithm of the disintegration constant is plotted against the logarithm of the maximum β-energy for the natural radioelements, two curves result (the Sargent curves, Fig. 4–3). These are in fact almost straight lines, so that an (approximate) empirical relationship

$$\log \lambda = a + b \log E_{\max} \tag{4–5}$$

can be derived. When the same operation is carried out for the artificial β-active isotopes, however, a number of other lines appear, and many isotopes do not fall on any of these. The half-lives of the β-emitters involved range from 0.03 sec (B^{12}) to 6×10^{14} years (In^{115}).

The varying energies of the electrons emitted in the same radioactive process were for many years a most difficult problem in nuclear physics, being in apparent contradiction to the conservation of energy. Moreover, since the electron has spin $\frac{1}{2}$, the conservation law demands that the spin of a nucleus formed by β-disintegration should differ from that of the initial nucleus by a half-integral. Experiment showed that either there was no spin change or else it changed by a whole number.

To overcome these difficulties, Pauli suggested the idea of a neutrino, ejected simultaneously with the electron. This particle would carry away the balance between the maximum energy of the spectrum and the actual energy of an individual electron, so that the spectrum of the neutrino should be complementary to that of the β-particles. The properties of the neutrino (mass very close to zero, zero charge, spin $\frac{1}{2}$) make its direct detection extremely difficult, and its energy spectrum cannot therefore be measured. There is, however, some indirect evidence which, without being decisive, gives plausibility to the neutrino hypothesis. If the electron were the only light particle emitted in β-disintegration, the momentum of the daughter nucleus would be constant; on the other hand, if a neutrino is emitted at the same time, there will be a distribution of energy depending upon the angular correlations between the two particles and governed by the law of conservation of momentum. This effect should be even more marked in electron capture, since the subsequent recoil of the nucleus would here be due solely to the neutrino, this being the only particle emitted. Experiments carried out with the recoiling nuclei in several transformations [3] such as

$$\mathrm{He}^6 \xrightarrow{\beta^-} \mathrm{Li}^6, \qquad \mathrm{Be}^7 \xrightarrow{\mathrm{e}} \mathrm{Li}^7, \qquad \mathrm{Ar}^{37} \xrightarrow{\mathrm{e}} \mathrm{Cl}^{37},$$

$$\mathrm{Cl}^{38} \xrightarrow{\beta^-} \mathrm{Ar}^{38}, \qquad \mathrm{Y}^{90} \xrightarrow{\beta^-} \mathrm{Zr}^{90},$$

and others, have given results which, although not definite, favor the existence of the neutrino. The study of the meson disintegrations

$$\pi \longrightarrow \mu \longrightarrow \mathrm{e}$$

has led to the same conclusion.

Reines and Cowan [4] have used an ingenious method in attempts to detect the reaction

$$\mathrm{p} + \nu \longrightarrow \mathrm{n} + \beta^+, \tag{4–5a}$$

which is in some ways the reverse of neutron disintegration (Section 2–6)

$$\mathrm{n} \longrightarrow \mathrm{p} + \beta^- + \nu.$$

Since an extremely low yield was expected, these authors exposed a fluorescent hydrogeneous liquid (toluene) containing cadmium to the stray neutrino flux coming from a powerful nuclear reactor. The positrons resulting from reaction (4–5a) interact with electrons to produce annihilation γ-rays, which can be detected with a scintillation counter; in addition, the γ-rays resulting from the capture of neutrons by cadmium can also be counted, using an appropriate coincidence circuit to take into account the very small time interval between the two processes. The measurements finally showed a small positive result in favor of the existence of the neutrino.*

Pauli's original suggestion was extended quantitatively by Fermi [5], who approached the problem by treating the proton and the neutron as two quantum states of the same particle. The interaction between these nucleons and the electron-neutrino pair is assumed to be analogous to the interaction between an atom and a radiative field in a change of quantum state. It was further suggested that the transformation might occur via a meson, which would finally go to an electron and a neutrino. Fermi deduced

---

* Further experiments using the method described have definitely proved the reality of reaction (4–5a), and hence the existence of the neutrino [C. L. Cowan, F. Reines, F. B. Harrison, H. W. Kruse, and A. D. McGuire, *Science*, **124,** 103 (1956)]. Similar experimental methods have confirmed the existence of the antineutrino [F. Reines, C. L. Cowan, F. B. Harrison, A. D. McGuire, and H. W. Kruse, *Phys. Rev.*, **117,** 159 (1960)].

TABLE 4–1

HALF-LIVES AND COMPARATIVE LIVES FOR SOME β-EMITTERS

	Nuclide	Half-life, sec	$f\tau$	E_{max}, Mev
Allowed transitions	S^{35}	7.6×10^6	1.9×10^4	0.166
	Mn^{57}	2.76×10^3	11.3×10^4	0.199
	Cu^{62}	6.30×10^2	8.4×10^4	2.6
	In^{117m}	7.02×10^3	14.1×10^4	1.73
First-order forbidden transitions	Ti^{51}	6.2×10^7	1.3×10^6	0.37
	Br^{80}	1.08×10^3	0.3×10^6	2.0
	I^{131}	6.9×10^5	3.9×10^6	0.59
Higher order forbidden transitions	Co^{55}	6.2×10^6	0.6×10^8	1.36
	Rb^{86}	1.7×10^6	1.5×10^8	1.57
	Au^{198}	2.3×10^5	0.1×10^8	0.82

a rather complex equation relating E_{max} and λ, which can be written in the simplified form

$$\lambda = kE_{max}^5 \tag{4–6}$$

or

$$\log \lambda = \log k + 5 \log E_{max}, \tag{4–6a}$$

thus giving the empirical relation (4–5). The constant k is different for the different types of transition defined by the selection rules, which depend on the changes of spin and parity of the nuclei

$$Z \rightarrow \begin{cases} Z - 1 \\ Z + 1 \end{cases}$$

and so in the last resort on the angular momentum l of the nucleon involved. This explains the existence of several lines in the Sargent diagram. In place of λ, the theory considers the "comparative life" which is the product $f\tau$, where τ is the average life and f is a function of Z and of E_{max}, and depends upon the form of the spectrum (Table 4–1).

According to the selection rules, a distinction is made between *allowed* transitions, which have a high probability and hence a very small half-life or comparative life, and *forbidden* transitions, of low probability. The allowed transitions are divided into favored and unfavored; forbidden transitions are subdivided according to the order of forbiddenness (first order, second order, etc.), the probability of disintegration decreasing with increasing order. In general, the half-life becomes about 100 times larger for an increase of one unit of order of forbiddenness. The transition rules put forward by Fermi were subsequently modified by Gamow and Teller [6].

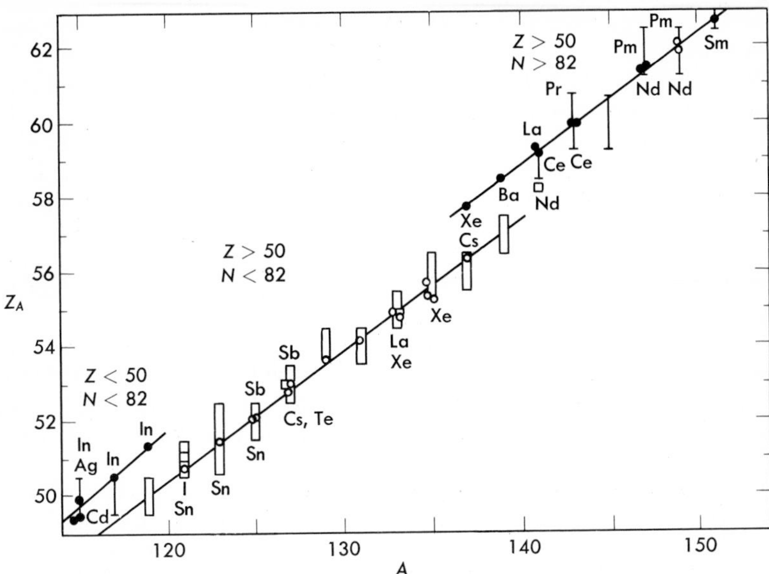

FIG. 4–4. Discontinuities in β-spectra at the magic numbers (Ref. 9).

It follows from the theory that the comparative lives of all β-emitters should be grouped around certain particular values, each of which would correspond to a Sargent curve. There are in fact a large number for which the value of log $f\tau$ is between 3.5 and 5, but other values are randomly distributed. Some examples of the relation between t, $f\tau$, and $E_{\max}$ are given in Table 4–1, based on the review by Konopinski [7]. Numerical tables of the energies of β-transformations have been published by King [8]. On the whole, Fermi's theory provides a satisfactory explanation of the various β-decay phenomena, and this in itself furnishes an indirect proof of the existence of the neutrino.

The nuclear spins deduced from the shell model generally permit allowed or forbidden transitions to be correctly predicted. This model also fits β-disintegration in various other ways, which are listed below.

(1) If the maximum energy of the β-spectrum is known, one can find Z_A, the number of protons in the most stable nuclide of a series of isobars with mass A (Eq. 3–12). If the δ-term in this equation is neglected and the expressions for $_ZM^A$ and $_{Z+1}M^A$ are introduced into Eq. (4–3), subtraction gives

$$\Delta E = E_{\max} = B_A(Z_A - Z - 0.5)/931. \qquad (4\text{–}7)$$

Now if numerical values are introduced into Eq. (3–12), Z_A is a virtually linear function of A, but in practice this linearity is found only between two successive magic numbers [9]. The magic numbers introduce discontinuities, so that the function Z_A/A is represented by several straight lines as shown in Fig. (4–4), which shows the data for odd values of A between 115 and 155; a displacement toward the ordinate occurs in the region of a magic number of protons, and toward the abscissa for a complete neutron shell.

(2) When $E_{\max}$ is plotted as a function of the number of neutrons for a given value of Z, separate lines are obtained for odd and even A, but both show discontinuities at the magic numbers $N = 50$, 82, 126, and, less clearly, at $N = 28$, corresponding to the decrease in the neutron binding energy immediately after these numbers [10]. Similarly, the spacing between the lines drawn for various values of Z increases at $Z = 50$, 82, and (possibly) 26. The graphs also show that the energy difference between two neighboring nucleons, one odd and the other even, decreases after a magic number.

(3) For a series of β-emitters with a given isotopic number $I(= N - Z)$, the disintegration energy decreases regularly with increasing N, but breaks appear at the magic numbers [11, 12, 13]. The values are 0.6 to 0.8 Mev for $N = 28$ or $Z = 20$, 28, or 50; 1 Mev for $N = 20$; and 1.9 Mev for $N = 50$ or 82.

(4) The difference ϵ between the neutron and proton pairing effects (Section 3–5), evaluated from β-disintegration energies, shows sharp variations and even changes of sign at certain magic numbers: $\epsilon = -0.7$ Mev for β-emitters with $Z < 20$, becomes $+0.3$ in the region of $Z > 20$ and $N > 28$, is once more negative (-0.1 to -0.4) between $Z > 28$ and $N < 50$, and again positive ($+0.4$) for $Z > 50$, $N > 50$, and for $Z > 82$ and $N > 126$ ($+0.1$). (See Ref. 9.)

Wu, *et al.* [14], have observed the anisotropic emission of electrons in the β-decay of nuclei oriented in a magnetic field, the preferred direction being that opposed to the nuclear spin. These authors showed that if a paramagnetic compound of Co^{60} is placed in an intense magnetic field, at a temperature close to absolute zero ($\sim 0.01°K$), the electrons ejected toward the North Pole exceed those emitted in the opposite sense by about 40%. The reverse effect, that of emission favored in the direction of the spin, has been observed [15] for the β^+-emitting nuclide Co^{58}. These results imply a nonconservation of parity in β-emissions, and a spatial asymmetry induced by these processes.

4–3 Complex and successive β-transitions. A nucleus formed by β-disintegration may initially be in some excited state, from which it subsequently decays to the ground state. If this is the case, the β-spectrum is accompanied by γ-emission and the total energy of the transition is shared between the electron, the neutrino, and the photon. In some systems, a fraction of the transitions leads directly to the ground state and the remainder to one or more excited levels (*branching*); the observed spectrum then consists of two superimposed components, each of which has a characteristic maximum energy. There are even systems in which the decomposition involves three related simple spectra, such as Cl^{38}, where the $E_{\max}$ are 1.11 Mev (31%), 2.77 Mev (16%), and 4.81 Mev (53%); there are two associated γ-rays of 1.6 and 2.15 Mev. The spectrum of Sb^{124} consists of five superimposed β-emissions. A further complication arises when the nuclide may undergo two different transformations such as β^-- and β^+-decay, or β^+-decay and electron capture. There

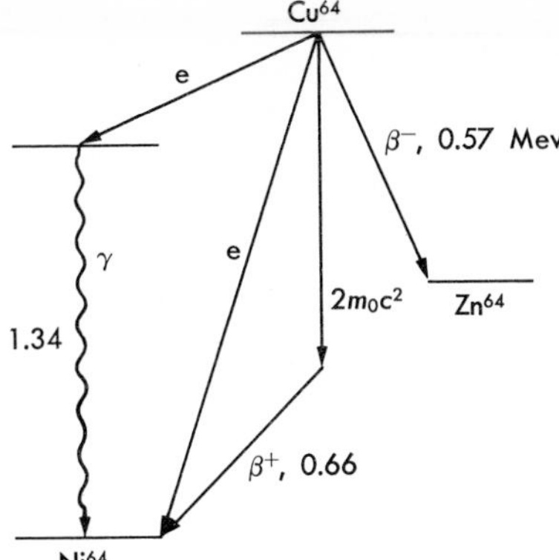

FIG. 4–5. The disintegration scheme of Cu^{64} [J. M. Hollander, I. Perlman, and G. T. Seaborg, *Revs. Modern Phys.*, **25**, 469 (1953)].

are many examples of this; a typical system is the decay of the nucleus Cu^{64}, which can decay by either of the transformations (Fig. 4–5)

$$Cu^{64} \rightarrow \begin{cases} Zn^{64} \\ Ni^{64}. \end{cases}$$

Another complex situation arises when the nuclide formed is itself unstable and decays by further electron emission. Successive β-transformations occur in the natural radioactive series

$$UX_1 \rightarrow UX_2 \rightarrow U2; \qquad ThB \rightarrow ThC \rightarrow ThC'; \qquad \text{etc.}$$

and more particularly among the fission products. Feather [13] has put forward the following rules for such successive β-emitters. In a disintegration series

$$Z^A \xrightarrow[\text{I}]{\beta^-} (Z+1)^A \xrightarrow[\text{II}]{\beta^-} (Z+2)^A$$

or

$$Z^A \xrightarrow[\text{I}]{\beta^+} (Z-1)^A \xrightarrow[\text{II}]{\beta^+} (Z-2)^A,$$

with Z even, the energy evolved in process I is smaller than that in II if A is even, and greater if A is odd. The difference between the two energies is generally much smaller when A is odd. These rules are self-explanatory when the variations in binding energy for even and odd nucleons are taken into consideration.

In place of the indirect transmission via $(Z+1)^A$, it might seem possible that a nucleus Z^A would decay directly to $(Z+2)^A$ by the virtually simultaneous emission of two electrons. The condition necessary for this double β-emission can be expressed by means of Eq. (3–8), provided that ${}_{Z+2}M^A$ is substituted for ${}_{Z+1}M^A$. Among the 65 known pairs of isobars with masses Z and $Z+2$, there are about 20 which, from their measured exact masses, appear to satisfy this condition [16]. This is so, for example, for the energy differences between ${}_{22}Ti^{48}$ and ${}_{20}Ca^{48}$, which is 4.3 Mev, between ${}_{42}Mo^{96}$ and ${}_{40}Zr^{96}$ (3.5 Mev), between ${}_{50}Sn^{116}$ and ${}_{48}Cd^{116}$ (2.5 Mev), between ${}_{54}Xe^{130}$ and ${}_{52}Te^{130}$ (3.25 Mev), and between ${}_{62}Sm^{150}$ and ${}_{60}Nd^{150}$ (4.1 Mev). These possible transformations are of interest, since their existence would allow a choice to be made between the two theories mentioned earlier (Section 2–6) as to the identity of the neutrino and the antineutrino [17]. If these two particles are not identical, the antineutrino emitted with the first electron cannot be captured by one of the neutrons of the daughter nucleus to give a second proton by the process $n + \bar{\nu} \rightarrow p + e^-$, and the double β-emission would therefore proceed by

$$Z^A \rightarrow {}_{Z+2}A + 2e^- + 2\bar{\nu}. \tag{4–8}$$

In the opposite case, there would be no neutrino emission, and we would have

$$Z^A \rightarrow {}_{Z+2}A + 2e^-. \tag{4–9}$$

The probability of this latter process is much the greater, the half-life being of the order of 10^{13} rather than 10^{21} years. It follows then that if the neutrino and the antineutrino are different, it will be virtually impossible to observe double β-emission even with the most sensitive modern instruments; half-lives of the order of 10^{13} years, on the other hand, are easily detectable. Much effort has gone into such researches, involving especially Zr^{96}, Sn^{124}, Cd^{116}, and Mo^{100}; despite some unconfirmed early positive results, there is no case in which double β-emission has been unambiguously identified [16, 18]. It has been possible merely to establish the lower limits for the half-lives, which are generally of the order of 10^{16} to 10^{17} years or longer. Nevertheless, it cannot yet be concluded that two nonidentical particles do exist, since there are great difficulties implicit in the experimental methods and in the identification of the nuclear process involved.*

4–4 Electron capture. This type of transformation, variously known as electron capture, K-capture, or orbital capture, is equivalent to, and in competition with, the emission of a positron. The condition of instability is expressed by an inequality analogous to Eqs. (3–8) and (3–9);

$${}_{Z+1}M^A - \frac{E}{c^2} > {}_ZM^A,$$

where the term in E is the binding energy of the electron captured from the K- or L-shell of the atom Z. When we compare this relation with Eq. (3–9), it is clear that the capture is energetically more favorable if $2m_0 \approx 1.02$ Mev $> E/c^2$, which is always the case, since even in the

* Recent experiments by C. L. Cowan and F. Reines, *Phys. Rev.*, **106,** 825 (1957), on the half-life of the possible double β-emission of Nd^{150} ($>10^{18}$ years) appear to definitely rule out the hypothesis of the identity of the neutrino and the antineutrino.

heaviest atoms the binding energy of an electron in the K-shell is only of the order of 0.1 Mev. Electron capture can therefore occur in certain nuclei such as Be^7 and Fe^{55}, which are stable to positron emission, and obviously when positron emission is possible, the probability of electron capture occurring is correspondingly increased.

The theoretical treatment of this process is a special case of Fermi's theory, from which it can be shown that the ratio of the probabilities of electron capture and positron emission depends on the type of the transition (i.e., whether allowed or forbidden) and increases with increasing Z. The capture process is in fact very frequently found with the heavy nuclei and is often in competition with α-emission. Of the natural radioactive nuclei, only K^{40} decays by this process, in competition here with electron emission.

Capture from the L-shell, which is in general less frequent than K-capture, was first demonstrated with the nuclide Ar^{37}, for which the ratio K-capture : L-capture was found to be 0.08 [19]. This ratio is much less than unity for other nuclei, but for Np^{235} it is greater than 10 [20] and for Am^{242} L-capture alone is observed [21].

The detection of K-capture is a good deal more difficult than positron emission, since the whole of the energy released is carried away by the neutrino, which, of course, cannot readily be detected. However, the vacant site in the K-shell is rapidly filled by an electron from a higher shell (L), and this transition is accompanied by the emission of an x-ray. The new hole is in its turn filled by an M-electron with the emission of another x-ray, and so on. These rays, characteristic of the atom ($Z - 1$) provide the main diagnostic evidence for K-capture [22].

Electron capture is associated with the emission of a continuous γ-spectrum (internal "bremsstrahlung," see Section 11–6) whose maximum energy corresponds to the transition energy, which can therefore be measured. This energy can also be determined if the transition goes by positron emission, producing the same nucleus either in an excited or the ground state. A further method depends on knowing three of the terms in a cycle involving four disintegrations, where the fourth (unknown) is an electron capture process; for example, the energy of the capture $Am^{244} \rightarrow Pu^{244}$ has been found to be 0.22 Mev from the cycle

$$\begin{array}{ccc} Np^{240} & \xleftarrow[5.23]{\alpha} & Am^{244} \\ \beta- \Big\uparrow 0.36 & & \Big\downarrow K \\ U^{240} & \xleftarrow[4.65]{\alpha} & Pu^{244} \end{array}$$

Similarly one finds 1.06 Mev for $At^{214} \rightarrow Po^{214}$ from

$$\begin{array}{ccc} Bi^{210} & \xleftarrow[8.95]{\alpha} & At^{214} \\ \beta- \Big\uparrow 0.06 & & \Big\downarrow K \\ Pb^{210} & \xleftarrow[7.83]{\alpha} & Po^{214} \end{array}$$

This procedure has been extensively used by Seaborg and his group at Berkeley [23, 24] for calculating the disintegration energies of several as yet unknown unstable heavy nuclides up to $Z = 103$.

The decay of many heavy nuclei involves various branching processes such as α and β, α and K-capture, and the like; the relative intensities vary considerably from one nuclide to another. The nuclides Pa^{230} and Am^{242} even undergo triple disintegration (α, β, and electron capture) although the intensity of the α-emission is extremely low.

Electron capture is typical of the interactions which can occur between a nucleus and its peripheral electrons. A further example of this, internal conversion, is discussed in Section 4–8.

4–5 Alpha transformations. If the nucleus is a collection of protons and neutrons, the α-particles emitted by radioactive nuclei cannot exist as such in the nucleus, but must be formed either in the course of the disintegration process or very shortly before it. This behavior can be compared with the vaporization of molecules of NaCl on heating a crystal made up of Na^+ and Cl^- ions. Alpha-particle emission occurs mainly with the heavy nuclei with $Z \geq 79$; of the natural radioactive nuclides of medium atomic weight, only ${}_{60}Nd^{144}$ and ${}_{62}Sm^{147}$ are α-emitters. Certain other rare earths nuclides (isotopes of Sm, Eu, Gd, Tb, and Ho) produced artificially in high-energy nuclear reactions are also α-active.

It was generally believed in the early years of radioactivity that all the α-particles emitted in any given radioactive transformation were of the same energy. The complexity of the α-spectrum was demonstrated by Rosenblum [25, 26] in 1929, who found that thorium-C emits several groups of particles, and it was subsequently established that in fact the majority of the natural α-emitting isotopes show this *fine structure.* More recent measurements have shown that the same is true for the transuranium elements, so that the complex nature of α-emission is a quite general phenomenon. It is due to the fact that the daughter nucleus can be produced in some excited state, from which it decays to the ground state by the emission of γ-rays equivalent to the difference in the disintegration energies of the ground state and the excited states. Spectroscopic study of the α-particle energies provides a valuable method for investigating the structure of heavy nuclei, especially in combination with γ-ray spectrometry. Figures 4–6 and 4–7 show the energy-level diagrams for the nuclei Io (Th^{230}, even-even) and Am^{241} (odd-odd) established from the fine structure in the α-spectra.

Certain very short-lived nuclides (e.g., RaC′, ThC′) emit a very small fraction (10^{-4} to 10^{-7}) of α-particles with energies much greater than that of the main group; radium-C′, for example, emits 28 particles with a range (in air) of 9 cm, and five of range 11 cm, per 10^6 particles with the normal range of 7 cm. These *long-range groups* of particles are produced when the disintegration process is sufficiently rapid for the α-particle to acquire the excess energy of the excited nucleus before this can be dissipated by photon emission.

With the exception of these rare events, α-particles are emitted by heavy nuclei with energies which fall for the most part between 4 and 6 Mev,

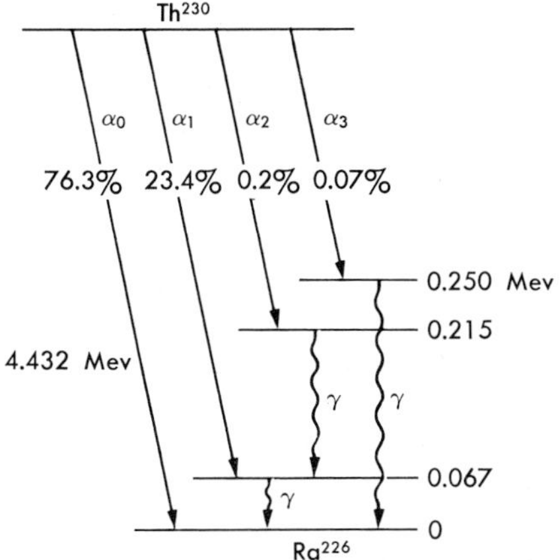

FIG. 4-6. The disintegration scheme of ionium (Th^{230}).

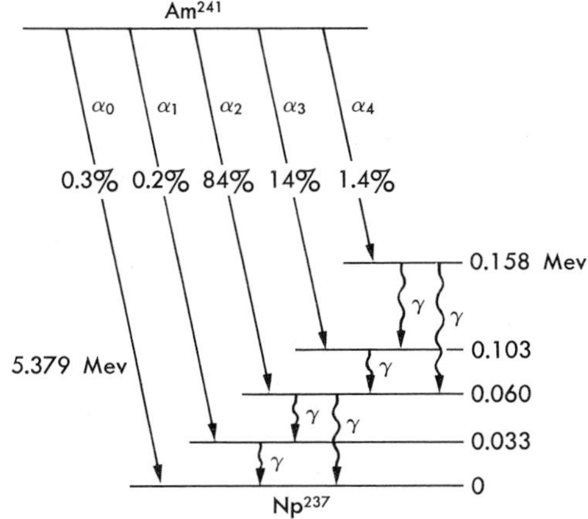

FIG. 4-7. The disintegration scheme of Am^{241} (Ref. 48).

rarely exceeding 7 Mev. We shall see later, however (Chapter 5), that in order to penetrate into a heavy nucleus, helium ions must be accelerated to energies of the order of 25 Mev, and that even then any transmutation which occurs is exoergic. This *activation energy* is necessary because for a particle to enter the nucleus it must first penetrate the potential barrier arising from the electrostatic repulsion at the surface of the positively charged nucleus, and this, of course, tends to repel particles of the same sign. The existence of such a barrier was first demonstrated in the classical experiments by Rutherford on the passage of α-particles from ThC′ (8.8 Mev) through uranium; Coulomb's law was found to hold down to a distance of approach of the particle to the nucleus of 3×10^{-12} cm. This result implies that the height of the electrostatic potential barrier around the uranium nucleus is at least 8.8 Mev. It is therefore difficult to under-

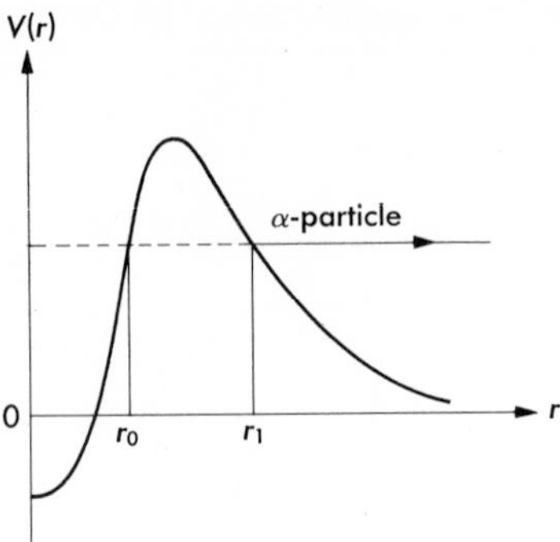

FIG. 4–8. The tunneling effect.

stand how particles with an energy much lower than this can overcome this barrier and be emitted from the nucleus.

The correct interpretation of this difficult question was eventually given independently by Gamow [27] and by Gurney and Condon [28, 29]. These authors assumed that the α-particle is preformed in the nucleus, and showed that it then follows from its associated wave properties that the particle has a very small but finite probability of penetrating the barrier (Fig. 4–8), even if its energy is less than the height of the latter (*the tunnel effect*). This probability, of which the disintegration constant is a measure, increases with the energy of the particle (E_α), with a decrease in the height of the barrier, (i.e., of Z), and with the width of the barrier (and hence with the radius r of the nucleus). The equation derived by Gamow,

$$\lambda = Ce^{-f(E,Z,r)}, \tag{4–10}$$

can be written for heavy nuclei in the simplified form

$$\log_{10} \lambda = 21.67 - 2 \log r - 1.725 \frac{A-4}{A} (Z-2)E_\alpha^{1/2} + 4.08 \frac{A-4}{A} (Z-2)^{1/2} r^{1/2}, \tag{4–11}$$

where r is in units of 10^{-12} cm and E_α in Mev. The expression (4–10) is of the same form as the well-known Arrhenius equation of chemical kinetics, and the coefficient C can be regarded as a frequency factor. Its value is in the region of 10^{20} sec^{-1}, which corresponds to α-particle velocities of the order of 10^8 cm·sec^{-1} and radii of about 10^{-12} cm for heavy nuclei. An α-particle therefore strikes the barrier approximately 10^{20} times/sec, but only crosses it after between 10^{13} and 10^{35} collisions. For bombarding particles which strike the nucleus with an energy of the order of a few Mev, the probability of penetrating the barrier is clearly very much smaller, explaining why no such penetration is detected.

It follows from Eq. (4–10) that the frequency factor is independent both of the energy and of Z, and is only slightly affected by changes in the radius. The transparency of the potential barrier and hence the half-life is, however, very sensitive to changes in these parameters. When the radius is increased by 25%, the probability of escape is multiplied by a factor of 10^3; when the energy is increased from 3 to 10 Mev, the probability increases by a factor of approximately 10^{26}. The exponential form of Eq. (4–10) accounts successfully then for the wide range of half-lives observed for α-emitters, extending as they do from a small fraction of a second to multiples of 10^9 years.

4–6 Alpha emission and nuclear structure. It can be seen from Eq. (4–11) that there must be a separate constant for each energy E_α, (i.e., for each component of the fine structure), so that the experimentally measured half-life for any given α-emitter is the resultant of the individual partial half-lives. For the α-active nuclides of the three natural radioactive families, since there is only a very small variation of Z and r within a given family, λ depends to a first approximation on E_α. This gives a qualitative explanation for the well-known empirical relation discovered by Geiger and Nuttall (Fig. 4–9). This can be written

$$\log \lambda = a + b \log R, \tag{4–12}$$

where a and b are constants; b is the same for all the natural α-emitters

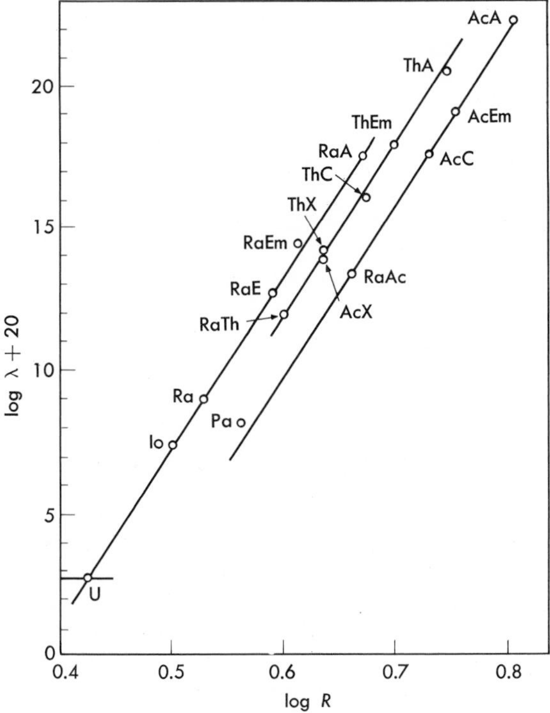

Fig. 4–9. The Geiger-Nuttall relation for the α-active natural radioelements.

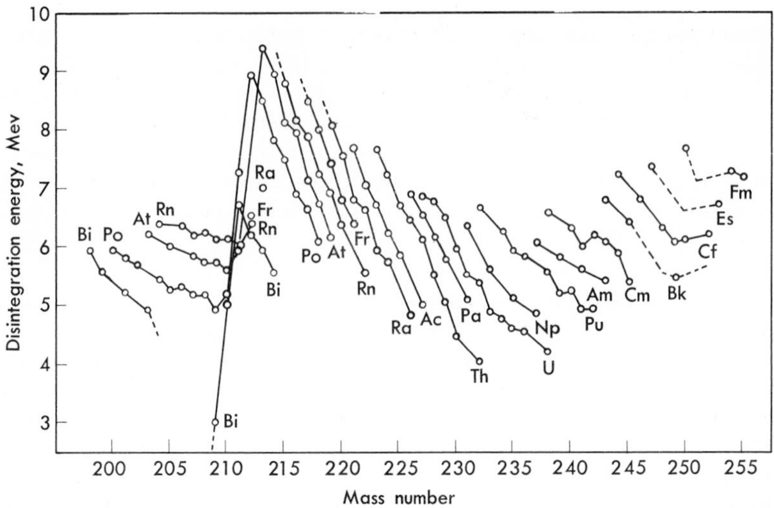

FIG. 4–10. The variation of α-disintegration energy with mass number (Ref. 24).

and a depends on the particular radioactive family; R is the *range* of the α-particle (i.e., the distance traversed by the particle in air before its energy is dissipated; see Section 11–3) and is clearly a measure of the energy of the particle.

In order to obtain information on the structure of nuclei, it is, however, more fruitful to consider the variation of parameters such as half-life, disintegration energy, and nuclear radius for each separate proton number Z or isotopic number I. As early as 1927, Fournier [30] examined the variation of α-particle velocities as a function of A for each value of Z and obtained a series of parallel lines, but with some anomalous points. A later approach suggested by Berthelot [31, 32] has proved very useful; this consists in plotting the logarithm of the half-life as a function of α-particle energy (i.e., Geiger-Nuttall curves), not for a whole family of natural radioelements, but for given values of Z. The resultant diagrams, like those obtained by plotting the energy as a function of Z for constant I, or of N for constant Z, are regular curves, with apparently anomalous points which emphasize the effect of the magic numbers at $Z = 82$ and $N = 126$. Later authors, notably Karlik [33, 34] and Feather [13] have obtained similar diagrams. The curves in Fig. 4–10, due to Perlman, Ghiorso, and Seaborg [35], show the variation of α-particle energy with mass number for the heavy nuclei up to Fm. These show that in general the energy increases with the decrease in mass, with the exceptions of isotopes of Bi, Po, and At, for which, after an initial increase, the energy falls and then rises again. This tendency toward inversion is also found, though less markedly, with the isotopes of Rn and Fr. These anomalies are exactly in agreement with the increased nuclear stability associated with the 126 neutron configuration. Similarly, for the isotopes of Po, the transition ${}_{84}\mathrm{Po}^{212} \rightarrow {}_{82}\mathrm{Pb}^{208}$ shows the greatest energy change, since this is the transformation of a nucleus containing 128 neutrons into the much more stable configura-

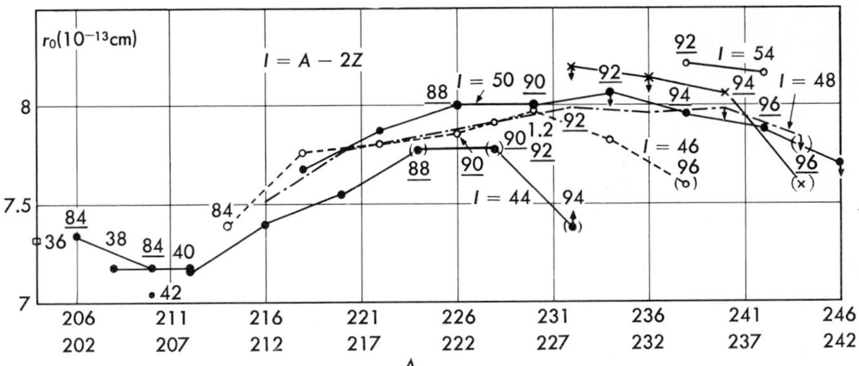

FIG. 4–11. The variation of nuclear radius with mass number (Ref. 38).

tion ($N = 126$), while the process ${}_{84}\text{Po}^{210} \rightarrow {}_{82}\text{Pb}^{206}$ is less exoergic, being a transition from 126 to 124 neutrons. The plot for the polonium isotopes becomes normal as one moves sufficiently far from this preferred configuration at Po^{208}.

The influence of shell structure on α-transitions is also evident among the nuclides of the rare earths, in the region of the magic number $N = 82$. The α-activity of the artificially produced isotopes ${}_{62}\text{Sm}^{146}$, ${}_{63}\text{Eu}^{147}$, ${}_{64}\text{Gd}^{148}$, ${}_{65}\text{Tb}^{149}$, and ${}_{66}\text{Dy}^{150}$ is undoubtedly due to the tendency of these nuclei to transform into ${}_{60}\text{Nd}^{142}$, ${}_{61}\text{Pm}^{143}$, ${}_{62}\text{Sm}^{144}$, ${}_{63}\text{Eu}^{145}$, and ${}_{64}\text{Gd}^{146}$, for all of which $N = 82$ [36, 37].

Further evidence of the importance of the magic numbers has been obtained from the Gamow equation (4–11). Rosenblum and Valadarès [38] have shown that the nuclear radii r, calculated by putting the known values of λ, E_α, and Z into this equation, vary regularly with the mass number for the α-emitters of the uranium and thorium families. The variation is, however, more pronounced in the region of $A = 208$, which is the sum of 82 protons and 126 neutrons. The influence of these magic numbers upon the dimensions of the nucleus shows itself even more markedly in a plot of r against A for constant isotopic number I. The radii fall rapidly towards $Z = 84({}_{84}\text{Po} - {}_{82}\text{Pb})$ for all values of I (Fig. 4–11), probably because the formation of a closed shell results in a contraction of the nucleus. A second minimum appears at $Z = 98$ (Cf) and suggests that a subshell may exist at $Z = 96$. Seaborg [39] has reached the same conclusion by considering the variation of the mean nuclear radius for the isotopic α-emitting nuclides as a function of Z. The variation of the radii with A for nuclides with Z between 98 and 100 appears to favor the existence of a subshell of neutrons at $N = 152$ [40, 41].

The contraction in nuclear size in the region of $N = 126$ and $Z = 82$ has also been established by Perlman and Ypsilantis [42], who have calculated the radii of 25 even-even α-emitters between Rn and Cm. These authors produced a Berthelot-type diagram showing the α-particle energy as a logarithmic function of the half-life. Virtually parallel curves are obtained for each value of Z, and for even-even nuclei, the calculated

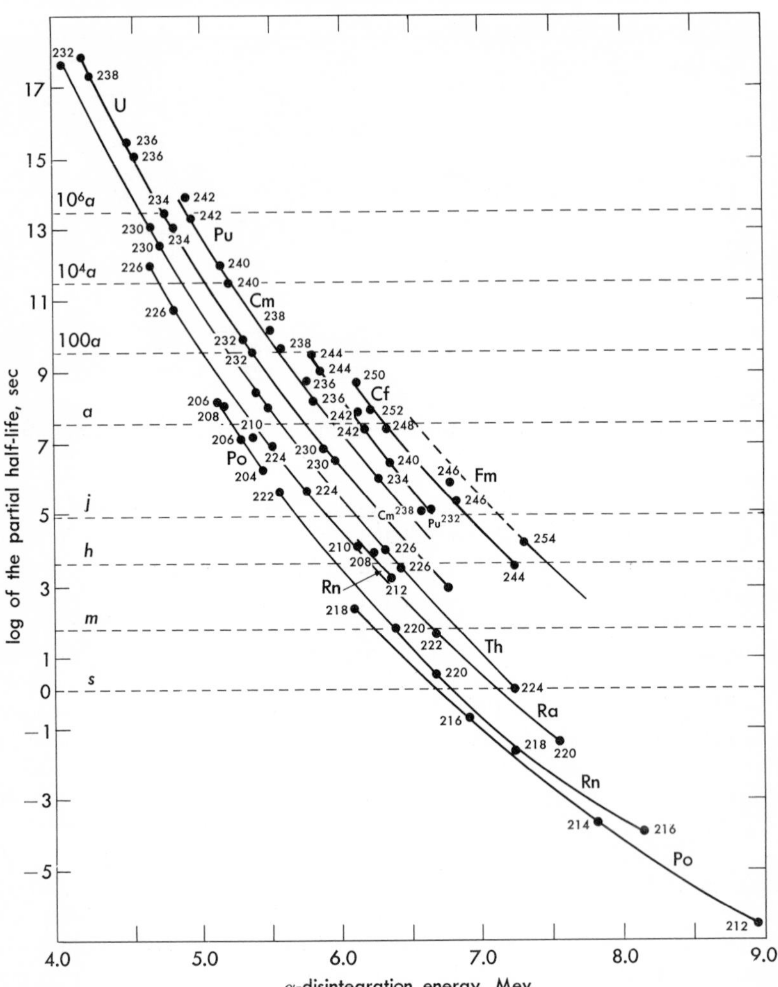

FIG. 4–12. The variation of half-life with α-disintegration energy for even Z and A (Ref. 35).

half-lives agree well with the values deduced from the equation, with the exception once again of certain nuclides around $Z = 82$ and $N = 126$ (Fig. 4–12). On the other hand, the half-lives of nuclei with even Z and odd A, odd Z and even A, and (especially) Z and A both odd, are very much higher than the theoretical values (Fig. 4–13); the measured half-lives are sometimes as much as 10^3 times larger than those given by Eq. (4–11). Perlman, *et al.* [35], believe that the deviations do not arise from the magic numbers alone, but from assuming (incorrectly) that the α-particle is preformed in the nucleus. In fact, for the unpaired nucleon to become part of the emitted α-particle, it must join with another nucleon with a different quantum number and with antiparallel spin. Consequently, the formation of the particle may necessitate a reorganization which will in-

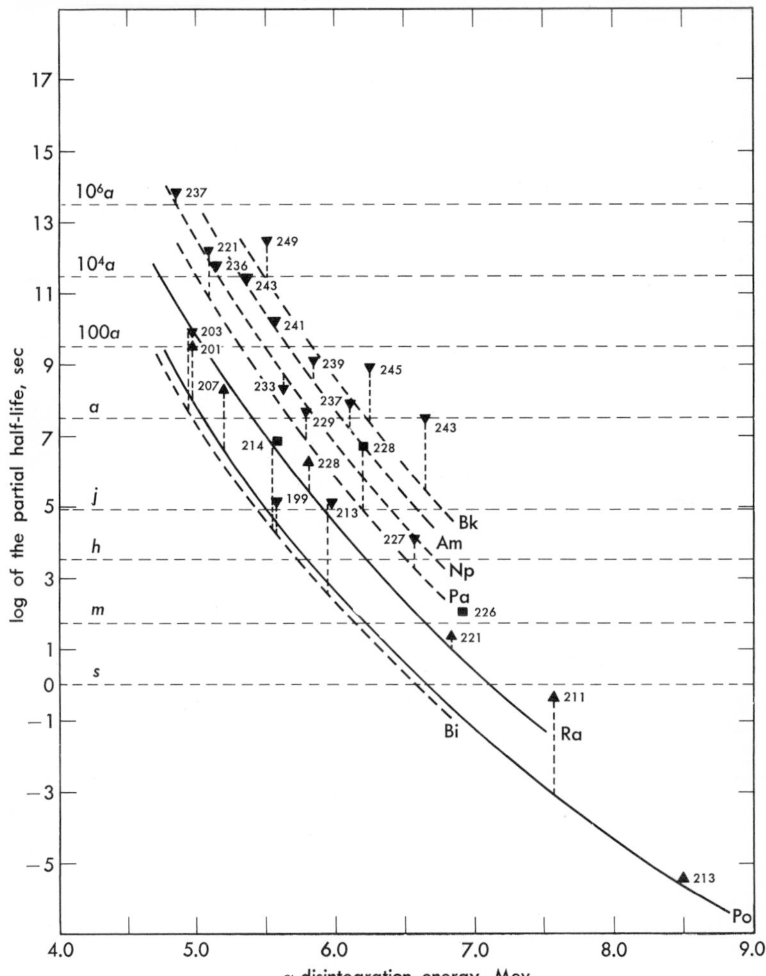

FIG. 4–13. · The variation of half-life with α-disintegration energy for odd Z and A (Ref. 35).

volve other nucleons, so that the emission will be delayed relative to the formation of a particle from nucleons of similar quantum states, as in even-even nuclides.

It should be noted that experiments by Rosenblum and Valadarès [43] suggest that the Gamow equation gives systematically low values for the relative intensities of the components of the fine structure. Furthermore, although these intensities generally decrease with energy as required by the theory, exceptions to this rule are known, notably for α-emitters with A odd: Ra^{223}, Ac^{227}, Pa^{231}, Th^{229}, and Am^{241}. For these and other reasons, various authors [44, 45] have suggested modifications of the Gamow relation without, however, bringing about any appreciable difference in the final results.

On the other hand, the Bohr-Mottelson collective model (Section 3–10) does seem to give a correct interpretation of some of the regularities observed in the fine structure of α-spectra. Rosenblum [26, 46, 47], for example, has pointed out that for the natural radioelements the energy differences between the nuclear levels, obtained from the fine structure of the long-range α-particles and from the γ-ray spectra, are often in the simple ratios 3/2, 2.5/2 . . . , or more generally in the form $(1 + 1/n)$ or $(2 + 1/n)$, where n is some small positive whole number. Similar regularities have been found for isotopes of the transuranium elements [48]. According to the collective model, such values are the result of the quantization of the rotational momentum, and it is thus possible to calculate the nuclear spins from the Bohr and Mottelson equations (3–21) and (3–22).

4–7 Gamma emission and internal conversion. It has already been stated that an excited nuclear state resulting from α- or β-disintegration decays to its ground state by the emission of a γ-ray whose quantum is equal to the energy difference between the two levels:

$$h\nu = E_2 - E_1.$$

A nucleus may be in an excited level, not only following a spontaneous radioactive process, but also as the result of external excitation, which may or may not be associated with a change in Z or A. Stabilization of the nucleus is also achieved in this case by the emission of a photon or, if the nucleus passes through intermediate states in decaying to the ground state, of a number of photons in cascade.

In many cases, decay to the fundamental level occurs by another process, *internal conversion*. Instead of being emitted in the form of photons, the excess energy of the nucleus is dissipated in the ejection of an electron from one of the outer shells (K, L, M, . . .) of the atom; the electron has an energy E_e given by

$$E_e = h\nu - E_{K,L,\ldots}, \tag{4–13}$$

where $h\nu$ is the energy of the equivalent photon and $E_{K,L\ldots}$ is the binding energy of the electron concerned. Unlike the spectra of nuclear β-emission, conversion electrons are monoenergetic and appear in the spectrum as discreet rays with energies determined by Eq. (4–13). This phenomenon can be regarded as an internal photoelectric effect (Section 11–5), taking place in two separate steps, namely the emission of a photon followed by its interaction with, and absorption by, the periphery electronic shells. This older picture of the process explains the name "internal conversion." Current theory assumes that there is a certain probability of direct interaction between the excited nucleus and the periphery electrons, and that this is in competition with the emission of electromagnetic radiation. The total internal conversion coefficient α is the ratio N_e/N_γ, where N_e is the number of de-excitations which occur by conversion and N_γ the number of photons emitted, both in unit time. The partial coefficients α_K, α_L, etc., have analogous definitions.

The relative probabilities of the two types of transitions depend on the energy difference between the two levels, on the atomic number, on the

TABLE 4–2

CONVERSION COEFFICIENTS IN THE L_{II}-SUBSHELL ($Z = 85$)

l	Electric		Magnetic	
	$E = 25.5$	76.5	25.5	76.5 kev
1	9.78×10^{-1}	5.71×10^{-5}	10.7×10	7.77×10^{-4}
2	2.02×10^{3}	7.64×10^{-4}	4.07×10^{2}	2.40×10^{-3}
3	1.84×10^{5}	4.38×10^{-3}	7.55×10^{3}	7.15×10^{-3}
4	9.19×10^{6}	1.71×10^{-2}	9.48×10^{5}	2.00×10^{-2}

polarity, and on the parity change. In classical electromagnetic theory, a polarity or multipole order is allotted to the radiations emitted by a system whose charge distribution varies in space and time. The radiation is characterized by a quantum number l referring to the angular momentum; for each value of l, two waves are emitted, one electric and one magnetic. By definition, the multipole order is equal to 2^l, so that a photon with an angular momentum characterized by $l = 1$ is dipolar (electric or magnetic); if $l = 2$, the photon is quadrupole, and so on. Furthermore, in the course of a transition between two levels, l can have one of the values $|I_i - I_f|$, $|I_i - I_f| + 1, \ldots, I_i + I_f$, where I_i and I_f are the spins of the initial and final levels. These variations, and those involving parity changes, impose selection rules analogous to those for β-transitions. For example, there can be no γ-transition between two levels which both have zero spin. The theoretical calculation of transition probabilities in terms of the various factors involved is tedious, approximate, and dependent upon the nuclear model. All the theories, however, lead to the following conclusions:

(1) De-excitation by γ-emission decreases rapidly with the multipolar order and increases with increasing energy.

(2) Internal conversion decreases when the energy increases, and increases with both polar order and with atomic number. These conclusions are illustrated in Table 4–2, which is based on the work of Rose [49], and refers to $Z = 85$.

4–8 Nuclear isomerism. When the transition between levels is associated with a large energy difference and is of low polarity, the half-life of the process is less than 10^{-12} sec, so that the decay is practically instantaneous. In some cases, however, the half-life can actually be measured, and the excited level is regarded as a *metastable state;* such levels, together with the ground state, are the *isomeric states* of the nuclide. This definition is rather imprecise, since it is affected by the sensitivity of the method of measuring the half-life; modern coincidence methods can be used to measure half-lives as small as 10^{-10} or 5×10^{-11} sec.

For a β-emitting nuclide represented by Z^A, β-transformation to the nuclide $(Z \pm 1)^A$ can take place by two different paths. If the isomers

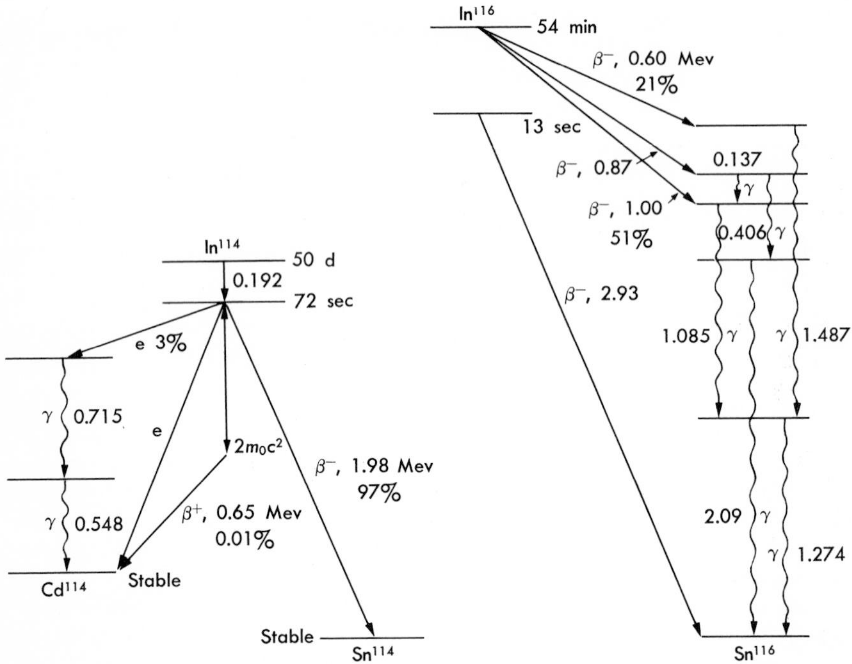

FIG. 4–14. The disintegration scheme of In^{114} [J. M. Hollander, I. Perlman, and G. T. Seaborg, *Revs. Modern Phys.*, **25,** 469 (1953)].

FIG. 4–15. The disintegration scheme of In^{116} [J. M. Hollander, I. Perlman, and G. T. Seaborg, *Revs. Modern Phys.*, **25,** 469 (1953)].

are genetically related, the metastable state decays by α-emission (with half-life t_1) to the ground state, which goes by β-emission (half-life t_2) to $(Z \pm 1)^A$. Such isomeric transitions are generally strongly converted. The isomers of In^{114} are a typical example; the metastable state decays with a half-life of 48 days to the ground state and this decays by β-emission to Sn^{114} and by β^+-emission or electron capture to Cd^{114}, with a mean half-life of 72 sec (Fig. 4–14). The second type of decay scheme is found when the isomers are independent of each other; both the excited state and the ground state decay by β-emission via intermediate states to the same isobaric nuclides with two different half-lives (e.g., $In^{116} \rightarrow Sn^{116}$; see Fig. 4–15). In many cases a definite fraction of the transitions proceeds by one mechanism and the remainder by another; thus the transition $Ge^{77m} \rightarrow As^{77}$ goes partially via the ground state of Ge^{77} and partly by direct β-emission.

Theory predicts that for γ-transitions of a given (high) polarity or with a given angular momentum, there will be a logarithmic relationship between the half-life and the energy of the transition, analogous to that for β-emission (Eq. 4–5). In testing this experimentally for transitions involving mixed γ-emission and internal conversion, the half-life t must be calculated from

$$t_\gamma = t(1 + \alpha), \tag{4–14}$$

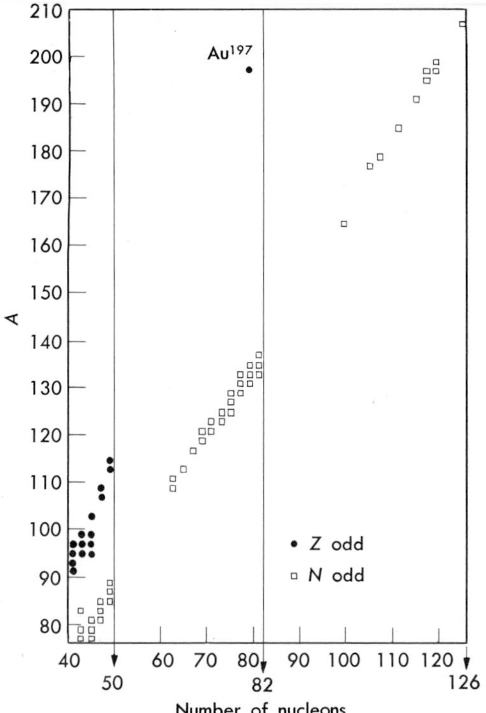

FIG. 4–16. "Islands" of isomerism (Ref. 53).

where t is the measured overall half-life and α is the conversion coefficient. Axel and Dankoff [50] have demonstrated that the logarithmic plot shows two virtually parallel straight lines, analogous to the Sargent curves, and corresponding to multipole orders of 4 and 5; some 60 isomeric transitions with relatively long half-lives ($t \geq 1$ sec) are grouped around these lines. There is also a third group of transitions, with very short half-lives (10^{-6} to 10^{-10} sec), for which there is no apparent energy dependence [51]. Virtually no metastable isomers are known with half-lives between 10^{-5} and 0.1 sec. Goldhaber and Sunyar [52] have established the following empirical relations between the average life τ and the energy E (in kev) for various spin changes:

$$\Delta I = 2, \qquad \log \tau = 4 - 5 \log E;$$
$$\Delta I = 3, \qquad \log \tau = 17.5 - 7 \log E;$$
$$\Delta I = 4, \qquad \log \tau = 27.7 - 9 \log E.$$

Nearly 200 pairs of isomers are currently known. For a number of nuclides, three isomers have been identified (Sb^{124}, Xe^{131}, Hg^{197}, Pb^{204}, etc.) and for some species four isomeric levels have been reported (Ta^{181}). Isomerism occurs much less frequently for even-even nuclides than for even-odd or odd-even. If the isomeric nuclides are placed on a plot of either Z or N as a function of the mass number, taking odd values only, the isomers are clearly grouped together in clusters which occur just before Z or N reaches the magic numbers 50, 82, or 126 (Fig. 4–16). For example, the odd isotopes of xenon with masses between 127 and 135 (N from 73 to 81) all exhibit nuclear isomerism, while Xe^{137} and Xe^{139}, with 83 and 85 neutrons, respectively, do not. The shell model explains these clusters by the fact that isomeric transitions correspond to the transition of an unpaired nucleon from one state to another; these states have different spins, and the transition probability increases with the difference between the spins [53, 54, 55]. These spin differences are large before the magic numbers and small after them (see Table 3–4).

4–9 The influence of chemical state. Electron capture and internal conversion cause a temporary disorganization of the electron shells of the atom because electrons are removed in these processes. This is also true of other radioactive disintegrations; as the α-particles or electrons ejected from the nucleus pass through the extranuclear electron cloud, they remove from it electrons associated with the excitation levels. This internal ionization [56, 57, 58] is similar to the ionization and excitation produced by the interaction of radiation with some external body (Chapter 11). The effect of these perturbations on the chemical composition of the medium, and the effects which arise from the mechanical recoil of the daughter atom after the emission of a particle from the nucleus are also discussed later (Chapter 17). For many years, the inverse effect, the influence of chemical composition on the rate of a nuclear transformation, was regarded as being negligible. This is certainly true for α-disintegrations, since here the energy changes involved are incomparably greater than those involved in chemical reactions. However, small, but by no means negligible, effects have been predicted theoretically and confirmed experimentally for both electron capture and internal conversion [59, 60].

Even with modern experimental techniques, the changes in the rate of decay can be observed only under exceptional circumstances. The most favorable conditions for observing the influence of chemical state on electron capture are to be found with nuclides of very low atomic number, where electrons are captured from a shell close to that containing the valence electrons. By changing the chemical constitution and consequently the electron density in the region of the nucleus, the probability of capture, and hence the half-life, is also changed. The difference should be especially acute between atoms in the elemental state and those which are in chemical combination.

This effect was confirmed by Segrè and his collaborators at Berkeley [59, 60] and by Bouchez, *et al.*, in Paris [61, 62] studying the L-electron capture of Be^7 (half-life 53.6 days). From measurements of the rate of decay of metallic beryllium and BeF_2, using a very sensitive differential method, Segrè found the relative difference in the half-lives to be

$$\frac{t(BeF_2) - t(Be)}{t(Be)} = 8.4 \times 10^{-4}.$$

The French workers found a value several times higher for this ratio. Be that as it may, there seems to be no doubt that the nuclide disintegrates more slowly when combined in an ionic compound.

The effect of chemical composition has also been detected by Bainbridge, *et al.* [63], who studied the isomeric transition of Tc^{99m} ($t = 6$ hr). The radiation emitted contains a strongly converted 2-kev component. These authors measured the half-life with metallic technetium (prepared either by electrolysis or by reduction with hydrogen at 1000°C), with anhydrous $KTcO_4$, and with dry precipitated Tc_2S_7. The half-life for the metal is 1.0003 greater than that for the sulfide and 1.003 times greater than for the pertechnetate. The differences have been discussed by Slater [64], who assumes that the 4p electrons are slightly more compressed in the pertechnetate ion than in the metal; the interatomic distances are 1.75 A for Tc-O and 2.73 A in the metal (i.e., for Tc-Tc). There is consequently a higher electron density in the ion and a higher probability of conversion. In agreement with this hypothesis, Bainbridge [65] has found that the half-life is lowered by 0.025% when technetium metal is compressed under a pressure of 100,000 atm.

More recently [66], it has been shown that the half-life of this isomeric transition in the metal decreases slightly at 4.2°K, at which temperature technetium becomes superconducting. If λ is the disintegration constant of Tc^{99m} at 293°K and λ' is the constant at 4.2°K, one finds $(\lambda' - \lambda)/\lambda = 6.4 \times 10^{-4}$. In a magnetic field, which suppresses the superconductivity, the difference decreases, and $(\lambda' - \lambda)/\lambda = 1.2 \times 10^{-4}$.

Finally, the chemical composition has been shown to affect the angular correlations between the γ-rays emitted by Cd^{111}. If a nuclide passes from an excited state A_1 to a state A_2 by the emission of radiation of energy $h\nu_1$, in a direction d_1, and A_2 goes to the ground state A_3 by the emission of $h\nu_2$ in a direction d_2, there will be some angle θ between d_1 and d_2. It is of interest to measure the relative probability of finding a given value of θ; this probability depends on the nature and properties of the levels A_1, A_2, and A_3, on the energies involved, and on the presence of an electric or magnetic field. According to d'Albers-Schönberg, *et al.* [67], the γ-rays emitted in cascade by Cd^{111}, an excited nuclide formed by electron capture from In^{111}, show a marked anisotropy when indium is in the liquid state or is a solvated ion, while the radiation is emitted isotropically by indium in the crystalline (metallic) state. It is suggested that in the latter case there is an interaction between the quadrupole moment of the nuclide and the nonhomogeneous electric field of the crystal which suppresses the anisotropy peculiar to the nucleus.

References

1. D. Palumbo and M. Santangelo, *Nuovo cimento,* **12,** Suppl. 1, 156 (1954).
2. A. V. Trofimov, *Doklady Akad. Nauk. S.S.S.R.*, **74,** 45 (1950).
3. O. Kofoed-Hansen, *β- and γ-Ray Spectroscopy,* K. Siegbahn, ed., North-Holland Publishing Co., Amsterdam, 1955, p. 357.
4. F. Reines and C. L. Cowan, *Phys. Rev.*, **90,** 492 (1953); **92,** 830 (1953).
5. E. Fermi, *Z. Physik.*, **88,** 161 (1934).

6. G. Gamow and E. Teller, *Phys. Rev.*, **49,** 895 (1936).
7. E. J. Konopinski, *Revs. Modern Phys.*, **15,** 209 (1945).
8. R. W. King, *Revs. Modern Phys.*, **26,** 327 (1954).
9. A. Pappas, R. Brightsen, and C. D. Coryell, *M.I.T. Progress Report*, May 1951, p. 71.
10. K. Way and M. Wood, *Phys. Rev.*, **94,** 119 (1954).
11. H. Suess, *Phys. Rev.*, **81,** 1071 (1951).
12. H. Suess and J. Jensen, *Arkiv Fysik*, **3,** 577 (1951).
13. N. Feather, *Nuclear Stability Rules*, Cambridge University Press, 1952.
14. C. S. Wu, E. Ambler, R. W. Hayward, D. D. Hoppes, and R. P. Hudson, *Phys. Rev.*, **105,** 1413 (1957).
15. H. Postma, W. J. Huiskamp, A. R. Miedima, M. J. Steenland, H. A. Tolhock, and C. J. Gorter, *Physica*, **23,** 259 (1957).
16. Y. B. Zeldovich, S. Y. Luk'yanov, and Y. A. Smorodinskii, *Uspekhi Fiz. Nauk*, **54,** 361 (1954).
17. W. H. Furry, *Phys. Rev.*, **56,** 1184 (1959).
18. R. G. Winter, *Phys. Rev.*, **99,** 88 (1955).
19. B. Pontecorvo, D. H. W. Kirkwood, and G. C. Hanna, *Phys. Rev.*, **75,** 982 (1949).
20. R. A. James, A. Ghiorso, and D. Orth, *Phys. Rev.*, **85,** 369 (1952).
21. G. D. O'Kelley, G. W. Barton, W. W. T. Crane, and I. Perlman, *Phys. Rev.*, **80,** 293 (1950).
22. L. W. Alvarez, *Phys. Rev.*, **54,** 486 (1938).
23. I. Perlman and F. Asaro, *Ann. Rev. Nuclear Sci.*, **4,** 157 (1954).
24. R. A. Glass, S. G. Thompson, and G. T. Seaborg, *J. Inorg. Nuclear Chem.*, **1,** 3 (1955).
25. S. Rosenblum, *Compt. rend.*, **188,** 1401 (1929); **190,** 1124 (1930).
26. S. Rosenblum, *J. phys. radium*, [7], **1,** 438 (1930).
27. G. Gamow, *Z. Physik*, **51,** 204 (1928).
28. R. W. Gurney and E. U. Condon, *Nature*, **122,** 439 (1928).
29. R. W. Gurney and E. U. Condon, *Phys. Rev.*, **33,** 127 (1929).
30. G. Fournier, *Compt. rend.*, **184,** 878 (1927).
31. A. Berthelot, *J. phys. radium*, **3,** 17, 52 (1942).
32. A. Berthelot, *Compt. rend.*, **227,** 829 (1948).
33. B. Karlik and T. Bernert, *Z. Physik*, **123,** 51 (1944).
34. B. Karlik, *Acta Phys. Austriaca*, **2,** 182 (1948).
35. I. Perlman, A. Ghiorso, and G. T. Seaborg, *Phys. Rev.*, **77,** 26 (1950); and Ref. 24.
36. O. J. Rasmussen, S. G. Thompson, and A. Ghiorso, *Phys. Rev.*, **89,** 33 (1953).
37. D. C. Dunlavey and G. T. Seaborg, *Phys. Rev.*, **92,** 206 (1953).
38. S. Rosenblum and M. Valadarès, *Compt. rend.*, **230,** 384 (1950); **236,** 196 (1953).
39. G. T. Seaborg, *Phys. Rev.*, **92,** 1074 (1953).
40. A. Ghiorso, S. G. Thompson, G. H. Higgins, B. G. Harvey, and G. T. Seaborg, *Phys. Rev.*, **95,** 293 (1954).
41. S. I. Larin and N. N. Kolesnikov, *Zhur. Eksp. i Teoret. Fiz.*, **28,** 243 (1955).
42. I. Perlman and T. J. Ypsilantis, *Phys. Rev.*, **79,** 30 (1950).

43. S. Rosenblum and M. Valadarès, *Compt. rend.*, **234**, 2359 (1952).
44. H. A. Bethe, *Revs. Modern Phys.*, **9**, 163 (1937).
45. M. A. Preston, *Phys. Rev.*, **71**, 865 (1941).
46. S. Rosenblum, *Compt. rend.*, **202**, 943 (1936); **234**, 202 (1952).
47. S. Rosenblum and M. Guillot, *Compt. rend.*, **204**, 345, 975 (1937).
48. F. Asaro and I. Perlman, *Phys. Rev.*, **91**, 763 (1953); **93**, 1423 (1954).
49. E. M. Rose, *J. phys. radium*, **16**, 520 (1955).
50. P. Axel and S. M. Dankoff, *Phys. Rev.*, **76**, 892 (1949).
51. R. Ballini, C. Levi, and L. Papineau, *C. E. A. Report* (*Saclay*), No. 179 (1952).
52. M. Goldhaber and H. W. Sunyar, *Phys. Rev.*, **83**, 906 (1951).
53. M. Goldhaber and D. R. Hill, *Revs. Modern Phys.*, **24**, 179 (1952).
54. L. W. Nordheim, *Phys. Rev.*, **75**, 1894 (1949).
55. E. Feenberg and K. C. Hammack, *Phys. Rev.*, **75**, 1877 (1949).
56. E. L. Feinberg, *J. Phys. russ.*, **4**, 424 (1941).
57. A. Migdal, *J. Phys. russ.*, **4**, 449 (1941).
58. P. Benoist-Gueutal, *Ann. phys.*, **8**, 593 (1953); also see the papers by J. Levinger, M. Riou, G. Charpak, and G. Renard in *J. phys. radium*, **16**, No. 7 (1955).
59. E. Segrè and C. Wiegand, *Phys. Rev.*, **75**, 39 (1949).
60. F. R. Leininger, E. Segrè, and C. Wiegand, *Phys. Rev.*, **76**, 897 (1949); **81**, 280 (1951).
61. R. Bouchez, P. Daudel, R. Daudel, and R. Muxart, *J. phys. radium*, **8**, 336 (1947).
62. R. Bouchez, P. Daudel, R. Daudel, R. Muxart, and A. Rogozinski, *J. phys. radium*, **10**, 201 (1949).
63. K. T. Bainbridge, M. Goldhaber, and E. Wilson, *Phys. Rev.*, **84**, 1260 (1951); **90**, 430 (1953).
64. J. C. Slater, *Phys. Rev.*, **84**, 1261 (1951).
65. K. T. Bainbridge, *Chem. Eng. News*, **30**, 651 (1952).
66. D. H. Byers and R. Stump, *Phys. Rev. Letters*, **1**, 219 (1958).
67. H. Albers-Schönberg, E. Heer, T. B. Novey, and R. Ruetschi, *Phys. Rev.*, **91**, 199 (1953).

CHAPTER 5

NUCLEAR REACTIONS

5–1 General principles. When a moving particle (i.e., a free nucleon or a nucleus) encounters another particle, kinetic energy is exchanged between them in accordance with the laws of conservation of energy and momentum. If the potential energy of the system is unchanged, so that kinetic energy is conserved in the collision, one speaks of *elastic scattering*. For an incident particle of mass m and energy E_0, the energy E_m acquired by the second particle of mass M, assumed to be at rest before the collision, is given by

$$E_m = \frac{4mM \sin^2 (\theta/2)}{(m + M)^2} E_0, \tag{5–1}$$

where θ is the angle between the initial and final paths of the incident particle.

The scattering process is *inelastic* if after the collision one of the particles is left in some excited state or has suffered a change or modification in composition or structure as a result of the collision. The nature and extent of such inelastic processes will depend on the nature of the projectile and target particles, and on the kinetic energy of the former.

The efficiency of the collisions in producing a given result, in other words, the yield, is expressed by the *microscopic cross section* σ. If p is the number of projectiles which, in unit time, strike a thin target x cm thick containing n_0 nuclei per cubic centimeter, then the number n of nuclei which are involved in a given process is

$$n = \sigma p n_0 x,$$

where σ is simply a proportionality coefficient, and it obviously follows that

$$\sigma = \frac{n}{p n_0 x} \cdot \tag{5–2}$$

The macroscopic cross section is given by $\Sigma = n_0\sigma$. For a target of atomic weight A and density ρ,

$$n_0 = \frac{\rho N}{A}, \qquad \Sigma = \frac{\rho N}{A} \sigma, \tag{5–3}$$

where N is Avagadro's number. Depending upon the nuclear interaction involved, one refers to the cross section for collision, absorption, excitation, etc. The total cross section σ_t is the sum of all these various partial cross sections. Nuclear dimensions are of the order of 10^{-02} cm, and since for processes involving fast particles σ_t is often of the same order as the geometrical area of nuclei, the units chosen for the cross section are $(10^{-12})^2$ or 10^{-24} cm^2, known as a *barn*.* Two subunits are also used, the millibarn, 10^{-27} cm^2 (mb), and the microbarn, 10^{-30} cm^2 (μb), for processes with low probabilities.

It is important to distinguish quite clearly between cross sections relating to a single nuclear species, such as Mg^{24}, Al^{27}, S^{32}, Ca^{42}, etc., and experimental values which refer to the natural mixture of isotopes. As a rule, barring the availability of the pure isotopes of a given element, yield determinations do not always allow the particular nuclide responsible for the observed phenomenon to be identified; this is certainly the case, for example, in the elastic scattering of neutrons.

Ignoring the very small effect of chemical composition on certain radioactive decay processes (already discussed in Section 4–10), we note that nuclear reactions are in principle independent of the chemical form of the target containing the nuclide in question. In practice, however, simple compounds in the purest possible form are used in order to avoid energy losses through various absorption phenomena and through secondary reactions, and to simplify the eventual chemical separation of the radioactive products. In Chapter 17 we discuss certain separations which are possible only if the reacting nuclide is initially present in some stable complex molecule (the Szilard-Chalmers effect). Generally however, the chemical form of the reacting nuclei will not be further considered in the present chapter.

As the result of an inelastic collision, a nucleus may undergo one of the following changes:

(a) The nucleus is simply excited to some higher energy level, from which it returns to its original state by the emission of one or more photons in cascade.

(b) The bombarding particle is captured with the resultant formation of a new nucleus, which may be stable or radioactive. The mass of this new species will, however, be less than the sum of the masses of the initial components; photons are emitted, with energies which are determined by this mass difference (in agreement with the Einstein equation) and by the kinetic energy of the projectile (after allowing for the recoil energy of the product nucleus).

(c) The target captures the projectile, and a nucleon or some very simple nuclide (e.g., a deuteron, α-particle, He^3) is ejected.

(d) For higher energy incident particles, capture may result in the "evaporation" of several nucleons or particles (2n, 3n, . . . 2pn, αn, etc.). The resultant nuclides, however, still have a mass and atomic number which are not too different from those of the original target nucleus.

(e) With sufficiently high-energy particles, of the order of 100 Mev, the nucleus throws out enough nucleons, either in the free state or in combination as nuclei, for the product nucleus to have a mass significantly lower than that of the target. This process is known as *spallation*. This name is sometimes more generally used [1] to include all transmutations involving

* "As big as a barn."

the ejection of free or combined nucleons following accelerated particle bombardment.

(f) In reactions between heavy nuclei ($Z > 70$) and protons with energies of 0.5 Bev or more, *fragmentation* occurs; this is the very fast and violent rupture of the nucleus into a light and a heavy excited fragment.

(g) The nuclide splits into two highly excited residues, each of similar mass, and releases a small number of nucleons (neutrons). This is the process known as *nuclear fission*. This process is also especially characteristic of the heavy elements, but much less energy is required than in (f), and it can often be brought about by neutrons of only thermal energies.

Depending on the mass balance, nuclear reactions are either exoergic or endoergic. Consider, for example, the first artificial transmutation discovered by Rutherford and his colleagues in the α-particle bombardment of nitrogen. The scintillations produced on a ZnS screen by particles with a range greater than that of the α-particles led to the conclusion that protons are emitted in the reaction

$$N^{14} + He^{4} \rightarrow H^{1} + O^{17}, \tag{5–4}$$

or, using modern nomenclature, N^{14} (α, p) O^{17}. This is a reaction of the type (c) above. The exact masses* of the four atoms involved are

$$\begin{aligned} \text{N } (14.00751) + \text{He } (4.00387) &= 18.01138 \\ \text{O } (17.00453) + \text{H } (1.00814) &= \underline{18.01267} \\ &\text{difference } 0.00129 \text{ amu.} \end{aligned}$$

The rest mass of the system has *increased* in the course of the reaction, which is therefore endoergic and an energy input of $0.00129 \times 931 = 1.172$ Mev is required (Section 3–4). This energy is not, however, all that is necessary, since some of the kinetic energy of the bombarding particle is transferred to the reaction products. The minimum energy required is given by $1.172\,[(14 + 4)/14] = 1.55$ Mev; this is the *threshold* of the reaction. In fact, the exact mass of O^{17} was not actually known when these experiments were carried out, and it was possible to determine it from the known initial energy of the α-particle and the kinetic energy of the products.

For a further example, consider the first transmutation carried out by Cockroft and Walton using accelerated protons:

$$\begin{matrix} Li^{7} & + & H^{1} & \rightarrow & 2\,He^{4} \\ 7.01822 & & 1.00814 & & 4.00387 \end{matrix} \tag{5–5}$$

This reaction is accompanied by a decrease in the total rest mass of

---

* The masses used in this chapter are taken from C. W. Li, W. Whaling, W. A. Fowler, and C. C. Lauritsen, *Phys. Rev.*, **83,** 512 (1951), and relate, in the absence of any statement to the contrary, to the neutral atoms. A more recent compilation has been given by A. H. Wapstra, *Physica,* **21,** 367, 385 (1955) and J. R. Huizenga, *Physica,* **21,** 410 (1955).

0.01862 amu, so that it is exoergic to this extent, with the release of $931 \times 0.01862 = 17.33$ Mev, either as the kinetic energy of the two α-particles, or in the emission of a photon.

The energy released or consumed in reactions such as (5–5) or (5–4) is usually designated by the letter Q, as in

$$N^{14} + n \rightarrow C^{14} + p + Q; \qquad Q = +0.60 \text{ Mev}. \tag{5–6}$$

From this reaction the exact mass of C^{14} can be determined from the relationship

$$C^{14} = 14.00751 + 1.00898 - \left(1.00814 + \frac{0.6}{931}\right) = 14.00771.$$

Reaction (5–6) differs from the two preceding ones in that the product nucleus is radioactive, but the mass and energy balance must hold equally well here as for transmutations giving stable nuclei.

The product nucleus of a nuclear reaction may be formed either in the ground state or, more often, in some excited level. In the latter case, decay to the ground state occurs by the emission of γ-radiation, equal in energy to the difference between the two states. The values of Q differ by the same energy; for example, if aluminum is bombarded with monoenergetic (7.3 Mev) α-particles, the product is Si^{30} and four groups of protons with energies of 9.3, 7.0, 5.5, and 4.6 Mev are ejected:

$$Al^{27} + He^4 \rightarrow Si^{30} + H^1 + Q. \tag{5–7}$$

In this reaction, the Q value for the production of Si^{30} in the ground state is 2.2 Mev, and the energies of the three excited states are 2.3, 3.8, and 4.7 Mev above this level [2].

A chemical reaction which is thermodynamically feasible proceeds at a measurable rate only if the activation energy necessary to overcome the potential barrier is available, and similarly, nuclear reactions involving positively charged particles take place only if the projectile particle can overcome the electrostatic repulsion which opposes its close approach to the target. This is true even for exoergic reactions. Only at sufficiently close approach do the specifically nuclear short-range forces bring about reaction. The *activation energy* is normally provided by the kinetic energy of the incident particle. The height of the coulombic barrier increases with the charge of the incident particle ze and with that of the target nucleus Ze and is given by the relation $E_b = Zze^2/R$, where R is the sum of the radii of the target nucleus and projectile. In contrast to this, the uncharged neutron requires no activation energy to take part in nuclear reactions, and the capture of thermal neutrons is consequently a very favorable process.

According to Bohr's statistical model of the nucleus (Section 4–10), nuclear reactions proceed in two successive steps. In the first stage, the loss of kinetic energy by the incident particle results in the formation of a compound nucleus; subsequently, after a large number of collisions between the nucleons inside this compound nucleus, the excess energy concentrates upon one nucleon or upon a small group of nucleons which escape from the nucleus (evaporation). The value of this dissociation energy is of the order of 8 Mev per nucleon. Since the two stages are independent of one another, the properties of the compound nucleus do not depend upon the nature of the processes by which it is formed. Thus the same excited O^{17} compound nucleus can be produced by any of the following processes:

$$O^{17} + \gamma, \quad O^{16} + n,$$
$$N^{15} + d, \quad N^{14} + t,$$
$$C^{13} + \alpha, \quad C^{14} + He^3.$$

Similarly, a given nuclear species can often be produced by a number of different transmutations; the β-active nuclide Mn^{56} (half-life 2.59 hours) can be prepared in the following ways:*

$$Mn^{55}\,(n, \gamma), \quad Mn^{55}\,(d, p), \quad Cr^{53}\,(\alpha, p), \quad Fe^{58}\,(d, \alpha),$$
$$Fe^{56}\,(n, p), \quad Fe^{57}\,(\gamma, p), \quad Co^{59}\,(\gamma, 2pn), \quad Co^{59}\,(n, \alpha),$$

and, in addition, by the spallation of iron, copper, or cobalt with very fast protons, of copper or arsenic with accelerated deuterons, and of copper with accelerated helium ions.

It also follows that once a compound nucleus has formed, it may decay in various ways, the probabilities of which are quite independent of the method of formation:

$$Al^{27} + \text{fast n} \rightarrow Al^{28*} \rightarrow \begin{cases} Al^{26} + 2n, \\ Al^{28} + \gamma, \\ Mg^{27} + p, \\ Na^{24} + \alpha, \end{cases}$$

$$C^{14} + d \rightarrow N^{16*} \rightarrow \begin{cases} B^{12} + \alpha, \\ C^{15} + p, \\ N^{15} + n. \end{cases}$$

As in molecular chemistry, some nuclear processes can go in either of two directions,

$$H^1 + n^1 \rightleftarrows H^2 + \gamma,$$
$$Be^9 + He^4 \rightleftarrows C^{12} + n^1.$$

Such systems can be treated by statistical methods similar to those applied to chemical equilibria. If $\sigma(a, v_a)$ and $\sigma(b, v_b)$ represent the cross sections for the reactions

$$A + a \rightleftarrows B + b$$

* The majority of the nuclear reactions mentioned in this chapter are taken from the review by D. Strominger, J. M. Hollander, and G. T. Seaborg, *Revs. Modern Phys.*, **30,** 585 (1958).

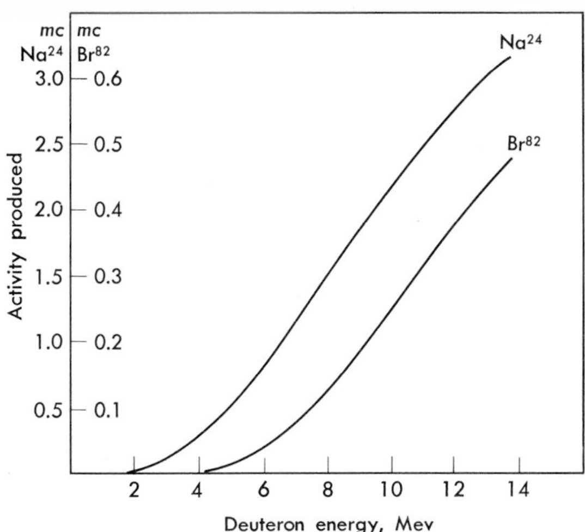

FIG. 5-1. Excitation functions for the Na^{23} (d, p) Na^{24} and Br^{81} (d, p) Br^{82} reactions. [E. T. Clarke and J. W. Irvine, Jr., *Phys. Rev.*, **66,** 231 (1944)]

for particles with velocities v_a and v_b, it can be shown [3] that

$$\frac{\sigma(a, v_a)}{\sigma(b, v_b)} = \frac{\lambda_a^2}{\lambda_b^2}, \tag{5-8}$$

where λ is the de Broglie wavelength for the particle in question.

The variation of the cross section (i.e., the yield) of a nuclear reaction with the energy of the incident particle is known as the *excitation function* and its graphical representation as an *excitation curve.* Apart from certain particular energy values, the excitation function is normally a smooth continuous function of the energy (Fig. 5-1), although the yield may decrease if other reactions which are favored at higher energies enter into competition with the reaction under consideration. The radiative capture of neutrons is an example of just such a system.

For most reactions, however, one finds significantly higher yields at certain particular incident energies, above and below which the cross section is much smaller, so that one or more relatively sharp maxima appear in the excitation curve (Fig. 5-2). According to the statistical model, these values correspond to the resonance energies of the energy levels of the compound nucleus. The extent of these high-yield regions, measured as the width of the excitation curve at half maximum, is the *resonance width,* denoted by Γ. For a given nuclear process $A(a, b)A'$, this is a measure of the probability that the compound nucleus $(A + a)$ will decompose in unit time into $(A' + b)$; more precisely, it is related to the average life τ of this process by

$$\Gamma_b = \frac{h}{2\pi\tau}. \tag{5-9}$$

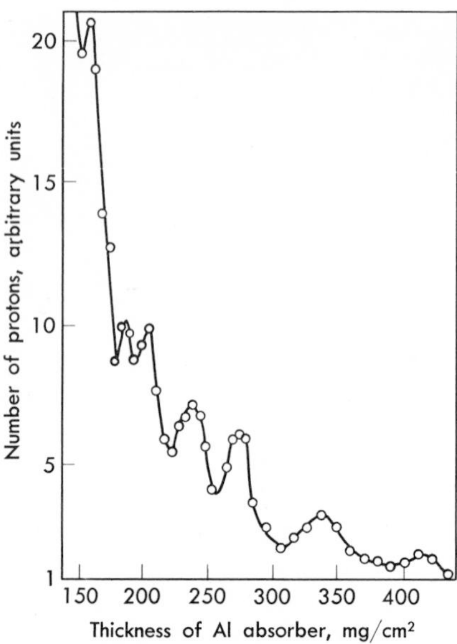

FIG. 5-2. Groups of protons produced in the Al^{27} (α, p) Si^{30} reaction. [J. E. Brolley, M. B. Sampson, and A. C. G. Mitchell, *Phys. Rev.*, **76,** 624 (1949)]

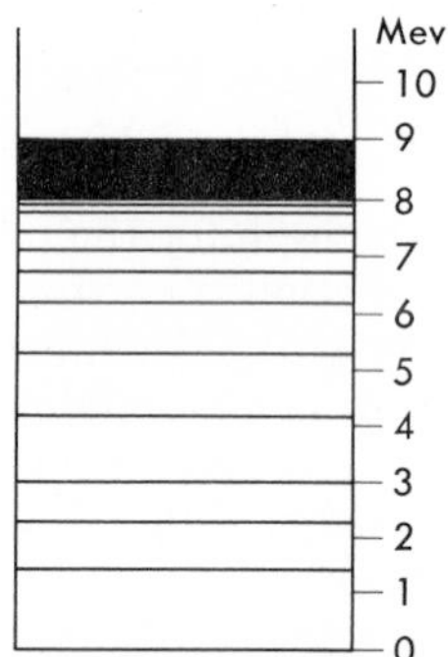

FIG. 5-3. The variation of the density of nuclear levels with energy.

The total resonance width measures the overall average life and is the sum of the various partial quantities; Γ has the dimensions of energy and is expressed in ev.

The distance between the levels decreases with increasing mass of the compound nucleus and with increasing energy (Fig. 5-3). For light nuclei ($A \sim 10$ to 25), the difference between the ground state and the first excited level is of the order of 1 Mev; it is $\sim$10 to 100 kev for an excitation of 8 Mev and about 1 kev in the 15-Mev region. For $A \sim 150$, the corresponding values are 0.1 Mev, 30 ev, and 1 to 10^{-2} ev. The width of the levels increases with the excitation energy to such an extent that for medium to high atomic weight compound nuclei at energies of 10 to 12 Mev, the levels are superimposed upon each other and the resonance vanishes.

5–2 Neutron reactions. The simplest type of nuclear reaction which occurs with neutrons is the so-called radiative capture. As early as 1934, Fermi and his collaborators demonstrated this process with the lightest nucleus,

$$H^1 + n^1 \rightarrow H^2 + \gamma,$$

and with the heaviest of the naturally occurring nuclides,

$$U^{238} + n \rightarrow U^{239} + \gamma \qquad (\beta\text{-active}, t_{1/2} = 23 \text{ min}),$$

and with very many other nuclides with masses between these two. Neutron capture results in the formation of an excited compound nucleus, the potential energy increase arising from the binding energy of the extra neutron, and eventually from the kinetic energy of the incident particle. De-excitation may occur by one of the four processes listed in the previous section; (a) photon emission, (b) the re-emission of a neutron, (c) the emission of a proton (less frequent with low-energy neutrons)

$$N^{14} + n \rightarrow C^{14} + p,$$

$$Cl^{35} + n \rightarrow S^{35} + p,$$

or (d) the emission of an α-particle

$$B^{10} + n \rightarrow Li^7 + \alpha,$$

$$Cl^{35} + n \rightarrow P^{32} + \alpha.$$

If the nucleus returns immediately to its ground state after the emission of a neutron [as in (b) above], the process is identical with elastic scattering. Inelastic collision with the formation of metastable states with measurable half-lives has been observed in a number of cases:

$$Y^{89}\,(n, n)\,Y^{89m}, \qquad t_{1/2} = 14 \text{ sec},$$
$$Ag^{107}\,(n, n)\,Ag^{107m}, \qquad 44.3 \text{ sec},$$
$$Ag^{109}\,(n, n)\,Ag^{109m}, \qquad 39.2 \text{ sec},$$
$$In^{115}\,(n, n)\,In^{115m}, \qquad 4.5 \text{ hr},$$
$$Au^{197}\,(n, n)\,Au^{197m}, \qquad 7.4 \text{ sec},$$
$$Pb^{207}\,(n, n)\,Pb^{207m}, \qquad 0.9 \text{ sec}.$$

The probability of processes (c) and (d) falls with increasing Z because of the increase of the electrostatic potential barrier which the proton or the α-particle must overcome in order to escape from the nucleus.

The result of the competition between elastic collision (n, n) and radiative capture depends on the energy of the neutron and on the mass of the target nucleus. Neutrons are generally classed as being slow (energies below 1 kev), intermediate ($1 < E < 500$ kev), fast ($0.5 < E < 10$ Mev), or very fast. Likewise nuclei are divided into light ($A < 25$), medium ($25 < A < 80$) and heavy, although these classifications obviously do not have too much significance.

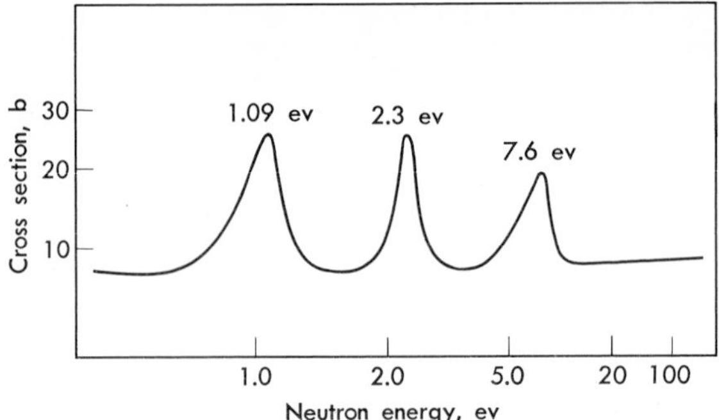

FIG. 5–4. Neutron resonances in Zr. [W. W. Havens, C. S. Wu, L. J. Rainwater, and C. L. Meaker, *Phys. Rev.*, **71**, 165 (1947)]

For slow neutrons, the capture cross section is inversely proportional to the velocity, and hence to the square root of the energy. This is the so-called $1/v$ law. In this energy region ($E = 1$ ev) the de Broglie wavelength ($\lambda = h/mv$) of the neutrons is of the order of 10^{-9} cm. This is several times greater than the dimensions of the nucleus, so that the interaction extends beyond the surface of the nucleus.

Deviations from the $1/v$ law may arise if the excitation energy of the compound nucleus brings it close to one of its energy levels, when resonance occurs (Fig. 5–4). The cross section is then given by an equation derived by Breit and Wigner [4],

$$\sigma_\gamma = \frac{\lambda^2}{4\pi} \frac{g\Gamma_\gamma\Gamma_n}{(E - E_0)^2 + \frac{1}{4}\Gamma^2}, \tag{5–10}$$

where E is the energy of the incident neutron, E_0 the resonance energy, Γ_γ and Γ_n the partial widths for capture and for elastic collision, Γ the total resonance width, and g a statistical factor which depends upon the spins of the neutron, the target nucleus, and the compound nucleus. Equations analogous to Eq. (5–10) hold for the resonances found in (n, x) reactions if Γ_x is substituted for Γ_γ; like Γ, Γ_n and Γ_x are measured in ev and are proportional to the probabilities of the processes in equation.

For slow neutrons, Γ_n is proportional to the velocity (or to $\sqrt{E}$), while Γ_γ is almost independent of energy. Since the density of the levels is very low in light nuclei (Section 5–1), resonance is rare and, apart from a few exceptions, the scattering is essentially elastic. For medium and heavy nuclei, Γ_n is generally markedly lower than Γ_γ. The values of Γ are usually of the order of 0.1 ev, but values 10 times larger or smaller than this are known; Γ_n is only 10^{-2} to 10^{-4} ev, although certain Mn and Co isotopes have exceptional values where Γ_n is $\sim$10 ev and Γ_γ about 0.1 ev. The nuclides Pd^{108}, Sm^{152}, and W^{186} have levels for which $\Gamma_n \approx \Gamma_\gamma \approx 0.1$ ev.

Table 5–1 gives some important resonance energies E_r and their widths Γ_γ for slow neutrons [6].

Table 5–2 lists the capture cross section and the total cross section for thermal neutrons for most of the elements and for a number of individual

TABLE 5–1

RESONANCE ENERGIES FOR SLOW NEUTRONS*

Nucleus	E_r, ev	Γ_γ, ev	Nucleus	E_r, ev	Γ_γ, ev
Mn^{55}	345	0.2	Hf^{177}	1.08	0.12
Co^{59}	123	0.3		2.34	0.16
As^{75}	46	0.05	Ta^{181}	6.1	—
Br	36	(0.1)		10.3	0.2
Rh^{103}	1.26	0.20		13.6, 20	(0.1)
Ag^{107}	15.9	~0.11	W^{182}	4.15	0.07
Ag^{109}	5.17	0.16	W^{183}	7.8	(0.1)
Cd^{113}	0.176	0.115	W^{186}	19.25	0.15
In^{115}	1.45, 38.6, 9	0.08	Re^{185}	4.4, 11	—
Sb	5.8, 15	(0.1)	Re^{187}	2.15	0.14
I^{127}	19.4	0.45		5.9, 7.2	—
Sm^{149}	0.096	0.074	Ir^{193}	1.27	~0.15
Eu^{153}	0.47	0.20	Au^{197}	4.87	0.15
Gd^{157}	0.028	0.12	U	6.5, 14	—
Dy	1.74	(0.1)			

* Taken from B. Feld, *Experimental Nuclear Physics*, E. Segrè, ed., **2,** 208 (1953).

isotopes. The importance of these figures in analytical chemistry is discussed in Chapter 22. It can be seen from Table 5–2 that σ_c is often approximately equal to σ_t for medium and heavy elements. For light elements, σ_c is small, generally less than 1 barn, and indeed in this mass region, the competing (n, p) and (n, α) reactions have very much higher cross sections (Table 5–3). For the medium atomic weight elements, the cross sections for thermal neutron capture may be as high as several barns. For (n, p) and (n, α), reactions, the neutron energy must be sufficiently high to overcome the endothermicity of the reaction and to increase the probability of escape of the charged product by the tunnel effect (Section 4–5). For neutrons with energies of the order of 10 Mev, the following are typical reactions:

$$Fe^{56}\,(n, p)\,Mn^{56}, \qquad Hg^{198}\,(n, p)\,Au^{198},$$
$$Hg^{200}\,(n, \alpha)\,Pt^{197}, \qquad Tl^{203}\,(n, \alpha)\,Au^{200}.$$

With increasing energy, competition from reactions such as (n, 2n), (n, 3n), (n, 2np), (n, nα), etc., becomes appreciable. Reactions involving only neutron emission have a threshold which is determined by the binding energy of the ejected neutron and by the recoil energy of the product nucleus; measurement of this threshold is in fact one of the methods available for the determination of the binding energy. Table 5–4 shows several examples of this type of reaction, with the threshold (in Mev). For medium or heavy nuclides, the energy required to remove a neutron is ~8 Mev.

TABLE 5–2

CAPTURE CROSS SECTIONS (σ_c) AND TOTAL CROSS SECTIONS (σ_t) FOR THERMAL NEUTRONS (0.025 EV) IN BARNS*

Element	σ_c	σ_t	Element	σ_c	σ_t
H^1	0.332	38	Rh^{103}	156	161
D^2	4.6×10^{-4}	7	Pd	8.0	11.6
Be^9	0.01	7	Ag	63	69
B	755	759	Cd	2450	—
C	3.4×10^{-3}	4.8	Cd^{113}	2.0×10^4	—
N	1.88	12	In	196	198
O	$<2 \times 10^{-4}$	4.2	Sn	0.62	4.6
Na^{23}	0.5	4.5	Sb	5.7	10
Mg	0.063	3.6	Te	4.7	9.7
Al^{27}	0.023	1.4	I^{127}	7.0	10.6
Si	0.16	1.8	Xe^{124}	74	—
P^{31}	0.2	5.2	Xe^{135}	2.7×10^6	—
S	0.52	1.6	Cs^{133}	29	—
Cl	33.6	49.6	Ba	1.2	9.2
Ar	0.66	2.1	La	9.3	—
K	2.07	3.5	Ce	0.73	—
Ca	0.44	—	Pr^{141}	11.6	—
Sc^{45}	24	48	Nd	46.2	—
Ti	5.8	10	Sm	5.6×10^3	—
V	4.98	10	Sm^{149}	40800	—
Cr	3.1	6.1	Sm^{151}	$\sim 10^4$	—
Mn^{25}	13.2	15.5	Eu	4.3×10^3	—
Fe	2.53	13.5	Gd	4.6×10^4	—
Co^{59}	37.0	44	Gd^{155}	$\sim 6.1 \times 10^4$	—
Ni	4.8	22.3	Gd^{157}	$\sim 2.4 \times 10^5$	—
Cu	3.77	11	Dy	950	1050
Zn	1.10	4.7	Hf	105	113
Ga	2.8	6.8	Ta	21	26
Ge	2.45	5.5	W	19.2	24.2
As^{75}	4.3	10.3	Re	86	100
Se	12.3	23.3	Os	15.3	—
Br	6.7	12.7	Ir	440	—
Kr	31	38.2	Pt	8.8	18.8
Rb	0.73	—	Au^{197}	98.8	108
Sr	1.21	11.2	Hg	380	400
Y^{89}	1.31	—	Tl	3.4	17.4
Zr	0.18	8	Pb	0.17	11.2
Nb^{93}	1.15	6.1	Bi^{209}	0.034	9
Mo	2.7	9.7	Th^{232}	7.56	—
Tc^{99}	22	—	U	7.68	—
Ru	2.56	8.6			

* Based on D. J. Hughes and R. B. Schwarz, *Neutron Cross Sections*, Brookhaven National Laboratory, 1958; see also Table 6–1 for values for uranium and the transuranium elements.

TABLE 5–3

YIELDS OF (n, p) AND (n, α) REACTIONS

Reaction	σ, barns, for thermal neutrons	Q, Mev
He^3 (n, p) H^3	5300	0.7637
Li^6 (n, α) H^3	950	4.785
B^{10} (n, α) Li^7	3990	2.79
N^{14} (n, p) C^{14}	1.86	0.626
Cl^{35} (n, p) S^{35}	~0.3	0.62

TABLE 5–4

(n, 2n) REACTIONS*

Initial nucleus	Product nucleus	Threshold, Mev
C^{12}	C^{11}	20.3
N^{14}	N^{13}	11.3
Mg^{24}	Mg^{23}	17.1
Mg^{25}	Mg^{24}	7.5
Cr^{50}	Cr^{49}	13.7
Zn^{64}	Zn^{63}	11.9
Sr^{87}	Sr^{86}	8.5
Mo^{97}	Mo^{96}	7.2
Sb^{121}	Sb^{120}	9.3
Nd^{150}	Nd^{149}	7.4
Ta^{181}	Ta^{180}	7.6
Au^{197}	Au^{196}	8.1
Pb^{208}	Pb^{207}	7.4
Th^{232}	Th^{231}	6.4
U^{238}	U^{237}	6.0

* Based on B. Feld, *op. cit.*

The emission of one or more neutrons along with a charged particle has been reported in a number of reactions, such as

$$O^{16}\,(n, 3np)\,N^{13}, \qquad N^{14}\,(n, 3np)\,C^{11},$$

$$O^{16}\,(n, 2n\alpha)\,C^{11}, \qquad Cu^{65}\,(n, n\alpha)\,Co^{61}.$$

For such processes, and especially for those involving the reaction of heavy nuclei with neutrons of about 100 Mev energy, Serber [5] and Goldberger [6] have suggested that the bombarding particle interacts directly with one or more of the nucleons in the nucleus before the incident energy can be distributed over the whole assembly of nucleons. (Such a sharing of the energy

TABLE 5–5

THE SPALLATION OF COPPER WITH 370-MEV NEUTRONS

Product	σ, mb	Reaction
$_{22}Ti^{45}$	0.078	(n, 3α p 6n)
$_{24}Cr^{49}$	0.35	(n, 2α p 6n)
$_{25}Mn^{51}$	0.76	(n, 2α 5n)
$_{25}Mn^{52}$	4.68	(n, 2α 4n)
$_{25}Mn^{56}$	2.81	(n, 2α)
$_{26}Fe^{52}$	0.134	(n, α p 7n)
$_{26}Fe^{58}$	1.24	(n, α p n)
$_{26}Fe^{59}$	2.44	(n, α p)
$_{27}Co^{55}$	0.415	(n, α 5n)
$_{27}Co^{58m}$	49	(n, α 2n)
$_{27}Co^{58}$	23.2	(n, α 2n)
$_{27}Co^{61}$	3.78	(n, 2p n)
$_{28}Ni^{57}$	0.54	(n, p 6n)
$_{28}Ni^{65}$	0.88	Cu^{65} (n, p)
$_{29}Cu^{61}$	15.1	(n, 3n)
$_{29}Cu^{62}$	37.1	(n, 2n)
$_{29}Cu^{64}$	56.6	(n, γ)

is assumed in the compound nucleus model, which does not hold for interactions with extremely high-energy nucleons, whose mean free path in the nucleus is greater than the nuclear diameter.)

The incident nucleon can escape after one or more collisions, having lost only a fraction of its kinetic energy. The nucleons with which it collided react in their turn with others, so that a cascade of interactions takes place inside the nucleus; this ends either by the nucleons in motion losing their kinetic energy in collision, or by escaping on reaching the surface. Since the incident nucleon can leave the nucleus after losing only a fraction of its initial energy, the nucleus is at least partially transparent to very fast nucleons. Depending upon the number and site of the collisions, differing nuclear changes can occur in this way. This mechanism has been used to explain the variety of products resulting from spallation reactions.

Qualitative confirmation of this cascade mechanism has been obtained experimentally by Hadley and York [7] for the spallation of C, Cu, and Pb by 90-Mev neutrons. Protons, deuterons, and tritons are emitted in decreasing proportions, and the protons and (especially) deuterons are projected forward with reference to the direction of the incident neutrons, as if the latter had picked up protons in flight. The angular distribution of the branches of the stars found in photographic emulsions from spallation reactions caused by 300-Mev neutrons also agrees with this theory [8]. The formation of deuterons by spallation of the constituents of emulsions by the high-energy neutrons in cosmic radiation was earlier reported by Cüer, Morand, and Van Rossum [9], who also proposed a mechanism involving the removal of a proton by the neutron.

The spallation of Cu has also been studied by Marquez [10], using neutrons with a maximum energy of 370 Mev. Table 5–5 lists the various products which were identified, with the cross sections σ. The nuclear reactions written in the final column are purely formal and do not presume to indicate the actual mechanism. For simplicity, it has been assumed that Cu^{63} is the only nuclide undergoing reaction (except for the production of Ni^{65} from Cu^{65}). The spallation of Al^{27} with neutrons of the same energy gave Mg^{27} (5.1 mb), Na^{24} (29.4 mb), F^{18} (6.8 mb), N^{13} (3.2 mb), and C^{11} (<3.4 mb).

For very high-energy neutrons, the cross section σ_t can be assumed to a first approximation to be close to the geometrical dimensions of the nucleus (πr^2). Measurements of σ_t for 14-, 25-, and 90-Mev neutrons have given values for the radii of various nuclei and confirmed the linear variation of r with $A^{1/3}$ (Section 3–3). A value of 1.37×10^{-13} cm is found for r_0 [11, 12, 13].

5–3 Proton reactions. We have already met the reaction (5–5),

$$Li^7 + p \rightarrow 2\alpha,$$

which in fact takes place in two stages, the process

$$Li^7 + H^1 \rightarrow Be^8 + \gamma, \tag{5–11}$$

being followed by

$$Be^8 \rightarrow 2\alpha. \tag{5–12}$$

The energy of the photon emitted in Eq. (5–11) is 17.3 or 3 Mev, depending on whether the Be^8 nucleus is formed in its ground state or in an excited level; in the latter case, the excess energy appears as the kinetic energy of the two α-particles. This is therefore effectively a radiative capture reaction. Since it is strongly exothermic, protons with energies as low as 13 kev will bring about reaction. Similar systems are

$$C^{12}\,(p, \gamma)\,N^{13}, \qquad F^{19}\,(p, \gamma)\,Ne^{20},$$

$$Al^{27}\,(p, \gamma)\,Si^{28}, \qquad Cd^{108}\,(p, \gamma)\,In^{109}.$$

The product nuclides in the first and last of these reactions are radioactive, while those of the other two are stable.

Resonance phenomena have been observed in most bombardments of light nuclei ($3 \leq Z \leq 17$) with protons of up to 3 Mev. The cross section is given by the Breit-Wigner equation, analogous to that for neutrons [Eq. 5–10]. Excited states can also be populated by the inelastic collision process (p, p); metastable states produced in this way include Rh^{103} (4.4 min) and In^{115} (4.5 hours). For this type of excitation, the proton energy must be high enough to allow the particle to penetrate the electrostatic potential barrier.

Lower energy protons often cause *coulombic excitation*, in which the nucleus acquires sufficient energy from the electrostatic interaction to pass to one of the two or three lowest excited levels from which, in the absence of metastable states, it decays to the ground state by γ-emission. Because of the low energies involved, the rotational levels predicted by the collective model have by far the greatest chance of being excited.

The cross section for coulombic excitation is very small, and the increase of σ with increasing proton energy is unimportant, since at higher energies the process is in any case masked by the formation and decomposition reactions of the compound nucleus. A theoretical treatment of coulombic excitation has been given by Ter-Martirosyan [14]. The first experimental evidence came from the bombardment of Ta^{181} with 1.75-Mev protons [15]; the energies of the two excited levels, 137 and 300 kev, agree well with the Bohr-Mottelson theory (Section 3–10). The excitation reactions of a very large number of other nuclei have subsequently been studied, and in general the results are in agreement with the theory.

At higher proton energies, light nuclei may disintegrate into two or three particles, sometimes giving different products:

$$Li^6 + H^1 \rightarrow He^3 + He^4, \qquad Be^9 + H^1 \rightarrow \begin{cases} Li^6 + He^4, \\ Be^8 + D^2, \end{cases}$$

$$B^{10} + H^1 \rightarrow B^8 + T^3, \qquad B^{11} + H^1 \rightarrow \begin{cases} Be^8 + He^4, \\ 3\,He^4, \end{cases}$$

$$N^{14} + H^1 \rightarrow C^{11} + He^4, \qquad O^{18} + H^1 \rightarrow N^{15} + He^4.$$

Reactions of the type Z^A (p, n) $(Z + 1)^A$, such as $Li^7 \rightarrow Be^7$, $B^{11} \rightarrow C^{11}$, $O^{18} \rightarrow F^{18}$, $F^{19} \rightarrow Ne^{19}$, etc., result in the formation of β^+-active nuclides. Such reactions are necessarily endoergic for two reasons; first, unless $(Z + 1)^A$ has a mass greater than $Z^A - m_0$ it would be β-active, and second, the mass of the neutron is greater than that of the proton. The threshold of the reaction is normally between 1 and 3 Mev. Reactions of the type Z^A (p, α), on the other hand, are generally exoergic, except where Z^A is some very stable light nuclide.

With increasing atomic number, the activation energy required for the proton to penetrate the potential barrier increases. As with α-particle emission, the probability of penetration from the exterior is a rapidly increasing function of the proton energy, and decreases with atomic number. It is also a function of the spin and of the radius of the nucleus, so that yield determination for reactions caused by proton or other charged particles is another of the methods available for estimating nuclear radii.

At sufficiently high proton energies, (p, α) reactions are still observed, but the emission of neutrons, either alone or with a proton, becomes predominant, since this type of process requires a lower activation energy for the ejection of the particle from the nucleus:

$$Cu^{65}\,(p, pn)\,Cu^{64}, \qquad Sb^{121}\,(p, pn)\,Sb^{120}, \qquad Ta^{181}\,(p, pn)\,Ta^{180},$$

$$Sr^{88}\,(p, 3n)\,Y^{86}, \qquad Co^{59}\,(p, 3n)\,Ni^{57}, \qquad I^{127}\,(p, 5n)\,Xe^{123},$$

$$I^{127}\,(p, 6n)\,Xe^{122}, \qquad Cs^{133}\,(p, 5, 6, 7n)\,Ba^{129,128,127},$$

$$Ta^{181}\,(p, 1\text{–}6n)\,W^{181-176}, \qquad Bi^{209}\,(p, 8n)\,Po^{202}, \qquad \text{etc.}$$

A number of nuclei will undergo spallation with protons with energies between 187 and 2200 Mev (2.2 Bev). In the bombardment of Al with 335-Mev protons, Marquez and Perlman [16] detected the formation of Na^{22}, Na^{24}, F^{18}, C^{11}, and Be^7, the formation cross sections being of the order of 10^{-2} to 10^{-3} mb; Be^7 is also formed in the spallation of C, Cu, Ag, and Au, the yield decreasing with the increasing atomic number of the target. With iron [17], one finds the formation of Cr^{51} (41), V^{49} (31), Cr^{49} (4.8), Cr^{48} (0.8), Cl^{38} (0.17), Na^{24} (0.026), and isotopes of Co, Ti, Sc, Ca, S, P, and Si; the cross sections are given in millibarns in parentheses.

In general, the cross sections fall off with the mass of the nuclide produced. The light particles He^4, He^3, and H^3 are found in the relative proportions 1.00: 0.048: 0.078 [18]. The bombardment of V, Mn, or Co with 187- or 370-Mev protons gives virtually the same product nuclides [19, 20, 21]. Some 35 nuclides have been identified in the products of the bombardment of copper with 340-Mev protons, including isotopes of Fe, Ti, Sc, Ca, Cl, S, P, and Na, as well as Zn, Ga, and Ge [22, 23]. As in neutron spallation, one can write reactions such as

$$_{29}Cu^{63}\,(p, 2p6n\alpha)\,_{26}Fe^{52}, \qquad _{29}Cu^{63}\,(p, pn6\alpha)\,_{17}Cl^{38}.$$

Zinc isotopes probably arise in (p, n) or (p, 2n) reactions, and Ga and Ge as the result of secondary reactions brought about by α-particles and lithium nuclei from spallation:

$$_{29}Cu^{63}\,(\alpha, n)\,_{31}Ga^{66}, \quad _{29}Cu^{65}\,(\alpha, n)\,_{31}Ga^{68}, \quad _{29}Cu\,(_3Li, xn)\,_{32}Ge.$$

The secondary reaction with lithium may also account for the formation of iodine isotopes in the spallation of Sn [16] and of At^{211} in that of Pb [24],

$$_{50}Sn\,(_3Li, xn)\,_{53}I, \qquad Pb^{208}\,(Li^8, 5n)\,At^{211}.$$

There is also evidence for the formation of Li^8 in bombardments of C, N, Ne, Ar, Kr, and Xe with 340-Mev protons or 190-Mev deuterons [25].

Bennett [26] has examined the products of the 400-Mev proton spallation of various elements with atomic numbers between 55 and 123, and concludes that the isotopes with the highest probability of formation are those close to the nuclear stability line (Fig. 3–4). In the bombardment of bismuth, the isotopes of Bi, Po, Tl, and Pb which are formed are generally neutron deficient, so that the expulsion of neutrons from the compound nucleus is more probable than is the expulsion of charged particles.

Analogous results have been obtained by Vinogradov, *et al.* [27] in the bombardment of bismuth with 480-Mev protons. These authors have also studied the spallation of copper by 480- and 680-Mev protons; by interpolating or extrapolating graphs of the formation cross sections of those radioactive nuclides with measurable half-lives as a function of the mass number for a given I or Z (Fig. 5–5), the formation cross sections of the stable products and those with very short half-lives could be estimated to a first approximation.

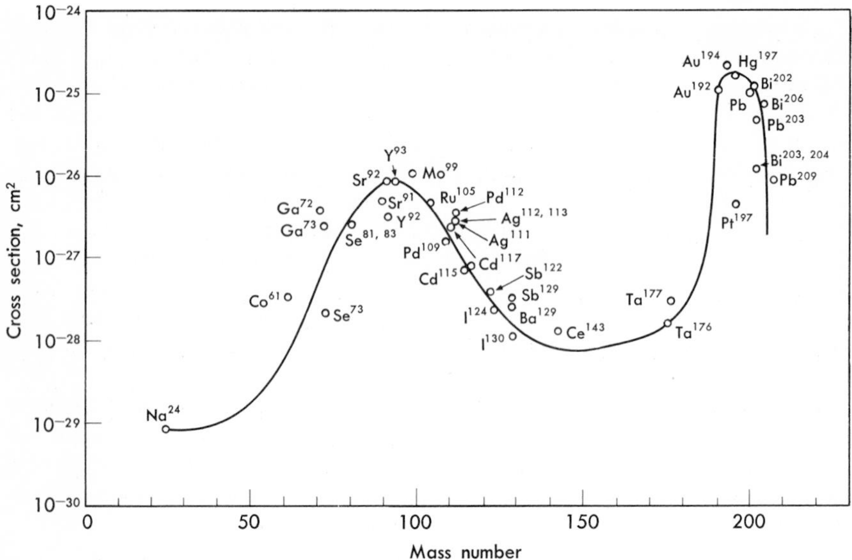

FIG. 5–5. Cross section of formation as a function of mass, for the radioactive nuclides produced in the 480-Mev proton bombardment of Bi (Ref. 27).

For the spallation of copper by 680-Mev protons, 43% of the total cross section corresponds to the formation of stable nuclides, 40.4% to the formation of neutron deficient isotopes, and 16.6% to neutron excess nuclides. The value of σ_t is 0.6×10^{-24} cm^2, equivalent to about 60% of the geometrical area of the cobalt nucleus. The most abundant products are isotopes of Cu, Ni, and Co, Fe^{55}, Mn^{53}, Cr^{51}, V^{49}, Ti^{47}, Se^{45}, Ca^{41}, and K^{39}. The majority of the radioactive isotopes formed by bombardment with 480-Mev protons are β^+-active or decay by K-capture, so that here too neutron deficient isotopes predominate. However, the radioactive products for which

$$\Delta Z\ (=Z_0 - Z) \geq 9,$$

where Z_0 is the atomic number of the target, are all β^--emitters. It also appears that nuclides whose formation requires the loss of one or more α-particles are formed in much higher yields than are their neighbors.

The predominant production of neutron-deficient isotopes has also been reported by Murin [28] for the bombardment of separated Cu, La, and Bi isotopes, and by Kurtchatov [29] for Ag. In agreement with the work discussed above, increasing proton energy was found to shift the maximum yield toward nuclides of lower atomic number. At these higher energies, fission is superimposed on spallation, and for heavy nuclei at particle energies of about 400 Mev, *fragmentation* also occurs [29a]. This involves rapid and violent rupture of the excited nucleus into two extremely unstable fragments, one light and one heavy, which have the same initial neutron : proton ratio as the target nucleus. The excitation energy is not shared uniformly between the constituents of the compound nucleus. The light fragment undergoes de-excitation by β^--emission, and the heavier one by the evaporation of several neutrons. This mechanism becomes significant for $Z > 70$; the cross section is of the order of 1 mb at 1 Bev, and 1 b at 2 to 3 Bev [29b]. The production of light fragments (Na^{24}, Cu^{67}) in the bombardment of Bi with 450- to 480-Mev protons, and of F^{18}, Mg^{28}, and P^{32} in the reaction of 1-Bev protons on Pb, is due to such fragmentation processes.

At these high energies, it becomes difficult to distinguish between these various processes, as has also been found in the bombardment of Cu with 2.2-Bev protons from the Brookhaven cosmotron [30, 31]. Altogether some 50 nuclides are produced, among which isotopes of Ga, Ge, Zn, Ni, Co, Fe, Sc, Ca, K, Cl, S, Na, were once again identified, as well as As^{71}, As^{72}, F^{18}, C^{11}, and Be^7. As before, it is necessary to assume a number of secondary reactions, such as Cu (y, xn), where y may be He^4, Be^7, or Li^8. From the yields obtained, the formation cross section for He^4 is 0.3 b and for Li^8 and Be^7 0.01 b; these particles would have energies of 30 to 40 Mev. Finally, a great many nuclides have also been identified in the bombardment of Ta, Au, and Bi [32] with very high-energy protons. The formation cross section decreases smoothly with increasing ΔZ, but is still appreciable even when as many as 60 nucleons are ejected. Among the products are isotopes of Pb, Tl, Ba, Sr, Br, Ge, and the α-emitting isotopes of the rare earths (Section 4–5).

The overall conclusion from these experiments is that the nature of the target has only a slight effect on the products, and that these are essentially located around the stability line (N/Z). The most probable products are those which result from the loss of two neutrons per proton [1]. The ejection of nucleons is largely due to direct interaction with the incident proton, but a certain number can also be lost from the excited residual nucleus by evaporation. Light particles (He, Li, Be) formed as primary products bring about secondary reactions, so that one result is the formation of nuclides with atomic numbers higher than that of the target.

Photographic observations on the interactions of fast protons (300 to 400 Mev) [8, 33] with nuclei in emulsions agree with the model proposed by Serber and Goldberger mentioned above. At higher energies, nucleon-nucleon collisions lead to π-meson formation. The cross section for the interactions studied in these experiments give a value of 1.3×10^{-13} cm for r_0, the elementary nuclear radius in Eq. (3–3).

Rudstam [34] has published empirical formulas relating the cross section for the formation of a nuclide by the spallation of a target of medium atomic number (51–75) to both the atomic number and atomic weight of the target.

5–4 Reactions involving deuterons and tritons. The deuteron is the relatively unstable combination of a proton and a neutron, with a rest mass of 2.01472, a charge of +1, spin $h/2\pi$, and a magnetic moment of 0.85765 nuclear magnetons. It obeys Bose-Einstein statistics. Since the deuteron has a quadrupole moment ($q = 2.74 \times 10^{-27}$ cm^2), its structure must be asymmetric, a fact of great significance in any theory of nuclear forces.

The deuteron can be broken down into its components either by its own accelerated ions, or by the absorption of a γ-ray, the so-called photonuclear effect:

$$D^2 + D^2 \rightarrow \begin{cases} H^1 + H^3, \\ He^3 + n, \end{cases} \tag{5-13}$$

$$D^2 + \gamma \rightarrow H^1 + n. \tag{5-14}$$

The reactions (5–13) are exoergic and can be brought about by deuterons with energies as low as 100 kev; both processes have similar cross sections. The measurement of the energy of the proton emitted in reaction (5–14) was applied by Chadwick and Goldhaber [35] to determine the binding energy of the deuteron, using the 2.615-Mev γ-rays from ThC″. The value found was 2.1 Mev. More precise measurements [36], based on the inverse reaction

$$p + n \rightarrow d + \gamma,$$

give a value of 2.230 Mev. The binding energy per nucleon is therefore very low, 1.115 Mev, corresponding to a fairly high nuclear radius of about 2.18×10^{-13} cm.

The properties of the deuteron make it a favorable projectile for use in transmutations and in particular for the preparation of radioactive nuclides in good yields. In effect, as the deuteron approaches the positively charged nucleus, it is deformed by the electrostatic forces which tend to repel the proton, so that the neutron has a high probability of being captured by the nucleus, by a (d, p) reaction, giving the same product as the (n, γ) process. This *stripping* mechanism, which does not require the formation of a compound nucleus, is known as the Oppenheimer-Phillips process, after the workers who established the theoretical basis of the reaction [37].: It is found to occur very frequently, even with deuterons having a kinetic energy lower than that necessary to penetrate the potential barrier. Typical examples are

$$Be^9\,(d, p)\,Be^{10}, \quad B^{11}\,(d, p)\,B^{12}, \quad Ar^{40}\,(d, p)\,Ar^{41},$$
$$Cu^{63}\,(d, p)\,Cu^{64}, \quad Br^{81}\,(d, p)\,Br^{82}, \quad Te^{128}\,(d, p)\,Te^{129},$$
$$Ba^{138}\,(d, p)\,Ba^{139}, \quad Ir^{193}\,(d, p)\,Ir^{194}, \quad Np^{237}\,(d, p)\,Np^{238}.$$

If the initial energy of the deuteron and its dissociation energy are known, the binding energy of the neutron captured by the nucleus can be calculated from measurements of the kinetic energy of the proton emitted in the (d, p) reaction. Harvey [38] has used this procedure to determine the energy of the "last" neutron in a number of nuclides, and has compared the values so obtained with those calculated from the Weizsäcker equation (3–10). The discontinuities associated with the magic numbers at $N = 50$, 82, and 126 are again evident; the binding energy of the 50th neutron is some 2 Mev greater than that of the 51st, and that of the 126th about 2.2 Mev greater than that of the 127th, and a significant difference also exists between the 82nd and the 83rd neutrons. The same discontinuities appear from the energetics of the reactions (n, 2n), (γ, n), (p, d), and (d, t), each of which corresponds to the removal of a neutron from the nucleus.

The (d, p) reaction can be regarded as a special type of *stripping reaction.* Such reactions occur mainly at high energies, and are a result of the relatively large size of the deuteron. When this particle penetrates into the force field of a nucleus, it may give up one of its two constituent particles, while the second particle flies off with a kinetic energy which may be as high as half the incident energy of the deuteron. Analogous to the (d, p) reaction, therefore, is the (d, n) process

$$N^{14}\ (d, n)\ O^{15}, \qquad Fe^{57}\ (d, n)\ Co^{58}, \qquad Sr^{86}\ (d, n)\ Y^{87},$$
$$Ba^{135}\ (d, n)\ La^{136}, \qquad W^{182}\ (d, n)\ Re^{183}, \qquad \text{etc.}$$

Applications of this reaction include the preparation of Tc isotopes from Mo, and the artificial production of Po^{210} from Bi. It is also used in various neutron sources (Table 11–11)

$$D + D, \qquad T + D, \qquad Li + D, \qquad Be + D, \qquad N + D, \qquad \text{etc.}$$

In spite of the importance of other competing reactions, the probability of the (d, n) process is not negligible, even with very high-energy deuterons. The (d, γ) capture process is already observable at much lower energies, although it has a lower probability than the stripping reaction, since an activation energy is necessary to overcome the coulombic repulsion before capture can take place. Typical examples are C^{12} (d, γ) N^{14} and Ba^{138} (d, γ) La^{140}. This latter reaction is in competition with other processes which need activation to bring about the ejection of charged particles, such as (d, t), (d, 2p), (d, α), etc., as in

$$Li^{7}\ (d, t)\ Li^{6}, \qquad P^{31}\ (d, t)\ P^{30}, \qquad Nb^{93}\ (d, t)\ Nb^{92},$$
$$Ag^{107}\ (d, t)\ Ag^{106}, \qquad Sn^{124}\ (d, t)\ Sn^{123}, \qquad U^{238}\ (d, t)\ U^{237},$$
$$Sc^{45}\ (d, 2p)\ Ca^{45}, \qquad Mo^{94}\ (d, \alpha)\ Nb^{92}, \qquad Al^{27}\ (d, p\alpha)\ Na^{24},$$
$$As^{75}\ (d, p\alpha)\ Ga^{72}.$$

The (p, d) or (p, pn) reaction mentioned above is in some ways the inverse of the stripping reaction, and to some extent the same is true of the (d, t) process. Instead of losing a neutron, the deuteron picks one up from the target nucleus to give a tritium nucleus. With medium or heavy nuclei, reactions such as (d, xn) or (d, txn) take place readily with deuterons of sufficiently high energy. In such reactions, x is generally between 1 and 9, as in

$$_{33}As^{75}\ (d, xn)\ _{34}Se, \qquad \text{with } x = 2, 4, 5, 7,$$
$$_{55}Cs^{133}\ (d, xn)\ _{56}Ba, \qquad 2, 7, 8,$$
$$_{57}La^{139}\ (d, xn)\ _{58}Ce, \qquad 2, 4, 6,$$
$$_{92}U^{238}\ (d, xn)\ _{93}Np, \qquad 1, 2, 4, 9,$$
$$As^{75}\ (d, pxn)\ As, \qquad 0, 2, 3, 4, 5, 6.$$

These last reactions also occur along with spallation in the bombardment of As with 200-Mev deuterons [39]. Among the other nuclides formed, isotopes of Se, Ge, Ga, Zn, Cu, Ni, Co, Fe, Mn, and Cr have been identified; a number of these are genetically related, such as

$$Se^{72} \xrightarrow{e} As^{72} \xrightarrow{\beta^+} Ge^{72},$$

$$Se^{71} \xrightarrow{\beta^+} As^{71} \xrightarrow{\beta^+} Ge^{71} \xrightarrow{\beta^+} Ga^{71}.$$

The spallation of copper [22, 40] and of silver [40] give almost the same products as those listed earlier for proton bombardment. The products detected in the bombardment of Sb [41], include Te, Sn, In, Cd, As, Cr, Ru, Mo, and Y. The mechanism of these reactions seems to follow principles similar to those involving neutrons and protons. Marquez [10] has compared the cross sections for the various nuclides obtained from the spallation of Sb with neutrons, protons, and deuterons and has shown that the relative yields are only slightly affected by the nature of the projectile. Vinogradov [27] reached the same conclusion, but has pointed out that for $\Delta Z \geq 7$ the yields fall off rapidly in neutron bombardments. The nuclide N^{17} has also been reported among the products for a wide variety of target materials (F, Na, Mg, S, Si, K, Ge, Gd, Au, Pt, Tl, Bi, etc.) [42, 43]; this disintegrates to

$$N^{17} \rightarrow O^{17*} \rightarrow O^{16} + n.$$

The singly charged H^3 ion, the triton, has also been used as a projectile in nuclear reactions. Although tritium occurs in nature in trace quantities (Section 7–1), the accelerated ions which are required in nuclear research are obtained either by the D-D reaction [Eq. (5–13)], or by the Li^6 (n, α) T reaction. The rest mass of the triton is 3.01700 amu, and it is β-active with a half-life of 12.4 years. Tritium undergoes nuclear decomposition when bombarded with its own accelerated ions with energies of 220 kev,

$$T + T \rightarrow He^4 + 2n + 11.32 \text{ Mev}.$$

The energy distribution of the emitted α-particles does not support the idea [44] that the two neutrons are associated as a very short-lived particle, the bineutron (${}_0n^2$).

A summary of the reactions of the triton shows their similarity to those found for deuterons:

(1) Oppenheimer-Phillips reactions: (t, p) and (t, d):

$$C^{12} \text{ (t, p) } C^{14}, \quad Mg^{26} \text{ (t, p) } Mg^{28}, \quad Al^{27} \text{ (t, p) } Al^{29},$$
$$Co^{59} \text{ (t, p) } Co^{61}, \quad Ag^{109} \text{ (t, p) } Ag^{111}, \quad Cu^{63} \text{ (t, d) } Cu^{64};$$

(2) (t, n) and (t, 2n) reaction:

$$O^{16} \text{ (t, n) } F^{18}, \quad S^{32} \text{ (t, n) } Cl^{34},$$
$$Cu^{63} \text{ (t, n) } Zn^{65}, \quad Ge^{76} \text{ (t, 2n) } As^{71};$$

(3) (t, α) and (t, He^3) reactions:

$$Li^7 \text{ (t, } \alpha\text{) } He^6, \quad Al^{27} \text{ (t, } He^3\text{) } Mg^{27}, \quad Ag^{109} \text{ (t, } He^3\text{) } Pd^{109}.$$

5–5 Alpha-particle reactions. The α-particle, the doubly charged helium nucleus, is an even-even nuclide, with zero spin and zero magnetic and electric moment, obeying Bose-Einstein statistics. It is an extremely stable particle; the energy of formation from two protons and two neutrons is given by

$$(2 \times 1.008142 + 2 \times 1.008922 - 4.003873)\, 931 = 28.28 \text{ Mev},$$

so that the binding energy is 7.07 Mev per nucleon. Bombardment with 90-Mev neutrons brings about the dissociation of the nucleus, with a wide range of possible reactions [45]:

$$\text{He}^4 + \text{n} \rightarrow \begin{cases} \text{p} + \text{t} + \text{n} & (42) \\ \text{p} + \text{d} + 2\text{n} & (15) \\ \text{d} + \text{t} & (13) \\ 2\text{d} + \text{n} & (7) \\ 2\text{p} + 3\text{n} & (0.8) \\ \text{He}^3 + 2\text{n} & (16) \end{cases}$$

The values in parentheses are the partial cross sections in millibarns for neutrons with energies $>$40 Mev; the total cross section is approximately 94 mb. The most important inelastic process is the removal of a proton to give a triton, the inverse of the stripping reaction. The (He^3, 2n) process has not been identified with certainty. Protons of 32 Mev will remove a neutron from the He nucleus [46]:

$$\text{He}^4 + \text{p} \rightarrow \text{He}^3 + \text{d}.$$

Since α-particles are doubly charged, they lend themselves to experiments involving coulombic excitation better than do protons, and since the potential barrier is higher, the light elements can be readily studied. A further advantage is that they produce less excitation of the lower electronic shells, and hence there is less masking of the γ-rays emitted in the de-excitation of the nucleus. Temmer and Heydenburg [47, 48] have carried out a systematic study of these processes with 6-Mev α-particles for many of the nuclides with Z between 20 and 92, with special emphasis on the rare earth region where the nuclei have incompletely filled shells. The Bohr-Mottelson theory predicts that a strong deformation should arise from this cause; rotational levels should therefore be observed, and in fact a large number of new nuclear levels were identified. For odd nuclei, two rotational levels were excited, but for even-even nuclei only one. The experimental cross sections and the energies were in excellent agreement with the theory.

For transmutations involving low-energy α-particles, natural sources such as radon, the active deposits, or polonium can be used. The α-particles from a mixture of RaC + RaC′ were used by Rutherford in the first artificial transmutation mentioned earlier [Eq. (5–4)]. Chadwick's experiments on the action of α-particles from polonium on various light elements resulted in the discovery of the neutron:

$$\mathrm{Be}^9\ (\alpha, \mathrm{n})\ \mathrm{C}^{12}, \qquad \mathrm{B}^{11}\ (\alpha, \mathrm{n})\ \mathrm{N}^{14}, \qquad \text{etc.}$$

A similar polonium source was used by Irène Curie and Frederic Joliot in their discovery of artificial radioactivity:

$$\mathrm{B}^{10}\ (\alpha, \mathrm{n})\ \mathrm{N}^{13}, \qquad \mathrm{Mg}^{24}\ (\alpha, \mathrm{n})\ \mathrm{Si}^{27}, \qquad \mathrm{Al}^{27}\ (\alpha, \mathrm{n})\ \mathrm{P}^{30}.$$

Natural α-particles do not have sufficient energy to penetrate the coulombic barrier of nuclei with atomic numbers greater than 20, so that a beam of accelerated helium ions (or helions) is usually used in studying the disintegration of such elements. Helions have been accelerated to energies as high as hundreds of Mev. Depending upon the velocity of the ions and the nature of the target, the compound nuclei formed may disintegrate by the loss of one or more neutrons, of one or more protons, or of both neutrons and protons:

$$\mathrm{Ag}^{109} + \alpha \rightarrow \begin{cases} \mathrm{Ag}^{111} + 2\mathrm{p}, \\ \mathrm{In}^{112} + \mathrm{n}, \\ \mathrm{In}^{111} + 2\mathrm{n}, \\ \mathrm{In}^{110} + 3\mathrm{n}, \\ \mathrm{Cd}^{109} + \mathrm{p} + 3\mathrm{n}, \\ \mathrm{Cd}^{107} + \mathrm{p} + 5\mathrm{n}, \end{cases}$$

$$\mathrm{Ir}^{191} + \alpha \rightarrow \begin{cases} \mathrm{Au}^{193} + 2\mathrm{n}, \\ \mathrm{Au}^{192} + 3\mathrm{n}, \\ \mathrm{Au}^{191} + 4\mathrm{n}. \end{cases}$$

$$\mathrm{Cs}^{133}\ (\alpha, 4\mathrm{n})\ \mathrm{La}^{133}.$$

A number of isotopes of the transuranium elements have been prepared by such reactions:

$$\mathrm{U}^{238}\ (\alpha, 2\mathrm{n})\ \mathrm{Pu}^{240}, \qquad \mathrm{Pu}^{239}\ (\alpha, \mathrm{p}2\mathrm{n})\ \mathrm{Am}^{240},$$
$$\mathrm{Pu}^{239}\ (\alpha, 1\text{–}5\mathrm{n})\ \mathrm{Cm}^{242-238}, \qquad \mathrm{Cm}^{242}\ (\alpha, 2\mathrm{n})\ \mathrm{Cf}^{244}, \qquad \text{etc.}$$

Inelastic collision (α, α) has been observed with helium ions (11 to 16 Mev) and In^{115}. Spallation of several of the nuclides already mentioned in the discussion of 190-Mev deuteron spallation (e.g., Cu, Sb, Sn) can also be brought about with 380-Mev helium ions. The nature of the products is much the same for the different projectiles. The yields are often several times higher than for deuterons, but are occasionally smaller because of various competing reactions.

Ions of the helium nucleus of mass 3 have also been used for some years as projectiles in nuclear bombardments. This isotope is a rare constituent of natural helium, being present as only 0.00013% of atmospheric helium. The rest mass of this atom is 3.016977 mass units, so that the binding energy per nucleon is given by

$$\tfrac{1}{3}\,(2 \times 1.008142 + 1.008482 - 3.016977)\ 931 = 2.57\ \text{Mev}.$$

The particle is a fermion, with spin one-half and a magnetic moment of 2.13 nuclear magnetons.

The bombardment of He^3 with its own ions (with energies of a few hundred kev) gives two reactions [49, 50]:

$$He^3 + He^3 \rightarrow Li^5 + p + 11 \text{ Mev},$$

$$He^3 + He^3 \rightarrow He^4 + 2p + 12.8 \text{ Mev}.$$

With 200-kev He^3 ions, the total cross section is about 2.5 μb. Other reactions reported for He^3 ions include

$$H^3\,(He^3, d)\,He^4, \quad C^{12}\,(He^3, d)\,N^{13}, \quad Si^{28}\,(He^3, p)\,P^{30},$$
$$C^{13}\,(He^3, t)\,N^{13}, \quad C^{12}\,(He^3, \alpha)\,C^{11}, \quad N^{14}\,(He^3, \alpha)\,N^{13}.$$

Clearly the particle may lose a neutron, a proton or both nucleons to the target nucleus, it may exchange a proton for a neutron, or it may even pick up a neutron from the target to form an α-particle.

5–6 Nuclear reactions with heavy ions. In nuclear chemistry the term "heavy ion" implies an ion with a mass greater than that of the helium ion, such as ${}_3Li^7$ (+3), ${}_4Be^9$ (+4), C^{12} (+6), etc. The charge : mass ratio of these species is sufficiently similar to that of the deuteron that they can be accelerated in a cyclotron under conditions similar to those used for the deuteron itself. For a given e/m ratio, the kinetic energy of the ion is proportional to its mass. With the techniques which have been developed over the last few years, it is now possible to obtain beams of ions such as C^{12} (+6), Li (+3), C^{13} (+6), N^{14} (+6), O^{16} (+6), Be^9 (+4), Ne^{20} (+9), etc., with energies equivalent to about 10 Mev per nucleon [51].

In particular, the ions C^{12} (+6), N^{14} (+6), and O^{16} (+6) accelerated to energies of the order of 100 Mev have been used in reactions with very heavy or very light nuclides; experiments have also been carried out on Pd [51], Cu [52], and In [53], which give neutron deficient nuclides:

$${}_{29}Cu^{65}\,({}_6C^{12}, 3n)\,{}_{35}Br^{74}, \qquad {}_{49}In^{115}\,({}_7N^{14}, 3n)\,{}_{56}Ba^{126}.$$

Photographic emulsions exposed to heavy ions show multi-branched stars, corresponding to the fragmentation of silver and bromine nuclei [54, 55].

In the higher mass region, this technique has been utilized for producing isotopes of the natural radioelements and the transuranic elements, and in particular for synthesizing the new elements ${}_{99}E$ and ${}_{100}Fm$ [56, 57] (Section 8–1):

$${}_{79}Au^{197}\,(C^{12}, 4n)\,{}_{85}At^{205}, \qquad {}_{82}Pb^{208}\,(C^{12}, 4n)\,{}_{88}Ra^{216},$$
$${}_{90}Th^{232}\,(C^{12}, 4n)\,{}_{96}Cm^{240}, \qquad {}_{92}U^{238}\,(C^{12}, 6n)\,{}_{98}Cf^{244},$$
$${}_{92}U^{238}\,(C^{12}, 4n)\,{}_{98}Cf^{246}, \qquad U^{238}\,(N^{14}, \alpha 5n)\,Bk^{243},$$
$$U^{238}\,(N^{14}, p3n)\,Cf^{248}, \qquad U^{238}\,(N^{14}, 6n)\,E^{246},$$
$$U^{238}\,(O^{16}, xn)\,Fm^{\sim 250}.$$

Using this method, we can synthesize nuclides with atomic numbers 6, 8, or more above the target nucleus. The products are usually neutron deficient and tend to transform their excess nuclear protons into neutrons by electron capture.

If the light elements between deuterium and sulfur are bombarded with N^{14} (+6) ions (average energy 19 Mev), a number of different reactions are observed [58, 59], such as

$$D^2 + N^{14} \rightarrow O^{15} + n, \qquad \sigma = 3\ \text{mb},$$

$$B^{10} + N^{14} \rightarrow \begin{cases} O^{15} + Be^9, & 50\ \mu b, \\ C^{11} + C^{13}, & 30\ \mu b, \end{cases}$$

$$C^{12} + N^{14} \rightarrow \begin{cases} F^{18} + Be^8, & 60\ \mu b, \\ Na^{22} + \alpha, & 0.5\ \text{mb}, \\ Na^{24} + 2p, & 80\ \mu b, \end{cases}$$

$$O^{16} + N^{14} \rightarrow \begin{cases} Al^{28} + 2p, & 0.2\ \text{mb}, \\ F^{18} + C^{12}, & 8\ \mu b. \end{cases}$$

Chackett and Fremlin [60, 61, 62] bombarded Al with 125-Mev N (+6) ions and identified the following radioactive products, arranged in order of decreasing yield: P^{32}, Al^{18}, Cl^{34}, K^{38}, P^{30}, S^{35}, Na^{24}, Si^{31}, Mg^{27}, N^{13}, and C^{11}. The formation of light products is attributed to a stripping reaction similar to the (d, p) process. The formation of the heavier nuclei may be caused by the target absorbing some of the nucleons of the projectile. If the disintegration energy of N^{14} into $(3\alpha + n + p)$ is virtually the same as the energy necessary for this nucleus to overcome the electrostatic potential barrier of Al^{27}, the projectile will break up in the latter's nuclear field into its constituents, so that the target is struck not by a single particle, but rather by a "buckshot charge." The capture of an α-particle will consequently be easier than that of a proton, since for equal velocities the α-particle will have four times as much energy, despite its double charge. The formation of Al is presumably due to direct excitation of the target nucleus, followed by the expulsion of nine neutrons.

To account for the heaviest products (K^{38}, Cl^{34}), it is suggested that the formation of the excited Ca^{41} compound nucleus is followed by the evaporation of a number of nucleons. Analogous results have been obtained in the bombardment of aluminum with accelerated O (+6) ions; in this case, the only products formed are K^{38}, Cl^{34}, P^{32}, P^{30}, Na^{24}, and F^{18}. Other nuclides, including those whose formation would be exoergic, were not detected. This is what would be expected if the transmutations are essentially due to the capture of 1, 2, or 3 α-particles:

$$Al^{27} + \alpha \rightarrow P^{31*} \rightarrow P^{30} + n,$$

$$Al^{27} + 2\alpha \rightarrow Cl^{35*} \rightarrow Cl^{34} + n,$$

$$Al^{27} + 3\alpha \rightarrow K^{39*} \rightarrow K^{38} + n.$$

The nuclides F^{18} and Na^{24} could be fission products:

$$Al^{27} + O^{16} \rightarrow \begin{cases} Mg^{24} + F^{19} \rightarrow F^{18} + n, \\ F^{18} + Mg^{25} \rightarrow Na^{24} + p. \end{cases}$$

The very low yield of P^{32} may be due to the emission of $(2\, He^4 + He^3)$.

In some cases, a simple stripping reaction leads to the transfer of a nucleon from the projectile to the target nucleus. An example of this is the bombardment of boron with N^{14} ions [62a], when C^{11} is produced with an appreciable cross section:

$$B^{10} + N^{14} \rightarrow C^{11} + C^{13} \qquad \text{(proton transfer)}.$$

A similar reaction is

$$Au^{197} + N^{14} \rightarrow Au^{198} + N^{13} \qquad \text{(neutron transfer)}.$$

Cohen, *et al.*, bombarded carbon with 29-Mev N (+6) ions [63] and compared the excitation functions for C (N, 2p) with those already published for the reactions Mg^{26} (p, 2p), Mg^{25} (p, α), and Mg^{25} (p, 2α). The compound nucleus is the same in both cases (Al^{26}). After making allowance for the difference in the energies necessary for the proton and the N (+6) particle to penetrate the potential barrier, the cross sections of the (p, 2p) and (N, 2p) reactions are similar, whereas those for the (N, α) and (N, 2α) processes have cross sections 2 to 4 times greater than for the analogous proton reactions. These authors concluded that in nitrogen ion bombardment, the compound nucleus does not attain the thermodynamic equilibrium required by the Bohr theory.

The formation of several α-emitting isotopes of Rn, At, and Po, with masses between 202 and 207, has been reported by Burcham [64] in the bombardment of Au with N (+6) ions. The suggested reactions are

$$Au^{197}\ (N, xn)\ Rn,$$

$$Au^{197}\ (N, pxn)\ At,$$

$$Au^{197}\ (N, dxn)\ Po.$$

Recent work with heavy ions has shown that a great deal of useful information can be obtained by using them to study coulombic excitation [65].

5-7 Photonuclear reactions. This topic includes all those nuclear reactions brought about by x- and γ-rays. It has been seen that the difference between adjacent energy levels is sometimes as low as a few kev, especially for the heavy nuclei; thus although x-rays originate in extranuclear transitions, their energies may be higher than those involved in certain nuclear changes. The term "x-ray" also covers the very high-energy electromagnetic radiation produced in accelerators by the deceleration of electrons in the coulombic field of a nucleus (Section 11-6).

Depending upon their energy, electromagnetic radiation may cause nuclear disintegration (as do accelerated particles), or may merely excite the nucleus to some unstable level from which it decays to a stable or metastable state. In the latter case, the isomer formed is identical with that produced in (n, n) or (p, p) reactions, and the transition to the ground state takes place by γ-emission. This effect was discovered by Pontecorvo and Lazard [66], using 1.85-Mev x-rays on In^{115}.

Later workers have found similar transitions with other indium isomers, and with Cd, Ag, Rh, and Au. Sufficiently high-energy electrons bring about the same isomeric transitions. The disintegration of the deuteron by 3.8-Mev electrons was first reported by Paul [67], and that of Be with 1.8-Mev electrons by Collins, *et al.* [68]; the cross sections are of the order of 10^{-30} to 10^{-31} cm^2. Reactions of the type (e, en) with 25- to 35-Mev electrons have been carried out on Cu^{63}, Zn^{64}, Ag^{109}, and Ta^{181} [69]. The yield relative to that of the simultaneous (γ, n) reaction process increases with the energy of the incident electron.

The first photonuclear reaction observed was the dissociation of the deuteron, and shortly afterward Szilard and Chalmers [70] observed the γ-ray decomposition of Be^9. Subsequent work has extended the (γ, n) reaction throughout the periodic system. It is equivalent to the (n, 2n) process and like the latter can be used for the determination of the binding energy of the last neutron by measuring the threshold of the reaction; discontinuities due to the magic numbers again appear. An important practical aspect is that the photoneutrons from a given reaction are monoenergetic (Section 11–10).

Photonuclear effects are generally investigated by means of the bremsstrahlung radiation produced in accelerating machines. This has a continuous spectrum, but the monoenergetic 17.3-Mev γ-rays emitted in the Li^7 (p, 2α) reaction have also been used [71]. The energy is high enough to split off a nucleon from any nucleus, including the removal of a proton from C^{12} or O^{16} and of a neutron from O^{16}.

The two types of reaction (γ, p) and (γ, n) are inevitably in competition with each other. For light nuclei, the cross sections of the two processes are not very different, but with increasing atomic number the yield of the (γ, p) process falls as a result of the increasing electrostatic barrier. The (γ, n) cross section shows little variation with atomic number up to $Z = 60$, where there is a sharp increase [72, 73]. Graphs of the (γ, n) and (γ, p) yields against the energy of the incident photon often show very wide maxima, the width being of the order of 6 Mev (*giant resonances*). The energy at the maximum decreases slowly with increasing nuclear mass; for Mg^{25}, for example, it is at 21 Mev, for Cu^{65} at 19 Mev, for Ag^{109} and Ta^{181} at 16 Mev. Goldhaber and Teller [74] have explained these maxima as resulting from dipolar vibrations brought about by collective motion of the protons relative to the neutrons. Levinger and Bethe [75] have, however, proposed a different mechanism.*

With photons of higher energy, the evaporation of several nucleons may occur, either alone or as deuterons or α-particles. The (γ, α) process is

* See U. S. Businaro and S. Gallone, *Nuovo cimento,* **1,** 1285 (1955) for a discussion of photonuclear reactions in terms of the collective model of the nucleus.

frequently found with light and medium nuclei:

$$C^{12}(\gamma, 3\alpha), \quad O^{16}(\gamma, \alpha) C^{12}, \quad O^{16}(\gamma, 4\alpha),$$
$$N^{14}(\gamma, 2\alpha) Li^{6}, \quad Cu^{63}(\gamma, \alpha) Co^{59}, \quad Br^{79,81}(\gamma, \alpha) As^{75,77},$$
$$Rb^{87}(\gamma, \alpha) Br^{83}, \quad S^{32}(\gamma, d) P^{30}, \quad B^{11}(\gamma, t) 2\alpha,$$
$$O^{16}(\gamma, t) N^{13}, \quad F^{19}(\gamma, 2n) F^{17}, \quad Na^{23}(\gamma, 3n) Na^{20},$$
$$Zn^{67}(\gamma, 4n) Zn^{63}, \quad Al^{27}(\gamma, 2p) Na^{25}, \quad N^{14}(\gamma, p2n) C^{11},$$
$$Co^{59}(\gamma, 2pn) Mn^{56}, \quad Na^{23}(\gamma, \alpha n) F^{18}, \quad Mo^{92}(\gamma, \alpha n) Zr^{87},$$
$$Mg^{24}(\gamma, \alpha pn) F^{18}, \quad Na^{23}(\gamma, \alpha 2p) N^{17}, \quad Bi^{209}(\gamma, 3\text{–}5n) Bi^{206-204},$$

$$Zn^{66}\left(\gamma, \begin{matrix} 3n \\ p3n \\ p4n \end{matrix}\right)\begin{matrix} Zn^{63} \\ Cu^{62}. \\ Cu^{61} \end{matrix}$$

Debs [76] has studied the photonuclear reactions of As, Ge, Ga, Zn, and Cu with 320-Mev x-rays. The product nuclides fall into two groups; those formed in relatively high yields in the (γ, n) process in the region of the giant resonance, and those with masses several units lower than the target ($As \rightarrow Co^{55}$, $Ge \rightarrow Cu^{61}$) and with low yields. The formation of the second group is believed to result from evaporation. In the irradiation of photographic plates with 27-Mev x-rays, Millar and Cameron [77] found tracks which they attribute to Li^8, probably coming from reactions such as $Ag^{107,109}(\gamma, Li^8) Ru^{99,101}$. The cross section is of the order of a microbarn [78].

5-8 Thermonuclear reactions. The condensation of the various isotopes of hydrogen, H, D, and T, to give heavier nuclides is always accompanied by a reduction of the rest mass and is therefore always exoergic:

$$\begin{aligned}
&(a) \quad H + H \rightarrow D + 0.43\ \text{Mev},\\
&(b) \quad H + D \rightarrow He^3 + 5.49\ \text{Mev},\\
&(c) \quad H + T \rightarrow He^4 + 19.8\ \text{Mev},\\
&(d) \quad D + D \rightarrow H + T + 4.03\ \text{Mev},\\
&(e) \quad D + D \rightarrow He^3 + n + 3.27\ \text{Mev},\\
&(f) \quad D + D \rightarrow He^4 + 28.83\ \text{Mev},\\
&(g) \quad D + T \rightarrow He^4 + n + 17.57\ \text{Mev},\\
&(h) \quad T + T \rightarrow He^4 + 2n + 11.32\ \text{Mev}.
\end{aligned}$$

The activation energies of these reactions are generally very small, so that the cross sections of processes (d), (e), and (g) are significant for deuterons with energies as low as 14 kev; at 25 kev, the cross sections are (d) 0.62, (e) 0.59 and (g) 1.14 mb, and at 100 kev 15.4, 15.2, and 4.9 mb respectively [79].

In chemical reactions, the activation energy is normally provided by the increase in the thermal vibration which results on increasing the temperature. For nuclear transformations, one must resort to the use of accelerators, since it is obviously impossible to reach sufficiently high temperatures in the laboratory to give the particles kinetic energies comparable to those mentioned above. Such temperatures exist in the stars, however, so that stellar conditions appear to be suitable for various thermonuclear reactions to occur. Using the Maxwell kinetic theory and equations governing the penetration of a coulombic barrier by charged particles, it has been shown [80] that the rate of reaction between two particles of mass A_1 and A_2 and atomic numbers Z_1 and Z_2 at an absolute temperature $T°$ is proportional to $\tau^2 e^{-\tau}$, where

$$\tau = 3\left(\frac{\pi^2 A e^4 Z_1^2 Z_2^2}{2\hbar k T}\right)^{1/3}. \tag{5–15}$$

Here A is the reduced mass $A_1A_2/(A_1 + A_2)$, and k is the Boltzmann constant. It follows from the exponential form of this equation that the rate increases rapidly with T and decreases rapidly with Z. If the rate of a thermonuclear reaction and the value of Q are both known, it is possible to calculate the energy produced per unit time. Such calculations have been carried out by Gamow and Critchfield [81] for a number of condensation reactions at various temperatures. For the very fast reaction (d) above, the energy liberated at 5×10^5 °C is only 10^{-7} cal/gm·sec, but at 10^6 °C it is already 300 cal; at 3×10^6 °C the energy release is 3×10^7 and at 10^7 °C it is 3×10^{12} cal/gm·sec. Such arguments illustrate why astrophysicists believe that one or another of these thermonuclear reactions may well constitute the source of energy which appears to have maintained the temperature of the sun, estimated at about 2×10^7 °C at the center, for millions of years.

The same problem also exists for the other stars. It was at one time believed that the constant temperature arose from a gradual gravitational contraction, which would be accompanied by the release of considerable amounts of heat. Calculations show, however, that if this phenomenon were the only source of energy in the stars, the age of the sun could not exceed 2×10^7 years. One must also reject hypotheses based on the disintegration and fission of heavy nuclei, despite the high exothermicity of these processes, since spectroscopic examination shows the absence of appreciable quantities of these elements in the sun. On the other hand, it is known that hydrogen constitutes a very large fraction of the mass of the sun.

Atkinson and Houtermans [82] were the first to suggest that the source of the sun's energy could be the condensation of four protons to form an α-particle. As far as the actual mechanism of this transformation is concerned, two reaction chains are currently considered to be possible: the *proton-proton* [83] and the *carbon-nitrogen* cycle [84, 85]. Neglecting neutrino emission, the proton-proton chain is

$$\begin{array}{lll}
\text{(a)} & \mathrm{H + H} & \rightarrow \mathrm{D} + e^+ \\
\text{(b)} & \mathrm{D + H} & \rightarrow \mathrm{He^3} + \gamma \\
\text{(c)} & \mathrm{He^3 + H} & \rightarrow \mathrm{He^4} + e^+ \\
\hline
\end{array}$$

$$4\mathrm{H} \rightarrow \mathrm{He^4} + 2e^+ + 24.75 \text{ Mev}.$$

Some authors [86, 87] replace reaction (c) by

$$He^3 + He^3 \rightarrow He^4 + 2H,$$

which it is believed would be much faster. Of these reactions, (a) is by far the slowest. Various authors have made estimates of the average life, and the final result depends, of course, upon assumptions made as to the solar conditions. Typical values would be: temperature 1.5 to 2×10^7 °C, density 125 to 80 gm/cm^3, hydrogen concentration 0.8 to 0.35, leading to values from 7×10^9 to 1.5×10^{10} years for the average life of reaction (a), an order of magnitude which is compatible with the age of the sun (Section 10–10).

A variation of this scheme is that proposed by Gamow and Critchfield [81]:

$$\begin{aligned} H + H &\rightarrow D + e^+, \\ D + H &\rightarrow He^3 + \gamma, \\ He^3 + He^4 &\rightarrow Be^7 + \gamma, \\ Be^7 &\rightarrow Li^7 + e^+, \\ Li^7 + H &\rightarrow 2He^4. \end{aligned}$$

The carbon-nitrogen cycle is

	Reaction	Mean life
(1)	$C^{12} + H \rightarrow N^{13} + \gamma$	1.3×10^7 yr,
(2)	$N^{13} \rightarrow C^{13} + e^+$	14 min,
(3)	$C^{13} + H \rightarrow N^{14} + \gamma$	2.7×10^6 yr,
(4)	$N^{14} + H \rightarrow O^{15} + \gamma$	3.2×10^8 yr,
(5)	$O^{15} \rightarrow N^{15} + e^+$	3 min,
(6)	$N^{15} + H \rightarrow C^{12} + He^4$	10^5 yr,

$$4H \rightarrow He^4 + 2e^+ + 24.75 \text{ Mev}.$$

These values refer to a temperature of 10^{13} °C, which is the value currently assumed for the center of the sun. Since the carbon reappears intact at the end of the cycle, it can be regarded as a catalyst. The average life of the cycle, which is determined by processes (1) and (4), is estimated at 3.3×10^8 years. This cycle is more favorable in terms of energy production than the proton-proton process. It is generally assumed, however, that this latter cycle is the predominant process in the temperature region 8 to 15×10^6 °C, and that the carbon-nitrogen cycle is the main one at higher temperatures, of the order of 20×10^6 °C.

Certain stars which are larger than the sun have luminosities, which, in view of their supposed hydrogen concentrations, are much higher than can be accounted for in terms of the production of a constant amount of energy from any of the above mechanisms. It has been suggested that after all the hydrogen present has been used up, the stars begin to contract; the density would, of course, increase and might reach values as high as

2×10^4 gm/cm^3, and at the same time the central temperature would become about 2×10^8 °C. A weakly endothermic reaction between He^4 nuclei would then begin to take place:

$$He^4 + He^4 \rightarrow Be^8 - 0.097 \text{ Mev},$$

followed by

$$Be^8 + He^4 \rightarrow C^{12} + 7.4 \text{ Mev}.$$

Despite the instability of Be^8, a very small fraction of the nuclides present (1 in 10^{10}) could exist as this, in dynamic equilibrium with other nuclei in the interior of the star. The C^{12} nucleus could subsequently undergo an exothermic condensation to give O^{16} ($Q \sim 7$ Mev), and this process could continue in decreasing intensity, with the production of Ne^{20}, Mg^{24}, Si^{28}, etc.

We shall see, however (Section 10–11), that some astrophysical theories suggest that at a certain stage in the evolution of stars, endothermic reactions may lead to their breakdown (novae and supernovae). Three explanations have been advanced as to the nature of these endothermic reactions. Hoyle [88] suggests that the synthesis of heavy nuclei becomes possible at the high energies and densities of the electronic gas. Gamow and Schönberg [89] believe that neutrinos, produced by β-disintegration and in synthetic reactions between nuclei and electrons, escape from the stars and so carry a significant fraction of the energy away with them. Examples of such reactions would be

$$He^3 + e^- \rightarrow H^3 + \nu,$$
$$O^{16} + e^- \rightarrow N^{16} + \nu,$$
$$Fe^{56} + e^- \rightarrow Mn^{56} + \nu.$$

A third hypothesis, put forward by Borst [90], assumes that the endothermic process is

$$He^4 + He^4 \rightarrow Be^7 + n - 19 \text{ Mev}.$$

On the cosmic scale, these are for the most part purely speculative hypotheses. The reality of thermonuclear reactions and the immense danger implicit in their misuse has, however, been proven by the fabrication of the so-called hydrogen bombs, which are discussed later (Section 6–11).

The laboratory-scale realization of temperatures at which the controlled fusion of light nuclei is possible, and hence peaceful use of thermonuclear energy, is still in the experimental stage [91, 92, 93, 94, 95]. The best that has been achieved so far is temperatures estimated at 5×10^6 °C, for periods of 2 to 5 milliseconds.

In the British experimental Zeta apparatus at Harwell, a series of condensers are used to produce a short discharge in an aluminum torus (diameter $\sim$ 10 ft) containing deuterium at about 10^{-4} mm Hg pressure. The gas is completely ionized and forms a *plasma*, a system of extremely high-energy positive ions and electrons. The magnetic field, produced by a current of about 200,000 amperes, perpendicular to the field, confines and constricts this current into a very dense and extremely hot filament, the so-called pinch effect. This filament is unstable and tends to break up and so dissipate its energy on the walls of the vessel under the effect of the smallest perturbations; to prevent such self-multiplying effects, an exterior longitudinal magnetic field of a few hundred gauss is used to keep the constituents of the plasma circulating in small circular trajectories and so isolate them from the walls of the vessel. Spectral analysis of the radiation emitted during the discharge puts the average kinetic energy of the positive ions at 300 ev. About 10^6 neutrons were emitted per discharge; these could have arisen from the reaction

$$D + D \rightarrow He^3 + n.$$

This explanation has, however, been refuted by Rose, Taylor, and Wood [96] whose further experiments led to the conclusion that the neutrons arose from collisions between the deuterons and stationary target materials. At the Second International Conference on the Peaceful Uses of Atomic Energy at Geneva in 1958, a number of other apparatuses based on different principles (Stellarator, magnetic mirror, revolving plasma, etc. [97]) were described and details given of their workings, but the progress which has been made with these does not seem to be appreciably greater than that already obtained from the apparatus just described. It is worth noting the estimate that for fusion reactions to become a useful source of energy, temperatures of the order of 300,000,000°C for deuterium, and 40,000,000°C for deuterium plus tritium, will be required.

5–9 The production of mesons and antinucleons, and their reactions. Pi-mesons, either charged or neutral, can be produced in the laboratory by the action of particles or photons with energies of about 200 Mev on target materials from hydrogen up to the heaviest atoms. The production of π-mesons is due to exchange interactions and to combinations between nucleons:

$$p + p \begin{cases} \rightarrow p + n + \pi^+, \\ \rightleftharpoons d + \pi^+, \\ \rightarrow p + p + \pi^0, \end{cases}$$

$$n + p \rightarrow \begin{cases} p + p + \pi^-, \\ n + n + \pi^+, \\ p + n + \pi^0, \\ d + \pi^0, \end{cases}$$

$$n + n \rightarrow \begin{cases} n + n + \pi^0, \\ n + p + \pi^-, \end{cases}$$

$$p + \gamma \rightarrow \begin{cases} p + \pi^0, \\ p + \pi^+, \end{cases}$$

$$n + \gamma \rightarrow \begin{cases} n + \pi^0, \\ p + \pi^-. \end{cases}$$

For example, the bombardment of deuterium with 340-Mev protons [98] gives the reactions

$$\mathrm{p} + \mathrm{d} \rightarrow \mathrm{He}^3 + \pi^0, \qquad \mathrm{p} + \mathrm{d} \rightarrow \mathrm{t} + \pi^+.$$

The total cross section is about 15 μb. Much effort has gone into the study of π-meson production by the action of accelerated particles or photons on He, C, Al, Ag, Pb, and other target atoms. Mu-mesons are always produced simultaneously, since they result from the spontaneous disintegration of charged pions. With fast protons, the yield of positive mesons per nucleon (σ/A) increases rapidly with the atomic number of the target [99], with a dependence on $Z^{2/3}$. For neutral pions from the reaction

$$\mathrm{p} + \mathrm{p} \rightarrow \mathrm{p} + \mathrm{p} + \pi^0,$$

the yield per proton is approximately constant up to Al, beyond which it decreases. For medium or higher mass targets, the total yield is approximately proportional to $A^{2/3}$ [100].

Measurement of the cross sections and angular distributions in the reactions

$$\mathrm{p} + \mathrm{p} \rightarrow \pi^+ + \mathrm{d},$$
$$\mathrm{n} + \mathrm{p} \rightarrow \pi^0 + \mathrm{d},$$

have confirmed that there is no charge dependence in the pion formation process [101].

The π^+/π^- ratio is greater than unity for targets with $Z > 1$ if the projectile is a proton, and less than unity for neutron bombardment. The yield falls off rapidly with increasing projectile energy. The threshold for γ-ray production of π^0-mesons is about 150 Mev; the yield for this photoproduction seems to go through a maximum in the 320-Mev region.

The interaction of charged mesons with nucleons in inelastic collisions may be either an exchange of charge,

$$\pi^+ + \mathrm{n} \rightarrow \pi^0 + \mathrm{p},$$
$$\pi^- + \mathrm{p} \rightarrow \pi^0 + \mathrm{n},$$

or radiative capture,

$$\pi^- + \mathrm{p} \rightarrow \mathrm{n} + \gamma,$$
$$\pi^+ + \mathrm{n} \rightarrow \mathrm{p} + \gamma.$$

For any given meson energy, the relative yields of these various processes depend on whether the nucleon in question is free or combined. With deuterium, 20-Mev π^+-mesons dissociate the target atom into two protons, with a cross section of 4×10^{-27} cm^2. For heavier nuclides, the transformations can be more complex, and may include spallation and fission.

The collision between a nucleon and a 1.5-Bev π^--meson gives various reactions [102]:

$$\pi^- + \mathrm{p} \rightarrow \begin{cases} \pi^- + \mathrm{p} + \pi^0, \\ \pi^- + \mathrm{n} + \pi^+, \\ 2\pi^0 + \mathrm{n}, \text{ etc.,} \end{cases} \qquad \pi^- + \mathrm{n} \rightarrow \begin{cases} \pi^- + \mathrm{n} + \pi^0, \\ 2\pi^- + \mathrm{p}, \text{ etc.} \end{cases}$$

The multi-branched stars seen on photographic plates after exposure to π-mesons indicate the fragmentation of the various nuclei in the emulsion (principally silver and bromine). Sugihara and Libby [103] bombarded bromine with 122-Mev π^--mesons and identified among the radioactive products isotopes of Se (34%), As (31%), Ge (21%), and Ga (7%). This implies a $(\pi^-, ypxn)$ reaction in which the yield falls off with increasing values of y. The most probable x/y ratio is between 3 and 4. In the bombardment of iodine, Winsberg [104] detected the formation of 25 isotopes of Te, Sb, In, Cd, Ag, and Pd. The maximum number of nucleons expelled is 18, giving Pd^{109}. The most probable number x of neutrons evaporated from the target is 6 for Te and Sb, 8 for Sn, and 10 for In. The relative percentage yields are Te 58, Sb 22, Sn 11, In 3, Cd 0.7, Ag 0.12, and Pd 0.3.

The products of the reaction of arsenic with 122-Mev negative pions included isotopes of Cu and Ga [105]; here the most probable value of x is 5.5. The bombardment of oxygen and nitrogen (either as dilute acid or a solution of NH_4NO_3) with 145-Mev negative pions gave in both cases C^{11}, in the form of a mixture of $C^{11}O$ and $C^{11}O_2$.

The photographic method [106] has been used to get evidence of the reactions which follow the capture of μ-mesons by nitrogen, oxygen, and carbon:

$$O^{16} + \mu^- \rightarrow 3\alpha + T + n,$$
$$N^{14} + \mu^- \rightarrow 3\alpha + 2n,$$
$$C^{12} + \mu^- \rightarrow 2\alpha + \begin{cases} p + 3n, \\ d + 2n, \\ t + n. \end{cases}$$

The interactions between muons and nuclei are much weaker than for pions. Winsberg [107] bombarded iodine with 35-kev mesons (using graphite to absorb pions) and found Te and Sb isotopes as products; the yields were 98 and 0.8% of the total cross section. The reactions could be of the type

$$\mu^- + p \rightarrow n + \nu \quad (+106 \text{ Mev}).$$

The principal process, however, is the expulsion of 1 to 4 neutrons from the target atom. Muons interact readily with iron, with the resultant evaporation of one or more neutrons [108]. The formation of Cu^{64} and Cu^{67} in the bombardment of zinc with pions may be due, at least in part, to the action of muons [109].

Apart from the direct interactions of mesons with nuclei, the emission or capture of mesons may modify nuclear reactions between a primary projectile and a target. This occurs, for instance, in the bombardment of ${}_{53}I^{127}$ with protons having energies of the order of 1 Bev [110]; the nuclides ${}_{52}Te^{127}$, ${}_{51}Sb^{127}$, and ${}_{55}Cs^{127}$ which are formed have the same mass as the target, but the atomic number is either 1 or 2 units lower, or 2 units higher. The formation of these species is attributed to the reactions

$$I^{127}\,(p, p\pi^+)\,Te^{127}, \qquad I^{127}\,(p, p2\pi^+)\,Sb^{127}, \qquad I^{127}\,(p, p2\pi^-)\,Cs^{127}.$$

Pions with energies of 750 Mev or more interact with nucleons to form heavy mesons (K^+, K^0) and hyperons, and these are also produced in nuclear reactions involving very high-energy protons or photons. The reaction

$$\pi^- + \mathrm{p} \rightarrow \Lambda^0 + K^0$$

has a threshold at 760 Mev; the cross section at 900 Mev is 0.6 b [111]. In competition with this process is the production of the $\Sigma^- + K^+$ pair, which, however, has a threshold at 890 Mev and a cross section of only 0.25 mb at 950 Mev. Two processes are known for positive pions:

$$\pi^+ + \mathrm{p} \rightarrow \begin{cases} \Lambda^0 + K^- + \pi^+, \\ \Sigma^+ + K^+; \end{cases}$$

1.01-Bev photons give

$$\gamma + \mathrm{p} \rightarrow \Lambda^0 + K^+,$$

with a cross section of 2 μb; the threshold is 910 Mev. It will be noted that in each case the production of a heavy meson is associated with hyperon formation, and vice versa.

These particles can, in their turn, cause the formation of further hyperons, and in these processes the baryon number is conserved. Examples include

$$K^- + \mathrm{p} \rightarrow \begin{cases} \Theta^0 + K^0, \\ \Sigma^- + \pi^+, \\ \Lambda^0 + \pi^0, \end{cases}$$

$$K^- + \mathrm{n} \rightarrow \begin{cases} \Sigma^- + \pi^0, \\ \Sigma^0 + \pi^-, \\ \Lambda^0 + \pi^-, \end{cases}$$

$$\Sigma^- + \mathrm{p} \rightarrow \begin{cases} \Sigma^0 + \mathrm{n}, \\ \Lambda^0 + \mathrm{n}, \end{cases}$$

$$\Sigma^- + \mathrm{d} \rightarrow \begin{cases} \Sigma^0 + 2\mathrm{n}, \\ \Lambda^0 + 2\mathrm{n}. \end{cases}$$

Some of the properties of heavy mesons and hyperons, and their behavior in nuclear reactions, show features which were obscure for many years, and for these reasons they were referred to as "strange particles." For example, because of their high instability (average lives between $\sim 10^{-8}$ and $\sim 10^{-13}$ sec), the yield for their production in nuclear reactions should be much lower than is actually the case. Similarly, several of these particles show multiple disintegration modes (Section 2–7), and as we saw above, they are always formed in pairs (heavy meson + hyperon). Finally, the relation $q = I_z + B/2$ [Eq. (3–13a)], which holds for nucleons and pions, is not valid for the strange particles and must be replaced [112] by

$$q = I_z + \frac{B}{2} + \frac{S}{2}, \tag{5–15a}$$

where, as before, q is the charge, I_z the isotopic spin, B the number of baryons, and S the *strangeness number*, which is a whole number with the same value for each member of a given multiplet of fundamental particles; $S = 0$ for nucleons and pions; $S = +1$ for the K^+, K^- doublet; $S = -1$ for the singlet Λ and for the triplet Σ^+, Σ^-, and Σ^0; and $S = -2$ for the doublet Θ^- and Θ^0. The classification of strange particles into multiplets (Section 3–8), together with the application of Eq. (5–15a), leads to a series of selection rules which have proved most helpful in understanding and predicting their interactions and transformations.

Certain experiments on the effect of cosmic rays upon photographic plates suggest that a nuclear fragment (*hyperfragment*) arising from a disintegration such as spallation can pick up a hyperon in place of a neutron for a very short time ($\sim 3 \times 10^{-12}$ sec) before disintegrating. This idea has been used by Danysz and Pniewski [113] to explain their experimental observation that a boron nucleus formed by the spallation of a silver or a bromine atom splits up into three or four charged particles, one of which is a μ-meson, at the end of its track in the emulsion. Analogous observations have been made with lighter primary fragments [114, 115]. For example, Rosselet, Weill, and Gailloud [116] detected the capture of a negative hyperon by a nucleus of the emulsion of a photographic plate exposed to cosmic radiation. A hyperfragment with unit charge is formed, and from measurements of the track lengths, etc., the process suggested is

$$\Sigma^- + \mathrm{C}^{12} \rightarrow 2\alpha + \mathrm{n} + \overset{*}{\mathrm{H}}{}^4 \qquad \text{(hyperfragment)}.$$

The formation of hyperfragments has also been observed in the interactions of heavy K^--mesons with a number of nuclei.

Of the unstable particles produced artificially, one of particular interest is the antiproton, the existence of which in cosmic radiation (Section 2–5) has been indirectly confirmed. On bombarding a copper target with 6.2-Bev protons from the Berkeley bevatron (Section 1–8), Segrè and his colleagues [117] observed the emission of several high-energy particles produced as a result of the proton-antiproton annihilation process. The production of one antiproton per 44,000 pions was identified with certainty.

Photographic investigation, undertaken in collaboration with Amaldi and his co-workers in Rome [118, 119], gave a mass of $1824 \pm 51m_0$ for the antiproton. The first photographic identification of this particle is shown in Fig. 5–6; the track L is that of the antiproton, which after traveling 9.31 cm in the emulsion, produces a nuclear explosion with an energy release of more than 825 Mev. The tracks a and b are pions, c is a proton, and the remainder are tracks of protons or α-particles all arising from the disintegration.

The Berkeley group has also used the bevatron to obtain evidence for the existence of the antineutron [120, 121]. The antineutron was produced in a bubble chamber, where it was formed by charge exchange in a collision between an antiproton and a proton:

$$\mathrm{p} + \overline{\mathrm{p}} \rightarrow \mathrm{n} + \overline{\mathrm{n}},$$

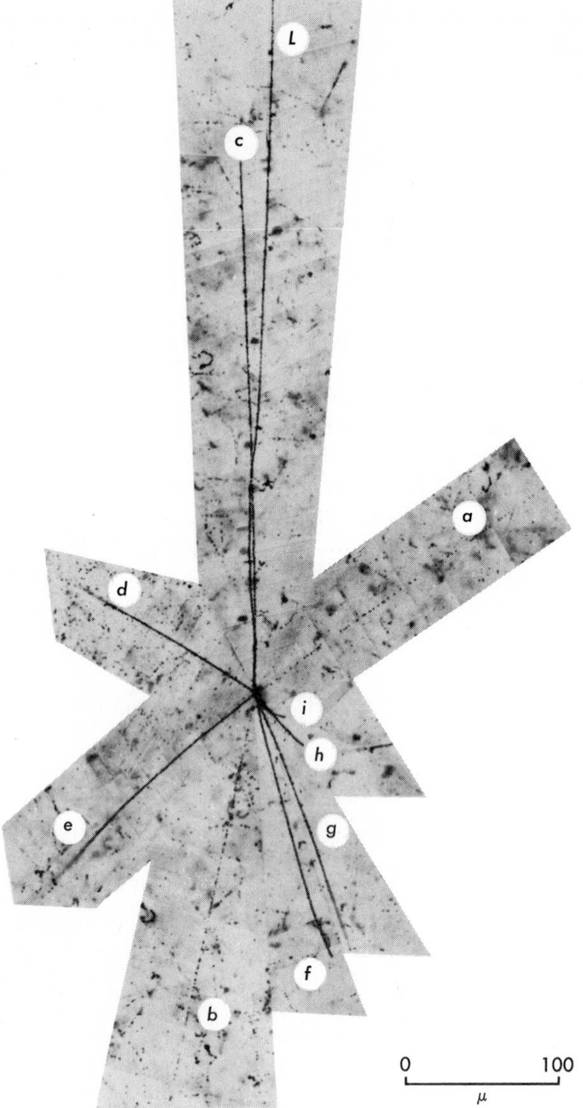

FIG. 5–6. Photographic evidence of the artificially produced antiproton (Ref. 120).

and was identified by the products of the antineutron-neutron annihilation. The antiprotons used in these experiments were produced by bombarding Be, C, or Pb with 6.2-Bev protons.

Very recently, the antihyperon $\bar{\Xi}^+$ has been discovered [121a] among the products of the proton-antiproton annihilation, being formed in the reaction

$$\bar{\mathrm{p}} + \mathrm{p} — [\Xi]^- + [\bar{\Xi}]^+.$$

TABLE 5-6

ENERGIES OF MESIC AND ELECTRONIC 2p → 1s TRANSITIONS

Atom	μ^--transition, kev	Electronic transition, kev
Al	350	
Si	410	
Ti	955	4.95
Cu	1550	8.96
Zn	1600	
Sb	3500	30.35
Hg	5800	
Bi	6020	
Pb	6020	88

5-10 Mesic atoms. Although all charged mesons (both $\mu^{\pm}$ and $\pi^{\pm}$) have extremely short average lives before being captured by nuclei, they can lose a large part of their kinetic energy in this time interval by means of the ionization and excitation processes known for other charged particles (Chapter 11). These are effectively complete in a time of about 10^{-11} sec. When their energy becomes sufficiently low, negative mesons are attracted by the coulombic field of the nucleus and may go into an extranuclear orbit, characterized by quantum numbers exactly as for an electron. The radiations emitted by these mesic atoms in the transition of the meson from an exterior shell into a deeper one are analogous to ordinary x-rays, except that for a given atom the energies involved are much higher. The probability of capture by the nucleus itself by the reactions described in the last section is, however, much too large for negative pions to get as far as the K-shell of heavy or medium atoms. The principles which govern the behavior of mesic atoms will therefore show up most clearly with μ^--mesons. The average life of the latter before capture is inversely proportional to Z^4 for light nuclei [122, 123], but varies more slowly for the heavy nuclei, reaching a value of 7×10^{-8} sec for $Z = 82$. This should be compared with an average life of only 10^{-18} sec for the 2p → 1s transition in lead.

The Bohr theory of the atom gives the binding energy of the meson in an orbit whose principal quantum number is n as

$$E_n = -\frac{207 m_0 Z^2 e^4}{2\hbar^2 n^2}, \tag{5-16}$$

where $207m_0 = m_\mu$, the mass of the muon. For $Z = 10$, the transition energy between two adjacent levels is a few hundred kev; for $Z = 50$, it is of the order of a few Mev. Table 5-6 shows the experimental values given by Fitch and Rainwater [124] for the 2p → 1s transitions in some mesic atoms and the corresponding energies for the electronic transitions.

It will be seen that the energies of the mesic transitions are considerably lower than those calculated from Eq. (5–16). The main reason for these differences is that the Bohr atom is a far from satisfactory model for these systems. The classical radius of an orbit of quantum number n in a mesic atom is given by

$$r = \frac{n^2\hbar^2}{Zm_\mu e^2}\cdot \tag{5–17}$$

For $n = 1$ and $Z = 82$, $r = 3.07 \times 10^{-13}$ cm, which is smaller than the nuclear radius, which for Pb is 8×10^{-12} cm; consequently a meson in the K-orbit of a heavy atom is in fact inside the nucleus. Wheeler [125, 126, 127] was the first to draw attention to this remarkable transparency of the nucleus to μ^--mesons. Before being captured by the lead nucleus, a μ^--meson in the K-shell travels some 5 meters through nuclear matter, equivalent to 10^{17} gm/cm^2. For such a species, the old Thomson idea of an atom with the negative charge inside a positive sphere seems to be a more convenient description than the Rutherford-Bohr model. The theoretical treatment of such atoms was initially developed by Wheeler, and subsequently by other authors [128]. It is necessary to take into account the finite size of the nucleus, whereas the Bohr theory regards the nucleus as a point. By assuming a uniform spherical distribution of nuclear charge, we find that the interaction potential in the interior of a nucleus of radius R is given by

$$V = -\frac{Ze^2}{R}\left(\frac{3}{2} - \frac{r^2}{2R^2}\right) \qquad (r \leq R), \tag{5–18}$$

and at the exterior

$$V = -\frac{Ze^2}{r} \qquad (r \geq R). \tag{5–19}$$

The high probability that mesons in the K- and L-shells will actually be inside the nucleus means that mesic atoms are extremely sensitive to variations in such nuclear properties as size, symmetry, and polarizability, etc. The study of such atoms therefore provides a very sensitive technique for the nuclear physicist; experimentally, one measures the energies and yield of the electromagnetic radiation (x-rays) emitted in the various orbital transitions. Furthermore, a mesic atom formed around a nucleus of atomic number Z interacts with the periphery electrons of this nucleus as would an atom of atomic number $Z - 1$; this can give rise to electronic transitions which do not normally occur.

Benedetti and others [129, 130] have measured the energies and the intensities of the x-rays emitted by mesic atoms with Z between 3 and 23. From the measurements made by Fitch and Rainwater [124] on the $2p \rightarrow 1s$ transitions in mesic atoms, it can be shown that the nuclear dimensions calculated from Eqs. (5–18) and (5–19) agree well with the relation (2–3), $R = r_0A^{1/3}$. The average value of r_0 is, however, about 1.2×10^{-13} cm, to be compared with values between 1.4 and 1.5×10^{-13} cm obtained from the other methods. It was pointed out, however, that the behavior of mesic atoms is sensitive to the charge density inside the nucleus, whereas most of the other methods for determining R depend on conditions at the surface. The anomaly can then be explained by supposing that the nuclear density is not uniform throughout but decreases from the center toward the surface of the nucleus according to some exponential law. Other authors [131] have attempted to get over the difficulty by making corrections to the values calculated from the other methods, and in this way making them practically equal to those obtained from the measurements on mesic atoms.

The formation of a mesic hydrogen atom may in certain conditions catalyze thermonuclear reactions (p + d, d + d, d + t, etc.). For example, the reaction

$$\mathrm{H} + \mathrm{D} + \mu^- \rightarrow \mathrm{He}^3 + \mu^-, \tag{5–20}$$

in which the energy released (5.5 Mev) is carried away by the muon, has been observed in a bubble chamber by Alvarez, *et al.* [132]. The catalytic reaction probably takes place in the following successive stages [133, 134]: (a) the formation of a mesic atom $\mathrm{H}\mu^-$; (b) irreversible exchange with a deuteron

$$\mathrm{H}\mu^- + \mathrm{D} \rightarrow \mathrm{H} + \mathrm{D}\mu^-;$$

(c) the formation of a "molecular ion" $\mathrm{HD}\mu^-$, with a diameter about 200 times smaller than that of the normal HD^+ molecule-ion; (d) nuclear reaction between H and D in the course of vibrational movement, the period of which is very much smaller than the average life of the meson. This is a fairly rare event, some 15 cases being observed per 2500 μ^-.

References

1. See, for example, D. H. Templeton, *Ann. Rev. Nuclear Sci.*, **2,** 93 (1953).
2. See the compilation of Q values by D. M. Van Patter and W. Whaling, *Revs. Modern Phys.*, **26,** 402 (1954).
3. I. Frenkel, *Theoretical Principles of Atomic Nuclei*, Moscow, 1950.
4. G. Breit and E. Wigner, *Phys. Rev.*, **49,** 519 (1936).
5. R. Serber, *Phys. Rev.*, **72,** 1008, 1114 (1947).
6. M. L. Goldberger, *Phys. Rev.*, **74,** 1269 (1948).
7. J. Hadley and H. York, *Phys. Rev.*, **80,** 345 (1950).
8. G. Bernardine, E. T. Booth, and S. J. Lindenbaum, *Phys. Rev.*, **85,** 826 (1952); **88,** 1017 (1952).
9. P. Cuer, M. Morand, and L. van Rossum, *Compt. rend.*, **238,** 481 (1949).
10. L. Marquez, *Phys. Rev.*, **88,** 225 (1952).
11. R. Sherr, *Phys. Rev.*, **68,** 240 (1945).
12. E. Amaldi, D. Bocciarelli, B. N. Cacciapuoti, and G. C. Trabacchi, *Nuovo cimento*, **3,** 203 (1946).
13. L. J. Cook, E. M. McMillan, J. M. Petersen, and D. C. Sewell, *Phys. Rev.*, **75,** 7 (1949).
14. K. A. Ter-Martirosyan, *J. Phys. russ.*, **22,** 284 (1952).
15. T. Huus and C. Zupancic, *Danske Videnskab. Selskab, Mat.-fys. Medd.*, **28,** No. 1, 3 (1953).

16. L. Marquez and I. Perlman, *Phys. Rev.*, **81,** 953 (1951).
17. G. S. Rudstam, P. C. Stevenson, and R. L. Folger, *Phys. Rev.*, **87,** 358 (1952).
18. G. R. Martin, S. J. Thomson, G. R. Wardle, and K. I. Mayne, *Phil. Mag.*, **45,** 410 (1954).
19. G. S. Rudstam, *Phil. Mag.*, **44,** 1131 (1953).
20. G. Andersson, *Phil. Mag.*, **45,** 621 (1954).
21. E. Belmont and J. M. Miller, *Phys. Rev.*, **95,** 1554 (1954).
22. R. E. Batzel, D. R. Miller, and G. T. Seaborg, *Phys. Rev.*, **84,** 671 (1951).
23. G. Wagner and E. O. Wiig, *J. Am. Chem. Soc.*, **74,** 1101 (1952).
24. D. H. Templeton and I. Perlman, *Abstracts of the 114th A. C. S. meeting*, 1948.
25. S. C. Wright, *Phys. Rev.*, **79,** 838 (1950).
26. W. E. Bennett, *Phys. Rev.*, **94,** 997 (1954).
27. A. P. Vinogradov, *et al.*, *Doklady Akad. Nauk S.S.S.R.*, July, 1955, p. 132 (*C.A.*, **50,** 6955c).
28. A. N. Murin, *et al.*, *Doklady Akad. Nauk S.S.S.R.*, 160 (*C.A.*, **50,** 6955i).
29. B. V. Kurchatov, *et al.*, *Doklady Akad. Nauk S.S.S.R.*, 178 (*C.A.*, **50,** 6955g).
29a. R. L. Wolfgang, E. W. Baker, A. A. Caretto, J. B. Cumming, G. Friedlander, and J. Hudis, *Phys. Rev.*, **103,** 394 (1956).
29b. J. M. Miller and J. Hudis, *Ann. Revs. Nuclear Sci.*, **9,** 159 (1959).
30. G. Friedlander, J. M. Miller, R. Wolfgang, J. Hudis, and E. Baker, *Phys. Rev.*, **94,** 727 (1954).
31. A. Turkevich and N. Sugarman, *Phys. Rev.*, **94,** 728 (1954).
32. N. Sugarman, R. B. Duffield, G. Friedlander, and J. M. Miller, *Phys. Rev.*, **95,** 1704 (1954).
33. W. O. Lock, P. V. March, H. Muirhead, and W. G. V. Rosser, *Proc. Roy. Soc. (London)*, **A230,** 215, 222 (1955).
34. S. G. Rudstam, *Phil. Mag.*, **46,** 344 (1955).
35. J. Chadwick and M. Goldhaber, *Proc. Roy. Soc. (London)*, **A151,** 479 (1935).
36. R. E. Bell and L. G. Elliott, *Phys. Rev.*, **79,** 282 (1950).
37. J. R. Oppenheimer and M. Phillips, *Phys. Rev.*, **48,** 500 (1935).
38. J. A. Harvey, *Phys. Rev.*, **81,** 353 (1951).
39. H. B. Hopkins, Jr. and B. B. Cunningham, *Phys. Rev.*, **73,** 1406 (1948).
40. D. R. Miller, R. C. Thompson, and B. B. Cunningham, *Phys. Rev.*, **74,** 347 (1948).
41. M. Lindner and I. Perlman, *Phys. Rev.*, **78,** 499 (1950).
42. N. Knable, E. O. Lawrence, C. E. Leith, B. J. Moyer, and R. L. Thornton, *Phys. Rev.*, **74,** 1217 (1948).
43. W. W. Chupp and E. M. McMillan, *Phys. Rev.*, **74,** 1217 (1948).
44. K. W. Allen, E. Almquist, J. T. Dewan, T. P. Pepper, and J. H. Sanders, *Phys. Rev.*, **82,** 262 (1951); see also B. L. Cohen and T. H. Handley, *Phys. Rev.*, **92,** 101 (1953).
45. P. E. Tannenwald, *Phys. Rev.*, **89,** 508 (1953).
46. J. Benveniste and B. Cork, *Phys. Rev.*, **89,** 422 (1953).
47. G. M. Temmer and N. P. Heydenburg, *Phys. Rev.*, **93,** 351 (1954).

48. N. P. Heydenburg and G. M. Temmer, *Phys. Rev.*, **95,** 629, 861 (1954).

49. E. Almquist, K. W. Allen, J. T. Dewan, and T. P. Pepper, *Phys. Rev.*, **91,** 1022 (1953).

50. W. M. Good, W. E. Kunz, and C. D. Moak, *Phys. Rev.*, **94,** 87 (1954).

51. G. B. Rossi, W. B. Jones, J. M. Hollander, and J. G. Hamilton, *Phys. Rev.*, **93,** 256 (1954).

52. J. M. Hollander, *Phys. Rev.*, **92,** 518 (1953).

53. M. I. Kalkstein and J. M. Hollander, *Phys. Rev.*, **96,** 730 (1954).

54. J. F. Miller, *Phys. Rev.*, **83,** 1261 (1951).

55. C. N. Chou, W. F. Fry, and J. J. Lord, *Phys. Rev.*, **87,** 671 (1952).

56. A. Ghiorso, G. B. Rossi, B. G. Harvey, and S. G. Thompson, *Phys. Rev.*, **93,** 257 (1954).

57. H. Atterling, W. Forsling, L. W. Holm, L. Melander, and B. Astrom, *Phys. Rev.*, **95,** 585 (1954).

58. L. D. Wyly and A. Zucker, *Phys. Rev.*, **89,** 524 (1953).

59. H. L. Reynolds and A. Zucker, *Phys. Rev.*, **91,** 496 (1953); **94,** 748 (1954).

60. K. F. Chackett, J. H. Fremlin, and D. Walker, *Phil. Mag.*, **45,** 173 (1954).

61. K. F. Chackett and J. H. Fremlin, *Phil. Mag.*, **45,** 735 (1954).

62. G. A. Chackett, K. F. Chackett, and J. H. Fremlin, *Phil. Mag.*, **46,** 1 (1955).

62a. H. L. Reynolds and A. Zucker, *Phys. Rev.*, **100,** 226 (1955).

63. B. L. Cohen, H. L. Reynolds, and A. Zucker, *Phys. Rev.*, **96,** 1617 (1954).

64. W. E. Burcham, *Proc. Phys. Soc. (London)*, **67A,** 555 (1954).

65. *Proceedings of the Conference on Nuclear Reactions*, Amsterdam, 1956.

66. B. Pontecorvo and R. Lazard, *Compt. rend.*, **208,** 99 (1939).

67. W. Paul, *Naturwiss.*, **36,** 31 (1949).

68. G. B. Collins, B. Waldman, and E. Guth, *Phys. Rev.*, **56,** 876 (1939).

69. K. L. Brown and R. Wilson, *Phys. Rev.*, **93,** 443 (1954).

70. L. Szilard and T. A. Chalmers, *Nature*, **134,** 494 (1934).

71. W. Bothe and W. Gentner, *Z. Physik*, **106,** 236 (1937); **112,** 45 (1939).

72. M. L. Perlman and G. Friedlander, *Phys. Rev.*, **74,** 442 (1948).

73. M. L. Perlman, *Phys. Rev.*, **75,** 988 (1949).

74. M. Goldhaber and E. Teller, *Phys. Rev.*, **74,** 1046 (1948).

75. J. S. Levinger and H. A. Bethe, *Phys. Rev.*, **78,** 115 (1950).

76. R. J. Debs, J. T. Eisinger, A. W. Fairhall, I. Halpern, and H. G. Richter, *Phys. Rev.*, **97,** 1325, 1327 (1955).

77. C. H. Millar and A. G. W. Cameron, *Phys. Rev.*, **79,** 182 (1950).

78. See also the review by E. W. Titterton, *Progress in Nuclear Physics*, Pergamon Press, London, **4,** 1 (1955).

79. W. R. Arnold, J. A. Phillips, G. A. Sawyer, E. J. Stovall, Jr., and J. L. Tuck, *Phys. Rev.*, **93,** 483 (1954).

80. E. E. Saltpeter, *Ann. Rev. Nuclear Sci.*, **2,** 41 (1953).

81. G. Gamow and C. L. Critchfield, *Theory of the Atomic Nucleus*, Oxford University Press, 1950.

82. R. d'E. Atkinson and F. G. Houtermans, *Z. Physik*, **54,** 656 (1929).

83. H. A. Bethe and C. L. Critchfield, *Phys. Rev.*, **54,** 248 (1938).

84. C. F. WEIZSACKER, *Physik. Z.*, **39**, 633 (1938).
85. H. A. BETHE, *Phys. Rev.*, **55**, 434 (1939).
86. W. A. FOWLER, *Phys. Rev.*, **81**, 655 (1951).
87. E. SCHATZMAN, *Compt. rend.*, **232**, 1740 (1951).
88. F. HOYLE, *The Nature of the Universe*, Oxford University Press, 1957.
89. G. GAMOW and M. SCHÖNBERG, *Phys. Rev.*, **59**, 539 (1941).
90. L. B. BORST, *Phys. Rev.*, **78**, 807 (1950); but see Ref. 80.
91. B. V. KOURCHATOV, *Bull. Atomic Scientists*, **12**, 269 (1956).
92. B. V. KOURCHATOV, *Progr. Phys. (U.S.S.R.)*, **59**, 603 (1956).
93. R. F. POST, *Revs. Modern Phys.*, **28**, 338 (1956).
94. P. C. THONEMANN, *et al.*, *Nature*, **181**, 217 (1958).
95. A. GIBSON, *Nature*, **181**, 803 (1958).
96. B. ROSE, A. E. TAYLOR, and E. WOOD, *Nature*, **181**, 1630 (1958).
97. A. S. BISHOP, *Project Sherwood*, Addison-Wesley Publishing Co., Reading, Mass., 1958.
98. W. J. FRANK, K. C. BANDTEL, R. MADEY, and B. J. MOYER, *Nature*, **94**, 1716 (1954).
99. R. SAGANE and W. DUDZIAK, *Nature*, **92**, 212 (1953); see also M. MECHTCHERIAKOV, *et al.*, *Doklady Akad. Nauk S.S.S.R.*, **100**, 673, 677 (1955) and A. TIAPKINE, *et al.*, *Doklady Akad. Nauk S.S.S.R.*, **100**, 689 (1955).
100. R. W. HALES and B. J. MOYER, *Phys. Rev.*, **89**, 1047 (1953).
101. R. H. HILDEBRAND, *Proceedings of the 1954 Glasgow Conference on Nuclear Physics*, Pergamon Press, London, 1955, p. 245.
102. J. CRUSSARD and W. D. WALKER, *Proceedings of the 1954 Glasgow Conference on Nuclear Physics*, p. 261.
103. T. T. SUGIHARA and W. F. LIBBY, *Phys. Rev.*, **88**, 587 (1952).
104. L. WINSBERG, *Phys. Rev.*, **90**, 343 (1953); **95**, 198 (1954).
105. A. TURKEVICH and J. B. NIDAY, *Phys. Rev.*, **84**, 1253 (1951); **90**, 342 (1953).
106. H. MORINGA and W. F. FRY, *Nuovo cimento*, **10**, 308 (1953).
107. L. WINSBERG, *Phys. Rev.*, **95**, 205 (1954).
108. M. ANNIS, H. C. WILKINS, and J. D. MILLER, *Phys. Rev.*, **94**, 1038 (1954).
109. S. C. FUNG and A. TURKEVICH, *Phys. Rev.*, **95**, 176 (1954).
110. I. M. LADENBANER, *U.S.A.E.C. report UCRL-8200*, (1958).
111. Based on J. GEHENIAU, *Les Particules Fondamentales*, Feuilles d'information, Brussels, 1959.
112. M. GELL-MANN and A. H. ROSENFELD, *Ann. Rev. Nuclear Sci.*, **7**, 407 (1957).
113. M. DANYSZ and J. PNIEWSKI, *Phil. Mag.*, **44**, 348 (1953).
114. C. F. POWELL, *Nuovo cimento*, Suppl. 11, 165 (1954).
115. J. CRUSSARD, *Proceedings of the Rochester Conference on High Energy Nuclear Physics*, 1954, p. 84.
116. P. ROSSELET, R. WEILL, and M. GAILLOUD, *Nuovo cimento*, **3**, 505 (1956).
117. O. CHAMBERLAIN, E. SEGRÈ, C. WIEGAND, and T. YPSILANTIS, *Phys. Rev.*, **100**, 947 (1956).
118. O. CHAMBERLAIN, W. W. CHUPP, G. GOLDHABER, E. SEGRÈ, C. WIEGAND, E. AMALDI, G. BARONI, C. CASTAGNOLI, C. FRANZINETTI, and A. MANFREDINI, *Nuovo cimento*, **3**, 447 (1956).

119. O. Chamberlain, W. W. Chupp, G. Goldhaber, E. Segrè, C. Wiegand, E. Amaldi, G. Baroni, C. Castagnoli, C. Franzinetti, and A. Manfredini, *Phys. Rev.*, **101,** 909 (1956).

120. B. Cork, G. R. Lambertson, O. Piccioni, and W. A. Wenzel, *Phys. Rev.*, **104,** 1193 (1956).

121. J. Button, T. Elioff, E. Segrè, H. M. Steiner, R. Weingard, C. Wiegand, and T. Ypsilantis, *Phys. Rev.*, **108,** 1557 (1957).

121a. H. N. Brown, *et al.*, *Phys. Rev. Letters,* **8,** 255 (1962); CERN Laboratories, *ibid,* p. 257.

122. J. W. Keuffel, F. B. Harrison, T. N. K. Godfrey, and G. T. Reynolds, *Phys. Rev.*, **87,** 942 (1952).

123. J. M. Kennedy, *Phys. Rev.*, **87,** 953 (1952).

124. V. L. Fitch and J. Rainwater, *Phys. Rev.*, **92,** 789 (1953).

125. J. A. Wheeler, *Revs. Modern Phys.*, **21,** 133 (1949).

126. J. A. Wheeler, *Phys. Rev.*, **92,** 812 (1953).

127. J. Tiomno and J. A. Wheeler, *Revs. Modern Phys.*, **21,** 144, 153 (1949).

128. L. N. Cooper and E. M. Henley, *Phys. Rev.*, **92,** 800 (1953).

129. S. de Benedetti, *Proceedings of the Rochester Conference on High Energy Nuclear Physics,* 1954, p. 57.

130. M. B. Stearns, M. Stearns, S. de Benedetti, and L. Leipuner, *Phys. Rev.*, **93,** 1123 (1954); **95,** 1353 (1954); **96,** 804 (1954); **97,** 240 (1955).

131. F. Bitter and H. Feshbach, *Phys. Rev.*, **92,** 837 (1953).

132. L. W. Alvarez, *et al.*, *Phys. Rev.*, **105,** 1127 (1957).

133. F. C. Frank, *Nature,* **160,** 525 (1947).

134. Y. B. Zeldovich, *Doklady Akad. Nauk S.S.S.R.*, **95,** 493 (1954).

CHAPTER 6

FISSION AND NUCLEAR REACTORS

6–1 Fission by thermal neutrons. Uranium, as it is found naturally, is a mixture of three isotopes, masses 234, 235, and 238, in the proportion 0.006 : 0.712 : 99.282. When the element, or some uranium compound, is bombarded with thermal neutrons, U^{238} captures a neutron to give the radioactive isotope U^{239}, which emits an electron to give Np^{239}, which in its turn β-decays to Pu^{239}:

$$U^{238} + n \rightarrow U^{239} \xrightarrow[23\text{ min}]{\beta-} Np^{239} \xrightarrow[2.3\text{ days}]{\beta-} Pu^{239} \xrightarrow[2.4 \times 10^{4}\text{ yr}]{\alpha}, \tag{6–1}$$

so that this series of transformations gives rise to the first transuranium elements (Chapter 8).

The isotope U^{235} undergoes a much more complex series of reactions. Only a small fraction (about 15%) goes to the active nuclide U^{236} (half-life 2.4×10^7 years); the majority of the compound nuclei (U^{235} + n) are formed in a highly excited state, and very rapidly break up into two extremely unstable fragments and a small number ν of neutrons:

$$_{92}U^{235} + n \rightarrow Z_1^{A_1} + Z_2^{A_2} + \nu n, \tag{6–2}$$

where $A_2 = 236 - A_1 - \nu$ and $Z_2 = 92 - Z_1$; the average value of ν is 2.46. This is the process known as *fission*,* written in the abbreviated form as U^{235} (n, f). The fragments are considerably neutron-excess, and decay by a series of successive β-emissions to give nuclides which are increasingly closer to the Z/N stability line in Fig. 3–4; for example,

$$_{52}Te^{137} \xrightarrow[1\text{ min}]{\beta} {_{53}I^{137}} \xrightarrow[22.5\text{ sec}]{\beta} {_{54}Xe^{137}} \xrightarrow[3.4\text{ min}]{\beta}$$

$$_{55}Cs^{137} \xrightarrow[27\text{ yr}]{\beta} {_{56}Ba^{137}}\text{ (stable)} \tag{6–3}$$

$$_{40}Zr^{97} \xrightarrow[17\text{ hr}]{\beta} {_{41}Nb^{97}} \xrightarrow[75\text{ min}]{\beta} {_{42}Mo^{97}}\text{ (stable)}. \tag{6–4}$$

The two disintegrations series (6–3) and (6–4) are complementary:

$$Z_1\,(52) + Z_2\,(40) = 92,$$

and

$$A_1\,(137) + A_2\,(97) + \nu\,(2) = 236.$$

---

* See Section 1–7 for the discovery of the fission process.

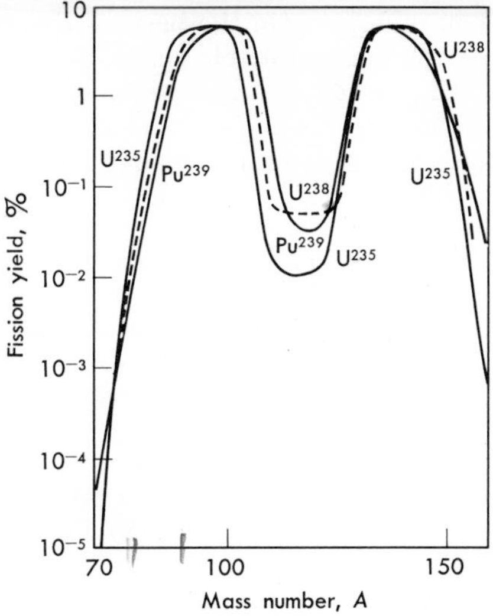

FIG. 6–1. Mass distribution of fission products.

The isotopes ${}_{52}Te^{137}$ and ${}_{40}Zr^{97}$ are not, however, unique values of $Z_1^{A_1}$ and $Z_2^{A_2}$, and in fact the fission process can take place via a large number of routes, since more than 200 different nuclides with atomic numbers between 30 (Zn) and 65 (Tb), and with mass numbers between 72 and 162, have been identified as fission products. All the members of a given chain are isobars, and each chain can be characterized by its mass number.

The overall result of these various modes of fission gives an average value of ~1.5 for the ratio A_1/A_2, and there is an asymmetric mass distribution for the nuclides formed. This is illustrated in Fig. 6–1, where the logarithm of the yield is plotted as a function of the mass number. This curve emphasizes the widely differing probabilities of formation for the various fission product series, varying between 6.4% (mass numbers 140 and 96) and 10^{-5}%. The probability of symmetrical fission, to give two equal fragments ($A_1 = A_2 = 118$), is only ~0.01%. The ratio of the yield at the maximum of the curve to that at the valley is approximately 650. The average mass numbers at half maximum height are 95 and 139. The most abundant fission products include

Zr^{95} (6.4%), Ba^{140} (6.3%), Cs^{137} (6.15%),
Tc^{99} and Ce^{144} (6.0%), Sr^{90} (5.8%), Y^{91} (5.4%),
Ru^{103} (3.0%), Pm^{147} (2.7%).

Corresponding to the asymmetric mass distribution, there must also be an initial asymmetric distribution of charge, showing up in the atomic number of the nuclides formed. There is as yet no completely reliable way of predicting the most probable charges Z_{p1} and Z_{p2} for two given complementary series. Among the various theories put forward, that of Coryell, Glendenin, and Edwards [1, 2], postulating *equal displacements*, seems to work best in practice. On the basis of the empirical data, these authors suggest that the most probable charge distribution is that giving the equality $Z_{A_1} - Z_{p_1} = Z_{A_2} - Z_{p_2}$, where Z_A is the charge of the stable nuclide at the end of the series. In other words, complementary chains of equal length are more probable than chains of different length; this is expressed by the relation

$$Z_{p_1} = Z_{A_1} - \tfrac{1}{2}(Z_{A_1} + Z_{A_2} - Z_F), \tag{6–5}$$

where Z_F is the charge of the fissile nucleus. Pappas [3, 4] has slightly modified this theory by taking into account the effect of the closed shells on nuclear stability in selecting the values of Z_A. Pappas also considers that the sum of the complementary masses should be equal to that of the compound nucleus which underwent fission, so that the approximately 2.5 neutrons which are spontaneously emitted should be included.

The two maxima in the distribution curve (Fig. 6–1) occur in the regions $A = 85$ and 135, corresponding to the neutron numbers $N = 50$ and $N = 82$. Mayer [5] and Meitner [6] believe that the essential cause of the asymmetric nature of fission lies in the stability of nuclides with these magic numbers. The first of these numbers is associated with $Z = 36$ and the second with $Z = 54$; since $Z_1 + Z_2 = 92$, the first fragment can have a 50-neutron shell for $Z = 36$ to 38, and the second an 82-neutron shell for $Z = 54$ to 56. In fact, there are eight chains beginning with $Z = 36$, and seven with $Z = 54$.

Another anomaly, namely the fine structure in the fission yield curve, has been attributed by Glendenin [7, 8, 9] to the effect of the magic numbers. The general smoothness of this curve corresponds to the fact that all the nuclides of any given chain have the same probability of formation. However, certain nuclides with neutron numbers close to 50 and 82 are formed with yields slightly above or below that of the rest of the chain. Glendenin believes that for a nucleus with $N = 51$ or 83 there will be a high probability of neutron loss to give a nuclide in the $N = 50$ series, which naturally disturbs the smooth distribution and the constancy of the yields. For example,

$$\begin{aligned}
&{}_{51}\mathrm{Sb}^{136} \to {}_{52}\mathrm{Te}^{136} \to {}_{53}\mathrm{I}^{136} \to {}_{54}\mathrm{Xe}^{136},\\
&{}_{51}\mathrm{Sb}^{135} \to {}_{52}\mathrm{Te}^{135} \to {}_{53}\mathrm{I}^{135} \to {}_{54}\mathrm{Xe}^{135} \to {}_{55}\mathrm{Cs}^{135} \to {}_{56}\mathrm{Ba}^{135},\\
&{}_{51}\mathrm{Sb}^{134} \to {}_{52}\mathrm{Te}^{134} \to {}_{53}\mathrm{I}^{134} \to {}_{54}\mathrm{Xe}^{134}.
\end{aligned}$$

Some fission products certainly do emit neutrons, described as *delayed neutrons* to distinguish them from those emitted spontaneously in the fission process itself. Several groups of these delayed neutrons are known; the decay follows an exponential law, so that they can be characterized by their half-lives. The values reported include

$$\begin{array}{ccc}
0.114 \text{ sec } (0.025\%), & 0.44 \text{ sec } (0.124\%), & 1.5 \text{ sec } (0.406\%),\\
4.5 \text{ sec } (0.18\%), & 19.8 \text{ sec } (0.23\%), & 54.3 \text{ sec } (0.035\%),\\
3 \text{ min } (8 \times 10^{-7}\%), & 12 \text{ min } (3 \times 10^{-9}\%), & 2 \text{ hr } (1.3 \times 10^{-10}\%).
\end{array}$$

The total intensity is 0.755%. The percentages given in parentheses (relative precision about 25%) are the intensities relative to the total neutron emission (i.e., both spontaneous and delayed). More recently a new group of delayed neutrons with a half-life of about 0.15 sec has been detected; the relative intensity is 0.02% [9].

At least three of these half-lives coincide with the half-lives of β-transitions in the chain in question; 54.3 sec is the half-life of $Br^{87} \rightarrow Kr^{87}$; 19.8 sec is that of $I^{137} \rightarrow Xe^{137}$; and 4.5 sec agrees with the half-life of Br^{89}. The half-lives 1.5 and 0.4 sec can probably be assigned to Sb^{135} and As^{85}. It is therefore very probable that the nuclides Kr^{87}, Xe^{137}, etc., are formed in a highly excited state and emit a neutron instantaneously, so that the half-lives for the neutron emission are in fact the half-lives of the preceding β-transition:

$$Br^{87} \xrightarrow{\beta} Kr^{87} \rightarrow Kr^{86} + n,$$

$$I^{137} \xrightarrow{\beta} Xe^{137} \rightarrow Xe^{136} + n.$$

Fission is accompanied by the release of a large amount of energy, corresponding to the decrease in the rest masses. The greater part of this energy appears as the kinetic energy of the two recoiling heavy fragments and of the 2.5 spontaneously emitted neutrons; the remainder is in the energy of the β- and γ-emissions, and of the neutrinos emitted in the radioactive transformations which follow the fission process itself. The average energy, determined calorimetrically, is 177 Mev [10], the energy of the γ-rays, neutrons, and the neutrinos which escape from the calorimeter must be added to this, giving a total energy of about 200 Mev. The amount carried away by the heavy fragments varies between 120 and 180 Mev, depending on the chain involved; for the most probable mode of fission, the energy is 156 Mev, of which 95 Mev is associated with the light fragment and the rest with the heavier fragment. Even for a given mass ratio A_1/A_2, there may be a considerable variation in the total kinetic energy, due to differences in the energies and number of neutrons emitted, as well as to variations in the initial charge distribution. The energy distribution curve (Fig. 6–2) is therefore not directly related to the mass distribution.

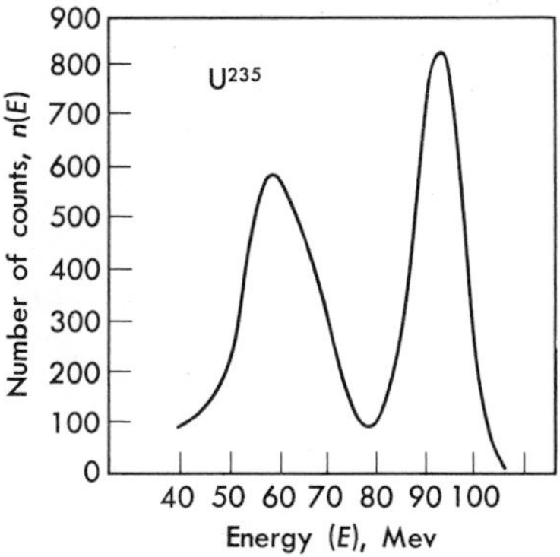

FIG. 6–2. Energy spectrum in the fission of U^{235}.

The energy spectrum of the emitted neutrons shows a pronounced maximum around 1 Mev; the average energy is approximately 2 Mev.

The nuclides U^{233}, Np^{237}, Pu^{239}, Pu^{241}, Am^{241}, and Am^{242} also undergo fission with thermal neutrons, and the principal features of these fission reactions are very similar to those just described for U^{235}. The average number of spontaneous neutrons [11] is U^{233}, 2.54; Pu^{239}, 2.88; Pu^{241}, 3.1. The fission yield curve for Pu^{239} has been determined both by radiochemical methods and mass spectrometrically and is shown in Fig. 6–1; the curve for U^{233} is similar. The peak-to-valley ratio is 150 for Pu^{239}, and 390 for U^{233} [12]. The average mass numbers at the half-height of the curve are 99 and 138, and 94 and 139, respectively.

The thermal neutron fission cross sections for a number of isotopes are given in Table 6–1, and for purpose of comparison the capture cross sections are also shown. These are only average values, however, since both fission and capture often show pronounced resonances in the thermal neutron region.

The fission of U^{235} is sometimes accompanied by the formation of a much lighter fragment, either an α-particle [13, 14, 15] or a triton [16]. The frequency of this emission is about 1 per 300 events for α-particles, and considerably lower for tritons. There is also some evidence of very rare fission events which give three or four fragments, all of comparable mass [17].

Table 6–1

Fission and Capture Cross Sections for Thermal Neutrons, in Barns

Nuclide	Fission	Capture
Th^{229}	45	—
Pa^{230}	1500	—
Pa^{232}	700	—
U^{232}	80	—
U^{233}	524	593
U^{235}	595	698
Natural U	4.2	3.5
Np^{234}	900	—
Np^{237}	0.019	170
Np^{238}	1600	—
Pu^{238}	18	425
Pu^{239}	729	1032
Pu^{241}	1055	1320
Am^{241}	3.13	700
Am^{242}	6400	8000
Am^{242m}	~2000	—
Am^{245}	1880	2040

6–2 Fission by fast particles and photons. As the energy of the incident neutron increases, the U^{235} fission yield falls off according to the $1/v$ law (Section 5–2), but even with very fast neutrons, fission still occurs. For U^{238}, on the other hand, fission can be brought about only by fast neutrons, with a threshold for the reaction at 0.92 Mev; the same holds for U^{234} (threshold 0.28 Mev), Th^{232} (1.05 Mev), Th^{230} ($\sim$1 Mev), Pa^{231} (0.45 Mev), and Np^{237} (0.25 Mev). It will be noted that the cross sections for the thermal neutron fission of these last two nuclides are extremely low (Table 6–1). The threshold increases rapidly with decreasing atomic number, so that for Bi^{209}, for example, it is of the order of 15 Mev. By using 84-Mev neutrons, Kelly and Wiegand [18] observed the fission of elements between bismuth and platinum; the fission yields relative to that for thorium are

Bi^{209},	0.019,	Tl,	0.0032,
Pb^{208},	0.0028,	Hg,	0.0023,
Pb^{207},	0.010,	Au,	0.0020,
Pb^{206},	0.007,	Pt,	0.0009.

Fission can also be induced by accelerated charged particles or by very high-energy photons. For U^{238}, the threshold is about 21 Mev for α-particles, about 8 Mev for deuterons, and approximately 7 Mev for protons; for Th^{232} the α-particle threshold is 23 Mev. The cross section for the fission of U^{238} by 100-Mev α-particles is approximately 1.5 b, and that for Th^{232} at 37.5 Mev is 0.6 b [19]; with 193-Mev deuterons, the values are respectively 1.3 and 1.2 b. Bismuth, lead, thalium, tantalum [20], and gold [21] will undergo fission with 190-Mev deuterons and 380-Mev α-particles, as will tungsten with 280-Mev deuterons [22]. The fission cross section for Bi with 190-Mev deuterons is 0.2 b [23]; for 220- to 340-Mev protons the corresponding values for U^{238}, U^{235}, and Th^{232} are 0.8, 1.0, and 0.35 b respectively. With 490-Mev protons, the value for U^{238} is 2 b, almost equal to the geometric cross section, but for bismuth at the same energy the cross section is only 0.07 b [24]. At such high energies, spallation reactions are superimposed upon the fission. Accelerated C^{12} (+6) ions can also be used to bring about the fission of U^{238}, with a cross section of the order of 0.1 b [25]. Other heavy ions behave similarly.

The fission of uranium by π^--mesons was first detected by Al-Salam [26], using photographic emulsions loaded with uranyl acetate, and was confirmed by John and Fry [27], who also observed the same reaction with μ^--mesons. Depending on the assumptions made as to the homogeneity of the emulsion, 37 or 18% of the pions and 15 or 7% of the muons captured by uranium cause nuclear fission. Perfilov, *et al.* [28], have studied the fission of uranium, bismuth, and tungsten by slow π^--mesons. The fission probability is estimated at between 30 to 40% for U, decreasing by a factor of about 10 for Bi, and with a further 10-fold reduction for W. The mass distribution is similar to that for fast-particle fission. These authors attribute the fission to nucleons with energies of about 70 Mev resulting from interaction with captured pions moving in a Bohr-type orbit. However, Sugarman and Haber [29], who investigated the fission of mercury by 122-Mev π^--mesons, estimate the effect of secondary neutrons and protons to be less than 1% in this case.

The 6.3-Mev γ-rays from the F^{19} (p, γ) Ne^{20} reaction are sufficiently energetic to bring about the fission of U^{238} and Th^{232}, with cross sections of 3.5 and 1.7 mb. The photofission thresholds for uranium, thorium, and plutonium are [30]:

Th^{232}	5.40 Mev,	U^{238}	5.08 Mev,
U^{233}	5.18,	Pu^{239}	5.31.
U^{235}	5.31,		

The near constancy of these values is quite remarkable. For each fissile nucleus, the thresholds quoted are almost equal to the sum of the threshold for neutron fission plus the binding energy of the neutron [31].

Bismuth undergoes fission with 85-Mev γ-rays [32] and gold with 315-Mev γ-rays [33]. Bernardini, Reitz, and Segrè [34] investigated the energy dependence of the cross section for the photofission of bismuth with γ-rays between 100 and 310 Mev and concluded that the primary process is the absorption of radiation to produce a π-meson; the subsequent capture of the pion by a nucleus causes fission.

Tantalum is the lightest element for which fission has been reported, but a number of spallation reactions involving elements of medium atomic number can also be regarded as fission processes. Batzel and Seaborg [35] have bombarded Cu, Ag, Br, Sn, and Ba with 340-Mev protons; in the case of Cu, the formation of Cl^{38} and Na^{24} was observed in addition to light species from the spallation process. The formation cross section for Na^{24} is only of the order of 10^{-8} b at 70 Mev, but this increases rapidly with increasing proton energy, reaching a value of 3 to 4×10^{-5} b at 340 Mev. These two nuclides can be considered either as being produced in spallation,

$$Cu^{63}\ (p,\ pn6\alpha)\ Cl^{38}, \tag{6–6}$$

$$Cu^{63}\ (p,\ p3n9\alpha)\ Na^{24}, \tag{6–7}$$

or as fission products,

$$Cu^{63} + p \rightarrow Cl^{38} + Al^{25} + n, \tag{6–8}$$

$$Cu^{63} + p \rightarrow Na^{24} + K^{39} + n. \tag{6–9}$$

The calculated thresholds for processes (6–6) and (6–7) are 170 and 110 Mev, whereas only about 50 Mev would be required for fission. Similar alternative routes can be postulated for the formation of Sc^{44} in the bombardment of bromine:

$$Br^{79}\ (p,\ pn7n7\alpha)\ Sc^{44} \qquad (180\ \text{Mev}),$$

$$Br^{79} + p \rightarrow Sc^{44} + P^{34} + 2n \qquad (80\ \text{Mev}),$$

and similarly for Na^{24}, Ga^{66} and Ga^{72} from the bombardment of tin, for Co^{61} from silver, and for Ga^{66} and Ga^{72} from barium. Batzel and

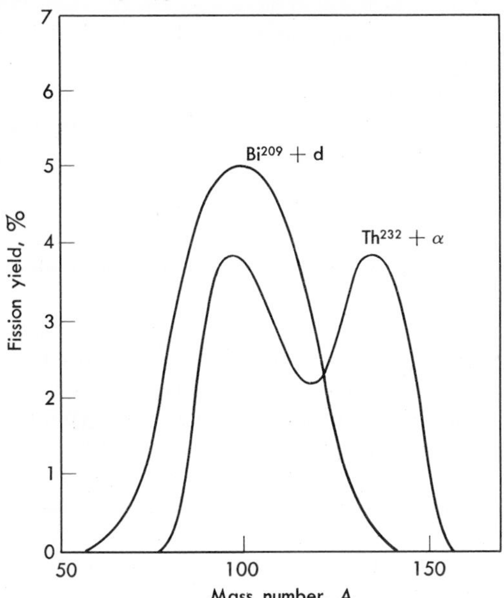

FIG. 6–3. Mass distribution of fission products form Th + α, and Bi + d.

Seaborg favor the fission reaction and believe that this process is possible for all nuclei, provided that sufficient energy is available and that this energy is not enough to cause spallation via intermediates such as α-particles, Be^7, or Li^8 (Section 5–3). We have already noted (Section 5–6) that Chackett considers that the ($Al^{27} + N^{14}$) compound nucleus can also undergo fission. Goeckerman and Perlman [23] have obtained the yield curve for the fission of Bi by 190-Mev deuterons, in which there is a maximum at $A = 100$ (Fig. 6–3); these authors suggest that the compound nucleus first evaporates a certain number of neutrons, forming, say, an excited Bi or Po nucleus:

$$Bi^{209}\ (d, 12n)\ \overset{*}{Po}{}^{199}, \tag{6–10}$$

and it is this latter nucleus which actually undergoes fission. An analogous mechanism involving the preliminary evaporation of 13 to 15 neutrons has been suggested by Kurtchatov [22] to explain results for the 280-Mev deuteron fission of tungsten.

Fission caused by high-energy particles generally differs from thermal neutron fission in the mass distribution of the products. With increasing energy, the distribution becomes more and more symmetrical, so that the two maxima in the curve flatten out, and finally only a single maximum is observed. Thus the yield curve for the fission products from Th^{232} with pile neutrons (mean energy $\sim$2.6 Mev) has the same asymmetric form as the curves shown in Fig. 6–1, but this asymmetry decreases if fission is induced by 11- to 16-Mev neutrons or 37-Mev α-particles [36, 37, 38.]

The distribution curve for the 200-Mev α-particle fission of bismuth shows only a single peak (Fig. 6–3), and the fission products are not identical with those formed in thermal neutron fission. The equal-displacement rule is no longer valid, and the neutron : proton ratio of the fragments tends to decrease. Equally, the number of neutrons emitted per fission increases with increasing incident energy; thus for U^{233}, the number of neutrons increases from 2.45 to 4.42 as the neutron energy increases from 0 to 15 Mev, and for U^{235} the corresponding values are 2.46 and 4.42. One result of these changes is that the heavy isotopes resulting from fission induced by high-energy particles are neutron deficient, and so decay either by positron emission or by electron capture.

The fission yield curve for the photofission of natural uranium with high-energy x-rays (up to about 300 Mev) can be divided into two components; one of these is asymmetric, with two peaks corresponding to low-energy fission, whereas the other component is symmetrical [39]. The average cross section for this latter mode of fission is 7 mb at energies between 16 and 300 Mev. The peak : valley ratio falls from 400 to 4 as the energy increases from 7 to 300 Mev. The average number of neutrons $\bar{\nu}$ emitted per event in fast neutron fission depends on the nature of the target. For uranium isotopes and for Pu^{239}, there is a linear increase in $\bar{\nu}$ with the incident energy of the projectile, the increase being approximately one unit per 8 Mev. At 15 Mev, $\bar{\nu}$ for U^{235} is 4.5, and for Pu^{239} it is 4.7 [40].

The symmetrical distribution in the case of Bi + D has been explained by Meitner [6] by assuming that after the evaporation of 12 neutrons, the compound nucleus does not have sufficient neutrons to form two fragments containing 50 and 82 neutrons, respectively. The tendency is therefore to split into two fragments of approximately equal mass, each of which has the same neutron excess relative to the 50-neutron closed shell.

If the energy of the incident particles is not too high (<14 Mev), the initial charge distribution is virtually the same for a number of fissile

TABLE 6–2

THE RATIO OF THE PROBABILITIES OF EVAPORATION OF 4 NEUTRONS, AND OF FISSION*

Target	Γ_n/Γ_f	Target	Γ_n/Γ_f
Ra^{226}	4.0	Pu^{238}	0.15
Th^{230}	0.48	Pu^{239}	0.20
Th^{232}	0.86	Pu^{240}	0.19
U^{233}	0.18	Pu^{242}	0.41
U^{234}	0.21	Am^{243}	0.52
U^{235}	0.27	Cm^{244}	0.15
U^{236}	0.32	Bk^{249}	0.36
U^{238}	0.58	Cf^{252}	0.27

* Taken from R. Vandenbosch and G. T. Seaborg, *Phys. Rev.*, **110,** 507 (1958).

nuclei, such as U^{235}, U^{233}, Th^{232}, and Pu^{233}. The half-lives of the delayed neutron emission appears to be the same for these various nuclides. The fraction of delayed neutrons in the fission of U^{238} is 2.9 times greater than for U^{235}.

It has already been noted (Section 5–3) that, at high energies, nuclear fission is in competition with spallation and with the evaporation of neutrons from the compound nucleus. The ratio of the probabilities of evaporation and of fission ($\Gamma_n/\bar{\Gamma}_f$) generally decreases with increasing proton number of the target; for a given value of Z, it varies with the mass number. Table 6–2 gives values of this ratio measured for various targets bombarded with ~40-Mev α-particles; Γ_n refers to the (α, 4n) reaction, and $\bar{\Gamma}_f$ is the average probability of fission of the compound nucleus after evaporating 1, 2, 3, or 4 neutrons.

6–3 Spontaneous fission. In addition to spontaneous α-disintegration, the very heavy nuclides also tend to undergo spontaneous fission, although for the natural radioelements the frequency of fission is much the smaller. The spontaneous fission of uranium was first observed by Petrjak and Flerov [41], who estimated the half-life for this process to be at least 10^{15} years. Some of the many subsequent measurements on rates of spontaneous fission are shown, together with the relative half-lives, in Table 6–3. In some cases, only the lower limits have been determined; for example, the spontaneous fission half-life for Ra^{226} is more than 10^{14} years, and for Th^{232} more than 10^{21} years.

It will be seen from the table that the half-life decreases with increasing atomic number, and that for a given Z there is often a decrease with in-

TABLE 6–3

SPONTANEOUS FISSION HALF-LIVES

Nuclide	Half-life, years	Nuclide	Half-life, years
U^{232}	$\sim 8 \times 10^{13}$	Cm^{248}	$\sim 4 \times 10^{6}$
U^{234}	1.6×10^{17}	Cm^{250}	$\sim 2 \times 10^{4}$
U^{235}	1.8×10^{17}	Bk^{249}	6×10^{8}
U^{236}	2×10^{16}	Cf^{246}	2.1×10^{3}
U^{238}	8×10^{15}	Cf^{248}	7×10^{3}
Pu^{236}	3.5×10^{9}	Cf^{249}	1.5×10^{9}
Pu^{238}	4.9×10^{10}	Cf^{250}	1.5×10^{4}
Pu^{239}	5.5×10^{15}	Cf^{252}	66
Pu^{240}	1.2×10^{11}	Cf^{254}	0.16
Pu^{242}	7.2×10^{10}	Es^{253}	7×10^{5}
Pu^{244}	2.5×10^{10}	Es^{254}	1.5×10^{5}
Cm^{240}	1.9×10^{6}	Fm^{254}	0.6
Cm^{242}	7.2×10^{6}	Fm^{255}	20
Cm^{244}	1.4×10^{7}	Fm^{256}	3×10^{-4}
Cm^{246}	2×10^{7}		

creasing mass. The ratio of the half-lives for spontaneous fission and α-emission is approximately 10^{-11} for U^{234}, and about 70 for Fm^{256}. As the mass increases, fission eventually becomes the predominant mode of decay; theory predicts that the spontaneous fission half-life is a continually decreasing function of Z^2/A (Section 6–4). At some sufficiently high value of this ratio, the fission half-life would become so small that the nucleus would split in half almost at the instant of formation, in a time of the order of 10^{-20} sec. This hypothetical nuclide of critical mass is sometimes referred to as *cosmium* [42]. It is found that when the half-lives are plotted against Z^2/A, the majority of the even-even nuclides fall on a straight line (Fig. 6–4) [43, 44, 45], but a number of fissile nuclei do not lie on this line, notably U^{234}, Pu^{244}, and Cm^{246}; the deviations increase with atomic number. Huizenga [46] has concluded from this that, contrary to the theory, a plot of the half-life against A passes through a maximum for constant Z. The rates of fission for odd nuclei are several orders of magnitude smaller than for the even-even nuclei, and a graph analogous to Fig. 6–4 would probably give two continuous curves.

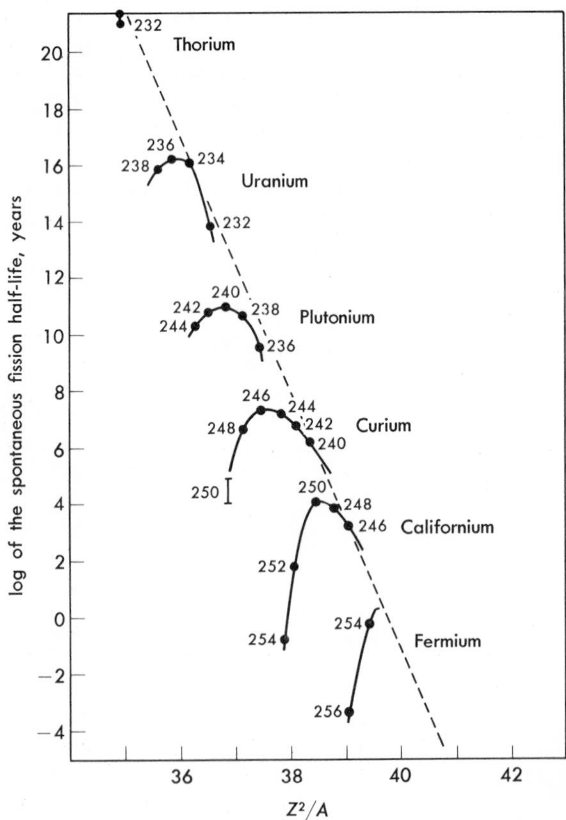

FIG. 6–4. Variation of half-life for spontaneous fission on Z^2/A for even-even nuclides. [After I. Halpern, *Ann. Rev. Nuclear Sci.*, **9**, 245 (1959)]

TABLE 6–4

AVERAGE NUMBER OF NEUTRONS ($\bar{\nu}$) EMITTED IN SPONTANEOUS FISSION*

Nuclide	$\bar{\nu}$	Nuclide	$\bar{\nu}$
Th^{230}	1.24	Pu^{242}	2.28
Th^{233}	1.36	Am^{242}	2.42
U^{234}	1.63	Cm^{242}	2.59
U^{236}	1.58	Cm^{244}	2.82
U^{238}	2.30	Bk^{249}	3.72
U^{239}	1.71	Cf^{246}	2.92
Np^{238}	1.67	Cf^{252}	3.84
Pu^{236}	2.17	Cf^{254}	3.90
Pu^{238}	2.28	Fm^{254}	4.05
Pu^{240}	2.23		

* Based on I. I. Bondarenko, *et al.*, *1958 Geneva Conference*, P. 2187, and I. Halpern, *Ann. Rev. Nuclear Sci.*, **9**, 245 (1959).

The average number $\bar{\nu}$ of neutrons emitted in the spontaneous fission of U^{238} is practically the same as in the thermal neutron fission of U^{235} (2.3 ± 0.20). Table 6–4 shows that with a few exceptions $\bar{\nu}$ increases with the mass of the nucleus. The mass [47] and charge [48] distribution curves are also very similar to those for the thermal neutron fission of U^{235}, and the same probably holds for the energy distribution in the spontaneous fission of Pu^{240} [49] and Cm^{242} [50].

6–4 The theory of nuclear fission. It has already been shown (Section 3–4) that the binding energy per nucleon is smaller for heavy nuclei than for those of medium mass. The Weizsäcker equation explains this as being the result of the increase in the electrostatic repulsion with increasing atomic number. It therefore follows that the division of a heavy nucleus of mass ${}_ZM^A$ into two nuclei of equal mass is an exoergic reaction, as can be proven by calculating the energy balance of the process, given by

$$E_f = 931\,({}_ZM^A - 2\,{}_{Z/2}M^{A/2}). \qquad (6\text{–}11)$$

A graph of E_f against A cuts the axis at $A = 83$, and the fission of all nuclei with masses greater than this is energetically possible. The reason for the stability of nuclides with masses below 238 to spontaneous fission is that fission requires an activation energy. The two fission fragments are positively charged and exert an electrostatic repulsion upon each other; if the corresponding potential energy is E_c, it can be shown from a potential energy diagram that the barrier for symmetrical fission is $E_c - E_f$. The variation of E_c with A is given schematically in Fig. 6–5. For nuclei with a mass of about 100, the difference $(E_c - E_f)$ is of the order of 50 Mev, so that this is the activation energy for symmetrical fission in this mass region. For heavy nuclei such as Th^{232}, U^{238}, or Pu^{239},

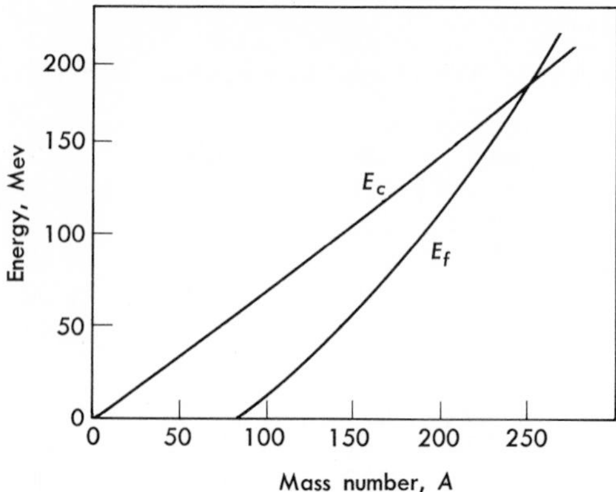

FIG. 6–5. Change of coulombic energy E_c and energy of fission E_f with mass number.

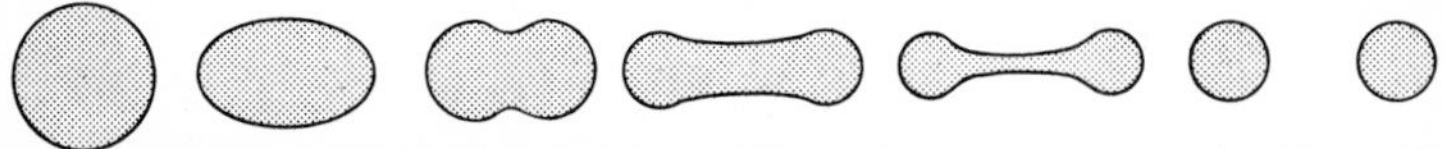

FIG. 6–6. Schematic representation of the fission of a nuclear "droplet."

$E_c - E_f$ is only 5 to 6 Mev, and in fact the threshold for photofission is of this order of magnitude, as is the energy required for fast neutron fission (threshold plus binding energy) (Section 6–2). For $A \approx 250$, $E_c \leq E_f$, and spontaneous fission becomes very rapid (Table 6–3).

Shortly after the discovery of fission, Meitner and Frisch [52] suggested that the liquid-drop model of the nucleus could be used to explain this process. The theory was developed quantitatively by Bohr and Wheeler [53] and by Frenkel [54]. A stable liquid drop will break in two if it is subjected to mechanical vibrations of sufficient amplitude (Fig. 6–6), and in the same way a spherical nucleus should undergo deformation or elongation as a result of excitation. For heavy nuclei (i.e., high Z) the charge, which is initially uniformly distributed, will tend to move toward regions of greatest curvature to reduce the repulsive energy, but the cohesive energy of the surface [i.e., the β-term in Eq. (3–10)] will fall off even more rapidly. This argument suggests then that the drop will pass through the successive stages shown in Fig. 6–6 and will finally end up by breaking into two fragments.

Fission therefore depends on the surface energy $E = 4\pi r_0^2 A^{2/3}\sigma$, and on the coulombic energy $E = \frac{3}{5}(Z/e)^2/r_0 A^{1/3}$, where r_0 is the elementary nuclear radius [Eq. (3–4)] and σ is the surface energy per cm^2. Calculations by Bohr and Wheeler show that the energy threshold for fission is given by

$$E_s = 8\pi\left(\frac{A}{2}\right)^{2/3} r_0^2\sigma - 4\pi A^{2/3} r_0^2\sigma + 1.7\,\frac{(Ze/2)^2}{(A/2)^{1/3} r_0} - \frac{3}{5}\,\frac{(Ze)^2}{A^{1/3} r_0}, \quad (6\text{–}12)$$

or,

$$\frac{E_s}{4\pi A^{2/3} r_0^2 \sigma} = 0.260 - 0.065 \frac{Z^2}{A} \cdot \frac{e^2/r_0}{4\pi r_0^2 \sigma} \cdot \qquad (6\text{–}13)$$

It follows from this that probability of a nucleus undergoing fission depends on the ratio Z^2/A. From this theory, the value of Z^2/A for the instantaneously spontaneous fissile hypothetical nucleus cosmium is given by

$$(Z^2/A)_{\text{crit}} = 10\left(\frac{4\pi}{3}\right) r_0 \frac{\sigma}{e^2} = 45, \qquad (6\text{–}14)$$

where $r_0 = 1.5 \times 10^{-13}$ cm and $4\pi r_0^2 \sigma = 13$ Mev. This is in approximate agreement with the value extrapolated from the straight line in Fig. 6–4, which gives a half-life of a few seconds for spontaneous fission for $Z^2/A \approx 43$. The spontaneous fission of nuclei with $Z^2/A < 45$ is attributed to a tunneling effect analogous to that invoked in the theory of α-disintegration (Section 4–5).

Furthermore, this theory explains the fact that U^{235}, and nuclides with an odd number of neutrons, will in general undergo fission more readily with thermal neutrons than U^{238} or other nuclides with even N. The calculated activation energies of 6.8 and 7.1 Mev for the compound nuclei U^{236} and U^{239} are not very different; however, the excitation energy due to the capture of a neutron by U^{235} is about 6.5 Mev, which is almost sufficient to bring about fission, but for U^{238} it is only 4.9 Mev. The difference in the behavior of the two isotopes is then attributed mainly to the pairing term (in δ) in Eq. (3–10), the U^{236} compound nucleus being even-even and U^{239} even-odd.

The Bohr and Wheeler theory is based on a spherical nuclear droplet, which is at best only an approximation, and other approximations are introduced for mathematical convenience. Frenkel and Metropolis [55] have used an electronic calculating machine to evaluate the fission thresholds more precisely from an equation derived from Eqs. (6–13) and (6–14), which gives E_s as a function of the ratio $(Z^2/A)/(Z^2/A)_{\text{crit}}$. The values found are not very different from those calculated directly from the Bohr-Wheeler theory, and do not always agree satisfactorily with experimental results. Thus the Frenkel-Metropolis treatment predicts a threshold for Th^{229} in the region of 1 Mev, whereas in fact this nuclide is already fissile with thermal neutrons with a cross section of ~45 b. Another drawback is that the constancy of the photofission threshold for several nuclides (Section 6–2) implies that Z and A have less influence on fission probability than this theory predicts. If the excitation energy E_f necessary to bring about fission is assumed to be approximately constant ($\approx$5.3 Mev) for all nuclides with Z between 88 and 96, then thermal neutron fission can be shown to depend on the difference $E_n - E_f$, where E_n is the binding energy of the prompt neutron. If this difference is negative, the nuclide is not fissile; if it is positive, fission will nearly always take place.

The asymmetric nature of the fission process is another difficult feature for this theory, which in fact predicts a rather greater probability for symmetrical fission. Frenkel [56] has tried to explain this anomaly by assuming a tunneling effect superimposed on the fission process; the probability of penetration through the barrier would be greater for unequal masses, for which there is a smaller reduced mass. Hill and Wheeler [42] have criticized this interpretation on the grounds that it would give a fission yield dependence on energy very different from that actually observed. These authors do not believe that the difficulty can be overcome by considering shell structure, since the compound nucleus cannot be affected by the structure of nuclides as yet unformed, and the absence of any favored distribution for even-even or even-odd products is taken as proof of this. They rather suggest that small initial asymmetries invariably associated with the transition state of the compound nucleus, which the collective model relates to the various modes of capillary oscillation, could be amplified by subsequent deformations, as would be predicted from classical hydrodynamics.

The greater deformation of nuclides of the same Z but greater mass could also explain some of the deviations from the Z^2/A dependence (Fig. 6–4). Ghiorso [57] has suggested that this is connected with a subshell of neutrons at $N = 152$ in the heaviest nuclei (Section 5–6). Several other authors have tried to explain the asymmetry in low-energy fission processes and its disappearance at higher energies by invoking the liquid-drop model, shell structure, or the statistical distribution of the energy levels available at the instant of fission [58].

6–5 Chain reactions. We have seen that the slow-neutron fission of U^{235} is accompanied by the emission of (on the average) 2.5 neutrons. These neutrons can of course bring about further fissions in their turn, either immediately or after some slowing down process, so that the number of neutrons multiplies and the overall rate of the process continually increases. This then is a genuine chain reaction, which can very rapidly result in the explosive disappearance of the uranium present, since an enormous amount of energy is liberated in each fission.

Several factors, however, serve to prevent the propagation of the chain in natural uranium. One important factor is that the cross section for the fission of U^{235} by fast neutrons is not very large. In addition, this nuclide is only 1/140th part of natural uranium, whose principal component (U^{238}) is fissile only with fast neutrons, with a relatively small cross section; for 2-Mev neutrons, the fission cross section is only 0.01 b, while that for elastic scattering is 4 b. Slow neutrons, on the other hand, are captured by U^{238} to give U^{239}, and there is a strong resonance at neutron energies of about 6 ev. Other elements present (or deliberately added) and the fission products formed may capture neutrons and so play their part in preventing the propagation of the chain. Finally, a certain number of neutrons inevitably escapes from the surface. The importance of these various factors can be modified to some extent by choosing appropriate conditions, so that the growth of the chain reaction can be controlled either to give a stationary state, as in a nuclear reactor, or to proceed explosively, as in an atomic bomb.

The ratio between the number of neutrons available for fission in two successive generations is called the *multiplication factor k;* the condition necessary for the maintenance of the chain is obviously $k = 1$. If $k > 1$, the number of neutrons increases in each generation and the chain is said to be *divergent*, which implies the system runs the risk of becoming explosive. If, on the other hand, $k < 1$, the chain is *convergent*, and reaction ceases after a limited number of generations.

The cross section for the thermal neutron fission of natural uranium is 4.18 b, and that for radiative capture 3.5 b. The total cross section is therefore 7.68 b, and the *average number of fast neutrons emitted per thermal neutron captured* by uranium is simply

$$\eta = \frac{2.5 \times 4.18}{7.68} = 1.36,$$

where 2.5 ($= \bar{\nu}$) is the average number of neutrons emitted in U^{235} fission. For pure U^{235}, $\eta = 2.08$, and for Pu^{239}, $\eta = 2.03$ [59]. A very small fraction of these fast neutrons are captured by U^{238} before thermalization and so cause the fission of this isotope. Let ϵ be the ratio between the total number of neutrons produced in fission and the number arising from thermal fission alone; ϵ is then the *fast-fission factor* and is slightly greater than 1. Further, let p be the fraction of neutrons thermalized before capture and f be the thermal utilization factor, which is the ratio between the number of thermal neutrons absorbed in the uranium and the total number absorbed in the whole system (i.e., by the uranium, the walls, impurities, etc.). It follows that for each thermal neutron absorbed by uranium in a generation there will be $\eta\epsilon pf$ neutrons available for the following generation. The product of these four factors (*the four-factor formula*) is in fact the multiplication factor k;

$$k = \eta\epsilon pf. \tag{6–15}$$

The value of η and ϵ can be increased by increasing the U^{235}/U^{238} ratio (i.e., by using uranium enriched in U^{235}) or alternatively, by substituting plutonium for uranium. It is easier to modify p and f by incorporating substances known as *moderators* into the assembly; these slow down fast neutrons by elastic collisions, without absorbing any appreciable number, so that neutron capture by U^{238} is markedly reduced. Heavy water, graphite, and beryllium are the most efficient materials for this purpose; it will be seen later that the number of collisions necessary to thermalize fast neutrons falls off rapidly with the atomic mass of the moderator (Section 11–10). Ordinary water, with its two protons which can capture neutrons, is considerably less desirable; the thermal neutron scattering cross section of the proton is 50 b, and the capture cross section is 0.31 b, whereas for deuterium, the corresponding values are 7 b and 0.00032 b. The presence of certain impurities such as boron in even trace quantities can cause a large decrease in the value of f, and consequently of k.

Equation (6–15) is strictly valid only for an infinite mass of fissile material or for any system in which loss of neutrons by escape from the surface can be neglected. With increasing mass, the loss of neutrons by escape, which is proportional to the surface area, is more than compensated for by the increase in the number of neutrons produced in the bulk, and for a given system, one reaches a critical mass for which the effective multiplication factor k_{eff} becomes equal to 1;

$$k_{\text{eff}} = k(1 - P), \tag{6–16}$$

where P is the probability of escape from the surface. In order to reduce the probability of escape, and hence to reduce the critical dimensions, the system is surrounded with a neutron reflector. Any material which acts as a moderator can equally well serve as a reflector (e.g., graphite, BeO, D_2O).

If $k_{\text{eff}} > 1$, the system is supercritical; alternatively for $k_{\text{eff}} < 1$, it is subcritical and the neutron density tends to decrease. For natural uranium, the critical mass is of the order of a few tons with heavy water, and about 10 times this with graphite. For pure U^{235}, the critical mass is only 2 to 3 kg.

6–6 The operation of thermal reactors. From what has just been said, the essential requisites for a natural uranium reactor are fissile material, which may be the metal or its oxide UO_2, a moderator, and a reflector. In the earliest reactors, the latter were in the form of graphite blocks, alternated with blocks or rods of metal. This method of building up the structure lead to the use of the name "atomic pile."

The proportions and dimensions of the pile are calculated so as to give a constant neutron density, so that $k_{\text{eff}} = 1$. In practice, a certain amount of fluctuation is inevitable, and in order to have a working margin of security, piles are constructed with k_{eff} a few percent greater than 1 (usually up to about 20%). The chain is prevented from becoming divergent by arranging control rods of materials such as boron steel, cadmium steel, or hafnium in the system. Since these three elements have very high cross sections for thermal neutron capture, they can quickly reduce the number of available neutrons. This control is carried out by means of some automatic arrangement; for example, the rods may be held in position above the pile by an electromagnet, so that when the multiplication factor exceeds a certain fixed value, the current activating the magnet is automatically cut off and the rods drop into the pile. Such an arrangement would not, however, be efficient if all the fission neutrons were emitted simultaneously. The average life τ of the great majority of the neutrons (i.e., the average interval between two successive generations) is in fact very small, being of the order of 0.001 sec in a heavy-water pile. Now the number of neutrons in the chain has an exponential time dependence given by

$$n = n_0 e^{rt/\tau}, \tag{6–17}$$

where r $(= k_{\text{eff}} - 1)$ is the so-called pile reactivity. The *time constant* of the pile τ/r is consequently extremely small even for low reactivities; thus for a heavy-water moderated reactor ($\tau = 0.01$ sec) $r = 0.005$, the number of neutrons increases by a factor of $e^5 = 150$ after $t = 1$ sec.

It must be remembered, however, that about 0.75% of the neutrons are from delayed emissions, with half-lives for the most part of the order of tens of seconds. This brings the average life τ up to about 0.1 sec. The dimensions of the pile are chosen so that it may be critical in terms of the whole neutron flux, and subcritical only for the prompt neutrons. Such a reactor, whose time constant is now of the order of 30 sec, has a certain inertia which makes it much easier to control. The reactivity is often quoted in units "per hundred thousand"; a reactivity of 100 on this scale therefore implies $r = 0.001$. The calculation of the critical dimensions of a reactor and the prediction of its behavior, which come under the heading of reactor kinetic theory, requires an exact knowledge of the properties of neutrons and especially of the laws which govern their collision, absorption, and diffusion in the materials involved, and of the cross sections and lifetimes of the relevent processes, etc. [50]. A discussion of the fundamental basis of these phenomena is to be found in Chapter 11.

Reactors are characterized by their power, that is to say by the number of fissions occurring in unit time. Each fission releases about 200 Mev of energy, equivalent to 3.2×10^{-4} erg, or 3.2×10^{-11} watts·sec, so that 3.1×10^{13} fissions/sec produce 1 kw of power. If, under the working conditions, n neutrons are produced per cubic centimeter, with an average velocity of v cm·sec^{-1}, the flux is nv neutrons per square centimeter per second. The flux Φ is related to A, the total number of fissions per unit time, by the relation

$$A = N\sigma\Phi V, \tag{6-18}$$

where σ is the fission cross section, N the number of fissile atoms per cubic centimeter, and V the volume of the reactor. The power P (in kw) is therefore

$$P = \frac{\sigma N\Phi V}{3.1 \times 10^{13}}\cdot \tag{6-19}$$

The average flux in a uranium pile working at 1000 kw/ton is generally about 3×10^{12} n·cm^{-2}·sec^{-1}. The maximum flux at the center of the pile is about three times higher [61]. The *integrated flux, nvt*, is the total number of neutrons received per square centimeter by a substance exposed to a flux nv for a time t.

For a given system, both the power and the neutron density increase with the reactivity. In principle, the power can be increased indefinitely, but in practice it is limited in most cases by the negative temperature coefficient of the reactivity, so that the reactivity decreases as the temperature rises. An increase in the reactivity and in the power therefore tends to decrease the divergence of the chain, and one result of this property is that reactors are to some extent self-controlling. There is therefore no risk of an explosion in a reactor which gets out of control, but the uranium and other materials will break up, melt, or undergo chemical reaction.

The heat produced by the reactor must in any case be dissipated in some way in order to maintain the pile characteristics, so that piles working at more than about 100 kw require some sort of cooling system. For thermal reactors, this generally involves circulating light or heavy water or some gas under pressure. Uranium metal is chemically rather reactive, and cannot be cooled directly. It is therefore protected by a metallic casing or "can," and for this purpose a metal is required which is resistant to corrosion, and at the same time has a negligible neutron-capture cross section. Aluminum is widely used for this in medium- or low-power reactors.

Another factor which brings about a decrease in the reactivity is the fact that a number of nuclides produced in significant yields in fission, especially Xe^{135} and Sm^{149}, have very high capture cross sections and so reduce the number of thermal neutrons available for chain propagation. In a natural-uranium graphite-moderated pile, the neutron balance is normally the following [62]: 2.5 neutrons are produced for each U^{235} fission (2.46 + 0.06 from U^{238}). These are consumed in the following way:

In the $U^{238} \rightarrow Np^{239} \rightarrow Pu^{239}$ process:	0.8
In the $U^{235} \rightarrow U^{236}$ process (i.e., capture to give the β-emitting nuclide):	0.2
Absorption in the moderator:	0.30
Absorption in the constructional materials:	0.05
Lost from the system by escape through the walls:	0.09
Chain propagation, plus marginal factors:	1.08
Total	2.52

The production of Pu^{239} contributes to an extension of the working life of the pile. If each U^{235} fission leads to 0.8 ($= \gamma$) Pu fissions, then the total number of fissions per atom of U^{235} is

$$1 + \gamma + \gamma^2 + \gamma^3 + \cdots + \gamma^n = \frac{1}{1 - \gamma} = 5, \tag{6–20}$$

since the 0.8 atoms of plutonium give rise in their turn to further $(0.8)^2$ plutonium atoms, and so on. One result of this is that U^{238} becomes, indirectly, fissile by slow neutrons. Since natural uranium contains only 0.7% of U^{235}, the maximum fuel burnup in a thermal reactor is 3.5%. Other factors, however, serve to alter the pile characteristics and so slow it down before the fuel is consumed; these include deterioration and deformation of the uranium and of the constructional materials as a result of the prolonged exposure to the intense radiations (Section 15–2), the variation of the pile characteristics due to the accumulation of fission products, etc.

The life of a reactor can be extended by periodically replacing the uranium rods which have been used up. The used rods are left for some time to allow the intense short-lived activities to decay away, and then chemically treated to extract plutonium and the fission products. These operations are carried out in some remote-control device. Remote control is also necessary for the innumerable physical measurements connected with the operation and control of a reactor, such as measurement of the power by

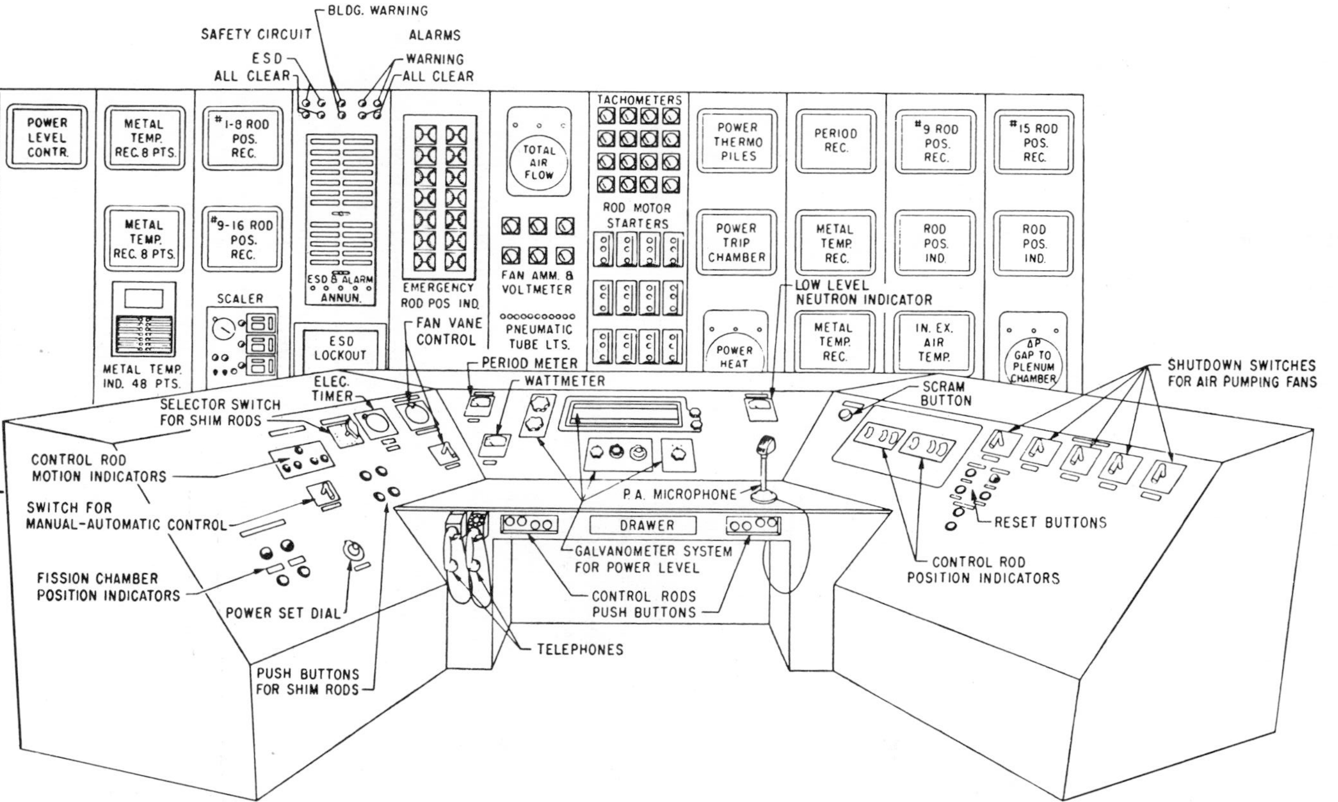

FIG. 6–7. Console and instrument panels of the Brookhaven air-cooled, graphite-moderated reactor. [Reproduced by permission from S. Glasstone, *Principles of Nuclear Reactor Engineering*, Van Nostrand, Inc., Princeton, N. J., 1955.]

means of the thermal neutron flux, measurement of the reactivity by the time constant of the pile, the detection of radioactive contaminents in the cooling fluids, the measurement of the pressure and rate of flow of this fluid, the adjustment of the boron or cadmium rods, the measurement of the temperature, the determination of the level in heavy-water piles, etc. [63]. The layout of the control room of a typical experimental reactor, that at the Brookhaven National Laboratory, is shown in Fig. 6–7.

Finally it must be noted that in order to give efficient radiation protection to the operating personnel, piles are surrounded by a thick wall of concrete and iron. Three feet of concrete reduces the radiation intensity by a factor of about 10^3.

6–7 The characteristics of some thermal reactors.* The first American pile (CP-1), constructed by Fermi and his co-workers at the University of Chicago, became divergent on December 2, 1942; the fuel consisted of 6 tons of metallic uranium and 40 tons of UO_2, with 385 tons of graphite as moderator, and the control rods were of cadmium-clad bronze. A shield of concrete some 1.5 m thick surrounded the pile, which was rectangular in shape, 9 m on the side and 6 m high. The power reached 100 w and the average thermal neutron flux was 4×10^6 n·cm^{-2}·sec^{-1}. The pile was dismantled after working for some months and transported to the Argonne National Laboratory, where 6 tons of uranium + UO_2 and 87 tons of graphite were added; it then functioned at 2 kw, with a flux of 10^8 n·cm^{-2}·sec^{-1} (CP-2).

Another reactor (CP-3) was constructed at Argonne in 1944 from 3 tons of uranium, with 6.5 tons of heavy water as moderator; 120 rods of uranium metal sheathed in aluminum dipped into this D_2O. The reflector was of graphite, and the reactor was surrounded by a lead-cadmium alloy screen and a concrete wall. Cooling was provided by circulating the heavy water. The power was 300 kw and the flux 5×10^{11} n·cm^{-2}·sec^{-1}. This reactor was subsequently modified in 1950 by the substitution of enriched uranium for natural uranium (CP-3′).

The first powerful reactor working with ordinary uranium (10 tons of metal) and moderated by heavy water (17 tons) seems to have been the NRX reactor at Chalk River in Canada. The water also acts as a coolant. This reactor, which became critical in 1947, had a power of 30,000 kw and a flux of 2×10^{13} n·cm^{-2}·sec^{-1}; it was completely modified in 1952 following an accident, and the power raised to 40,000 kw and the maximum flux to 7×10^{13} n·cm^{-2}·sec^{-1}. More powerful still are the Hanford reactors, which also use uranium metal and graphite. Details of their construction and working have been kept secret, but they are known to be designed for plutonium production and to have a power of (at least) several hundred thousand kilowatts. The first medium-power reactor of the U.S.S.R. Academy of Sciences also uses uranium metal (45 tons) and graphite as moderator and reflector. A second heavy-water moderated reactor (5000 kw) is designed for the study of reactor physics and of beams of neutrons.

---

* Based largely on papers presented at the 1955 Geneva Conference.

In the BEPO pile at Harwell, England, 40 tons of uranium metal are distributed in 900 channels of the graphite moderator; the total weight of the graphite reflector is 850 tons. Cooling is by the circulation of air, the temperature of the exit gas being 80°C. The biological shield consists of 3000 tons of concrete and 6000 tons of steel. A small part of the power (6000 kw) is recovered and used for heating the surrounding buildings. The Norwegian pile JEEP contains 2.2 tons of uranium metal, seven tons of D_2O, and more than 40 tons of graphite; its power is 350 kw and the flux 10^{12} n/cm^2·sec. This reactor is cooled by circulating heavy water in a closed circuit. The French pile at Chatillon was originally of UO_2 and heavy water; it required no cooling because of its low power (only a few kilowatts, hence its name ZOE—zero energy, uranium oxide, heavy water, or in French, Zéro énergie, Oxyde d'urane, Eau lourde). Subsequent improvements have included the replacement of the uranium oxide by 1.9 tons of uranium metal and the installation of a cooling system involving the circulation of heavy water in a closed system (4.5 tons D_2O).

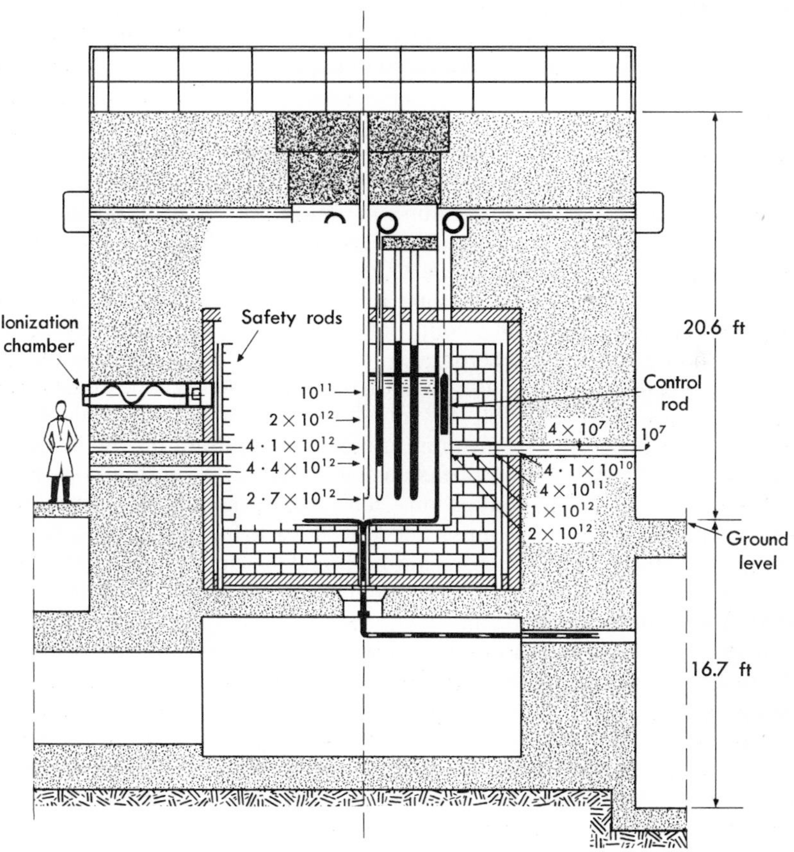

Fig. 6–8. The layout of the P-2 reactor at Saclay. (The figures in the center show the neutron flux at reduced power.)

The reflector is of graphite. The current power is some 150 kw, which can be increased; the flux in the axial channel is 7×10^9 n/cm^2·sec·kw, so that the total flux is about 10^{12} n·cm^{-2}·sec^{-1}. The flux in the thermal column let into the protective concrete wall, perpendicular to the axial channel, is 4×10^{11} n·cm^{-2}·sec^{-1}.

The P-2 pile at Saclay also works with uranium metal (approximately 3 tons) and heavy water contained in an aluminum tank some 2 m in diameter and 2.5 m high. Aluminum sheaths protect 136 rods of uranium, 2.8 cm in diameter and 2.15 m long, which dip into the heavy water which partly fills the tank. Around and below this is the graphite reflector, 90 cm thick (57 tons). This assembly is placed in the upper chamber of a concrete block, the dimensions of the chamber being $4.06 \times 9.06 \times 3.75$ m^3; the thickness of the lateral walls is 2.25 m. The inside of the shield is covered with blocks of cast iron (Fig. 6–8). Cooling is carried out by circulating carbon dioxide along the length of the rods at 8 atm pressure, the exit temperature of the gas being 130°C. Control rods of cadmium provide the safety factor in the working of the pile. The power is 2400 kw and the flux in the axial channel 8×10^{12} n·cm^{-2}·sec^{-1}. The biological shield is pierced by 37 vertical channels and 25 horizontal ones which are used for control purposes and for the irradiation of materials.

6–8 Other types of reactors. Apart from their power, reactors are classified on the basis of (a) the velocity of the neutrons which propagate the chain (i.e., slow, fast, or intermediate), (b) the nature of the fuel (natural uranium, enriched uranium, or plutonium), (c) the physical condition of the fuel (*heterogeneous*, as in those just described, or *homogeneous*), (d) the purpose for which the reactor is designed, such as plutonium production, high neutron flux, isotope or power production, the study of materials and pile operating conditions, the training of personnel, etc. (*experimental* or research reactor).

Thermal reactors which use natural uranium fuel can be regarded as *converters* since they are able to transform U^{238} into the fissile Pu^{239}. With enriched uranium, or uranium mixed with plutonium, the chain can be maintained by the action of fast neutrons on U^{238}, with a consequent increase in the U $\rightarrow$ Pu conversion. The use of moderators is no longer necessary, and the critical mass is reduced to a few kilograms, but the cooling of such powerful reactors can no longer be achieved by the normal methods and it may be necessary to use liquid metals (sodium, alkali metal alloys, mercury, or bismuth).

An important type of fast reactor, which could well have considerable economic importance in the peaceful uses of atomic energy, is the self-generating or "*breeder*" reactor. The aim is to balance the "neutron economy" in such a way as to get a conversion factor greater than 1, so that the fissile material produced compensates, or more than compensates, for the fissile material used up. For example, using plutonium as fuel, the number of neutrons emitted per fission $\bar{\nu} = 2.9$; in the absence of a moderator, and using natural uranium or U^{238} as a reflector, this should give under ideal conditions 1.9 neutrons for the $U^{238} \rightarrow Np^{239} \rightarrow Pu^{239}$ transmutation, the third neutron being required for the propagation of the chain. In practice, the conversion factor is defined not by $\bar{\nu}$ but by η, the number of fast neutrons produced per neutron absorbed in the *fuel*. For the thermal neutron fission of U^{235} or Pu^{239}, η is almost 2 [59], so that the gain in breeding in thermal reactors is virtually zero. If U^{233} is used as fuel and Th^{232} as "fertile material," one finds $\eta = 2.3$ with thermal neutrons. This uranium isotope does not occur naturally, but is formed by neutron capture on Th^{232}:

$$Th^{232} \xrightarrow{(n,\,\gamma)} Th^{233} \xrightarrow{\beta-} Pa^{233} \xrightarrow{\beta-} U^{233}.$$

With this type of breeder reactor, a gain of 10 to 15% should be possible, and Th could then be reasonably regarded as a nuclear fuel. Some American fast reactors [59] have η significantly greater than 2 (2.23 for U^{235}, 2.7 for Pu^{239}) so that the conversion factor should be appreciably greater than unity. However, physical and radiochemical measurement of Pu production in the Idaho breeder reactor (1400 kw) have so far (1956) given conversion factors between 0.99 and 1.02 [64]. It seems, therefore, that the parasitic absorption of neutrons by the constructional materials, the cooling liquid, and fission products is very important. This pile (EBR 1) "burns" U^{235} at 350°C and is cooled by a sodium-potassium alloy; the heat carried away by the coolant is utilized for producing steam at 230°C, which drives a turbine giving some 200 kw of electricity.

In contrast with these results, Holmes, *et al.* [65, 66] have given the conversion factor of the British fast reactor ZEPHYR as 2.1 ± 0.2 at zero power (1 to 2 w). This very favorable result could be due to a very small capture : fission ratio, plus a large U^{238} contribution to the fission; these factors are probably the result of a favorable neutron spectrum [67]. The plutonium core of this reactor, 15 cm in diameter and 15 cm high is surrounded by an envelope of uranium. Control is achieved by using rods of this metal placed in the vertical channels. This reactor has no cooling and practically no protective shield. To date there seem to have been no reactors based on neutrons slowed down to energies above thermal.

A reactor using enriched uranium may also work as a thermal reactor, so that ordinary water will suffice for cooling. One example is the experimental reactor at the U.S.S.R. Academy of Sciences; the fuel (3.5 kg of uranium containing 10% U^{235}) is in the form of rods (24 × 16 elements) protected by aluminum or some aluminum alloy. The rods dip into an aluminum tank filled with ordinary water which serves both as a moderator-reflector and as coolant. The entrance temperature of this water is 30°C, and is not more than 31°C at the exit. The safety and control rods are of boron carbide, and the flux is 2×10^{12} n·cm^{-2}·sec^{-1}.

Another reactor (RFT), working in the same Academy since 1952, uses 15% enriched uranium, with graphite and ordinary water as moderator. The water circulates under an initial pressure of 12 atm, the entrance temperature being 20 to 30°C, rising to 50 to 65°C at the exit; the temperature of the graphite may reach 470°C. This reactor has a power of 10,000 kw, and a maximum flux at the center of 2×10^{14} n·cm^{-2}·sec^{-1}.

An interesting reactor using enriched uranium (E 443) has been constructed in the United Kingdom [68]. The core consists of 2.5 kg of uranium, in the form of an aluminum alloy, placed in the center of an aluminum tank. Heavy water circulates through this for cooling purposes, and also acts as a reflector for the upper part. A 60-cm layer of graphite, contained in a steel tank under an atmosphere of helium, serves as reflector for the bottom and the sides. The design power is 10,000 kw, and the flux 10^{14} n·cm^{-2}·sec^{-1}. This reactor should be capable of producing 30,000 curies of high specific activity Co^{60} per annum.

There are several small-sized reactors, moderated and cooled by ordinary water, which are working or under construction [69, 70] in the United States, and are used for materials testing. These have extremely high specific powers (i.e., kw/gm) and fluxes greater than 10^{14} n·cm^{-2}·sec^{-1}. Highly enriched uranium alloyed with aluminum is sandwiched between aluminum plates; the active core, $40 \times 70 \times 60$ cm in dimension, consists of 45 elements containing 10 sandwiches each. Between 3 and 4 kg of uranium are used, with layers of beryllium and graphite around the core as reflectors; water under pressure circulates between the elements and through holes in the beryllium. The MTR reactor at Arco, Idaho, is of this type, and has a power of 30,000 kw, a flux of 10^{14} fast neutrons/cm^2·sec, and a slow neutron flux which is twice as high. A similar reactor at Oak Ridge (LITR) has a working power of 3000 kw and a maximum flux of 4×10^{13} n·cm^{-2}·sec^{-1}.

A variant of this type is the so-called swimming-pool reactor [71]. The fuel assembly, 3 to 3.5 kg of 90% enriched U, is placed at the bottom of a large pool (100 to 200 cubic yards) containing ordinary water which acts as moderator, reflector, coolant, and partial protection. A reactor of this design has been operating at Oak Ridge since 1951, at a power of 100 kw, and several others are under construction. A 100 kw swimming-pool reactor was exhibited by the United States Government at the International Conference for the Peaceful Uses of Atomic Energy held at Geneva in 1955. The core of this reactor consisted of 15.25 kg of uranium, of which 3.66 kg was U^{235}, and 74 kg of aluminum. The water in the pool constantly gives off a blue color as the result of the absorption of radiation from the active material (Cerenkov radiation, see Section 11–6).

All the reactors considered so far are heterogeneous, but an increasing number of homogeneous reactors are being constructed using enriched uranium, since these offer several advantages. In particular, they have a smaller volume and give intense neutron fluxes, since, according to Eq. (6–19), the flux is proportional to the power per unit volume or unit mass, and a homogeneous reactor gives a relatively high power for a small volume.

From this point of view, reactors moderated with heavy water have many advantages over those moderated with graphite, since the latter require a much greater mass. The first homogeneous reactor LOPO (low-power water boiler) was constructed at Los Alamos, New Mexico, in 1954 [72, 73, 74]; 15 liters of solution containing 580 gm of U^{235} and 3378 gm of U^{238} as uranyl sulfate are held in a stainless-steel sphere. The reflector is a mixture of graphite and BeO. The power of this reactor is only

0.05 w, but the same laboratory has a second boiling-water reactor (SUPO) using 870 gm of U^{235} and 5341 gm of U^{238} as uranyl nitrate, which has a maximum power of 45 kw and a flux in the neighborhood of 10^{13} n·cm^{-2}·sec^{-1}. The cooling water also acts as moderator; the temperature of the 12.7 liters of solution is 75°C. Similar reactors have been set up at the University of North Carolina (power 10 kw) and by the North American Aviation Corporation (1 to 1500 w). This latter organization has also constructed a homogeneous solid reactor, using an intimate mixture of uranium powder and graphite [75] with a graphite reflector and a heavy-water cooling system. This reactor works at 135 kw and 204°C.

The total number of reactors operating throughout the world in August 1955 has been estimated at between 40 and 50, and this figure had reached or exceeded 400 by the end of 1960.

6-9 The utilization of the energy of the fission process. We have already seen that enormous quantities of energy are released in the fission process. The "combustion" of one gram of natural uranium by slow neutrons, in other words the total fission of the U^{235} alone, would release 160 kwh. The total fast-neutron fission of a gram of uranium in a breeder reactor with a 50% yield would give about 70 times this amount (11,250 kwh), equivalent to the heat obtained by the combustion of 1.4 tons of coal. The total world reserves of uranium are still not known completely, but an estimated value is 25 million tons, corresponding to 2.5×10^{17} kwh, representing a potential energy at least 500 times greater than that available from the world's known mineral resources of coal and oil. In addition to this, the fission of thorium, which is three times more abundant than uranium, will obviously also be of great potential use when the operation of breeder reactors, or some other more efficient technique, has been perfected.

The conversion of the heat given off into some other form of energy, such as electricity, raises several difficult physical, chemical, metallurgical, and technological problems. For a number of rather obvious reasons which we cannot go into here, it is only recently that appreciable effort has been devoted to solving these problems. At the present time, however, the evidence is that a number of countries are showing increasing interest in the peaceful uses of nuclear energy, and a number of practical attempts have been made to transform this energy into electricity.

The first electrical power station using fission energy on a practical scale started working in the U.S.S.R. in June, 1954 [76]. The driving power is a thermal reactor containing 550 kg of 5% enriched uranium; the fuel and the graphite moderator are placed in an hermetically sealed steel tank filled with nitrogen or helium, and the reactivity is controlled by rods of boron carbide. The thermal power is 30,000 kw and the average flux 5×10^{13} n·cm^{-2}·sec^{-1}. The coolant (ordinary water) circulates under a pressure of 100 atm, and at 260 to 270°C, through a series of heat exchangers by which the heat is transferred to a second circuit; in this, steam is generated and used to drive a 5000 kw turbogenerator. This double circuit system eliminates any danger of radioactive contamination in the turbines and associated machinery, which work exactly as in an ordinary power station. In its first year of working the reactor provided 15×10^6 kwh, which were fed into the general grid system of the country. Other power stations of from 50 to 200 megawatts, each driven by two powerful reactors, are in the course of construction, and other projects are being considered.

The Russian experiments suggest that the cost of providing electricity from nuclear sources is greater than that from a large coal-fired power station, but is comparable with the costs of a low-power station. Increases in the capacity of nuclear power stations and technological improvements based on experience with the pilot stations, as well as the advantages of using breeder-reactors, etc., should certainly bring about a considerable reduction in the cost. The cost of the energy is not, however, the only important criterion in assessing new energy sources. The extent to which a country possesses natural resources (hydroelectric power, gasoline, coal, etc.), its state of industrial development, the geographical separation of an industrial region from the sources of natural energy, and the purpose for which the energy is required are equally important factors which must be considered and which may well be decisive. It therefore seems likely that in the course of the next few years we shall see rapid developments in the construction of nuclear reactors in several countries, with the construction of pilot stations being followed by increasingly powerful power stations.

The first large uranium graphite reactor built in France is that at Marcoule (Gard), the 40,000-kw G-1 reactor, which produces plutonium, and which has a small (5000 kw) electrical power plant using the hot air from the reactor. In this way it is possible to recover a substantial part of the electricity used. Two other piles (G-2 and G-3), each of 200,000 kw, should produce 30 megawatts of electricity each and many kg of plutonium per year. In the United Kingdom, several reactors with a total power output of 400 to 800 megawatts are proposed for the next few years, and by 1975 a third or perhaps a half of the electricity consumed should be produced from nuclear energy. In the United States [77] the construction of various types of high-power reactors is under way, notably boiling-water and breeder reactors.

One especially interesting development is the use of sodium as coolant, since this allows the reactor to be run at a higher temperature, giving better thermal efficiency. The circulation of liquid metals presents a number of very difficult technological problems in itself, and in particular requires the use of constructional materials which must not only have satisfactory nuclear characteristics, but must also be resistant to heat and to corrosion, and must have a number of other specific chemical and mechanical properties. Zirconium seems to be the most suitable element for this purpose, and research on the physical and chemical properties and the preparation of this metal, together with beryllium, hafnium, and titanium, has increased considerably in recent years.

In a boiling-water reactor, using either heavy or light water, steam can be produced directly in the active zone, thereby eliminating the necessity for heat exchangers. Heterogeneous mixtures of plutonium and U^{238} have been suggested for breeder reactors, as has a homogeneous aqueous solution of U^{235} compounds in D_2O contained in a vessel through which a suspension of ThO_2 in heavy water is circulated under pressure. Similar projects using enriched UO_2 powders have been discussed in Holland [78.] Theoretical studies and preliminary technological work has been carried out at Brookhaven [79] on the construction of a breeder reactor to give cheap electrical power. The fuel would be a solution of U^{235} in molten bismuth, and the moderator a sphere of graphite traversed by channels containing Th_3Bi_5 dispersed in liquid bismuth. A number of original techniques have been used in solving various problems concerning the constructional materials, corrosion, heat exchange, the continuous elimination of gaseous fission products, rare earths, polonium, protactinium, etc.

6-10 The use of fission products and their radiation. The number of reactors in the world continues to increase without respite. Irrespective of the purpose for which they are built, and of their design, one result is that there is a continual production of enormous quantities of radioactive nuclides, in great excess of current requirements. These products are being used in a variety of ways in research in physics, chemistry, biology, medicine, and technology, but there are as yet insufficient economic outlets for them. Subsequent chapters will illustrate numerous examples of these research applications, which can be divided into two groups, the direct utilization and the indirect utilization of the radiations.

Neutrons from a reactor can be used to produce a large number of the radioactive isotopes which are not formed in fission, as well as fission product nuclides in a pure radiochemical state. Examples of the use of the radiations from nuclides produced in a reactor are: as sources of ionization for dissipating static electrical charges; for activating phosphorescent substances or phosphorescent tubes; for radiography or autoradiography of metals or other materials; for the polymerization of organic compounds to give plastic materials; the production of electricity from various cells; oxidation and halogenation processes; the sterilization of food or pharmaceutical or medical products; etc. The majority of these applications are only under preliminary study at present, and in any case are only rarely feasible on a large scale.

The indirect use of the radiations to characterize and identify the emitting atom has, of course, been developed more fully. Thus ionization measurements or photographic methods can be used to follow the change of state of an atom, or changes from one molecular form to another. Since the physico-chemical properties of a radioactive atom are virtually identical with those of its inactive isotopes, the former may be used to locate the inactive isotopes, which are thereby "traced" by the radioactivity. This is the principle of the *radioactive indicator* method, already mentioned in Chapter 1, and fully described in several later chapters. A radionuclide or a mixture of radioactive isotopes can be obtained from the pile undiluted by inactive isotopes; such unweighable quantities are at the *tracer*, or *indicator*, *level*. The study of the physico-chemical properties of elements in solution at such very high dilutions gives valuable information in electrochemistry, analytical and colloid chemistry, etc. (Chapters 19–24). The principal fission products available for such research are set out in Table 18–1.

It is clear, however, that the demand for radioisotopes is far behind their rate of production, and obviously this situation will become increasingly worse as the number of nuclear reactors increases. The problem of disposing of radioactive residues from fission processes will therefore become increasingly difficult. To illustrate the magnitude of the problem at present, it should be noted that in the United States, such waste materials are placed in special steel boxes which are sealed and stored in some remote unpopulated region; after a suitable period, these are sunk in the ocean with heavy concrete blocks.

Glueckauf [80] has estimated that an annual world consumption of 1000 tons of nuclear fuel would produce stocks of residual fission products more than a year old with an activity of the order of 3×10^{11} Mev·curie (1 Mev · curie = 0.0059 w). At this level a stationary state would be established, since radioactive decay would be balanced by further production. If this amount were to be dispersed uniformly throughout the oceans of the world, the specific activity increase of the seas would be about equal to that due to the K^{40} already present. If, however, it were possible to remove the highly abundant and highly active nuclides Sr^{90} and Cs^{137} before disposal, the stationary level would be lowered to 1/1000 of the above value. From a biological point of view, the improvement would be even greater, since the toxicity of the Sr^{90} β-particles is about 25 times greater than for the other fission products. On the other hand, the release of Kr^{55}, another important fission product, into the atmosphere would give a (stationary) activity in the air less than that already caused by cosmic radiation.

After examining the various different possible solutions to this problem, Glueckauf has concluded that the most rational scheme of treatment would be the following:

1. Concentration of the solutions by about a factor of 200 by evaporation.

2. Quantitative separation of strontium and ceasium, which should be sealed up separately for about 50 years, unless they could be utilized as sources of radiation or heat. After 50 years, the activity would be sufficiently reduced to enable them to be dumped in the deserted regions of the earth or in the depths of the oceans, possibly after high temperature conversion into ceramic material.

3. The residual solution should be stored for 15 years, after which the hazard would be negligible. Some of the very rare and precious metals could then be extracted from it; for example, ruthenium would have accumulated to the extent of 38 kg/ton of fissile material; also present would be technetium (29 kg/ton), rhodium (26 kg/ton), palladium (7 kg/ton), xenon (13 m^3/ton), neptunium, and americium.

It should be noted that the overall radioactive decay of fission products follows an approximate law,

$$A_t = A_0 t^{-a}, \tag{6–21}$$

in which it is usual to set $a = 1.2$, although in fact this varies slightly during the decay.

6–11 Atomic weapons. The so-called atomic bombs are in fact of two principal sorts, fission bombs of U^{235} or Pu^{239} (A-bomb) and thermonuclear weapons (H-bomb). In the A-bomb, two or more masses of fissile material, each less than the critical mass, are brought together mechanically to give a mass greater than the critical mass immediately before the explosion. The bomb includes a device to prevent too rapid a separation of the fragments produced, a neutron reflector, and a parachute to allow the explosion to take place at a predetermined height. It has been estimated that the bombs dropped over Hiroshima (U^{235}) and Nagasaki (Pu^{239}) in 1945 were equivalent in destructive power to 20 kilotons of TNT, so that if the efficiency was 2%, the explosive mass must have been about 50 kg. The total weight of each of these bombs has been estimated at a few tons. From official or semi-official statements, it seems that much more efficient and more powerful bombs (up to some 25 times), atomic shells, etc., have subsequently been manufactured.

The principle of the H-bomb is the liberation of energy in the thermonuclear reactions discussed in Section 5–8. It seems that at least two types of weapon have been made. In one, a mixture of liquid tritium and deuterium undergoes very high-temperature fusion:

$$D + T \rightarrow He^4 + n + 17.57 \text{ Mev } (10^8 \text{ kcal/mole}). \qquad (6\text{–}22)$$

This reaction is no doubt accompanied by such processes as D + D, T + T, etc. [reactions (d), (e), (f), (h) of Section 5–8], which are all exoergic. In the other type of bomb, the fuel is the natural isotopic mixture of lithium (or its light isotope Li^6) and deuterium, as the compound LiD:

$$Li^6 + D \rightarrow 2He^4 + 22.3 \text{ Mev } (5.1 \times 10^8 \text{ kcal/mole}). \qquad (6\text{–}23)$$

$$Li^7 + D \rightarrow 2He^4 + n + 15.1 \text{ Mev } (3.5 \times 10^8 \text{ kcal/mole}). \qquad (6\text{–}24)$$

In either case, to initiate the reaction (i.e., to get the reactants to a sufficiently high temperature for condensation to occur), a uranium or plutonium fission bomb is used as "detonator." The power of such H-bombs is equivalent to 50 megatons of TNT, which is about 2500 times greater than that dropped on Hiroshima.

The nuclear reactions in the H-bomb do not give radioactive products directly, but the neutrons and other radiations emitted in the thermonuclear reactions can activate the surrounding matter, especially by the N^{14} (n, p) C^{14} reaction in air. It seems, however, that the effects of at least one of the American thermonuclear bombs, that exploded on March 1, 1954, in the Eniwetok archipelago in the Pacific (Section 14–11), were in fact chiefly due to fission phenomena rather than fusion.

The United States authorities have published the measured activities at various distances from the explosion after different time intervals. From these values, using the estimated power of current A-bombs, it has been calculated [81] that the total activity of the H-bomb was only 40 times greater than that of the detonator. Radiochemical analysis by Japanese workers of the ashes from the explosion have shown that the radioactivity of the debris was due almost exclusively to fission products or to transuranium elements. According to Nishiwaki [82], chemical analysis has shown the presence of radioactive isotopes of strontium, yttrium, zirconium, niobium, ruthenium, silver, antimony, tellurium, iodine, barium, lanthanum, cerium, praesodymium, and neodymium (all of which are fission products), U^{237}, Pu^{239}, Ca^{45}, and S^{35}. The presence of the latter two nuclides is probably the result of neutron activation of the earth close to the explosion (Section 14–11). From these results, Rotblat has concluded that the bomb probably contained a detonator (U^{235} or Pu) at the center, surrounded by the thermonuclear mass (LiD), around which was a thick envelope of uranium. Fast neutron fission of this could have accounted for about 80% of the explosive power of the device.

The explosion of a nuclear weapon occurs in a few millionths of a second, with a temperature at the center of about 10 to 20 million degrees celsius. One of the primary manifestations is the formation of a tremendously bright "fireball," which rapidly expands, changes color, and transforms itself into a gigantic cloud, which climbs towards the sky in the shape of a mushroom. The height of this is about 10 to 15 km for an A-bomb. The mechanical effects appear as blast and shock waves, which rapidly cause massive destruction, to which are added the effects of the heat waves. For a hydrogen bomb, the radius of total destruction is several miles. Consequently the trial explosion of such a bomb in the Eniwetok archipelago in November, 1952, resulted in the complete disappearance of the Elugelab Island, some 3 miles long. The area of severe and partial destruction was 10 miles in radius.

The fireball, whose diameter has been estimated at about 3 miles for an H-bomb, hollows out a crater of 1 to 2 miles diameter in the ground, and hundreds of feet deep. Hundreds of thousands of tons of earth are broken down into powder in this way, and are carried upwards by the mushroom cloud and eventually thrown into the upper atmosphere. The larger contaminated particles fall fairly quickly in the region of the explosion, but the fall of the much finer material is extremely slow and can occur months or even years later at practically any point on the globe, depending on wind movements. The distribution of radioactivity in this way is called *fallout*, and has been the subject of much attention because of the inherent danger which it presents. This topic will be further discussed in Chapter 14 in its relation to the biological and genetic effects of radiation.

It seems quite possible that nuclear explosions may have considerable effect on atmospheric conditions, although this is not at all understood at the moment. Debierne [83] has calculated that the explosion of a 10-kg fission bomb releases sufficient heat to raise the temperature of 5×10^7 kg of air to 10,000°C. Another probable result would be the reaction of nitrogen and oxygen to give 5×10^4 kg of NO, which would be rapidly oxydized to NO_2 and HNO_2, thus forming a large number of condensation centers for water vapor. Debierne suggested that the accumulation of water droplets in a layer 40 km above the ground over the whole of the earth's surface could hardly fail to bring about some atmospheric changes.

Other factors which have been discussed in this connection are the formation of condensation centers on powdered debris, and changes in the normal electrical conditions in the atmosphere due to the effect of ionizing radiations. Some authors [84, 85, 86, 87] suggest that climatic observations made during the last few years (during which about 60 A- and H-bombs had been tested in various parts of the globe) do not justify these apprehensions. They recognize, however, that the phenomena in question are too complex and are subject to such appreciable fluctuations that only a long and detailed series of experimental observations could decide the issue. The hazards involved in such explosions are, of course, far too great for such experiments to be undertaken.

References

1. C. D. Coryell, L. E. Glendenin, and R. R. Edwards, *Phys. Rev.*, **75,** 337 (1949).

2. C. D. Coryell and L. E. Glendenin, eds., *Radiochemical Studies: The Fission Products,* National Nuclear Energy Series, Div. IV-9, McGraw-Hill, New York, 1951, p. 489.

3. A. C. Pappas, *U.S.A.E.C. report AECU-2806.*

4. A. C. Pappas, *1955 Geneva Conference,* P. 881.

5. M. Goeppert-Mayer, *Phys. Rev.*, **74,** 235 (1948); **78,** 16 (1950).

6. L. Meitner, *Nature,* **165,** 561 (1950).

7. L. E. Glendenin, *Thesis,* M.I.T., (1949).

8. L. E. Glendenin, E. P. Steinberg, M. G. Inghram, and D. C. Hess, *Phys. Rev.*, **84,** 860 (1951): see also D. R. Wiles, B. W. Smith, R. Horsley, and H. G. Thode, *Can. J. Phys.*, **31,** 419 (1953).

9. P. J. Bendt and F. R. Scott, *Phys. Rev.*, **97,** 744 (1955).

10. M. C. Henderson, *Phys. Rev.*, **58,** 774 (1940).

11. V. Kalachnikova et al., *Acad. Sci. U.S.S.R.* (Physics section), July 1–5, 1955, p. 161.

12. L. E. Glendenin and E. P. Steinberg, *1955 Geneva Conference,* P. 614.

13. S. T. Tsien, Z. W. Ho, L. Vigneron, and R. Chastel, *J. phys. radium,* **8,** 165 (1947); *Nature,* **159,** 773 (1947).

14. L. L. Green and D. L. Livesey, *Trans. Roy. Soc. (London),* **A241,** 323 (1948).

15. K. W. Allen and J. T. Dewan, *Phys. Rev.*, **82,** 527 (1950).

16. E. L. Albenesius, *Phys. Rev. Letters,* **3,** 274 (1959); see also J. C. Watsón, *Phys. Rev.*, **121,** 230 (1961).

17. L. Rosen and A. M. Hudson, *Phys. Rev.*, **78,** 533 (1950); see also J. C. Watson, Ref. 16, *and* N. A. Perfilov, I. F. Romanov, and Z. I. Solovieva, *Russian Prog. Phys.*, **71,** 471 (1961).

18. E. L. Kelly and C. Wiegand, *Phys. Rev.*, **73,** 1135 (1948).

19. A. S. Newton, *Phys. Rev.*, **75,** 17 (1949).

20. I. Perlman, R. H. Goeckermann, D. H. Templeton, and J. J. Howland, *Phys. Rev.*, **72,** 352 (1947).

21. J. Jungerman, *Phys. Rev.*, **79,** 632 (1950).

22. B. Kurchatov, *et al.*, Ref. 11, p. 120.

23. R. H. GOECKERMANN and I. PERLMAN, *Brookhaven Conference Reports*, C9, 12 (1949); *Phys. Rev.*, **73,** 1127 (1948); **76,** 628 (1949).

24. A. VINOGRADOV, *et al.*, Ref. 11, p. 27.

25. J. M. HOLLANDER, quoted by W. J. WHITEHOUSE, *Progr. in Nuclear Phys.*, O. R. Frisch, ed., **2,** 120 (1952).

26. S. G. AL-SALAM, *Phys. Rev.*, **84,** 254 (1951).

27. W. JOHN and W. F. FRY, *Phys. Rev.*, **91,** 1234 (1953).

28. N. PERFILOV, *et al.*, Ref. 11, p. 79.

29. N. SUGARMAN and A. HABER, *Phys. Rev.*, **92,** 730 (1953).

30. H. W. KOCH, J. MCELHINNEY, and E. L. GASTEIGER, *Phys. Rev.*, **77,** 329 (1950).

31. J. R. HUIZENGA and R. B. DUFFIELD, *Phys. Rev.*, **88,** 959 (1953).

32. N. SUGARMAN, *Phys. Rev.*, **79,** 532 (1950).

33. R. B. DUFFIELD and J. GINDLER, quoted by R. W. SPENCE and G. P. FORD, *Ann. Rev. Nuclear Sci.*, **2,** 399 (1953).

34. G. BERNADINI, R. REITZ, and E. SEGRÈ, *Phys. Rev.*, **90,** 573 (1953).

35. R. E. BATZEL and G. T. SEABORG, *Phys. Rev.*, **79,** 528 (1950); **82,** 607 (1951).

36. A. TURKEVICH and J. B. NIDAY, *Phys. Rev.*, **84,** 52 (1951).

37. A. TURKEVICH, J. B. NIDAY, and A. TOMPKINS, *Phys. Rev.*, **89,** 552 (1953).

38. A. S. NEWTON, *Phys. Rev.*, **75,** 17 (1949).

39. R. A. SCHMITT and N. SUGARMAN, *Phys. Rev.*, **95,** 1260 (1954).

40. R. B. LEACHMAN, *1958 Geneva Conference*, P. 2467.

41. K. PETRJAK and G. FLEROV, *Doklady Akad. Nauk S.S.S.R.*, **28,** 500 (1940).

42. D. L. HILL and J. A. WHEELER, *Phys. Rev.*, **89,** 1102 (1953).

43. G. T. SEABORG, *Phys. Rev.*, **85,** 157 (1952).

44. W. J. WHITEHOUSE and W. GALBRAITH, *Nature*, **169,** 494 (1952).

45. P. R. FIELDS, M. H. STUDIER, L. B. MAGNUSSON, and J. R. HUIZENGA, *Nature*, **174,** 265 (1954).

46. J. R. HUIZENGA, *Phys. Rev.*, **94,** 158 (1954).

47. J. MACNAMARA and H. G. THODE, *Phys. Rev.*, **80,** 471 (1950).

48. W. J. WHITEHOUSE and W. GALBRAITH, *Phil. Mag.*, **41,** 429 (1950).

49. E. SEGRÈ and C. WIEGAND, *Phys. Rev.*, **94,** 157 (1954).

50. G. C. HANNA, B. G. HARVEY, N. MOSS, and P. R. TUNNICLIFFE, *Phys. Rev.*, **81,** 466 (1951).

51. Taken from M. DEUTSCH, in *The Science and Engineering of Nuclear Power*, C. GOODMAN, ed., Addison-Wesley Publishing Co., Reading, Mass., Vol. I, 1947, p. 75.

52. L. MEITNER and O. R. FRISCH, *Nature*, **143,** 239 (1939).

53. N. BOHR and J. A. WHEELER, *Phys. Rev.*, **56,** 426 (1939).

54. J. FRENKEL, *J. Phys. Russe*, **1,** 125 (1939); *Phys. Rev.*, **55,** 987 (1939).

55. S. FRANKEL and N. METROPOLIS, *Phys. Rev.*, **72,** 914 (1947).

56. J. FRENKEL, *J. Phys. Russe*, **10,** 533 (1946).

57. A. GHIORSO, *1955 Geneva Conference*, P. 718.

58. P. FONG, *Phys. Rev.*, **102,** 434 (1956); for a thorough discussion of this topic, see also I. HALPERN, *Ann. Rev. Nuclear Sci.*, **9,** 245 (1959).

59. W. H. ZINN, *1955 Geneva Conference*, P. 814.

60. See C. Goodman, ed., *The Science and Engineering of Nuclear Power*, Addison-Wesley Publishing Co., Reading, Mass., 1952; S. Glasstone and M. C. Edlund, *Elements of Nuclear Reactor Theory*, Van Nostrand, New York, 1952; *and* Ref. 11.

61. V. Raievski, *Onde Elec.*, No. 321, 1953.

62. J. D. Cockcroft, *Nature*, **171,** 411 (1953).

63. For such measurements, see J. D. Trimmer and W. H. Jordan, *Nucleonics*, **9,** No. 4, 60 (1951); B. Jacrot, F. Netter, and V. Raievski, *Electricité*, March 1953; M. Surdin and J. Weill, *Electricité*, May, June, 1953.

64. C. E. Crouthamel and E. Turk, *1955 Geneva Conference*, P. 721.

65. J. E. R. Holmes, D. D. McVicar, H. Rose, R. D. Smith, and C. R. Shepherd, *1955 Geneva Conference*, P. 404.

66. J. E. R. Holmes, *J. Nuclear Energy*, **1,** 47 (1954).

67. A. M. Weinberg, *1955 Geneva Conference*, P. 862.

68. H. J. Grout and F. W. Fenning, *1955 Geneva Conference*, P. 402.

69. J. R. Huffman, *Nucleonics*, **12,** No. 4, 21 (1954).

70. A. M. Weinberg, T. E. Cole, and M. M. Mann, *1955 Geneva Conference*, P. 490.

71. W. M. Breazeale, *Nucleonics*, **10,** No. 11, 56 (1952).

72. L. D. P. King, *1955 Geneva Conference*, P. 488.

73. R. Chalker, *Science*, **119,** 9 (1954).

74. M. E. Remley, *Science*, **119,** 21 (1954).

75. A. M. Stelle, *Science*, **119,** 15 (1954).

76. N. A. Nikolayer and D. I. Blockhintsev, *1955 Geneva Conference*, P. 615: this paper gives a discussion of the merits and demerits of other types of nuclear power stations.

77. J. A. Lane, *1955 Geneva Conference*, P. 476: this paper also contains a discussion of the costs of installation and power production.

78. H. de Bruyn, *et al.*, *1955 Geneva Conference*, P. 936, 938.

79. F. T. Miles and C. Williams, *1955 Geneva Conference*, P. 494: see also *Nucleonics*, **12,** No. 7, 11–42 (1954).

80. E. Glueckauf, *1955 Geneva Conference*, P. 398.

81. J. Rotblat, *Bull. Atomic Scientists*, **11,** 171 (1955).

82. Y. Nishiwaki, *J. Atomic Scientists* (*G.B.*), **4,** 279 (1955).

83. A. Debierne, *Compt. rend.*, **222,** 1124, 1352 (1946); **224,** 1220 (1947).

84. L. Machta and D. L. Harris, *Science*, **121,** 75 (1955).

85. H. Wexler, L. Machta, D. H. Pack, and F. D. White, *1955 Geneva Conference*, P. 276.

86. G. Sutton, *Nature*, **175,** 319 (1955).

87. J. D. Cockcroft, *Nature*, **175,** 873 (1955).

CHAPTER 7

THE NATURAL RADIOELEMENTS

7–1 Tritium. In the discussion of thermonuclear reactions (Section 5–7), we noted the hypothesis that helium and other light stable elements are continually being synthesized in the stars. There is no definite evidence of any such primary production of heavy radioelements under present cosmic conditions. Only very long-lived ($t_{1/2} > 10^8$ years) active isotopes are found in nature; these must have been formed at a period when cosmic conditions were very different from those existing at present, or else they are the daughter products of other nuclides.

However, two light radioactive nuclides, both β^--emitters, are being continually produced in the earth's atmosphere by the action of cosmic radiation. These are tritium, H^3 or T, which has a half-life of 12.4 years and a maximum β-energy of 18.9 kev, and radiocarbon, C^{14}, with a half-life of 5568 years and a maximum energy of 155 kev. The neutron component of cosmic radiation reacts with nitrogen in the following ways [1]:

$$N^{14} + n \rightarrow C^{12} + H^3 - 4.5\ \text{Mev}, \tag{7–1}$$

$$N^{14} + n \rightarrow 3He^4 + H^3 - 11.5\ \text{Mev}, \tag{7–2}$$

$$N^{14} + n \rightarrow C^{14} + H^1 + 0.62\ \text{Mev}. \tag{7–3}$$

Of these, Eq. (7–3) has by far the largest yield. Tritium is also formed in the disintegration of various heavier nuclides by cosmic radiation (spallation, "star" formation) [2, 3]. Traces of Be^7, an active nuclide with a half-life of 53.6 days, have been found in rain water; this no doubt arises from a similar process, as do P^{32}, Cl^{36}, Cl^{38}, Ar^{37}, etc., which have also been detected [4, 5]. The monsoon rainfall over Bombay contains 2400 Be^7 atoms/cm^2 of the collecting surface [6].

Grosse, Libby, and their collaborators [1] identified tritium in Norwegian surface waters, after electrolytic concentration (Section 9–9) to 10^{-7} of the original volume. Subsequent measurements [7] of the tritium concentration in a large number of samples of natural waters from various sources (rain, snow, rivers, lakes, sea, reservoirs, etc.) revealed wide variations of between 1.5 and 67 atoms of T per 10^{18} atoms of H. These values correspond to an average rate of production of 0.14 tritium atoms·sec^{-1}·cm^{-2} over the earth's surface, if we make the assumption that tritium is transferred to the oceanic and continental waters as quickly as it is formed. Fireman [2] has given rather higher values, from 0.4 to 9 tritium atoms·sec^{-1}·cm^{-2}, and T/H ratios as high as 8×10^{-16}. These measurements may have been partly falsified by the presence of tritium arising from thermonuclear explosions.

Faltings and Harteck [8, 9] had previously detected the presence of tritium in molecular hydrogen at an altitude of 70 km. The intense ultraviolet radiation at this altitude decomposes water molecules, so that hydrogen exists in the free state. The measured T/H ratio was of the order of 5×10^{-5}. A very similar ratio was found [10] in molecular hydrogen in the He-Ne fraction from the liquefaction of normal atmospheric air. Harteck has calculated that the total quantity of molecular tritium (T_2) is 2 gm, and that present as HTO is 6000 gm (2000 moles of T). Thus in spite of the very high HT/H_2 ratio, compared with HTO/H_2O, the absolute quantity of tritiated water may be 3000 times larger than the amount of T_2. Harteck attributes this to oxidation by ozone.

Tritium must also be produced in certain rocks and minerals of the earth's crust, especially in $LiAl(SiO_3)_2$, since there is an abnormally high abundance of the stable daughter element He^3 in such rocks. The tritium is probably produced by the nuclear reaction

$$Li^6 + n \rightarrow He^4 + T, \tag{7–4}$$

involving neutrons from the spontaneous fission of uranium, and more especially from (α, n) reactions initiated by natural α-emitters. This process (7–4), however, makes only a very small contribution to the total rate of tritium production.

Since tritium has a half-life of 12.4 years, the concentration in "aged" water (e.g., samples stored in such a way as to prevent contamination from the atmosphere) decreases with this half-life. The tritium content can therefore be used [11] to estimate the age of rain waters and agricultural products (especially wine), and similarly in hydrology to determine the accumulation time of subterranean waters, and in meteorology to investigate the origin of water vapor in the atmosphere, since vapor from surface water will have a very much higher tritium content than that coming from the ocean depths.

The physico-chemical properties of tritium and its compounds are significantly different from those of "normal" hydrogen; this question will be discussed later in Section 9–2.

7–2 Radiocarbon and archeological dating. The presence of natural radiocarbon in the atmosphere was first discovered by Libby and his colleagues [12, 13]. The most likely product of reaction (7–3) is atomic radiocarbon, which is extremely reactive chemically and so is rapidly oxidized to $C^{14}O_2$. This mixes with normal carbon dioxide and so penetrates into the vegetable and animal kingdom by photosynthesis and metabolism, and also enters into chemical equilibria with carbonates dissolved in natural waters [14].

If it is assumed, with Libby [15, 16], that the cosmic radiation intensity has remained constant over a period equal to at least several half-lives of C^{14} (approximately 5600 years), then the specific activity of this "exchange reservoir" has also been constant for this period, due to the stationary state set up between the disintegration of C^{14} and the formation of fresh nuclei by process (7–3). Libby has estimated the elementary carbon content of the reservoir at 8.3 gm/cm^2 of the earth's surface; of this, 7.25 gm is present in inorganic compounds in solution in the oceans. A neutron flux of 2.4 $n \cdot sec^{-1} \cdot cm^{-2}$ over the earth's surface is calculated to give 19 ± 4 disintegrations of C^{14} per minute per gram of carbon [17, 18] (neglecting the production of tritium). Anderson has carried out a large number of determinations of the C^{14} content of modern woods, and finds that on the average 1 gm of carbon gives 15.3 disintegrations per minute. The C^{14}/C^{12} ratio in plants is slightly lower than that in carbonates (Section 10–4), which form the principal component of the exchange reservoir; for such materials, the C^{14} activity corresponds to 16.5 disintegrations per minute per gram. This is in good agreement with the theoretical estimates.

Taking this agreement as proof of a constant cosmic radiation flux, Libby has worked out an extremely important method for determining the age of carboniferous materials of animal or vegetable origin. The results of this method have done much to provide further proof of the validity of the original hypothesis. A constant specific activity is maintained in living matter only as long as its carbon exchanges with atmospheric carbon dioxide by metabolic processes. On the death of the plant or animal, the radiocarbon content decreases according to the ordinary radioactive disintegration law (Eq. 4–2) and this loss is no longer compensated by the uptake of C^{14} from the atmosphere. It therefore follows that if the specific activity of a sample from an organism which died t years ago is compared with the present specific activity of living matter (15.3 disintegrations per minute per gram), the age t can be found. Libby has checked the validity of the method using samples of known origin, with ages as great as 5000 years, and has found good agreement. A vast number of other measurements have subsequently been carried out by Libby and his collaborators, and by workers in other laboratories, to determine the age of varied samples of widespread origin; several examples are quoted below.

Since the specific activity of C^{14} in living matter is very low, and decreases further with age, the experimental method is very delicate, and extremely careful sample preparation and radiometric techniques are required. Libby has used an anticoincidence arrangement of several internal-grid-wall Geiger counters mounted around one central counter. In this setup, counts are not recorded if an ionizing particle passes through two counters and the central counter, which contains the sample being measured. In this way it has been possible to reduce the "background" of the apparatus (i.e., stray pulses arising from cosmic radiation and from the intrinsic activity of the materials of which the counters are made) to five counts per minute.

The measurements are carried out on samples prepared as elemental carbon (lampblack), obtained by combustion of the initial material, followed by high temperature reduction of CO_2 with magnesium. The upper limit for age determinations with this technique is of the order of 20,000 years, but this limit can be increased to 45,000 years, either by using scintillation counters [19], in which the C^{14} is present as toluene, or by filling a counter with $C^{14}O_2$ under pressure [20]. For counters filled with C_2H_2, the maximum measurable age is 30,000 years [21, 22]; the acetylene is prepared by the reduction of $SrCO_3$ with Mg to give SrC_2, which is then treated with water:

$$2SrCO_3 + 5Mg \rightarrow SrC_2 + 5MgO + SrO, \quad (7\text{-}5)$$

$$SrC_2 + 2H_2O \rightarrow Sr(OH)_2 + C_2H_2. \quad (7\text{-}6)$$

The examples given of the interesting historical and archeological results obtained by this method are taken from the very large number of determinations carried out principally by Libby.

It has been generally supposed that the last advance of large glaciers across the American continent occurred about 25,000 years ago, but C^{14} measurements on samples of wood and turf has fixed this epoch at 11,000 years ago. This implies a more rapid geological development than had previously been assumed, reduces the interval between ancient and more recent civilizations, and also throws light upon certain aspects of tribal migration.

Samples taken from an Icelandic post-glacial tomb covered by a flow of lava show that the direction of the earth's magnetic field was the same 5000 years ago as it is today, since the orientation of the solidified lava is determined by this field.

Three hundred pairs of sandals discovered recently in a grotto in the State of Oregon, woven from vegetable cord, were made about 9400 years ago. A sample of wooden roof beam found in Iraq dates from the reign of Hammurabi of Babylon, 3945 ± 106 years ago; from this it has been possible to work out the correct relationship between the ancient Babylonian calendar and our own.

The age of the famous primitive cave frescoes at Lascaux (Dordogne) is estimated at 15,500 ± 900 years on the basis of the C^{14} content of wood found in the cave. The Biblical scrolls found a few years ago near the Dead Sea, the authenticity of which has been the subject of some controversy, have been dated from their linen wrapping as being about 1900 years old.

The method has also been applied to the determination of the age of the tombs of the Pharaohs, in which grains of wheat were found; these, incidentally, retained their germinating power. The remains of the Taimyr mammoth in Siberia have a C^{14} age of 12,000 years [23].

7-3 Natural radioelements of medium atomic weight. All the naturally occurring radioactive nuclides with Z between 6 and 81 are very long-lived. Since they are generally mixed with stable isotopes, their activity has virtually no effect on the chemical behavior of the element. Their geochemical significance is discussed in Chapter 10. Table 7-1 lists these nuclides, with their half-lives, and the radiations emitted. The list is divided into two groups; group A contains those elements whose radioactivity is established, and group B those whose activity requires further investigation, including the as yet unconfirmed activities reported for Pb^{204} and Bi^{209}.

TABLE 7–1

NATURAL RADIOACTIVE ISOTOPES WITH $Z \leq 83$

Z	Nuclide	Abundance, %	$t_{1/2}$, years	Mode of decay
		Group A		
19	K^{40}	0.0119	1.3×10^9	β^-, e
23	V^{50}	0.25	4×10^{14}	e
37	Rb^{87}	27.85	6.15×10^{10}	β^-
49	In^{115}	95.77	6×10^{14}	β^-
57	La^{138}	0.089	2×10^{11}	β^-, e
60	Nd^{144}	23.87	1.5×10^{15}	α
62	Sm^{147}	15.07	1.25×10^{11}	α
71	Lu^{176}	2.6	2.1×10^{10}	β^-, e
75	Re^{187}	62.93	5×10^{10}	β^-
		Group B		
19	K^{38}	10^{-8}	1.1×10^9	β^+, e
51	Sb^{123}	42.75	1.3×10^{13}	e
58	Ce^{142}	11.07	5×10^{15}	α
64	Gd^{152}	0.20	1.08×10^{14}	α
72	Hf^{174}	0.20	2×10^{15}	α
73	Ta^{180}	0.01	$10^7 - 10^{11}$	β
74	W^{178}	$\sim 10^{-7}$	6×10^8	α
78	Pt^{190}	0.012	$\sim 10^{12}$	α
82	Pb^{204}	1.48	3×10^{16}	α
83	Bi^{209}	100	2×10^{17}	α

Of the species in Table 7–1, the activity of K^{40} has been longest known, although its half-life and decay scheme, 88% β-emission and 12% electron capture, have been definitely established only in the last few years. Despite its very low activity and very small isotopic abundance (0.0119%), K^{40} plays an essential part in the thermal equilibrium of the earth, because of the high abundance of potassium compared with other elements. The nuclear energy from 1 gm of potassium is only 2.6×10^{-6} cal·year^{-1}, whereas uranium in equilibrium with its daughter products releases 0.73 cal·year^{-1}, and thorium and its decay products 0.20 cal·year^{-1}. However, the abundance of potassium, in granitic rocks, for example, is estimated as 3.5 weight per cent, while that of uranium is only 4×10^{-4} and of thorium 15×10^{-4}%. The relative abundances in other types of rock are very similar. It follows from this that potassium gives off 0.9 cal·year^{-1}·gm^{-1} of silicate rock, and uranium and thorium 3 cal·year^{-1} [24]. Because of the abundance of these three elements over the whole earth (crust plus mantle plus core), it could be that potassium contributes almost as much energy as the three natural radioactive families toward maintaining the earth's thermal condition. Since it has a much shorter half-life than the longest-lived members of these series, its relative contribution was presumably even more important in the early stages of the earth's development, some three or four thousand million years ago (Section 9–10), when the heat which it released was sufficient to keep the terrestrial mantle in a molten state for hundreds of millions of years [25].

Although very sensitive methods are currently available for the detection of very low activities (especially photographic methods, see Section 16–8), the positive identification of the necessarily low activity of a natural radionuclide becomes more doubtful, and more likely to be due to contamination, as the assumed half-life becomes longer. In addition to methods involving direct measurement, the instability of a natural nuclide can be deduced if its eventual descendant is found in abnormally high isotopic abundance in some common mineral. Kohman [26] has suggested that this approach can be used to detect the previous natural occurrence of "extinct" radionuclides, which have completely decayed away because of their short half-life, but which could have existed for a sufficiently long time to accumulate a measurable amount of daughter product. This method should be applicable to half-lives of the order of 10^8 years. Kohman has quoted the example of the nuclide Fe^{60}, which could β-decay to Ni^{60}, and so change the isotopic composition of the nickel impurity in aged iron minerals; the half-life of Fe^{60} is estimated at about 10^8 years.*

7–4 Technetium and promethium. Minute traces of these two elements are present in nature, being formed either in spontaneous fission or by the action of cosmic ray or fission neutrons on related elements. For example, from the known half-lives of U^{238} and Tc^{99}, and the fission yield of Tc^{99}, the Tc^{99}/U^{238} ratio is calculated to be 1.5×10^{-12}. Promethium does not appear to occur naturally in detectable quantities; for technetium this point is as yet undecided. Both the isobaric rules and nuclear shell structure theory predict that all the isotopes of technetium ($Z = 43$) and promethium ($Z = 61$) are unstable, and in fact all the artificially prepared isotopes of these two elements are radioactive. The half-lives of all the promethium isotopes, and of most of those of technetium, are too short to be compatible with the survival of these species since the formation of the terrestrial crust.

The masses of the known isotopes of technetium are between 92 and 107; the isotope of mass 98 has recently been prepared [27] by bombarding Mo with 22-Mev protons, and has a half-life of 1.5×10^7 years. There are two isomers of Tc^{97}; the ground state decays with a half-life of 2.6×10^6 years. The natural occurrence of these isotopes is obviously rather improbable. Several attempts to find this element in terrestrial minerals and in meteorites have so far given negative or rather doubtful results. However, in 1951 Moore [28] detected lines in the solar spectrum which he attributed to technetium, the spectrum of which is well established. This

* Roy and Kohman, *Can. J. Phys.*, **35**, 649 (1957) have recently prepared Fe^{60} by bombarding copper with 400-Mev protons; it is a β-emitter with a half-life of the order of 3×10^5 years.

result has recently been confirmed [29], and Merrill [30] has identified technetium lines in the spectra of at least 13 S-type stars. These results encouraged a number of authors to use sensitive radiometric methods in a search for this element in terrestrial minerals.

Alperovitch [31, 32] bombarded samples of colombite, yttro-tantalite, and other minerals with slow neutrons in the Brookhaven reactor and detected the formation of Tc^{99m}, which could have been produced in the Tc^{98} (n, γ) capture process. A similar result was obtained by Herr [33]. It would, however, be rather premature to conclude that technetium exists in the terrestrial crust, since it is possible that Tc^{99} was formed by some other nuclear process, such as

$$Mo^{98}\ (n, \gamma)\ Mo^{99} \xrightarrow{\beta} Tc^{99},$$

for example.*

The first artificially prepared isotopes of technetium were isolated by Perrier and Segrè [34, 35], who bombarded molybdenum with 5-Mev deuterons; the nuclear reaction is ${}_{42}Mo$ (d, n) ${}_{43}Tc$. The name of the element was chosen by these workers to emphasize its artificial origin. Other isotopes have been obtained either by the bomdardment of Mo, or from fission products. Weighable quantities are now available, so that the physical and chemical properties of the element and many of its compounds are quite well known. It is a homologue of manganese and rhenium, with properties similar to those of these elements, and especially of rhenium. The established technetium valence states are VII, VI, and IV [36, 37]; polarographic work also suggests the existence of V and II states, and perhaps of a Tc^- ion, analogous to Re^-.

The pertechnetate ion TcO_4^- can be obtained by dissolving bombarded molybdenum targets, or cathodic deposits of technetium, in HNO_3/HCl or HNO_3/H_2SO_4 mixtures. The solution is pink in color. At the tracer level, Tc (VII) largely coprecipitates with the insoluble perrhenates of Tl, Cs, and Rb, and with the insoluble perchlorates [38], so that it probably forms sparingly soluble pertechnetates with these cations. Similarly, nitron perrhenate and perchlorate carry down TcO_4^- virtually completely. Unlike the perrhenates, but by analogy with other oxygenated ions, solutions of pertechnetates (5×10^{-5} to $5 \times 10^{-4}\ M$) are efficient in protecting steel against corrosion in aereated water, even at 250°C [39, 40]; protection occurs even at a surface coverage of 3×10^{12} Tc atoms/cm^2.

A dark brown sulfide, Tc_2S_7, insoluble in 0.4 to 5 M HCl, has been prepared. Precipitation is quite incomplete in stronger acid (10 M), from which rhenium sulfide precipitates fairly well, if slowly. This, therefore, gives a method of separating the two elements by fractional precipitation. Another method makes use of the fact that when a stream of wet HCl at 200°C is passed into a solution in H_2SO_4 at 80°C, rhenium distills off completely, whereas technetium volatilizes very slowly. By contrast, the

* Later experiments by Boyd and Larson, *J. Phys. Chem.*, **60,** 707 (1956), appear to rule out quite definitely the existence of technetium in terrestrial minerals, and its existence in the sun has also been questioned, C. de Jager, *Bull. Astronom. Inst. Netherlands,* **13,** 13 (1956).

two sulfides distill simultaneously in a current of chlorine at 100°C. Paper chromatography can be used to separate technetium and rhenium from molybdenum [41]. Molybdenum can also be separated from Tc with 8-hydroxyquinoline, which forms an insoluble Mo complex in acetic acid solution, or by using the nonprecipitation of Mo with nitron. Another method involves extraction with tetraphenylarsonium chloride in chloroform solution [42]. The pertechnetate ion can also be extracted from alkaline solution into pyridine or methyl ethyl ketone [43].

In alkaline solution, hydrazine reduces pertechnetate to technetate TcO_4^{2-}, which probably undergoes dismutation to TcO_4^- and TcO_2. An oxide, TcO_3, is also known. Pertechnetates are reduced by $SnCl_2$, concentrated HCl, KI, hydroxylamine, and hydrazine in acid solution, to TcO_2. This dioxide can also be obtained by electrolytic reduction at a platinum cathode in alkaline solution [44], under which conditions rhenium and molybdenum remain in solution. In concentrated HCl solution, zinc apparently reduces technetium compounds to the divalent state (TcO), which coprecipitates with iron, manganese, and zirconium hydroxides [38].

Technetium metal can be prepared by reduction of the sulfide with hydrogen at 1100°C. It is hexagonal, with a compact structure, isomorphous with rhenium, osmium, and ruthenium [45]. The calculated density of Tc^{99} is 11.487. Unlike rhenium, technetium metal does not dissolve in boiling $H_2O_2 + NH_4OH$ solution. Several hundred lines have been identified in the technetium spark spectrum [46, 47]; the lines recommended for qualitative detection are those at 4927.2, 4261.9, 4095.3, 4088.4, 4031.3, and 3237.0 A. Less than a microgram of the element can be detected in this way. The x-ray spectrum has been obtained with a 0.7-mg sample of technetium [48].

A long and difficult search was necessary for the discovery of *promethium*, the element obviously missing from the rare earth series, whose members all have very similar chemical properties. The first identification of two isotopes of elements 61 (masses 147 and 149) was by Marinsky, Glendenin, and Coryell in work on fission chemistry [49]. The name "promethium" was suggested by Mrs. Coryell to emphasize the release of energy in nuclear reactors, which resulted in the discovery of the element, and which recalled the snatching of Prometheus from fire. About a dozen isotopes of promethium, produced either in fission or by the fast particle bombardment of Nd and Pr, are known at present. The longest lived is Pm^{145} ($t_{1/2} \sim 30$ years) which decays by electron capture to Nd^{145}.

Comparatively large quantities of Pm are produced in reactors; Seaborg [50] has calculated that a 100-kw reactor produces 1 mg/day. The presence of several other rare earths means that the extraction of Pm is extremely difficult, the most efficient method using ion exchange chromatography. Chemically, promethium behaves as would be predicted for a rare earth lying between neodymium and samarium, with only a single trivalent state; the nitrate is pink and the chloride yellow. The lines in the spark spectrum most suitable for identification of Pm are at 4086.0, 3980.6, 3910.4, and 3711.7 [46]. The arc spectrum [51], the absorption spectrum of the chloride and the nitrate [52], and the x-ray spectrum [53] have also been studied, using milligram quantities of the element.

7–5 The four natural radioactive series. The naturally occurring heavy radioelements fall into three families or series, beginning with U^{238}, U^{235}, and Th^{232} respectively. Various successive α- and β-emissions finally transform these to stable lead isotopes, with masses 206, 207, and 208 (Figs. 7–1, 7–2, and 7–3). The members of any one series are therefore

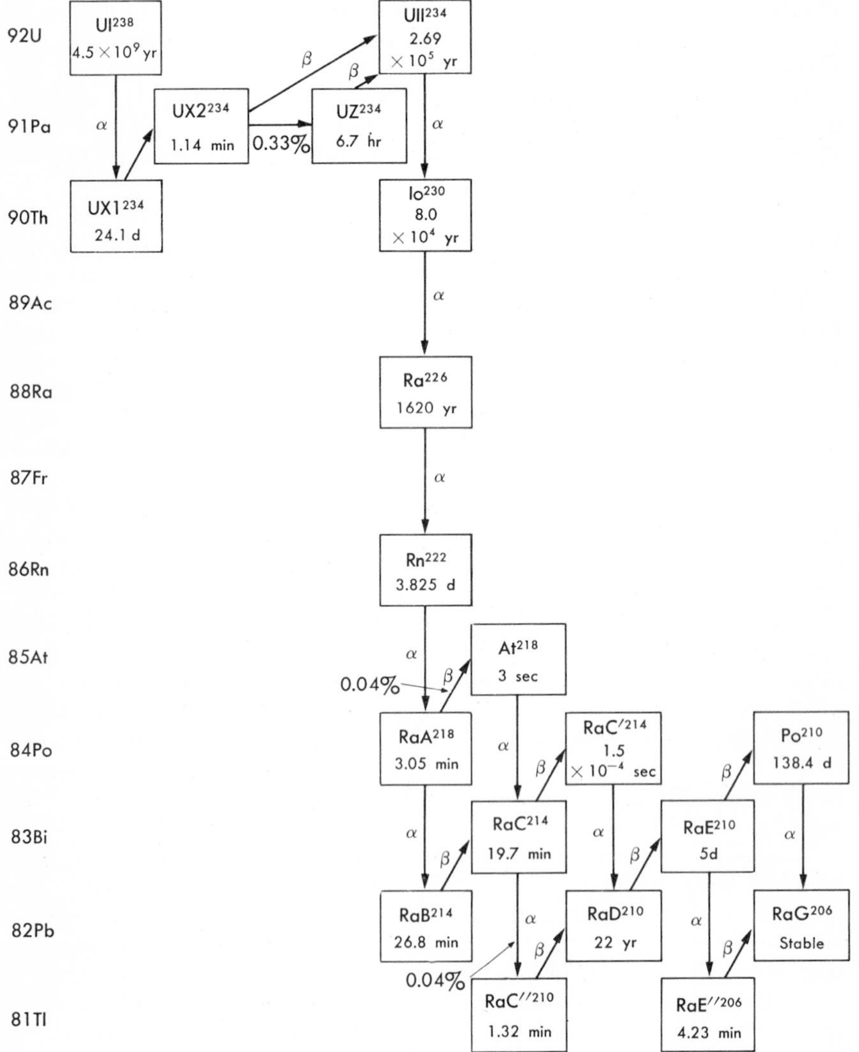

FIG. 7–1. The uranium (4n + 2) series.

genetically related, and their mass numbers are given by the general formulae, 4n for the thorium series, (4n + 2) for the uranium series, and (4n + 3) for the U^{235} (or actinium) series. This arises because the α-decay of a nuclide of mass A obviously gives a nuclide of mass $A - 4$, while β-decay produces an isobar, so that all the members of a radioactive family fit the same mass formula as the mother element.

For many years, the search for the (4n + 1) family gave only negative results, but these elements were eventually obtained artificially [54, 55] by two different routes, both of which involved U^{233} as an intermediate.

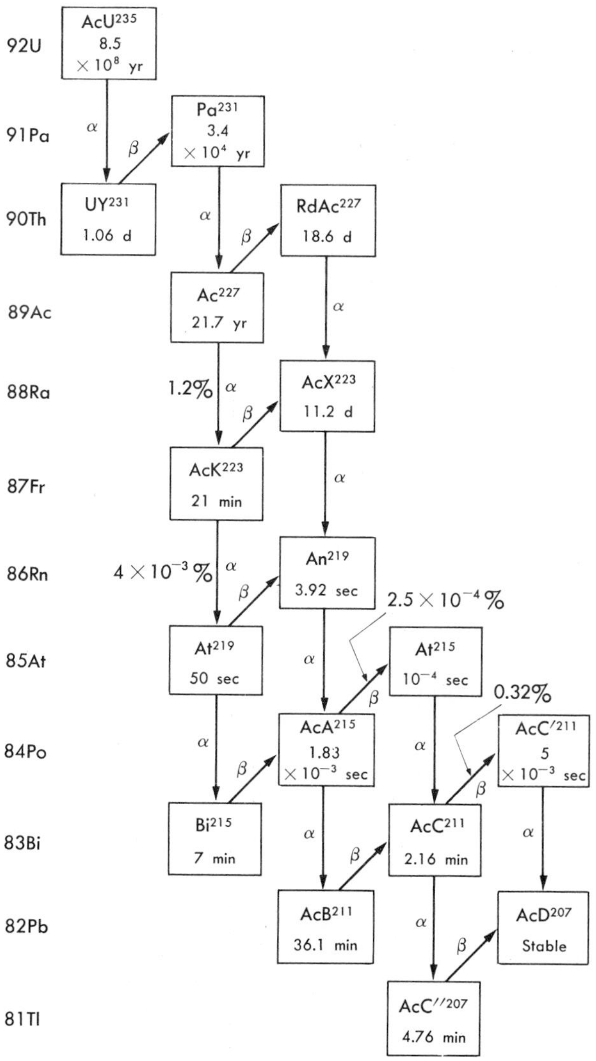

FIG. 7-2. The actino-uranium (4n + 3) series.

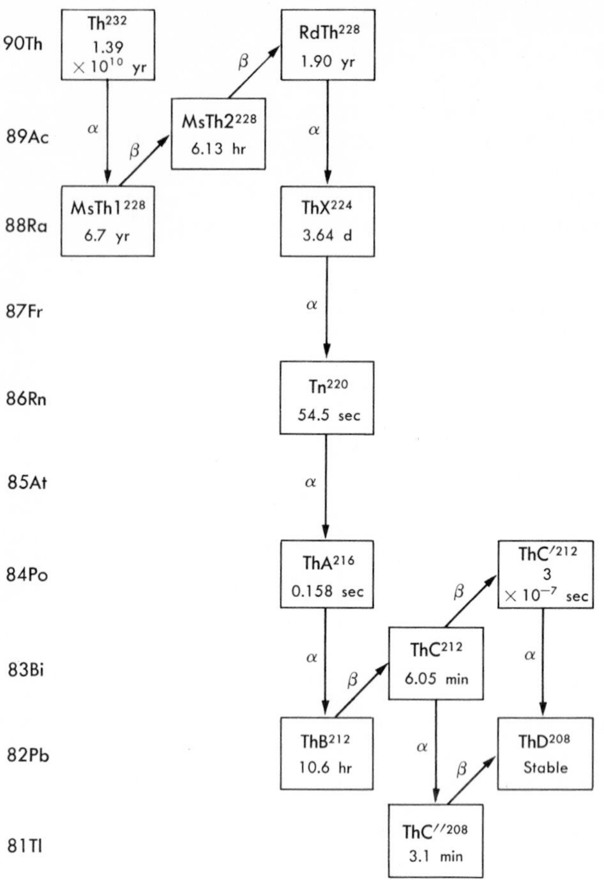

FIG. 7–3. The thorium (4n) series.

This nuclide can be obtained either by

$$U^{238}\,(\alpha, n)\,Pu^{241} \xrightarrow[14\text{ yr}]{\beta} Am^{241} \xrightarrow[475\text{ yr}]{\alpha} Np^{237}$$

$$\xrightarrow[2.2 \times 10^{6}\text{ yr}]{\alpha} U^{233}\,(1.6 \times 10^{5}\text{ yr}), \qquad (7\text{–}7)$$

or by the Th^{232} (n, γ) reaction (Section 6–8). The daughter elements of U^{233} are shown in Fig. 7–4. This series has been named the *neptunium* series, since Np is the longest-lived member. The presence of Np^{237} has subsequently been detected in minute traces [56] in pitchblende from the Congo; the Np^{237}/U^{238} ratio is estimated as 1.8×10^{-12}. It probably arises from the β-decay of U^{237}, which could be formed by an (n, 2n) reaction on U^{238} with fast neutrons from uranium fission.

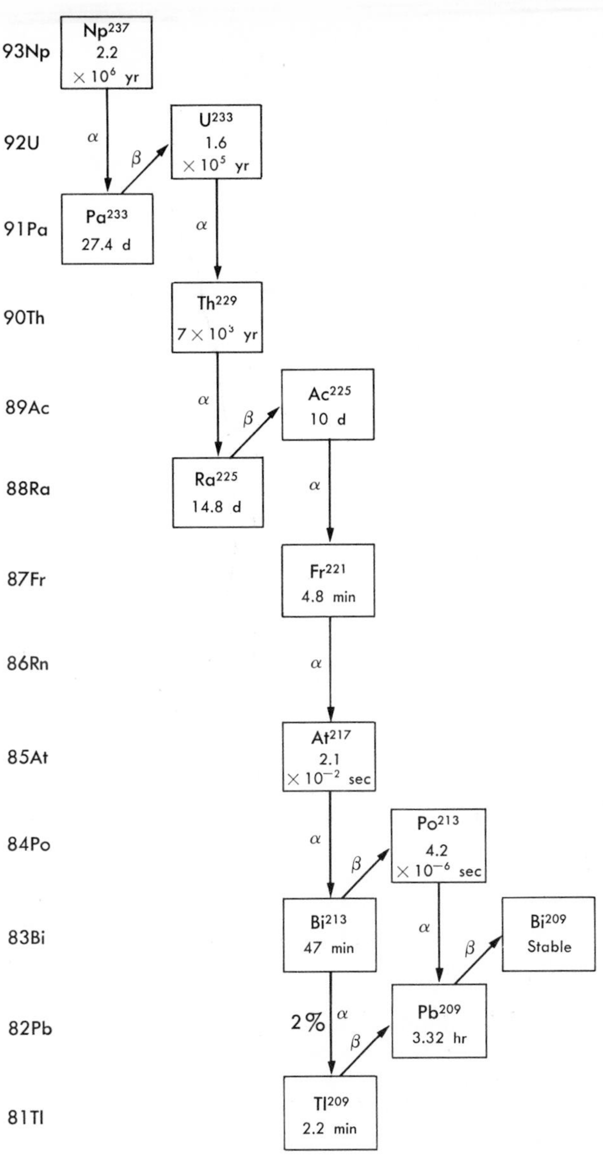

FIG. 7-4. The neptunium (4n + 1) series.

Thus, although trace quantities of the fourth radioactive family are found in nature, its origins are quite different from those of the other three series. It should be noted that unlike the other radioactive families, the (4n + 1) series ends with a bismuth isotope, and also that it contains no isotope of radon. The latter, however, occurs in the *collateral series*, that is, in the chains of related elements which are of different origin from the main series, but which are linked with it through common members.

TABLE 7–2

COLLATERAL RADIOACTIVE CHAINS

4n

$$U^{228} \xrightarrow[9.3\text{ min}]{\alpha} Th^{224} \xrightarrow[1\text{ sec}]{\alpha} Ra^{220} \xrightarrow[3 \times 10^{-2}\text{ sec}]{\alpha} Rn^{216} \xrightarrow[10^{-4}\text{ sec}]{\alpha} Po^{212}\ (\text{ThC}')$$

$$Pa^{228} \xrightarrow[22\text{ hr}]{\alpha} Ac^{224} \xrightarrow[2.9\text{ hr}]{\alpha} Fr^{220} \xrightarrow[27.5\text{ sec}]{\alpha} At^{216} \xrightarrow[3 \times 10^{-4}\text{ sec}]{\alpha} Bi^{212}\ (\text{ThC})$$

4n + 2

$$Pa^{230} \xrightarrow[17.7\text{ d}]{\beta} U^{230} \xrightarrow[20.8\text{ d}]{\alpha} Th^{226} \xrightarrow[30.9\text{ min}]{\alpha} Ra^{222} \xrightarrow[38\text{ sec}]{\alpha} Rn^{218} \xrightarrow[0.019\text{ sec}]{\alpha} Po^{214}\ (\text{RaC}')$$

$$Pa^{226} \xrightarrow[1.8\text{ min}]{\alpha} Ac^{222} \xrightarrow[5.5\text{ sec}]{\alpha} Fr^{218} \xrightarrow[5 \times 10^{-3}\text{ sec}]{\alpha} At^{214} \xrightarrow[2 \times 10^{-6}\text{ sec}]{\alpha} Bi^{210}\ (\text{RaE})$$

4n + 3

$$U^{227} \xrightarrow[1.3\text{ min}]{\alpha} Th^{223} \xrightarrow[0.1\text{ sec}]{\alpha} Ra^{219} \xrightarrow[10^{-3}\text{ sec}]{\alpha} Rn^{215} \xrightarrow[10^{-6}\text{ sec}]{\alpha} Po^{211}\ (\text{AcC}')$$

$$Pa^{227} \xrightarrow[38.3\text{ min}]{\alpha} Ac^{223} \xrightarrow[2.2\text{ min}]{\alpha} Fr^{219} \xrightarrow[0.02\text{ sec}]{\alpha} At^{215} \xrightarrow[10^{-4}\text{ sec}]{\alpha} Bi^{211}\ (\text{AcC})$$

Thus the bombardment of thorium with 100-Mev α-particles gives rise to the series [57]

$$Th^{232}\ (\alpha, 7n)\ U^{229} \xrightarrow[58\text{ min}]{\alpha} Th^{225} \xrightarrow[8\text{ min}]{\alpha} Ra^{221} \xrightarrow[30\text{ sec}]{\alpha} Rn^{217} \xrightarrow[10^{-3}\text{sec}]{\alpha} Po^{213}, \tag{7–8}$$

which connects with the main series via Po^{213}. The bombardment of thorium with accelerated α-particles or deuterons results in various (α, xn) or (d, xn) reactions, which give several other collateral series with masses of 4n, (4n + 2), and (4n + 3) (Table 7–2). With the exception of Pa^{230}, the members of these chains are α-emitters, although some isotopes of actinium and protactinium also partially decay by electron capture; in addition Pa^{230} has a very small α-branching disintegration (about 0.003%).

7–6 Polonium. Polonium is the lightest heavy element for which no stable isotope is known. It is also the first radioactive element which was discovered (by Pierre and Marie Curie); the isotope Po^{210} (radium-F) occurs in pitchblende from St. Joachimstahl, Czechoslovakia, to the extent of about 0.1 mg/ton. The half-life of this isotope is 138.4 days. Subsequent work has identified more than 20 other isotopes, either in the natural radioactive series, or by artificial preparation, with mass numbers extending from 192 to 218 [58, 59, 60]. They are all radioactive, being mostly α-emitters, with half-lives varying from 3×10^{-7} sec (ThC′, Po^{212}) to 103 years (Po^{209}). Radium-F remains the polonium isotope most widely used in research in nuclear physics and in radiochemistry. In addition to the ease with which it can be prepared in the pure state, its half-life is neither inconveniently long nor too short, there are no radioactive daughter products, and the radiation emitted is practically all α-particles, in high intensity.

Quantities of Po^{210} are normally expressed either in curies (or fractions of a curie), or in electrostatic units (esu). The curie was originally defined as that quantity of a radioelement of the uranium family which would be in radioactive equilibrium with 1 gm of radium; this quantity corresponds in practice to 3.65×10^{10} disintegrations per second. As currently defined, one curie is the quantity of any nuclide which undergoes 3.700×10^{10} disintegrations per second, and is therefore independent of any experimental specific activity found for radium itself. The specific activity of any radioactive source is the activity per unit mass or unit volume, measured in curies, or in units derived from this (i.e., millicuries, microcuries), or in other units (counts per minute, etc.).

One millicurie of polonium corresponds to 2.24×10^{-7} gm. The quantity m of Po^{210} (in grams) which produces a saturation current I (esu) over a solid angle of 2π in an air-filled ionization chamber is given by

$$I = m \frac{\lambda N}{A} ke, \qquad (7\text{–}9)$$

where λ is the decay constant of Po^{210}, k is the number of ion pairs produced by an α-particle from polonium along its total track length in air (1.52×10^5), A the atomic weight, N Avogadro's number, and e the electronic charge; 1 esu of polonium corresponds to 1.67×10^{-10} gm, or 1/1340 mc.

Apart from uranium minerals and residues resulting from their treatment, Po^{210} can also be obtained from the following sources: (a) old radon ampoules containing the long-lived active deposit (RaD + E + F); (b) radium salts; (c) Bi^{210} (RaE) produced artificially in the Bi^{209} (d, p) or Bi^{209} (n, γ) reactions.

The majority of investigations on the chemistry of polonium have been made with unweighable quantities of the element, using various tracer techniques (Chapters 20 and 21). More recently, however, weighable quantities of the element, obtained by neutron bombardment of bismuth, have been used in a number of laboratories. It has been possible to confirm or modify some of the older observations, and a number of new facts have been established. Some caution must be used, however, in the interpretation of results obtained with very high concentrations of polonium, because of the effects of the intense radiation and of the radiolytic products on the chemical reactions of the element, especially in terms of its redox behavior.

Polonium is the higher homologue of tellurium, and like tellurium is tetravalent in the most stable state. The tetravalency was established indirectly by radiochemical methods based on isomorphism [60] (Section 21–3), and has been confirmed with weighable quantities of various Po(IV) compounds. The oxide PoO_2 is yellow, with a face-centred cubic structure [61, 62], but a less stable red tetragonal modification can also be obtained. The oxide is prepared by the action of oxygen on the metal at 250°C. The tetrachloride $PoCl_4$ can be prepared by heating the metal with Cl_2, or PoO_2 with HCl (or other anhydrous chlorine compounds), or by dissolving the metal in HCl [63, 64]. It is light yellow in color, melts at about 300°C in a sealed tube, and boils at 390°C. The red tetrabromide (M.P. ~ 324°C) is formed by the action of bromine on the metal [65].

From earlier tracer studies [60, 66, 67], it was concluded that reducing agents such as hydrazine, SO_2 in acid solution, oxalic acid, or pyrogallol will convert Po(IV) in solution to a lower oxidation state, assumed to be the trivalent state. Recent experiments on weighable quantities show, however, that an unstable Po(II) state is formed, but do not exclude the possible existence of an unstable trichloride. Even in very strong acid solution, the solubility of the nitrate does not exceed 4.6×10^{-3} mole/liter (for 8 *M* HNO_3 at 45°C) [68]. The chloride $PoCl_2$ is a dark red solid, which sublimes at 200°C with slight decomposition. Its aqueous solution (dilute HCl) is pink in color and undergoes rapid atmospheric oxidation to Po(IV). Strong reducing agents such as $SnCl_2$, hydrazine in alkaline solution, $TiCl_3$, $Na_2S_2O_4$, and NaH_2PO_2 precipitate metallic polonium from solution [66, 67]. Electrolysis of an acid or alkaline solution deposits polonium at both electrodes, as the metal at the cathode and very probably as the oxide PoO_3 at the anode. The electrochemical properties of polonium are discussed in greater detail in Chapter 20.

Paneth [69, 70] prepared a very unstable volatile hydride (PoH_2) by the action of magnesium powder upon an hydrochloric acid solution, or by spark discharge. The existence of Na_2Po compounds, isomorphous with Na_2Te, and also of volatile $Po(CH_3)_2$, has been reported [71]. Various metallic polonides (Pb, Hg, Zn, Ni, Pt) have recently been prepared on the milligram scale. In sum then, polonium is known to have the valency states II, III (?), IV, VI, —II.

In weak acid solution, polonium salts have a strong tendency to hydrolyse to the colloidal state. In very acid solution, or in solutions containing large quantities of alkali salts, anionic complexes such as $[PoCl_6]^{2-}$ and $[Po(NO_3)_6]^{2-}$ are formed. In alkaline solution, a polonite Na_2PoO_3, analogous to sodium tellurite, is very probably formed [72].

The crystal structure of metallic polonium, obtained by cathodic deposition, has been studied by x-ray diffraction methods [73, 74]. Two varieties have been distinguished, α-Po which is cubic, and rhombohedral β-Po, with a transition point at about 36°C. The melting point is 254°C, and the density 9.4; vapor pressure measurements suggest a boiling point at about 960°C [75]. The metal can be easily volatilized, and this has been used in one method of preparing the pure element. Recently [76] 139 lines in the high-frequency spectrum have been identified, and 48 in the spark spectrum. The ionization potential of the neutral atom is estimated from these measurements to be 8.43 ev.

7–7 Astatine and radon. The first isotope of *astatine* ("unstable") was obtained by Segrè and his collaborators [77] by the bombardment of bismuth with accelerated helium ions, the reaction being Bi^{209} (α, 2n) At^{211}. This isotope has a half-life of 7.5 hours, disintegrating by both α-emission (40%) and *K*-capture (60%). Shortly after this work, Karlik and Bernert [78, 79] detected a very weak branching β-emission in the decay of RaA (5×10^{-2}%), giving At^{218}, an α-emitter with a half-life of 1.4 to 2 sec. This result was confirmed by Walen [80]. Karlik and Bernert [81] reported analogous branchings in the thorium and actinium series, giving At^{216} and At^{215}, although energy considerations suggest that only At^{215} can be formed; this has been confirmed by Avignon [82]. The nuclide At^{216}, an α-emitter with a half-life of 3×10^{-4} sec, can, however, be prepared artificially. A very weak branching ($4 \times 10^{-3}\%$) in Fr^{223} (AcK) leads to At^{219}, an α- and β-emitter with a half-life of 0.9 min [83]. Some 20 other isotopes of astatine are known at the present time, the longest lived having a half-life of 8.3 hours. This short half-life renders any study of the properties of the element extremely difficult. Only a small number of papers have been published [77, 84, 85, 86] on its chemical behavior, which still remains largely uninvestigated.

Astatine is a homologue of iodine, but as would be expected from its position in the periodic system, the metallic character, which already shows up slightly in iodine, is more apparent in astatine. Because of this, results reported with solutions at concentrations of only 10^{-15} *M* must be interpreted with caution, especially when analogies are being drawn with the homologue. The following conclusions, however, seem to be fairly well established. On heating bombarded bismuth to its melting point in a high vacuum, astatine distills from the target and can be collected as the element in a tube cooled in liquid nitrogen. In this state it is very stable in aqueous solution or in weak nitric acid solution; this is shown particularly by partition coefficient measurements between organic solvents (C_6H_6, CCl_4) and aqueous solutions (0.01 *M* HNO_3). As would be expected, the extraction coefficients are very high, being greater than for iodine at comparable concentrations.

Extraction into organic solvents has been extremely useful in studying astatine, and this technique has also been applied in work on the valency states, and in chemical separations. The element itself is reduced by Zn or SO_2 to give At^-, which coprecipitates quantitatively with AgI or TlI in acid or alkaline solution (by forming insoluble astatides). This coprecipitation does not occur in concentrated nitric acid solution, which oxidizes astatine to a positive oxidation state, as do Fe(III), Hg(II), and Br_2; in this state, astatine is not precipitated with AgI or $AgIO_3$. On the other hand, if a more powerful oxidizing agent such as HOCl or $K_2S_2O_8$ is used, coprecipitation with $AgIO_3$ is complete. It appears from this that astatine has two positive valencies, the higher state being the pentavalent (AtO_3^-).

After nitric acid oxidation, astatine migrates to the anode, and so must be in solution in some anionic state (AtO_3^-, AtO^-?); more energetic oxidation does not change this. Electrolysis in nitric acid solution deposits the element on both electrodes, but the significance of these electrolytic results is not clear.

The first isotope of *radon*, Rn^{220} (thoron), was discovered by Owens and Rutherford in 1899. Sixteen isotopes of the element are known at present, of which Rn^{222} (radon itself) the daughter element of radium, has the longest half-life of 3.825 days. Radon is an inert gas, and is therefore formally zero-valent. Like the other heavy inert gases, it can, however, form definite compounds held together by Van der Waals forces. Nikitin [87, 88, 89] has reported evidence for the existence of a hydrate $Rn \cdot 6H_2O$

isomorphous with $H_2S{\cdot}6H_2O$ and $SO_2{\cdot}6H_2O$. When these latter compounds are crystallized in the presence of radon, the distribution of the radon hydrate between the crystals and the aqueous phase obeys the Berthelot-Nernst law (Section 21–3), which is a criterion of isomorphism. Helium does not form compounds of this type, so that this property can be used to separate the two gases. Phenol and *p*-chlorophenol also form similar molecular clathrate compounds with radon.

Radon is soluble in water, and to a greater extent in alcohols and various other organic solvents. It is strongly adsorbed by a number of solids, and this property is sometimes used in purifying the gas.*

When radon is generated in some crystalline radium compound (or thoron from a thorium compound), or from Ra incorporated in another solid, the gas spontaneously liberated from the solid in differing extent. The ratio between the number of Rn atoms liberated and the number formed by radioactive disintegration in unit time is the *emanating power*. This parameter is very sensitive to changes in the surface state, in the structure, and in the chemical composition. The various physico-chemical applications of this property are discussed later in Chapter 21.

7–8 The cisuranium elements. Under this heading we shall consider the five elements with atomic numbers between 87 and 91, preceding uranium in the seventh long period of the periodic system.

The first isotope of element 87, *francium*, was discovered by Mlle. Perey [90] while studying the radiations emitted by actinium. She was able to show that in addition to the well-established β-decay, this element has a small α-branching (1.2%) to give Fr^{223} (AcK, half-life 21 min). Seven other isotopes of lower mass, and with shorter half-lives, have since been prepared artificially. In agreement with its position in the periodic system, francium is an alkali metal, and the most electropositive element. Experiments on coprecipitation and mixed crystallization have demonstrated the marked analogy between this element and its homologue caesium. For example, the solubility of the simple metal salts generally increases from potassium to caesium, and the solubility of the double salts decreases in the same order. In agreement with this, francium is carried down virtually completely on crystals of Cs_2PtCl_6, Cs_2BiCl_5, Cs_2SbCl_5, Cs_2SnCl_6, and $Cs_2Na[Co(NO_2)]_6$, but is only partly coprecipitated with caesium perchlorate, picrate, and tartrate [91]. In dilute solution, potassium tartrate can be precipitated and francium left in solution. Carrier-free francium [92] can be obtained by coprecipitation with silico-tungstic acid in concentrated HCl solution; after the precipitate is dissolved in water, francium can be separated by ion exchange.

Some 13 isotopes of *radium* are currently known; the isotope of mass 226, first discovered by Pierre and Marie Curie and Bémont, has the longest half-life (1620 years). It is a divalent element, with all the characteristic properties of an alkaline earth metal. The metal itself can be ob-

* The activity picked up by greases exposed to radon, and often attributed to adsorbed radon, may in fact be due to the adsorption of the active deposit (J. Labeyrie, personal communication).

tained by electrolytic reduction at a mercury cathode [93] or by decomposition of the nitride [94]. It melts at about 700°C.

The half-life of the *actinium* isotope of mass 227, estimated from the increase in activity of its initially pure parent (Pa^{231}), is 21.7 years [95, 96], although smaller values, even as low as 9 years, have also been obtained with preparations extracted from minerals. In addition to the natural isotope MsTh-2, nine other isotopes with masses between 221 and 231 have been prepared artificially.

Actinium is homologous with lanthanum and chemically analogous to the rare earth elements (lanthanides). In separation procedures, it acts as a more basic homologue of these elements. One anomaly has been found in the fractional crystallization of the double magnesium nitrates of the rare earths, namely Ac does not come out at the beginning with La, but is found between Nd and Sm. Ion exchange methods have been used to obtain the element in the carrier-free state [97, 98]. Actinium forms an insoluble hydroxide, fluoride, iodate, phosphate, carbonate, and oxalate.* Milligram quantities of Ac in more than 95% purity were obtained by the neutron bombardment of one gram of radium [99, 100]. About a milligram of the metal was obtained by reduction of the fluoride with Li at 1200°C; the metal forms face-centered cubic crystals, and melts at 1050°C.

Natural *thorium* is a mixture of two isotopes, Th^{232} (1.4×10^{10} years) and Th^{228} (RdTh, 1.9 years); each of the three natural radioactive series contains two thorium isotopes (UX-1 and Io, UY and RdAc, etc.). Five other isotopes have been prepared artificially. The element is homologous with Hf and Zr, but, in agreement with its position in the periodic system, is more basic. The normal valency is the very stable tetravalent state, which is found even in the nitride Th_3N_4, although the corresponding compounds of Zr and Hf, ZrN and HfN, contain the trivalent state. Reduction of ThI_4 with metallic thorium at about 600° gives ThI_3 and ThI_2, which react vigorously with water, producing hydrogen and tetravalent Th [101, 102]. This behavior is similar to that shown by the lower iodides of Hf and Zr, and different from the very stable CeI_3. The only significant similarity between thorium and cerium is the formation of an insoluble fluoride ThF_4 not found with Zr and Hf, but whereas this is very stable, CeF_4 decomposes easily giving off HF and (probably)F_2.†

The first isotope of *protactinium*, Pa^{234} (UX2), was discovered in 1913 by Fajans and Göhring who named it "brevium" because of its short half-life (1.17 min). There is also a nuclear isomer, UZ, with a half-life of 6.7 hours. In addition to the isotope Pa^{231}, from which the element is named, there are eleven others with masses between 224 and 237.

The chemistry of protactinium can be summarized very briefly [103, 104] by stating that it is the higher homologue of tantalum and niobium, but

---

* A detailed discussion of the nuclear and chemical properties of Ac is given by F. T. Hagemann in *The Actinide Elements*, G. T. Seaborg and J. J. Katz, eds., McGraw-Hill, New York, 1954, p. 14; and by G. Bouissières, *Nouveau Traité de Chimie Minérale de Pascal*, Vol. VII, 1960.

† For a discussion of the chemistry of thorium, see L. I. Katzin in *The Actinide Elements, op. cit.*, p. 66.

that it also has certain other characteristics which bring it nearer to hafnium and zirconium. The relation to the first two elements is well illustrated in the difficulties involved in the chemical handling and separation of the element. Protactinium is in fact chemically one of the most inert elements; it forms compounds which are generally insoluble and are easily hydrolysed. Like its homologues and some elements in group IV (Ti, Zr, Hf), its behavior is considerably affected by the properties of the other elements which are present; in particular, the tendency to hydrolyse and the solubility are often sharply changed in some way. Because of these effects, conclusions about the chemical properties based on experiments carried out in the presence of related elements (either because they occur naturally with Pa, or because they have been deliberately added as "carriers," see Section 21–1) must be treated with more than usual caution.

Protactinium is a pentavalent element in its normal state, although for many years there was some controversy as to whether it bore the closest resemblance to pentavalent tantalum or tetravalent zirconium. In fact it must show analogies with both these elements, since in the periodic table changes of properties are due to increasing ionic radius (vertically) and in the opposite sense to increasing valency (horizontally). This means that an element has characteristics in common not only with its homologue, but also with the element immediately to the left of the latter (the *diagonal rule*). Examples relevant to the present chapter are thorium with lanthanum [and hence with Ce(III)], polonium with antimony, and protactinium with hafnium (and hence with Zr). The strict analogies between the homologues of groups IV and VI in the 5th and 6th periods (more than in the 6th and 7th periods) are the result of the lanthanide contraction, which reduces the difference in ionic (and atomic) radii of the homologues in the 5th and 6th periods, and so reduces the chemical differences. This factor does not arise in going from the 6th to the 7th period, so that a new rare earth family does not appear, and the change in the properties is therefore more pronounced. These comments will again be relevant in discussing the classification of the elements of the 7th period of the periodic table (Section 8–8).

Since it is more electropositive than tantalum, protactinium does not form compounds analogous to the tantalates. It also appears to have less tendency to form complexes, although its compounds dissolve in aqueous HF or alkaline fluoride to give complex ions such as $[PaF_7]^{2-}$. The solubility of Pa in such media is great, as it is in solutions containing citrate, tartrate, or other complexing ligands. The solubility in strong mineral acids such as HCl, H_2SO_4, or dilute HNO_3 is very small. It can be easily extracted from these solutions by a large number of organic solvents, including di-isopropyl ketone, methyl dioctylamine, theonyltrifluoro acetone, tributyl phosphate, etc.

When treated with zinc amalgam in hydrofluoric solution, or with Cr^{2+} in HCl, Pa(V) passes to the less stable Pa(IV) state [105], in which it shows analytical properties in common with the neighboring tetravalent elements, with a strong tendency to form insoluble compounds (fluoride, iodate, phosphate, double potassium sulfate, phenyl arsonate). A black oxide, PaO_2, has also been prepared by the reduction of Pa_4O_9 with hydrogen at 1600°C [106]. No trivalent compounds of protactinium are known in solution, but the hydride PaH_3 can be prepared by the action of hydrogen on the metal at 250 to 300°C.

The metal itself was first prepared by Grosse and Agruss [107] using either the dissociation of the oxides with 35-kv electrons in vacuo, or the dissociation of halide vapors on a tungsten filament at a pressure of 10^{-5} mm. It can also be obtained by the reduction of PaF_4 with barium at 1500°C [106]. Thin layers of the metal can be deposited on Pt, Au, Cu, Ni, or Pb by cathodic reduction in HF solution at pH 6 [108, 109]. From the cathodic deposition potential on various metals, and the concentration dependence, the normal potential of the $Pa/[PaF_7]^{2-}$ electrode is estimated at approximately -1 v [110]. Very small quantities, probably of a superficial peroxide, can be anodically deposited on Pt or Pb [111]. The metal has a tetragonal structure, with a calculated density of 15.37. Its optical spectrum has been investigated between 2650 and 5800 A [112, 113]; the lines recommended for spectroscopic analysis are those at 4291.3, 4248.1, 4217.2, 4056.1, 4018.2, 4012.9, 3970.0, 3957.8, 2980.5, 2959.7, 2940.2, 2909.6, and 2743.9 A. The limit of detection is about 0.2 μg. The x-ray spectrum has been studied by Beuthe and Grosse, and by Dolejsek and Marek [114, 115, 116].

7-9 Uranium. The nuclear properties of the most important uranium isotopes, U^{238}, U^{235}, and U^{233} have already been discussed. The last named does not occur naturally, and eleven others with masses between 227 and 240 have also been synthesized.

Uranium is a homologue of tungsten and molybdenum, and like these elements its most stable valency is VI. In particular it forms UF_6, analogous to MoF_6 and WF_6; all three compounds are volatile, and have very similar infrared and Raman spectra [117]. Uranium hexafluoride is, of course, very important in nuclear chemistry because of its use in the separation of U^{235} (Section 9-7). In solution the valencies VI, V, IV, and III are known; of these the trivalent state is less stable than in the homologues, in agreement with the general rule for the effect of atomic weight on the lower valencies in the same A subgroup of the periodic system.

Other differences between uranium and its homologues are due to its higher electropositivity and to differences of the same type as those noted above between protactinium and tantalum. In the hexavalent state, uranium exists in aqueous solution as the uranyl ion UO_2^{2+}; this is, however, less basic than PaO_2^+, and forms uranate salts. Unlike tungsten and molybdenum, uranium cannot be incorporated into heteropoly acids as M′ in $H_m[M_n(M'O_p)_q]$. This is apparently limited to the three elements V, Mo, and W, no doubt because of their particularly favorable atomic radii, but like many other elements, uranium can occur in these acids as the central atom M. Various authors [118, 119, 120] have shown, however, that hydrolysis of UO_2^{2+} leads to the formation of polynuclear complexes $U_2O_5^{2+}$, $U_3O_8^{2+}$, $U_3O_8(OH)_3^-$, etc., which is typical of the group VI A elements. In the solid state, the uranates formed by U(IV), U(V), and U(VI) (MUO_3, MUO_4, M_2UO_5, and M_3UO_6, where M is an alkaline earth metal) showed marked analogies, both in constitution and in properties, with the corresponding wolframates and molybdates [121].

The large scale use of uranium in nuclear reactors has raised a large number of chemical and metallurgical problems, which have resulted in a considerable increase in our knowledge of the properties of the element. Only two examples will be given. For the construction of aqueous homogeneous reactors, it is important to know the solubility and resistance to hydrolysis of various uranyl salts at high temperatures. These properties have recently been studied [122] for the nitrate, sulfate, chromate, phosphate, and chlorides up to temperatures exceeding 300°C, and the binary and ternary phase diagrams established. The effects of the products of the radiolytic decomposition of the solvent, H_2 and H_2O_2, on these systems have also been examined. Similarly it has been suggested that in the projected U^{233}-Bi homogeneous reactor (Section 6–8) the rare earths produced in fission could be extracted by treatment with a molten KCl-LiCl mixture at 450°C, leaving the uranium in the metallic phase. For these purposes, the partition coefficients of various components and equilibrium constants of reactions such as

$$3LiCl + La \rightleftharpoons 3Li + LaCl_3$$

have been measured at temperatures as high as 1000°K [123].

Other advances which have been made in the general study of uranium* include:

1. The preparation of high purity uranium metal by various techniques, including the reduction of the oxides or halides with Mg, Ca, CaH_2, or alkali metals, electrolytic reduction of a molten flux, and thermal dissociation of the iodide. As a consequence of this, much more precise measurement of the various physical constants of the metal is possible than was previously the case. Thus the melting point of 99% pure uranium† is 1133°C [124], whereas the values in the prewar literature, doubtless obtained with oxide-contaminated metal, are above 1800°C. The boiling point is 3900°C, and the density, at 20°C, 19.1. The resistance of uranium metal to corrosion has also been widely studied in various media.
2. An improvement in extraction methods for minerals with a low uranium content.
3. A considerable improvement in the analytical and separation methods for uranium compounds, especially by those methods involving extraction with organic solvents such as ethyl ether, ketones, pentaether, tributyl and dialkyl phosphates, and chelate complexes.
4. A wider knowledge of the chemistry of uranium fluorine compounds, and of the chemistry of fluorine in general.

---

* For a general discussion of the chemistry of uranium, see H. R. Hoekstra and J. J. Katz, in *The Actinide Elements*, *op. cit.*, p. 130, and J. J. Katz and E. Rabinowitch, *The Chemistry of Uranium*, McGraw-Hill, New York, 1951.

† Allendorfer, *Z. Naturforsch.*, **5a**, 234 (1950) gives 1090°C for the melting point of 99.96% pure U.

5. Information on the oxidation state, V, which can be obtained by the electrolytic reduction of UO_2^{2+} at a mercury cathode, by reducing U(VI) with U(IV) or zinc amalgam, or (better) by dissolving UCl_5 in water.

Following P. Kauranen (*Ann. Acad. Scient. Fennicae*, **A6**, 96, 1962), there exists a small α branching in RaD (1.7×10^{-8}) with formation of Hg^{206}, radioactive β^- with a half-life of 8.5 min (see Fig. 7–1).

References

1. A. V. Grosse, W. M. Johnston, R. L. Wolfgang, and W. F. Libby, *Science*, **113**, 1 (1951).
2. E. L. Fireman, *Phys. Rev.*, **91**, 922 (1953).
3. E. L. Fireman and D. Schwarze, *Phys. Rev.*, **94**, 385 (1954).
4. J. R. Arnold and H. Ali Al-Salih, *Science*, **121**, 451 (1955).
5. J. R. Arnold, *Geochemical Symposium*, Minneapolis, 1955.
6. P. S. Goel, S. Jha, D. Lal, P. Radhakrishna, and Rama, *Nuclear Phys.*, **1**, 196 (1956).
7. S. Kaufman and W. F. Libby, *Phys. Rev.*, **93**, 1337 (1954).
8. V. Faltings and P. Harteck, *Z. Naturforsch.*, **5a**, 438 (1950).
9. P. Harteck, *J. Chem. Phys.*, **22**, 1746 (1954).
10. A. V. Grosse, A. D. Kirshenbaum, J. L. Kulp, and W. S. Broecker, *Phys. Rev.*, **93**, 250 (1954).
11. W. F. Libby, *Proc. Natl. Acad. Sci. U. S.*, **39**, 245 (1953).
12. E. C. Anderson, W. F. Libby, S. Weinhouse, A. F. Reid, A. D. Kirschenbaum, and A. V. Grosse, *Science*, **105**, 576 (1947).
13. E. C. Anderson, W. F. Libby, S. Weinhouse, A. F. Reid, A. D. Kirschenbaum, and A. V. Grosse, *Phys. Rev.*, **72**, 931 (1947).
14. See, however, E. S. Deevey, M. S. Gross, G. E. Hutchinson, and H. L. Kraybill, *Proc. Natl. Acad. Sci. U. S.*, **40**, 285 (1954).
15. W. F. Libby, *Phys. Rev.*, **69**, 671 (1946).
16. W. F. Libby, *Radiocarbon Dating*, Chicago University Press, Chicago, 1952.
17. E. C. Anderson and W. F. Libby, *Phys. Rev.*, **81**, 64 (1951).
18. E. C. Anderson, *Ann. Rev. Nuclear Sci.*, **2**, 63 (1953).
19. B. L. Funt, S. Sobering, R. W. Pringle, and W. Turchinetz, *Nature*, **175**, 1042 (1955).
20. G. J. Fergusson, *Nucleonics*, **13**, No. 1, 18 (1955).
21. H. E. Suess, *Science*, **120**, 5, 457 (1954).
22. A. R. Crathorn, *Nature*, **172**, 632 (1953).
23. A. Tromifov, quoted by A. P. Vinogradov, *Bull. Acad. Sci. U.S.S.R.*, No. 3, 3 (1954).
24. Based on values given by T. P. Kohman and N. Saito, *Ann. Rev. Nuclear Sci.*, **4**, 401 (1954).
25. F. Birch, *J. Geophys. Research*, **56**, 107 (1952) (quoted in Ref. 24).
26. T. P. Kohman, *Science*, **119**, 851 (1954).
27. G. E. Boyd, J. R. Sites, Q. V. Larson, and C. R. Baldock, *Phys. Rev.*, **99**, 1030 (1955).
28. C. E. Moore, *Science*, **114**, 59 (1951).
29. H. Hubenet, C. de Jager, and C. Zwaan, *Mem. Soc. roy. sci. Liège*, **14**, 471 (1954).

30. P. W. Merrill, *Science,* **115,** 484 (1952).
31. E. A. Alperovitch, *Thesis,* Columbia University, 1954.
32. E. A. Alperovitch and J. M. Miller, *Nature,* **176,** 299 (1955).
33. W. Herr, *Z. Naturforsch.,* **9a,** 907 (1954).
34. C. Perrier and E. Segrè, *R. C. Lincei,* **25,** 723 (1937).
35. C. Perrier and E. Segrè, *J. Chem. Phys.,* **5,** 715 (1937); **7,** 155 (1939).
36. E. E. Motta, G. E. Boyd, and Q. V. Larson, *Phys. Rev.,* **72,** 1270 (1947).
37. S. Fried, *J. Am. Chem. Soc.,* **70,** 442 (1948).
38. J. B. Gerlit, *1955 Geneva Conference,* P. 671.
39. G. H. Cartledge, *J. Am. Chem. Soc.,* **77,** 2658 (1955).
40. G. H. Cartledge, *J. Phys. Chem.,* **59,** 979 (1955).
41. M. Lederer, *Anal. Chim. Acta,* **12,** 146 (1955).
42. S. Tribalat and J. Beydon, *Anal. Chim. Acta,* **8,** 22 (1953).
43. W. Goishi and W. F. Libby, *J. Am. Chem. Soc.,* **74,** 6109 (1952).
44. L. B. Rogers, *J. Am. Chem. Soc.,* **71,** 1507 (1949).
45. R. C. L. Mooney, *Phys. Rev.,* **72,** 1269 (1947).
46. D. L. Timma, *J. Opt. Soc. Am.,* **39,** 898 (1949).
47. W. F. Meggers and B. F. Scribner, *J. Opt. Soc. Am.,* **39,** 1059 (1949).
48. L. E. Burkhart, W. F. Peed, and B. G. Saunders, *Phys. Rev.,* **73,** 347 (1948).
49. J. A. Marinsky, L. E. Glendenin, and C. D. Coryell, *J. Am. Chem. Soc.,* **69,** 2781 (1947).
50. G. T Seaborg, *Am. Scientist,* **36,** 361 (1948).
51. C. Feldman, *J. Am. Chem. Soc.,* **71,** 3841 (1948).
52. G. W. Parker and P. M. Lantz, *J. Am. Chem. Soc.,* **72,** 2834 (1950).
53. L. E. Burkhardt, W. F. Peed, and E. J. Spitzer, *Phys. Rev.,* **75,** 86 (1949); **76,** 143 (1949).
54. F. Hagemann, L. I. Katzin, M. H. Studier, A. Ghiorso, and G. T. Seaborg, *Phys. Rev.,* **72,** 252 (1947); **79,** 435 (1950).
55. A. C. English, T. E. Cranshaw, P. Demers, E. P. Hincks, J. A. Harvey, J. V. Jelley, and A. N. May, *Phys. Rev.,* **72,** 253 (1947).
56. D. F. Peppard, G. W. Mason, P. R. Gray, and J. F. Mech, *J. Am. Chem. Soc.,* **74,** 6081 (1952).
57. A. Ghiorso, W. W. Meinke, and G. T. Seaborg, *Phys. Rev.,* **74,** 695 (1948); **75,** 314 (1949); **81,** 782 (1951); **85,** 429 (1952).
58. S. Rosenblum and H. Tyren, *Compt. rend.,* **239,** 1205 (1954).
59. H. Atterling, W. Forsling, and B. Astrom, *Physica,* **22,** 1193 (1956).
60. M. Guillot, *J. Chim. Phys.,* **28,** 14, 92 (1931).
61. H. W. Martin, *J. Phys. Chem.,* **58,** 911 (1954).
62. K. W. Bagnall and R. M. W. D'Eye, *J. Chem. Soc.,* **1954,** 4295.
63. K. W. Bagnall, R. M. W. D'Eye, and J. H. Freeman, *J. Chem. Soc.,* **1955,** 2320.
64. K. W. Bagnall, *1955 Geneva Conference,* P. 439.
65. E. F. Joy, *Chem. Eng. News,* **32,** 3848 (1954).
66. M. Haïssinsky and M. Guillot, *J. phys. radium,* **5,** 419 (1934).
67. M. Haïssinsky and M. Guillot, *Bull. soc. chim. France,* **2,** 239 (1935).
68. E. Orban, *U.S.A.E.C. report MLM-973,* (1954).
69. F. A. Paneth, *Ber.,* **51,** 1704 (1918).
70. F. A. Paneth and A. Johannsen, *Ber.,* **55,** 2622 (1922).

71. V. G. KHLOPINE and A. SAMARTZEVA, *Compt. rend. acad. sci. U.S.S.R.*, **4,** 433 (1934).
72. M. HAÏSSINSKY, *J. Chim. Phys.*, **30,** 27 (1933).
73. W. H. BEAMER and C. R. MAXWELL, *J. Chem. Phys.*, **14,** 569 (1946); **17,** 1293 (1949).
74. C. R. MAXWELL, *J. Chem. Phys.*, **17,** 1288 (1949).
75. L. S. BROOKS, *J. Am. Chem. Soc.*, **77,** 3211 (1955).
76. G. W. CHARLES, D. J. HUNT, G. PISH, and D. L. TIMMA, *J. Opt. Soc. Am.*, **45,** 869 (1955).
77. D. R. CORSON, K. R. MACKENZIE, and E. SEGRÈ, *Phys. Rev.*, **58,** 672 (1940).
78. B. KARLIK and T. BERNERT, *Naturwiss.*, **31,** 298, 413 (1943).
79. B. KARLIK and T. BERNERT, *Z. Physik,* **123,** 51 (1944).
80. R. WALEN, *Compt. rend.*, **227,** 1090 (1948).
81. B. KARLIK and T. BERNERT, *Naturwiss.*, **31,** 492 (1943); **32,** 44 (1944).
82. P. AVIGNON, *J. phys. radium,* **11,** 521 (1950).
83. E. K. HYDE and A. GHIORSO, *Phys. Rev.*, **90,** 267 (1953).
84. G. L. JOHNSTON, R. F. LEININGER, and E. SEGRÈ, *J. Chem. Phys.*, **17,** 1 (1949).
85. G. W. BARTON, A. GHIORSO, and I. PERLMAN, *Phys. Rev.*, **82,** 13 (1951).
86. W. M. GARRISON, J. D. GILE, R. D. MAXWELL, and J. G. HAMILTON, *Anal. Chem.*, **23,** 204 (1951).
87. B. A. NIKITIN, *J. Gen. Chem. Russ.*, **9,** 1176 (1936).
88. B. A. NIKITIN, *Compt. rend. acad. sci. U.S.S.R.*, **24,** 565 (1939).
89. B. A. NIKITIN and E. M. IOFFE, *Doklady Akad. Nauk S.S.S.R.*, **85,** 809 (1952).
90. M. PEREY, *Compt. rend.*, **208,** 97 (1939).
91. M. PEREY, *J. Chim. Phys.*, **43,** 155, 262 (1946).
92. E. K. HYDE, *J. Am. Chem. Soc.*, **74,** 4181 (1952).
93. M. CURIE and A. DEBIERNE, *Compt. rend.*, **151,** 523 (1910).
94. E. EBLER, *Ber.*, **43,** 2613 (1910).
95. I. CURIE and G. BOUISSIÈRES, *Cahiers Phys.*, No. 26, 1 (1944).
96. J. M. HOLLANDER and R. F. LEININGER, *Phys. Rev.*, **80,** 915 (1950).
97. G. T. YANG and M. HAÏSSINSKY, *Bull. soc. chim. France,* **16,** 546 (1949).
98. C. K. MCLANE and S. PETERSON, in *The Transuranium Elements* (N.N.E.S., IV–14B), McGraw-Hill, New York, 1949, p. 1385.
99. F. HAGEMANN, *J. Am. Chem. Soc.*, **72,** 768 (1950).
100. J. G. STITES, M. L. SALUTSKY, and B. D. STONE, *J. Am. Chem. Soc.*, **77,** 237 (1955).
101. J. S. ANDERSON and R. M. W. D'EYE, *J. Chem. Soc.*, **1949,** S 244.
102. E. HAYEK and T. REHNER, *Experientia,* **5,** 114 (1949).
103. G. BOUISSIÈRES and M. HAÏSSINSKY, *Bull. soc. chim. France,* **18,** 557 (1951).
104. R. E. ELSON, in *The Actinide Elements,* G. T. SEABORG and J. J. KATZ, eds., McGraw-Hill, New York, 1954, p. 103.
105. G. BOUISSIÈRES and M. HAÏSSINSKY, *Bull. soc. chim. France,* **18,** 146 (1951).
106. P. A. SELLERS, S. FRIED, R. E. ELSON, and W. H. ZACHARIASEN, *J. Am. Chem. Soc.*, **76,** 5935 (1954).

107. A. V. Grosse and M. S. Agruss, *J. Am. Chem. Soc.*, **56,** 2200 (1934).
108. H. Emmanuel and M. Haïssinsky, *Compt. rend.*, **206,** 1102 (1938).
109. J. Danon and C. Ferradini, *Compt. rend.*, **234,** 1361 (1952).
110. C. Ferradini, *J. Chim. Phys.*, **51,** 286 (1954).
111. M. Haïssinsky, *J. Chim. Phys.*, **43,** 66 (1946).
112. H. Schuler and H. Gollnow, *Naturwiss.*, **22,** 511 (1934).
113. F. S. Tomkins and M. Fred, *J. Opt. Soc. Am.*, **39,** 357 (1949).
114. H. Beuthe and A. V. Grosse, *Z. Physik,* **61,** 170 (1931).
115. V. Dolejsek and J. Marek, *Z. Physik,* **97,** 70 (1935).
116. Y. Cauchois, *J. phys. radium,* **13,** 113 (1952).
117. T. G. Burke, F. D. Smith, and A. H. Nielsen, *J. Chem. Phys.*, **20,** 447 (1952).
118. J. Faucherre, *Compt. rend.*, **227,** 1367 (1948).
119. J. Sutton, *J. Chem. Soc.*, **1949,** S 275.
120. T. V. Arden, *J. Chem. Soc.*, **1949,** S 299.
121. R. Scholder and L. Brixner, *Z. Naturforsch.*, **10b,** 178 (1955).
122. C. H. Secoy, *1955 Geneva Conference*, P. 821.
123. D. W. Bareis, R. H. Wiswall, and W. E. Winsche, *Nucleonics,* **12,** No. 7, 40 (1954).
124. A. I. Dahl and H. E. Cleaves, *J. Research Natl. Bur. Standards,* **43,** 513 (1949).

CHAPTER 8

THE TRANSURANIUM ELEMENTS

8–1 The properties of the transuranium nuclides. As a result of the synthesis of elements 93 and 94 (Section 1–7), sufficient information about the radioactive properties and chemical behavior of these two elements became available for a successful search for their existence in various minerals to be undertaken. As a result of this work, minute quantities of Np^{237} and Pu^{239} were extracted [see Section 7–5 for the discovery of neptunium and the $(4n + 1)$ radioactive family]. Quantities of Pu^{239} of the order of a microgram were isolated, starting with one ton of pitchblende [1]; the Pu^{239}/U^{238} ratio in pitchblende from various sources, and in monazites [2], is of the order of 3 to 12×10^{-12}.

The various methods by which nuclides with atomic numbers between 93 and 103 can be prepared artificially have already been outlined in Chapter 5. In principle, when uranium or plutonium receive a sufficiently intense neutron flux from a reactor, the various isotopes of all the heavier elements are formed successively as the result of (n, γ) reactions followed by β-decay [3]. Thus einsteinium (Es, $Z = 99$) and fermium (Fm, $Z = 100$) were first detected in uranium which had been exposed to the extremely intense neutron flux of a thermonuclear explosion [4]. It is suggested that in such a flux, the uranium nuclides could capture up to 17 neutrons, to give U^{253} and U^{255} in particular, and that these would decay by successive β-disintegrations to Es^{253} and Fm^{255}. Other nuclides discovered in the debris resulting from a thermonuclear explosion include Pu^{246}, Am^{246}, Cm^{250}, and Cf^{254}.

Naturally enough, the yields from this procedure fall off rapidly with increasing atomic number. A more useful method is to bombard appropriate targets with accelerated ions such as deuterons, helium ions, C^{6+}, N^{6+}, or O^{6+}. By making use of nuclear reactions such as (d, xn), (α, xn), (α, pxn), (C^{6+}, xn), etc., it has been possible to prepare transcurium isotopes in quantities which cannot be weighed, but which are sufficient for the essential nuclear characteristics to be determined. Lists of the transuranium nuclides known at present, with their half-lives and modes of disintegration, are given in Tables 8–1 and 8–2.

The first isotope of americium, mass 241, was discovered in 1944 by Seaborg, James, and Morgan, who bombarded uranium with 40-Mev helium ions:

$$U^{238}\ (\alpha, n)\ Pu^{241} \xrightarrow{\beta} Am^{241}.$$

Seaborg and his collaborators were also responsible for the discovery of curium in the same year by the bombardment of plutonium $Pu^{239}\ (\alpha, n)\ Cm^{242}$ Berkelium was discovered in 1949, $Am^{241}\ (\alpha, 2n)\ Bk^{243}$, and californium in 1950 by the reaction $Cm^{242}\ (\alpha, 2n)\ Cf^{244}$. The relevant

TABLE 8–1

THE ISOTOPES OF Np, Pu, Am, AND Cm*

Mass	Np		Pu		Am		Cm	
	$t_{1/2}$	disintegration	$t_{1/2}$	disintegration	$t_{1/2}$	disintegration	$t_{1/2}$	disintegration
231	~50 min	α						
232	13 min	e	36 min	α, e				
233	35 min	α, e	20 min	α, e				
234	4.4 d	e, β^-	9 hr	α, e				
235	410 d	α, e	26 min	α, e				
236	22 hr	β^-, e	2.85 yr	α				
236*m*	>5000 yr							
237	2.2×10^6 yr	α	45.6 d	α, e	1.3 hr	α, e		
237*m*	6×10^{-8} sec	γ	0.18 sec	γ				
238	2.1 d	β^-	86.4 yr	α	1.86 hr	e	2.5 hr	α, e
239	2.33 d	β^-	24360 yr	α	12 hr	α, e	2.9 hr	e
239*m*			1.1×10^{-9} sec and 1.83×10^{-9} sec	γ				
240	63 min	β^-	6580 yr	α	47 hr	e	26.8 d	α
240*m*	7.3 min	β^-						
241	16 min	β^-	13.25 yr	α, β^-	457.7 yr	α	35 d	α, e
241*m*	3.4 hr	β^-						
242			3.79×10^5 yr	α	16 hr	β^-, e	162.5 d	α
242*m*					152 yr	γ, α		
243			4.98 hr	β^-	7950 yr	α	35 yr	α
244			7.6×10^7 yr	α	26 min	β^-, e	18.4 yr	α
245			10.1 hr	β^-	2.0 hr	β^-	7500 yr	α
246			10.85 d	β^-	25 min	β^-	6620 yr	α
247							$>4 \times 10^7$ yr	α
248							4.2×10^6 yr	α, fission
249							63 min	β^-
250							1.7×10^4 yr	fission

* See Table 6–2 for the spontaneous fission half-lives of these nuclides.

TABLE 8–2

THE ISOTOPES OF THE TRANSURANIUM ELEMENTS*

Mass	Bk		Cf		Es		Fm		Md	
	$t_{1/2}$	disintegration	$t_{1/2}$	disintegration	$t_{1/2}$	disintegration	$t_{1/2}$	disintegration	$t_{1/2}$	disintegration
243	4.5 hr	α, e								
244	4.4 hr	e	25.3 min	α						
245	4.95 d	α, e	44 min	α, e						
246	1.9 d	e	35.7 hr	α	7.3 min	e				
247	4×10^3 yr		2.7 hr	e						
248	16 hr	β^-	250 d	α	25 min	e, α	0.6 min	α, e		
249	314 d	α, β^-	470 yr	α	2 hr	e, α	2.5 min	α		
250	3.1 hr	β^-	9.3 yr	α	8 hr	e	30 min	α		
251			660 yr	α	1.5 d	e, α	7 hr	e, α		
252			2.55 yr	α, fission	~140 d		22.7 hr	α		
253			20 d	β^-	20.03 d	α	4.5 d	α, e		
254			56.2 d	fission	480 d	α	3.2 hr	α, fission		
254*m*					38.5 hr	β^-, e	21.5 hr	β^-		
255					24.2 d	β^-	3.2 hr	α, fission	0.5 hr	e
256					1 hr	β^-	160 min	fission	1.5 hr	e

* See Table 6–2 for the spontaneous fission half-lives of these nuclides.

sections of Chapters 1 and 5 should be consulted for the history of the discovery of elements 93, 94, 99, and 100. The first isotope of mendelevium (Md, $Z = 101$) was prepared by Seaborg and his group by the bombardment of a target of Es^{253} (10^9 to 10^{10} atoms) with a very intense beam of 41-Mev helium ions [5]. This gives Md^{256}, which decays by K-capture to Fm^{256}. Only about 20 atoms of this isotope were prepared in these experiments.

In 1957, a group of Swedish, English, and American workers claimed that element 102 had been obtained by bombarding a target of curium with $^{13}C^{6+}$ ions [6],

$$Cm^{244}\ (C^{6+}, 4n \text{ or } 6n)\ 102^{253 \text{ or } 251} \qquad (t_{1/2} \sim 10 \text{ min}).$$

This nuclide was reported to emit 8.5-Mev α-particles; the new element was given the name nobelium. Ghiorso, *et al.* [7], however, were not able to confirm these results, and claim that by irradiating a similar Cm^{244} target with accelerated C^{12} ions they obtained an α-emitting isotope of element 102, with a half-life of three seconds; this nuclide would be of mass 254. A group of Russian workers [8] have discovered a new nuclide which emits 8.8-Mev α-particles, from the bombardment of plutonium with accelerated O^{16} ions; Pu^{241} (O^{16}, xn) 102. This could be the same nuclide as that prepared by Ghiorso and his co-workers. The first isotope of element 103, Lawrencium (Lw), of mass 257, has been prepared [8a] by the nuclear reaction

$$_{98}Cf^{250-252} + {_5}B^{10,11} \rightarrow {_{103}}Lw^{257} + x\text{n}.$$

This nuclide emits 8.6-Mev α-particles and has a half-life of 8 ± 2 sec.

The fission behavior of the most important nuclides of this group of elements has already been discussed in Chapter 6.

8–2 The uranides. From the chemical properties of the transuranium elements, it is possible to divide them into two groups—the uranides, which includes neptunium, plutonium, americium, and uranium itself, and the curides, comprising curium, berkelium, californium, einsteinium, fermium, mendelevium, nobelium, and lawrencium. The characteristic feature of the uranides is their multiple valencies, which in aqueous solution extend from III to VI. The curides are all trivalent in solution, although berkelium also has a tetravalent state, and curium forms solid CmO_2 and CmF_4. The differences and the similarities between the two groups are discussed later.

With increasing atomic number, the stability of the higher valencies of the uranides decreases, and there is a corresponding increase, first in the stability of the tetravalent state, and then in that of the trivalent state. It follows from this that the IV and V oxidation states are more important in the aqueous solution chemistry of neptunium than is the case for uranium, although both elements have the characteristic hexavalency. The most stable state for plutonium is IV, and for americium III; no tetravalent compounds of this latter element are known in solution. Various suboxides

TABLE 8–3

OXIDATION AND REDUCTION OF THE URANIDES

	air			air, I_2, Fe^{3+}		
U III		IV				VI
				V		
	Zn + HCl			Hg cathode		
	air, cold HNO_3		air, $HClO_4$, hot HNO_3		Cl_2, BrO_3^-, MnO_4^-, Ce^{4+}	
Np III		IV		V		VI
	Zn, Hg cathode		I^-, Fe^{2+}, SO_2		I^-, Sn^{2+}, N_2H_4, SO_2	
	Cl_2, Ce^{4+}, MnO_4^-		Ce^{4+}, BrO_3^- at 85°,		hot MnO_4^-, O_3, $S_2O_8^{2-}$	
Pu III		IV				VI
				V		
	Sn^{2+}, Zn, SO_2, NH_2OH		I^-, NH_2OH, NO_2^-		I^-, SO_2, N_2H_4	
	air (high temp)		NaOCl + K_2CO_3		O_3, $S_2O_8^{2-}$, Ag^{2+}	
Am III		IV		V		VI
			I^-, N_2H_4, Fe^{2+}			

TABLE 8–4

THE REDOX POTENTIALS OF THE URANIDES (IN VOLTS)*
IN 1 *M* $HClO_4$ SOLUTION

U	−1.80	III	−0.63	IV	+0.58	V	+0.06	VI
					+0.334			
				+0.677				
Np	−1.83	III	+0.155	IV	+0.739	V	+1.137	VI
			0.447					
						+0.938		
					+1.022			
Pu	−2.03	III	+0.982	IV	+1.172	V	+0.913	VI
					+1.0427			
				+1.69				
Am	−2.32	III	+2.44	IV	+1.04	V	+1.60	VI
				+1.74				

* Values use the European sign convention.

(NpO, PuO, AmO) with metallic properties, and a hydride ($AmH_{2.7}$) have been prepared. Attempts to reduce Am^{3+} to Am^{2+} in solution have failed. The differing stability of the oxidation states of the uranides is illustrated by the typical reagents required for the various redox reactions shown in Table 8–3.

It can be seen that it is necessary to use a mercury cathode to reduce U(VI), whereas Pu(VI) and Am(VI) can be reduced by either sulfur dioxide or ferrous sulfate. Similarly, to obtain the hexavalent states of these latter elements, energetic oxidizing agents such as potassium bromate or persulfate must be used, while the salts of U(IV) are oxidized spontaneously, though slowly, by air.

The oxidation-reduction potentials also show the stabilization of the lower valencies with increasing atomic number; the data in Table 8–4 relate to perchloric acid media. These potentials are, for the most part, only approximate values, first because they vary slightly with the nature of the anion, and second because in some cases the calculations have been made from rather uncertain data, and without taking activity coefficients into account. Only those potentials which correspond to simple electron transfer (M^{3+}/M^{4+}, MO_2^+/MO_2^{2+}) are reversible. Despite these reservations, on the whole the table shows correctly the change in the redox behavior with increasing oxidation state for a given element, and for a given couple, shows the changes in the series uranium-americium.

Finally, the stabilization of the lower valencies with increasing atomic number is also shown by the oxides and halides of the uranides (Table 8–5).

TABLE 8–5

Oxides	Chlorides
UO, U_2O_3, UO_2; U_3O_8, UO_3 NpO, NpO_2, Np_3O_8 PuO, Pu_2O_3, PuO_2 AmO, Am_2O_3, AmO_2	UCl_3, UCl_4; UCl_5, UCl_6 $NpCl_3$, $NpCl_4$ $PuCl_3$ $AmCl_3$
Fluorides	**Bromides and Iodides**
UF_3, UF_4, UF_5, UF_6 NpF_3, NpF_4, NpF_6 PuF_3, PuF_4, PuF_6 AmF_3, AmF_4	UBr_3, UBr_4; UI_3, UI_4 $NpBr_3$, $NpBr_4$; NpI_3 $PuBr_3$; PuI_3 $AmBr_3$; AmI_4

In a given valency state, all the uranides show very similar properties, due to the very similar ionic radii for equal charge. The trivalent compounds are chemically like those of actinium; the tetravalent state shows analogies with Th(IV) and Pa(IV), but also with Zr(IV) and even Ti(IV) (e.g., the formation of insoluble compounds; peroxide formation; extraction into organic solvents). Some of the differences between the pentavalent uranides and Pa(V) are quite pronounced (see below). Comparable solid compounds of uranides in the same valency state are isomorphous, and have similar lattice constants. The hydroxides, fluorides, iodates, carbonates, ferrocyanides, and oxalates of the tri- and tetravalent elements are sparingly soluble in water, as are the periodates, phosphates, hypophosphates, and phenylarsenates of the tetravalent species. The hexavalent uranides form characteristic double acetates $NaMO_2(CH_3COO)_3$, where M = U, Np, Pu, or Am; these are all isomorphous, and insoluble in water. Other similarities include the solubility of the nitrates in ether, and the formation of oxinates with 8-hydroxyquinoline. The neptunates and plutonates are analogous to the uranates.

The gradual decrease in the ionic radii of the uranides in a given valency state with increasing atomic number is shown in Table 8–6

TABLE 8–6

THE IONIC RADII AND COVALENT BOND LENGTHS OF THE URANIDES, IN A*

	M^{3+}	M^{4+}	M(V)	M(VI)
U	1.03	0.93	1.50	1.42
Np	1.01	0.92	1.49	1.41
Pu	1.00	0.90	1.48	1.40
Am	0.99	0.89	1.47	1.39

* Taken from W. H. Zachariasen, in *The Actinide Elements*, G. T. Seaborg and J. J. Katz, eds., McGraw-Hill, New York, 1954, p. 769.

As for uranium, the pentavalent ions exist as NpO_2^+, PuO_2^+, and AmO_2^+, and the hexavalent states as NpO_2^{2+}, PuO_2^{2+}, and AmO_2^{2+} (neptunyl, plutonyl, and americyl). The structures of these ions have been established by x-rays [10] and by infrared studies of the aqueous solutions [11] and of the crystalline sodium double acetates [12]; the MO_2^{2+} groups have a linear (or quasi-linear) structure. The vibrational frequency and the force constants of the M—O bonds decrease in the order $k_{U-O} > k_{Np-O} > k_{Pu-O} > k_{Am-O}$, the actual values of k being 0.705, 0.698, 0.675, and 0.612 megadyne/cm. The M—O bond distances apparently decrease in the same order; this is attributed to a contraction of the electronic orbitals with increasing nuclear charge from uranium to americium. Decreasing bond strength in the same order, despite this contraction, is ascribed to increasing interaction with electrons outside the valency shell.

The absorption spectra of UO_2^{2+} [13], NpO_2^{2+} [14], and PuO_2^{2+} [13, 15] in perchlorate solution in the 400-mμ region show fine structure, which is attributed to symmetrical vibrations of the linear O—M—O group. This structure is not, however, found in the spectra of AmO_2^{2+} [16]. The MO_2^{2+}, MO_2^+, M^{4+}, and M^{3+} ions are all colored in aqueous solution (although the color of UO_2^+ is not known).

The uranides all tend to undergo disproportionation and mutual oxidation-reduction reactions between the various valency states (i.e., reproportionation). Thus a perchlorate solution initially containing PuO_2^+ changes in time to give a mixture of Pu^{3+}, Pu^{4+}, PuO_2^+, and PuO_2^{2+}, in which the latter species predominates; PuO_2^+ is absent in the mixture obtained when Pu^{4+} is the initial species. Similarly a solution of AmO_2^+ eventually gives a mixture containing Am^{3+}, AmO_2^+, and (especially) AmO_2^{2+}. Pentavalent uranium undergoes disproportionation to U^{4+} and UO_2^{2+} only at a pH below 2.5 [17].

The tendency for an ion M^{z+} to disproportionate depends on the difference between the potentials corresponding to the $M^{z+}/M^{(z+1)+}$ and $M^{(z-1)+}/M^{z+}$ couples. In the case of MO_2^+ ions, the reactions involved are [17]

$$\text{(a)} \qquad MO_2^+ \rightarrow MO_2^{2+} + e^-,$$

$$\text{(b)} \qquad M^{4+} + 2H_2O \rightarrow MO_2^+ + 4H^+ + e^-.$$

For an ion to be stable the difference $E_a - E_b$ should be positive, as is the case, for example, for NpO_2^+ in 1 M $HClO_4$, for which the difference is $1.137 - 0.739 = 0.398$ v, and the disproportionation is only very slight. On the other hand, the value for UO_2^+ is -0.52 v, and disproportionation occurs readily. The PuO_2^+ ion, with $E_a - E_b = -0.26$ v, lies between these two. Reaction (b) depends on the acidity of the solution, varying with the fourth power of the H^+ ion concentration, so that at room temperature the potential becomes more negative by 4×0.058 v for unit pH change. Consequently the difference $(E_a - E_b)$ becomes more positive with increasing pH, and the ion MO_2^+ becomes increasingly stable. It should be realized, however, that hydrolysis of the M^{4+} and MO_2^+ ions may become significant, and that this does not vary with pH in the same way for the two species. Kraus, *et al.*, have calculated the potentials for the $M^{4+}/$

MO_2^+ and MO_2^+/MO_2^{2+} couples at various pH's for uranium, neptunium, and plutonium. A graphical representation of these results can be used to find the pH range in which each MO_2^+ ion has the greatest stability.

The NpO_2^+ ion has less tendency to disproportionate than PuO_2^+, and practically pure solutions can be prepared either by reduction of Np(VI) (with Sn^{2+} or hydrazine) or by the oxidation of Np(IV) (with Ce^{4+} or hot HNO_3). Dilute solutions are blue-green in color; NpO_2^{2+} solutions are pale pink in 1 N $HClO_4$, and dark yellow-green in 2 N H_2SO_4.

The instability of Pu(V) is due to the reaction

$$2PuO_2^+ + 4H^+ \rightleftharpoons Pu^{4+} + PuO_2^{2+} + 2H_2O; \qquad (8\text{–}1)$$

Pu(IV) subsequently reacts with Pu(V),

$$PuO_2^+ + Pu^{4+} \rightleftharpoons PuO_2^{2+} + Pu^{3+}. \qquad (8\text{–}2)$$

When the concentration of Pu^{3+} is sufficiently high, dismutation occurs via the reaction

$$PuO_2^+ + Pu^{3+} + 4H^+ \rightleftharpoons 2Pu^{4+} + 2H_2O, \qquad (8\text{–}3)$$

followed by reaction (8–2). An equilibrium is set up between the various valency states, and at a given temperature the equilibrium constant depends on the acidity. At 25° in 0.5 N HCl, the equilibrium constant is

$$\frac{[\mathrm{Pu(VI)}][\mathrm{Pu(III)}]}{[\mathrm{Pu(V)}][\mathrm{Pu(IV)}]} = K = 8.5. \qquad (8\text{–}4)$$

Reactions (8–1) through (8–3) are accompanied by the disproportionation of Pu^{4+},

$$3Pu^{4+} + 2H_2O \rightleftharpoons 2Pu^{3+} + PuO_2^{2+} + 4H^+. \qquad (8\text{–}5)$$

In perchloric acid solution, this equilibrium is established in the following steps [18]:

$$Pu^{4+} + H_2O \rightleftharpoons PuOH^{3+} + H^+, \qquad (8\text{–}6)$$

$$PuOH^{3+} + H_2O \rightleftharpoons Pu(OH)_2^{2+} + H^+, \qquad (8\text{–}7)$$

$$Pu(OH)_2^{2+} + PuOH^{3+} \rightarrow Pu^{3+} + PuO_2^+ + H_2O + H^+, \qquad (8\text{–}8)$$

$$PuO_2^+ + Pu^{4+} \rightleftharpoons Pu^{3+} + PuO_2^{2+}. \qquad (8\text{–}9)$$

Reaction (8–8) is probably the slowest, and would therefore determine the overall rate of dismutation.

The equilibrium constant for reaction (8–5) also varies with the acidity; in 0.052 M $HClO_4$,

$$\frac{[\mathrm{Pu(VI)}][\mathrm{Pu(III)}]^2}{[\mathrm{Pu(IV)}]^3} = K' = 252, \qquad (8\text{–}10)$$

compared with a value of $K' = 14.2$ in 0.102 N $HClO_4$. These reactions can be studied either by emf measurements or by spectrophotometry.

Solutions of Pu^{3+} and Pu^{4+} are either blue, green, or purple in color, depending upon the composition of the medium.

For americium, disproportionation occurs via the stoichiometric reaction [19]

$$3AmO_2^+ + 4H^+ \rightleftharpoons 2AmO_2^{2+} + Am^{3+} + 2H_2O, \qquad (8\text{–}11)$$

with Am(IV) probably acting as an intermediate.

The high potentials of the PuO_2^{2+}/Pu^{4+} and PuO^{2+}/Pu^{4+} couples, and of the corresponding couples for americium, explain the ease with which hexavalent and pentavalent compounds of these elements are reduced in aqueous solution to lower oxidation states by their own α-emission [20, 21] and by external ionizing radiation [22]. With uranium the reverse effect is observed, namely the oxidation of lower valency states to uranyl compounds, for example, by γ-rays from Co^{60} [23, 24].

The uranide ions in their different oxidation states are easily hydrolysed and readily form strong complexes with several anions. The tendency of the trivalent state to hydrolyse increases slightly from uranium to americium, as would be expected from the decreasing ionic radii; the relative hydrolysis of the MO_2^+ and MO_2^{2+} ions goes in the opposite sense, however, corresponding to the decreasing M—O bond length. The ease of hydrolysis of the U^{4+} ion is similar to that for Pu^{4+} [25]. For a given uranide, hydrolysis and complex formation decrease in the order $M^{4+} > MO_2^{2+} > M^{3+} > MO_2^+$. Anions which form complexes include F^-, Cl^-, NO_3^-, $C_2O_4^{2-}$, CO_3^{2-}, and many organic ions. It is noteworthy that the tetravalent fluorides, which are insoluble in water, dissolve in excess ammonium carbonate or oxalate, as well as in very concentrated NH_4F or KF solutions. Complex formation finds application in the elution (and separation) of uranides from ion exchange resins.

The differing stabilities of the various oxidation states of the uranide elements mean that they are relatively easy to separate. All that is necessary is to treat a mixture of the elements in question with an oxidizing or reducing agent which reacts with one (or two) components of the mixture and not with the others. Thus the separation of uranium from plutonium (for example, in the uranium rods from a reactor) can be achieved [26] by partition between aqueous nitric acid and a solution of tributyl phosphate in some paraffinic hydrocarbon, followed by reduction of plutonium to the trivalent state with hydrazine or ferrous sulfamate, and back extraction into water. In general, the (VI) and (IV) valent states are easily extracted into basic organic solvents, the (III) and (V) states much less so. By choosing suitable acidity and temperature conditions, neptunium can be separated from plutonium [27, 28] by oxidizing the tetravalent salts to Np(V) with potassium bromate and precipitating Pu(IV) as the fluoride or as the potassium double sulfate. Several other analogous procedures have been successfully applied to the separation of these elements. The quantitatively different ion exchange behavior of the transuranium elements has also been used (Section 21–8).

Table 8–4 emphasizes the strongly electropositive character of the metals of the uranide group, whose potentials (corresponding to the M/M^{3+}

electrode) lie between those of magnesium and beryllium. A further striking feature of the metals is the existence of several allotropic modifications. Neptunium exists in three allotropic forms; α (orthorhombic), stable between 0 and 278°C; β (tetragonal), stable between 278 and 550°C; and γ (cubic) at still higher temperatures. The melting point is 640°C. The density of the α-form is 20.45, and of the β-form 19.36 (at 313°C). The metal can be prepared by the reduction of NpF_3 or NpF_4 with barium vapor at 1200°C. Plutonium has six allotropic forms [29, 30, 31, 32]:

(1) α (monoclinic), density 19.816, transition point 122°C;
(2) β (monoclinic, F.C.), $d = 17.77$, transition point 203°C;
(3) γ (orthorhombic), $d = 17.14$, transition point 317°C;
(4) δ (cubic, F.C.), $d = 15.9$, transition point 453°C;
(5) δ' (tetragonal), $d = 16.0$, transition point 477°C;
(6) ϵ (cubic, B.C.), $d = 16.5$, melting point 639.5°C.

Intermetallic compounds and eutectics of plutonium with a number of other metals have been reported [33, 34], including beryllium ($PuBe_{13}$), aluminum (Pu_3Al, $PuAl$, $PuAl_2$, $PuAl_3$, $PuAl_4$), magnesium, indium, copper, iron, nickel, osmium, and lead. The crystal structures and the equilibrium phase diagrams have been worked out for most of these systems. Plutonium metal also forms carbides, silicides, and amalgams. Despite its strongly electropositive nature, the metal is attacked only slowly by water, concentrated nitric acid, ammonium fluoride, or 2.5 N sodium hydroxide solution; this is probably due to the formation of a passive surface layer.

Quantities of plutonium of the order of 1 mg/cm^2 can be deposited cathodically, either as an oxide or hydroxide, by the electrolysis of Pu(VI) in 0.1 to 0.2 M potassium hydroxide solution [35, 36], or Pu(IV) in oxalate solution [37]. A technique similar to that reported for thorium and actinium [38] can be used to deposit thin oxide films of plutonium, americium, and curium [39] by electrolysis of salts in acetone-alcohol mixtures.

Americium metal has been prepared by reducing AmF_3 with barium vapor at above 800°C. The density is only 11.7. Preliminary measurements by Wallman [40, 41] show that the melting point of the metal is between 825 and 875°C, which is higher than for the two preceding uranide elements, Np and Pu, both of which melt at 640°C. Precise measurements are difficult because of the formation of an oxide layer on the metal. The crystal structures of the allotropic forms of americium metal are as yet uncertain, but it appears that the most stable form at room temperature is a double hexagonal structure (α-form), and that a face-centered cubic form appears at higher temperatures [41]. In some conditions, however, a hexagonal structure, different from the α-form, is obtained.

8-3 The curides. For curium, the most thoroughly studied element of this group, only the trivalent state has been identified in solution, although the tetravalent solid compounds CmO_2 and CmF_4 are also known. Berkelium has two valency states (III and IV) in solution, the latter being obtained by the oxidation of Bk(III) with bromate or dichromate. At

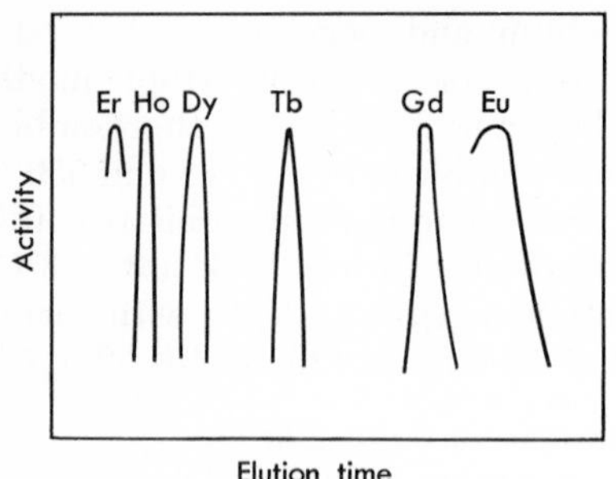

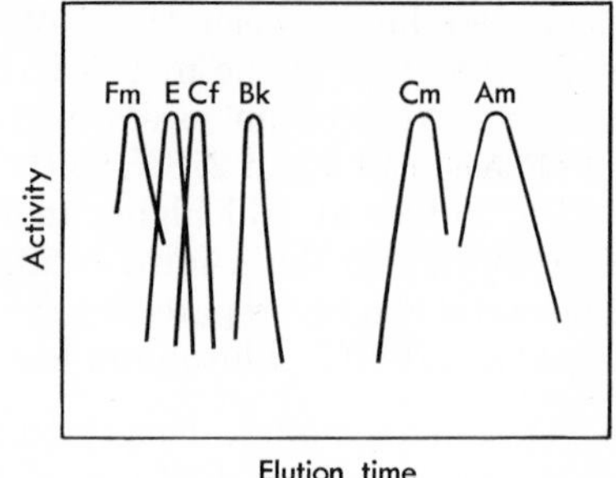

FIG. 8–1. The separation of the lanthanide and transplutonium elements by ion exchange chromatography (Refs. 42 and 43).

present, the quantities of californium, einsteinium, and fermium available are too small for a definitive study of their chemical properties, and since only a few atoms of mendelevium and nobelium can be obtained in each experiment, nothing can be stated about their chemistry other than that a trivalent state is suggested by extrapolation, and by their ion exchange behavior. Seaborg and his collaborators [32, 33] have shown that the transplutonium elements, from americium (III) to fermium, when eluted from the resin Dowex-50 with ammonium citrate or lactate at 87°C, separate in the inverse order of their atomic numbers, so that fermium elutes first, followed by einsteinium, californium, berkelium, curium, and americium (Fig. 8–1). The same order was found [44] for the Am–No series eluted from Dowex-50 with ammonium α-hydroxyisobutyrate. This is the behavior to be expected from the decrease in ionic radius with increasing atomic number, which causes stronger complex formation with the anion in question. This behavior is analogous to the rare earths (Eu–Yb), which are the homologues of the transplutonium elements in the actinide hypothesis.

The above order is not always found, however. When a mixture of Y, La, Ce(III), Eu, Am, and Cm is eluted from Dowex-50 with 3.2 M HCl, the order of elution is Y, Cm, Am, Eu, Ce, and La; with 9.3 M HCl, the order becomes Cm = Y, Am, Eu, Ce, and La; finally with 12.2 M acid one finds Am, Cm, Y, Eu, and La [46]. It will be seen that the order of elution of the rare earths remains unchanged when the acidity is altered, whereas an inversion is observed for Cm and Am. A similar inversion occurs in the room temperature elution of a mixture of americium and the lower curide elements with 12.5 M HCl in 20% ethanol, Am coming between Cm and Bk [42]. If this mixture is adsorbed on the anion resin Dowex-1 and eluted with concentrated HCl, Am comes through with Cm, and Cf ($Z = 98$) is found between Es ($Z = 99$) and Fm ($Z = 100$). The same inversion for californium occurs on eluting with NH_4SCN at 87°C [46]. It is probable that the tendency for complex formation, which governs these ion exchange separations, varies in a different order for the lanthanides and for the trivalent transplutonium elements, and that for the latter it may depend on the complexing agent, and on the physico-chemical conditions of the medium.

An examination of the main properties of the transuranium elements shows indisputably that neptunium, plutonium, and americium are not homologues of rhenium, osmium, and iridium, but that with uranium they form a chemically homogeneous group of elements. This group is characterized by the same maximum hexavalency; by the existence of three other oxidation states, with gradual stabilization of the trivalent state from uranium to americium; and by the similar properties of the elements in the same valency state. The stabilization of the trivalent state is quite definite beyond curium, where it becomes predominant, or even unique. This group then is a *horizontal anomaly* in the periodic table, similar to the lanthanide group, but obviously more complex. This chemical complexity almost certainly corresponds to a complex electronic structure, which as we shall see has not yet been definitely established (at least for the uranides) because of the frequently contradictory conclusions drawn by different authors from their measurements.

8-4 The electronic structure of the transuranium elements: theoretical considerations. In the early stages of the atomic theory, Bohr [47] pointed out that the electron distribution in the seventh long period could probably produce a situation similar to that found for the rare earths. In the sixth period, extra electrons added beyond cerium go into the 4f shell rather than the 5d shell started at lanthanum; similarly, the filling of the 6d orbits might be interrupted somewhere after actinium, and the new electrons would be found in the lower 5f shell. The number of valency electrons would remain unchanged, thereby giving rise to a new family of "rare earths," all with very similar properties.

It will become clear that, in fact, theory cannot establish precisely the atomic number of the element in which the first 5f electron appears. This point is, however, critical in terms of the chemical properties of the elements with the 5f configuration, since, by analogy with the lanthanides, it determines the predominant valency of the new series. A comment first made by Bohr has considerable importance in this respect, and also in considering the properties to be expected from the filling of 5f shells. Since these electrons are further from the nucleus than 4f electrons, the energy difference between 5f and 6d electrons will be less than for the 4f and 5d configurations. Since the 4f electrons lie below the 5f, the effect of the latter on the chemical properties will not be the same as in the lanthanides, especially in terms of valency, at least for atoms with only a small number of f electrons. Experimental observation must therefore be used to determine the relation between electron configuration and physico-chemical properties. Additionally, it would be rash to conclude that an atom of atomic number $(Z - 1)$ contains $(n - 1)$ 5f electrons merely on the grounds that the atom with atomic number Z has $5f^n$, since there are several cases known in which the number of electrons in a given energy level increases by 2 for unit increase in atomic number. This latter situation is even more probable in the present case, in which the differences between the energies of the 5f and 6d levels are small for small values of n.

Finally, as Jorgensen [49, 50] has emphasized, for elements like the uranides with multiple valencies, identification of the electronic structure

TABLE 8-7

THE ENERGIES OF THE 6d AND 5f CONFIGURATIONS FOR $Z = 90$ TO 98

Element	Configuration	Energy, ev
Th	$6s^2p^6d^27s^2$	652,439
	$5f6s^2p^6d7s^2$	652,422
Pa	$6s^2p^6d^37s^2$	669,653
	$5f^26s^2p^6d7s^2$	669,626
U	$6s^2p^6d^57s$	687,780
	$5f^36s^2p^6d7s^2$	687,766
Np	$6s^2p^6d^57s^2$	707,725
	$5f^66s^2p^4d7s^2$	707,699
Pu	$6s^2p^6d^67s^2$	724,167
	$5f^56s^2p^6d7s^2$	724,151
Am	$6s^2p^6d^77s^2$	742,914
	$5f^66s^2p^6d7s^2$	742,917
Cm	$6s^2p^6d^87s^2$	762,349
	$5f^76s^2p^6d7s^2$	762,377
Bk	$6s^2p^6d^97s^2$	783,453
	$5f^86s^2p^6d7s^2$	783,513
Cf	$6s^2p^6d^{10}7s^2$	801,327
	$5f^96s^2p^6d7s^2$	801,428

(i.e., 5f or 6d) of one oxidation state is not sufficient evidence for conclusions to be drawn about the structure in another state, which may well be quite different. In particular, a structure established for a gaseous atom or ion should not be uncritically allocated to the corresponding ion in solution.

In principle, a large number of methods can be used to establish, or at least to suggest, the electronic configuration of a given element, but the interpretation of the results is frequently subject to some uncertainty. For this reason then, it is necessary to consider all the data available from the various methods, and to attempt to draw a consistent conclusion from this overall picture. We shall, therefore, now review the results obtained by various authors on the elements with Z between 90 and 98 using one or other of the following methods: (a) theoretical calculations, (b) emission spectra, (c) absorption and fluorescent spectra, (d) x-ray spectra, (e) magnetic susceptibilities, (f) paramagnetic resonance, (g) specific heats, (h) lattice constants, (i) chemical evidence. The values for the transcurium elements ($Z > 98$) are still too fragmentary to make any serious contribution to solving this problem. It is, in any case, generally agreed that, as in curium, the added electrons go into the 5f shell.

Quantum mechanical methods can be used to calculate the most stable electronic configuration of an atom containing Z electrons, or in other words, to find the energy levels corresponding to the lowest total potential energy. The first attempt was made by Sugiura and Urey in 1926 using the published values of the x-ray spectral terms [50]. They concluded that if the first 4f electron in the sixth period appears at cerium ($Z = 58$), which is confirmed experimentally, then the first 5f electron cannot appear before $Z = 95$. Later, Wu and Goudsmit [51] calculated that the 5f orbitals would start to be filled at $Z = 92$ or 93; Goeppert-Mayer [52] found a slightly different result, with $Z = 91$ or 92 as the first element with 5f electrons. These results illustrate the limitations of the method, which has been used more recently by Cap [53], who calculated the total energy of the neutral atoms from $Z = 90$ to $Z = 98$ for the 5f and 6d configurations, using the method due to Slater [54]. The values (in ev) found by Cap are shown in Table 8–7; for each pair, the higher absolute value corresponds to the most stable configuration, with a precision estimated at 6 or 8 ev. It can be seen from these calculations that the 6d configuration is more stable than the 5f up to plutonium, that the reverse is true beyond curium, and that the two configurations have about the same stability for americium. These results therefore agree with those reported by Sugiura and Urey. It should also be noted that Lehmann [55], using the method of Slater and Koster [56], has calculated the energy levels in the atom, and the energy bands in the metal, for thorium, uranium, and plutonium; the results show that thorium contains only 6d electrons, with 5f electrons below these in uranium and plutonium.

8–5 Spectral evidence. Investigation of *emission spectra* is probably the most reliable method for identifying the energy levels in a gaseous atom, either neutral or ionized. A number of authors have studied the spectrum of thorium [57, 58], and all agree that in the ground state the neutral atom has a $6d^27s^2$ structure. The 5f electrons are also absent from Th^+, for which the lowest levels are $6d7s^2$, $6d^27s$, and $6d^3$ [59]. The ground state of Th^{2+} is also $6d^2$, with the 5f6d level above this, the energy difference between the two levels being 809.9 cm^{-1} [60]. Only the ground state of Th^{3+} has a 5f configuration.

The spark spectrum of protactinium has been studied by Tomkins and Fred [61], who measured several lines in the 2650 to 4370 A region, but have not identified the energy levels concerned.

The arc and spark spectra of uranium have been measured by Keiss, Humphreys, and Laun [62]; from the (approximately) 9000 lines identified, the ground state of the neutral atom is $5f^36d^17s^2$. The lowest term in the U^+ spectrum corresponds to $5f^37s^2$ [63, 64]. The spectrum of uranium contains many more lines than that of its analog neodymium, whose neutral ground state has been identified [65] as $4f^46s^2$. The lowest levels of Nd^+ correspond to $4f^46s$ and $4f^45d$ configurations.

The spectra of plutonium has been investigated by a number of authors. The work of McNally, including the Zeeman effect, suggests a $5f^67s$ configuration for the ground state of the Pu^+ ion [66, 67]. The structure found for the neutral atom is $5s^67s^2$ [68].

The spark spectrum of americium has been studied by Tomkins and Fred [61, 69], who detected some 3000 lines; from an analysis of the terms involved, these authors propose that the configuration of the ground state of the neutral Am atom is $5f^7 7s^2$, and $5f^7 7s$ for the Am^+ ion; certain $5f^6 6d$ levels were also identified. The energy for the $5f^7 \rightarrow 5f^6 d$ transition is much greater for the Am^+ ion than for the neutral atom, so that the stability of the 5f configuration increases with charge. This conclusion will reappear repeatedly in what follows.

Conway, Moore, and Craine [70] have measured the arc and spark spectra of curium, but it has not so far been possible to analyze the terms involved.

The *absorption spectra* of certain tri- and bivalent lanthanide compounds, both in the solid state and in aqueous solution, show several sharp bands of relatively low intensity. These have been generally interpreted as corresponding to forbidden transitions between different states in the 4f shell, the forbiddenness being partially removed by crystal field perturbations or other interactions. Their sharpness is attributed to the fact that since the 4f electrons are in lower levels, and so are protected by the 5s and 5p electrons from the electric field of the crystal which would otherwise lead to band widening by a Stark effect. These 4f electrons therefore behave virtually as electrons in the gaseous state.

The bands in the absorption spectra of the trivalent uranides (and the higher valency states) and of curium are also sharp, and there has been a tendency to regard this as proof of the presence of 5f electrons. However, Stewart [71], who measured the spectra of U^{3+}, Np^{3+}, Pu^{3+}, and Am^{3+} in perchlorate solution, has emphasized two important differences between these spectra and those of the lanthanides; (a) the intensities are some 10 to 100 times higher, and (b) the bands are often appreciably wider. Sjoblom and Hindman [14] have reached similar conclusions by studying the absorption spectra of the Np perchlorates in the III, IV, V, and VI oxidation states. For Np^{3+}, the bands are narrow between 350 and 1050 mμ, but diffuse between 225 and 300 mμ; these latter bands correspond to transitions in the $5f^x 6d$ levels. There are strong interactions with the external field, and these increase with the charge of the ion.

The absorption spectra of the crystalline uranium compounds UF_4, UCl_4, UCl_3, and of a solution of UCl_4 in a propanol-propane-propene mixture were measured at 77°K by Sancier and Freed [72], who compared the spectra with those of $PrCl_3$ and $NdCl_3$. These authors believe that the UCl_4 spectrum is similar to that of $PrCl_3$, but that the similarity between the spectra of UCl_3 and $NdCl_3$ is less pronounced. The results show, however, that the bands in the uranium spectra are much wider and more diffuse than in those of either of the lanthanides. The bands in the absorption spectra of certain crystalline uranium (IV) fluorine compounds (UF_4, $NaUF_5$, KUF_5, Na_2UF_6) also vary in complexity from one compound to another, depending on the symmetry of the electrical field produced by the fluoride ions [73]. Finally, the absorption spectrum of UO_2 in solid solution in ThO_2 shows four discrete bands, but there is also a large intense band between 650 and 700 mμ [74].

If it is assumed that the uranides contain 5f electrons, then these interact much more strongly with the medium than do 4f electrons, especially in Np and U. We shall see that no matter what property of the uranide is examined, this same conclusion cannot be avoided. Furthermore, Starke [75] has pointed out that certain ions of the transition metals, such as Mn^{2+} and Co^{2+} [76], also have narrow bands in their absorption spectra. From this point of view then, the uranides occupy an intermediate position between the transition elements and the lanthanides. It should be noted that the absorption spectra of compounds of the 7th period elements have been used to support the existence of a thoride series [77, 78].

Jorgensen [79] has studied the absorption spectra of aqueous solutions of uranium in its different valency states. Although the U(IV) spectrum does not have particularly narrow bands, and is more strongly affected by the anion than is the case with the lanthanides, the interpretation invokes transitions in the 5f level. The narrow bands in the visible region of U(III) could have the same origin, but the wide intense bands in the ultraviolet are attributed to the allowed transition $5f^3 \rightarrow 5f^2 6d$. Jorgensen believes that the same transitions are involved in the spectra of Pa(IV), Np(III), Pu(III), and Pu(IV) [80]. Axe [83] has measured the absorption spectrum of Pa(IV) in crystalline Cs_2ZrCl_6 between 200 and 1600 mμ, and also finds evidence for the probable existence of a 5f electron in this species.

Jorgensen [48, 80] has also used the Condon and Shortly theory of the electrostatic interaction between electrons in partially filled shells to calculate the energy levels of the various 5f configurations. When the 5f and 6d levels are compared, it is found that the latter are higher in the uranides (i.e., less stable), and that the difference between the 6d and 5f configurations increases in favor of the latter more rapidly with oxidation state than with atomic number. The electrostatic interaction is about 30% lower for the uranides than for the lanthanides; in other words, the 5f shells have greater radii than the 4f. It follows that the screening of 5f electrons is not much greater than for 6d electrons, which could explain their interaction with the crystal field and their contribution to chemical properties (for example, in valency), in the same way as the d electrons.

The absorption spectra of NpO_2^{2+} and PuO_2^{2+} have further been investigated by Eisenstein and Pryce [84] using the configurational f-d model discussed later. It should also be noted that infrared spectra of the uranium, neptunium, and plutonium hexafluorides are analogous to the I.R. spectra of MoF_6 and WF_6, which are their homologues in the "uranide" classification [85, 86].

Related to the absorption spectra are the *fluorescent spectra* of the chlorides of the trivalent uranides [87] and curium [88], in dilute solution in anhydrous $LaCl_3$ single crystals. These spectra, which can be obtained by excitation with ultraviolet radiation or by self-excitation for α-emitting elements (Pu, Am, Cm), are related to the absorption spectra. Since certain lanthanide compounds also exhibit fluorescent spectra, it is tempting to deduce that the uranides have similar electronic structures. It must be remembered, however, that uranyl compounds, stripped of their valency electrons, have a well-known characteristic strong fluorescence, whereas the plutonyl ion with two uncoupled electrons does not fluoresce [89].

X-ray spectra. We noted earlier that Sugiura and Urey, by analyzing the x-ray terms of thorium and uranium, deduced that the first 5f electron should not appear before $Z = 95$. However, Cauchois [90] suggests from discontinuities in the x-ray absorption edges of the heavy metals that the f and d states are mixed in thorium, protactinium, and uranium. Theoretical treatment of this has led Freidel [91] to the same conclusion; Freidel suggests that these 5f electrons behave similarly to the d electrons in the transition metals.

Borovsky and Barinsky [92] have studied the M-series fine structure in the emission and absorption x-ray spectra of UO_3, and have also concluded that in U the 5f levels are mixed with the 6d and 7p levels. The structure depends on the oxidation state, and the intensities and widths of the rays are very different from those of the lanthanides. A comparable study of thorium dioxide and nitrate in the solid state shows the presence of an f electron in the weakly excited levels [93]. More recently, Roof [94] has measured the x-ray absorption coefficients and the variation of the screening constant for solutions of Th, U, and Pu. From the results, he concludes that 5f electrons are not present in thorium and uranium.

8–6 Magnetic measurements. A considerable amount of work has been done by the magnetic method in the hope of determining electronic configurations, especially of uranium compounds. The 6d structure was apparently favored until a few years ago, when the "actinide" hypothesis instigated a new series of measurements and interpretations, which illustrate the difficulty of reaching any unambiguous conclusions in this field.

It is worth first restating the theoretical basis of the method, since this will make an understanding of the experimental results much easier. The paramagnetism of atoms or ions is the result of the presence of unpaired electrons, and is expressed by the Langevin equation

$$\chi = \frac{N\mu^2}{3kT}, \tag{8–12}$$

where χ is the molar susceptibility, N is Avagadro's number, μ is the permanent magnetic moment, k is the Boltzmann constant, and T is the absolute temperature. The quantum theory treatment developed by Hund leads to the relation

$$\mu = g\sqrt{J(J+1)}, \tag{8–13}$$

where μ is in Bohr magnetons, and g is the Landé factor, given by

$$g = 1 + \frac{J(J+1) + S(S+1) - L(L+1)}{2J(J+1)},$$

where S and L are the total spin and angular momentum vectors, and J is the total resultant vectorial sum of S and L (Russell-Saunders coupling). In general then, the magnetic moment is due to the spin contribution of the unpaired electrons and to their orbital motion. Substances in which all the electrons are paired are diamagnetic, or show a very weak temperature-independent paramagnetism.

Equation (8–12) can be written in the same form as the Curie law:

$$\chi = C/T, \tag{8–14}$$

TABLE 8–8

Number of electrons	6d		5f	
	$\chi \times 10^6$	μ, Bohr magnetons	$\chi \times 10^6$	μ, Bohr magnetons
1	1245	1.73	2685	2.54
2	3333	2.83	5390–6140	3.58–3.81
3	6250	3.87	5455	3.62
4	10500	4.90	3010	2.68

but in fact the experimental dependence is often given by

$$\chi = \frac{C}{T + \Delta}, \tag{8–15}$$

where Δ is the Weiss constant. There are two reasons for the decrease in the susceptibility, expressed by Δ: (a) at high concentrations of magnetic ions, a strong coupling between the spins of unpaired electrons in neighboring ions can modify the magnetic moment, but this can be avoided with solids by dilution with an isomorphous diamagnetic substance (for example, UO_2 with ThO_2) so that the ions with unpaired electrons are sufficiently separated by ions in which all the electrons are paired; (b) the electrical field due to the neighboring ions causes a decrease in the orbital contribution to the magnetic moment. It is important to realize that these two effects are appreciable, so that the Weiss constant is high for paramagnetic compounds of the transition elements with unpaired electrons (e.g., in the 5d level). In such species, the orbital contribution is virtually zero and the magnetic moment arises from the "spin-only" contribution. The value of g then becomes 2.0023, and Eq. (8–13) can be written approximately

$$\mu = 2\sqrt{S(S + 1)}. \tag{8–16}$$

In contrast, it would be expected that for the lowlying f electrons, protected from ionic interactions by the s and p electrons, a complete orbital contribution would be involved. This is the case for the lanthanides, for which the magnetic moments calculated from Eq. (8–13) have been confirmed experimentally.

The molar susceptibilities and the values of χ corresponding to the $d^1d^2d^3d^4$ and $f^1f^2f^3f^4$ configurations are shown in Table 8–8. The experimental values given for χ or μ are generally corrected for the diamagnetism of the molecule, which, however, exerts an almost negligible contribution to the overall magnetism.

Thorium compounds. Since the Th atom is stripped of its valence electrons in the tetravalent state, Th(IV) compounds should be diamagnetic. In fact, the dioxide ThO_2 has a very weak temperature-independent paramagnetism, with $\chi = 32 \times 10^{-6}$, comparable to the susceptibilities of TiO_2 or ZrO_2 [95]; ThS_2 is not paramagnetic [96]. More interesting is the fact that the compounds ThS, Th_2S_3 [96], Th_2Se_3, and ThI_3 [97] are not paramagnetic and so contain no f electrons. For ThI_3, for example, one finds $\chi = 355 \times 10^{-6}$, compared with a value of $\chi = 2411 \times 10^{-6}$ for CeF_3 with one 4f electron.

Uranium metal. The molar susceptibility of the metal at room temperature is approximately 400×10^{-6} [98], to be compared with a value of 5350×10^{-6} for neodymium (which is the homologue of uranium on the actinide hypothesis). Bates and Mallard [99] have measured the paramagnetism of uranium between 20 and 350°C, and find that it increases slowly with temperature; the variation is similar to that found for the transition elements ruthenium, rhodium, and iridium. It was concluded from this that the unpaired electrons are in the d level.

Trivalent uranium. The theoretical value of μ for U^{3+} in the $6d^3$ state is 3.87, and in the $5f^3$ state 3.62, so that susceptibility measurements can only decide between these two with difficulty. In general, the experimental values are lower than both these theoretical magnetic moments. For UCl_3 and $U_2(SO_4)_3$ in aqueous solution, Lawrence [100] finds $\mu = 3.22$ and 3.17. Similar values ranging from 3.03 to 3.31 have been found by Dawson for the trivalent uranium halides in the solid state [97]. According to this author, the temperature dependence of the susceptibility of these compounds is closer to that for compounds with d electrons than for Nd_2O_3 ($4f^3$), for example.

On the other hand, Handler and Hutchinson [101] have found $\mu = 3.80$ for UCl_3 in dilute solution in $LaCl_3$ crystals, and have concluded that the structure is $5f^3$, although this moment is in fact nearer to the theoretical value for the $6d^3$ state. Finally, Trzebiatowski, Sliwa, and Stalinski [102] have measured the susceptibility of UH_3 and UD_3 between 190 and 460°K and find that the Curie-Weiss law is obeyed, with $\mu = 2.44$. Below 172°K, UH_3, and UD_3 (below 174°K) show ferromagnetic behavior, which would seem to indicate the presence of d electrons. These results have been confirmed by Gruen [103], who finds $\mu = 2.79$ for UH_3 and concludes that the orbital moment of the electrons is completely suppressed in this compound. The ferromagnetic behavior of the hydride has also been reported by Lin and Kaufmann [104].

Tetravalent uranium. These compounds contain two unpaired electrons; as already noted, a $6d^2$ structure corresponds to $\mu = 2.83$, and a $5f^2$ structure to $\mu = 3.58$ or 3.81. All the older measurements (i.e., before 1948), and a number of recent experiments have given values close to 2.8, or at any rate closer to this than to 3.6. This is the case in the work of Lawrence [100] mentioned above, in which $\mu = 2.95$ for $U(ClO_4)_4$, UCl_4, and $U(SO_4)_2$ in aqueous solution. Bose and Dhar give an average value of 2.42 for the oxalate, nitrate, and UO_2, and conclude that the paramagnetism is due to the "spin-only" contribution [105]. The same conclusion was reached by Sucksmith from measurements with various U(IV) solid compounds [106]. Similarly, Bommer gave $\mu = 2.7$ for UCl_4 [107], and Haraldsen and Bakker 2.92 for UO_2 [108]. More recently Howland and Calvin have found $\chi = 3690 \times 10^{-6}$ for UCl_4 [109], and Stoenner and Elliott [110] $\chi = 3636 \times 10^{-6}$ at 20°C, values which are closer to the theoretical value for $6d^2$ (3333×10^{-6}) than for $5f^2$. Picon and Flahaut [111] give

$\chi = 3011 \times 10^{-6}$ for UOS, and 3137×10^{-6} for US_2, a value close to that reported by Eastman, *et al.* [96].

Trzebiatowski and Selwood [112] have measured the paramagnetism of UO_2 diluted with the isomorphous diamagnetic compound ThO_2. With increasing dilution, the Weiss constant decreases from 220 to 26°C, in contrast to what is found when Nd_2O_3 is diluted with La_2O_3, where the Weiss constant is virtually independent of concentration. Extrapolation to infinite dilution gives μ between 2.7 and 2.9, again in good agreement with the theoretical value for $6d^2$. The same result was obtained by Slowinski and Elliot [113] for this system ($\mu = 2.86$), and by Dawson, who measured the paramagnetism of UO_2 diluted with ThO_2, and of UF_4 diluted with ThF_4 [97], and found $\mu = 2.82$ or 2.92. Sacconi [114] found values between 2.7 and 2.8 for μ in various complexes of tetravalent uranium with organic compounds such as benzoylacetone, benzoylmethane, and nitrosophenylhydroxylamine. Sacconi himself regards this result as being in favor of the $5f^2$ configuration by assuming that the complexes are 8-coordinate, as in the model proposed by Pauling.

More recent measurements, especially those carried out by Elliott, Hutchison, and their collaborators [115–118], contrast sharply with these results, since the magnetic moments of UF_4, various complex fluorides, the anhydrous or hydrated sulfate, oxalate, and other organic compounds of U(IV) are found to lie between 3.2 and about 3.8, and are interpreted as being due to 5f electrons. The differences found between the theoretical and (generally lower) experimental values are attributed by these authors to the effect of the overall electrical field due to the charges around each ion, an effect established theoretically for outer electrons such as 5d or 6d, but not for 4f electrons.

Pentavalent uranium. ($\mu = 1.73$ for $6d^1$ and 2.54 for $5f^1$.) Rudorff and Menzer [119] have measured the susceptibility of crystalline $LiUO_3$ and $NaUO_3$, and find values of $\mu = 1.81$ and 1.66 respectively. The magnetic moments of UCl_5 and of $UCl_5 \cdot SOCl_2$ also agree with the 6d configuration. The value found by Handler and Hutchison [101] for UCl_5 ($\mu = 2.0$) is also closer to that for a 6d electron than for the 5f configuration.

Hexavalent uranium. Uranyl compounds in solution show a very weak temperature-independent paramagnetism, with various authors finding χ to be between 57 and 110×10^{-6} [95, 120]. Eisenstein and Pryce [84] have interpreted this result on the assumption that the O—U—O bonds are strongly covalent in nature, due to hybridization of the s, p, d, and f orbitals. It follows that there is an axially symmetrical electrical charge distribution along the O—U—O axis, which, as already noted, has a linear structure. The same structure is suggested by these authors for NpO_2^+, NpO_2^{2+}, PuO_2^{2+}, and AmO_2^{2+}. The effect of the axial field on the magnetic property of unpaired 5f electrons could well be greater than that of the crystal field. A similar model has been proposed by Elliott [121]. According to Eisenstein and Pryce, this model explains the weak paramagnetism of the uranyl group; a purely 6d structure would result in diamagnetism. It should be noted, however, that other U(VI) compounds such as UO_3 [95] or UF_6 [122] also exhibit a paramagnetism which is of the same order as that of the uranyl group. Moreover, compounds of Cr(VI), Mn(VII),

Th(IV), and of certain cobaltammines, etc., none of which contain unpaired electrons, have a weak temperature-independent paramagnetism (the molar susceptibility of $Cr_2O_7^{2-}$, for example, is 62.1×10^{-6} [120]). Although the origin of this paramagnetism is not at all clear at the moment, it is generally believed that the electrons are not completely paired in these compounds [122].

Transuranium compounds. Calvin, *et al.*, have measured the magnetic susceptibilities of the Np(IV), Np(VI), and Pu(IV) sulfates and the Np(V) and Pu(IV) chlorides at 20°C [109, 123]. Measurements for the three Np valency states have also been carried out by Gruen and Hutchison [124] (between 14 and 320°K) and by Dawson [97], and by Lewis and Elliott [125] for various plutonium compounds. For Np(IV), with three unpaired electrons, as for U^{3+}, the moments ($\mu = 3.03$ and 3.31) are lower than the theoretical values (6d or 5f). For Np(V) and Pu(VI), with two unpaired electrons, the experimental results are generally close to the theoretical values for $6d^2$ [Np(V) 2.96 to 3.08; Pu(VI) 2.82 to 2.95], save for the value of 3.17 found by Gruen and Hutchison for Np(V) (cf. Table 8–8). In particular, for the double acetate $NaPuO_2(CH_3COO)_3$, Dawson [108] has found that the Curie law is obeyed between 90 and 300°K, with a Weiss constant of zero; nevertheless, the average magnetic susceptibility corresponds to $\mu = 2.83$, in exact agreement with the theoretical value for the $6d^2$ structure.

For the sulfate and the double acetate of NpO_2^{2+}, with only one unpaired electron, the values found are slightly higher than those calculated for the "spin-only" case (6d), but much lower than those calculated for the 5f configuration [127], as shown in the table below:

$\chi \times 10^6$			
Temp, °K	Experimental	Spin-only	5f
300	1660	1240	2660
77	5760	4830	10,460
64	6880	5810	12,500

Curious results were obtained by Weinstock and Malm [127] with NpF_6, for which the measured susceptibilities are very low, increasing from 443 to 887×10^{-6} as the temperature increases from 300 to 640°K. No precise interpretation was offered, but the authors believe that this could be a crystal field effect.

On the other hand, the following values of μ for solid Pu(IV) compounds, from measurements by Lewis and Elliott over the temperature range 77 to 334°K, favor a $5f^4$ configuration, taking into consideration the perturbations produced by the crystal field [128]:

PuF_4, 2.90 $Pu(SO_4)_2{\cdot}4H_2O$, 2.96 $Rb_4Pu(SO_4)_4{\cdot}2H_2O$, 2.98

$Pu(C_2O_4)_2{\cdot}6H_2O$, 2.99 Me_4NPuCl_6. 1.99

A similar result was found by Dawson [97] for the magnetic susceptibility of PuF_4 diluted with ThF_4; extrapolation to infinite dilution gives $\chi = 3020 \times 10^{-6}$, in excellent agreement with the theoretical value of 3010×10^{-6} for $5f^4$. The magnetic behavior of PuO_2 diluted with ThO_2 is more complex, and the possibility is not excluded that some electrons occupy 6d levels in this compound.

Like uranium hexafluoride, crystalline PuF_6 shows a weak paramagnetism, which varies only slightly with temperature (170×10^{-6} at room temperature). This has been interpreted [129, 130] as the result of a strong interaction between f electrons and the crystal field. Measurements on Pu^{3+} compounds, with five unpaired electrons, give values considerably lower than those predicted for the $5f^5$ configuration, but the temperature variation of the susceptibility, which passes through a minimum, is similar to that for Sm^{3+} [109, 131, 132]. The susceptibilities of americium nitrate [109] and trifluoride [133], and of americium metal [134], are also lower than the calculated values for a $5f^6$ configuration; that for a solid solution of CmF_3 in LaF_3 at room temperature is extremely high (2650×10^{-6}), and comparable with that of Gd^{3+}, with its $4f^7$ structure [135].

Nevertheless, Crane, Howland, Calvin, *et al.*, who carried out the measurements on americium and its compounds, allocate it a 5f structure, in the same way that most authors presume 5f configurations for the various compounds of neptunium and plutonium, and then assume that there are significant effects due to the anion, to the dipoles of water molecules, or to the ligand field. These factors, however, play no appreciable part in the case of the lanthanides. More frequently these f configurations are assumed *a priori*, and models and parameters are then sought to reconcile the results with the theory (see, for example, Eisenstein and Pryce [84], Elliott [121], Gruen and Hutchison [124]). Thus in order to interpret the magnetic susceptibilities of solid Np compounds, the latter two authors considered 14 different models, all of which assumed a 5f structure but differed in the crystal field symmetry, in the ground state of the ion, and in the nature of the spin-orbital coupling. Some of these models allowed a satisfactory explanation of the results for Np(V) and Np(VI) compounds, but none agreed with the data for Np(IV).

One of the arguments advanced in favor of the f structure for the actinides consists in comparing the variation of magnetic susceptibilities with atomic number with the analogous variation for the lanthanides. Figure 8–2, given for the first time by Howland and Calvin [109] and completed by Katz and Seaborg [44] with data for curium and gadolinium, shows this comparison. The following comments must be made about this argument:

1. Apart from the points for Cm and Gd, the rest of the actinide curve (Np–Am) obviously lies below the curve for the lanthanides; this is a brief statement of the experimental facts discussed above.

2. The first lanthanides Ce, Pr, Nd, and Pm are compared, not with their actinide hypothesis analogues [Th(III), Pa(III), only known in PaH_3, which probably does not have an ionic structure, U(III), and Np(III)], but with the higher oxidation states of Np and Pu. It is difficult not to agree with the remark made by Selwood [136] that "by the appropri-

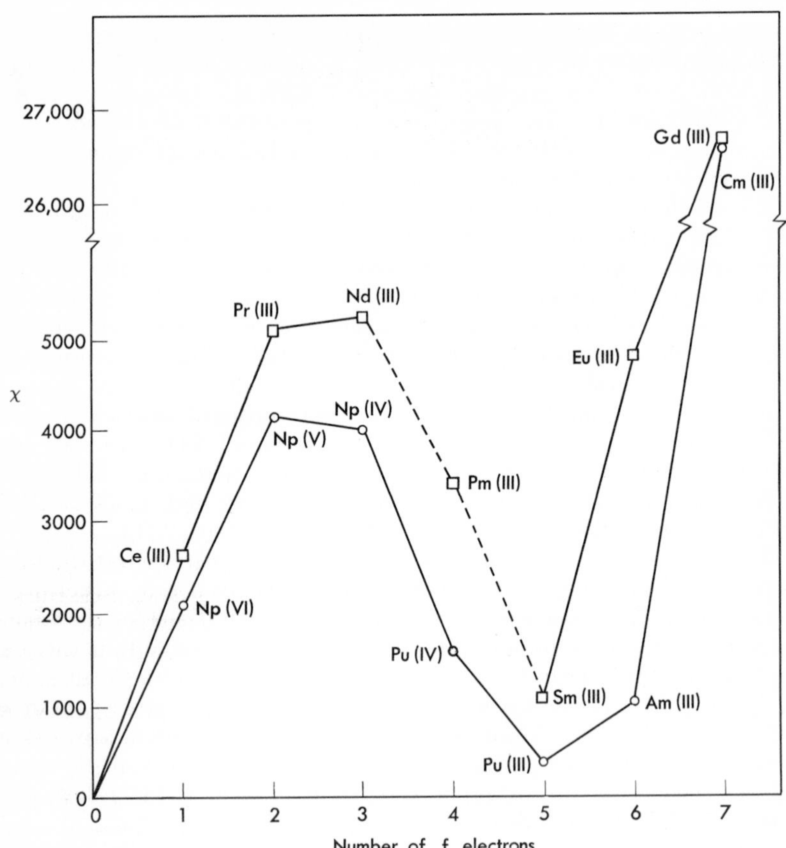

FIG. 8–2. The magnetic susceptibilities of the lanthanide and transuranium elements.

ate selection of values and the omission of certain others it is also possible to construct curves with two maxima for the transition elements, similar to the curve for the lanthanides." Selwood has in fact given such a curve for the "scandides" in the third period of the periodic system.

Thompson and Muga [137] have used a special micro-apparatus to measure the magnetic susceptibility of 0.23 μgm of Bk and of 0.056 μgm of Cf at low temperatures, and conclude that the former contains nine 5f electrons and the latter $5f^{10}$. Thus the picture derived from magnetic data is quite clear for Th, which contains no 5f electrons, and for Cf, Bk, Cm, and perhaps Am, which contain 10, 9, 7, and 7 5f electrons, respectively. The situation is much more complex, however, for the elements between Th and Am; for these, the way in which the electrons are distributed apparently varies with the oxidation state, and perhaps even with the physical state. Gaseous uranium, for example, contains three f electrons, although the metal itself seems to have virtually none. From a review of the magnetic data published up to 1952, Dawson [97] has concluded that uranium, neptunium, or plutonium ions containing one or two electrons would have these in the d level, while three or more electrons would be in the f shell.

Paramagnetic electron resonance. This method, discovered by Zavoisky [138] in 1944, can be used to determine the energy difference between the sublevels produced in the magnetic field splitting of a spin quantum level. To measure this effect, a paramagnetic crystal (preferably a single crystal) is placed in a static magnetic field H, whose strength can be varied continually; an oscillating electromagnetic field of frequency ν is then applied at right angles to the magnetic field. The paramagnetic substance absorbs energy to an extent which depends on the oscillating field. The absorption is a maximum at a resonance level, which is set up when the magnetic field H fulfills the condition

$$h\nu = g\beta H, \tag{8-17}$$

where g is the Landé factor and β the Bohr magneton. The values of ν are in the microwave region ($\lambda = 1$ to 10 cm), and radar techniques are used to detect the energy absorption. As in susceptibility measurements, dilution of the paramagnetic substance by diamagnetic material is very useful. The effects are greater, and more easily detected, if measurements are made at very low temperatures (liquid air, hydrogen, or helium). A sharp maximum is obtained, from which g and hence the magnetic moment $g\beta$ can be determined. As in the case of the magnetic susceptibility, the value of g depends upon the spin, on the orbital angular moment, on the coupling, and on the interaction of the ligand field with the orbital moment. When the field has axial symmetry, g is split into $g_{\parallel}$ parallel to, and $g_{\perp}$ perpendicular to the axis of symmetry: if the angular moment is completely suppressed by interaction with the medium, g is isotropic and equal to 2.0023.

A value close to this (2.1) was found by Ghosh, Gordy, and Hill [139] for powdered UF_4, from which they deduced a d configuration. Results with UF_3 can be interpreted as arising from a mixed 5f-6d ground state, although calculations by O'Brien, taking into account the crystal symmetry, suggest that these results are compatible with a $5f^3$ structure [140]. However, Hutchison, *et al.*, who applied this method to UCl_3 diluted in a single crystal of $LaCl_3$, found $g_{\parallel} = 4.153$ and $g_{\perp} = 1.520$, close to the values for neodymium compounds, which have an f structure [141]. A similar conclusion was reached by Bleaney, Llewellyn, and Jones [142] from measurements at 20°K on U^{3+} and Nd^{3+} introduced into single crystals of CaF_2 or SrF_2. In the case of uranium, however, a hyperfine structure is found, due to interaction with the F^- ions, but this is absent in neodymium. The paramagnetic resonance of $RbNpO_2(NO_3)_3$ and $RbPuO_2(NO_3)_3$ has been measured by Bleaney, *et al.* [143], and that of the double acetate $NaPuO_2(CH_3COO)_3$ by Hutchison and Lewis [144]. The interpretation of these results by Eisenstein and Pryce [84], based on the model noted earlier, implies the hybridization of s, p, d, and f electrons, although these authors assume a predominantly d structure in the neptunyl rubidium double nitrate. It will be noted that the result for the plutonium double acetate does not agree with the magnetic susceptibility measurements mentioned earlier, which led to a 6d configuration. The paramagnetic resonance spectrum of $CmCl_3$ in $LaCl_3$ [145] suggests a structure in some ways similar to that of $GdCl_3$; the g values correspond to a $5f^7$ configuration.

Finally, this method has been applied to tetravalent Pa^{231} in crystals of Cs_2ZrCl_6, for which the paramagnetic resonance spectrum was determined at 40°K [80, 146, 147]. Analysis of the results leads to the conclusion that there is probably a 5f electron localized on the protactinium ions in the solid. A study of the electron energy levels in a beam of Pa^{233} atoms by Winocur [148] suggests that the configuration is probably $5f^26d7s^2$. Hubbs and Marrus [149] have used this same technique to measure the hyperfine structure of the Zeeman effect in neptunium and propose a $5f^46d7s^2$ structure, although $5f^26d^37s^2$ cannot be excluded.

Specific heats. The specific heats of uranium and neptunium dioxides are closely related to the magnetic properties. Jones, Gordon, and Long [150] have shown that the specific heat curve for UO_2 has a sharp maximum at 28.7°K, and a similar result was reported by Westrum, Hatcher, and Osborne [151] for NpO_2. The same effect is found with ferrous carbonate and pyrolusite (MnO_2), in which it is associated with antiferromagnetism [152]. Westrum, *et al.*, explain this as being due to the loss of magnetic entropy by the electrons which are responsible for the antiferromagnetism (generally d electrons).

The temperature variation of both the atomic and electronic specific heats of metallic uranium between 10 and 295°K also agrees closely with that for the transition metals [153].

8–7 Ionic size and crystal structure. We have already noted that the gradual decrease in the ionic radii of the uranides in a given oxidation state is similar to the lanthanide contraction. Such a decrease is, however, also found in the transition elements in the periods preceding the lanthanides, as for example,

Ti^{3+}	V^{3+}	Cr^{3+}	Mn^{3+}	Fe^{3+}	
0.69	0.66	0.64	0.62	0.60	(A),

to be compared with,

Th^{4+}	Pa^{4+}	U^{4+}	Np^{4+}	Pu^{4+}	Am^{4+}	
0.99	0.96	0.93	0.92	0.90	0.89	(A),

or,

Th^{3+}	...	U^{3+}	Np^{3+}	Pu^{3+}	Am^{3+}	
1.08		1.03	1.01	1.00	0.99	(A).

The contraction for the first five terms of the second series is 0.09 A, exactly equal to that of the first series, and is not very different (0.08 A) for the series of the trivalent ions (the radius of Th^{3+} is interpolated). The contraction is 0.07 A for the lanthanides from Ce^{3+} to Sm^{3+} (1.034 − 0.964).

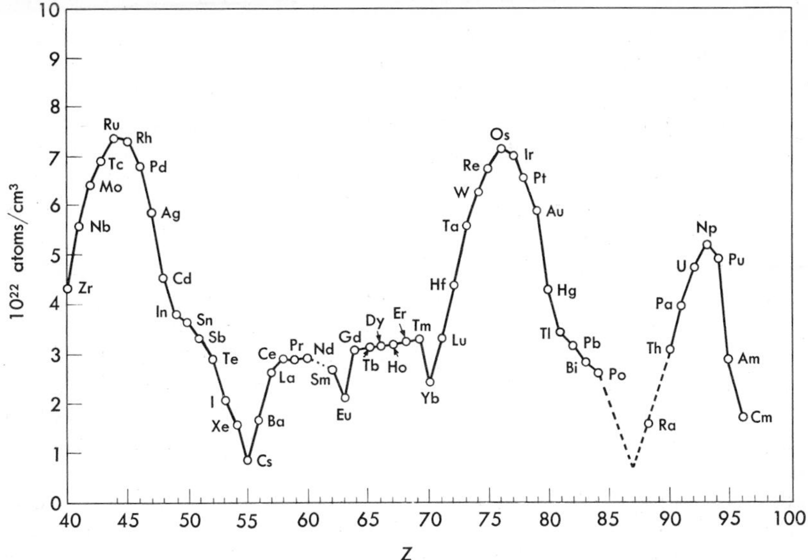

Fig. 8–3. The atomic densities of the elements as a function of Z (Ref. 154).

According to Zachariasen [7], to whom we owe most of our knowledge of the crystallographic properties of the elements of the seventh period, the contraction is much less pronounced in the atomic radii in the series

Th	Pa	U	Np	Pu	
1.79	1.63	1.54	1.52	1.51	(A).

The rapid change of atomic radius from thorium to uranium is characteristic of the 6d orbitals being filled, accompanied by an increase in the valence state in the metal. For example, if protactinium metal contained one 5f electron, its radius would be 1.76 A. Zachariasen also rules out the presence of 5f electrons in uranium metal, and neptunium cannot have more than one 5f electron. The difference between the atomic radii of Pa and Th is 0.16 A, very close to that between Nb and Zr, or between Ta and Hf (0.14 A). In the same way, the Pa-O distance in PaO would be 2.71 A, instead of the value of 2.48 A found by Zachariasen.

The important difference between the lanthanide metals and the elements of the seventh period is illustrated very clearly on an atomic volume curve, which is a well-known characteristic expression of changes in the fundamental properties of the elements. If the known densities of the elements from radium to curium are plotted in this way [154], the peaked curve obtained is quite different from that for the lanthanides (Fig. 8–3). Instead of the slight slope for the latter elements from lanthanum to gadolinium with a slight minimum at europium, there is a rapid rise to neptunium, followed by an equally rapid descent to curium, the last element for which the density is known. It is, however, possible that the value assumed for curium (7 gm/cm^3) may be lower than the actual density, since it was determined on a very small quantity of material, but, even so, the difference between the two curves is considerable, both in form and in the values involved.*

It was noted earlier that the uranide metals have several crystalline modifications, in which the elements have at least two different coordination numbers; this parallels the complex structure of β-tungsten and β-manganese, but neither thorium nor the lanthanide metals have this property. Finally, it should be noted that the atomic radius of americium in the α-phase (corresponding to the trivalent state) is 1.82 A, much larger than the other three uranide metals; according to Seaborg and Katz [33], this is the first transuranium element to resemble the lanthanides in the metallic state in terms of its density and crystal structure.

The very similar dimensions of the uranides and the neighboring elements in the same oxidation state have important results in the crystal chemistry of these elements. It is well known that for equal charge and chemical constitution, two compounds are isomorphous if the dimensional differences do not exceed a certain limit, which is generally very small. This explains the isomorphism frequently found with the seventh period elements, already noted for the uranides. Thus the uranium and neptunium tetrachlorides are isomorphous with those of thorium and protactinium, and also with $ZrCl_4$, since the ionic radius of Zr^{4+} (0.89 A) is the same as that of U^{4+}. The same is true of the tetrafluorides and the dioxides; ZrO_2 is isomorphous with the other oxides only at high temperatures. These oxides and UO_2 have a fluorite structure, whereas the homologues of uranium dioxide, WO_2 and MoO_2, have different crystal structures, since W^{4+} and Mo^{4+} have much smaller ionic radii (0.68 A). Makarov [155] has recently discussed the miscibility and isomorphism of the alloys formed by thorium, uranium, and the first transuranium elements, and the isomorphism of various compounds of these elements (halides, hydrides, oxides, borides, carbides, etc.). He concludes that there is a strong relationship among these elements and their respective homologues in the sixth period, and that their crystal chemistry is very different from that of the lanthanides. Dwight [156] has reached the same conclusion for thorium from a study of the crystal structure of intermetallic compounds with the general formula AB_3, but does not believe that uranium shows any great similarity to the molybdenum group. (See, however, Section 7–8.)

The arguments outlined above also explain the isomorphism frequently observed between the trivalent lanthanides and the uranides and curides, and similarly between the (rare) tetravalent lanthanide compounds and the tetravalent uranides (for example, CeO_2, ThO_2, UO_2, etc.). Here again the ionic radii are very similar in both series.

---

* According to new (preliminary) results reported by J. C. Wallmann, *18th International Congress of Chemistry*, Munich, 1959, communication A 317, curium has a density of approximately 13. If this is confirmed, the final part of the curve in Fig. 8–3 between Pu and Cm would be virtually the same as that for the lanthanides between Sm and Gd. The sharp rise from thorium to neptunium has no analogue whatsoever in the lanthanide series.

It is clear, therefore, that isomorphism is not a reliable indication of isoelectronic structures, and still less does it necessarily imply the filling of f orbitals. Manganates and chromates are isomorphous, as are sulfates and selenates, and permanganates with perchlorates. The oxides of the 3d transition elements, Ti_2O_3, V_2O_3, Cr_2O_3, and Fe_2O_3 also have isostructural modifications, as do the iodides TiI_2, MnI_2, FeI_2, and CoI_2 [157].

8–8 Chemical evidence and conclusions. Too much emphasis cannot be placed on the care necessary in trying to reach conclusions about electronic configuration from chemical properties, or vice versa, despite the fact that chemical properties are clearly determined by electronic structure. The relation between these are only simple for those elements which are close neighbors of the inert gases (i.e., the alkali metals, the alkaline earths, the halogens), and it would be extremely difficult if not impossible to deduce one from the other for the transition elements, especially for the three triads. Even the trivalency of the lanthanides would not be deduced from their configuration, which is most frequently $4f^n6s^2$. The problem becomes even more difficult for elements with a 5f structure, since both the theoretical predictions of Bohr (noted earlier) and the evidence of the physical properties emphasize that the behavior of the first 5f electrons would not differ greatly from that of the 6d electrons.

The same care must be observed in selecting chemical properties of an element with the intention of deducing its electronic structure, its relation to neighboring elements, and its place in a vertical group or horizontal series of the periodic system. Although 90 years have elapsed since Mendeleev established the classification which bears his name, the principles which he used and the criteria which he adopted to characterize chemical elements remain indisputably valid. The periodic classification relies in the first place on the valency states, and in particular on the maximum valency, and then considers the relative stability of the various oxidation states in solution and in the solid or gaseous state, the electropositivities (especially the electrochemical properties), the basicity, etc. Finally, it should not be forgotten that the properties frequently change down the group and along the periods in a sharp or complex fashion which cannot always be expressed by means of simple analogies.

These considerations suggest a comparison of the valencies of the seventh period elements with those of the lanthanides, which certainly have $4f^n$ structures. These valencies are shown in Table 8–9, with the most stable valency italicized and those states only known in the solid state given in parentheses. This table emphasizes quite clearly the special position of the four uranides U, Np, Pu, and Am, with their four valencies of 3, 4, 5, 6. These multiple valencies give rise to a very complex chemistry, comparable to that of the elements in the last two transition metal groups in terms of the oxidation-reduction reactions, disproportionation, complex formation, etc. Because of the appreciable differences in the redox potentials, separations of the uranides from each other (and from the cisuranium elements) are certainly much simpler than in the rare earth group, which are a classical example of extremely difficult chemical separation. In view

TABLE 8–9

Ac	Th	Pa	U	Np	Pu
3	(2, 3), *4*	4, *5*	3, 4, 5, *6*	3, 4, *5*, *6*	3, *4*, 5, 6
La	Ce	Pr	Nd	Pm	Sm
3	*3*, 4	*3*, (4)	*3*	*3*	2, *3*

Am	Cm	Bk	Cf	Es	Fm	Md	No
3, (4), 5, 6	*3*, (4)	*3*, 4	*3*	*3*	*3*	*3*	*3*
Eu	Gd	Tb	Dy	Ho	Er	Tm	Yb
2, *3*	*3*	*3*, (4)	*3*	*3*	*3*	*3*	2, *3*

of these facts, it is impossible to see why the uranides should be regarded as homologues of neodymium, promethium, samarium, and europium. The differences are emphasized by the fact that the latter two elements can be reduced in aqueous solution to the divalent state, which has not as yet been achieved for plutonium and americium.

In terms of the valencies then, the analogy between the two series appears only at curium, even though this element, in addition to its trivalency, can form tetravalent compounds in the solid state. In this it is unlike gadolinium, in which the half-filled 4f shell ($4f^7$) is particularly stable. Since it seems certain that curium is isoelectronic with gadolinium, it can again be concluded that the 5f electrons are much less strongly bound than the 4f, even when there are already seven in the shell. A similar comment can be made about berkelium with its valencies of III and IV, of which the second is less stable. In general, however, the trivalent state seems to be predominant, if not unique, beyond curium.

The gradual stabilization of the lower valency state from Am to Cm, particularly the trivalency, can be taken as further evidence in favor of the 5f structure. However, this stabilization of the lower valency states with increasing atomic number is found not only in the lanthanides but also in those elements which certainly have a d structure. This is illustrated in Table 8–10, which shows the oxides and fluorides of the last two triads, whose elements also exhibit multiple valency.

TABLE 8–10

Oxides	Fluorides
RuO, Ru_2O_3, RuO_2, RuO_4	RuF_5
Rh_2O_3, RhO_2, RhO_3	RhF_3, RhF_4
PdO, Pd_2O_3	PdF_2, PdF_3
OsO, Os_2O_3, OsO_4	OsF_4, OsF_6
IrO, Ir_2O_3, IrO_2	IrF_4, IrF_6
PtO, PtO_2	PtF_2 (?), PtF_4, PtF_6 (unstable)

This table should be compared with that of the corresponding uranide compounds (Table 8–5). It follows, therefore, that if the uranides contain 5f electrons in the solid state, as is very probably the case in certain oxidation states, the effect of these on the chemical behavior is obviously different from that of a 4f configuration, and to some extent resembles the influence of d electrons.

Even less convincing is the argument, advanced in favor of the actinide hypothesis, that the properties of the elements in the same valency state are very similar, and that in the trivalent state they are similar to those of the lanthanides. First, it should not be forgotten that the similar properties of isovalent elements is one result of similar ionic or atomic size (as is isomorphism), and is not an exclusive characteristic of the rare earths. For example, the compounds of Cr^{2+}, Mn^{2+}, Fe^{2+}, Co^{2+}, Ni^{2+}, and Cu^{2+} show many common features, although the stabilities differ, and the same applies to V^{3+}, Cr^{3+}, Mn^{3+}, Fe^{3+}, and Co^{3+}. Zirconium, which has a d structure, shares many analytical properties with thorium and cerium, despite the latter's f electron. Second, while it is quite true that very pronounced similarities exist between the tetravalent and pentavalent uranides, there are also marked differences between the latter and Th(IV) and Pa(V) respectively. For example, one of the marked characteristics of Pa(V) is its strong tendency to hydrolyze, even in acid solution (in the absence of complexing anions such as F^-), but in contrast, the pentavalent uranides are relatively stable to hydrolysis [25]. Thus the pentavalent uranium chloride is ionic in 2×10^{-3} N solution even at pH 3, and the solubility of Pu(V) in neutral solution exceeds 50 mg/liter.

The hydrolytic behavior of Th(IV) appears quite different from that of U(IV) or Pu(IV). The first step in the hydrolysis of these latter two species is the simple monomeric reaction

$$M^{4+} + H_2O \rightleftharpoons MOH^{3+} + H^+, \qquad (8\text{–}18)$$

followed by slow irreversible polymerization of the hydrolysis products. For thorium, on the other hand, reaction (8–18) is unimportant and even in very dilute solution various polymeric species such as $Th_4(OH)_8^{8+}$, $Th_5(OH)_8^{8+}$, etc., are formed reversibly, with various equilibria set up between them. Irreversible polymer formation only occurs under special conditions [158, 159]. Other differences have been discussed by Kraus [25].

The similarities in the properties of the trivalent species extend neither to Pa(III) compounds, which for all practical purposes do not exist, nor to the Th(III) halides, which in their metallic appearance, color, and chemical behavior resemble the trihalides of zirconium and hafnium. For this reason, all the chemical arguments brought forward in favor of the 5f hypothesis based on the properties of trivalent uranium and the transuranium elements are worthless for the cisuranium elements. This particularly applies to the most interesting work by Peppard and his collaborators on the partition of uranium and the trivalent transuranics between aqueous solution and various organic solvents [160]. These authors found in several systems that the logarithm of the partition coefficient varies linearly with atomic number, giving two straight lines which intersect at curium, similar to the results found with the lanthanides.

These experiments then justify the division of the elements in question into uranides and curides, but do not allow extrapolation to protactinium and thorium.

There are a number of other differences between the trivalent transuranium elements and the lanthanides which must be taken into account. For example, the lanthanides can be precipitated from nitrate solution with fluosilicic acid without carrying down either Am(III) or curium [161]. We discussed earlier some of the inversions found in the elution of Am(III)/Cm and Cf/Es, for which there are no analogies in the lanthanides. More significant perhaps is the effect of acidity in the HCl elution of Pu, Am, and Cm, and of the lanthanides and actinium from Dowex-50 [45]; at acidities above 6 N, the transuranics are eluted very much more rapidly than the lanthanides or actinium. This is due to the very strong tendency of the trivalent transuranium elements to form complexes, which is attributed by Diamond, Street, and Seaborg [45] to hybridization of the 5f, 6d, and 7s orbitals, as proposed by Eisenstein and Pryce to explain the metal-oxygen bond in the MO_2^+ and MO_2^{2+} ions.

Glueckauf and McKay [162] were the first to propose that hybridization of the s, p, d, and f orbitals in the uranyl, neptunyl, and plutonyl ions could explain, among other things, the extraction and solvation of the nitrates of these ions in organic solvents. These authors suggest that this behavior, which has been studied in detail by Katzin and Sullivan [163], is quite exceptional and strikingly different from that of other elements. Connick and Hugus [164] have supported this suggestion for other reasons, but Katzin [165] has argued that there is in fact a strong similarity between the behavior of uranyl nitrate and certain transition metal nitrates in organic solvents. A theoretical analysis of this problem has been attempted by Coulson and Lester [166]. Although a definite conclusion was not possible, these authors suggest that the ionic character of the O—U—O bond is at least as great as the covalent character, that the 5f orbitals do not have sufficient spatial extension to achieve efficient hybridization, and finally that a possible sd^2 hybridization in uranium would perhaps be more satisfactory than that involving f orbitals. It should be noted, however, that recent experiments by Choppin and Chatham-Strode [167] on Cm/Am inversions in chromatographic elution show that under certain conditions the nature of the resin affects the results, which can be explained, only with difficulty, in terms of orbital hybridization.

This discussion of the chemical aspects of the problem can be concluded by stating that the properties of thorium, protactinium, and uranium completely justify their usual place in the Mendeleev periodic table, in which they appear as homologues of hafnium, tantalum, and tungsten, respectively. Certain differences in the chemical behavior of the two series of homologues have been used to support the opposite view [168–170], and although these differences certainly exist, the comments made at the beginning of this section on the change of properties in the periodic system and on the essential characteristic criterion (namely the maximum valency) considerably reduce the weight of these arguments. Other aspects of this question are discussed in the preceding chapter in terms of the chemistry of protactinium (Section 7–8).

TABLE 8–11

Element	5f	5f-6d	6d	7s
Fr				1
Ra				2
Ac			1	2
Th			2	2
Pa		2?	1	2
U		3	1	2
Np		4	1	2
Pu		5	1	2
Am		6	1	2
Cm	7		1	2
Bk	9			2
Cf	10			2
...	...	...	...	...
...	...	...	...	...
Lw	14		1	2

From this review of the known properties of the elements of the seventh period and their electronic structure, it can be concluded with great certainty that thorium contains no 5f electrons, and that curium and the transcurium elements have the $5f^n$ structure with $n = 7$ for $Z = 96$, 9 for $Z = 97$, up to $n = 14$ for $Z = 103$. The conclusions are less definite for the uranides, since contradictory results are reported by different authors. It seems in fact that the electronic configuration here depends upon the oxidation state of the element in question.

One other important and unambiguous conclusion arises from the discussion. The effect of the 5f electrons on the chemical and physical properties of the uranides is markedly different from that of the 4f electrons in the lanthanide series, and is similar to the influence of the d electrons in the transition elements. These conclusions can be expressed schematically by saying that the electronic structure of the uranides is mixed 6d-5f in character, with the 6d character being more pronounced in uranium (very stable hexavalency) and the 5f in americium (III the most stable valency). This emphasizes the considerable interaction between the 5f electrons and the medium, and removes the ambiguity implicit in the "actinide" hypothesis, according to which a 5f structure implies the same chemical consequences as a 4f structure.

The electronic distribution in the outermost shells deduced from these arguments are listed in Table 8–11. This electronic structure corresponds to the following evolution of chemical properties in the seventh period: (a) francium and the elements up to uranium are the homologues of caesium-tungsten; (b) a tetrad of uranides characterized by identical oxidation states and similar properties (except in terms of stability); (c) a curide series, from curium to lawrencium. Despite the existence of Cm(IV) in the solid state and of Bk(IV), this latter series is characterized

TABLE 8–12. PERIODIC TABLE OF THE ELEMENTS

Group Period	a I b	a II b	a III b	a IV b	a V b	a VI b	a VII b	VIII	O
1	1 H 1.0080								2 He 4.003
2	3 Li 6.940	4 Be 9.013	5 B 10.82	6 C 12.010	7 N 14.008	8 O 16.000	9 F 19.00		10 Ne 20.183
3	11 Na 22.997	12 Mg 24.32	13 Al 26.97	14 Si 28.09	15 P 30.979	16 S 32.066	17 Cl 35.457		18 Ar 39.944
4	19 K 39.100 29 Cu 63.542	20 Ca 40.08 30 Zn 65.377	21 Se 44.96 31 Ga 69.72	22 Ti 47.90 32 Ge 72.60	23 V 50.95 33 As 74.91	24 Cr 52.01 34 Se 78.96	25 Mn 54.93 35 Br 79.916	26 Fe 27 Co 28 Ni 55.85 58.94 58.69	36 Kr 83.80
5	37 Rb 85.48 47 Ag 107.880	38 Sr 87.63 48 Cd 112.41	39 Y 88.92 49 In 114.76	40 Zr 91.22 50 Sn 118.70	41 Nb 92.91 51 Sb 121.76	42 Mo 95.95 52 Te 127.61	43 Tc 98.91 53 I 126.91	44 Ru 45 Rh 46 Pd 101.7 102.91 106.7	54 Xe 131.3
6	55 Cs 132.91 79 Au 197.2	56 Ba 137.36 80 Hg 200.61	57 La* 138.92 81 Tl 204.39	72 Hf 178.6 82 Pb 207.21	73 Ta 180.88 83 Bi 209.00	74 W 183.92 84 Po 210	75 Re 186.31 85 At 210	76 Os 77 Ir 78 Pt 190.2 193.1 195.23	86 Rn 222
7	87 Fr 223	88 Ra 226.05	89 Ac 227 96 Cm*** 247	90 Th 232.12	91 Pa 231	92 U** 238.07			

*Lanthanides	57 La 138.92	58 Ce 140.13	59 Pr 140.92	60 Nd 144.27	61 Pm 145	62 Sm 150.43	63 Eu 152.0	64 Gd 156.9	65 Tb 159.2	66 Dy 159.2	67 Ho 164.94	68 Er 167.2	69 Tm 169.4	70 Yb 173.04	71 Lu 175.0

**Uranides	92 U 238.07	93 Np 237	94 Pu 244	95 Am 243	***Curides	96 Cm 247	97 Bk 247	98 Cf 251	99 Es 254	100 Fm 253	101 Md 256	102 No 254	103 Lw 257

by a predominant trivalency, and its members are homologous with the lanthanides gadolinium-lutecium (Table 8–12). Although complex, such a classification retains the main purpose of the periodic system, which attempts to represent the essential chemical properties of the elements to the greatest possible extent, and to illustrate their similarities and differences.

References

1. D. F. Peppard, M. H. Studier, M. V. Gergel, G. W. Mason, J. C. Sullivan, and J. F. Mech, *J. Am. Chem. Soc.*, **73,** 2529, 3278 (1951).

2. C. A. Levine and G. T. Seaborg, *J. Am. Chem. Soc.*, **73,** 3278 (1951).

3. G. T. Seaborg, in *The Actinide Elements*, G. T. Seaborg and J. J. Katz, eds., McGraw-Hill, New York, 1954, p. 189.

4. A. Ghiorso, *et al.*, *Phys. Rev.*, **100,** 1048 (1955).

5. A. Ghiorso, B. G. Harvey, G. R. Choppin, S. G. Thompson, and G. T. Seaborg, *Phys. Rev.*, **98,** 1518 (1955).

6. P. R. Fields, A. M. Friedman, J. Milsted, H. Atterling, W. Forsling, L. W. Holm, and B. Astrom, *Phys. Rev.*, **107,** 1460 (1957).

7. A. Ghiorso, T. Sikkeland, J. R. Walton, and G. T. Seaborg, *Phys. Rev. Letters*, **1,** 17, 18 (1958).

8. G. N. Flerov, *et al.*, 1958 *Geneva Conference*, P. 2299; *Doklady Akad. Nauk. SSSR*, **120,** 73 (1958).

8a. A. Ghiorso, *et al.*, *Phys. Rev. Letters*, **6,** 473 (1961).

9. W. H. Zachariasen, in *The Actinide Elements*, *op. cit.*, p. 769.

10. W. H. Zachariasen, *Acta Cryst.*, **1,** 277, 281 (1948).

11. L. H. Jones and R. H. Penneman, *J. Chem. Phys.*, **21,** 542 (1953).

12. L. H. Jones, *J. Chem. Phys.*, **23,** 2105 (1955).

13. M. Kasha, *J. Chem. Phys.*, **17,** 348 (1949).

14. R. Sjoblom and J. C. Hindman, *J. Am. Chem. Soc.*, **73,** 1744 (1951).

15. R. H. Betts and B. G. Harvey, *J. Chem. Phys.*, **16,** 1089 (1948).

16. S. E. Stephanou, J. P. Nigon, and R. H. Penneman, *J. Chem. Phys.*, **21,** 42 (1953).

17. K. A. Kraus, G. L. Johnson, and F. Nelson, *U.S.A.E.C. report AECD-2460* (1948).

18. S. W. Rabideau, *J. Am. Chem. Soc.*, **75,** 798 (1953).

19. G. N. Iakovlev and T. N. Kossiakov, *1955 Geneva Conference*, P. 676.

20. R. E. Connick, M. Kasha, W. H. McVey, and G. E. Sheline in *The Transuranium Elements* (N.N.E.S., IV–14B), McGraw-Hill, New York, 1949, p. 559.

21. L. B. Asprey and S. E. Stephanou, *U.S.A.E.C. report AECD-924*, (1950).

22. M. Pagès, C. Ferradini, and M. Haïssinsky, *Compt. rend.*, **245,** 1128 (1957).

23. J. W. Boyle, C. J. Hochandel, T. J. Sworski, J. A. Ghormley, and W. F. Kieffer, *1955 Geneva Conference*, P. 741.

24. M. Haïssinsky and M. Duflo, *J. Chim. Phys.*, **53,** 970 (1956).

25. K. A. Kraus, *1955 Geneva Conference*, P. 731.

26. B. GOLDSCHMIDT, P. REGNAUT, and I. PREVOT, *1955 Geneva Conference*, P. 349.

27. A. M. VOROBIEV and I. K. SCHVETZOV, *1955 Geneva Conference*, P. 674.

28. G. T. SEABORG, in *The Actinide Elements, op. cit.*, p. 189.

29. W. B. H. LORD, *Nature*, **173,** 534 (1954).

30. J. G. BALL, J. A. L. ROBERTSON, P. MARDON, J. A. LEE, and E. T. ADAMS, *Nature*, **173,** 535 (1954).

31. C. S. SMITH, *Phys. Rev.*, **94,** 1068 (1954).

32. E. R. JETTE, *J. Chem. Phys.*, **23,** 365 (1955).

33. S. KONOBÉEVSKI, *Sess. Acad. Sci., U.S.S.R.*, July 1–5, 1955, Chem. Section, p. 362.

34. A. B. MCINTOSH and T. J. HEAL, *Materials for Nuclear Engineering*, Temple Press, London, 1960.

35. M. MILLER, *U.S.A.E.C. report MDDC–469.*

36. H. W. MILLER and R. J. BROUNS, *Anal. Chem.*, **24,** 536 (1952).

37. F. L. MOORE and G. W. SMITH, *Nucleonics*, **13,** No. 4, 66 (1955).

38. S. COTELLE and M. HAÏSSINSKY, *Compt. rend.*, **206,** 1644 (1938).

39. V. DEDOV and V. KOSSIAKOV, *1955 Geneva Conference*, P. 675.

40. J. C. WALLMANN, *17th International Congress of Chemistry*, Munich, 1959.

41. D. B. MCWHAN, J. C. WALLMAN, B. B. CUNNINGHAM, L. B. ASPREY, F. H. ELLINGER, and W. H. ZACHARIASEN, *J. Inorg. Nuclear Chem.*, **15,** 185 (1960).

42. K. STREET, S. G. THOMPSON, and G. T. SEABORG, *J. Am. Chem. Soc.*, **72,** 4832 (1950).

43. S. G. THOMPSON, B. G. HARVEY, G. R. CHOPPIN, and G. T. SEABORG, *J. Am. Chem. Soc.*, **76,** 6229 (1954).

44. J. J. KATZ and G. T. SEABORG, *The Chemistry of the Actinide Elements*, Methuen, London, 1957.

45. R. M. DIAMOND, K. STREET, and G. T. SEABORG, *J. Am. Chem. Soc.*, **76,** 1461 (1954).

46. S. G. THOMPSON, B. G. HARVEY, G. R. CHOPPIN, and G. T. SEABORG, *U.S.A.E.C. report UCRL–2591*, (1954); see also L. WISH, E. C. FREILING, and L. BUNNEY, *J. Am. Chem. Soc.*, **76,** 3444 (1954).

47. N. BOHR, *Z. Physik*, **9,** 1 (1922).

48. C. K. JORGENSEN, *J. Inorg. Nuclear Chem.*, **1,** 301 (1955).

49. C. K. JORGENSEN, *16th International Congress of Chemistry*, Paris, 1957.

50. Y. SUGIURA and H. C. UREY, *Danske Videnskab. Selskab*, **7,** No. 13, 3 (1926).

51. T. Y. WU and S. GOUDSMIT, *Phys. Rev.*, **43,** 496 (1933).

52. M. GOEPPERT-MAYER, *Phys. Rev.*, **60,** 184 (1941).

53. F. CAP, *Experientia*, **6,** 291 (1950).

54. J. C. SLATER, *Phys. Rev.*, **36,** 57 (1930).

55. G. W. LEHMAN, *U.S.A.E.C. report NAA–SR–1659* (1956); *NAA–SR–1839* (1957).

56. J. C. SLATER and G. F. KOSTER, *Phys. Rev.*, **94,** 1498 (1954).

57. P. SCHUURMANS, quoted in Ref. 44.

58. W. F. MEGGERS, *Science*, **105,** 514 (1947).

59. T. L. DE BRUIN, P. SCHUURMANS, and P. F. A. KLINKENBERG, *Z. Physik*, **121,** 667 (1943); **122,** 23 (1944).

60. T. L. de Bruin, P. F. A. Klinkenberg, and P. Schuurmans, *Z. Physik*, **118,** 58 (1941).

61. F. S. Tomkins and M. Fred, *J. Opt. Soc. Am.*, **39,** 357 (1949).

62. C. C. Kiess, C. J. Humphreys, and D. D. Laun, *J. Research Natl. Bur. Standards*, **37,** 57 (1946).

63. J. van den Bosch, *Physica*, **15,** 503 (1949).

64. J. R. McNally, *Phys. Rev.*, **77,** 417 (1950).

65. W. E. Albertson, G. R. Harrison, and J. R. McNally, *Phys. Rev.*, **61,** 167 (1942).

66. P. M. Griffin and J. R. McNally, *J. Opt. Soc. Am.*, **45,** 63 (1955).

67. J. R. McNally, *J. Opt. Soc. Am.*, **45,** 901 (1955).

68. J. Hubbs, *et al.*, quoted in Ref. 44.

69. M. Fred and F. S. Tomkins, *J. Opt. Soc. Am.*, **47,** 1076 (1957).

70. J. G. Conway, M. F. Moore, and W. W. T. Crane, *J. Am. Chem. Soc.*, **73,** 1308 (1951).

71. D. Stewart, *U.S.A.E.C. report ANL–4812*, (1952).

72. K. M. Sancier and S. Freed, *J. Chem. Phys.*, **20,** 349 (1952).

73. M. D. Gruen and M. Fred, *J. Am. Chem. Soc.*, **76,** 3850 (1954).

74. M. D. Gruen, *J. Am. Chem. Soc.*, **76,** 2117 (1954).

75. K. Starke, *Z. anorg. Chem.*, **251,** 251 (1943).

76. J. Gielessen, *Ann. Physik*, **22,** 537 (1935).

77. F. Ephraim and M. Mezener, *Helv. Chim. Acta*, **16,** 1257 (1933).

78. V. M. Goldschmidt, *Norsk Fys. Tids.*, **3,** No. 3, 179 (1942).

79. C. K. Jorgensen, *Acta Chem. Scand.*, **10,** 1503 (1956).

80. C. K. Jorgensen, *Thesis*, Copenhagen, 1957.

81. C. K. Jorgensen, *Danske Videnskab. Selskab Mat.-fys. Medd*, **30,** No. 22 (1956).

82. C. K. Jorgensen, *Acta Chem. Scand.*, **11,** 53 (1957).

83. J. D. Axe, *U.S.A.E.C. report UCRL–9293*, 1960.

84. J. C. Eisenstein and M. H. L. Pryce, *Proc. Roy. Soc.* (*London*), **A229,** 20 (1955); **A238,** 31 (1956).

85. J. N. Hawkins, H. C. Mattraw, and W. W. Sabol, *J. Chem. Phys.*, **23,** 2191 (1955).

86. J. G. Malm, B. Weinstock, and H. H. Claassen, *J. Chem. Phys.*, **23,** 2192 (1955).

87. D. M. Gruen, J. G. Conway, R. D. McLaughlin, and B. B. Cunningham, *J. Chem. Phys.*, **24,** 1115, 1275 (1956).

88. J. G. Conway, J. C. Wallmann, B. B. Cunningham, and B. B. Shalimoff, *J. Chem. Phys.*, **27,** 1416 (1957).

89. G. N. Walton, G. Hutton, and J. Dalziel, quoted in Ref. 97.

90. Y. Cauchois, *J. phys. radium*, **14,** 73S (1953).

91. J. Friedel, *Proc. Phys. Soc.* (*London*), **66A,** 333 (1953).

92. I. B. Borovsky and R. L. Barinsky, *Compt. rend. acad. sci. U.S.S.R.*, **72,** 31 (1950); I. B. Borovsky, personal communication.

93. R. L. Barinsky, *Bull. Acad. Sci. U.S.S.R.* (Phys. section), **20,** 133 (1956).

94. R. B. Roof, *Phys. Rev.*, **113,** 820 (1959).

95. W. Tilk and W. Klemm, *Z. anorg. Chem.*, **240,** 355 (1939).

96. E. D. Eastman, L. Brewer, L. A. Bromley, P. W. Gilles, and N. L. Lofgren, *J. Am. Chem. Soc.*, **72,** 4019 (1950).

97. J. K. DAWSON, *Nucleonics,* **10,** No. 9, 39 (1952).

98. C. J. KRIESSMAN and T. R. MCGUIRE, *Phys. Rev.,* **85,** 71 (1952).

99. L. F. BATES and J. R. MALLARD, *Proc. Phys. Soc.* (*London*), **63B,** 520 (1950).

100. R. W. LAWRENCE, *J. Am. Chem. Soc.,* **56,** 776 (1934).

101. P. HANDLER and C. A. HUTCHISON, *J. Chem. Phys.,* **25,** 1210 (1956).

102. W. TRZEBIATOWSKI, A. SLIWA, and B. STALINSKI, *Rozniki Chemii,* **28,** 12 (1954).

103. D. M. GRUEN, *J. Chem. Phys.,* **23,** 1708 (1955).

104. S. T. LIN and A. R. KAUFMANN, *Phys. Rev.,* **102,** 640 (1956).

105. D. M. BOSE and H. G. DHAR, *Z. Physik,* **48,** 716 (1928).

106. W. SUCKSMITH, *Phil. Mag.,* **14,** 1115 (1932).

107. H. BOMMER, *Z. anorg. Chem.,* **247,** 249 (1941).

108. H. HARALDSEN and R. BAKKER, *Naturwiss.,* **28,** 127 (1940).

109. J. J. HOWLAND and M. CALVIN, *J. Chem. Phys.,* **18,** 239 (1950).

110. R. STOENNER and N. ELLIOTT, *J. Chem. Phys.,* **12,** 950 (1951).

111. M. PICON and J. FLAHAUT, *Compt. rend.,* **237,** 1160 (1953).

112. W. TRZEBIATOWSKI and P. SELWOOD, *J. Am. Chem. Soc.,* **72,** 4504 (1950).

113. E. SLOWINSKI and N. ELLIOTT, *Acta Cryst.,* **5,** 768 (1952).

114. L. SACCONI, *Acad. Lincei,* **6,** 639 (1949).

115. C. A. HUTCHISON and N. ELLIOTT, *J. Chem. Phys.,* **16,** 920 (1948).

116. N. ELLIOTT, *Phys. Rev.,* **76,** 431 (1949).

117. C. A. HUTCHISON, *J. Chem. Phys.,* **27,** 707 (1957).

118. C. A. HUTCHISON and C. M. HERZFELD, *J. Chem. Phys.,* **23,** 1650 (1955).

119. W. RUDORFF and W. MENZER, *Z. anorg. Chem.,* **292,** 197 (1957).

120. S. FREED and C. KASPER, *J. Am. Chem. Soc.,* **52,** 4671 (1930).

121. R. J. ELLIOTT, *Phys. Rev.,* **89,** 659 (1953).

122. R. S. NYHOLM, *Quart. Revs.,* **7,** 377 (1953).

123. M. CALVIN, M. KASHA, and G. E. SHELINE, *U.S.A.E.C. report AECD–2002* (1948).

124. D. M. GRUEN and C. A. HUTCHISON, *J. Chem. Phys.,* **22,** 386 (1954).

125. W. B. LEWIS and N. ELLIOTT, *J. Chem. Phys.,* **27,** 904 (1957).

126. J. K. DAWSON, *J. Chem. Soc.,* **1952,** 2705.

127. B. WEINSTOCK and J. G. MALM, *J. Chem. Phys.,* **27,** 594 (1957).

128. W. B. LEWIS and N. ELLIOTT, *J. Chem. Phys.,* **27,** 904 (1957).

129. D. M. GRUEN, J. G. MALM, and B. WEINSTOCK, *J. Chem. Phys.,* **24,** 905 (1956).

130. B. WEINSTOCK and J. G. MALM, *J. Inorg. Nuclear Chem.,* **2,** 380 (1956).

131. N. ELLIOTT and W. B. LEWIS, quoted in Ref. 97.

132. J. K. DAWSON, C. J. MANDELBERG, and D. DAVIES, *J. Chem. Soc.,* **1951,** 2047.

133. W. W. T. CRANE, J. C. WALLMAN, and B. B. CUNNINGHAM, *U.S.A.E.C. report UCRL–846* (1950).

134. P. GRAF, B. B. CUNNINGHAM, C. H. DAUBEN, J. C. WALLMAN, D. H. TEMPLETON, and H. RUBEN, *J. Am. Chem. Soc.,* **78,** 2340 (1956).

135. W. W. T. CRANE, quoted in Ref. 44.

136. P. W. SELWOOD, *Magnetochemistry,* Interscience Publishing Corp., New York, 1956; see also Ref. 43.

137. J. G. THOMPSON and M. L. MUGA, *1958 Geneva Conference,* P. 718.

138. E. Zavoisky, *J. Phys. U.S.S.R.*, **9**, 245 (1945).
139. S. N. Ghosh, W. Gordy, and D. G. Hill, *Phys. Rev.*, **96**, 36 (1954).
140. M. C. M. O'Brien, *Proc. Phys. Soc. (London)*, **A68**, 351 (1955).
141. C. A. Hutchison, P. M. Llewellyn, E. Wang, and P. Dorain, *Phys. Rev.*, **102**, 292 (1956).
142. B. Bleaney, P. M. Llewellyn, and D. A. Jones, *Proc. Phys. Soc. (London)*, **B69**, 858 (1956).
143. B. Bleaney, P. M. Llewellyn, M. H. L. Pryce, and G. R. Hall, *Phil. Mag.*, **45**, 991, 992 (1954).
144. C. A. Hutchison and W. B. Lewis, *Phys. Rev.*, **95**, 1096 (1954).
145. P. R. Fields, A. Friedman, B. Smaller, and W. Low, *Phys. Rev.*, **105**, 757 (1957).
146. J. D. Axe, R. Kyi, and H. J. Stapleton, *J. Chem. Phys.*, **32**, 1961 (1960).
147. R. Kyi, *U.S.A.E.C. report UCRL–9109* (1960).
148. J. Winocur, *U.S.A.E.C. report UCRL–9174* (1960).
149. J. C. Hubbs and R. Marrus, *Phys. Rev.*, **110**, 287 (1958).
150. W. M. Jones, J. Gordon, and E. A. Long, *J. Chem. Phys.*, **20**, 695 (1952).
151. E. F. Westrum, J. B. Hatcher, and D. W. Osborne, *J. Chem. Phys.*, **21**, 419 (1953).
152. H. Bizette and B. Tsai, *Les phenomènes cryomagnetiques*, Centre National de la Recherche Scientifique, Paris, 1949, p. 164.
153. K. Clusius and U. Piesbergen, *Helv. Phys. Acta*, **31**, 302 (1958).
154. R. Gregoire, *Bull. soc. chim. France*, **1953**, 16.
155. E. Makarov, *The Crystal Chemistry of the Compounds of U, Th, Pu and Np*, Moscow, 1958.
156. A. E. Dwight, *Nature*, **187**, 505 (1960).
157. A. G. Maddock, *16th International Congress of Chemistry*, Paris, 1957.
158. A. Dobry-Duclaux, S. Guinand, and A. Mathieu-Sicaud, *J. Chim. Phys.*, **50**, 501 (1953).
159. A. Dobry-Duclaux, *J. Chim. Phys.*, **50**, 507 (1953).
160. D. F. Peppard, G. W. Mason, R. Sironen, and S. McCarty, *16th International Congress of Chemistry*, Paris, 1957.
161. S. G. Thompson, R. A. James, L. O. Morgan, and I. Perlman, in *The Transuranium Elements* (N.N.E.S. IV–14B), McGraw-Hill, New York, 1949, p. 1339.
162. E. Glueckauf and H. A. C. McKay, *Nature*, **165**, 594 (1950).
163. L. I. Katzin and J. C. Sullivan, *U.S.A.E.C. report AECD–2537*.
164. R. E. Connick and Z. Z. Hugus, *J. Am. Chem. Soc.*, **74**, 6012 (1952).
165. L. I. Katzin, *Nature*, **166**, 605 (1950).
166. C. A. Coulson and G. R. Lester, *J. Chem. Soc.*, **1956**, 3650.
167. G. R. Choppin and A. Chatham-Strode, *J. Inorg. Nuclear Chem.*, **15**, 377 (1960).
168. B. Purkayastha, *Nucleonics*, **3**, No. 5, 2 (1948).
169. T. Szabo, *Phys. Rev.*, **76**, 147 (1949).
170. G. T. Seaborg, *Nucleonics*, **5**, No. 11, 16 (1949).

CHAPTER 9

ISOTOPE EFFECTS AND THE SEPARATION OF ISOTOPES

9–1 Physical isotope effects. In Section 1–3 we saw that the concept of isotopy had to be introduced into nuclear chemistry at the beginning of this century to explain the difficulties constantly found when attempts were made to separate certain radioelements from ordinary elements, such as radium-D from lead or uranium-X_1 from thorium. Soddy [1] defined isotopes as "species which occupy the same place in the periodic system, which are chemically identical, and which very probably cannot be separated by means of their ordinary physical properties." It is now known that the second part of this definition is only an approximation, which becomes increasingly closer to reality as the ratio of the masses of the isotopes concerned comes closer to unity. *Isotope effects* are defined as the physical or chemical differences between isotopes of the same element or compounds containing these isotopes. Two molecules are said to be *isotopic* if they have the same chemical constitution and structure, but differ in that one or more atoms in one are isotopically different from the corresponding atoms in the other.

Although isotope effects are usually very small, they are often measureable, and may be sufficient to allow isotopic mixtures to be fractionated, or even separated completely. They arise from the inequality of the masses, spins, or other nuclear properties. For example, the differences in the vibrational spectra of isotopic molecules are due to the mass differences; these spectral effects led to the discovery of a number of isotopes of light elements, such as D, C^{13}, N^{15}, O^{17}, and O^{18}. For the sake of simplicity, consider a diatomic molecule A_1A_2 and neglect the anharmonicity of the vibration; the vibrational energy is then given by

$$E_v = (v + \tfrac{1}{2})hc\omega, \tag{9–1}$$

where v is a quantum number 0, 1, 2, . . . ; ω, the frequency in cm^{-1} (wave numbers), is

$$\omega = \frac{1}{2\pi c}\sqrt{k/\mu}, \tag{9–2}$$

in which μ is the reduced mass $(A_1A_2)/(A_1 + A_2)$ and k is the force constant. For two isotopic molecules A_1 A_2 and $A_1'A_2$,

$$\frac{\omega}{\omega'} = \sqrt{\mu'/\mu}. \tag{9–3}$$

We shall find that a large number of chemical isotope effects arise from differences in the vibrational energies corresponding to the quantum state $v = 0$. Equation (9–1) shows that for $v = 0$, the so-called zero-point energy is not in fact zero:

$$E_0 = \tfrac{1}{2}hc\omega. \tag{9–4}$$

TABLE 9-1

THE FUNDAMENTAL FREQUENCIES, ZERO-POINT ENERGIES, AND DISSOCIATION ENERGIES OF DIATOMIC ISOTOPIC MOLECULES

Molecule	ω_0, cm^{-1}	E_0, kcal/mole	D, kcal/mole
H_2	4405.3	6.212	102.80
HD	3817.1	5.390	103.62
D_2	3118.8	4.411	104.60
HT	3608.4	5.073	—
DT	2845.6	4.030	—
T_2	2553.8	3.603	—
NaH	1170.8	1.610	51.6
NaD	845.3	1.202	52.0
HCl^{35}	2989.0	4.236	102.1
DCl^{35}	2143.5	3.046	103.3
HCl^{37}	2987.5	4.234	102.1
HI	2309.5	3.274	71.6
DI	1639.5	2.329	72.5
$C^{12}O^{16}$	2167.4	3.090	222
$C^{13}O^{16}$	2119.2	3.021	—
$C^{12}O^{18}$	2115.2	3.016	—
N_2^{14}	2359.6	3.364	225
N_2^{15}	2279.6	3.249	—

For two isotopic molecules

$$\frac{E_0}{E_0'} = \sqrt{\mu'/\mu}, \tag{9-5}$$

so that the heavier molecule has the lower vibrational energy.

Table 9-1 gives the fundamental frequency ω_0, the zero-point energy E_0, and the dissociation energy D for a number of isotopic molecules [2]. It will be seen that the differences fall off with increasing isotopic mass, and that for two isotopic molecules, $\Delta D \approx \Delta E_0$.

The rotational spectra of isotopic molecules also differ, but the effects in this case are smaller, being important only for the hydrogen isotopes. The rotational energy is given by

$$E_r = \frac{h^2}{8\pi^2 I} \cdot J(J+1), \tag{9-6}$$

where the moment of inertia I is proportional to the reduced mass μ, so that the following relation holds:

$$\frac{E_r}{E_r'} = \frac{\mu'}{\mu}. \tag{9-7}$$

An important isotope effect shows up in the two varieties of the H_2 molecule, ortho- and parahydrogen [3, 4]. The rotational moment of the molecule is either an odd multiple (o-H_2) or even multiple (p-H_2) of $h/2\pi$, depending on the relative orientation of the spins of the two nuclei (i.e., either parallel or antiparallel). The wave function of the first species is antisymmetrical, and that of the second symmetrical. Experimentally, the differences show up in differing intensities in the rotational spectra, and in the specific heat, thermal conductivity, and viscosity.

At low temperature the predominant species at equilibrium is that with zero rotational energy, ($J = 0$), i.e., parahydrogen. The o-$H_2 \rightarrow p$-H_2 conversion is catalyzed by paramagnetic substances (NO, O_2, Fe^{2+}, Co^{2+}, Nd^{3+}, etc.), which favor reorientation of the spin; a magnetic field has a similar effect. At ordinary temperatures, the o/p ratio is three for H_2 and two for D_2. The heteronuclear molecule HD exists in only one form. The rate of ortho $\rightarrow$ para conversion, brought about either by temperature change or by interaction with a paramagnetic gas, is two to four times greater for H_2 than for D_2.

Helium shows an isotope effect of a completely different nature. Liquid helium of mass 4 undergoes an allotropic transition at 2.18°K (the λ-point) from the He(I) phase to He(II). The first species is a normal liquid, but He(II) has an extremely curious behavior [5], since it shows thermal superconductivity and superfluidity due to a sharp decrease in the viscosity under certain conditions. For example, the rate of flow of He(II) through very fine capillary tubes is independent of the pressure applied to the liquid, and is virtually independent of the length of the tube. If an empty glass test tube is placed in a vessel containing a certain level of He(II), the tube proceeds to fill to the same level, as if the glass were permeable to the liquid. In fact, the liquid creeps along the walls of the vessel and covers them with an invisible thin film.

If one end of a tube containing He(II) is heated, the liquid flows in a sense opposite to that of the flow of heat (the thermomechanical or *fountain effect*). The London-Titza theory [6, 7, 8] explains this as being due to the fact that a large number of the He^4 atoms, which obey Bose-Einstein statistics, are in a degenerate state below the λ-point. They can therefore move with virtually no exchange of energy and internal friction. The isotope He^3 obeys Fermi statistics and shows normal liquid phase behavior.

Although He^6, produced in the Be (n, α) reaction, follows Bose-Einstein statistics, it does not appear to have the superfluidity of He^4(II) in capillary motion [9]. This has been attributed to the extremely low experimental concentration of He^6 (atom fraction 10^{-19}), so that the degeneracy temperature would only be reached in the region of absolute zero. It should be noted, however, that Landau [10, 11] has developed a theory of quantum hydrodynamics in which the superfluidity of He(II) is explained without recourse to the statistics of the particles. This treatment predicts that moving He^4 transports no impurity whatsoever, even one that is isotopic with He^4.

At very low temperatures, He^3/He^4 and H_2/D_2 mixtures show deviations from Raoult's law and from ideal solution behavior. Prigogine [12] has shown that this is due to the existence of a positive excess energy of mixing, arising from the mass differences. At 0°K, the stable state corresponds to separation of the pure isotopes.

As the following sections show, significant and measurable thermodynamic isotope effects are found with elements much heavier than hydrogen and helium. The same is true of isotopic spectral shifts, which have been measured for elements as heavy as mercury, bismuth, thorium, uranium, and plutonium [13, 14]. Thus taking the U^{238} line at 4244.373 A as a standard, the isotopic shift for U^{235} is 0.251 A, for U^{234} 0.298 A, and for U^{233} 0.396 A, in each case toward the violet.

An interesting isotope effect is found in the superconductivity of certain medium and heavy elements. Maxwell [15, 16] measured the superconductivity of high purity Hg^{198}, obtained by neutron activation of gold, and found a very small increase in the transition temperature T_c at which normal conductivity gives place to superconductivity, of the order of 0.01° per unit mass relative to natural mercury. This effect was subsequently confirmed by other workers, with isotopes of tin, thalium, and lead; at a given voltage, the superconductivity appears at a temperature which increases with decreasing mass. A theoretical relation, $M^{1/2}T_c$ = constant, derived by Fröhlich [17] and by Bardeen [18], is at least approximately confirmed. This treatment assumes that superconductivity is the result of interactions between the electrons and the lattice vibrations of the metallic crystals.

9–2 Isotope effects in hydrogen and its compounds. Differences in molecular properties such as density, boiling point, freezing point, latent

TABLE 9–2

THE PHYSICAL PROPERTIES OF MOLECULAR HYDROGEN*

Property	H_2	HD	D_2	T_2
Boiling point, °K	20.39	22.13	23.67	25.04
Freezing point, °K	13.95	16.60	18.65	—
Latent heat of vaporization at the boiling point, cal/mole	216	—	293	333
Latent heat of fusion, cal/mole	28.0	37.0	47.0	—
Critical temperature, °K	32.99	35.41	38.96	—
Critical pressure, atm	12.77	14.64	16.28	—
Critical volume, cm³/mole	65.5	62.3	60.3	—
Temperature at triple point, °K	13.96	16.60	18.73	20.62
Pressure at triple point, mm Hg	54.0	92.8	128.6	162.0
Density of liquid	0.08	—	0.170	0.182
Enthalpy ΔH^0 at 25°C, kcal/mole	0	+0.15	0	0
Free energy ΔG^0, kcal/mole	0	−0.36	0	0
Entropy S^0, cal/mole·degree	31.23	34.39	34.62	39.39

* Based on E. R. Grilly, *J. Am. Chem. Soc.*, **73,** 843, 5307 (1951); H. J. Hoge and R. D. Arnold, *J. Research Natl. Bur. Standards,* **47,** 63 (1951); H. J. Hoge and J. W. Lassiter, *J. Research Natl. Bur. Standards,* **47,** 75 (1951); A. H. Kimball, H C. Urey, and I. Kirshenbaum, *Bibliography on Heavy Hydrogen Compounds,* McGraw-Hill, New York, 1949.

Table 9–3

The Physical Properties of H_2O and D_2O*

Property	H_2O		D_2O		HDO	T_2O
Boiling point, °C	100		101.42			
Freezing point, °C	0		3.8			
Temperature of maximum density, °C	3.96		11.6			
Latent heat of vaporization at 25°C, kcal/mole	10.515		10.844			
Latent heat of fusion, kcal/mole	1.436		1.515			
Density at 20°C	0.99823		1.10530			
Maximum density	1.000 at 4°C		1.106 at 11.6°C			
Dielectric constant	81.5		80.7			
Cryoscopic constant	1.859		2.050			
Viscosity at 25°C, millipoise	8.91		10.99			
Dissociation constant at 20°C	5.11×10^{-15}		1.49×10^{-15}			
Zero-point energy, cal/mole	13.219		9.664			
Electrode potential H_2/H^+ at 25°C, volts	0		−0.0035 (in D_2O)			
Mobility H_3O^+/H_2O at 18°C, ohm^{-1}	315.2		213.7			
Mobility OH^-/H_2O at 25°C, ohm^{-1}	197.6		119.0			
	Gas	Liquid	Gas	Liquid	Gas	Gas
ΔH^0, kcal/mole	−57.80	−68.32	−59.25	−70.40	−58.45	—
ΔG^0, kcal/mole	−54.63	−56.68	−55.74	−58.29	−55.32	−55.43
Entropy, cal/mole·degree	45.13	16.67	47.38	18.08	46.92	—

* From I. Kirshenbaum, *The Physical Properties of Heavy Water*, McGraw-Hill, New York, 1954, and Ref. 2.

heat, rate of diffusion, etc., are naturally most obvious for isotopes of hydrogen and their compounds. Tables 9–2 and 9–3 give the most important properties of the isotopic molecules of molecular hydrogen and water; Table 9–4 lists the comparable parameters for the molecules H_2O_2 and D_2O_2. Comparisons of these values show that the differences decrease with increasing molecular mass, although they never disappear completely.

The vapor pressures of a pair of isotopic molecules at a temperature T°K are related by a general equation of the type

$$\log \frac{p_1}{p_2} = \frac{a}{T} + b. \tag{9–8}$$

For H_2O and D_2O, $a = 268.84$, $b = -16.9987$; $p_1 = p_2$ at 491°K. For H_2O^{16} and H_2O^{18}, $a = 3.20$, $b = -0.0068$; $p_1 = p_2$ at 490°K.

The solubilities of various salts and organic compounds are much lower in heavy water than in ordinary water, with differences up to as much as 30% in some cases. Some typical values are: KCl in H_2O, 6.81 at 0°C.; in

TABLE 9–4

THE PHYSICAL PROPERTIES OF H_2O_2 AND D_2O_2

Property	H_2O_2	D_2O_2*
Freezing point, °C	−0.43	1.5
Density at 0°C	1.473	1.557
Viscosity at 0°C, millipoise	18.19	19.75
Heat of vaporization at 25°C, kcal/mole	12.345	12.526

* From P. A. Giguère, *Bull. soc. chim. France,* **1954,** 720.

D_2O, 5.69 (moles per 100 mole of solvent); $K_2Cr_2O_7$ in H_2O, 0.358 at 5°; in D_2O, 0.236; CdI_2 in H_2O, 4.34 at 25°; in D_2O, 3.21. Similarly, the ratio of the solubilities of triethylamine in H_2O and D_2O at 25°C is 1.43; for benzene and carbon disulfide the ratios are 1.21 and 1.26 respectively. The conductivities of electrolytes, ionic mobilities, and acid and base constants are also lower in D_2O.

The substitution of D for H in crystalline hydrogenous compounds may cause an appreciable change in the lattice constants if the structure involves hydrogen bonding, as in $(COOH)_2 \cdot 2H_2O$ and KHF_2 [19, 20]. In the case of KH_2PO_4, the substitution brings about a large enough change that crystals of KD_2PO_4 have a completely different structure, with lower symmetry. The cell constants of crystals involving OH bonds (for example, $CuSO_4 \cdot 5H_2O$) are not, however, sensibly changed by the substitution of D for H.

Finally, it should be noted that the partial substitution of D for H in a molecule containing several hydrogen atoms may produce sufficient assymetry to give a measurable optical activity. This has actually been observed [21, 22] in deutero-3-trans-*p*-menthane:

```
CH3         CH2 —CH2
   \       /        \
    CH·CH            CH—CH3
   /       \        /
CH3         CHD—CH2
```

$[\alpha]_D^{25°} = -0.14°$;

in dideutero-2, 3-trans-*p*-menthane:

```
CH3         CH2 —CH2
   \       /        \
    CH·CH            CH—CH3
   /       \        /
CH3         CHD—CHD
```

$[\alpha]_D^{25°} = -0.09°$;

and in α-deuteroethylbenzene, $C_6H_5 \cdot CHDCH_3$, for which $[\alpha]_D^{25°} = -0.30°$ [23].

9–3 Isotope effects in chemical equilibria. Chemical isotope effects are due either to differences in the chemical potentials (i.e., to measurable differences in the equilibrium state) or to differences in kinetic behavior. The former have been studied both theoretically and experimentally, especially in terms of *isotopic exchanges*, in view of the importance of these in isotopic separation methods.

Consider a system containing gaseous $N^{14}H_3$ and an aqueous solution of $N^{15}H_4OH$. The two isotopes will distribute between the two phases by the exchange process

$$N^{15}H_3 + N^{14}H_4^+ \rightleftharpoons N^{15}H_4^+ + N^{14}H_3, \tag{9–9}$$

so that at equilibrium

$$K = \frac{[N^{14}H_{3(g)}][N^{15}H^+_{4(aq)}]}{[N^{14}H^+_{4(aq)}][N^{15}H_{3(g)}]}. \tag{9–10}$$

If the chemical potentials of isotopic molecules were exactly equal, there would be no isotope effect and K would be 1, whereas in fact $K = 1.034$ at 25°C.

Statistical thermodynamics* can be applied to the calculation of the equilibrium constants for various exchange reactions [24, 25, 26]. For a reaction of the type

$$y\text{MA}_x + x\text{NA}'_y \rightleftharpoons y\text{MA}'_x + x\text{NA}_y,$$

the equilibrium constant can be written as

$$K = [f(\text{MA}_x)/f(\text{MA}'_x)]^y/[f(\text{NA}_y)/f(\text{NA}'_y)]^x, \tag{9–11}$$

where the *partition functions* f are related to the free energy of the molecules by the relation $-RT \log f = G^0$. These functions replace the molecular concentrations or thermodynamic activities of classical thermodynamics. The partition function expresses the probability of each molecule being in a given energy state, and is the product of the various factors which contribute to the energy state of the molecule

$$f = f_{\text{tr}} f_{\text{el}} f_{\text{v}} f_{\text{r}} f_{\text{sp}} = \sum_i g_i e^{-E_i/kT}. \tag{9–12}$$

The summation $\sum$ applies to all energy states; translational tr, electronic el, vibrational v, rotational r, and a contribution from the nuclear spin sp; g is the *degeneracy*, a statistical factor which expresses the number of different ways in which the energy state in question can be achieved.

In order to calculate the equilibrium constant of a given exchange reaction, it is necessary to substitute values for f in Eq. (9–11). Fortunately these values are often known from spectroscopic data, at least for light

---

* Bigeleisen, *J. Chem. Phys.*, **21,** 1333 (1953), has also calculated the enthalpy, entropy, and specific heat differences for gaseous isotopes.

isotopic molecules. The influence of f_{el} and f_{sp} is zero or negligibly small. The vibrational energy comes in especially in the term corresponding to the zero-point energy E_0 [Eq. (9–4)]. If E_0 is known for a diatomic isotopic molecule, it can be simply calculated for a second molecule from Eq. (9–5), and the same applies to the rotational energies [using Eq. (9–7)]. For these molecules, the ratio of the partition functions is given by

$$\frac{f_1}{f_2} = \frac{\sigma_2}{\sigma_1}\left(\frac{M_1}{M_2}\right)^{3/2}\left[\frac{I_1(1 - e^{-u_2})e^{-u_1/2}}{I_2(1 - e^{-u_1})e^{-u_2/2}}\right], \tag{9–13}$$

where M is the molecular mass, I the moment of inertia, and $u = hc\omega_0/kT$ where ω_0 is the fundamental vibrational frequency in cm^{-1}; σ is the sym, metry number, which is a measure of the number of identical positions which the molecule can assume when rotated through 360° around each axis of symmetry. This depends on the number of atoms in the molecule in question. For a diatomic homonuclear molecule ($N^{14}N^{14}$), $\sigma = 2$, and for a heteronuclear diatomic molecule ($N^{14}N^{15}$), $\sigma = 1$; similarly $\sigma = 2$ for $CO^{16}O^{16}$, and 1 for $CO^{16}O^{18}$ an analogous equation can be derived for linear polyatomic molecules, which have only a single moment of inertia. For other molecules with n atoms,

$$\frac{f_1}{f_2} = \frac{\sigma_2}{\sigma_1}\left(\frac{M_1}{M_2}\right)^{3/2}\left(\frac{A_1B_1C_1}{A_2B_2C_2}\right)^{1/2}\prod\left[\frac{(1 - e^{-u_2})e^{-u_1/2}}{(1 - e^{-u_1})e^{-u_2/2}}\right], \tag{9–14}$$

where Π is the product of the u-functions for $(3n - 6)$ vibrations; A, B, and C are the principal moments of inertia. These are not generally known for heavy isotopic molecules, and spectroscopic values are also lacking, but the fundamental frequencies can sometimes be evaluated from certain rules, such as that proposed by Teller and Redlich [27, 28]

$$\prod\left(\frac{u_2}{u_1}\right) = \left(\frac{M_2}{M_1}\right)^{3/2}\left(\frac{A_2B_2C_2}{A_1B_1C_1}\right)^{1/2}, \tag{9–15}$$

so that Eq. (9–14) can be simplified to

$$\frac{f_1}{f_2} = \frac{\sigma_2}{\sigma_1}\prod\left[\frac{u_1(1 - e^{-u_2})e^{-u_1/2}}{u_2(1 - e^{-u_1})e^{-u_2/2}}\right]. \tag{9–16}$$

This equation is also valid for diatomic isotopic molecules. Taken together with Eq. (9–11), it shows that the equilibrium constant for exchange reactions depends essentially on the symmetry numbers and on the u-functions, and hence on the zero-point energies. With increasing temperature, u approaches zero and the value of the factor in brackets (*the free energy factor*) approaches unity, so that the equilibrium constant is then given by the ratio of the symmetry numbers. For example, for the reaction

$$\begin{array}{cccc} & H_2 + & D_2 \rightleftharpoons & 2HD, \\ \sigma = & 2 & 2 & 1 \end{array}$$

so that at high temperature, in the absence of an isotopic effect arising

TABLE 9–5

EQUILIBRIUM CONSTANTS FOR EXCHANGE REACTIONS AT 25°C

Reaction	K experimental	K theory
$H_2 + D_2 \rightleftharpoons 2HD$	3.28	3.33
$H_2 + T_2 \rightleftharpoons 2HT$	—	2.56
$H_2O + D_2O \rightleftharpoons 2HDO_{(g)}$	—	3.27
$H_2O + T_2O \rightleftharpoons 2HTO_{(g)}$	—	3.42
$HD + H_2O \rightleftharpoons HDO + H_2$	3.7	3.78
$HT + H_2O \rightleftharpoons HTO + H_2$	6.26	6.19
$H_2 + DCl \rightleftharpoons HCl + HD$ (at 17°C)	1.45	1.53
$PH_2D + H_2O \rightleftharpoons PH_3 + HDO_{(g)}$	—	1.52*
$C^{12}O_2 + C^{13}O \rightleftharpoons C^{13}O_2 + C^{12}O$	—	1.086†
$C^{12}O^{2-}_{3(aq)} + C^{13}O_{2(g)} \rightleftharpoons C^{13}O^{2-}_{3(aq)} + C^{12}O_{2(g)}$ (at 0°C)	1.017	1.016
$C^{12}O^{2-}_{3(aq)} + C^{14}O_{2(g)} \rightleftharpoons C^{14}O^{2-}_{3(aq)} + C^{12}O_{2(g)}$ (at 0°C)	—	1.024
$HC^{12}N_{(g)} + C^{13}N^-_{(aq)} \rightleftharpoons HC^{13}N_{(g)} + C^{12}N^-_{(aq)}$ (at 18°C)	1.026	1.030‡
$N^{15}H_{3(g)} + N^{14}H^+_{4(aq)} \rightleftharpoons N^{14}H_{3(g)} + N^{15}H^+_{4(aq)}$	1.034	1.035
$N^{15}O_2^- + N^{14}O_3^- \rightleftharpoons N^{14}O_2^- + N^{15}O_3^-$	—	1.09
$\frac{1}{2}CO_2^{16} + H_2O^{18} \rightleftharpoons \frac{1}{2}CO_2^{18} + H_2O^{16}$ (at 0°C)	1.046	1.044
$S^{34}O_{2(g)} + HS^{32}O^-_{3(aq)} \rightleftharpoons S^{32}O_{2(g)} + HS^{34}O^-_{3(aq)}$	—	1.019
$S^{36}O_{2(g)} + HS^{32}O^-_{3(aq)} \rightleftharpoons S^{32}O_{2(g)} + HS^{36}O^-_{3(aq)}$	1.043	1.039
$Cl^{37}O_3^- + Cl^{35}O_4^- \rightleftharpoons Cl^{35}O_3^- + Cl^{37}O_4^-$	—	1.035
$Cl^{35}Cl^{37}_{(g)} + Cl^{35}O^-_{3(aq)} \rightleftharpoons Cl^{35}Cl^{35}_{(g)} + Cl^{37}O^-_{3\,(aq)}$	—	1.077
$Br^{79}Br^{81} + Br^{79}O_3^- \rightleftharpoons Br^{79}Br^{79} + Br^{81}O_3^-$	—	1.007
$I^{127}I^{129} + I^{127}O_3^- \rightleftharpoons I^{127}I^{127} + I^{129}O_3^-$	—	1.0028
$I^{127}I^{131} + I^{127}O_3^- \rightleftharpoons I^{127}I^{127} + I^{131}O_3^-$	—	1.005

* Ref. 29.
† Ref. 30.
‡ See D. R. Stranks and G. M. Harris, *J. Am. Chem. Soc.*, **75,** 2015 (1953) for the equilibrium constants of other exchange reactions involving C^{14}.

from the zero-point energies,

$$K_{\lim} = \frac{f[HD]^2}{f[H_2]f[D_2]} = \frac{\sigma_{H_2} \cdot \sigma_{D_2}}{\sigma_{HD}} = 4, \tag{9–17}$$

corresponding to a purely statistical distribution of each isotope between the various molecules involved.

Table 9–5 gives the calculated constants K for certain exchange reactions, together with a number of experimental results.

A number of generalities can be deduced from this table. Thus it can be seen that isotope effects generally decrease with increasing mass; ($K - 1$) approximately doubles when the mass difference doubles S^{34} and S^{36}, I^{129} and I^{131}). When the exchange involves two isotopic atoms in different valency states, the heavier isotope tends to concentrate in the higher valency compound (ClO_3^- and ClO_4^-, NO_2^- and NO_3^-). If the exchange involves partition between water and the gaseous phase of a compound, which is in the same molecular state in both phases, the heavier molecule tends to concentrate in the liquid phase. If the molecule is dissociated or ionized in the liquid phase, the heavy isotope concentrates in this phase when the dissociated form has the larger number of modes of vibration; in the opposite case, the liquid is enriched in the lighter isotope [31]. In the partition of HCN between water and the gaseous phase, N^{15} concentrates slightly in the liquid phase, and C^{13} in the gas.

In the crystallization of the hydrated salts $Na_2SO_4 \cdot 10H_2O$, $Na_2CO_3 \cdot 10H_2O$, $BaCl_2 \cdot 2H_2O$, and $CaSO_4 \cdot 2H_2O$, the crystals contain relatively less O^{18} than the solvents [32], and the same is found in the precipitation of HgO and Ag_2O by alkali [33]. Other examples of isotope effects in the partition of compounds such as carbonates and phosphates between two phases are discussed in Chapter 10.

9–4 Kinetic isotope effects. Isotopic molecules often react at slightly different rates due to differences in the activation energies. In addition to this, for light molecules containing hydrogen isotopes, the collision frequency may be smaller for the heavier isotope (D or T), which reduces the rate constant accordingly.

The theory of such kinetic isotope effects was originally given by Eyring [34, 35], and more recently by Bigeleisen [36, 37] using the absolute rate theory. This theory relates the rate constant k of a reaction to the formation of an intermediate transitory compound, the activated complex or transition state, which is assumed to be in thermodynamic equilibrium with the reacting species. This equilibrium state is defined by the ratio of the partition coefficients in an equation analogous to Eq. (9–11). Bigeleisen has shown that the effect of isotopes on the reaction rate can be treated in a manner similar to that used for equilibrium systems, and has established that the ratio of the rate constants for two isotopic molecules is given by

$$\frac{k_1}{k_2} = \frac{\sigma_1 \sigma_2^{\ddagger}}{\sigma_2 \sigma_1^{\ddagger}} \cdot \left(\frac{\mu_2}{\mu_1}\right)^{1/2} [1 + \Sigma\varphi(u_i) - \Sigma\varphi(u^{\ddagger})], \qquad (9\text{–}18)$$

in which as usual the symbol $\ddagger$ refers to the activated complex; the $\varphi(u)$ terms are functions of the fundamental frequencies ω_0 and hence of the zero-point energies E_0; μ is the reduced mass of the activated complex in the reaction direction, i.e., of the atoms involved in the bond whose rupture determines the rate of reaction. The frequency of bond breaking in the complex depends on the ratio μ_2/μ_1. The free energy factor (in u) affects the equilibrium between the complex and the reacting species. The heaviest isotopic molecule has the lower vibrational frequency, and hence

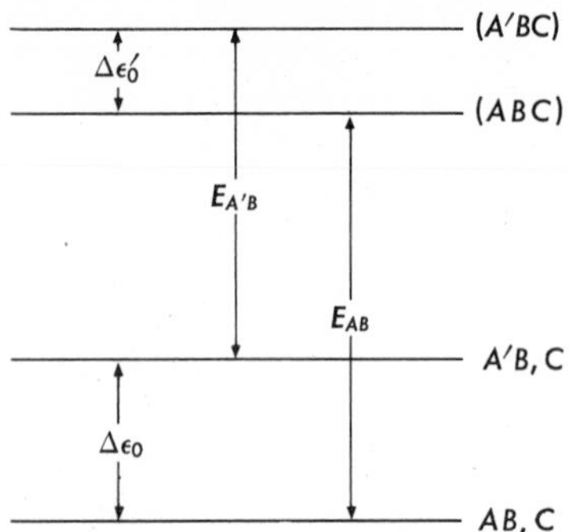

FIG. 9–1. The energy levels of the isotopic molecules AB and $A'B$, and of their activated complexes with C (schematic).

the smaller zero-point energy, but on the other hand, the zero-point energy of the activated complex is lower for the heavier molecule (see the energy level scheme in Fig. 9–1); in general, $\Delta E_0 > \Delta E_0^{\ddagger}$. It follows that the maximum difference in the activation energies in a reaction involving two isotopic molecules is equal to the difference in their zero-point energies. This occurs when the isotopic atoms are very loosely bound in the activated complex; one then has $\Delta E_0^{\ddagger} \approx 0$, and the isotope effect is at a maximum. If hydrogen isotopes are involved, the relation between the rate constants is more complex, since differences in the rotational energies must also be taken into account.

Bigeleisen has calculated the maximum ratios between the rate constants for reactions involving isotopic molecules; some of the values found for reactions at 25°C are given in Table 9–6. It will be seen that the effects decrease with increasing mass, but that for a large difference (Ca^{40}, Ca^{45}) the effects are not negligible, even for medium atomic weight elements. Like thermodynamic isotope effects, kinetic effects decrease with increasing temperature, since the free energy factor approaches unity.

Bigeleisen has distinguished between two types of kinetic effects, *intermolecular* and *intramolecular*. In the first case, the rate constants of two distinct molecules are compared, as for example, in the decarboxylation of malonic acid,

$$H_2C\begin{matrix}\diagup C^{12}OOH \\ \diagdown C^{12}OOH\end{matrix} \xrightarrow{k_1} CH_3{\cdot}C^{12}OOH + C^{12}O_2,$$

and (9–19)

$$H_2C\begin{matrix}\diagup C^{13}OOH \\ \diagdown C^{12}OOH\end{matrix} \xrightarrow{k_2} CH_3{\cdot}C^{12}OOH + C^{13}O_2.$$

TABLE 9–6

MAXIMUM KINETIC ISOTOPE EFFECTS AT 25°C

Isotopes	K_1/K_2
H/D	18
H/T	60
B^{10}/B^{11}	1.3
C^{12}/C^{13}	1.25
C^{12}/C^{14}	1.50
N^{14}/N^{15}	1.14
O^{16}/O^{18}	1.19
Na^{22}/Na^{23}	1.03
P^{31}/P^{32}	1.02
S^{32}/S^{35}	1.05
Ca^{40}/Ca^{45}	1.08
I^{127}/I^{131}	1.02

The intramolecular effect relates to the difference between rate constants measured on the same molecule,

$$
H_2C\begin{cases} C^{13}OOH \xrightarrow{k_2} CH_3{\cdot}C^{12}OOH + C^{13}O_2, \\ C^{12}OOH \xrightarrow{k_3} CH_3{\cdot}C^{13}OOH + C^{12}O_2. \end{cases} \tag{9–20}
$$

The intramolecular effect is always superimposed on the intermolecular effect. The ratio of the rate constants for intermolecular reactions is often written as k_2/k_1, and for intramolecular reactions as k_3/k_2 (or k_2/k_3). More frequently the notation k_{14}/k_{12}, k_{12}/k_{13}, etc., is used, where the subscripts refer to the mass numbers of the isotopes concerned. Kinetic effects are sometimes expressed as the percentage $100[(k_1/k_2) - 1]$.

Bigeleisen has shown that in intramolecular effects involving light isotopes, the zero-point energy can be neglected, and under these circumstances Eq. (9–18) reduces to

$$
\frac{k_3}{k_2} = S\left(\frac{\mu_2}{\mu_1}\right)^{1/2}, \tag{9–21}
$$

where S is the overall symmetry factor. The isotopic effect is then independent of temperature, and is quite easily calculated. This is not true of intermolecular effects, for which the calculation of k_1/k_2 requires a knowledge of the vibrational frequencies of the isotopic molecules and of the activated complex, so that a model structure must be assumed for the latter. One consequence of this is that agreement between theory and experiment is generally much better for intramolecular than for intermolecular isotope effects.

It is not usually possible to measure the ratio of the rate constants with initially isotopically pure molecules, and the natural or enriched mixture containing one of the isotopes (for example, D, C^{13}, C^{14}, N^{15}, etc.) in high dilution is employed. Mass-spectrometric or radiometric methods are then used to measure the relative concentration of the two isotopes after various reaction times, and a relation between concentration and time is established in the usual way. For example, in the decarboxylation of 2-,4-,6-trimethylbenzoic acid, $C_6H_2(CH_3)_3C^{13}OOH$ [38], we find

$$\log\left[1 + \left(\frac{n_0 - n}{n_0}\right)\left(\frac{x}{1 - x}\right)\right] = \left(\frac{k_{13}}{k_{12}} - 1\right)\log(1 - x), \quad (9\text{–}22)$$

where x is the fraction of acid decomposed after time t, n the concentration of $C^{13}O_2$ at the same time, and n_0 the concentration at the completion of the reaction. If the expression on the left-hand side of the equation is plotted against $\log(1 - x)$ for various values of x, a straight line is obtained with a slope of

$$\frac{k_{13}}{k_{12}} - 1.$$

9–5 Experimental results. Kinetic isotope effects have been detected and measured in a considerable (and increasing) number of reactions, especially those involving isotopes of carbon. In Table 9–7, some of the results of these measurements are collected, and where possible, compared with the theoretical values.

This comparison is particularly important for the differences between the two carbon isotopes C^{13} and C^{14} in the same reaction. Theory predicts that in the breaking of a C—C, C—O, or C—N bond, the ratio

$$\frac{(k_{12}/k_{14}) - 1}{(k_{12}/k_{13}) - 1} \quad (= \alpha)$$

should be 2 (Table 9–5). Table 9–7 shows that this is approximately true for the dehydration of oxalic acid, for the nonenzymatic hydrolysis of urea, and for the decarboxylation of malonic acid. A number of earlier measurements on this latter compound and its derivatives always gave values of approximately 3 for α, the isotope effect for C^{14} being twice as large as the theoretical value [58, 59, 60]. Recent careful measurements by Yankwich, quoted in Table 9–7, apparently eliminate this deviation, but it is not clear whether the differences found in certain other cases (malonic acid derivatives, trimethylbenzoic acid, and the reaction of benzoic anhydride with C_2H_5OH or $CH_3 \cdot C_6H_4 \cdot NH_2$) are also due to experimental error, or to some error in the theoretical treatment.

The anomalous results found for the hydrolysis of urea by urease is probably connected with the enzymatic mechanism of this reaction. In other cases, the role of the solvent has been invoked in explaining the results. For example, in the decarboxylation of malonic acid in quinoline solution, it has been found that the isotope effect decreases with decreasing temperature [61, 62], in apparent contradiction to theory, which requires that the variation is always in the inverse sense. The influence of the solvent on kinetic isotope effects in various organic molecules has been studied experimentally by Ropp and Raaen [63]. These authors have also examined the effect of substituents (Cl, NO_2, CH_3, OCH_3) in such molecules.

The decrease in the rate of reaction with increasing mass for heavy isotopic molecules, predicted by theory, is confirmed by virtually all the examples given in Table 9–7. It has also been verified in a large number of other cases, including the breaking of the C^{12}—C^{12} and C^{12}—C^{13} bonds in propane by thermal cracking, or by electron bombardment in a mass spectrometer [64]; the thermal decomposition of $Ni(CO)_4$ [65]; and the decomposition of mercurous formate $HC^{14}OO$ Hg [57a]. The rate of assimilation of $C^{12}O_2$ in the photosynthesis of green algae is greater than that of $C^{13}O_2$, and *a fortiori* of $C^{14}O_2$, although different authors report discordant values depending on the differences measured; from 2.6 to 4.3% for $C^{13}O_2$ [66, 67, 68] and from 10.5 to 17% for $C^{14}O_2$ [69, 70, 71]. The $C^{12} = 0$ group reacts more quickly than $C^{14} = 0$ in the reaction of benzophenone with 2-, 4-dinitrophenylhydrazine [72]

$$C_6H_5{\cdot}C^{14}O{\cdot}C_6H_5 + NH_2{\cdot}NH{\cdot}C_6H_3(NO_2)_2$$
$$\rightarrow (C_6H_5)_2C = N{\cdot}NH{\cdot}C_6H_3{\cdot}(NO_2)_3 + H_2O \quad (k_{12}/k_{14} = 1.1 \text{ at } 27°\text{C}).$$

Equally, the molecule $C_4H_9Cl^{35}$ reacts more quickly than $C_4H_9Cl^{37}$ with $AgNO_3$ or NaOH in alcohol solution, with $k_{35}/k_{37} = 1.008$ [73].

Deuterated molecules also react more slowly in general than their light analogs. Examples of this include:

(a) the mutarotation of glucose in acetic acid solution ($k_H/k_D = 2.4$ to 2.6) [74];

(b) the decomposition of nitramide ($k_H/k_D = 2$ to 5.2) [75, 76];

(c) the oxidation of CH_3CHDOH to CH_3CDO [77];

(d) the reaction $CH_3I + DI \rightarrow CH_3D + I_2$ ($k_H/k_D = 1.42$ at 270°C) [78];

(e) the decomposition of $CHCl_3$ by 50 to 70-ev electrons ($k_H/k_D \approx 3$) [79];

(f) the photochlorination of $CHCl_3$ and $CDCl_3$ [80];

(g) the reaction of metals with H_2O or D_2O vapor [81].

However, there are a number of protolytic reactions, involving the transport of H^+ or D^+ from one molecule to another, in which the deuterated molecules react more quickly.* Thus the dismutation of UO_2^+ is 1.7 times faster in heavy water than in H_2O [82]. Other examples of this effect with deuterium will be discussed in Section 23–2 in terms of the mechanism of acid-base catalysis.

A number of similar inversions have also been reported for a few reactions involving isotopic carbon molecules (e.g., the iodination of acetone and the condensation of benzylbenzoic acid; see Table 9–7); these have not, however, always been confirmed. Where genuine, this behavior appears to have its origin in the kinetics of the reaction. Thus if a reaction

* Several other H/D isotope effects are discussed by K. Wiberg, *Chem. Revs.*, **55**, 13 (1955).

TABLE 9–7

KINETIC ISOTOPE EFFECTS

Reaction	Temp, °C	Experimental result	Theory	Ref.
$HC^{14}OOH \xrightarrow{H_2SO_4} H_2O + C^{14}O$	0	$k_{14}/k_{12} = 0.89$	0.88	39, 40
$C^{13}OOH \xrightarrow{k_2} C^{13}O_2 + C^{12}O + H_2O$ | $C^{12}OOH \xrightarrow{k_3} C^{12}O_2 + C^{13}O + H_2O$	100	k_2/k_3 $= 1.027\text{–}1.033$	1.023–1.03	41, 42
Same reaction, with C^{14} instead of C^{13}	103	$k_2/k_3 = 1.055$	1.043–1.06	42
$C^{13}O + \frac{1}{2}O_2$ (heterogeneous combustion)	~600	$k_{13}/k_{12} = 0.985$	0.983	43
$C^{14}O + \frac{1}{2}O_2$ (heterogeneous combustion)	~600	$k_{14}/k_{12} = 0.959$	0.966	43
$CH_2(C^{13}OOH)(COOH) \rightarrow CO_2 + CH_3COOH$	138	$k_{12}/k_{13} = 1.028$	1.021	44
Same reaction, with C^{14} instead of C^{13}	138	$k_{12}/k_{14} = 1.054$	1.038	44
$C_6H_2(CH_3)_3C^{13}OOH \rightarrow CO_2 + C_6H_3(CH_3)_3$	60	$k_{12}/k_{13} = 1.038$	1.041	38, 45
Same reaction, with C^{14} instead of C^{13}	60	$k_{12}/k_{14} = 1.101$	1.078	45
$(C_6H_5 \cdot C^{14}O)(C_6H_5 \cdot C^{12}O)O + C_2H_5OH \rightarrow C_6H_5 \cdot C^{14}OOH + C_6H_5 \cdot C^{12}OOC_2H_5$	30	$k_{12}/k_{14} = 1.127$	1.043	46

$C_6H_5 \cdot C^{12}O \rangle O + CH_3 \cdot C_6H_4 \cdot NH_2 \rightarrow C_6H_6 + C_6H_5 \cdot C^{14}O \cdot O \cdot C^{12}O \cdot NH_2 \cdot C_6H_4 \cdot CH_3$	30	$k_{12}/k_{14} = 1.073$	1.041	46
Hydrolysis of $C_6H_5\ COOC_2H_5$	20	$k_{14}/k_{12} = 0.86$	0.86–0.88	47
Hydrolysis of urea ($NH_2 \cdot C^{13}O \cdot NH_2$)	100	$k_{12}/k_{13} = 1.055$	1.043	48
Hydrolysis of $NH_2 \cdot C^{14}O \cdot NH_2$	100	$k_{12}/k_{14} = 1.10$	1.08	48
Hydrolysis of $NH_2 \cdot C^{14}O \cdot NH_2$ by urease	30	$k_{12}/k_{14} = 1.032$	1.102	48
Hydrolysis of $NH_2 \cdot C^{13}O \cdot NH_2$ by urease	30	$k_{12}/k_{13} = 1.010$	1.053	48
$CH_3 \cdot C^{14}OOH \xrightarrow{\text{wet oxidation}} C^{14}O_2$	25	$k_{12}/k_{14} = 1.06$	1.075	49
$CCl_3 \cdot C^{13}OO^- + H_2O \rightarrow CHCl_3 + HC^{13}O_3^-$	70	$k_{12}/k_{13} = 1.034$	1.04	50
$Ba(OH)_2 + C^{13}O_2 \rightarrow BaC^{13}O_3 + H_2O$*	25	$k_{12}/k_{13} = 1.011–1.014$	—	51
Polymerisation of styrene, and of vinyl chloride	25	$k_{14}/k_{12} = 0.93$	—	52
$C^{14}H_3 \cdot CO \cdot CH_3 + 2NaOH + I_2 \rightarrow NaI + CH_3I + C^{14}H_3 \cdot COONa$	—	$k_{14}/k_{12} = 1.03–1.06$	—	53
o-benzylbenzoic acid → anthraquinone	100	$k_{14}/k_{12} = 1.074$	—	54
phthalamide → phthalimide + $N^{15}H_3$	136	$k_2/k_3 = 1.015$	1.016	55
$NH_4NO_3^{18} \rightarrow N_2O + 2H_2O$	220	$k_{16}/k_{18} = 1.023$	1.026	56
Reduction of $H_2O^{16}O^{18}$ by Fe(II), Cr(II), Cu(I), Sn(II)	25	$k_{18}/k_{16} = 0.93–0.95$	0.939	57

* Ropp, Raaen, and Weinberger [57*a*] find no isotope effect in the absorption of $C^{13}O_2$ by caustic soda or benzylamine.

occurs in two or more successive steps and the elementary rate controlling process regenerates the initial isotopic molecule [for example, the reverse step in the UO_2^+ equilibria in Eq. (9–23)], the overall rate will be greater for the heavier molecule:

$$UO_2^+ + D^+ \rightleftharpoons UO_2D^{2+}; \qquad UO_2^+ + UO_2D^{2+} \rightarrow UO_2^{2+} + UO_2D^+. \tag{9–23}$$

On the other hand, if the isotopes are initially present as free atoms (H, D, Cl^{35}, Cl^{37}), the u_i term in Eq. (9–18) is zero, so that the ratio k_1/k_2 may be less than unity.

Finally it should be noted that there will naturally be no isotope effect if the isotopic atoms do not form part of the bond which is broken in the reaction in question. For instance, no isotope effect was found in the decarboxylation of amino-benzoic acid [83]:

$$NH_2 \cdot C_6H_4 \cdot C^{13}OOH \rightarrow C_6H_5 \cdot NH_2 + C^{13}O_2.$$

The reaction follows a second order kinetic law; the rate-determining process is probably the attack of a proton on the α-carbon atom of the amphoteric ion $^+NH_3 \cdot C_6H_4 \cdot COO^-$, which is formed in a preliminary step. The activation energy of this process will be greater than that for rupture of the C—C bond, and identical for both isotopic molecules. Zero isotope effects have also been found in the Cannizzaro reaction with benzaldehyde [84],

$$2C_6H_5 \cdot C^{14}HO + H_2O \rightarrow C_6H_5 \cdot CHOH + C_6H_5 \cdot COOH,$$

for the condensation of benzaldehyde to $C_6H_5 \cdot CHOH \cdot CO \cdot C_6H_5$, for the decarboxylation of benzilic acid $(C_6H_5)_2 \cdot COH \cdot C^{14}OOH$ [84], and for the pyrolysis of lithium acetate [85] and barium adipate [86].

In a number of cases, the extent of the isotope effect depends on the reagent used [87]; the ratio k_{12}/k_{14} for the oxidation of oxalic acid with bromine is 1.022, with Fenton's reagent (ferrous sulfate plus hydrogen peroxide) 1.016, with potassium permanganate 1.026, and with potassium permanganate in the presence of manganous ions 1.035.

The influence of different elementary processes on isotope effects provides a useful method of studying reaction mechanisms. Such applications are discussed in Chapter 23.

9–6 The separation of isotopes by statistical physical methods. The differences in the physical and chemical properties of the isotopes of a given element are extremely small, but despite this, various long and laborious methods can be used to separate isotopes, or at least to obtain fractions which are richer in one isotopic component of the initial mixture. The degree of separation of a mixture of two isotopes is usually expressed by a fractionation or separation factor α. For simplicity, the discussion will be limited to binary isotopic mixtures. Let N_1 and n_1 be the numbers of molecules (or gram molecules) of two constituents per unit volume in one of the fractions or phases obtained by some separation procedure, and N_2 and n_2 the numbers in a second fraction. Further let $N_1 > N_2$, so that $n_1 < n_2$. Then by definition

$$\alpha = \frac{N_1/N_2}{n_1/n_2} \qquad (\alpha > 1), \tag{9-24}$$

and the enrichment factor is then $(\alpha - 1)$.

In most methods, α is very close to unity for a single elementary process, and the enrichment is negligible, so that the number of separations or "stages" must be multiplied; one example of this is the use of the countercurrent principle as in distillation. For x stages, the overall separation factor is $A = \alpha^x$. After a certain time, a stationary state is reached, corresponding to the limit of enrichment which can be achieved with the arrangement in question. Working in cascade* (i.e., circulating the enriched fractions through several units) increases the separation.

In principle, any property which varies with the mass may form the basis of an isotopic fractionation method. A number of techniques have been proposed or actually used for such separations, but these differ in their practical importance. Some techniques will only give limited enrichments, whereas with others, such as isotopic exchange and thermal diffusion, complete separation can be achieved under favorable conditions. These latter two methods are statistical in nature, as are diffusion through porous membranes, centrifugation, distillation, chemical exchange, etc.; the differences being made use of are those between the *average* properties of isotopic molecules, such as the mean kinetic energy. Such methods are especially suitable for isotopes of the light elements, but if very careful precautions are taken, they can even be applied to the separation of U^{235}. Although isotope effects increase with decreasing temperature, temperature rise may increase the efficiency of the separation if the increase in rate more than compensates for the decrease in the thermodynamic equilibrium constant. We shall merely outline here the principles of these separation methods.

Fractional distillation. This method depends on the differing vapor pressures P_1 and P_2 of two pure isotopic molecules; the separation factor is given by

$$\alpha = \frac{(N_1/N_2)_{\text{vap}}}{(n_1/n_2)_{\text{liq}}} = \frac{P_1}{P_2}. \tag{9-25}$$

If the lighter component (index 1) is the more volatile, $\alpha > 1$; for example, $\alpha = 1.007$ for the molecules H_2O^{16} and H_2O^{18}. A countercurrent distillation is carried out in a reflux column, containing up to several hundred plates (real or theoretical); this involves filling the column with small ball bearings, or glass or stainless steel helices, which serve to increase the

* The theory of cascade operation is discussed by K. Cohen, *Theory of Isotope Separation* (N.N.E.S., III-16) McGraw-Hill, New York, 1951, and in C. Goodman, ed., *The Science and Engineering of Nuclear Power*, Vol. II, Addison-Wesley, Reading, Mass., 1949, p. 19.

contact surface for the liquid-vapor equilibrium. For p plates, the overall separation factor is $A = \alpha^{p+1}$. In practice, equilibrium is never completely reached, and the effective number of plates is calculated from measured enrichments.

The yields from fractional distillation are always very small, and the method is useful only if the mixture of isotopes is available in large quantities and at comparatively low cost. It has been applied with some success to such systems as the enrichment of C^{13} by the low temperature distillation of CO, the enrichment of O^{18} by the distillation of C_2H_5OH and (more especially) water, and to argon. Thode [88] has obtained 150 cm^3 of H_2O enriched 6.5 times in O^{18} and 2.7 times in O^{17} by a distillation lasting 120 days through three columns 8 m long. By using several specially designed columns, Dostrowsky [89] was able to bring about a considerable enrichment in these two oxygen isotopes, and even to obtain complete separation of O^{18}.

In all these fractionations, the heavier isotopic molecule concentrates in the liquid phase, and this is also true in the fractionation of chlorine isotopes by distillation of $CHCl_3$ and CCl_4, and of the isotopes of oxygen in the fractionation of CH_3OH [90]. On the other hand, the heavy carbon isotope C^{13} concentrates in the vapor phase in this latter distillation (i.e., of CH_3OH) as it does in the distillation of benzene. It appears that if the isotopic atom is in a central position in a molecule, such as

```
Cl     Cl            H      OH
  \   /                \   /
    C         or         C      ,
  /   \                /   \
Cl     Cl            H      H
```

the heavier isotopic molecule has the high vapor pressure. Bradley [91] has discussed this apparent anomaly on the basis of statistical thermodynamics.

Diffusion. Graham's law states that the rate of diffusion of a gas through a porous solid is inversely proportional to the square root of the molecular weight, provided that the pore diameter is small compared with the mean free path of the molecules. It follows that the diffusion of a gaseous mixture of two isotopic molecules will give an initial separation factor

$$\alpha = \sqrt{M_1/M_2}.$$

This equation is strictly valid only if the exit pressure from the porous membrane is zero. The separation factor tends to decrease as the diffusion proceeds, since the pressure of the lighter constituent of the mixture decreases more rapidly than does that of the heavier constituent. If the diffusion is allowed to proceed to completion, there will naturally be no separation at all, so that some compromise must be found, as for example by restricting the process to the diffusion of half the gas; for the $C^{12}H_4/C^{13}H_4$ mixture, α (initial) $= 1.03$ and $\alpha_{1/2} = 1.02$.

Hertz [92] increased the efficiency of this method considerably by using a large number of porous tubes and mercury diffusion pumps. By this means, the apparatus could be operated continually and automatically in cascade, so that the lighter and the heavier fractions were displaced in opposite directions (the countercurrent principle). Using a system of 50 pumps, Hertz was able to separate the hydrogen-deuterium mixture completely, and also obtained practically pure Ne^{20}. The method was subsequently further improved by replacing the tubes by the mercury vapor jets in the pumps, which then functioned as porous membranes. With this system, considerable enrichment of the isotopes of nitrogen, oxygen (H_2O^{16}/H_2O^{18}), carbon ($C^{12}H_4/C^{13}H_4$), and argon was obtained. This technique was used in the United States during the period 1942 to 1945, for the separation of U^{235} for atomic weapon work. Using some thousands of pumps, gaseous UF_6 (boiling point 56°C) was circulated through thousands of special membranes, with pores about 10^{-5} mm in diameter [93].

Thermal diffusion. Separation methods based on the Soret effect (thermal diffusion) are much more efficient than those involving simple diffusion. Establishing a temperature gradient in an initially homogeneous fluid mixture sets up a concentration gradient by a diffusion mechanism; the light molecules tend to concentrate in the hot regions, and the heavier molecules in the colder zones. For elastic spherical molecules, the concentration difference between two zones with temperatures T and T' is given by [94, 95]

$$\Delta c_1 = \frac{17}{3}\left(\frac{M_1 - M_2}{M_1 + M_2}\right)\frac{c_1 c_2}{9.15 - 8.25 c_1 c_2}\log\left(\frac{T}{T'}\right), \tag{9-26}$$

where c_1 is the mole fraction of the constituent with a molecular weight of M_1, and c_2 that of M_2.

By itself, this type of diffusion only brings about a very low isotopic separation, since ordinary diffusion works against the thermal diffusion and thus tends to re-establish the homogeneity of the system. A simple and ingenious apparatus introduced by Clusius and Dickel [96, 97], however, increased the efficiency of this method considerably. These authors used a long vertical tube, cooled on the outside and electrically heated to 750°C in the center by means of a coaxial resistance wire; consequently, in addition to thermal diffusion, there is a thermal syphoning effect which causes a current of hot gas to rise to the top in the center of the tube and cold gas to descend down the walls of the tube. The combination of these two effects sets up a countercurrent, which tends to concentrate the lighter molecules at the top of the tube and the heavier ones at the bottom. The separation factor is given by [98]

$$\alpha = \exp\left[\frac{k(M_1 - M_2)}{M_1 + M_2}\cdot\frac{\Delta T^{4/3}}{T_m^{5/3}}\right], \tag{9-27}$$

where ΔT is the temperature gradient, T_m the average temperature, and k a constant depending on the dimensions of the tube and on the experimental conditions. In practice, several tubes are used, joined by narrower tubes so that the gas circulates between the bottom of the main tube and the upper end of the next.

Clusius and Dickel used a series of five or six tubes, with a total length of over 30 m, 8.4 cm in diameter, with a platinum wire 0.4 mm in diameter passing down the center. This gave virtually pure isotopes of chlorine (masses 35 and 37), neon (mass 22), krypton (masses 84 and 86), oxygen (mass 18), and nitrogen (mass 15, using a tube 82 m long), and considerable enrichments of various other isotopes. The separation procedure took several weeks or months. Enrichments of heavy methane and of He^3 have been achieved by Nier [99, 100], and of tritium and deuterium by Seaborg [101].

The technique can also be applied to the separation of isotopes in the liquid state, but since diffusion is some 10^4 to 10^5 times slower than for gases, the procedure is less efficient. The systems for which this has been tried include H_2O/D_2O, C_6H_6/C_6D_6, and $U^{235}F_6/U^{238}F_6$.

Centrifugation. A gaseous mixture in the terrestrial gravitational field tends to undergo separation, governed by the barometric formula

$$\alpha = \exp\left[\frac{-\ \Delta Mg\ \Delta h}{RT}\right], \tag{9–28}$$

where g is the gravitational constant, Δh the difference in altitude, and ΔM the mass difference. An analogous relation can be derived for the separation of two isotopes in a centrifugal field [102]:

$$\alpha = \exp\left[\frac{-\ v^2\ \Delta M}{2RT}\right]. \tag{9–29}$$

For $T = 290°$K, $\alpha = \exp\left[-2.07 \times 10^{-11} v^2\ \Delta M\right]$, where v is the linear rate of displacement. Since this increases with the length of the axis of rotation, α increases with increasing diameter of the centrifuge. Modern ultracentrifuges give fields equivalent to several hundred thousand g, so that good enrichments can be achieved. With a diameter of 10 cm and a rotation of 1500 rev/sec, $v = 450$ m/sec, so that $\alpha = 0.913$ for $\Delta M = 2$; this means that the difference between the center and the periphery for the O^{16}/O^{18} ratio in H_2O, for example, is 4.35%.

This method is especially suitable for the heavy elements, since the separation factor depends not on the ratio of the masses, but on the difference between them, so that in principle the separation of U^{235} and U^{238} should be more efficient than that of hydrogen and deuterium. For the same reason, α is independent of the state of combination of the isotopes. This method has been applied to the enrichment of the chlorine isotopes in CCl_4 [103] and of the bromine isotopes in C_2H_5Br [104], and has also been used on a semi-industrial scale for the partial separation of uranium isotopes [93].

9–7 Chemical methods. *Isotopic exchange methods.* The theoretical treatment of isotopic exchanges was first given by Urey, who has made some elegant applications of this method, which depends on the enrichment of one isotope in a liquid phase at the expense of a gaseous phase, making use of deviations from unity in the equilibrium constant of heterogeneous exchange reactions. In this respect, the method is very similar to a statistical process such as fractional distillation, and in fact is likewise normally carried out in a multistage reflux system.

One example of this technique is the separation of the isotopes of nitrogen (natural N^{14}/N^{15} ratio = 262), using the reaction

$$N^{14}H^{+}_{4(aq)} + N^{15}H_{3(gas)} \rightleftharpoons N^{15}H^{+}_{4(aq)} + NH_{3(gas)}, \qquad (9\text{–}30)$$

for which the equilibrium constant at 25°C is 1.035 (Table 9–5). A solution of an ammonium salt (chloride, nitrate, or sulfate) passes down a long column, up which gaseous ammonia is rising (Fig. 9–2). When the liquid reaches the bottom of the column, it reacts with hot caustic soda solution, and ammonia enriched in N^{15} is released. At the end of several cycles, part of the solution and the enriched gas are transferred to a second (smaller) column, where the same series of operations is repeated. By using a multistage apparatus, highly enriched or even pure N^{15} can be obtained. Analogous reactions have been used to concentrate the heavy isotopes of hydrogen (H_2O + HD), oxygen ($CO_2^{16} + H_2O^{18}$), sulfur ($S^{32}O_2 + H_2S^{34}O_3^-$), and carbon. In the latter case, one available reaction is

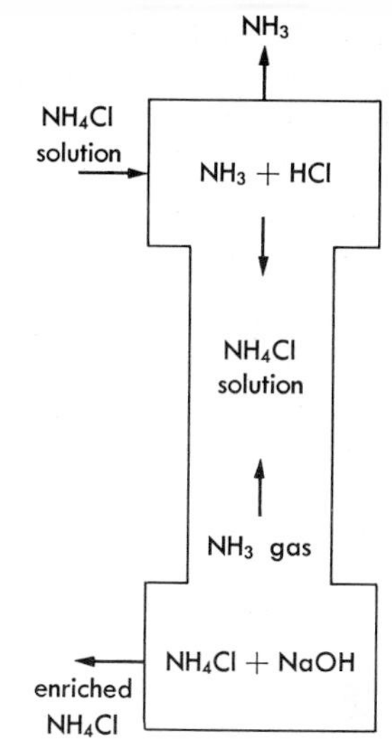

FIG. 9–2. The chemical fractionation of the nitrogen isotopes (Ref. 2).

$$HC^{12}N_{(gas)} + C^{13}N^{-}_{(aq)} \rightleftharpoons HC^{13}N_{(gas)} + C^{12}N^{-}_{(aq)}, \qquad (9\text{–}31)$$

for which $\alpha = 1.026$.

The rate of exchange reactions can generally be accelerated by filling the column with some appropriate catalyst, such as aluminum or steel helices. Hydrocyanic acid is, however, strongly poisonous, and, furthermore, easily polymerizes in solution, although this latter drawback can be overcome by adding an inhibitor such as Na_2S or Na_2SO_3 to the solution. The exchange between $C^{12}O_2$ and $HC^{13}O_3^-$ is more practical, except that it is very slow and there is no known catalyst to accelerate it.

Bernstein and Taylor [105] have proposed a method for enriching C^{13} in a homogeneous system by combining the $C^{12}O_2 + C^{13}O$ exchange reaction with thermal diffusion by establishing hot and cold currents in the column. This procedure has been applied to the separation of the nitrogen isotopes using the $N^{14}O + N^{15}O_2$ exchange [106].

The isotopes of lithium have been fractionated [107] by exchange between lithium amalgam and lithium chloride dissolved in alcohol, or lithium bromide in alcohol-dioxane solution. Very fine droplets of the amalgam pass down a column 18 m long containing the solution, and are chemically decomposed on reaching the bottom; the ionic lithium so formed is then added to the ascending electrolyte. After passing 10 liters of amalgam down the column, the Li^7/Li^6 ratio was 11.6, compared with the initial value of 5.1. From this change, the standard electromotive force of the $Li^7/Li^+/Li^6$ cell is calculated to be 0.0006 v.

The separations described above are based on equilibrium isotope effects. The different kinetic behavior shown by isotopic molecules can also be used to separate or fractionate isotopes by working in cascade. The decarboxylation of malonic acid, and the faster assimilation of $C^{12}O_2$ by green leaves, relative to $C^{13}O_2$, have been suggested for the enrichment of C^{13} [108, 109].

Exchange on ion-exchange resins. A chromatographic column can be compared to a distillation column in which the ionic exchanges (or alternate adsorption and desorption, see Section 21–8) occurring along the column determine the number of plates. The elementary separation factor here depends on the equilibrium constant of the ion exchange reactions (or adsorption isotherms); the overall separation factor depends on the characteristics of the column itself, such as height, particle diameter, rate of elution, etc.

Taylor and Urey [110] were the first to attempt to fractionate the isotopes of lithium, potassium, and nitrogen (as NH_4^+) by ion exchange in a column of synthetic zeolite (Na^+ form) 33 m in length. The Li^6 cations displace Na^+ ions from the resin more readily than Li^7, but the latter are more easily eluted by sodium chloride solution. The head fraction thus obtained is therefore enriched in Li^7. Taylor and Urey were able to obtain a 25% change in the relative isotopic abundance for lithium, and a 10% change for the isotopes of potassium and nitrogen. In these two latter cases, the heavy isotopes concentrated in the zeolite. A significant fractionation of the potassium isotopes (masses 39 and 40) has also been achieved by Brewer [111] using a short column (10 cm) filled with zeolite sand. Similarly a few milligrams of virtually pure Li^7 were obtained by running a normal solution of lithium acetate down a 90 cm column containing zeocarb resin at a very low flow rate, but the yield was very poor [112]. Chlorine isotopes have been fractionated by ion exchange of KCl on a 150-cm column containing the resin amberlite IRA-400, followed by elution with KNO_3. The concentration of Cl^{37} in the head and tail fractions was 25.12 and 24.03 atom percent, compared with an initial value of 24.6% [113].

9–8 Electrochemical methods. *Electrolysis.* The electrolytic method has proved particularly efficient for the separation of the isotopes of hydrogen. The technique most frequently used involves electrolysis of NaOH or KOH solutions at nickel electrodes, but separations have also been achieved in acid media and with various cathodes. The light isotope is released preferentially at the cathode, so that the solution is enriched in deuterium, and by using a multistage technique, 99% pure heavy water can be obtained. The actual experimental factor depends on the condi-

Table 9–8

Electrolytic Separation Factors for Deuterium at 20°C

Cathode	Electrolyte	α
Pt	0.5 N KOH	6.5–7.6
Pb	0.5 N KOH	7.2–7.4
Fe	0.5 N KOH	6.9–7.6
Ni	0.5 N KOH	5.5
Cu	0.5 N KOH	6.8
Ag	0.5 N KOH	5.3–6.6
Pt	0.5 N H_2SO_4	5.7
Hg	0.5 N HCl	3.3
Sn	0.2–0.5 N H_2SO_4	3.0
Ni	0.2–0.5 N H_2SO_4	7.0
Ag	0.2–0.5 N H_2SO_4	6.0

tions, such as the nature of the electrolyte and of the cathode, the state of the cathode surface, the current density, and the temperature. The data in Table 9–8 show that it is quite easy to get separation factors as high as 5 or more [114].

With Hg, Sn, Ni, or Ag cathodes, the separation factor decreases with current density, but with Pt the reverse is found. The separation factor also decreases with increasing temperature, but when α is small, an increase is sometimes observed. There is probably also a decrease with increasing D/H ratio.

Various authors have tried to relate the influence of these factors on α with the effect which they have upon the hydrogen over-voltage, and hence to deduce arguments which favor one or other of the mechanisms proposed to explain this over-voltage. None of the conclusions which have been drawn can be regarded as unambiguous, but it seems clear that the separation is largely due to kinetic effects. The differences between the zero-point energies for the $H^+_{(aq)}$ and $D^+_{(aq)}$ ions are insufficient to explain the observed fractionations, except for values of $\alpha \approx 3$, since the equilibrium constant for the exchange reaction

$$H_2O + HD \rightleftharpoons HDO + H_2 \qquad (9\text{–}32)$$

is 3.7.

Ultrasonic irradiation during the electrolysis raises the separation factor, and decreases the temperature coefficient; experiments by Mason, Biddick, and Boyd [115] showed that with a polished Pt cathode, ultrasonic radiation raised α from 6.6 to 7.1 at 5°, from 4.4 to 6.0 at 30° and from 3.8 to 5.4 at 50°C. This is explained as being due to the rapid elimination of gas from the electrode surface, which otherwise inhibits the surface catalyzed reaction (9–32).

As would be predicted, the separation factor for tritium is still higher than for deuterium. Eidinoff [116], using a platinum cathode and a current density of 0.1 amp/cm^2, found values in the region of 14 for a 10% solution of NaOH, 10^{-11} N in tritium.

Electrolytic separation has also been applied to the isotopes of oxygen. Using iron or nickel anodes and solutions of NaOH or KOH, separation factors of the order of 1.01 are found. It seems likely that the exchange reaction

$$H_2O^{18} + O_2^{16} \rightleftharpoons H_2O^{16} + O^{16}O^{18}, \tag{9-33}$$

which concentrates heavy oxygen in the gaseous phase, works against the electrolytic enrichment [117].

Small separation factors (1.02 to 1.05) have also been found for the electrolysis of lithium salts at a mercury cathode; Li^6 concentrates in the amalgam formed with the cathode, and Li^7 concentrates in the solution [117]. Yacoubyan [118] obtained a very slight enrichment of Cl^{37} after long electrolysis of concentrated HCl + KCl solutions between graphite electrodes at 10°C; the atomic weight of chlorine increased from 35.46 to 35.48. Other applications include the enrichment of potassium isotopes using KCl solution and platinum electrodes ($\alpha = 1.055$), and of nitrogen using NH_4Cl solution and a mercury cathode ($\alpha = 1.006$).

A slight separation of hydrogen isotopes can be produced in a discharge tube [119]. The passage of a continuous current causes a pressure change near the electrodes, and these differ slightly for the two isotopes; no such effect was found with xenon.

Ionic migration. Differences in the mobilities of isotopic ions in solution or in a molten salt provide another method of separating isotopes. The techniques used are similar to those involved in the determination of transport numbers by the Hittorf method. If one isotope is much less abundant than the other, with an initial concentration c_0, the enrichment is given by [120]

$$c_t = c_0 + 2\,\frac{c_0\,\Delta wt}{\sqrt{\pi Dt}}, \tag{9-34}$$

which can also be written

$$\frac{c_t}{c_0} = 1 + 2\,\frac{\Delta w}{w}\cdot\frac{wt}{\sqrt{\pi Dt}}, \tag{9-35}$$

where c_t is the concentration of the rarer ion in a plane reached in time t in moving toward the electrode of opposite sign, w is the mobility, Δw the difference in the mobilities of the two isotopic ions, and D the diffusion coefficient. It follows that the enrichment increases with the distance wt traveled by the ions, and decreases with the length of diffusion $\sqrt{Dt}$. In other words, the enrichment increases with the current intensity; it is rapid at the beginning of the experiment, but subsequently drops off because of diffusive mixing. Appreciable enrichments can be obtained only in long experiments.

In order to avoid the use of excessively long tubes, countercurrent techniques are employed, and the overall migration of the ions is compensated by the continual addition of electrolyte solution moving in the opposite direction, so that only the light ion moves toward the electrode. Convection currents are suppressed by using a sintered glass diaphragm. This technique has been applied [121] to the fractionation of potassium isotopes by electrolyzing K_2SO_4 or KCl solution between platinum electrodes in a U-shaped cell. The alkali produced at the cathode is neutralized by the continual addition of acid, and vice versa at the anode. After passing a current of 0.5 amp for 19 days through a cathode volume of 11 cm^3, the K^{39}/K^{41} ratio changed from 14.2 to 24.0, corresponding to $\alpha = 1.0022$. A comparable procedure [122] was used for the enrichment of Rb^{85} by the electrolysis of rubidium hydroxide. Similarly, electrolysis of chloride solutions [123] increased the Cl^{35} abundance from 75.76 to 80.70%.

Perhaps more useful from a practical point of view is the method developed by Klemm [120, 124, 125, 126] using the migration of ions in molten salts. For example, a four-day electrolysis of LiCl at 650°C gave 1 gm of salt with a Li^6 abundance of 16.1%, compared with the initial value of 7.5% (relative to the total lithium). Similarly the abundance of Ag^{109} changed from 48.6 to 51% after 20 hours of electrolysis of AgI at 230°C. Appreciable enrichments were also obtained in isotopes of lithium, zinc, cadmium, and thalium by the electrolysis of their molten halides, and of Cl^{35} by the electrolysis of lead chloride. The isotope effect is here defined by the ratio

$$\mu = \frac{\Delta w/w}{\Delta M/M},$$

and from this Klemm has established, for the six electrolytes studied, the empirical relation

$$\mu = -0.15 \frac{2.1M_-}{2.1M_- + M_+}, \tag{9–36}$$

where M_+ and M_- are the masses of cation and anion. This relation has recently also been verified for the fractionation of silver isotopes by migration in molten AgCl [126] and of copper isotopes in CuCl [127, 128] at 530°C. Klemm has also tried to get enrichment of Cu^{63} by the diffusion of Cu_2S in Ag_2S [129].

Finally, in this discussion of electrochemical methods, a technique proposed by Haeffner [130] should also be noted, although the mechanism involved is far from clear. This author passed an electric current through mercury in a vertical glass tube (2 mm in diameter) at 15°C and found an enrichment of the light isotopes near the positive electrode and of heavy isotopes near the cathode. For instance, by passing a current of 22.6 amps for 2000 hours, the abundance of Hg^{198} increased by 2.5% at the anode, and that of Hg^{204} decreased by 3.46%; similarly, at the cathode there was a decrease of 3.8% for Hg^{198} and an enrichment of 4.2% for Hg^{204}. Similar results have been obtained with liquid gallium at 40°C [131].

9–9 Mass spectrometry and electromagnetic separations. Unlike the statistical methods discussed so far, electromagnetic separation methods give very high separation factors, and with modern techniques it is possible to prepare very pure isotopes in quantities of the order of one gram

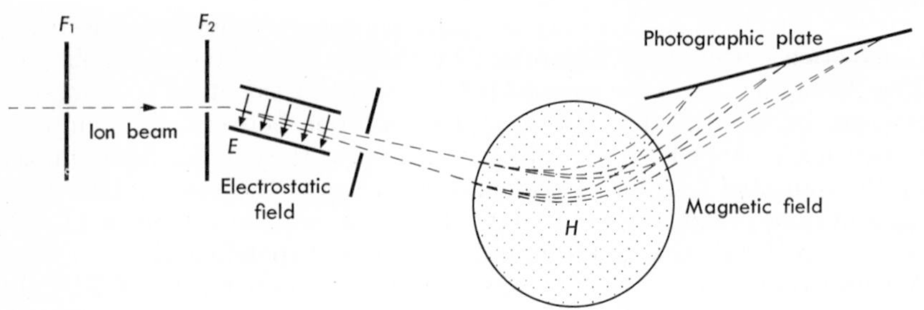

FIG. 9–3. The principle of Aston's mass spectrograph.

per day. Furthermore, there is the considerable advantage that several isotopes can be separated at the same time. Finally, these methods can be applied to all elements, irrespective of atomic weight, provided that the element in question forms some volatile compound.

The technique employed has been developed from mass spectroscopy, which is based on the different movement of gaseous ions in an electric and/or magnetic field depending upon their charge, mass, and energy. In the first apparatus, built by J. J. Thomson, the focusing of the "positive rays" was achieved by the parallel orientation of two fields, which deflected the particles successively in two perpendicular directions, and canalized those with the same mass/charge ratio (M/ne) into parabolas. In the apparatus developed by Aston, the ion beam from a discharge tube is canalized by two slits $F_1 + F_2$ (Fig. 9–3) and passes through an electric field E and a magnetic field H so arranged that all particles with the same M/ne ratio are concentrated at one point (or more precisely, form small spots upon some detecting screen such as a photographic plate). The individual isotopic masses can be determined from the distance between the points of the "spectrum" thus formed and the point corresponding to the initial (undeflected) direction of the beam.

Using this *mass spectrograph*, Aston was able to show that the atomic weight of isotopes, relative to $O^{16} = 16.0000$, are whole numbers to a first approximation, and that many elements have fractional atomic weights because they are mixtures of isotopes. Subsequent refinements made to this apparatus by Aston increased the precision of the measurements, and isotopic masses and mass defects could be determined to within about 10^{-4} mass units.

Other workers responsible for the development of mass spectrographs or spectrometers include Dempster, Bainbridge, Mattauch, and Nier. In the apparatus designed by Bainbridge, very high-energy ions (15 to 20 kev) produced in a discharge tube are dispersed in an electric field, according to their velocities, and are subsequently focused in a magnetic field perpendicular to the electrostatic field. The resolving power $M/\Delta M$ is very high, and may easily be as much as 10^4.

The first *mass spectrometer*, in which the isotopic composition of an element is determined by measuring electrical currents, was designed by Dempster. In the type of apparatus using a magnetic field, the vapor of the element concerned is ionized by bombardment with high-energy electrons from a heated filament, or by a high-frequency spark. The ions first cross a potential gap E, so that ions with the same M/e acquire the same kinetic energy, and then pass through a thin slit into an intense homogeneous magnetic field in which they move along a semicircle (of radius r); after passing through a second slit, the ions are focused on a detector connected to an electrometer. In this way, the intensity and the abundance of each isotope can be determined. The mass is then given by

$$M = \frac{H^2 r^2 e}{2E}. \tag{9–37}$$

The ionization currents are very small, usually of the order of 10^{-10} amp, which in terms of quantities of material corresponds to about 10^{-8} gm/day for a medium atomic weight element. In order to get weighable quantities of separated isotopes, it was necessary to improve the techniques for producing ion beams with intensities millions of times greater than those just quoted. Increasing the intensity, however, causes poor focusing and hence poor separation; this drawback is connected with the creation of space charges. These difficulties have been overcome in a number of powerful modern electromagnetic separators such as the Calutron (California University Cyclotron). Focusing is generally by a nonhomogeneous magnetic field, and the positive space charges are neutralized by electrons in the beams [132]. Beam currents of more than tens of milliamps can be obtained from modern machines, corresponding to the collection of tens of milligrams per hour.

Up to the present time, it has been possible to separate weighable quantities of about 200 stable isotopes of some 40 elements in high purity. These isotopes are used in many different ways in nuclear physics and physical chemistry. In addition to their application as indicators in kinetics or biochemistry (Chapters 23 and 24), they can be used in studying the properties of individual isotopes (exact mass, thermodynamic constants, optical spectra, spin, conductivity, cross section in various elastic and inelastic processes, nuclear energy levels, etc.) and also in investigating certain nuclear reactions, especially those which involve a rare isotope whose reactions may be masked in the natural mixture of isotopes.

Mass spectrometers are, of course, particularly applicable to the determination of isotopic abundances, but they are also widely used in chemical analysis, in leak detection, in determining ionization potentials (Section 14–1) and dissociation energies, in chemical kinetics (especially for detecting free radicals), and in many other techniques. They are becoming increasingly indispensable tools in physico-chemical laboratories.

Figure 9–4 shows the mass spectra of mercury before and after pile neutron bombardment [133], and is a neat example of the use of mass spectrometry. These curves show the changes in isotopic composition which follow neutron capture; about 23% of Hg^{196} and 19% of Hg^{199} have disappeared, and the relative abundance of Hg^{200} has increased by 4%. It can therefore be directly deduced that neutron capture in mercury is due to the isotope 196 and 199; the isotope Hg^{197} does not, however,

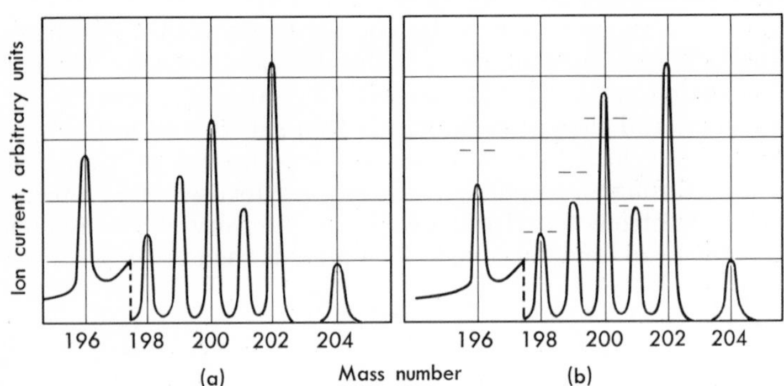

FIG. 9–4. Changes in the mass spectrum of mercury after neutron bombardment (Ref. 133).

appear in diagram (b) since it is radioactive, with a half-life of 43 min. Several other applications of mass spectrometry are discussed in the relevant specialized texts [134, 135, 136].

9–10 Photochemical separations and other methods. Certain separation methods, which are not of general applicability, can be used in isolated cases when the conditions are particularly favorable. If, for example, a light source with a sufficiently narrow spectral band is available to excite one molecular species but not its isotopic molecule, the first species can be made to react and to eventually decompose, and in this way the isotopes will be separated, since they end up in different chemical states. Such a system arises with the ultraviolet radiation from a mercury lamp emitting the intense 3663.27 A line, which coincides with the absorption band of the $Cl^{35}O_2$ molecule, while the 3654.83 A line coincides with the absorption in $Cl^{37}O_2$. Kuhn, *et al.* [137], filtered out the second ray, and irradiated gaseous ClO_2 at low pressure with the former, and showed that this resulted in an increase in the Cl^{35}/Cl^{37} ratio in the chlorine released in the reaction

$$2ClO_2 + h\nu \rightarrow Cl_2 + 2O_2 \tag{9–38}$$

from 3.41 to 3.57. The increase is quite small, in view of the fact that the intensities of the two rays are virtually equal. Billings, *et al.* [138], used a mercury lamp containing pure Hg^{198}, and excited natural mercury vapor to bring about the photochemical decomposition of water

$$Hg + H_2O \rightarrow HgO + H_2.$$

Since only Hg^{198} is excited, the oxide produced is appreciably enriched in this isotope.

In Chapter 17, we shall discuss the conditions under which a radioactive atom can be separated from its inactive isotopes (or active isomers) by making use of the radiation emitted in nuclear transformations (the Szilard-Chalmers effect).

The superfluidity of He^4(II) has been used to separate He^4 from He^3, which does not show this property (Section 9–1); the enrichment factor may be as high as 3×10^4 [139, 140, 141].

A number of other procedures have been proposed for isotope separation, without having so far found any practical application. These include the flow of a gas through a capillary heated at one end and cooled at the other; the distribution of some species between two immiscible solvents; the boiling of azeotropic mixtures; the ionization of polyatomic molecules in high-voltage generators, etc.

Finally, it should be noted that some stable isotopes can be prepared in a high state of purity by an appropriate nuclear reaction. A good example of this is Hg^{198}, which can be obtained by the neutron irradiation of gold;

$$Au^{197}\,(n, \gamma)\,Au^{198} \xrightarrow{\beta} Hg^{198}.$$

In addition to the photochemical use of this isotope (see above), it has been proposed as a standard of length; it emits a green line ($\lambda = 5461$ A), which can be measured with an accuracy better than 1 in 10^6, so that 1 m = 1,831,249.21 λ. A similar proposal is based on the corresponding emission from Hg^{202}, which can be prepared in the pure state by mass-spectrometric methods. It is currently preferred, however, to define the meter in terms of the orange radiation of Kr^{86}, which can be prepared in a high state of purity; 1 m = 1650763.73 λ (Comité Consultatif pour la Définition du Mètre, 1957).

References

1. F. Soddy, *Radium*, 4th ed., Murray, London, 1920, p. 229.
2. A. I. Brodsky, *Isotope Chemistry*, Academy of Sciences, Moscow, 1957.
3. K. F. Bonhoeffer and P. Harteck, *Z. physik. Chem.*, **B4,** 113 (1929).
4. A. Eucken and K. Hiller, *Z. physik. Chem.*, **B4,** 142 (1929).
5. J. G. Daunt and R. S. Smith, *Revs. Modern Phys.*, **26,** 172 (1954).
6. F. London, *Phys. Rev.*, **54,** 947 (1938).
7. H. London, *Proc. Roy. Soc.* (*London*), **A171,** 484 (1939).
8. L. Tisza, *J. phys. radium*, **1,** 164, 350 (1940).
9. L. Guttman and J. R. Arnold, *Phys. Rev.*, **92,** 547 (1953).
10. L. D. Landau, *J. Exptl. Theoret. Phys.* (*U.S.S.R.*), **11,** 592 (1941).
11. L. D. Landau and I. Pomerantchuk, *Doklady Akad. Nauk S.S.S.R.*, **59,** 669 (1948).
12. I. Prigogine, R. Bingen, and J. Jeener, *Physica*, **20,** 383, 516 (1954).
13. C. Keim, *Ann. Rev. Nuclear Sci.*, **1,** 263 (1952).
14. W. M. Jones, *Ann. Rev. Phys. Chem.*, **5,** 91 (1954).
15. E. Maxwell, *Phys. Rev.*, **78,** 477 (1950); **79,** 173 (1950).
16. E. Maxwell, *Physics Today*, **5,** No. 12, 14 (1952).
17. H. Frohlich, *Phys. Rev.*, **79,** 845 (1950).
18. J. G. Bardeen, *Revs. Modern Phys.*, **23,** 263 (1951).
19. J. M. Robertson and A. R. Ubbelohde, *Proc. Roy. Soc.* (*London*), **A170,** 22, 241 (1939).

20. A. R. UBBELOHDE, *Proc. Roy. Soc. (London)*, **A173,** 417 (1939).
21. E. R. ALEXANDER, *J. Am. Chem. Soc.*, **72,** 3796 (1950).
22. E. R. ALEXANDER and A. G. PINKUS, *J. Am. Chem. Soc.*, **71,** 1786 (1949).
23. E. L. ELIEL, *J. Am. Chem. Soc.*, **71,** 3970 (1949).
24. H. C. UREY, *J. Chem. Soc.*, **1947,** 562.
25. H. C. UREY and D. RITTENBERG, *J. Chem. Phys.*, **1,** 137 (1933).
26. J. BIGELEISEN and M. GOEPPERT-MAYER, *J. Chem. Phys.*, **15,** 261 (1947).
27. E. TELLER, quoted by C. K. Ingold, *et al.*, *J. Chem. Soc.*, **1936,** 971.
28. O. REDLICH, *Z. physik. Chem.*, **B28,** 371 (1935).
29. R. E. WESTON and J. BIGELEISEN, *J. Chem. Phys.*, **20,** 1400 (1952).
30. R. B. BERNSTEIN and T. I. TAYLOR, *J. Chem. Phys.*, **16,** 903 (1948).
31. L. WALDMANN, *Naturwiss.*, **31,** 205 (1943).
32. R. V. TEIS, *Doklady Akad. Nauk S.S.S.R.*, **99,** 585 (1954).
33. R. B. BERNSTEIN and H. G. PARS, *J. Am. Chem. Soc.*, **77,** 4433 (1955).
34. H. EYRING, *J. Chem. Phys.*, **3,** 107 (1935).
35. H. EYRING and F. W. CAGLE, *J. Phys. Chem.*, **56,** 889 (1952).
36. J. BIGELEISEN, *J. Chem. Phys.*, **17,** 344, 425, 675 (1949).
37. J. BIGELEISEN, *J. Phys. Chem.*, **56,** 823 (1952).
38. A. A. BOTHNER-BY and J. BIGELEISEN, *J. Chem. Phys.*, **19,** 755 (1951).
39. J. BIGELEISEN, *J. Chem. Phys.*, **17,** 425 (1949).
40. G. A. ROPP, A. J. WEINBERGER, and O. K. NEVILLE, *J. Am. Chem. Soc.*, **73,** 5573 (1951).
41. J. G. LINDSAY, D. E. MCELCHERAN, and H. G. THODE, *J. Chem. Phys.*, **17,** 589 (1949).
42. A. FRY and M. CALVIN, *J. Phys. Chem.*, **56,** 897 (1952).
43. R. W. ATTREE, F. BROWN, G. E. DUNN, and M. LOUNSBURY, *Can. J. Chem.*, **32,** 921 (1954).
44. P. E. YANKWICH, A. L. PROMISLOW, and R. F. NYSTROM, *J. Am. Chem. Soc.*, **76,** 5893 (1954).
45. W. H. STEVENS, J. M. PEPPER, and M. LOUNSBURY, *J. Chem. Phys.*, **20,** 192 (1952).
46. V. F. RAAEN and G. A. ROPP, *J. Chem. Phys.*, **21,** 1902 (1953).
47. G. A. ROPP and V. F. RAAEN, *J. Chem. Phys.*, **20,** 1823 (1952).
48. J. A. SCHMITT, A. A. MYERSON, and F. DANIELS, *J. Phys. Chem.*, **56,** 917 (1950).
49. E. A. EVANS and J. L. HUSTON, *J. Chem. Phys.*, **19,** 1214 (1951).
50. J. BIGELEISEN and T. L. ALLEN, *J. Chem. Phys.*, **19,** 760 (1951).
51. P. BAERTSCHI, *Helv. Chim. Acta*, **35,** 1030 (1952).
52. F. INGLEY and A. ROCHE, quoted by G. Ropp, Ref. 48.
53. A. ROE and E. L. ALBENESIUS, *J. Am. Chem. Soc.*, **74,** 2402 (1952).
54. W. H. STEVENS and D. A. CROWDER, *Can. J. Chem.*, **32,** 792 (1954).
55. F. W. STACEY, J. G. LINDSAY, and A. N. BOURNS, *Can. J. Chem.*, **30,** 135 (1952).
56. L. FRIEDMAN and J. BIGELEISEN, *J. Chem. Phys.*, **18,** 1325 (1950).
57. A. E. CAHILL and H. TAUBE, *J. Am. Chem. Soc.*, **74,** 2312 (1952).
57a. G. A. ROPP, V. F. RAAEN, and A. J. WEINBERGER, *J. Am. Chem. Soc.*, **75,** 3694 (1953).
58. G. A. ROPP, *Nucleonics*, **10,** No. 10, 22 (1952).
59. J. BIGELEISEN, *Ann. Rev. Nuclear Sci.*, **2,** 221 (1952).

60. P. E. YANKWICH, *Ann. Rev. Nuclear Sci.*, **3,** 235 (1953).

61. P. E. YANKWICH and A. L. PROMISLOW, *J. Am. Chem. Soc.*, **76,** 4648 (1954).

62. P. E. YANKWICH and H. S. WEBER, *J. Am. Chem. Soc.*, **77,** 4513 (1955).

63. G. A. ROPP and V. F. RAAEN, *J. Chem. Phys.*, **22,** 1223 (1954).

64. O. BEECK, J. W. OTVOS, D. P. STEVENSON, and C. D. WAGNER, *J. Chem. Phys.*, **16,** 255 (1948).

65. R. B. BERNSTEIN, *J. Phys. Chem.*, **56,** 893 (1952).

66. G. A. ROPP, V. F. RAAEN, and A. WEINBERGER, *J. Am. Chem. Soc.*, **75,** 3694 (1953).

67. H. C. UREY, *Science*, **108,** 489 (1948).

68. P. BAERTSCHI, *Helv. Chim. Acta*, **36,** 773 (1953).

69. D. L. BUCHANAN, D. NAKAO, and G. EDWARDS, *Science*, **117,** 541 (1953).

70. J. W. WEIGL and M. CALVIN, *J. Chem. Phys.*, **17,** 210 (1949).

71. J. W. WEIGL, P. M. WARRINGTON, and M. CALVIN, *J. Am. Chem. Soc.*, **73,** 5058 (1951).

72. F. BROWN and D. A. HOLLAND, *Can. J. Chem.*, **30,** 438 (1952).

73. R. M. BARTHOLOMEW, F. BROWN, and M. LOUNSBURY, *Can. J. Chem.*, **32,** 979 (1954).

74. W. H. HAMILL and V. K. LA MER, *J. Chem. Phys.*, **4,** 144 (1936).

75. V. K. LA MER and J. GREENSPAN, *Trans. Faraday Soc.*, **33,** 1266 (1937).

76. S. LIOTTA and V. K. LA MER, *J. Am. Chem. Soc.*, **60,** 1967 (1938).

77. J. W. CORNFORTH and G. POPJAK, *Nature*, **164,** 1053 (1949).

78. T. W. NEWTON, *J. Chem. Phys.*, **18,** 797 (1950).

79. V. H. DIBELER and R. B. BERNSTEIN, *J. Chem. Phys.*, **19,** 404 (1951).

80. T. W. NEWTON and G. K. ROLLEFSON, *J. Chem. Phys.*, **17,** 718 (1949).

81. W. G. HENDERSON and R. B. BERNSTEIN, *J. Am. Chem. Soc.*, **76,** 5344 (1954).

82. F. R. DUKE and R. C. PINKERTON, *J. Am. Chem. Soc.*, **73,** 2361 (1951).

83. W. H. STEVENS, J. M. PEPPER, and M. LOUNSBURY, *Can. J. Chem.*, **30,** 529 (1952).

84. W. H. STEVENS and R. W. ATTREE, *J. Chem. Phys.*, **18,** 574 (1950).

85. A. ROE and J. B. FINLAY, *J. Am. Chem. Soc.*, **74,** 2442 (1952).

86. J. BIGELEISEN, A. A. BOTHNER-BY, and L. FRIEDMAN, *J. Am. Chem. Soc.*, **75,** 2908 (1953).

87. C. A. BUNTON and D. R. LLEWELLYN, *Research*, **5,** 443 (1952).

88. H. G. THODE, S. R. SMITH, and F. O. WALKING, *Can. J. Research*, **22B,** 127 (1944).

89. I. DOSTROWSKY, D. R. LLEWELLYN, and B. H. VROMEN, *J. Chem. Soc.*, **1952,** 3509.

90. F. BAERTSCHI, W. KUHN, and H. KUHN, *Nature*, **171,** 1018 (1953).

91. D. C. BRADLEY, *Nature*, **173,** 260 (1954).

92. G. HERTZ, *Z. Physik*, **79,** 108 (1932); **91,** 810 (1934).

93. H. D. SMYTH, *Atomic Energy for Military Purposes*, Princeton University Press, Princeton, 1945.

94. S. CHAPMAN, *Phil. Mag.*, **38,** 182 (1919).

95. R. S. MULLIKEN, *J. Am. Chem. Soc.*, **44,** 1035 (1922).

96. K. CLUSIUS and G. DICKEL, *Naturwiss.*, **26,** 546 (1938); **27,** 148, 487 (1939).

97. K. CLUSIUS, *Helv. Chim. Acta*, **33,** 2134 (1950).

98. L. Waldmann, *Naturwiss.*, **27,** 230 (1939).
99. A. O. Nier, *Phys. Rev.*, **57,** 30 (1940).
100. B. B. McInteer, L. T. Aldrich, and A. O. Nier, *Phys. Rev.*, **76,** 946 (1948).
101. G. T. Seaborg, A. C. Wahl, and J. W. Kennedy, *J. Chem. Phys.*, **8,** 639 (1940).
102. F. A. Lindemann and F. W. Aston, *Phil. Mag.*, **37,** 523 (1919).
103. J. W. Beams and C. Skarstrom, *Phys. Rev.*, **56,** 266 (1939).
104. R. F. Humphreys, *Phys. Rev.*, **56,** 684 (1939).
105. R. B. Bernstein and T. I. Taylor, *J. Chem. Phys.*, **16,** 903 (1948).
106. W. Spindel and T. I. Taylor, *J. Chem. Phys.*, **23,** 1318 (1955).
107. G. N. Lewis and R. T. McDonald, *J. Am. Chem. Soc.*, **58,** 2519 (1936).
108. M. Calvin and P. Yankwich, U. S. Patent 2,511,667, 1950.
109. J. W. Weigl and M. Calvin, *J. Chem. Phys.*, **17,** 210 (1949); see also Ref. 65.
110. T. I. Taylor and H. C. Urey, *J. Chem. Phys.*, **6,** 429 (1938).
111. A. K. Brewer, *J. Am. Chem. Soc.*, **61,** 1597 (1939).
112. E. Glueckauf, K. H. Barker, and G. P. Kitt, *Discussions Faraday Soc.*, **7,** 199 (1949).
113. T. Langvad, *Acta Chem. Scand.*, **8,** 526 (1954).
114. H. S. Taylor and S. Glasstone, ed., *Treatise on Physical Chemistry, Vol. 1,* Van Nostrand, New York, 1943, pp. 66–68.
115. D. F. Mason, R. E. Biddick, and C. A. Boyd, *J. Chem. Phys.*, **19,** 1551 (1951).
116. M. L. Eidinoff, *J. Am. Chem. Soc.*, **69,** 2507 (1947).
117. M. Dole, *Chem. Revs.*, **51,** 263 (1952).
118. K. V. Yacoubyan, *Helv. Chim. Acta,* **22,** 808 (1939).
119. W. Groth and P. Harteck, *Naturwiss.*, **27,** 390 (1939).
120. A. Klemm, *J. Chim. Phys.*, **49,** C 18 (1952).
121. A. K. Brewer and S. L. Madorsky, *J. Research Natl. Bur. Standards,* **38,** 137 (1947).
122. E. R. Ramirez, *J. Am. Chem. Soc.*, **76,** 5237 (1954).
123. S. L. Madorsky and S. Straus, *J. Research Natl. Bur. Standards,* **38,** 185 (1947).
124. A. Klemm, *Z. Naturforsch.*, **6a,** 487 (1951).
125. A. Klemm, *Z. Elektrochem.*, **58,** 609 (1954).
126. A. Klemm and A. Lunden, *Z. Naturforsch.*, **10a,** 282 (1955).
127. S. Floberg, *Arkiv Fysik,* **8,** 7 (1954).
128. A. Lunden, *Arkiv Fysik,* **8,** 15 (1954); see also M. Chemla and P. Süe, *Compt. rend.*, **236,** 2397 (1953).
129. A. Klemm, *Z. physik. Chem.*, **A193,** 29 (1944).
130. E. Haeffner, *Nature,* **172,** 775 (1953).
131. G. Nief and E. Roth, *Compt. rend.*, **239,** 162 (1954); see also A. Klemm, *Z. Naturforsch.*, **9a,** 1031 (1954).
132. R. Bernas, *J. phys. radium,* **14,** 34 (1953).
133. M. G. Inghram, D. C. Hess, and R. J. Hayden, *Phys. Rev.*, **71,** 745 (1947).
134. G. A. Barnard, *Modern Mass Spectrometry,* Institute of Physics, London, 1953.

135. C. Keim, *Ann. Rev. Nuclear Sci.*, **1**, 263 (1952).
136. K. I. Mayne, *Reports on Progress in Physics*, **15**, 24 (1952).
137. W. Kuhn, H. Martin, and K. H. Eldau, *Z. physik. Chem.*, **B50**, 213 (1941).
138. B. H. Billings, W. J. Hitchcock, and M. Zelikoff, *J. Chem. Phys.*, **21**, 1762 (1953).
139. C. T. Lane, H. A. Fairbank, L. T. Aldrich, and A. O. Nier, *Phys. Rev.*, **73**, 256 (1948).
140. T. Soller, W. M. Fairbank, and A. D. Crowell, *Phys. Rev.*, **91**, 1058 (1953).
141. B. N. Eselson and B. G. Lazarev, *Doklady Akad. Nauk S.S.S.R.*, **72**, 265 (1950).

CHAPTER 10

THE GEOCHEMICAL, GEOLOGICAL, AND ASTROPHYSICAL APPLICATIONS OF RADIOACTIVITY

10–1 Geochemistry and cosmochemistry. The chemical composition of the earth and the sun, and of the celestial bodies in general, is a measure of the relative stability of nuclei, and is therefore closely related to nuclear structure and to the physical conditions under which the elementary constituents of matter formed nuclei. The investigation of the terrestrial chemical composition is the concern of a comparatively new science, *geochemistry*, although the name itself was introduced as long ago as 1838 by the Swiss chemist Schoenbein [1]. The purpose of geochemistry is to investigate the global distribution and local concentration of the elements in the earth's crust and in other layers, their chemical state, their movement (both in space and in time), their physico-chemical behavior under different thermodynamic conditions, and eventually to establish their overall history. The development of nuclear chemistry has significantly increased the scope of geochemistry by extending the investigations to the isotopes of the elements, and to the effect of radioactivity on the various phenomena in question.

The first systematic research on the chemical composition of rocks was carried out by W. Clarke (1847–1931) and H. Washington (1867–1943). Despite the limited methods available to these pioneers, their results provided the foundation for geochemistry, which has expanded remarkably during the last thirty years; among the chemists and radiochemists responsible for this expansion were Vernadski, Fersman, Goldschmidt, Hevesy, Paneth, H. Brown, Urey, and many others. There has been a continued increase in the sensitivity of the chemical methods of analysis, and the introduction of physical methods (spectroscopy, radioactivity, x-rays, mass spectrometry), and the improved selection of samples, have produced more complete and more precise data, extending to the rarer metals and the other minor constituents of the lithosphere, hydrosphere, biosphere, and atmosphere.

These analytical results have been supplemented by indirect geophysical measurements (density, magnetism, seismography) on the globe as a whole. More detailed information on the composition of the interior of the earth is available from analyses of meteorites. As far back as 1850 Baisse suggested that these bodies which fall from the sky are similar in composition to the earth itself. This view is now generally accepted. It is believed that meteorites are genetically related to the solar system, being either the fragments of some large planet [2] or the debris of a collision between asteroids [3, 4, 5] (miniature planets orbiting between Mars and Jupiter).

Parallel to such geochemical researches, astrophysicists have investigated the composition of the atmosphere of the sun and of various other stars, and of interstellar gases and intergalactic nebulae, by visible, ultraviolet, and infrared spectroscopy. The most reliable methods depend on comparing the position and intensities of the "ultimate rays" of the elements with laboratory standards, but the quantitative interpretation of the results is extremely difficult and frequently ambiguous. This is related to the assumptions which must be made about the density and turbulence of the stellar atmosphere, the temperature of the inversion layer, the excited state of the emitting atoms, etc. In particular, there is no certainty that results obtained for the atmospheres can be extended to include the interior of the stars, the homogeneity of which is still a rather controversial subject. The assumption that the violent convection currents necessarily present in rotating stars produce complete mixing of the constituents is rejected by some authors.

Indirect information on the composition of stars comes from results on their luminosities, masses, densities, and temperatures. We saw earlier (Section 5-8) that the temperatures are related to the assumptions made about the thermonuclear reactions going on in the stars.

10-2 The natural abundances of the elements. Meteorites are the most important source of information on the distribution of the elements in nature. They are generally divided into three principal groups (or *phases*); (a) stony meteorites (*aeroliths*) consisting essentially of magnesium and iron silicates; (b) iron meteorites or *siderites*, containing about 90% iron and 8% nickel; (c) mixed phases of iron and stone (*siderolithes*). There may also be a fourth and less important glassy phase, the *tectites*. The aeroliths can themselves be divided into two subgroups, chondrites and achondrites, the first being entirely aggregates of rounded grains or chondrules, and the second only partly chondritic. One frequent component of meteorites is troilite, an iron sulfide with a structure identical with that of terrestrial mineral pyrites, and containing 1.7% (Ni + Co). Urey [3] has suggested that the chondrites were produced in the high-temperature zone at the center of a collision between asteroids, and that the achondrites and the ferrous phase are the peripheral fragments.

It is probable that meteorites suffer appreciable changes and losses before reaching the earth's surface at the end of their travel through interplanetary space, possibly including close approach to the sun. In particular, gases and volatile elements, or those which tend to form volatile compounds, will be partially or completely lost. The traces of helium and argon found in meteorites are of radiogenic origin. It is also possible that the absence of gas is due to the fact that the original planets were too small to have a gravitational field strong enough to retain an atmosphere of gas. Mercury, for example, whose mass is some 20 times smaller than that of the earth, has no atmosphere around it. The composition of the atmospheres of the larger planets is similarly related to their size. The atmospheres of Jupiter and of Saturn contain appreciable quantities of methane, whereas in those of our earth, and of Venus and Mars, carbon is present as carbon dioxide; ammonia is also abundant in the atmosphere around Jupiter.

In order to establish the average proportion of each element in meteorites, it is necessary to evaluate the most probable ratios between the masses of the various phases. This is, however, a rather uncertain procedure, since the conditions of fall and preservation mean that iron meteorites are recovered more frequently than stony meteorites. In addition, very small meteorites are rapidly destroyed, or else are not observed at all. Despite these factors, it appears established that the aeroliths are very similar in composition to the terrestrial silicate layer, although the aeroliths are always anhydrous, and correspond to a more reducing medium than the earth. The predominance of iron and nickel in siderites also corresponds to current views on the composition of the interior of our planet. On the other hand, the meteoritic isotopic abundances of a number of elements are generally more constant than in the terrestrial crust. This suggests that the elements in meteorites have undergone comparatively small isotope effects during the course of time, and that the isotopic abundances are not very different from those in primeval matter.

Of the stellar spectra which have been studied, that of the sun is naturally the best known. The hydrogen lines are certainly the most intense in this spectrum, followed by helium [6]. The lines of some 65 other elements have also been detected. Rare gases heavier than neon have not been identified; other elements apparently absent include the halogens heavier than fluorine, arsenic, caesium, promethium, holmium, rhenium, and those elements with $Z > 80$, excepting lead and thorium. For this last element, and for argon, cadmium, and gold, only one spectral line has been identified. Some of the missing elements also have low terrestrial abundances, and some of the others have ionization or excitation potentials which are too high for the spectra to be readily accessible, although this is not true of caesium, thalium, and bismuth. (See Section 7–4 for technetium.) Struve [7] estimates the relative total abundances as hydrogen 70%, helium 26%, the oxygen group 1.4%, the metals 0.4%; other authors have suggested rather different H/He ratios.

Values for the composition of the other stars are much less numerous and less reliable. The difficulties involved in these determinations were discussed earlier. These are emphasized by the fact that the differences between the values reported for the same star by different authors are often several times greater than those found by one author for different stars. On the whole, the composition varies slightly from one star to the next, with an average very close to that found for meteorites, although there are appreciable differences in the volatile elements, and in those light elements which can take part in thermonuclear reactions. Thus for certain *R*-class stars, the C^{12}/C^{13} ratio is between 50 and 3.4, and for *N*-class stars between 19 and 1, to be compared with the normal value of about 90 in the atmosphere and the terrestrial biosphere. It is also possible that the D/H ratio is different in the atmospheres of the sun and of the earth [8].

Despite these (and other) deviations, there is a general tendency among astrophysicists and geochemists to regard the distribution of matter as being approximately uniform throughout the universe, and in particular to take the meteorites as a model of the *cosmic abundances*. It should not

TABLE 10–1

THE RELATIVE NATURAL ABUNDANCES OF THE ELEMENTS

Element	Abundance	Element	Abundance	Element	Abundance
H	3.5×10^8	Ni	1340	Ce	0.023
He	3.5×10^7	Cu	4.6	Pr	0.0096
Li	1.0*	Zn	1.6	Nd	0.033
Be	0.16*	Ga	0.65	Sm	0.012
B	0.2*	Ge	2.5	Eu	0.0028
C	8×10^4	As	4.8	Gd	0.017
N	16×10^4	Se	0.25	Tb	0.0052
O	22×10^4	Br	0.42	Dy	0.02
F	90	Rb	0.07	Ho	0.0057
Ne	9000–24,000	Sr	0.4	Er	0.016
Na	460	Y	0.1	Tm	0.0029
Mg	8870	Zr	1.5	Yb	0.015
Al	880	Nb	0.009	Lu	0.0048
Si	10,000	Mo	0.19	Hf	0.007
P	130	Ru	0.093	Ta	0.003
S	3500	Rh	0.038	W	0.17
Cl	170	Pd	0.032	Re	0.004
Ar	130–2200	Ag	0.027	Os	0.035
K	69	Cd	0.026	Ir	0.014
Ca	670	In	0.01	Pt	0.087
Sc	0.18	Sn	0.62	Au	0.0082
Ti	26	Sb	0.017	Hg	<0.00006*
V	2.5	Te	0.0016*	Tl	0.001*
Cr	95	I	0.018	Pb	<0.02
Mn	77	Cs	0.001	Bi	0.002
Fe	18,300	Ba	0.039	U	0.0002
Co	99	La	0.021		

* See text below.

be forgotten, however, that only a very limited fraction of cosmic material has been explored so far, and that from the surface only, so that it would be unwise to push these generalizations too far.

Goldschmidt [9] was the first to establish a synthetic table of average abundances by weighting the contributions from various sources (terrestrial volcanic rocks, meteorites, the sun, etc.). Following improvements in analytical methods and the compilation of new and more precise values on the chemical and isotopic composition, Brown [10] has extended and revised the Goldschmidt values. Brown has taken the meteoritic values in most cases, and the solar and stellar abundances for some of the light elements. The resultant table (Table 10–1) has been completed by adding a number of values (marked by asterisks) from Urey's compilation [3]; the abundances are relative to Si = 10,000.

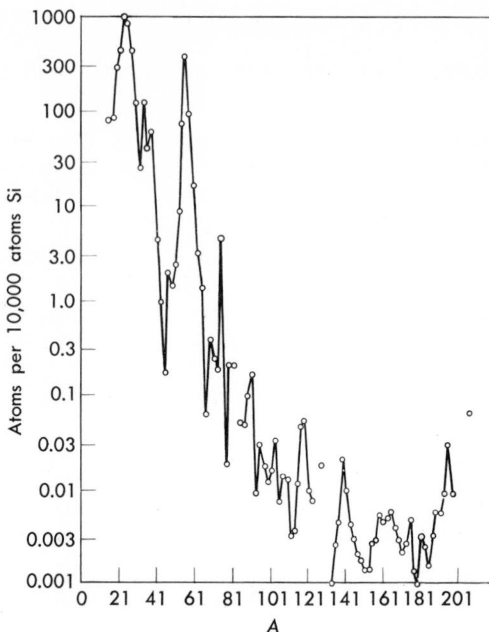

FIG. 10–1. The abundances of the elements, relative to 10,000 atoms of Si (Ref. 10).

Even if the values in the table are merely regarded as orders of magnitude, a number of extremely interesting conclusions emerge. The predominant abundance of hydrogen and of helium have already been noted; after helium, the abundance decreases very markedly, lithium, beryllium, and boron being extremely rare elements. Carbon, nitrogen, and oxygen are more abundant than silicon, and of the same order of magnitude, and the same is true of magnesium, and probably neon. A series of less abundant elements follow, up to iron, which is obviously more abundant than its neighbors. Beyond nickel the abundances decrease again, more without any very marked changes appearing.

The general tenor of these variations is shown in Fig. 10–1, in which the logarithms of the relative abundances are plotted as a function of the atomic weight. Among the general irregularities and fluctuations, it will be noted that those elements whose atomic weights are multiples of four (Oddo's rule), and more especially those which are multiples of two (Harkin's rule), are more abundant than their immediate neighbors. There are also maxima corresponding to the magic numbers 8, 50, 82, and 126. Finally, it will be seen that some elements normally thought of as rare are in fact more abundant than others regarded as being more common; for instance, hafnium is more abundant than bismuth and mercury, gallium is 17 times more abundant than barium, and europium is seven times more abundant than cadmium in volcanic rocks [1]. Some of these results are due to the wide terrestrial dispersion of the elements concerned.

Similarly, other elements are associated with their homologues, or other chemically similar elements, so that their separation is very difficult, and this may make them appear rarer than is in fact the case.

If the isotopic abundances are considered instead of those of the elements, it is possible to arrive at isobaric, isotopic, and stability rules similar to those described in Chapter 3 [11].

10-3 Isotopic variations in hydrogen and oxygen. Apart from any physico-chemical isotope effects, volatile elements may undergo small isotopic fractionations due to the effect of gravity. Thus the (free) deuterium/hydrogen ratio in the earth's atmosphere [12] is about 25% greater than would be predicted from the thermodynamic equilibrium

$$H_2O + HD \rightleftharpoons HDO + H_2,$$

and this enrichment of deuterium in the air could be at least partly due to the effect of the earth's gravitational field. With increasing altitude, the barometric formula predicts a decrease in the light isotopes, but convection currents tend to overcome this separation. Thus, despite previous claims, the isotopic composition of oxygen and nitrogen does not vary up to an altitude of 51.6 km [13].

Most of the older measurements on isotopic composition of hydrogen in natural waters were made by very sensitive density methods, so that the results are related to density changes, and are sometimes expressed in units of 10^{-6} (or γ). These results are only of limited value, since they necessarily include variations in the oxygen isotopes, which may be opposed in sign to those in hydrogen. The data suggested a fairly constant density for the waters from large rivers and open lakes, and small variations in water from the seas and oceans. Determinations can now be carried out on the isotopes of oxygen and hydrogen separately, either by mass spectrometry or by the simultaneous measurement of density and refractive index [14]. The amount of the very rare oxygen isotope O^{17} is generally neglected.

The average deuterium content of hydrogen from the fresh waters of the rivers and lakes (in the United States) is 0.0148 atom percent, but the actual value may vary between 0.0135 and 0.0154%, depending on the source; for oceanic water, the results lie between 0.0153 and 0.0156% [15]. Likewise, the relative abundance of O^{18} in different waters varies between limits of $+32$ and -17×10^{-4} atom percent relative to fresh water. The actual value depends upon the climatic conditions, and is lower in the cold regions [16]. In sea water, there is a slight increase with the salinity [17]. In the Pacific Ocean a depth dependence is found, with a maximum at 800 m [18], at which the dissolved oxygen content is a minimum; this has been attributed to a faster metabolism of O^{16} than O^{18} by the various plants and marine micro-organisms in the water.

The other effects are the result of the differing vapor pressures of the various molecules H_2O, HDO, H_2O^{16}, H_2O^{18}, which produce an increased concentration of the heavy isotopes in rain, but fractionations probably

TABLE 10–2

OXYGEN ISOTOPE RATIOS

Origin of sample	O^{18}/O^{16}
Fresh water	1.000
Ocean water	1.009
Water from the Dead Sea	1.020
Atmospheric air	1.03
O_2 from photosynthesis	1.006
CO_2 from the air	1.040
Carbonates	1.039
Sedimentary silicates*	1.03

* Ref. 23.

also occur in other natural physico-chemical processes. Measurements on Arctic glaciers and waters [19] show that the deuterium content may be slightly greater, and the O^{18} unchanged from normal, or vice versa, depending on the origin of the sample. Water from snow has a slightly lower deuterium content than normal water, the difference corresponding to 4 to 6 γ; the O^{18} content may be higher (1.5 to 3 γ). The same composition has been found for rivers and mountain lakes fed from glaciers. Baertschi, however, has found that the O^{18} content of snow waters is below normal [20]; this author has also found variations as high as 1% in mineral waters.

The H/D isotopic composition of water vapor in natural gases appears to be normal, but there is a 21% decrease in the deuterium content of molecular hydrogen from the *soffioni* at Lardarello, Italy [21].

The isotopic composition of oxygen has been determined mass spectrometrically in a large number of substances other than water. The values in Table 10–2 [22] are compared with the ratio $O^{18}/O^{16} = 1$ in fresh water (actually equal to 0.204/99.75). (See also Fig. 10–2.) The high O^{18} content of CO_2 and carbonates is most probably the result of the exchange reactions

$$\tfrac{1}{2}CO^{16}_{2(\text{gas})} + H_2O^{18}_{(\text{liq})} \rightleftharpoons \tfrac{1}{2}CO^{18}_{(\text{gas})} + H_2O^{16}_{(\text{liq})} \qquad (K = 1.046 \text{ at } 0°\text{C}), \tag{10–1}$$

$$\tfrac{1}{3}CO_3^{16(2-)} + H_2O^{18} \rightleftharpoons \tfrac{1}{3}CO_3^{18(2-)} + H_2O^{16} \qquad (K = 1.036 \text{ at } 0°\text{C}). \tag{10–2}$$

The O^{18} enrichment of atmospheric air is more difficult to understand. Oxygen in the air is in fact produced by photosynthesis in vegetable matter, especially by oceanic plant life, according to the well-known equation

$$n CO_2 + n H_2O \rightarrow (CH_2O)_n + n O_2. \tag{10–3}$$

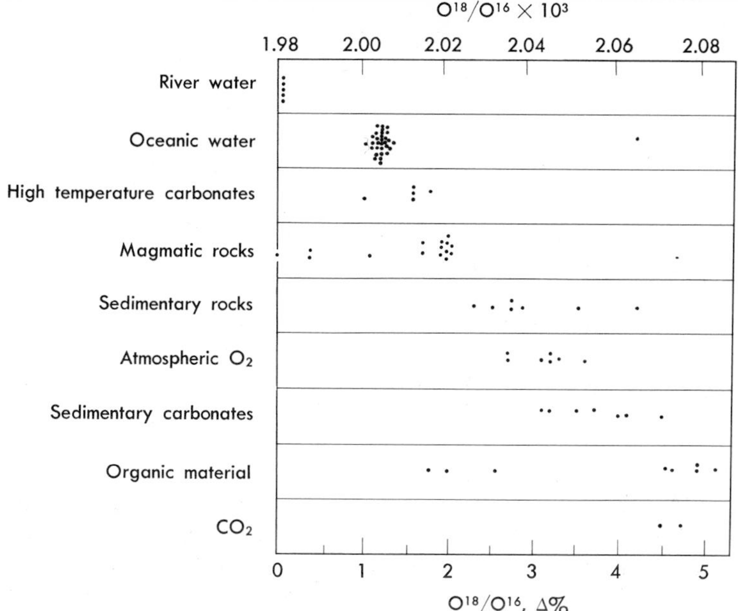

FIG. 10–2. O^{18}/O^{16} isotopic ratios (based on A. Vinogradov, Ref. 109).

Various authors have used molecules labeled with O^{18} to demonstrate that the oxygen produced comes originally from H_2O and not from CO_2 [24, 25]. The table shows, however, that oxygen from photosynthesis is not very different in composition from that in normal water. The equilibrium constant of the exchange reaction

$$H_2O^{18} + \tfrac{1}{2}O_2^{16} \rightleftharpoons H_2O^{16} + \tfrac{1}{2}O_2^{18} \qquad (K = 1.017 \text{ at } 0°\text{C}) \qquad (10\text{–}4)$$

is too small to explain the differences observed, but Roake and Dole [26, 27] have shown that under ultraviolet irradiation in a discharge tube at low pressures, the process

$$CO_2^{18} + O_2^{16} \rightarrow CO_2^{16} + O_2^{18} \qquad (10\text{–}5)$$

goes appreciably even at −50°C. The analogous exchange involving H_2O and O_2 does not occur, and these authors have therefore suggested that the anomalous value in atmospheric oxygen may be due to the exchange process (10–1), followed irreversibly by process (10–5) occurring in the upper atmosphere, where there is a high ultraviolet light intensity. This hypothesis implies, however, an increased O^{18}/O^{16} ratio in these upper layers, which is contrary to the observations made by Dole himself [13], and noted earlier. Another possibility is that the inverse of photosynthesis, the mineralization of oxygen released in process (10–3), may be slower for the heavier isotope, which would lead to its enrichment in the atmosphere. Measurements on oxygen dissolved in the Pacific Ocean have in fact shown an O^{18} enrichment. The fractionation factor for these processes is, however, too small to explain the ratio of 1.03 in air.

Relatively large variations in O^{18} content have also been found in natural silicates [23, 28, 29]. The sedimentary rocks are richer in O^{18} than the igneous rocks, and among the latter, acidic rocks are richer than the basic ones. The differences between these various silicates, which may be as much as 2.4%, are principally attributed to exchanges between the surface layer and the surrounding water during erosion and sedimentation processes:

$$SiO_2^{16} + H_2O^{18} \rightleftharpoons SiO^{16}O^{18} + H_2O^{16} \qquad (K = 1.03 \text{ at } 15°C). \tag{10–6}$$

The equilibrium constant favors the concentration of heavy oxygen in the silicate phase. Igneous rocks formed at high temperature are closer to the normal composition, since the isotopic effects tend to disappear with increasing temperature. In agreement with these arguments, the isotopic composition of oxygen in meteorites, assumed to be virtually unaffected by physico-chemical processes, is generally identical with that in basic volcanic rocks. Spectral analyses by McKellar [30] show that the relative oxygen isotopic abundances in the atmospheres of *M*-type stars are not significantly different from the terrestrial value.

The isotopic composition of oxygen in sedimentary iron oxides is the same as in river waters. Haematites and magnetites formed by contact with carbonates,

$$FeCl_2 + CaCO_3 \rightarrow FeO + CO_2 + CaCl_2,$$

$$3FeO + CO_2 \rightleftharpoons Fe_3O_4 + CO,$$

are richer in O^{18}, like the carbonates themselves; reduction gives water with a density 6 to 7 γ higher than that of normal water [31, 32].

The distribution of O^{18} between water and carbonates, phosphates, silicates, and other oxy-anions varies with temperature, the temperature coefficient being -0.176% per degree for carbonates [33], -0.128 for silicates [23], $+0.0188$ for sulfates, and $+0.0068$ for phosphates [34, 35]. For calcium carbonate precipitated under conditions similar to those under which it is formed naturally, there is a linear relation between the isotopic composition and the temperature over the range from -1.2 to $+79.8$°C [33]:

$$t° = 18 - 5.47 \cdot \Delta O^{18}, \tag{10–7}$$

where ΔO^{18} is the difference between the O^{18}/O^{16} ratio (in parts per thousand) of the sample in question and of a standard carbonate. Urey [36] has suggested that these variations can be used to establish a geological paleo-temperature scale for the formation of carbonates in the ocean depths. When some marine animal with a carbonaceous shell or skeleton (e.g., a belemnite or some other mollusc) spends its lifetime in contact with water, the O^{18} content of its carbonate depends on the ambient temperature. After death, the fossil falls to the bottom of the ocean, and if the conditions are such that the exchange ceases (i.e., a well-preserved thick shell), the isotopic composition of the carbonate will be the same today as it was at the time of death. The O^{18}/O^{16} ratio could then serve as a thermometer which registers the temperature at which the animal lived, subsequently preserved for many millions of years. There are several assumptions implicit in this ingenious technique, and some of these are difficult to verify. In particular it is assumed that: (a) at the instant of formation of the deposit, the carbonate was in isotopic equilibrium with the surrounding water; (b) the isotopic composition has not changed in the course of geological time, which implies the absence of secondary exchanges, diffusion, and recrystallization; (c) the isotopic composition of the oceanic water is uniform, and has remained constant since the formation of the deposit.

From a practical point of view, the selection of well-preserved samples is quite critical, and because of the very small temperature coefficient involved, an extremely sensitive mass spectrometer must be used for the determinations. Despite these difficulties and uncertainties, measurements by Urey and his collaborators [34, 35] have convinced them that, provided the necessary precautions are taken, the method can in some cases at least give useful information on the temperature and climatic conditions of distant epochs. The precision of the method could be increased by performing the abundance measurements on both carbonates and phosphates. Teis [37] has applied this method to carbonates of hydrothermal or magmatic origin, and Emiliani and Epstein [38] have used it on marls from the Lower Pleistocene which contain the shells of foraminifera.

10–4 Isotopic variations in boron, lithium, and carbon. Variations in the boron isotopic abundances as high as 3 or 4% have been reported by Thode, *et al.* [39] The isotopic composition of the samples examined varied with the place of origin, although it was not possible to show any relation with the physical or geochemical state. This result has an important consequence in terms of the use of boron as a standard in precise measurements of neutron capture cross sections, since the B^{10} content, on which these

TABLE 10–3

ISOTOPIC ABUNDANCES IN CARBON

Sample	C^{12}/C^{13}
Atmospheric CO_2	91.5
Limestone	88.8–89.4
Shells of marine animals	89.5
Sea water	89.3
Meteorites	89.8–92
Coal, wood	91.3–92.2
Petroleum, pitch	91.3–92.8
Algae, spores	92.8–91.3

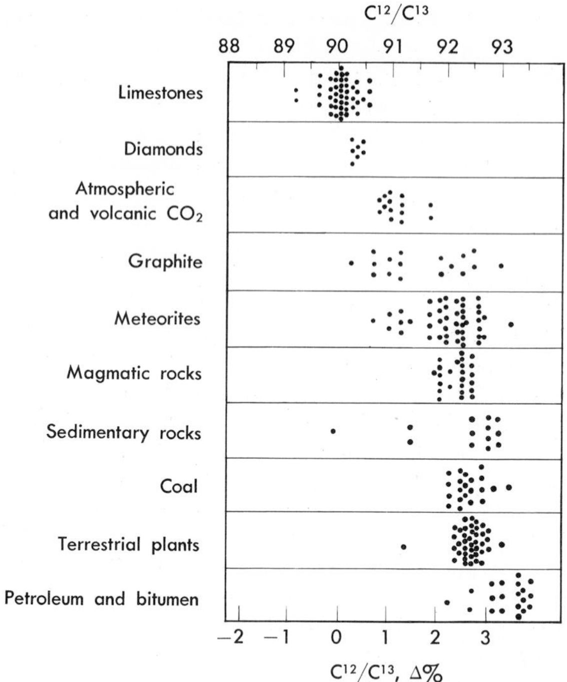

FIG. 10–3. C^{12}/C^{13} isotopic ratios (Ref. 109).

measurements are based, is not rigorously constant. For lithium, it has been found that the Li^7/Li^6 ratio in various minerals varies between 12.47 and 12.72.

The C^{12}/C^{13} ratio of a number of different carbonaceous materials has been measured mass spectrometrically by Nier and his collaborators [41]; the results are collected in Table 10–3. (See also Fig. 10–3.)

Plants show small variations from one to the other; thus terrestrial vegetables are slightly richer in C^{13} than are marine plants [42, 43, 44]. Nier's results show that compared with free CO_2, vegetable and animal carbon tends to concentrate C^{12}, whereas inorganic carbon is enriched in C^{13}. These variations are principally due to two effects; first, the assimilation of $C^{12}O_2$ in photosynthesis is more rapid than that of $C^{13}O_2$ (Section 9–5) and second, in the precipitation of carbonates, $C^{13}O_3^{2-}$ concentrates in the solid phase. These two effects work in the same sense. In general, oxidized compounds tend to be enriched in C^{13}, and reduced compounds in C^{12} [44], in agreement with the rule previously stated for isotopic exchange processes (Section 9–3).

Rankama [38] has suggested that the differences between the isotopic abundances of carbon in inorganic and animal material are sufficiently well established to serve as a criterion of the biogenic origin of a substance containing carbon; the lower limit for the C^{12}/C^{13} ratio in biogenic compounds appears to be 90.5. Rankama believes that this would provide a means of investigating the history of life, at least as far back as the pre-Cambrian era. Craig [44] and Trofimov [47] have criticized these conclusions. The latter author has found C^{12}/C^{13} ratios greater than 92 in various magmatic, basaltic, and granitic rocks; the ratio in meteorites is also close to this value. Petroleum is generally considered to be of biogenic origin, but it is only slightly higher enriched in C^{13} (Section 14–1), although it is possible that further fractionation has occurred during geological time.

10–5 Isotopic variations in silicon and sulfur. Reynolds and Verhoogen [48] have found (mass spectrometrically) variations of the order of 0.3% in the Si^{28}/Si^{30} ratio in various minerals and rocks, and Allenby [49] has reported values up to 1.3%. The Si^{30} content generally decreases on going from minerals which crystallized at high temperatures (olivine) to those deposited at lower temperatures (quartz, geyserite). With a few exceptions, these variations are in the same sense as those discussed above for the O^{16}/O^{18} ratio in silicates; the sedimentary and acidic rocks tend to concentrate the heavy isotope, while the basic rocks are richer in Si^{28}. Grant [50] has interpreted these fractionations by a thermodynamic argument based on the effect of isotope exchange during the separation of silicates from the magna or from solutions, plus the action of erosion. This latter process is cumulative in effect.

Despite the slightly greater masses of the sulfur isotopes, appreciable isotopic variations have been found, and these are generally larger than for silicon. The enrichments are the result of the equilibrium constants for the exchange reactions between the various valency states. For example, Tudge and Thode [51] have calculated a value of $K = 1.075$ at 25°C for the process

$$H_2S^{34} + S^{32}O_4^{2-} \rightarrow H_2S^{32} + S^{34}O_4^{2-}. \qquad (10\text{–}7a)$$

Measurements carried out by Thode and his co-workers [52] with sulfur from different sources (native sulfur, pyrites, natural sulfates, waters containing sulfur, etc.) show differences of the order of 4% in the S^{32}/S^{33} ratio, and of 8% in S^{32}/S^{34}; the heavy isotopes are more concentrated in the sulfates than in elementary sulfur, and more concentrated in elementary sulfur than in sulfides. Small variations are found for the same valency state; for instance, the S^{32}/S^{34} ratio in native sulfur varies between 21.89 and 22.30 [52a] (Fig. 10–4).

For meteoritic sulfur, this ratio is fairly constant at 21.2, which is approximately the value found for terrestrial igneous rocks, although very small differences have been noted between the relative abundances in samples from these two sources [53, 54]. The generally constant isotopic abundance in meteorites suggests that the latter were formed at high temperatures, which do not favor isotope effects, and that the primeval terrestrial abundance was also constant and close to the meteoritic value. It follows that the fractionations observed are the consequence of the various physicochemical and biochemical processes occurring under terrestrial conditions. Thode [55, 56] suggests that the fractionation of sulfur isotopes by reaction

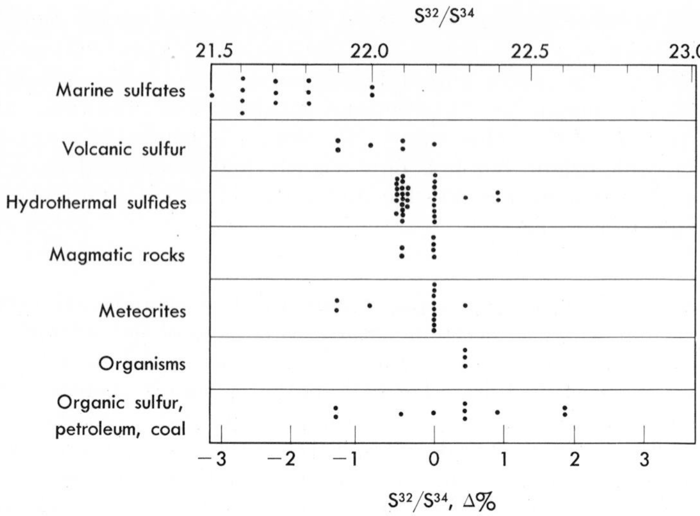

FIG. 10–4. S^{32}/S^{34} isotopic ratios (Ref. 109).

(10–7a) takes place via the biochemical cycle of this element in the sea, involving vegetable metabolism and bacterial redox reactions:

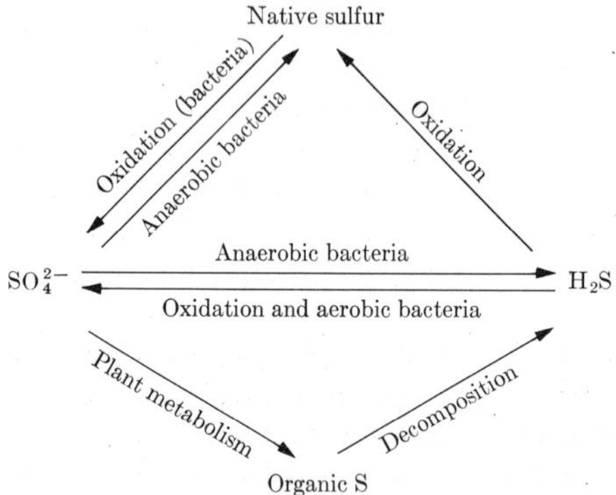

Thode has pointed out that the isotopic composition of sulfur in shales and limestones is related to the geological age of these materials. The data indicate an increased biological activity in the seas 200 to 300 million years ago, and the onset of biogenic fractionation 700 to 800 million years ago. This period must have seen the appearance of the autotrophic sulfur bacteria, with carbon dioxide and carbonates as their only source of carbon. The free energy changes associated with the oxidations $S^{2-} \rightarrow S \rightarrow SO_4^{2-}$ could have contributed to the development of already existing primitive organisms.

Thode has obtained confirmation for the fractionation mechanism shown above from deposits of native sulfur formed by action of plankton bacteria on sulfates, since the S^{34} abundance was 3.9% lower than in the starting material. It is worth noting that calcite from the same deposits contains 3.3 to 5.5% less C^{13} than normal carbon. It is probable that microbiological oxidation of organic carbon to carbonate and the reduction of sulfate to sulfide occur simultaneously.

With increasing atomic weight, the natural fractionation of isotopes becomes less and less important. A number of elements show some variations in isotopic abundance, but these are connected with various nuclear effects. These are discussed in later sections.

10–6 The constancy of atomic weights. Isotope effects which can be measured in the laboratory must of necessity also occur in nature. The physico-chemical equilibria between the isotopes of an element depend on the medium, and since these themselves change with time, the relative abundances are not absolutely identical in different compounds or different phases. The many and varied dynamic processes which take place continually, even in apparently inert matter, also tend to bring about fractionation of isotopes by the kinetic effects discussed previously. Finally, considerable variations in atomic weight are found in elements with one or more radioactive isotope, or with isotopes which are genetically related to radioactive nuclides. We have already seen that there are an appreciable number of naturally occurring radioactive elements; the variations in atomic weight due to this cause are discussed later in this chapter.

The fact that atomic weights were formerly believed to be constant is due to the differences between the relative abundances generally being very small, and so escaping detection by the analytical methods available 30 or 40 years ago. Apart from the changes due to radioactive processes, the variations are most marked for the light elements such as H, C, N, and O. Even for these elements, the heavy isotopes were undetected before 1930, since they are present in only very small proportions in the natural mixture of isotopes. The relative isotopic abundances given in Table 3–3, and hence the average atomic weights, refer to the natural mixtures most frequently found.

The problem of the atomic weight of oxygen is especially important. Physical atomic weights refer to the atom O^{16}, taken by definition as having a mass of 16.0000 units, so that no ambiguity exists on this scale. This is not true of chemical atomic weights, which are based on the natural isotopic mixture of oxygen, and this suggests that the proportions of the three isotopes O^{16}, O^{17}, and O^{18} present in such a standard mixture should be defined. The chemical atomic weight, currently taken as $O = 16.0000$, corresponds to an isotopic mixture with an average mass 1.000275 times that of O^{16}. It would seem logical to use the physical atomic weight scale in chemistry also, despite the temporary disturbance which such a change would cause.

An alternative solution would be to combine both scales on some new standard, such as taking hydrogen as unity. This would change all the present atomic weights by about 0.8%. Wichers [57] has proposed the mono-isotopic element fluorine as the basis of a new common scale, giving it a mass of 19.0000 instead of its present chemical weight of 18.9992.

TABLE 10–4

RADIOACTIVE MINERALS (CONTAINING U AND Th)*

Mineral	Chemical composition	% U	% Th	Principal sources
Pitchblende	U_3O_8	60–90		Congo, Canada, Bohemia, Saxony, Colorado
Becquerelite	$2UO_3 \cdot 3H_2O$	74		Congo, Bavaria
Curite	$2PbO \cdot 5UO_3 \cdot 4H_2O$	60–70		Congo
Gummite	$UO_3 \cdot nH_2O$	40–70	0–0.3	Congo, Saxony, Czechkoslovakia, U.S.A., Canada
Uraninite	$UO_2 \cdot UO_3$	65–75	0.5–10	Karelia, Japan, U.S.A., Canada
Broeggerite	variety of uranite	48–75	6–12	Norway
Cleveite (or niveite)	variety of uranite	48–66	3.5–4.5	Norway, Texas, Japan, Saxony
Autunite†	$Ca(UO_2)_2(PO_4)_2 \cdot nH_2O$	50–60		France, Madagascar, Saxony, Portugal, U.S.A.
Carnotite	$K_2O \cdot 5UO_3 \cdot V_2O_5 \cdot nH_2O$	50–55		U.S.A., Congo, U.S.S.R., Australia
Ferghanite	$UO_3 \cdot V_2O_5 \cdot 6H_2O$	65		Turkestan

Troegerite	$(UO_2)_3(AsO_4)_2 \cdot 12H_2O$	56		Saxony
Soddite	$12UO_3 \cdot 5SiO_2 \cdot 14H_2O$	~70		Congo
Sklodowskite	$MgO \cdot 2UO_3 \cdot 2SiO_2 \cdot 6H_2O$	50–60		Congo
Casolite	$PbO \cdot UO_3SiO_2 \cdot H_2O$	~40		Congo
Betafite	$(U, Ca)(Nb, Ta, Ti)_3O_8 \cdot nH_2O$	20–26	1	Madagascar
Liebigite	U and Ca carbonates	~30		Austria, Saxony, U.S.S.R.
Johannite	$CuO_3 \cdot 2UO_3 \cdot 2SO_4 \cdot 7H_2O$	40–50		Czechkoslovakia, Saxony, U.S.A.
Thorianite	$(Th, U)O_2$	4–28	60–90	Ceylon, Madagascar
Thorite, orangite	$ThSiO_4 \cdot H_2O$	1–19	40–70	Norway, U.S.A.
Pilbarite	$PbO \cdot UO_3 \cdot ThO_2 \cdot 2SiO_2 \cdot 4H_2O$	~27	~30	Australia
Monazite	Phosphates		0.1–15	Brazil, India, U.S.S.R., Norway, Madagascar

* Based on data given by Maurice Curie, *Le Radium*, Baillière, Paris, 1925; and J. J. Katz and E. Rabinowitch, *The Chemistry of Uranium*, (N.N.E.S., VIII-5) McGraw-Hill, New York, 1951.

† There are several other minerals containing uranium phosphates mixed with other phosphates, such as Cu (chalcolite), Mn (fritzcheite), Ba (uranocircite), Mg (saleite), Pb (parsonite, stasite), etc. The uranium content is between 50 and 60%.

This would increase all chemical atomic weights by only 0.004%, and lower the physical masses by 0.02%.

Mattauch and others [58, 59] have, however, pointed out a number of drawbacks to this scheme, both in the mass-spectrometric determination of exact masses and in the measurement of the energy release in nuclear reactions. In both types of experiment, the accuracy of the measurement depends on the mass of the standard atom being simply related to the masses of a sufficiently large number of other atoms. This is not the case for F^{19}, but these conditions are satisfied by C^{12}, probably more than by any other element, and in practice C^{12} is widely used in mass spectrometry as a secondary standard. The adoption of this scale would require chemical atomic weights to be divided by only 1.000043, and in terms of the precision of the present values, this would only involve changes for a small number of elements. Greater changes would be necessary in the physical atomic weights, however, since the present unit is 0.0318% lower than that based on C^{12}.

The selection of C = 12.0000 as the basis for atomic weights was made definite by the XVIIIth International Congress of Pure and Applied Chemistry at Montreal (Canada) in 1961.

10–7 Radioactive minerals. The primary source of those radioelements in the three natural radioactive families are uranium and thorium minerals. Geochemically, these two elements are *lithophiles* (i.e., they are concentrated in the silicate layer) and *oxyphiles*, combining with oxygen to form oxides, silicates, phosphates, and other oxygenated compounds; they do not occur as halides, sulfides, etc. Table 10–4 lists some typical minerals which contain uranium or thorium, or both, in appreciable proportions. Several other minerals, such as uranolepidite (oxides), samarskite, euxenite, fergusonite (niobo-titanates or niobo-tantalates), also contain appreciable quantities of uranium. Minerals which contain several percent uranium are relatively rare, although those which contain only a few parts per thousand are much more widespread.

In well-preserved minerals, uranium and thorium are in equilibrium with their radioactive daughter products. In the uranium family, the longest-lived species, apart from the isotopes of uranium itself, is ionium, with a half-life of 8.2×10^4 years. Equilibrium is reached (to within 1%) after seven half-lives, so that for Io this requires 5.74×10^5 years; 8.2×10^6 years are required to be within 0.1% of equilibrium. The time to reach complete equilibrium is appreciably shorter for the thorium family, for which the longest lived member after thorium is $MsTh_1$, with a half-life of 6.7 years. If the amount of one member of a given radioactive family is known, the equilibrium quantities of all the others can be simply calculated from the relation

$$\lambda_1 N_1 = \lambda_2 N_2 = \cdots \lambda_n N_n. \qquad (10\text{–}8)$$

This does not, of course, apply to the stable products of the disintegration processes (Pb^{206}, Pb^{207}, Pb^{208}, and He^4), which also accumulate in radio-

Table 10–5

The Abundance of U and Th in Igneous Rocks

	U, gm/ton	Th, gm/ton
Granitic rocks	3.95	12.95
Intermediate rocks	2.61	9.97
Basalts	0.83	5.0
Basic rocks	0.96	3.9
Ultrabasic rocks	0.83	2.0
Sedimentary rocks	1.2–4	1–10

active minerals from the decay of uranium and thorium, increasing as the quantities of these elements decrease.

Uranium and, to a lesser degree, thorium are *dispersed* elements [60]; that is, they are widely spread in trace concentrations in all minerals, rocks, soils, and waters. The wide dispersion of uranium is due partly to its tendency to form hexavalent compounds, which go into solution and are subsequently deposited in secondary minerals.

Acidic rocks contain more uranium and thorium than basic rocks, and more thorium than uranium. Table 10–5 shows some average concentrations in igneous rocks, although there are, of course, considerable fluctuations from one place to another. Uranium and thorium contents as high as 200 gm/ton have been reported for certain Italian volcanic rocks [61]; the value in lava from Vesuvius is 30 to 46.5 gm/ton [62]. Determinations on lavas from various localities (including Italy) by Adams [63] gave values very similar to those in Table 10–5, and showed the same influence of basicity.

Stony meteorites are more basic than the ultrabasic terrestrial rocks, and in agreement with the general rule suggested, they contain even less uranium (about 0.36 gm/ton on the average). The uranium content of iron meteorites is smaller again, from 0.001 to 0.005 gm/ton; in fact, Read and Turkevich could find no trace of uranium at all (that is, $<5 \times 10^{-4}$ gm/ton) in two iron meteorites, despite the highly sensitive method employed (neutron irradiation followed by a search for the fission product Ba^{140} or the neutron capture product Np^{239} [64].

Bituminous shales, pitch, and petroleum-bearing nappes are always rich in uranium; average values of 100 gm/ton have been reported for petroleum [65]. A number of attempts have been made to relate the formation of petroleum with radioactivity (Section 14–2). Finally, it should be noted that uranium has been detected in several living organisms, both terrestrial and marine. The concentration in protoplasm varies from 10^{-4} to $10^{-9}\%$.

10–8 Radioelements in water and in the air. The average uranium concentration in the seas and oceans, determined by means of the fluorescence of uranyl salts [66] is 1.3×10^{-6} gm/liter. At the surface, the concentration is lower (1.1×10^{-6} gm/liter) than in the depths (1.4×10^{-6}

gm/liter at about 1000 m), but there is a decrease of about 10 to 20% near the seabed [67]. The average radium concentration is 0.6 to 1×10^{-13} gm/liter, which corresponds to only 10 to 15% of the amount required for equilibrium with the uranium (from the half-lives). Recent determinations of the uranium content of the Pacific Ocean gave a total uranium concentration of 2.5×10^{-6} gm/liter, suggesting an even greater radium deficiency. The method used consisted in extracting uranium into a solution of butyl phosphoric acid in some organic solvent, and subsequently counting the fission products from U^{235} [68]. The thorium concentration is several hundred times lower (5×10^{-9} gm/liter) than that of uranium, and Petterson [69] has suggested that thorium precipitates and carries down ionium (Th^{234}) into the sedimentary layers (red clay, radiolaria, or diatomaceous slime). Piggot and Urry [70, 71] have confirmed this hypothesis, since radium was found in excess, in terms of the uranium content, at the surface of oceanic deposits. Direct determinations of ionium by autoradiography have also shown that this isotope is not in equilibrium with radium [72]. Various theories have been advanced as to the precise mechanism by which the oceanic waters lose their ionium and radium, such as coprecipitation of ionium with ferric hydroxide [69], the biological action of aquatic organisms on radium salts, and the adsorption and ion exchange of Ra^{2+} and Io^{4+} [73].

Urry and Piggot's measurements show that the radium content of the upper layer of the ocean sediments varies regularly with depth, increasing to a maximum over the first 10 cm, decreasing again to a depth of 60 to 70 cm, and remaining constant thereafter. The interpretation of these results involves the perturbation of the radioactive equilibrium following the precipitation of ionium, and the assumption that ionium and radium do not diffuse through the sediments. In the freshly precipitated layers, ionium is in excess with respect to radium and uranium. With increasing depth, and hence increasing age of the sediment, the quantity of radium increases until it is again in equilibrium with its parent. Since the quantity of uranium in the sediments is smaller than that which would be in equilibrium with the precipitated ionium, the activity due to the latter and to the radium subsequently decreases in the deeper layers until equilibrium has been re-established. It therefore follows that by measuring the radium content of successive layers, the uranium and thorium concentration can be calculated, and the age of the deposit then worked out from the radium deficiency. This method should be applicable to sediments with ages equal to four or five half-lives of ionium, i.e., of the order of 400,000 years.

The method has been criticized by Petterson, following measurements carried out during the Swedish *Albatross* expedition to the Pacific and Atlantic Oceans, organized in 1947 and 1948 by the Gothenburg Oceanographic Institute [74, 75, 76]. The results showed that the concentration does not change regularly with the depth, but that secondary maxima and minima occur. These may be due to differing rates of vertical or horizontal diffusion of the two elements, or to differences in the rates of sedimentation or precipitation. It seems possible, however, to allow for these variations in using the method. Various authors have used the results, along with other oceanographic data, in attempts to establish the climatic conditions of previous geological epochs [77, 78].

The radon content of the surface waters of the oceans is greater than the equilibrium quantity. The excess is probably due to the contribution carried out to sea by large rivers, themselves fed from springs enriched in radon picked up from the ground over which they flow. As the water gets farther away from its source, radon is lost both by radioactive decay and by out-gassing, so that streams and rivers are less active than springs, some of which are well known for their high radioactivity.

The average amount of uranium in rivers [79] is 10^{-6} gm/liter; the radium content is 0.7×10^{-13} gm/liter, and the thorium content 2×10^{-8} gm/liter. The radon content of the air varies between 5×10^{-13} and 10^{-14} curie/liter. Measurements carried out at Saclay (near Paris) by Labeyrie [80] show that there are daily fluctuations in the radon level, with an average value of 3×10^{-13} and a maximum of 3×10^{-12} curie/liter. The air over London contains 2 to 3×10^{-12} curie/liter, but the actual value varies with the atmospheric conditions [81].

The contribution made by tritium and C^{14} to the radioactivity of the atmosphere has already been discussed in Chapter 7. It is worth noting that the body of an adult man weighing some 155 lb contains 1.7×10^9 atoms of tritium, 8.1×10^{14} atoms of C^{14}, and 1.2×10^{21} atoms of K^{40}, corresponding to 3, 3100, and 19,000 disintegrations per second respectively [82].

10–9 The age of minerals by the lead and helium methods. Age determinations by radioactive methods are based on a principle similar to that involved in using an egg timer as a clock. If the rate of fall of the sand is known, a period of time t can be determined by weighing the quantity which has fallen in this period. In the radioactive "egg timer," the "sand" is some stable disintegration product (Pb, He, Ar^{40}, Sr^{87}, etc.) of a long-lived radioactive nuclide (U, Th, K^{40}, Rb^{87}) whose decay constant measures the rate of production. A fundamental assumption in such methods is that the decay constant has remained constant throughout geological time.

Consider a mineral which contains uranium but neither thorium nor ordinary lead at the instant of its formation. Let there be N atoms of U^{238} in 1 gm, at a time $t = 0$. After a time t, which is sufficiently long for radioactive equilibrium to be set up, the radioactive decay law (Section 4–1) gives for $(N_0 - N_t)$ atoms of U^{238} decayed, and hence of Pb^{206} formed,

$$(N_0 - N_t) = N_{206} = N_0(1 - e^{-\lambda_{238}t}), \tag{10–9}$$

where λ_{238} is the decay constant of U^{238}. It follows from this that

$$\frac{N_{206}}{N_{238}} = \frac{N_0(1 - e^{-\lambda_{238}t})}{N_0 e^{-\lambda_{238}t}} = e^{\lambda_{238}t} - 1. \tag{10–10}$$

Since the U^{235}/U^{238} ratio in minerals is 1/139, one can also write

$$\frac{N_{207}}{N_{238}} = \frac{1}{139} \cdot e^{\lambda_{235} t} - 1, \tag{10–11}$$

where N_{207} is the number of Pb^{207} atoms per gram, and λ_{235} is the decay constant of U^{235}.

For values of t which are not too large ($<1.2 \times 10^9$ years), the exponential functions in Eqs. (10–10) and (10–11) can be expanded into series, and the term $\lambda_{238}t$ retained in Eq. (10–10), and the two first terms, $\lambda_{235}t - [(\lambda_{235}t)^2/2]$, retained in Eq. (10–11). If the ratios N_{206}/N_{238} and N_{207}/N_{238} are transformed into the mass ratio [Pb]/[U], the age t is given approximately, but sufficiently accurately [83], by

$$t = t_1 - \frac{a}{2} t_1^2, \tag{10–12}$$

where t_1, the so-called "linear age," is directly proportional to the [Pb]/[U] ratio and a is constant. An analogous relation can be established for thorium minerals, starting from the equation

$$\frac{N_{208}}{N_{232}} = e^{\lambda_{232} t} - 1, \tag{10–13}$$

where N_{208} is the number of atoms of Pb^{208} formed in a time t in a mineral containing N_{232} atoms of thorium, whose decay constant is λ_{232}.

Figures 7–1 and 7–3 show that the transformation of an atom of U^{238} into Pb^{206} is accompanied by the formation of 8 atoms of helium; equally, the total change $U^{235} \rightarrow Pb^{207}$ gives 7 He atoms, and $Th^{232} \rightarrow Pb^{208}$ gives 6 He atoms. Formulas analogous to the above can therefore be established to allow age determinations to be based on the amount of helium which has accumulated.

Calculations using precise exponential equations show that 1 gm of uranium produces 1.4×10^{-10} gm of lead and 1.195×10^{-4} mm^3 of helium per year, and that 1 gm of thorium produces 4.47×10^{-11} grams of lead and 2.9×10^{-5} mm^3 of helium per year. If the treatment is restricted to the linear age t_1 and the contribution of Pb^{207} neglected, then for a mineral containing [U] gm of uranium, [Th] gm of thorium, [Pb] gm of radiogenic lead, and [He] mm^3 of helium, one has

$$t_1 = c\,\frac{[\mathrm{Pb}]}{[\mathrm{U}] + k[\mathrm{Th}]} = c'\,\frac{[\mathrm{He}]}{[\mathrm{U}] + k'[\mathrm{Th}]} \cdot 10^6 \text{ years}. \tag{10–14}$$

Accepted values for the decay constants and masses give $c = 7370$, $k = 0.35$, $c' = 8800$, and $k' = 0.27$. The value of the constant a in Eq. (10–12) is 1.95×10^{-10}.

These methods of age determination are experimentally very sensitive, and special precautions must be observed in their use, especially in the choice of samples. Thus if the mineral has been altered in the course of geological time, selective and nonequivalent losses of uranium, thorium, and lead or one of their intermediates may have occurred, and the age found would then include an appreciable error. Alternatively if the mineral is found to contain Pb^{204}, which is not radiogenic in origin, then the mineral must have contained ordinary lead at the instant of its formation, and an appropriate correction must be made in calculating the age.

The helium method was particularly developed by Paneth and his collaborators [84, 85, 86, 87], who built up precise techniques for the determination of very small quantities of gases in solids. In the most recent variant of the method, helium is liberated by dissolving the solid in $H_2SO_4 + K_2S_2O_8$, or in an acid solution of $CuCl_2 + KCl$, in order to prevent the formation of large quantities of hydrogen. Any traces of this gas which are present are burned in a palladium furnace, nitrogen is eliminated in a barium furnace, and the inert gases are fractionated and separated in a series of tubes containing activated charcoal cooled in liquid nitrogen. A pumping system circulates the gas through the apparatus; the pressure is finally measured in a Pirani gauge. Quantities of the order of 2×10^{-7} cm^3 of helium can be detected in this way, even if initially diluted with hundreds of cubic centimeters of hydrogen. Radon and thoron are determined in a separate apparatus. Paneth has applied this method especially to age determination on meteorites. Khlopin, Gerling, and their collaborators in the U.S.S.R., and Evans, Keevil, and others in the United States have carried out similar measurements on igneous rocks [88].

Despite the high accuracy of the measurements, there are uncertainties in the results because of the losses which may take place through cracks and fissures, and of incomplete retention in the minerals. Losses of helium are especially likely when the gas is under pressure in aged minerals, and when radiation has caused breakup of the crystal lattice. The values found for *terrestrial* minerals are often lower than those obtained by the lead method, and different ages have been found for minerals from the same rock.

There are always inherent errors in chemical methods which involve the measurement of absolute quantities of accumulated disintegration products, and the accuracy of the age determination can be increased by measuring the ratio of two lead isotopes (*isotope methods*). Since U^{235} and U^{238} have different half-lives, the AcD/RaG ratio varies with the age according to the equation

$$\frac{N_{207}}{N_{206}} = \frac{1}{139} \cdot \frac{e^{\lambda_{238} t} - 1}{e^{\lambda_{238} t} - 1}. \tag{10-15}$$

A further advantage of this method is that only a fraction of the total amount of lead present is required for the isotopic analysis. Nier [89, 90, 91] has applied this method to a large number of minerals, using mass-spectrometric techniques for the isotopic analysis. Another variation of the method [92] consists in measuring radiochemically the RaD/Pb ratio (RaD $= Pb^{210}$). Since at radioactive equilibrium $N_{238}\lambda_{238} = N_{210}\lambda_{210}$, determination of this ratio gives the [Pb]/[U] ratio.

There may, however, be errors in these methods too. For instance, there may have been greater losses of Rn^{222} compared with the much shorter lived An(Rn^{219}). To obtain reliable results, therefore, several procedures should be combined, by measuring the ratios Pb^{206}/U^{238}, Pb^{207}/U^{235}, Pb^{207}/Pb^{206}, and possibly Pb^{208}/Th^{232}.

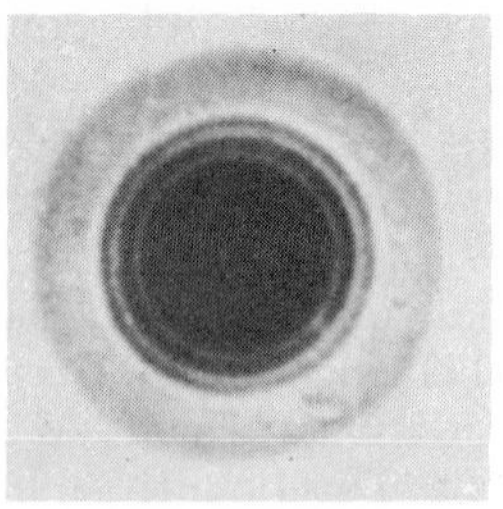

Fig. 10–5. A pleochroic halo from a Canadian mica containing uranium. [Micrograph by G. H. Henderson, reproduced by A. Holmes, *Endeavour,* **6,** 99 (1947).]

10–10 Other methods of age determination. Some granitic micas contain microscopic radioactive inclusions, which produce circular colorations in the mineral. When thin sections are examined, several colored (black-brown) rings can be distinguished, with radii corresponding to the range of the various α-particles emitted by the included substance. When examined under polarizing light, these rings show pleochroism, and hence the name of *pleochroic halos* (Fig. 10–5). If the intensity of blackening is assumed to be proportional to the total number of α-particles emitted since the formation of the mineral, the age can be calculated, provided that the uranium and thorium concentrations are known. The extremely small quantities of matter involved are practically beyond the limits of chemical analysis, but Henderson [93] overcame this difficulty by comparing photometrically the blackening in rings produced by the uranium and actinium series, and so derived the U^{238}/U^{235} concentration ratio. In recent work with nuclear photographic plates (Section 16–8), direct measurement of the α-activity of the inclusions has been combined with photometry of the haloes [94, 95].

Henderson's measurements showed that the radii of the haloes in pre-Cambrian rocks, which are more than 10^9 years old, correspond to the present α-particle ranges. Since the ranges are proportional to the energies, which are themselves related to the half-lives by the Geiger-Nuttall law (Section 4–5), Henderson has concluded from these measurements that the disintegration constants have remained unchanged throughout geological time, at least to a first approximation. It should be remembered, however, that because of the log-log form of this relation, a considerable change could have occurred without the effects showing up in the radii of the haloes. It is worth noting that no one has so far identified the radioelement responsible for the low radius pleochroic halo (1.74μ).

One effect of radiation on minerals is to induce a thermoluminescence (Section 16–3), and it has been suggested that the intensity of this could serve as a measure of the age of the mineral [96]. The values obtained by this method depend, however, very markedly on the history of the sample, and must be treated with some reserve. Similar remarks apply to the procedure [97] utilizing the structural alterations caused in minerals by α-bombardment, which show up in changes in the lattice constants, for example (transformation to the metamict state, see Section 15–4). This method has been applied to radioactive zircons which have not been appreciably altered and which have not undergone large temperature changes [98]. It cannot be applied to uraninites, whose structure can be chemically changed by the surrounding oxygen.

One of these chemical modifications has in fact been proposed as a method of determining the age of such minerals, which are mixtures of the oxides UO_2 and UO_3. Ellsworth [99] has suggested that uranium in these uranites is initially in the form of UO_2, and that as it is transformed into lead, the overall reactions are

$$UO_2 \xrightarrow{8\alpha} PbO + O_2, \qquad UO_2 + O_2 \rightarrow UO_3,$$

so that the UO_2/UO_3 ratio should be a function of the age. Khlopin has tried to apply this method to various uraninites, but the results are not always concordant, and the values found are much higher than those obtained by the lead method.

According to Wasserstein [100], there is a contraction in the unit cell of uraninites in the course of time due to the U → Pb transformation, since the atomic radius of the latter is smaller than that of uranium. This author believes that this change in cell size could be used in age determinations, and has evaluated the contraction at 0.004 A/10^8 years.

The spontaneous fission of uranium can also be used for age measurements [101]. The fission products found include the stable xenon isotope of mass 129, 131, 132, 134, and 136, which accumulate in uranium minerals and can be measured very accurately. If [Xe] is the number of xenon atoms per gram of mineral and [U] the number of U^{238} atoms, one can derive the relation

$$t = \frac{1}{\lambda_\alpha}\left[\frac{[\mathrm{Xe}]}{a[\mathrm{U}]\lambda_f/\lambda_\alpha} + 1\right], \tag{10–16}$$

where λ_α and λ_f are the decay constants for uranium α-decay and spontaneous fission respectively, and a (=0.19) is the fraction of fission chains which result in the formation of a stable xenon isotope. The values of t found for certain uraninites are, however, lower than those given by the lead method (1.26×10^9 instead of 1.85×10^9 years). Some of the xenon probably escapes from the mineral in the course of geological time.

The argon isotope Ar^{38} is found in uranium minerals in large excess with respect to Ar^{36}, and this probably is due to nuclear reactions [102] such as

$$Cl^{35}\,(\alpha,\mathrm{p})\,Ar^{38} \qquad \text{or} \qquad Cl^{35}\,(\alpha,\mathrm{n})\,K^{38} \xrightarrow{\beta^+} Ar^{38}.$$

The argon in some potassium minerals also has an atomic weight appreciably higher than that of atmospheric samples. For example, Gentner [103, 104, 105] has shown mass spectrometrically that the Ar^{40}/Ar^{36} ratio in sylvines (KCl) and various other potassium minerals is greater than 10^3, and may even exceed 5000, whereas for atmospheric argon the value is

239. The excess of Ar^{40} arises from the transformation

$$K^{40} \xrightarrow{e} Ar^{40},$$

which occurs in competition with the β^--decay of K^{40} to form Ca^{40}. The age of the mineral can therefore be determined from the equation

$$N_{40} = N_K \frac{\lambda_e}{\lambda} (e^{\lambda t} - 1), \tag{10–17}$$

where N_{40} is the number of atoms of Ar^{40} per gram arising from the electron capture of K^{40}, the number of atoms of which per gram at time t is N_K; λ_e is the partial decay constant for this process and λ the overall decay constant. The accuracy of the argon analysis has been considerably increased by using isotopic dilution methods together with mass spectrometry [106, 107]; this technique is further considered in Section 22–4. The ages of potassium feldspars determined in this way lie between 2.5×10^8 and 1.9×10^9 years, in agreement with results obtained by the lead method. Ages of the order of 4.5 to 4.8×10^9 years have been found for chondrites which contain argon [107, 108, 109].

Instead of measuring the argon, one can determine the age by measuring the amount of Ca^{40} in the mineral; Eq. (10–17) can still be used, provided that λ_β is substituted for λ_e [110, 111]. This method can be used for minerals such as lepidolites, which do not contain appreciable quantities of nonradiogenic calcium, and also for meteorites [112]. The lepidolites also contain very little nonradiogenic strontium, so that their age can be determined* by measuring the amount of Sr^{87} which has formed by β-decay of Rb^{87}. Such measurements frequently give values significantly higher than those obtained by other methods; however, the value taken for the half-life of Rb^{87} was $\sim 6 \times 10^{10}$ years, whereas more recent determinations give values of 4.7 or 4.3×10^{10} years [113]. Another explanation is that the minerals examined may have lost some rubidium. A further difficulty is that the Sr^{86}/Sr^{88} ratio in certain biotites and feldspars varies between 0.116 and 1.022 [114]. Since neither of these isotopes is radiogenic, the reason for this variation is not at all clear, but the result must cast some doubt on the validity of using strontium isotopes in age determinations.

Measurements on lepidolites and biotites from Southern Rhodesia, from Manitoba, Canada, and from parts of the United States give ages between 3 and 4×10^9 years. The oldest uranium minerals dated by the lead technique are the uraninites from North Karelia, with ages between 1.8 and 2×10^9 years, and those from Manitoba with ages of approximately 2.2×10^9 years. Recent work on uranites from Northern Rhodesia gives an age of 2.62×10^9 years by the Pb^{207}/Pb^{206} method [115].

Excessively high ages, up to $\sim 6 \times 10^9$ years, have been found for certain meteorites by the helium method [116], but some doubt has been cast on these results [117, 118], since some of the helium may have come from nuclear reactions in the meteorites as the result of bombardment by cosmic

* L. H. Ahrens, Ref. 63, p. 331, gives a bibliography on this method; see also T. Kohman and N. Saito, *Ann. Rev. Nuclear Sci.*, **4**, 401 (1954).

radiation during their passage through space. Mass-spectrometric analysis of the helium has shown that in fact meteoritic helium is a mixture of He^3 and He^4, and that the ratio varies from one sample to another [119, 120]. Urey [121] has stated that iron meteorites should contain neither uranium nor thorium [64], since these two electropositive metals tend to concentrate in the silicate and troilite phases, which are permeable to helium.

10-11 The age of the lithosphere and of the earth. The ages found for minerals set lower limits on the age of the terrestrial crust or of the lithosphere. Many attempts have been made to establish the upper limits for the age of the earth, or to find an approximate value for this age. The methods used always involve the relative abundance of genetically related elements, or of isotopic ratios, but the fundamental premises of these arguments frequently contain arbitrary assumptions or hypotheses which cannot be checked. A good deal of confusion has resulted, and different interpretations have been put upon the results. Thus the value which some authors take as the age of the lithosphere or of the Sial layer (silica-aluminum), is regarded by others as the age of the earth, of the sun, of uranium, of the elements, or even the maximum age of matter or the age of the universe.

Most of these methods depend on the isotopic composition of lead, determined mass spectrometrically by Nier [89, 90] and more recently by other authors [122–126], on samples from a number of lead minerals of known age. It has been suggested [127] that this composition corresponds to the mixing of two fractions. The first of these, the *primary* or *primordial lead*, always has the isotopes 204, 206, 207, and 208 in the same proportion, and was uniformly mixed with the other elements before the solidification of the terrestrial crust. At t_0, the instant of formation of rocks containing varying amounts of uranium and thorium as well as lead, the quantity of lead begins to increase as the result of radioactive disintegrations, until at a time t_m various geological processes cause all the lead to separate completely and crystallize into minerals which are virtually free of the radioactive parent elements. The lead accumulated in the time interval $t_0 - t_m$ then constitutes the second fraction. The time t_0 has been given various other meanings, but the one just defined seems to be generally accepted.

Suppose that the present Pb^{206}/Pb^{204} ratio is α, and the ratio Pb^{207}/Pb^{204} is β, and that α_0 and β_0 were the corresponding ratios at time t_0; from the hypothesis just discussed, α_0 and β_0 are then universally constant on the terrestrial scale. It follows quite simply that the ratio between the number of atoms Pb^{207}/Pb^{206} produced in the time interval $t_0 - t_m$ is

$$\frac{\beta - \beta_0}{\alpha - \alpha_0} = \frac{1}{139} \frac{e^{\lambda_{235} t_0} - e^{\lambda_{235} t_m}}{e^{\lambda_{283} t_0} - e^{\lambda_{238} t_m}}. \qquad (10\text{-}18)$$

If α and β are known for three samples, for at least two of which t_m is different, α_0, β_0, and t_0 can be calculated. The same result can be obtained graphically by plotting α as a function of β for various minerals having the same age t_m [128, 129]. Since this is a linear function, straight

TABLE 10–6

THE AGE OF THE TERRESTRIAL CRUST

Author	Age, $\times 10^9$ yrs.	Ref.
Gerling	3.23	127
Holmes	3.35	128
Houtermans	2.9	129
Collins	3.5	130
Bullard	3.29	131

lines or *isochronic lines* are found, with a common point of intersection corresponding to α_0 and β_0 (Fig. 10–6). An analogous result can be obtained by assuming that the U/Th ratio is constant, and hence determining the Pb^{208}/Pb^{206} ratios in minerals for various values of t_m.

The values found in this way by various authors for t_0 are listed in Table 10–6. The corresponding values of α vary between 10.95 and 12.5, and of β between 13.5 and 14.1. The higher values in the table are virtually the same as those found for the oldest lepidolite samples.

A higher value of t_0 has recently been obtained from isotopic analysis of lead from the meteorite Canyon Diablo [132, 133, 134]. The troilite from this meteorite contains only traces of uranium and only small amounts of lead (the U/Pb ratio is 1/2000) so that the isotopic composition of this lead should be very close to that of the primordial terrestrial metal; α_0 and β_0 should therefore follow directly. From these values, and the α and β ratios for various tertiary leads of known geological age, $t_0 = 4.56 \times 10^9$ years. This figure is very similar to that given above for the age of meteor-

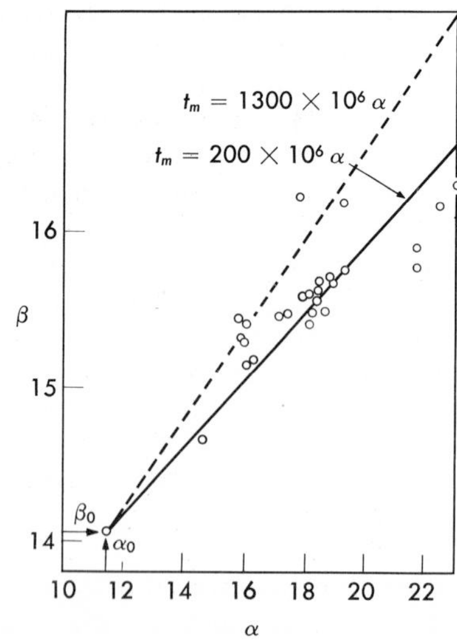

FIG. 10–6. Isochronic lines for the determination of geological ages.

TABLE 10–7

THE AGE OF THE EARTH

Author	Age, $\times 10^9$ yrs.	Ref.
Koczy	5.3	138
Baranov	4.85	139
Alpher	5.3	135
Vinogradov	5.0	123
McCrady	5.1	140
Collins	5.5	130
Allan	5.4	141

ites as determined by the argon method. The weak point in the isochronic method is that it is often necessary to reject some results which give widely discordant ages [135].

Measurements of the isotopic composition of lead in its minerals show that the ratios of Pb^{206}, Pb^{207}, and Pb^{208} to Pb^{204} decrease fairly smoothly with the age of the mineral (Fig. 10–6). This suggests [136, 137] that in fact all terrestrial lead with masses 206, 207, and 208 is radiogenic, coming from the disintegration of U^{238}, U^{235}, and Th^{232}. If it can be further assumed that the Pb/U and Pb/Th ratios have remained unchanged since the formation of the earth (apart from radioactive decay), the age of the earth can be evaluated either by extrapolating the age to the time at which $Pb^{206} = Pb^{207} = Pb^{208} = 0$, or by calculating this time from Eqs. (10–10), (10–11), and (10–13). The data for Pb^{206} and Pb^{207} give the values for the age of the earth listed in Table 10–7. Baranov [139] has obtained an age which is significantly higher from the Pb^{208}/Th^{232} ratio, and he has therefore concluded that this lead isotope is not entirely radiogenic.

The "uranium age" implies the time which has elapsed since the production of this element in terrestrial matter ceased. This age is close to the values given above if some plausible assumption is made about the initial relative abundances of U^{238} and U^{235}. If these are assumed to have been equal, an age of 6.05×19^9 years is obtained from the present ratio of 1/139 and the ratio of the half-lives. This value is, however, certainly an upper limit, since from the isobaric rules, the abundance of U^{235} should in fact be less than that of U^{238}. If the U^{235}/U^{238} ratio is put at 0.5, the age becomes 5.1×10^9 years [139].

Similar estimates have been made by assuming that all the atmospheric Ar^{40} has come from the disintegration of terrestrial K^{40}, but contradictory results are obtained by different authors [142–145], depending on the assumptions made about the abundance of potassium, the length and extent of the solidification of the terrestrial crust, the retention of the gas by minerals, etc.

Despite the uncertainties implicit in all the methods described, the results of the various determinations consistently give 3.5 to 4.5×10^9

years for the age of the terrestrial crust, and 5 to 5.3×10^9 years for the age of the earth or of the elements (under terrestrial conditions). It is, however, necessary to take into consideration that the improved, and increased number of methods available have resulted in the accepted age being almost doubled over the last few years. These latter results may themselves be subsequently modified. From the present data, it can be deduced that the interval Δt between the formation of the earth and its solidification was of the order of 0.5 to 1.5×10^9 years. An independent attempt to evaluate this time interval has been made by Katkoff, Schaeffer, and Hastings [146], who have noted the unusually high isotopic abundance of Xe^{129} (26.44%) relative to its neighbors of mass 128 (1.92%) and 130 (4.08%). According to a rule proposed by Aten [147], an isotope of odd mass always has a lower abundance than the sum of the abundances of its neighboring even isotopes; Xe^{129} appears to be the only exception to this rule. Katkoff, *et al.*, therefore suggest that an appreciable fraction of this isotope is radiogenic, coming from the decay of I^{129}, which is an "extinct" nuclide, in the sense that the word is used by Kohman (Section 7–3); I^{129} is known as a fission product, however, with a half-life of 1.72×10^7 years. If it is assumed that I^{129} and I^{127} were equally abundant at the instant of their formation, and that the fraction of xenon which has passed into the earth's atmosphere, with respect to the total I^{129} disintegrated, is the same as for Ar^{40}/K^{40}, a value of 2.7×10^8 years is deduced for Δt, much smaller than the figure given above.

The assumptions and hypotheses made in this method are, however, open to question. In particular, Suess and Brown [148] have pointed out that the radiogenesis of Xe^{129} is by no means certain, and the deviation from the Aten rule may be due, not to an abnormally high abundance of Xe^{129}, but to abnormally low abundances of its neighbors Xe^{128} and Xe^{130}, since Xe^{131} also has a high abundance (21.18%), although it is not radiogenic.

10–12 The formation of the elements. Nucleogenesis. If it is assumed that the elements are uniformly distributed throughout the universe, at least as far as the regions which have been explored are concerned, it is natural to speculate about the physical conditions which governed this distribution. The distribution is known to be related to nuclear stability, but it is also desirable to define as quantitatively as possible the thermodynamic and kinetic factors (temperature, pressure, density, concentration, rates of nuclear reactions, etc.) which produced the abundances shown in Fig. 10–1. It seems quite clear that these conditions have subsequently changed considerably. Some astrophysicists have related this problem to the so-called "age of the universe"; this is a concept which has frequently produced confusion, especially if attempts are made to give it the philosophical significance of a beginning or "creation." The age of the universe can have no other significance than to define a given period in the history of the universe under which the conditions were such that matter began to change to the state in which it is found at the present time. This comment also applies to theories of *"the expanding universe,"* according to which initially highly compressed matter at an extremely high temperature began to expand and to cool in a manner governed by certain laws. But as Tolman [149] has pointed out, "expansion does not necessarily imply creation with no previous history"; it could for example have been preceded by a contraction [149, 150].

A theory known as the α, β, γ theory (the authors being Alpher, Bethe, and Gamow [151, 152]), extended by Alpher and Herman [153, 154], considers that the formation of all the elements occurred exactly at the beginning of this expansion process. According to this view, the primitive material "the *ylem*," consisted only of neutrons; a very important assumption is that the density of the radiations or of their equivalent mass, calculated from the Einstein equation [Eq. (2–2)], was much greater than the density ρ_m of matter. On this basis, using a relativistic treatment, it can be shown that under the conditions stated, the absolute temperature T of the universe and ρ_m varied with the time t (in seconds) since the beginning of the expansion according to the equations

$$T = 1.52 \times 10^{10} t^{-1/2} \qquad (°\text{K}), \tag{10–19}$$

and

$$\rho_m = 4.48 \times 10^{-3} t^{-3/2} \qquad (\text{gm/cm}^3). \tag{10–20}$$

When the density of the radiations becomes appreciably smaller than ρ_m, one has

$$T = T_0 t^{-2/3} \qquad (°\text{K}), \tag{10–21}$$

where T_0 is the temperature at which the two densities become equal, and corresponds to $t \approx 10^{14}$ sec.

At $t = 1$ sec, $T = 1.5 \times 10^{10°}$, but after 300 sec, $T \approx 10^{9°}$, a temperature interval favorable for triggering-off neutron reactions. The first process would be the dissociation of neutrons into protons and electrons, at a rate determined by the disintegration constant of the neutron. With decreasing temperature, deuterons could be formed by the n + p process, and subsequent successive neutron captures would then give rise to all the other elements. Provided that the interval between two successive captures was sufficiently long for the unstable nuclides to transform into their stable isobars, neutron capture would remain the rate controlling process for the overall rate.

A simplifying (and probably oversimplified) assumption [155] is that $\log \sigma$ (σ = capture cross section) varies linearly with the mass number A up to $A = 100$, and that for the heavier nuclides, σ is approximately constant. The usual kinetic equations can then be written for the time dependence of the number of nuclides of mass $A = 1, 2, 3, \ldots, 92$, in which the cross section appears as a rate constant

$$-dN_A/dt = \Phi(t)(\sigma_A N_A - \sigma_{A-1} N_{A-1}), \tag{10–22}$$

where Φ is the neutron flux. By choosing appropriate values for Φ and the time interval Δt (initial nucleon density 5.4×10^{17} n/cm^3, corresponding to $\rho_m = 8.9 \times 10^{-7}$ gm/cm^3 at $t = 142$ sec and $T = 1.28 \times 10^{9}$°K), integration of Eq. (10–22) gives a curve which coincides fairly well with the known abundances (Fig. 10–7). The time interval Δt should be compatible with the disintegration constant of the neutron, and should be of

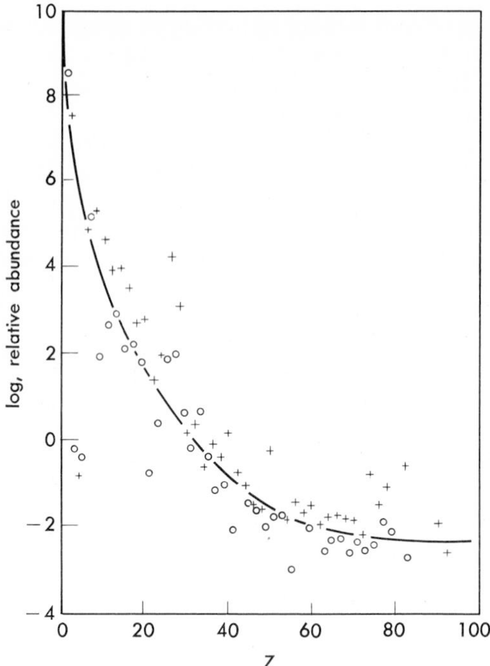

FIG. 10–7. Semilog plot of the abundances of the elements as a function of atomic number (Ref. 154).

the order of 6000 sec (since the beginning of the expansion process). At the end of this time the density would be 10^{-9} gm/cm^3, and the temperature 2×10^{8}°K.

Equations (10–19), (10–20), and (10–21) give a method of calculating the time which has passed since the beginning of the expansion, i.e., the "age of the universe." The value put forward by Gamow in 1949 [156] was 1.8×10^9 years, which is lower than that actually found for the oldest minerals, but on revising some of the constants, Gamow has subsequently found an age of 3×10^9, and more recently 5×10^9 years [150, 151]. This is of course very close to the value calculated for the age of the earth (Section 10–11).

A number of objections raised against this theory have not so far been satisfactorily answered [155, 158, 159].

1. The calculated density (10^{-9} gm/cm^3) is too small to account satisfactorily for the total mass of the universe.

2. The initial neutron density is too high to account for the present cosmic He/H ratio, since helium should be in excess of hydrogen, whereas the opposite is the case.

3. Since nuclides of mass $A = 5$ and $A = 8$ do not exist naturally, their formation by capture is unlikely, and there is no obvious mechanism by which the production of these elements is bypassed in going from He^4 to Li^6, and from Li^7 to Be^9. Attempts have been made to overcome

this difficulty by introducing thermonuclear reactions such as

$$\mathrm{He}^4\,(\mathrm{T}, \gamma)\,\mathrm{Li}^7 \qquad \text{or} \qquad \mathrm{He}^4\,(\mathrm{He}^3, \gamma)\,\mathrm{Be}^7,$$

but the cross sections of these processes are too small to provide the solution to this problem.

4. A nuclide Z^A cannot be formed either by capture if Z^{A-1} does not exist, nor by β-decay from $(Z - 1)^A$ if the latter is stable; this would be the case for Xe^{128} and some other nuclides.

5. The maximum in the abundance curve at iron cannot be explained without introducing further assumptions.

An essential point in the Gamow theory is the rapid dynamic formation of the elements. In contrast to this, many authors [160–166] have suggested a statistical mechanism based on the ideas of thermodynamic equilibria. Klein and his collaborators [163, 164] have used the methods of molecular chemistry to determine the distribution of a number of components between various molecular species and phases under given physical conditions (temperature, pressure) and given chemical potentials. The principal basis of this argument is the fact that the observed abundances have an obvious relation to the binding energy of the nuclides. If the chemical potentials of the neutron and of the proton are μ and λ, related to the concentrations by

$$c_n \propto e^{\mu/kT} \qquad \text{and} \qquad c_p \propto e^{\lambda/kT},$$

the concentration c of a nuclide (N, Z) in an energy level E is given by

$$c(N, Z) = g\left(\frac{2\pi AkT}{h^2}\right)^{3/2} \exp\left[\frac{\mu N + \lambda Z - E}{kT}\right], \qquad (10\text{–}23)$$

where k is the Boltzmann constant, h Planck's constant, g the degeneracy (Section 9–3) or multiplicity of the level in question, and $A = N + Z$. In the ground state, E is given by the mass defect. This equation contains three unknown parameters, μ, λ, and T, and by adjusting the values of the latter to fit with the known abundances of certain nuclides, Klein has found

$$\mu = -7.6 \text{ Mev}, \qquad \lambda = -11.6 \text{ Mev}, \qquad kT \approx 1 \text{ Mev}, \quad T \approx 10^{10}\,^\circ\mathrm{K}.$$

Such a temperature is sufficiently high to explain the production of the heaviest elements.

The calculated density of matter $[\rho_m = \sum c(N, Z)A]$ on this basis is of the order of 10^7 to 10^8 gm/cm^3, which is 10^{16} to 10^{17} times higher than that which the α, β, γ theory assumed to exist at the time of formation of the elements. Temperatures and densities of this magnitude would be possible in the interior of stars at a certain point in their development. The process would be so rapid that the equilibrium between the debris (the elements), dispersed in space by the catastrophe, would be quickly "frozen," and the distribution would thereafter remain virtually unchanged.

The agreement between the observed values and theory is, however, only satisfactory up to $A \approx 40$ to 60. For the heavier elements, the theoretical values bear no relation whatsoever to the known abundances, being about 10^{100} times too small for the heaviest elements. Various attempts have been made to improve on this by considering the influence of the excited states, and of gravitational and electrostatic effects, all of which favor the formation of heavy nuclides, but although these corrections do in fact reduce the differences between theory and experiment quite considerably, there is still considerable difficulty in explaining the abundances of all the elements from a single equilibrium state. Moreover, any mechanism should show how the equilibrium distribution corresponding to certain temperature and density conditions has been preserved until the present time.

A number of different stellar models have been set up [163, 167, 168, 169] in attempts to get over these difficulties; the one summarized here is due to Hoyle. In a star with a mass some 10 times greater than the sun, the hydrogen reserve is consumed (to form helium) in about 10^8 years. The radiative energy losses in this helium star are not compensated by thermonuclear reactions, and the star slowly contracts until the density is about 10^7 gm/cm^3, and the temperature 4×10^{9}°K. These conditions are favorable for endothermic synthetic reactions which give medium weight nuclei, but the absorption of energy increases the rate of the contraction, so that there is an acceleration in the rotational movement of the star. These processes can continue for about 10^6 years, at the end of which the density is 10^8 to 10^9 gm/cm^3; the rotational movement becomes so great that the star is no longer stable and explodes in the form of a *nova*. The elements present are therefore dispersed throughout space. In other cases, the density rapidly reaches 10^{12} gm/cm^3, and the explosion is in the form of a *supernova*, releasing neutrons, which bring about the synthesis of the heaviest elements. In both cases, the explosions are assumed to be so rapid that the equilibrium between the elements is quickly "frozen," and the distribution preserved.

There are also a number of theories which adopt a position intermediate between the two just discussed. According to Jensen and Suess [170], the present distribution of the elements reflects some initial thermodynamic equilibrium, which has been considerably modified by nonequilibrium processes occurring during the "annealing." On the other hand, Mayer and Teller [171] believe that two different processes are responsible for the formation of the light nuclei ($Z < 34$) and the heavy ones. Thermonuclear reactions, especially those involving protons, are believed to have produced the first group, whereas the second group could be fission fragments from a *polyneutron*, a primordial cold, liquid, nuclear species, only slightly smaller in dimensions than a star. The nuclides produced by neutron evaporation from these excited fragments would have a Gaussian distribution, and Mayer and Teller have shown that this theory gives satisfactory calculated isotopic abundances in the region $62 < Z < 78$, in which the influence of the closed shells is small. It is not known, however, if this theory accounts satisfactorily for the abundances of all elements and nuclides, and in particular if the conditions described for the formation of the light nuclei are compatible with those postulated for the formation of the heavy nuclei.

References

1. K. Rankama and T. G. Sahama, *Geochemistry*, Chicago University Press, Chicago, 1950, p. 8.
2. H. Brown and C. Patterson, *J. Geology*, **56,** 85 (1948).
3. H. C. Urey, *The Planets*, Yale University Press, New Haven, 1952.
4. H. C. Urey, *Geochim. Acta*, **2,** 269 (1952).
5. H. C. Urey and H. Craig, *Geochim. Acta*, **4,** 36 (1953).
6. C. E. Moore, *Science*, **119,** 449 (1954).
7. O. Struve, *Stellar Evolution*, Princeton University Press, Princeton, 1950.
8. C. de Jager, *Mem. Soc. roy. sci. Liège*, **14,** 460 (1953).
9. V. M. Goldschmidt, *Norske Videnskaps-Akad., Mat-Naturv. Klasse*, **1937,** No. 4.
10. H. Brown, *Revs. Modern Phys.*, **21,** 625 (1949).
11. H. E. Suess, *Experientia*, **5,** 266 (1949).
12. P. Harteck and H. E. Suess, *Naturwiss.*, **36,** 218 (1949).
13. M. Dole, G. A. Lane, D. P. Rudd, and D. A. Zaukelies, *Geochim. Acta*, **6,** 65 (1954).
14. A. I. Brodsky, O. K. Skarre, E. Dontzova, and M. M. Slutskaya, *J. Phys. Chem. Russ.*, **10,** 731 (1937).
15. I. Friedman, *Geochim. Acta*, **4,** 89 (1953).
16. W. Dansgaard, *Nature*, **174,** 234 (1954).
17. S. Epstein and T. Mayeda, *Geochim. Acta*, **4,** 213 (1953).
18. N. M. Rakestraw, D. P. Rudd, and M. Dole, *J. Am. Chem. Soc.*, **73,** 2976 (1951).
19. A. I. Brodsky, *Isotope Chemistry*, Academy of Sciences, Moscow, 1957.
20. P. Baertschi, *Helv. Chim. Acta*, **36,** 1352 (1953).
21. G. Boato, G. Careri, and G. G. Volpi, *Nuovo cimento*, **9,** 539 (1952).
22. H. G. Thode, *Research*, **2,** 154 (1949).
23. S. R. Silverman, *Geochim. Acta*, **2,** 26 (1951).
24. S. Ruben, M. Randall, M. Kamen, and J. L. Hyde, *J. Am. Chem. Soc.*, **63,** 877 (1941).
25. A. P. Vinogradov and R. V. Teis, *Compt. rend. acad. sci. U.S.S.R.*, **33,** 490 (1941).
26. W. E. Roake and M. Dole, *J. Am. Chem. Soc.*, **72,** 36 (1950).
27. M. Dole, *Science*, **109,** 77 (1949).
28. P. Baertschi, *Nature*, **166,** 112 (1950).
29. P. Baertschi and S. R. Silverman, *Geochim. Acta*, **1,** 317 (1951).
30. A. McKellar, quoted in Ref. 23.
31. E. Dontsova, *Doklady Akad. Nauk S.S.S.R.*, **71,** 905 (1950).
32. A. P. Vinogradov and E. I. Dontsova, *Doklady Akad. Nauk S.S.S.R.*, **85,** 1341 (1952).
33. J. M. McCrea, *J. Chem. Phys.*, **18,** 849 (1950).
34. H. C. Urey, H. A. Lowenstam, S. Epstein, and C. R. McKinney, *Bull. Geol. Soc. Am.*, **62,** 399 (1951).
35. S. Epstein, R. Buchsbaum, H. A. Lowenstam, and H. C. Urey, *Bull. Geol. Soc. Am.*, **62,** 417 (1951).
36. H. C. Urey, *Science*, **108,** 489 (1948).
37. R. V. Teis, *Doklady Akad. Nauk S.S.S.R.*, **72,** 73 (1950).

38. C. Emiliani and S. Epstein, *J. Geology*, **61,** 171 (1953).

39. H. G. Thode, J. MacNamara, F. P. Lossing, and C. B. Collins, *J. Am. Chem. Soc.*, **70,** 3008 (1948).

40. A. E. Cameron, *J. Am. Chem. Soc.*, **77,** 2731 (1955).

41. B. F. Murphey and A. O. Nier, *Phys. Rev.*, **59,** 771 (1941).

42. F. E. Wickman, *Nature*, **169,** 1051 (1952).

43. F. E. Wickman, *Geochim. Acta*, **2,** 243 (1952).

44. H. Craig, *Geochim. Acta*, **3,** 53 (1953).

45. K. Rankama, *Geochim. Acta*, **5,** 142 (1954).

46. K. Rankama, *J. Geology*, **56,** 199 (1948).

47. A. V. Trofimov, *Doklady Akad. Nauk S.S.S.R.*, **85,** 169 (1952).

48. J. H. Reynolds and J. Verhoogen, *Geochim. Acta*, **3,** 224 (1953).

49. R. J. Allenby, *Geochim. Acta*, **5,** 40 (1954).

50. F. S. Grant, *Geochim. Acta*, **5,** 225 (1954).

51. A. P. Tudge and H. G. Thode, *Can. J. Research*, **28B,** 567 (1950).

52. H. G. Thode, J. MacNamara, and C. B. Collins, *Can. J. Research*, **27B,** 361 (1949).

52a. B. Lazard, G. Nief, and E. Roth, *J. Chim. Phys.*, **49,** 60 (1952).

53. J. MacNamara and H. G. Thode, *Phys. Rev.*, **78,** 307 (1950).

54. A. Trofimov, *Doklady Akad. Nauk S.S.S.R.*, **66,** 181 (1949).

55. H. G. Thode, J. MacNamara, and W. H. Fleming, *Geochim. Acta*, **3,** 235 (1953).

56. H. G. Thode, R. K. Wanless, and R. Wallouch, *Geochim. Acta*, **5,** 286 (1954).

57. E. Wichers, *J. Am. Chem. Soc.*, **78,** 3235 (1956).

58. J. Mattauch, *J. Am. Chem. Soc.*, **80,** 4125 (1958).

59. T. P. Kohman, J. H. Mattauch, and A. Wapstra, *J. Chim. Phys.*, **55,** 393 (1958).

60. W. Vernadski, *La Geochimie*, Alcan, Paris, 1934.

61. V. Caglioti, C. Bettinali, and F. Salvetti, *Atti Convegno Geol. Nucl.*, **1,** 36 (1955).

62. M. Ferretti-Sforzini, C. Festa, and F. Ippolito, *Atti Convegno Geol. Nucl.*, **1,** 57 (1955); for the possible role of radioactivity in volcanic action, see J. Noetzlin, *Compt. rend*, **208,** 1100, 1662 (1939), and A. Dauvillier, *Compt. rend.*, **237,** 1202 (1953).

63. J. Adams, *Symposium on Nuclear Geology*, Wiley and Sons, New York, 1955, p. 89.

64. G. W. Reed and A. Turkevich, *Nature*, **176,** 794 (1955).

65. S. I. Tomkeieff, *Science Progress*, **34,** 696 (1946).

66. F. Hernegger and B. Karlik, *Akad. Wiss. Wien, Abt. IIa*, **144,** 217 (1935).

67. F. F. Koczy, *Akad. Wiss. Wien, Abt. IIa*, **158,** 113 (1950).

68. D. C. Stewart and W. C. Bentley, *Science*, **120,** 50 (1954).

69. H. Pettersson, *Wiener Anzeiger*, No. 1, 1937, quoted in Ref. 74.

70. C. S. Piggot and W. D. Urry, *J. Wash. Acad. Science*, **29,** 405 (1939).

71. C. S. Piggot and W. D. Urry, *Am. J. Sci.*, **239,** 81 (1941).

72. N. Isaac and E. Picciotto, *Nature*, **171,** 742 (1953).

73. H. D. Holland and J. L. Kulp, *Geochim. Acta*, **5,** 214 (1954).

74. H. Pettersson, *Nature*, **167,** 942 (1951).

75. T. Bernert, *Akad. Wiss. Wien, Abt. IIa*, **160,** 99 (1951).

76. V. S. Kroll, *Nature,* **171,** 742 (1953); see also V. I. Baranov and L. Kouzmina, *Doklady Akad. Nauk S.S.S.R.*, **97,** 483 (1954).

77. J. L. Hough, *J. Geology,* **58,** 254 (1950); **61,** 252 (1953).

78. H. L. Volchok and J. L. Kulp, *Bull. Geol. Soc. Am.*, **62,** 1487 (1951); **63,** 1386 (1952).

79. F. F. Koczy, Ref. 63, p. 120.

80. J. Labeyrie, *L'Onde Electr.*, **35,** 929 (1955).

81. W. Anderson, W. V. Mayneord, and R. C. Turner, *Nature,* **174,** 424 (1954).

82. I. Asimov, *J. Chem. Educ.*, **32,** 84 (1955).

83. N. B. Keevil, *Am. J. Sci.*, **237,** 195 (1939).

84. F. A. Paneth and K. Peters, *Z. physik. Chem.*, **134,** 353 (1926).

85. F. A. Paneth and W. D. Urry, *Z. physik. Chem.*, **152 A,** 127 (1931).

86. E. Glueckauf, *Proc. Roy. Soc. (London),* **A185,** 98 (1945).

87. K. F. Chackett, P. Reasbeck, and E. J. Wilson, *Geochim. Acta,* **3,** 261 (1953).

88. For a bibliography, see P. M. Hurley, Ref. 63, p. 301.

89. A. O. Nier, *J. Am. Chem. Soc.*, **60,** 1571 (1938).

90. A. O. Nier, *Phys. Rev.*, **55,** 153 (1939).

91. A. O. Nier, R. W. Thompson, and B. F. Murphey, *Phys. Rev.*, **60,** 112 (1941).

92. F. Begemann, H. Buttlar, F. G. Houtermans, N. Isaac, and E. Picciotto, *Geochim. Acta,* **4,** 21 (1953).

93. G. H. Henderson, *Proc. Roy. Soc. (London),* **A145,** 591 (1934); **173,** 250 (1939).

94. I. Hayase, *Am. Mineral.*, **39,** 761 (1954).

95. S. Deutsch, D. Hirschberg, and E. Picciotto, *Experientia,* **11,** 172 (1955).

96. F. Daniels, C. A. Boyd, and D. F. Saunders, *Science,* **109,** 440 (1949); **117,** 343 (1953).

97. H. D. Holland and J. L. Kulp, *Science,* **111,** 312 (1950).

98. P. M. Hurley and H. W. Fairbairn, *Bull. Geol. Soc. Am.*, **64,** 659 (1953).

99. H. V. Ellsworth, *Am. J. Sci.*, **209,** 127 (1925).

100. B. Wasserstein, *Nature,* **174,** 1004 (1954); **175,** 605 (1955); **176,** 159 (1955); for a critical discussion of this method, see H. R. Hoekstra and J. J. Katz, *Nature,* **175,** 605 (1955).

101. V. G. Khlopin, E. K. Gerling, and N. V. Baranovskaya, *Bull. Acad. Sci. U.S.S.R.*, serie chem., **1947,** 599.

102. W. H. Fleming and H. G. Thode, *Phys. Rev.*, **90,** 857 (1953).

103. F. Smits and W. Gentner, *Geochim. Acta,* **1,** 22 (1950).

104. W. Gentner, R. Prag, and F. Smits, *Geochim. Acta,* **4,** 11 (1953).

105. W. Gentner, F. Jensen, and K. K. Mehnert, *Z. Naturforsch.*, **9a,** 176 (1954).

106. G. J. Wasserburg and R. J. Hayden, *Geochim. Acta,* **7,** 51 (1955).

107. G. J. Wasserburg and R. J. Hayden, *Phys. Rev.*, **97,** 86 (1955).

108. E. K. Gerling and T. G. Pavlova, *Doklady Akad. Nauk S.S.S.R.*, **77,** 85 (1951).

109. E. K. Gerling and K. G. Rik, quoted by A. P. Vinogradov, *Bull. Acad. Sci. U.S.S.R.*, serie geol., No. 3, 3 (1954).

110. M. G. Inghram, H. Brown, C. Patterson, and D. C. Hess, *Phys. Rev.*, **80,** 916 (1950).

111. L. H. Ahrens, *Geochim. Acta,* **1,** 312 (1951).

112. C. Festa and M. Santangelo, *Ann. Geofisica,* **3,** 251 (1950).

113. I. Geese-Bahnisch, *Z. Physik,* **142,** 565 (1955). K. F. Flynn and L. E. Glendenin, *Phys. Rev.*, **116,** 744 (1959).

114. L. Aldrich, *et al.*, *Phys. Rev.*, **89,** 631 (1953).

115. A. Holmes, *Nature,* **173,** 612 (1954).

116. W. J. Arrol, R. B. Jacobi, and F. A. Paneth, *Nature,* **149,** 235 (1942).

117. C. A. Bauer, *Phys. Rev.*, **72,** 354 (1947); **74,** 225, 501 (1948).

118. H. E. Huntley, *Nature,* **161,** 356 (1948).

119. F. A. Paneth, P. Reasbeck, and K. I. Mayne, *Geochim. Acta,* **2,** 300 (1952).

120. G. R. Martin, *Geochim. Acta,* **3,** 288 (1953).

121. H. C. Urey, *Nature,* **175,** 321 (1955).

122. C. B. Collins, R. M. Farquhar, and R. D. Russell, *Can. J. Phys.*, **31,** 402 (1953).

123. A. P. Vinogradov, I. K. Zadorozhnyi, and S. I. Zykov, *Doklady Akad. Nauk S.S.S.R.*, **85,** 1107 (1952).

124. H. F. Ehrenberg, *Z. Physik,* **134,** 317 (1953).

125. P. Eberhardt, J. Geiss, and F. G. Houtermans, *Z. Physik,* **141,** 91 (1955).

126. H. F. Ehrenberg, *Z. Naturforsch.*, **9a,** 951 (1954).

127. E. K. Gerling, *Compt. rend. acad. sci. U.S.S.R.*, **34,** 259 (1942).

128. A. Holmes, *Nature,* **157,** 680 (1946); **159,** 127 (1947).

129. F. Houtermans, *Z. Naturforsch.*, **2a,** 322 (1947).

130. C. B. Collins, R. M. Farquhar, and R. D. Russell, *Phys. Rev.*, **88,** 1275 (1952).

131. E. C. Bullard and J. P. Stanley, quoted in T. P. Kohman and N. Saito, *Ann. Rev. Nuclear Sci.*, **4,** 401 (1954).

132. C. Patterson, H. Brown, G. Tilton, and M. G. Inghram, *Phys. Rev.*, **92,** 1234 (1953).

133. C. Patterson, G. Tilton, and M. G. Inghram, *Science,* **121,** 69 (1955).

134. F. Houtermans, *Nuovo cimento,* **10,** 1623 (1953); **12,** suppl. 1, 17 (1954).

135. R. A. Alpher and R. C. Herman, *Phys. Rev.*, **84,** 1111 (1951).

136. S. Meyer, *Akad. Wiss. Wien, Abt. IIa,* **146,** 175, 581 (1937).

137. I. E. Starik, *Bull. Acad. Sci. U.S.S.R.*, serie geol., No. 2 (1937).

138. F. F. Koczy, *Nature,* **151,** 24 (1943).

139. V. I. Baranov, *1st Conference on Cosmography,* Moscow, 1951, p. 108.

140. E. McCrady, *Trans. Am. Geophys. Union,* **33,** 156 (1952), quoted by V. J. Linnenbom, Ref. 145.

141. D. W. Allan, R. M. Farquhar, and R. D. Russell, *Science,* **118,** 486 (1953).

142. A. Rostagni, *Geofis. pura e appl.*, **18,** 128 (1950).

143. H. Tatel, *J. Geophys. Research,* **55,** 329 (1950).

144. K. F. Chackett, *Phys. Rev.*, **81,** 1057 (1951).

145. V. J. Linnenbom, *J. Chem. Educ.*, **32,** 58 (1955).

146. S. Katkoff, O. A. Schaeffer, and J. M. Hastings, *Phys. Rev.*, **82,** 688 (1951).

147. A. H. W. Aten, *Phys. Rev.*, **73,** 1206 (1948).
148. H. E. Suess and H. Brown, *Phys. Rev.*, **83,** 1254 (1951).
149. R. C. Tolman, *Revs. Modern Phys.*, **21,** 374 (1949).
150. G. A. Gamow, *Atomes (Paris)*, **9,** 100 (1954).
151. R. A. Alpher, H. Bethe, and G. A. Gamow, *Phys. Rev.*, **73,** 803 (1948).
152. R. A. Alpher, R. C. Herman, and G. A. Gamow, *Phys. Rev.*, **74,** 1198 (1948); **75,** 332 (1949).
153. R. A. Alpher and R. C. Herman, *Revs. Modern Phys.*, **22,** 153, 406 (1950).
154. R. A. Alpher and R. C. Herman, *Ann. Rev. Nuclear Sci.*, **2,** 1 (1953).
155. E. Fermi, *Conference on Atomic Physics*, Accad. Lincei, Rome, 1952.
156. G. A. Gamow and C. L. Critchfield, *Theory of the Atomic Nucleus*, Oxford University Press, 1949.
157. G. A. Gamow, *Revs. Modern Phys.*, **21,** 367 (1949).
158. D. Ter Haar, *Revs. Modern Phys.*, **22,** 119 (1950).
159. J. Podolanski and D. Ter Haar, *Mem. Soc. roy. sci. Liège*, **14,** 19 (1954).
160. G. I. Pokrowski, *Physik. Z.*, **32,** 374 (1931).
161. C. F. Weizsäcker, *Physik. Z.*, **38,** 176 (1937); **39,** 633 (1938).
162. S. Chandrasekhar and L. H. Henrich, *Astrophys. J.*, **95,** 288 (1942).
163. O. Klein, G. Beskow, and L. Treffenberg, *Arkiv. Mat. Astron. Fysik*, **B33,** No. 1 (1946).
164. G. Beskow and L. Treffenberg, *Arkiv. Mat. Astron. Fysik*, **A34,** Nos. 13, 17 (1947).
165. H. C. Urey and C. A. Bradley, *Phys. Rev.*, **38,** 718 (1931).
166. C. Lattes and G. Wataghin, *Phys. Rev.*, **69,** 237 (1946).
167. G. B. van Albada, *Astrophys. J.*, **105,** 393 (1947).
168. F. Hoyle, *Proc. Phys. Soc. (London)*, **59,** 972 (1947).
169. F. Hoyle, *The Nature of the Universe*, Oxford University Press, 1957.
170. J. H. D. Jensen and H. E. Suess, *Naturwiss.*, **34,** 131 (1947).
171. M. Goeppert-Mayer and E. Teller, *Phys. Rev.*, **76,** 1226 (1949).

CHAPTER 11

DISSIPATION OF THE ENERGY OF RADIATIONS IN MATTER

11–1 Introduction. The corpuscular and electromagnetic radiations emitted in radioactive transformations generally have high kinetic energies, and, as the radiations pass through matter, this energy is rapidly lost in interactions with the components of the substance concerned. Leaving aside the relatively rare nuclear reactions discussed previously, we find that radiation may cause permanent or transitory changes in those molecules which are struck, or which are in the neighborhood of such events. In studying such interactions, there are two main (and necessarily related) problems: first, the way in which the radiations dissipate their energy, and second, the changes caused by the absorption of this energy in matter. The present chapter is devoted to the first of these topics.

A fast-moving charged particle (α-particle, proton, deuteron, fission fragment, etc.) or a high-energy photon (x- or γ-ray) loses energy in striking a molecule or an atom, and there is a resultant change in the direction of motion; these changes are governed by the laws of conservation of energy and of momentum. The processes are *inelastic collisions* if the potential energy of the struck molecule is changed by excitation or ionization, and *elastic* when its kinetic energy alone is increased.

Charged particles and electromagnetic radiations dissipate their energy in different ways and according to different laws. Only one single elementary process is involved in the dissipation of photon energy, and as a result, the absorption of a beam of x- or γ-rays follows an exponential law. In contrast to this, a very large number of collisions are required to stop an α-particle or a fast-moving proton completely, and ignoring statistical fluctuations, this number is the same for identical particles with the same energy. It therefore follows that for an ionizing particle with a given initial energy passing through a given medium, the *range* can be defined as the distance traveled by the particle before it is stopped completely. This path, which can be detected by the dense ionization produced, is virtually a straight line for this type of particle, as can be clearly demonstrated by Wilson cloud-chamber experiments, or some appropriate photographic technique. Scattering by nuclei cause marked changes in the path of the incident particle, but it is very rare, and too little momentum is transferred in collisions with electrons to cause any appreciable change in direction.

The collision between a high-velocity free electron and a stationary bound electron in an atom is quite different, since the exchange of momentum is sufficiently large for the path to show multiple deviations. It is possible to distinguish between heavy particles and primary electrons, or electrons produced in the absorption of a high-energy photon, by the differing tracks produced on a photographic plate (Fig. 11–1). It will be convenient to consider neutrons separately, since they do not cause direct

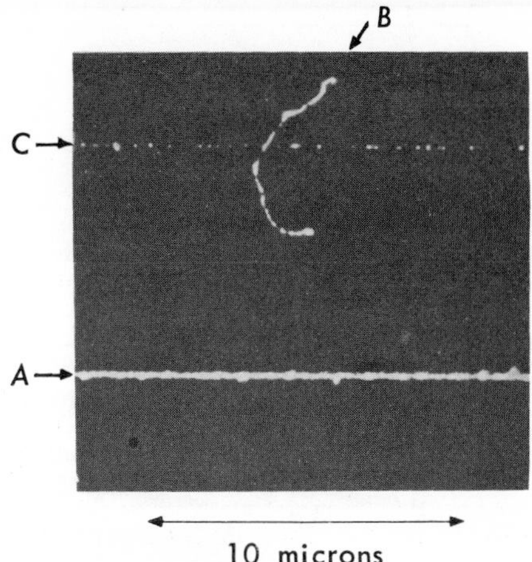

FIG. 11-1. Cloud-chamber photograph of the passage of a fast electron (200 kev, track C), a slow electron (20 kev, track B), and a proton (track A) (Ref. 58).

ionization of matter, although elastic collisions with protons or other atoms transfer kinetic energy to the struck atoms, and so move them from their position (Section 11-10).

Energy transfer between charged particles and molecules or atoms occurs essentially by excitation and ionization. The energy of each individual excitation process is of the order of a few electron volts, up to about 15 ev. In ionization, the energy transferred must be at least equal to the lowest ionization potential of the molecule or atom, but it may be much higher when the electron removed acquires a finite kinetic energy (i.e., above zero). In a small fraction of the collisions, when a moving particle passes very close to an orbital electron, the latter is removed with an energy of several hundred or even thousand ev, and this in its turn can cause a secondary path of ionization, which is denser than that from the faster primary electron.

The number of secondary electrons, (δ-*rays*; see Fig. 11-2) produced per unit track length increases with decreasing energy of the initial ionizing particle. Their maximum velocity is twice the velocity of this particle, corresponding to a maximum energy given by

$$E_\delta = 4\,\frac{m}{M}\,E, \tag{11-1}$$

where m is the mass of the electron, and M and E the mass and energy of the initial particle. Lea [1] has calculated the number of δ-rays with an energy greater than W ev produced per micron of path in water by α-particles and protons with various incident energies. Some of the results of these calculations are reproduced in Tables 11-1 and 11-2.

When an electron which has been detached from an ionized molecule in a gas has lost most of its kinetic energy, it may attach itself to another

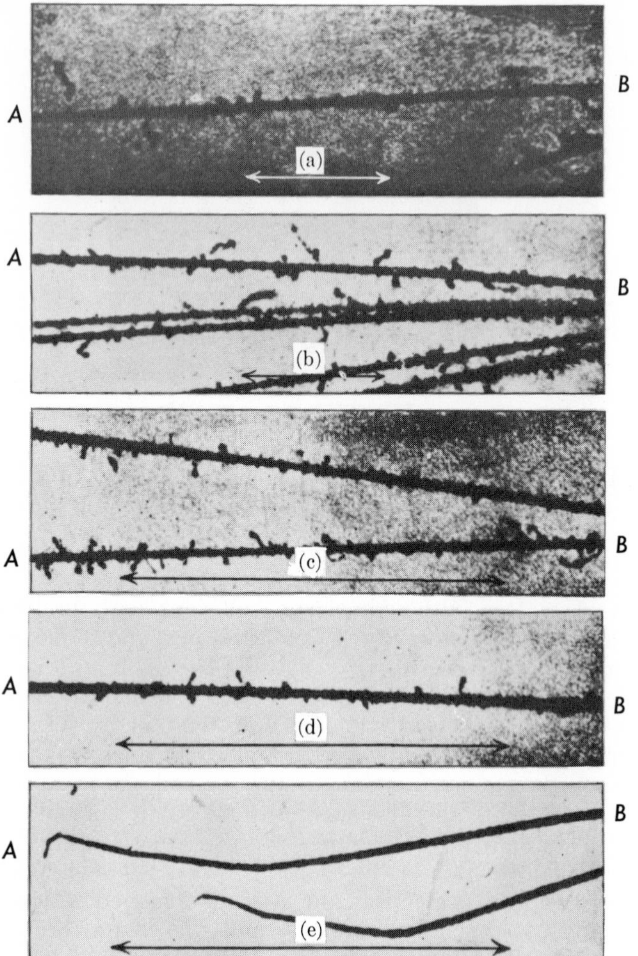

FIG. 11–2. Cloud-chamber photographs of the tracks of α-particles of decreasing energy, and of δ-rays. [T. Alper, *Z. Physik*, **76,** 172 (1932).]

molecule or atom, provided that the electron affinity of the latter is sufficiently large to allow it to form a negative ion. If this is not the case, the "ion-pair" consists of a positive ion and an electron.

The number of ion-pairs produced by the particle per unit track length (measured in centimeters for a gas, and in microns for a liquid or solid) gives the *specific ionization* or the linear ion density, whereas the *total ionization* is the number of ion-pairs produced by the particle along the whole of its path. For a given energy, the specific ionization increases with the mass of the particle.

Some of the energy dissipated in a gas as ionization produces chemical changes by changes in internal energy, but the remainder is virtually

TABLE 11–1

THE PRODUCTION OF δ-RAYS IN WATER BY α-PARTICLES AND PROTONS

E, Mev / W, kev	2		4		5	6		8		10
	α	p	α	p	α	α	p	α	p	p
0.1	231.4	15.66	121.5	7.921	98.15	82.31	5.301	62.22	3.984	3.191
0.25	78.64	6.042	45.13	3.113	37.03	31.38	2.096	24.02	1.580	1.267
0.55	23.07	2.546	17.34	1.365	14.80	12.85	0.9304	10.12	0.7055	0.5681
1.1	—	1.089	5.768	0.634	5.544	5.136	0.4447	4.336	0.3412	0.2767
2.25	—	0.3440	—	0.2641	0.810	1.191	0.1965	1.378	0.1551	0.1277
3.75	—	0.0591	—	0.1216	—	—	0.1015	0.246	0.0838	0.0707
5.5	—	—	—	0.0536	—	—	0.0562	—	0.0498	0.04355
10.5	—	—	—	—	—	—	0.0100	—	0.0151	0.01580

TABLE 11–2

THE PRODUCTION OF δ-RAYS BY ELECTRONS PASSING THROUGH WATER

W, kev \ E, kev	12	24	48	96	192
0.1	1.433	0.7579	0.4011	0.2326	0.1442
0.55	0.2226	0.1261	0.06942	0.04117	0.02586
1.1	0.09432	0.05757	0.03299	0.02001	0.01274
2.25	0.03309	0.02369	0.01467	0.009287	0.006055
5.5	0.00212	0.006024	0.004725	0.003340	0.002313
10.5	—	0.000842	0.001722	0.001462	0.001103
22.5	—	—	0.000108	0.000443	0.000419
45	—	—	—	0.000032	0.000142

entirely degraded as the heat released in neutralization and combination reactions. The average temperature rise is, however, negligible, even for very high dose rates. Local temperature changes may, however, be quite large and are fundamental to the theory of "hot spots," which has been used in attempts to explain the chemical and biological effects of radiation [2].

11–2 Stopping power. The *stopping power* of a substance is the energy loss which an ionizing particle undergoes per unit track length, and is expressed in kev/cm (or kev/μ for condensed media), or in ergs/cm (1 kev $= 1.602 \times 10^{9}$ erg). The *atomic* stopping power is the energy loss per centimeter divided by the atomic density, and is expressed in ev·cm^2/atom. The *mass* stopping power is the energy loss per centimeter divided by the specific mass, and is expressed in kev·cm^2/mg. For example, 1 kev/cm in hydrogen [3] is equivalent to 1.861×10^{-17} ev/cm^2·atom, or 11.12 kev·cm^2/mg; in air, the equivalent values are 1.861×10^{-17} and 0.7734, respectively, and in aluminum 1.658×10^{-18} and 37×10^{-5}. The *relative* stopping power s is the ratio between the stopping powers of a given substance and that of air for identical particles with the same energy, and is equal to the inverse ratio of the thicknesses which for equal atomic density would give the same stopping power for the particle in question;

$$s = \frac{d_0\rho_0 A}{d\rho A_0},$$

where d, ρ, and A are the thickness, density, and atomic weight of the substance, and d_0, ρ_0, and A_0 are the same parameters for air; A_0, the average atomic weight of air, is taken as 14.4.

The stopping power of a monotomic gas, of atomic number Z, containing n atoms per cubic centimeter, for a heavy particle (proton, deuteron,

TABLE 11-3

AVERAGE EXCITATION POTENTIALS, I (ev)

Element	I	Element	I
H	15.6	Co	309
He	34.5	Cu	325
Li	34.0	Zn	340
Be	60.4	Kr	390
C	76.4	Ag	428
N	81	Sn	479
O	99	Pb	810
Al	150	U	881
Ar	195	(air	87)
Fe	243	(H_2O	65)

α-particle) with charge ze and velocity v is given by the classical Bohr theory as

$$-\frac{dE}{dx} = \frac{4\pi e^4 z^2 n}{mv^2} B, \tag{11-2}$$

where m is the rest mass of the electron and B, the *stopping number*, is given by the quantum relation established by Bethe [4, 5, 6] and Bloch [7, 8]:

$$B = Z \log_e \left[\frac{2mv^2}{I(1 - \beta^2)} - \beta^2 \right] \cdot \tag{11-3}$$

In this formula, I is the geometrically averaged excitation potential for all the ionization and excitation potentials of the atom; $\beta = v/c$, c being the velocity of light. For nonrelativistic velocities (i.e., for small values of β),

$$B = Z \log_e \frac{2mv^2}{I} \cdot \tag{11-3a}$$

A similar but more complex relationship can be derived for electrons [9], which for small values of β is of the same form as Eq. (11-2), with $B = Z \log_e (1.66mv^2/2I)$; for energies where $E \gg mc^2$,

$$-\frac{dE}{dx} = 2\pi \frac{ne^4 Z}{mc^2} \left(\log_e \frac{E}{2mc^2 I} + \frac{1}{8} \right) \cdot \tag{11-4}$$

Bloch [5] suggests that the average excitation potential is proportional to the atomic number, so that $I = kZ$, with $k = 11.5$. Experiments by Mano [10], however, show that this proportionality holds only for $Z > 20$, for which k is approximately 10.5; for smaller values of Z, the values vary appreciably. More recent measurements [9] give $k = 8.8$ for $Z > 47$, so that k apparently decreases with increasing atomic number. Values of I (in ev) for a number of elements are given in Table 11-3.

The average excitation potentials appear to vary slightly with the velocity of the ionizing particle, and this is probably one of the reasons why various authors using different techniques, and particles with different energies, have reported discordant values for these parameters.

Equation (11–2) is valid only when the velocity of the incident particle is greater than the velocities of *all* the orbital electrons in the atoms of the absorbing material. The velocity of an electron of energy ϵ ($= \frac{1}{2}mv^2$) is equal to that of an incident particle of mass A, when the energy of the latter $E = (A/m)\epsilon$. For example, $\epsilon = 545$ kev for a 4-Mev α-particle, equal to the energy of the electrons in the K-shell of the oxygen atom. This is consequently a very significant limitation, since it implies that the equation is not in fact rigorously applicable even for the stopping power of such α-particles in oxygen, and its validity is further reduced for heavier atoms. Furthermore, positively charged particles of comparatively low energy (less than 1 Mev for α-particles, and less than 0.2 Mev for protons) can capture an electron from an atom and lose it in a subsequent collision, in which the charge is no longer the initial charge ze. There is as yet no satisfactory theory which gets over all these difficulties, although some improvement can be brought about by introducing a correction term into Eq. (11–3a) to make this equation valid for those energies at which electron capture can be neglected. The factor B then becomes

$$B = Z \log_e \frac{2mv^2}{I} - C_k. \tag{11–5}$$

At very high energies, it is necessary to take into account the effect of polarization of the atoms in the absorbing medium [11, 12]; this tends to decrease the energy transfer, especially for high-energy incident particles.

From Eqs. (11–2) and (11–4), the specific ionization should show an initial decrease with increasing particle energy, then pass through a minimum, and subsequently increase because of the relativistic correction. This minimum is in fact observed, being reached for energies of the order of 1 Mev for electrons (Fig. 11–3). At the minimum, the specific ionization is 46.1 ions/cm in air, 6.48 in hydrogen, 8.13 in helium, and 53.1 in argon [13].

11–3 The ranges of α-particles and protons. The range of a particle is the length of its path from the point at which it has an incident energy of E, up to the point where this energy has been degraded to $E = 0$. This range is therefore obtained by integrating the equation for the loss of energy between the limits $E = E$ and $E = 0$,

$$R = \int_0^E \frac{dE}{-\,dE/dx} = \frac{M}{z^2}\,\frac{m}{4\pi e^4 n} \int_0^{v_1} \frac{v^3\,dv}{B}, \tag{11–6}$$

where $E = \frac{1}{2}Mv^2$, and M is the mass of the particle. Although this integration is not difficult mathematically, the equation does not in fact give very precise results, since corrections are necessary to take into account electron captures and losses at low energies. After such empirical corrections

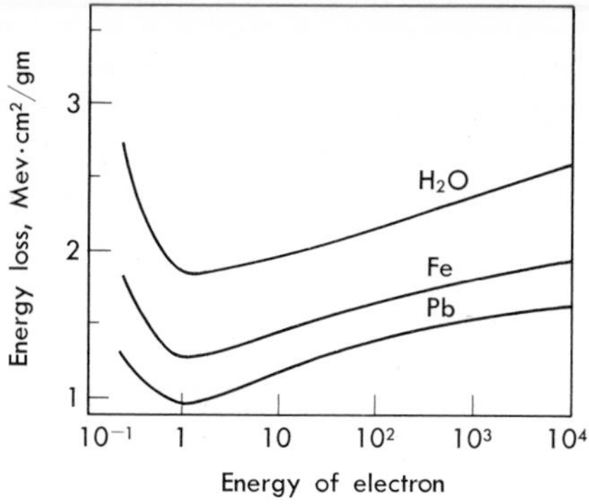

FIG. 11-3. The rate of loss of energy by electrons as a function of energy in different media.

are introduced, this equation can be used to calculate the range of a particle of mass M and charge z_1e if the range of another particle, of mass M_2 and charge z_2e is known for the same velocity or energy. Blackett and Lees [14] have used this method to establish equations which are valid for protons and α-particles in air at 15°C and 760 mm Hg pressure:

$$R_H(v) = 1.007R_\alpha(v) - 0.20 \text{ (cm)}, \tag{11-7}$$

$$R_H(E) = 1.007R_\alpha(3.972E) - 0.20 \text{ (cm)}. \tag{11-8}$$

The constant term (0.20) is introduced as a correction to take into account the fact that electron capture and loss are not the same for α-particles and protons with equal velocities or energies. Apart from this correction, the energy loss is four times smaller for a proton than for an α-particle with the same energy, since the atomic number (1 for the proton and 2 for the α-particle) comes into Eq. (11-2) as Z^2. Since the mass ratio is 1.007/4.0, and the energy is given by $E = \frac{1}{2}Mv^2$, the decrease in velocity after a given distance is virtually the same for both particles.

The arguments developed so far can strictly be applied only to monatomic gases. There is no precise theory of stopping power for polyatomic gases at present [15], but the evidence is that the influence of chemical bonding on the energy loss is very small. In agreement with this, it is usual to use the empirical Bragg and Kleeman *additivity rule*, which states that the atomic stopping power is independent of the state of chemical combination and the physical state of the absorbing atom, and is proportional to the square root of the atomic weight. This rule is most often applied to the *average stopping power* relative to air (S) along the whole path of a particle with a given initial energy; this is not the same as the *true* relative stopping power s, since the energy loss varies with the velocity. S is the ratio of the ranges R_0/R, corrected for the atomic densities, where R_0 is the range in air; $S = R_0n_0/Rn$, where n is the number of atoms per cubic centimeter.

The additivity rule states that for a compound A_aB_b, the stopping power is given by $S_{AB} = aS_A + bS_B$. Gray [16] has made a careful examination of a number of experimental values, and has shown that in only three cases is the deviation from the additivity rule more than 3%; it does not exceed 1.5% in 38 other measurements involving 15 compounds containing H, O, C, and N. Allowing for experimental errors, Gray concludes that the overall influence of chemical combination is extremely small. More recent work by Thompson [17] on the slowing down of 340- to 200-Mev protons in various organic compounds containing C, H, O, N, and Cl has shown that the deviations from additivity are as much as 2% for hydrogen compounds; for the other compounds examined, the rule is valid to within ~1%.

There is some uncertainty as to the rigorous application of the additivity rule to compounds in the condensed state. Polarization by neighboring atoms, which depends on the dielectric constant of the medium, can reduce the energy transfer between the particle and the struck atom, especially at higher energies. This question, too, has been investigated experimentally by Gray [16], who concludes from a series of precise measurements with mica that oxygen has sensibly the same atomic stopping power in the gas and in the crystal states. Deviations of 15 to 20% were, however, found from linear additivity in a number of organic liquids (alcohol, ether, carbon disulfide, etc.), but Gray suggests that the experimental technique (involving the visual observation of scintillations on a ZnS screen) was unreliable. Similarly, results [18, 19, 20] implying differences of the order of 15% between the stopping powers of water vapor and liquid water have been criticized by Carvalho and Yagoda [21]. These authors found that the α-particles from Po (5.3 Mev) and RaC′ (7.68 Mev) have the same stopping power in liquid and solid water, and obey the additivity rule. Ellis, Rossi, and Failla [22] have reached a similar conclusion by measuring the ionization produced when the Po α-particles are partially absorbed in acetylene and in a very thin film of polystyrene, since the differences between the stopping powers of these two substances is less than 1%. The corresponding difference for water as vapor and as liquid is less than 5%, below the limits of experimental error.

Platzman, however, has questioned this conclusion [15] and suggests that the stopping power should depend on the state of aggregation, not only because of polarization effects but also because of the appreciable differences between the excitation levels in the crystalline and vapor states of the same substance. For metals at least, it has been shown theoretically [23] that the conductivity electrons make a contribution to the stopping power not correctly expressed by Eq. (11–2), and this is especially important for metals of low atomic weight. By taking into account polarization effects, A. Bohr [12] has calculated $I = 60$ ev for the excitation potential of metallic beryllium, significantly lower than the value found in the vapor phase. Precise measurements by Madsen and Venkateswarlu [24] of the stopping power for 1-Mev protons have confirmed this result.

Table 11–4 shows the range of the α-particles from RaC′ (7.68 Mev) in different metals [25], and Table 11–5 the range of α-particles and protons

TABLE 11–4

THE RANGE OF THE RaC′ α-PARTICLES IN METALS

Metal	R, μ
Li	129.1
Mg	57.8
Al	40.6
Ca	78.8
Fe	18.7
Ni	18.4
Cu	18.3
Zn	22.8
Ag	19.2
Cd	24.2
Pt	12.8
Au	14.0
Pb	24.1

TABLE 11–5

THE RANGES AND PRIMARY IONIZATION OF PROTONS AND α-PARTICLES IN WATER

Energy, Mev	Range in water, μ		Primary ionization, ions/μ	
	α	Protons	α	Protons
1	5.3	23	5207	398.2
2	10.1	73	2883	217.0
3	16.8	147	2031	151.8
4	25.1	241	1581	117.7
5	35.2	355	1301	96.56
6	47.0	486	1109	82.13
7	60.3	642	968	71.63
8	75.5	813	860.5	63.62
9	91.6	1004	775.4	57.31
10	108.4	1211	706.4	52.19

with energies between 1 and 10 Mev in liquid water, together with the number of primary ionizations per micron of the path (i.e., without the δ-rays). These latter values are from calculation by Lea [1], taking the energy required to produce an ion-pair as 35 ev, as in air.

Several empirical relations have been proposed to relate the initial energy E of a heavy ionizing particle and its range R; these are generally of the type

$$R = aE^n. \tag{11–9}$$

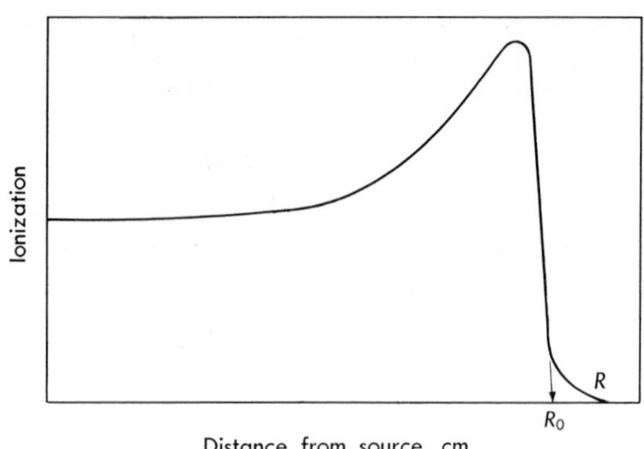

FIG. 11–4. The Bragg curve for α-particles.

With $n = \frac{3}{2}$, this is the Geiger equation for the natural α-emitting elements, with ranges in air between 3 and 7 cm approximately. For protons with energies between a few Mev and 200 Mev, $n = 1.8$. In fact, however, n increases with energy; for α-particles with ranges below 3 cm, $n \approx 1.4$, and for R greater than 7 cm, $n = 2$.

It should be noted that the ranges discussed so far are *mean* ranges. In dealing with gases, where very precise measurements are possible, this should not be confused with the *extrapolated range*. The energy losses in a beam of initially monoenergetic charged particles are subject to statistical fluctuations, so that all the particles are not stopped at exactly the same distance from the emitting source (*straggling*). This can be seen in the Bragg curve for a beam of particles; the specific ionization is shown as a function of the residual range (Fig. 11–4), and a distribution of ranges around the most probable value (the mean range) can be seen. The extrapolated range R_0 is obtained by extrapolating the final steeply descending part of the curve to the axis. The difference between the two ranges is only about 0.7%.

An important practical problem arises with solid α-emitters, which partially absorb the emitted particles. Such a source is said to constitute an infinitely *thick layer* when the thickness of the layer of material is greater than the range of the particles in the material concerned. A characteristic property is that in these circumstances the ionization current produced in the surrounding gas phase is independent of the thickness; for example, a thick layer of U_3O_8 gives a current of 1.75×10^{-3} esu/cm^2. The measured activity is proportional to the concentration of radioactive atoms (Fig. 11–7); multiplying this by the weight of the layer gives the *activity product*, which is proportional to the total number of radioactive atoms in the source. A more frequently used parameter is the *specific activity*, which is the activity (in either absolute or arbitrary units) per unit mass of the radioactive substance.

A layer is *infinitely thin* if virtually none of the emitted particles are absorbed. If n is the number of particles emitted per cubic centimeter per second from an infinitely thin layer of material over a 4π solid angle, and

n' is the number of particles escaping from the surface of a thick layer per square centimeter per second, it follows [26, 27] that

$$n = \frac{n'R}{4}, \tag{11-10}$$

where R is the range of the particles in the solid. The ionization current produced by these particles, in ion-pairs per square centimeter per second is

$$i = fknR, \tag{11-11}$$

where k is the number of ion pairs produced by an α-particle along the whole of its path in the gas phase above the source, and f is a coefficient which increases slightly with α-particle energy, as shown by the values

R_0, cm	1	2	3	5	8
f	0.11	0.13	0.14	0.145	0.15

The use of thick layers and the relevant theory are important in separating radioelements from inactive material, and in measurements using radioactive tracers.

11-4 The absorption of electrons. Fast electrons undergo a very large number of collisions with the absorbing medium before losing their energy completely, and because of this, the initially straight tracks show deviations which are particularly large toward the end of the path. There is consequently a very much greater spread of ranges for electrons than for the heavy particles, and this makes the experimental determination of an average range very difficult. It is, however, possible to define an extrapolated range for a beam of initially monoenergetic electrons by extending the linear descending part of the absorption curve to the point at which it intercepts that part of the curve which is parallel to the abscissa (Fig. 11-5). The abscissa normally represents the mass of absorbent per square centimeter, and the ordinate shows the intensity of β-radiation as measured by some ionization technique.

The loss of energy is proportional to the atomic number and to n, the number of atoms per cubic centimeter, and so approximately to $\rho Z/A$, where A is the atomic weight of the absorbent, since $nZ = N\rho Z/A$, where N is Avogadro's number and ρ the density of the medium. The variation of Z/A with Z is, however, fairly small (0.5 for aluminum, and 0.4 for lead), so that it is reasonable to assume that the absorption depends essentially on the density of the absorbing medium, and that for a given density it is almost independent of atomic number. If the absorption is expressed as a function of the product of the density and the thickness (gm/cm^2), the values will vary only slightly with the nature of the absorbent.

Experimentally, it is found that the absorption of β-particles, with their complex spectrum of heteroenergetic electrons, can be represented to a

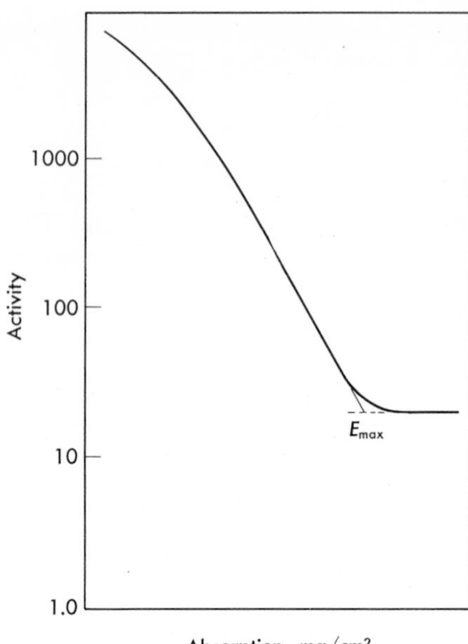

FIG. 11–5. The range of β-particles.

good approximation by the exponential equation

$$I = I_0 e^{-\mu x} = I_0 e^{-(\mu/\rho)\cdot(m/s)}, \tag{11–12}$$

where I/I_0 is the measured fraction of the initial intensity of ionization after the radiation has passed through x cm of absorbent, μ is the total *absorption coefficient,* m the mass, and s the surface area of the absorbent, so that μ/ρ is the *mass absorption coefficient,* which is approximately independent of atomic number. The intensity is reduced by half after a thickness given by $x = \log_e 2/\mu = 0.693/\mu$. Writing this thickness as $(m/s)_{1/2}$ in gm/cm^3 and the maximum energy of the β-spectrum as E_{max} (Mev), one has the approximate relationship [28]

$$E_{max} = \left(31 \frac{m}{s}\right)_{1/2}^{0.75} = 23.4 \left(\frac{m}{s}\right)_{1/2}^{0.75}. \tag{11–13}$$

For $0.6 < E_{max} < 5$ Mev, Perey has proposed the relation [29]

$$E_{max} = \frac{(m/s)_{1/2} + 0.008}{0.047}. \tag{11–14}$$

Various other empirical relations have been suggested relating the extrapolated range (in gm/cm^2) and E_{max}. Of these, the best known is that of Feather [30]:

$$R = 0.543\, E_{max} - 0.160. \tag{11–15}$$

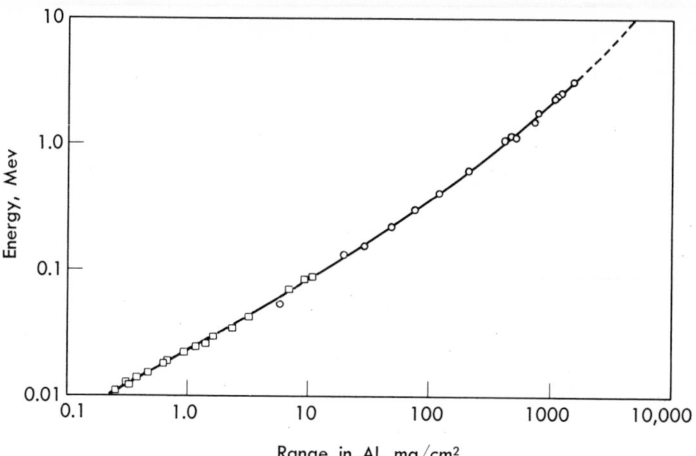

Fig. 11–6. The range of electrons in aluminum as a function of their energy (Ref. 32).

Using more recent data on the absorption of β-particles, Glendenin and Coryell [31] have proposed an equation valid for $E_{max} > 0.8$ Mev:

$$R = 0.542\, E_{max} - 0.133, \tag{11–16}$$

or, for $R > 0.3$ gm/cm^2,

$$E_{max} = 1.85\, R + 0.245. \tag{11–17}$$

For $0.15 < E_{max} < 0.8$,

$$E_{max} = 1.99\, R^{0.725}, \tag{11–18}$$

or

$$R = 0.407\, E_{max}^{1.38}. \tag{11–19}$$

For monoenergetic electrons with energies above 0.6 Mev, it has been suggested [9] that

$$R = 0.526\, E - 0.094. \tag{11–20}$$

Another empirical relation, analogous to Eq. (11–9) for heavy particles, relates the ranges of slow electrons ($v/c < 0.6$) to their velocity

$$R = kv^n \tag{11–21}$$

with n decreasing with v from 4 to 2.

No single relation is valid over the whole range of energies, but Glendenin [32] has produced an empirical logarithmic curve giving the range as a function of E for electron energies between 0.01 and 3 Mev, and has extrapolated this up to 10 Mev (Fig. 11–6). This curve is particularly useful for energies below 0.8 Mev, in which region the empirical formulae have only limited usefulness.

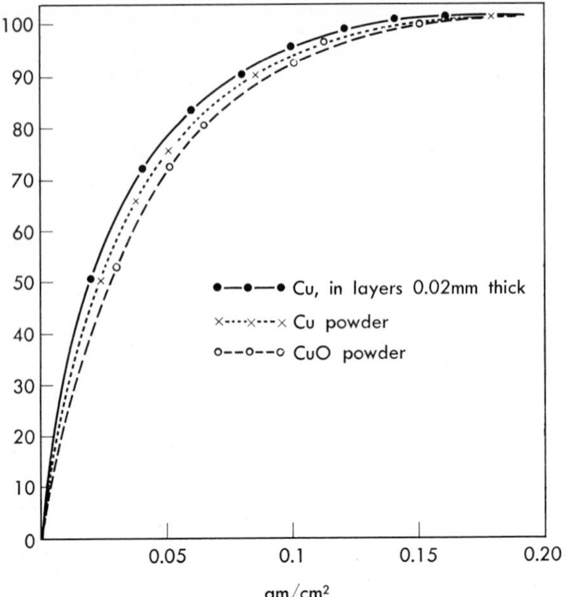

FIG. 11–7. The self-absorption of β-particles in copper (Ref. 35).

A series of experiments by Fournier [33] on the absorption on the RaE β-particles by metals gave the relation

$$\frac{\mu}{\rho} = a + bZ, \tag{11–22}$$

where the constants are $a = 15$ and $b = 0.142$. Solid or liquid compounds, represented by the formula A_aB_b, can be divided into two groups; the first group, which includes SiO_2, MnO_2, Al_2O_3, KBr, $NaNO_3$, C_8H_{10}, CCl_4, CS_2, etc., obey an additivity law defined as

$$\frac{\mu}{\rho} = \frac{aA_A(\mu/\rho)_A + bA_B(\mu/\rho)_B + \cdots}{M},$$

where A_A, A_B, . . . , are the atomic weights of the components, and M is the molecular weight of the compound. The other group, which includes water, hydrated compounds, CaF_2, ZnS, etc., shows deviations from the additivity law of the order of 8 to 10% or more. It is difficult to see how these differences arise, although it should be noted that the simple equations given above are not always valid with β-emitters other than RaE [34].

For a β-emitting substance whose thickness is not negligibly small, the self-absorption is given by [35]

$$I = k(1 - e^{-\mu x}),$$

with (11–23)

$$k = \frac{I_0}{1 - e^{-\mu\epsilon}},$$

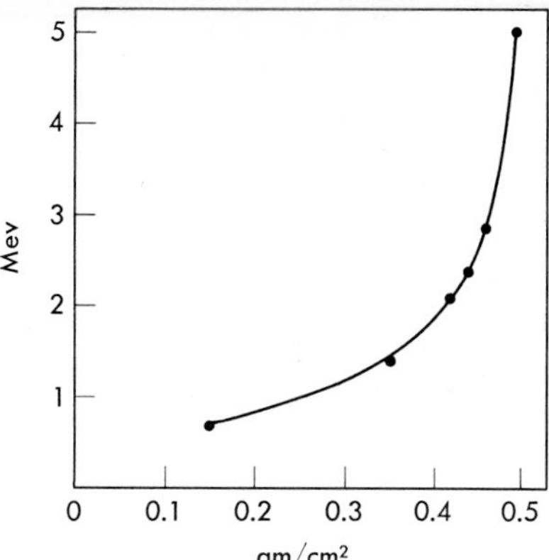

FIG. 11–8. The minimum thickness of a "thick layer" as a function of β-particle energy (Ref. 35).

where I/I_0 is the fraction of the activity measured on an infinitely thin layer, x is the thickness of the source, and ϵ the thickness of a monomolecular layer of this substance. With increasing x, I goes assymptotically to a limiting value, equal to k for $x =$ infinity. In practice (Fig. 11–7) a "thick layer" (Section 11–3) is reached fairly quickly in the case of β-particles whose maximum energy is of the order of 5 Mev or less. When the self-absorption is essentially due to atoms which are isotopic with the emitting nuclide, the minimum surface density needed to get a thick layer depends on the maximum energy of the emitted radiation, as shown in Fig. 11–8.

Broda, *et al.* [29], have shown that the thickness of self-absorbing material necessary to reduce the radiation intensity by one-half is, on the average, 2.2 times greater than the "half-thickness" of an external absorbent (although there are appreciable deviations from this figure).

Self-absorption often depends on the conditions under which the measurement is carried out, and in particular can be affected by the nature and thickness of the support which carries the active material. In fact, some of the radiation initially emitted toward the support is reflected by the latter toward the detecting instrument. For a given source, the amount of this *back-scattering* increases with the atomic number and the thickness of the support, up to some limiting thickness. For "thick layers," self-absorption in the sample compensates for this back-scattering. The maximum energy of the scattered electrons also increases with the atomic number of the reflecting material. These effects can be minimized by using extremely thin supports of very light material, such as aluminum, nylon, polystyrene, or some other plastic. For example, the ratio between the activity of a RaE source measured with different supports in a "thick layer" and that found with virtually no back-scattering is 1.1 for paper, 1.5 for nickel, and 1.78 for platinum. Appreciable errors can obviously occur if the nature of the support is not properly considered in making counting measurements.

TABLE 11–6

THE RANGE AND PRIMARY IONIZATION OF ELECTRONS IN WATER

Electron energy, kev	Range, μ	Electron energy, kev	Primary ionization, ions/μ
0.1	0.00301	0.1	1697
0.5	0.01963	0.45	469.5
1.0	0.05344	1.1	214.5
2.0	0.1595	1.9	132.1
4.0	0.5089	3.75	71.96
10	2.517	9.5	31.90
20	8.464	17.5	18.70
50	42.69	45	8.452
100	141.2	95	4.603
150	278.1	135	3.786
180	374.3	165	3.349
240	590.7	225	2.846
300	832.0	270	2.592
420	1366	390	2.241
480	1651	450	2.166

Table 11–6, based on data by Lea [1], gives the range and primary ionization per unit path length μ in water for electrons with energies between 0.1 and 480 kev. The calculation of the number of ion-pairs is based on a value of 32.5 ev for the energy required to produce an ion-pair (Section 12–2).

11–5 Recoil rays. The conservation of momentum requires that when a particle of mass m and velocity v is ejected from an atom whose initial mass is M, the residual atom recoils with a velocity $V = mv/(M - m)$. Thus, when a heavy atom emits an α-particle, the recoiling atom has an initial velocity about 2% of that of the α-particle; the kinetic energies are in the same ratio, given by $(M - m)V^2/mv^2$. For example, a Rn atom produced by the emission of a 4.8-Mev α-particle from Ra has a kinetic energy of 86 kev, and a RaG atom from the emission of a 5.3-Mev α-particle from RaF (Po^{210}) 103 kev. The recoil atoms, sometimes known as a-rays, resemble α-particles in having a definite range in a gas, and in causing ionization along this path [37]. At the beginning of the track, the linear ionization density is greater than for α-particles of the same energy, since a heavier particle undergoes a greater energy loss per unit length; beyond about half the range, the ionization falls off rapidly. The range of the a-rays in air is about 0.1 to 0.2 mm, depending on the gas and the initial velocity in a way similar to that already discussed for α-particles.

The ionization produced by recoil atoms suggests that they carry an electric charge. Experiments by Wertenstein [37] on the recoil atoms

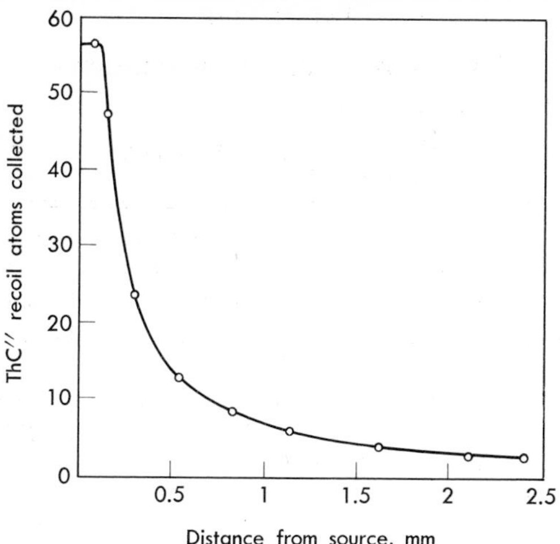

FIG. 11-9. The range of recoil particles.

formed by RaC in a very high vacuum show that these are initially emitted as neutral atoms, and acquire a charge in collisions with residual gas molecules. The ions have a positive charge, so that the recoil atoms can be collected on a negatively charged metal plate placed close to that on which the radioactive source is deposited [38, 39]. This technique has been used to separate pure radioelements from their parent substances. Wertenstein [37], and later Chamié [40], measured the numbers of recoil atoms (RaB or ThC″) collected on a charged or neutral surface as a function of distance from the source. Chamié found that only 8% of the recoiling ThC″ atoms emitted in the α-disintegration of ThC were collected on an uncharged receiver placed less than the recoil range away from the source. With increasing distance, the quantity collected falls off rapidly (Fig. 11-9), and for distances of the order of 1 cm, a strong electric field (800 v/cm) must be applied; in this way, a maximum of 30% of the recoiling atoms can be collected. This behavior is quite different from the diffusion of gaseous molecules, and has led Langevin [41] to suggest that the recoiling atoms are strongly re-absorbed by the emitting source. This theory gives a hyperbolic relationship for the diffusion of recoiling atoms, which has been verified experimentally [40, 42].

Recoil also occurs in β-emission, but because of the very low mass of the electron, it is much less important and much more difficult to investigate. For example, in the case of RaB, whose β-spectrum has a maximum energy of 1.1 Mev, the recoil energy of the RaC atoms is only 0.4 ev. Even this small recoil energy has been utilized in the separation of very short-lived radioactive species for studies of their nuclear properties, although the efficiency of the method is very low.

The important applications of the recoil method in radiochemistry are discussed in Chapter 17; it has been particularly useful in research on fission and the higher transuranium elements (Chapter 8).

TABLE 11–7

HEAT LOSS FROM RADIOELEMENTS

Element	Heat loss, cal/curie·hr	Element	Heat loss, cal/gm·hr
UI	20.9	U → RaG	9.2×10^{-5}
UII	23.0	Th → ThD	2.2×10^{-5}
Io	23.6	K	2.6×10^{-5}
Ra → RaC″	140	Rb	3.6×10^{-5}
Po^{210}	27.4	Sm	3×10^{-4}
U → RaG	262	Pu^{239}	1.64
Pu^{239}	26.5	T	275
T	2.8×10^{-2}		

11–6 Thermal effects. The final result of the degradation of the kinetic energy of the radiation from radioactive substances (and of the recoil atoms) by matter is the release of this energy in the form of heat. This thermal effect was discovered in 1903 by Pierre Curie and Laborde [43], who measured the heat given off by radium in a Bunsen calorimeter. This evolution of thermal energy has played a critical part in the development of theories of nuclear transformation, since it demonstrates quite clearly the enormous amount of energy involved in such changes. For example, 1 gm of Ra in equilibrium with Rn and the short-lived active deposit (RaA + B + C) evolves about 136 cal/hr, of which 89.9% arises from α-particles and recoil atoms, 3.5% from β-particles, and 6.6% from γ-rays [25]. The total overall transformation of 1 gm·atom of Ra to (inactive) Pb releases 7.7×10^8 cal, which is about 4×10^6 times the amount of heat involved in the most energetic chemical reactions.

The amount of heat released per hour from a number of radioactive materials is shown in Table 11–7.

The radioactive elements play an essential part in the thermal condition of the earth. Quantitative discussions of this question are difficult (and often contradictory) because of the lack of definite information on the relative abundances of the radioelements in the very deep terrestrial layers, and on the thermal conductivity of the various layers. The values shown in Table 11–8 are from calculations by Dauvillier [45], based on measurements on rocks and meteorites; we saw earlier (Section 10–2) that the elementary composition of iron meteorites is believed to be similar to that at the center of the earth. The second column of Table 11–8 gives the estimated quantity of radioelements (expressed as grams of Ra) in these layers. The third column gives the energy release (in 10^{12} cal·sec^{-1}). The loss of the heat by conduction through the surface of the globe (including oceanic and other waters) is evaluated by Dauvillier as 24×10^{12} cal·sec^{-1}; the energy remaining is attributed by this author to various volcanic processes.

TABLE 11–8

Layer	Radio-elements,* 10^{13} gm Ra	Energy release, 10^{12} cal·sec^{-1}
Sial (Si-Al)	175.8	65.1
Sima (Si-Mg)	80.0	29.6
Core	20.3	7.5
Total	276.1	102.2

* Estimated.

It seems certain that radioactive elements played a most important part in distant geological times, when they were present in considerably greater quantities. A number of authors agree that at a certain point sufficient heat was deposited by radioactive processes to melt the whole terrestrial mass. The importance of potassium in geothermal conditions was noted earlier in Section 7–3. Kapustinsky [46] has estimated that comparatively small quantities of radioelements would be sufficient to maintain the center of the earth at a temperature of the order of 2000 to 2500°C. This author suggests that because of the enormous pressure (evaluated at 1.5 to 3×10^6 atm) in the central zone, of about 2500 km radius, matter behaves as it does in the region of absolute zero; the entropy tends to zero, the electrical and thermal conductivities are very high, and the specific heat is very low. Electrons which are normally in high-energy orbits are considerably compressed, and are forced into lower quantum number orbits, constituting a sort of plasma which moves uniformly around the different atomic nuclei, so that the elements lose their chemical individuality and are in a homogeneous metallic state.

11–7 Electromagnetic radiation. The electromagnetic radiations extend over an extremely wide energy region, from the Hertzian waves to γ-radiation with energies up to a few Bev from very powerful accelerating machines. The interactions of these radiations with matter depends on their energy, and may involve merely a perturbation of the orientations of the constituents of a crystal, or of the rotational and vibrational levels of a molecule, or the excitation or ionization of molecules, or finally the production of photonuclear reactions, which may include fission, spallation, or meson production. The ultraviolet region, which corresponds to molecular dissociation energies, is separated from soft x-rays by the Holweck-Schumann region (wavelength from a few tenths to ten angstrom units), which is extremely difficult to study experimentally. The ionizing electromagnetic radiations are therefore usually regarded as including x-rays (from about 5 kev) and γ-rays, although ultraviolet radiation with a wavelength of a few thousand angstroms has sufficient energy to ionize several molecules, including water.

Leaving aside *coherent* scattering by crystals, governed by the Bragg equation, and nuclear reactions, three principal interactions of x- and γ-rays with matter can be distinguished: the photoelectric effect, the Compton effect, and pair production (to form an electron plus a positron). The total absorption coefficient of the radiation is therefore the sum of these three partial coefficients,

$$\mu = \mu_{\mathrm{PE}} + \mu_{\mathrm{CE}} + \mu_{\mathrm{PP}}, \tag{11–24}$$

where μ is a proportionality coefficient for the *attenuation*, or decrease in the intensity of the radiation ΔI caused by passing through a small thickness Δx

$$\Delta I = \mu I \, \Delta x. \tag{11–25}$$

For homogeneous radiation, μ is constant, so that integration of Eq. (11–25) gives

$$I = I_0 e^{-\mu x}. \tag{11–26}$$

Thus the γ-rays from Co^{60} are attenuated by 6% on passing through 1 cm of water, by 12% after 2 cm, and by 23% after 4 cm. The thicknesses required to absorb 90% of this γ-radiation (in gm/cm^2) are H_2O, 43.2; Al or Fe, 51.7; Pb, 46.5; and U, 38.0.

The thickness x can be expressed in centimeters, as in Eq. (11–12), and μ is then a *linear* coefficient; if x is in grams per square centimeter, we have the *mass* coefficient μ/ρ, where ρ is the density; x in atoms per square centimeter gives the *atomic* absorption coefficient σ_a, and finally x in electrons per square centimeter gives the electronic coefficient σ_e,

$$\frac{\mu}{\rho} = \sigma_a \frac{N}{A} = \sigma_a n = \sigma_e \frac{NZ}{A}, \tag{11–27}$$

where N is Avagadro's number, A is the atomic weight of the absorber, and n is the number of atoms per gram. Equations similar to Eq. (11–27) can be written for the partial coefficients μ_{PE}, μ_{CE}, and μ_{PP}.

When a photon with an energy $h\nu$ strikes an atom, it may remove an electron, which will have a kinetic energy given by

$$E = h\nu - I, \tag{11–28}$$

where I is the ionization potential of the quantum level from which the electron has been removed. The photon itself disappears during this process. The absorption coefficient μ_{PE} for this *photoelectric effect* is the principal component of the total absorption coefficient at energies below 50 kev for light elements such as aluminum, and below 500 kev for lead. In fact, μ_{PE} increases rapidly with the atomic number Z; an empirical equation derived by Lea [1], valid for wavelengths (λ) lower than those of the characteristic radiation of the absorbent, states that

$$\mu_{\mathrm{PE}} = 0.0089\rho \frac{Z^{4.1}}{A} \lambda^n. \tag{11–29}$$

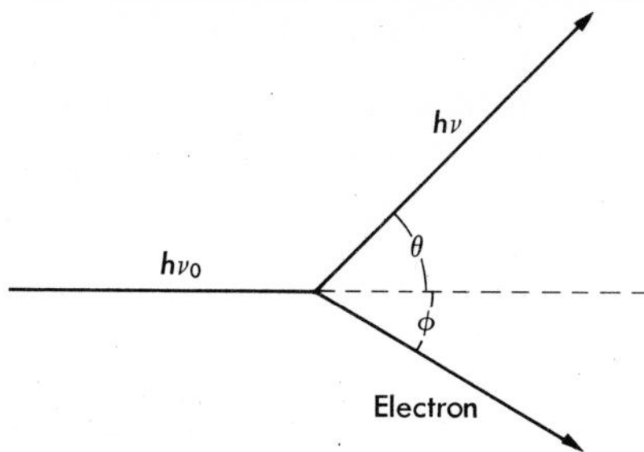

FIG. 11–10. The Compton effect.

With λ in angstroms, $n = 3.05$ for N, C, and O, and 2.85 for the elements between Na and Fe. Alternative values of 4.5 or 4.6 have been suggested for the exponent of Z.

The coefficient μ_{PE} is the sum of the coefficients μ_K, μ_L, . . . , which represent the contribution made by the various electron levels K, L, . . . , to the total absorption, provided that the frequency of the incident radiation is sufficient to ionize the shell in question. For wavelengths lower than those of the K-shell, theory gives the approximate relation

$$\mu_{\text{PE}} = 48.5\lambda^{3.5}Z^5, \tag{11–30}$$

which is not very different from the empirical Eq. (11–29). The contribution from the L-shell is about one-fifth of that from the K-shell for heavy elements, and about one-eighth for the light elements; the contributions of the M- and N-shells are about one-quarter of that of the L-shell.

The *Compton effect* begins to occur when the energy of the photon exceeds about 10 kev. This process is an elastic collision between the photon and an electron which is only weakly bound to an atom. If the binding energy of this electron can be neglected, the process is similar to a collision between two particles with conservation of energy and momentum. At low energies, when the wavelength of the photon is comparable to the size of an atom, the scattering is coherent and the photon passes on with its initial energy. When the energy $h\nu_0$ is greater than the binding energy of the electrons in the atom, the photon changes direction by an angle θ, giving a secondary photon of energy $h\nu$; the electron moves off at an angle ϕ with a kinetic energy E_e (Fig. 11–10). The wavelength λ of the scattered quantum is related to that of the incident quantum λ_0 by the Compton-Debye equation

$$\lambda - \lambda_0 = \frac{h}{mc}(1 - \cos\theta) = 24.17(1 - \cos\theta)10^{-11}\text{ cm.} \tag{11–31}$$

The constant $h/mc = 24.17$ X-units (1X = 0.001 A) is known as the *Compton wavelength.*

The electron scattering coefficient σ_{CE}, which expresses the ratio of the average energy emitted to the energy received, is given by the Klein

TABLE 11–9

THE PROPORTIONS AND ENERGIES OF PHOTOELECTRONS AND COMPTON ELECTRONS IN WATER

Photon energy, kev	Photoelectrons		Recoil electrons	
	Proportion, %	Energy, kev	Proportion, %	Average energy, kev
5.108	99.4	5.11	0.6	0.05
10.217	95.5	10.22	4.5	0.19
20.433	72.5	20.43	27.5	0.75
51.083	15.1	51.08	84.9	4.20
107.27	21	107.127	97.9	15.56
153.25	0.8	153.25	99.2	28.22
199.22	0.4	199.22	99.6	43.04
306.50	0.1	306.50	99.9	83.55
510.83	0.1	510.83	99.9	175.95
715.16	0.0	715.16	100	280.67
1021.66	0.0	1021.66	100	452.56

and Nishina equation [47]

$$\sigma_{\mathrm{CE}} = \frac{2\pi e^4}{m^2c^4}\left\{\frac{1+\omega}{\omega^2}\left[\frac{2(1+\omega)}{1+2\omega} - \frac{1}{\omega}\log_e(1+2\omega)\right] + \frac{1}{2\omega}\log_e(1+2\omega) - \frac{1+3\omega}{(1+2\omega)^2}\right\}\mathrm{cm}^2, \qquad (11\text{–}32)$$

where $\omega = h\nu_0/mc^2 = h\nu_0/0.51$ Mev. When ω tends towards zero (that is, λ very large), this reduces to the classical Thompson relation

$$\sigma_{\mathrm{CE}} = \frac{8\pi}{3}\cdot\frac{e^4}{m^2c^4} = 6.62\times 10^{-25}\ \mathrm{cm}^2, \qquad (11\text{–}33)$$

so that the cross section is independent of ν_0; or in other words, the scattered radiation has the same frequency as the incident radiation (i.e., at such energies there is no Compton effect). On the other hand, if $h\nu_0$ is very much larger than the energy of the electron (mc^2), we have

$$\sigma_{\mathrm{CE}} = \frac{\pi e^4}{m^2c^4}\left(\frac{1}{2\omega} + \frac{1}{\omega}\log_e 2\omega\right)\cdot \qquad (11\text{–}34)$$

The scattering coefficient is therefore almost inversely proportional to ν.

The energy E_e of the Compton electron varies continuously with the angle from zero to a maximum value obtained when the electron recoils

Table 11–10

Mass Absorption Coefficients,* cm^2/gm

$h\nu$, Mev	Water	Al	Fe	Pb
0.1	0.171	0.169	0.370	5.46
0.2	0.137	0.122	0.146	0.942
0.3	0.119	0.104	0.110	0.378
0.5	0.0967	0.0844	0.0840	0.152
1.0	0.0706	0.0614	0.0598	0.0703
2.0	0.0493	0.0431	0.0422	0.0456
3.0	0.0396	0.0353	0.0359	0.0413
5.0	0.0302	0.0284	0.0314	0.0430
8.0	0.0242	0.0243	0.0298	0.0471
10.0	0.0221	0.0232	0.0300	0.0503

* From U. Fano, *Nucleonics*, **11,** No. 8, 8 (1953). The review by C. M. Davisson and R. D. Evans, *Revs. Modern Phys.*, **24,** 79 (1952), gives values for the total, photoelectric, Compton, and pair production absorption coefficients for 24 elements with Z between 1 and 85, and for γ-energies between 0.1 and 8 Mev.

in the direction of the emission of the photon $h\nu_0$ ($\theta = 180°$, $\phi = 0$ in Fig. 11–10); this means that

$$E_{\max} = h\nu_0 - \frac{mc^2}{2} = h\nu_0 - 0.25 \text{ Mev}. \tag{11–35}$$

The maximum angle of scattering ϕ of the recoil electrons is 90°, and such an electron therefore has zero energy.

The energy loss suffered by a beam of photons due to the Compton effect is therefore made up of two parts: the energy acquired by the electron σ_a and that which is scattered σ_s. For $h\nu = 1.6$ Mev, $\sigma_a = \sigma_s$; for greater energies $\sigma_a > \sigma_s$, and vice versa for lower energies.

Since σ_{CE} is independent of Z and since the Z/A ratio changes only slowly with Z, Eq. (11–27) suggests that the mass and electron scattering coefficients for the Compton effect depend very little on the nature of the absorber.

Table 11–9 contains values taken from Lea [1] for the proportions and energies of the Compton electrons and photoelectrons for photons with energies between 5 kev and 1.02 Mev. Table 11–10 gives the total mass absorption coefficients for photons with energies between 0.1 and 10 Mev in water and in aluminum, iron, and lead [31]. It will be seen that in the middle energy region, where the Compton effect predominates, the coefficients are not very different for these four different absorbers. The dependence on Z is, however, very marked at low energies, where the absorption is essentially due to the photoelectric effect. Finally, the influence of atomic number shows up again at high energies, where *pair production*

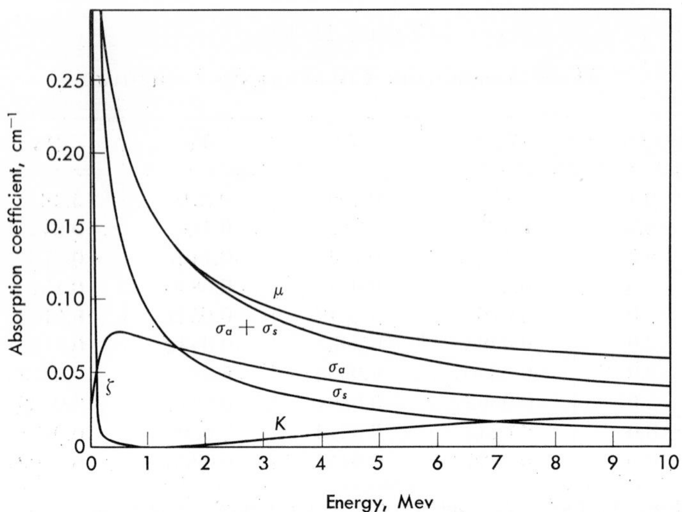

FIG. 11–11. The absorption of γ-rays in aluminum; μ, total absorption coefficient; σ_a, Compton absorption coefficient for electrons; σ_s, Compton scattering; K, pair production coefficient; ζ, photoelectric effect coefficient.

occurs. This latter process, already discussed in Chapter 2, requires a minimum photon energy of 1.02 Mev, since this value is equivalent to $2m_0c^2$. Theory predicts that the extent of this process first increases rapidly with the difference $(E - 2m_0c^2)$, and then varies linearly with $\log E$ (up to $E = 137m_0c^2$, beyond which the theory is no longer valid). Energy dissipation by this process in lead is equal to that by the Compton effect at $E = 4.7$ Mev. At a given energy, its importance increases with atomic number, and is proportional to Z^2.

The change of the total absorption coefficient and the partial coefficients with energy up to 10 Mev in aluminum, and up to 13 Mev in lead, are shown in Figs. 11–11 and 11–12. It will be seen that in the latter case there are two very different energies at which the coefficient μ has the same value, above $\mu = 0.45 \text{ cm}^{-1}$.

To express the overall photon absorption in a compound containing different atoms with atomic numbers Z_1, Z_2, etc., the concept of *effective atomic number* is used. For energies below 1.02 Mev, the mass absorption coefficient can be written

$$\frac{\mu}{\rho} = n_0 \left[\frac{\mu}{\rho_{\text{CE}}} + k(a_1 Z_1^m + a_2 Z_2^m + \cdots)\lambda^n\right], \tag{11–36}$$

where n_0 is the total number of electrons per gram and a_1, a_2, etc. are the electron fractions for each atomic species [Eq. (11–29)]. The effective atomic number $\overline{Z}$ is therefore defined by replacing Eq. (11–36) by the relation

$$\frac{\mu}{\rho} = n_0 \left(\frac{\mu}{\rho_{\text{CE}}} + k\overline{Z}^m\lambda^n\right) \cdot \tag{11–37}$$

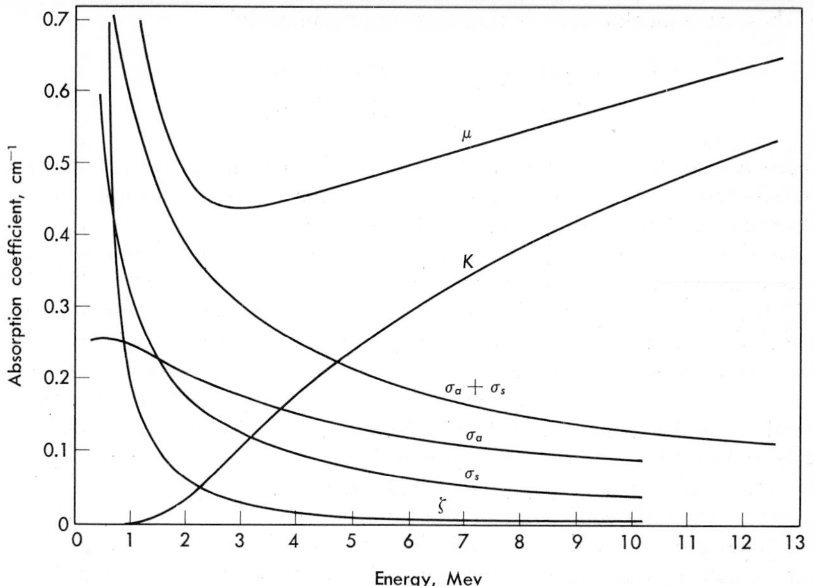

FIG. 11–12. The absorption γ-rays in lead. (Same notation as in Fig. 11–11.)

Irrespective of the mode of absorption of high-energy photons (photoelectric, Compton, or pair production), the main result is the release of electrons. The discussion in Section 11–4 on the energy loss and ionization by electrons is, of course, also applicable to these secondary electrons.

11–8 Secondary radiations. Excitation and ionization are not the only processes by which fast electrons dissipate their energy in an absorbing medium. With increasing electron energy, an entirely different process, involving the emission of electromagnetic radiation in the coulombic field of the nuclei of the absorber, becomes increasingly important. This "slowing-down radiation," or *bremsstrahlung*, is favored by the small mass of the electron; as this is accelerated in the nuclear field, classical electromagnetic theory requires that it emit radiative energy, of the same type as the radiation of the continuous spectrum of ordinary x-rays. A quantum treatment of this phenomena was given by Heitler [48], who established the following equation for the energy loss in this process:

$$-\left(\frac{dE}{dx}\right)_{\text{rad}} = \frac{4ne^2Z^2}{137m^2c^4}(E + mc^2)\left[\log_e \frac{2(E + mc^2)}{mc^2} - \frac{1}{3}\right]. \quad (11\text{–}38)$$

Whereas the stopping power by collision with electrons is proportional to the atomic number of the absorber [Eq. (11–2)], the radiative loss depends on Z^2, and on the energy of the electron. The ratio of the energy losses by these two mechanisms is therefore approximately

$$\frac{(dE/dx)_{\text{rad}}}{(dE/dx)_{\text{ion}}} = \frac{kZ^2E}{Z} = \frac{ZE}{800}, \tag{11–39}$$

where E is in Mev. For lead ($Z = 82$) each mechanism makes an equal contribution at $E = 6.9$ Mev, and at $E = 47$ Mev for aluminum. Bremsstrahlung radiation can be neglected completely below 1 Mev.

Another way in which fast charged particles moving through a condensed medium lose their energy via radiation is the *Cerenkov* effect [49, 50]. When such a particle has a uniform velocity v greater than the speed of light in the medium concerned (c/r, where r is the refractive index), the electromagnetic field tends to decrease the momentum by the emission of low-energy radiation. This effect has been observed with liquids as different as water, benzene, acetone, glycerine, and sulfuric acid. The partially polarized light emitted is generally in the blue-violet region of the spectrum. With a strong source of high-energy β-particles being absorbed in water, the pale blue color of the radiation is visible to the naked eye. It is localized into a cone around the direction of the incident radiation, and its intensity is inversely proportional to the density of the medium. The angle θ of the cone is given by the relation $\cos\theta = c/rv$; for water $\theta = 30°$.

The theory of this effect was established by Frank and Tamm [51, 52], and further developed by Fermi [11], Beck [53], and A. Bohr [12], who took into consideration the effect of the polarization of the medium. Frank and Tamm calculated the loss of energy due to the Cerenkov effect, and showed that the number of photons with a frequency between ν and $\nu + d\nu$ per unit path length of a particle of charge e is given by

$$n(\nu)\,d\nu = 4\pi^2 \frac{e^2}{hc^2}\left(1 - \frac{1}{r^2\beta^2}\right) d\nu, \tag{11–40}$$

where $\beta = v/c$. With $\beta = 0.75$ (that is, 0.5-Mev electrons) and $r = 1.33$, the refractive index of water, 10 photons with λ between 4000 and 6000 A are produced per millimeter.

Absorption of a γ-quantum by the photoelectric effect also produces secondary radiation. When the photon removes an electron from the K-shell, the energy made available by the formation of the "hole" can be used up in two ways. The first of these involves the passage of a L- or M-electron into the K-shell, with the emission of a quantum of *fluorescent radiation* characteristic of the K- or L-shell. The second process is the removal of an electron from the level immediately above, with the formation of a new hole, which in its turn is filled by an electron from an outer shell. These two effects then involve either the emission of a quantum, or the loss of a further electron. The atom is therefore ionized twice (or even more). This is the so-called *Auger effect*, the probability of which increases with decreasing atomic number.

The Auger effect can occur each time an electron is removed from a deep electron level, irrespective of the cause of this removal. Thus Platzman [15] has estimated that 4% of the energy dissipated in water by a 3-Mev proton is used in ionizing the K-shell of oxygen, and this proportion increases with the energy of the ionizing particle. This process takes place in a time of the order of 10^{-15} sec, and is accompanied by a considerable transfer of energy; for example, the ionization potential of the K-shell in oxygen is 540 ev, and in a carbon atom 284 ev. If the atom ionized is part of some polyatomic molecule, the greater part of the energy will be dissipated inside this molecule and will cause tremendous dissociations and ionizations, over and above that expected from the average energy consumed in ion-pair formation. These processes do not occur with the Compton effect, which involves only those electrons in the outer shells of the atom.

11–9 The measurement of radiation and dosimetry. The energy dissipated by x- or γ-rays is generally expressed in terms of the ionization produced by means of secondary electrons, or by the *quantity of radiation* (the *dose*). In radiology, this is normally measured in *roentgen* units (r). The definition adopted by the International Commission on Radiological Units and Measurements in 1957 states that the *roentgen* is a *dose of exposure* to x- or γ-radiation such that the associated corpuscle emission produces ions of either sign, carrying a total quantity of electricity equal to 1 esu, in 0.001293 gm of dry air. The weight of air in this definition is that of 1 cm^3 at 0°C and 760 mm Hg pressure. One roentgen corresponds to the production of 1.61×10^{12} ion-pairs per gram of air, or to the absorption of 83.7 ergs in one gram of air (see below for the "rep").

This definition of the roentgen is not, however, completely unambiguous, and has given rise to some confusion; for instance, in some cases the roentgen is taken as the unit of ionization, or a unit of energy absorbed. The dose should be quite clearly distinguished from the *dose absorbed* and the *intensity* of the dose. The dose is the quantity of radiation propagated in air at a given point, and is independent of the system which is to be irradiated; the dose absorbed is by definition the quantity of energy absorbed per unit mass of a given substance, and therefore depends on the absorbing properties of the latter. The *integrated dose* is the dose multiplied by the total mass irradiated.

The roentgen is not a unit which can be converted directly into other units of energy, such as the erg, the electron volt, or the calorie. It is measured by the ionization produced in air *at a given point*, and the quantity of energy E absorbed per unit mass of another substance can be derived from this by means of the relation derived by Gray [54],

$$E = jWs,$$

where j is the number of ion-pairs per gram of air, W is the average energy required to produce an ion-pair in air, and s is the relative stopping power. For a given number of roentgens, the energy absorbed per gram differs considerably from one substance to another, depending upon the effective atomic number and on the density. In addition, it varies with the wavelength of the radiation because of the complex wavelength dependence of

TABLE 11–11

THE NUMBER OF ERGS/GM DISSIPATED PER ROENTGEN

Tissue	Photon wavelength, A				
	1.0	0.6	0.3	0.1	0.015
Muscle	87.0	87.1	88.0	93.8	94.7
Fat	42.1	42.6	48.0	83.6	89.2
Bone	883	828	797	245	157

the various absorption coefficients; for the photoelectric coefficient, there is also a change with the atomic number. Table 11–11, containing values calculated by Spiers [55], illustrates this very neatly.

Under standard geometrical conditions, however, the radiation dose (in r) from an x-ray generator or from a given radioactive source is characteristic of the source itself. In the case of radioactive substances, the dose is proportional to the quantity of radioelement present, and to the exposure time. Furthermore, for a quasi point source, the dose at a given point is inversely proportional to the square of the distance from the source to this point, so that for any radioelement one can define the dose in roentgens (for example) per hour 1 cm from a 1-mc source.

From a practical point of view, the use of roentgens in radiology probably has a number of advantages, but in experimental work on the physical and chemical effects of radiations, it is much more rational to use an energy unit like the erg or the electron volt. This latter unit is particularly useful, since the *G unit* is used in radiation chemistry to express the yield as the *number of molecules* (or equivalents) *transformed per 100 ev* (Chapter 12). These units also have the advantage that the effects caused by different ionizing radiations, such as γ's, α's, protons, etc., can be compared directly.

Radiologists tend to use units derived from the roentgen for this purpose, especially the *roentgen equivalent physical* (rep), which has been defined as the "quantity of radiation which produces a dissipation of energy equal to 93.1 ergs/gm." This corresponds to the energy dissipated in 1 gm of water exposed to a quantity of radiation equal to 1 r (assuming that 32.5 ev are required to produce an ion-pair in air); using the more recent value of 34 ev (Section 12–2), the numerical value in this equation becomes 97.4 ergs/gm. More recently the International Commission on Radiological Units [56] has recommended the use of the *rad*, which corresponds to the absorption of 100 ergs/gm. This is an energy density, which, unlike the roentgen, is independent of the absorbing material and of the type of radiation involved.

Experimentally, the dosimetry of electromagnetic radiation [57, 58] involves the use of ionization chambers, of which there are two principal types. In the "wall-less" airfilled chamber, all the secondary radiation is absorbed before reaching the walls, either because it is sufficiently soft or because the air is under pressure. In this way, the ionization current can be measured absolutely, but this technique requires the complete collection of all the ions, and the uniformity of the electrical field is very critical.* For this reason, more frequent use is made in medical dosimetry of the "cavity chamber" or the "air-wall" chamber (the Victoreen), which has been carefully studied and developed by Gray. The chemical composition of the walls are such that its mass stopping power is equivalent to that of air; this is achieved by the use of appropriate conducting plastics, containing a small proportion of some heavy element. The ionization produced per unit mass of air is therefore exactly the same as that produced by the same flux of x- or γ-rays in a "wall-less" chamber. Ionization chambers of this type must be standardized at several different wavelengths using standard "wall-less" chambers.

The intensity of corpuscular radiation (that is, α- or β-particles) is determined either by measuring the ionization produced, or by collecting the total charge carried, or by calorimetry. For an α-emitter such as Po or Rn, or a very soft β-emitter such as tritium or C^{14}, uniformly dissolved in a liquid which completely absorbs the radiation (i.e., an internal source) the intensity of the dose absorbed is proportional to the concentration of the radioelement at that instant; the intensity is equal to the number of particles emitted in unit time, multiplied by the energy of each particle, and divided by the mass of the liquid. To get the dose absorbed for radon, or any other short-lived nuclide, it is necessary to allow for radioactive decay; the average dose absorbed is proportional to the number of millicuries decayed during the irradiation period. For times of the order of a few hours, the correction for the decay of polonium is negligible; it is about 0.5% per day for the first 5 to 10 days after a measurement of intensity. Chemical methods of dosimetry are discussed in Section 13-8.

Table 11-12 gives the conversion factors between the various units of dose absorbed. In the case of radon it was necessary to allow for the α-particles from the short-lived daughter products (RaA + C + C′) but the energy loss via β-particles and γ-rays has been neglected [59].

With electromagnetic radiation, roentgens are easily converted into other units, when the Compton effect predominates and the absorbent has a stopping power similar to that of water, so that 1 r can be assumed to be equivalent to 93.1 ergs/gm (or 97.4 on the more recent value).

Occasionally, and especially in older publications, the energy is expressed as a number of ion-pairs produced. The ionization is generally assumed to be in air, and all that is needed to obtain the energy in ev is to multiply the numbers given by 32.5 for x- and γ-rays, and by 35 for α-particles.

11-10 Neutrons. Table 11-13 lists the characteristics of some of the most important neutron sources. It will be seen that neutrons emitted in γ-induced nuclear reactions are monoenergetic, and that in other cases

---

* See Rogozinski, *J. Radiolog. Elektrol.*, **19,** 639 (1935), who has constructed an ionization chamber for soft x-rays, and Singer, *Am. J. Roentgen.*, **44,** 428 (1940), who used a chamber filled with air at 10-atm pressure.

TABLE 11–12

EQUIVALENT ENERGY UNITS

	erg	ev	calorie, 15°C	kw·hr	mc Po^{210}/hr	μc Rn^{222} decayed
1 erg =	1	6.242×10^{11}	2.389×10^{-8}	2.778×10^{-14}	8.954×10^{-7}	1.856×10^{-6}
1 ev =	1.602×10^{-12}	1	3.828×10^{-20}	4.45×10^{-26}	1.424×10^{-18}	2.959×10^{-18}
1 cal =	4.186×10^{7}	2.612×10^{19}	1	1.163×10^{-6}	37.48	77.77
1 kw·hr =	8.6×10^{13}	2.247×10^{25}	8.60×10^{5}	1	3.223×10^{7}	6.688×10^{7}
1 mc Po^{210}/hr =	1.1168×10^{6}	7.022×10^{17}	2.668×10^{-2}	3.102×10^{-8}	1	2.075
1 mc Rn^{222} decayed =	5.382×10^{5}	3.384×10^{17}	1.286×10^{-2}	1.495×10^{-8}	0.4819	1

TABLE 11–13

NEUTRON SOURCES

Source	Nuclear process	Half-life	Neutron energy, Mev	Yield, 10^4 n/curie·sec
Be + Ra (α)	Be^9 (α, n) C^{12}	1620 yr	max. intensity at 4 Mev	1700
Be + Rn (α)	Be^9 (α, n) C^{12}	3.825 d	—	1500
Be + Ra (γ)	Be^9 (γ, n) 2α	1620 yr	—	—
Be + Po (α)	Be^9 (α, n) C^{12}	138 d	max. intensity at 3.5 Mev	300*
B + Ra (α)	B^{10} (α, n) C^{13} B^{11} (α, n) C^{14}	1620 yr	max. intensity at 3 Mev	680
D_2O + Ra (γ)	D^2 (γ, n) H	1620 yr	0.12	0.1
D_2O + D	D^2 (d, n) He^3	—	minimum 2.45	10^8–10^{10} n/sec
Li + D	Li^7 (d, n) 2α	—	minimum 13.3	10^8–10^{10} n/sec
Li + H	Li^7 (p, n) Be^7	—	minimum 0.029	10^8–10^{10} n/sec
Be + Sb^{124}	Be^9 (γ, n) 2α	60 d	0.024	100
Be + Na^{24}	Be^9 (γ, n) 2α	14.8 hr	0.83	13
D_2O + Na^{24}	D (γ, n) H	14.8 hr	0.22	27
Be + La^{140}	Be (γ, n) 2α	40 d	0.62	0.8
U + n	fission (reactors)	—	complex	10^{10}–10^{14} n/cm^2·sec

* The neutron yields from γ-reactions refer to 1 gm of Be or D_2O placed 1 cm from the γ-ray source. Most of the values in the last two columns are taken from Feld, Ref. 60.

there is an energy spectrum, of differing complexity. Fast neutrons quickly lose their energy by elastic and inelastic collisions before being captured by a nucleus or undergoing spontaneous disintegration. Since they have no electric charge, they do not ionize directly, but by means of the charged particles liberated either in these collisions or in nuclear reactions. For example, a vessel filled with the gas BF_3 functions as an ionization chamber when neutrons pass through it due to the reaction B^{11} (n, α) Li^7. Equally, a fast neutron moving through a hydrogenous substance collides with protons, which consequently acquire a velocity determined by the laws of conservation of energy and of momentum.

Neutrons can be detected by means of these secondary particles, and this can be used to measure the neutron intensity. In addition to the BF_3 chamber, another method used depends on the activation of metallic foils, or of thin layers of some appropriate compound, which become radioactive on neutron capture. Gold, indium, manganese, silver, and dysprosium are most frequently employed for this purpose. The slow neutron fission of uranium, and the fast neutron fission of thorium, are also used. In all these cases, the radioactivity produced is measured by one of the usual methods (ionization chamber, proportional counter, Geiger counter, scintillation counter, etc.). Finally, a measuring device containing some hydrogenous substance (either a gas in an ionization chamber or counter, or a liquid or solid in some scintillation counting device) can be used as a neutron counter by measuring the recoil protons produced.

In Section 6–6, we saw that a knowledge of the laws which govern the slowing down of neutrons, and of their spatial distribution after passing through different materials, is most important in the design and operation of a reactor. Long before the discovery of fission, however, Fermi and his collaborators (Amaldi, D'Agostino, Pontecorvo, Rasetti, and Segrè [61, 62]) had used a variety of experimental techniques to study the capture and scattering of neutrons, especially in hydrogenous materials. From this they worked out the essential laws, which were finally extended and developed in a more exact manner by several other authors (Dunning, Pegram, etc., in the United States; Halban and Preiswerk in France; Kurtchatov, Bjerge, Goldhaber; theoretical work by Bethe, Wigner, Placzeck, Langevin, etc.).

The first experiments by Fermi and his co-workers on the production of artificially active radioelements by neutrons which had previously passed through a layer of paraffin or water gave evidence of the *thermalization* of neutrons, i.e., the lowering of their energy by successive collisions to an average value corresponding to that of a gas at room temperature. This energy $\overline{E}$ is equal to $\frac{1}{2}mv^2 = 3kT$, where k is the Boltzmann constant (8.6×10^{-5} ev). At 290°K, E is about 0.04 ev, but the value usually taken for thermal neutrons is the energy corresponding to the most probable velocity, $E = kT = 0.025$ ev, $v = 2200$ m/sec.

The direct proof of the thermalization was given by Moon and Tillman [63, 64], who measured the effect of temperature on the capture. The Maxwell distribution of thermal neutron velocities (with a tailing off toward high energies, where the distribution is inversely proportional to $E^{3/2}$) was established by Dunning, *et al.* [65], who measured the velocities of the thermal neutrons directly, using a mechanical velocity selector consisting of a wheel with alternating discs of aluminum and cadmium (to absorb the thermal neutrons) rotating at a known rate. The velocity of the neutrons is determined by the ratio l/t, where l is the distance between the source and the detector, and t, the *time of flight*, is the time interval during which neutrons can pass through to the detector. Another procedure currently employed for measuring the velocity of neutrons from an accelerator consists in modulating the accelerating potential (say for deuterons in the Be + D reaction), so that the deuterons strike the beryllium target periodically for a very short period, of the order of a few microseconds or milliseconds. After passing through a layer of paraffin, the slowed neutrons reach a BF_3 ionization chamber, placed a distance l away. By means of a suitable electronic apparatus, a counter connected to the chamber gives the time of flight t, from the delay with respect to the emission.

Monoenergetic beams of slow neutrons (0.01 to 1 ev) can be obtained, and their velocities measured by the methods of crystal spectrometry. In this energy region, the de Broglie wavelength λ is of the same order as the interplanar distances, so that neutrons are reflected by crystals with intensity maxima given by the Bragg law for the diffraction of x-rays

$$n\lambda = 2d \sin \theta, \tag{11–41}$$

where n is a whole number, d is the distance between the crystal planes, and θ is the incident angle between the neutron beam and these planes; $\lambda = h/Mv = h(2ME)^{-1/2} = 0.286E^{-1/2}$, where M is the mass of the neutron and E its energy in ev. For energies between 0.01 and 0 ev, λ varies between 2.86 and 0.286 A; for $E = kT$ at 25°, $\lambda = 1.8$ A. The velocity of the neutrons is given by

$$v = \frac{nh}{2Md \sin \theta}. \tag{11–42}$$

Hydrogenous substances are preferred for slowing neutrons, since the energy transfer to the struck atom increases with decreasing atomic mass A. It can be shown that for a neutron with an energy E_0 before the collision and E after it, the average parameter,

$$\xi = \overline{\log_e E_0/E}, \tag{11–43}$$

is given by

$$\xi = 1 - \frac{(A-1)^2}{2A} \log_e \frac{A+1}{A-1}. \tag{11–44}$$

Equations (11–43) and (11–44) show that for hydrogen, $\log_e E/E_0 = 1$, so that on the average, each collision with a hydrogen atom reduces the energy to $E_0/e = E_0/2.72 = 37\%\ E_0$. For a heavy atom (that is, $A > 6$),

$$\xi = \frac{2}{A + \frac{2}{3}} \approx \frac{2}{A}. \tag{11–45}$$

TABLE 11–14

THE SLOWING DOWN OF NEUTRONS

A	$\overline{\Delta E}$, kev	ξ	n
H^1	1000	1	18
D^2	888	0.72	24
He^4	640	0.43	41
Be	360	0.207	50
C	284	0.16	111
O	222	0.12	145
Al	137	0.072	240
Fe	69	0.035	552
U	16.7	0.0084	2100

For isotropic scattering, the average energy transferred to the struck atom is

$$\overline{\Delta E} = E_0 \frac{2A}{(A+1)^2}, \tag{11–46}$$

and the maximum energy which a neutron can lose in a collision (i.e., in direct frontal collision) is given by the ratio

$$\frac{E}{E_0} = \left(\frac{A-1}{A+1}\right)^2. \tag{11–47}$$

The number of collisions necessary to reduce the energy of a neutron from E_0 to E is

$$n = \frac{1}{\xi} \log_e \frac{E_0}{E}. \tag{11–48}$$

Table 11–14 gives values of ξ, $\overline{\Delta E}$, and n for $E_0 = 2$ Mev, and for $E = kT$ (see also Table 15–1).

For a Maxwellian distribution of velocities, the neutron density can be calculated from the Boltzmann equation used in the kinetic theory of gases. This treatment is based on the conservation principle; that is to say, in the stationary state an equal number of neutrons arrive and disappear by diffusion and capture in a given elementary volume. We shall consider here only certain important points related to problems of thermal diffusion (especially in a hydrogenous medium) and the relations between them; typical values will be given for a number of cases [66, 67].

As in the kinetic theory of gases, the diffusion coefficient D is related to the *mean free path* of the neutron, the distance between two successive collisions, and to its velocity v, by the relation $D = \lambda v/3$. For neutrons, however, three quite separate mean free paths must be considered: that for scattering λ_d, for capture λ_c, and for transport λ_t. These are the reciprocals

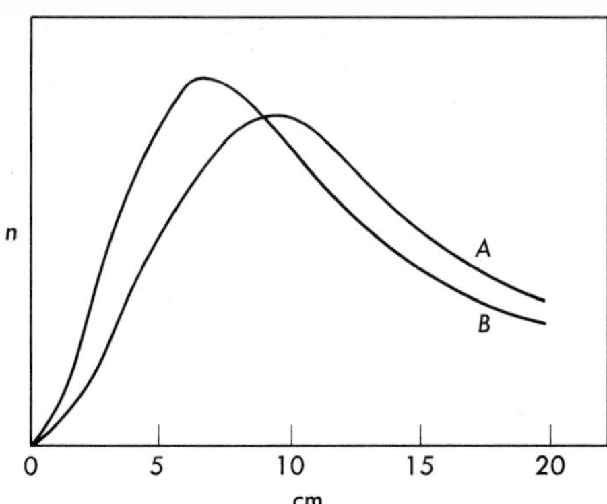

FIG. 11–13. Neutron densities in water as a function of distance from the source; A, thermal neutrons, B, 1-ev neutrons.

of the respective macroscopic cross sections multiplied by n, the number of atoms of the material per cubic centimeter,

$$\lambda_{\rm d} = \frac{1}{n\sigma_{\rm d}}, \qquad \lambda_{\rm c} = \frac{1}{n\sigma_{\rm c}}, \qquad \lambda_{\rm t} = \frac{1}{n\sigma_{\rm t}}.$$

The mean free path for transport $\lambda_{\rm t}$ is related to $\lambda_{\rm d}$ by the relation

$$\lambda_{\rm t} = \frac{\lambda_{\rm d}}{1 - \overline{\cos\theta}}, \tag{11–49}$$

where $\overline{\cos\theta}$ is the mean cosine of the scattering angle; this is a measure of the average distance which the neutron has traveled in the initial direction after a large number of collisions. For hydrogen, $\overline{\cos\theta} = \frac{2}{3}$, scattering in the forward direction being preferred. The ratio $\lambda_{\rm c}/v$ is the *average life* τ of the neutrons, being the average time interval between the production of a neutron and its disappearance by capture (Table 11–15).

The total cross section $\sigma_{\rm tot}$ (for scattering and capture) relates to the *transmission* of a narrow beam through an absorber. The absorption of a beam of monokinetic neutrons obeys an exponential law

$$N_x = N_0 e^{-n\sigma_{\rm tot}x} = N_0 e^{-\mu x}, \tag{11–50}$$

where N_0 is the initial flux (i.e., the number of neutrons per square centimeter per second), and N_x the flux after passing through the absorber whose thickness is x (see p. 334).

The parameter $L^2 = \lambda_{\rm t}\lambda_{\rm c}/3$ is the *thermal diffusion length*, which measures the distance after which the neutron density n has decreased to n/e (where e is the base of natural logarithms). The curves in Fig. 11–13 represent the neutron densities in water as a function of the distance from the source, for thermal neutrons (A) and for neutrons with an energy of 1 ev (B).

TABLE 11–15

THE PROPERTIES OF MODERATORS*

Moderator	Density	λ_e, cm	τ, sec	λ_t, cm	L, cm	γ_∞	Stopping power, cm^{-1}	Moderator ratio
H_2O	1.00	51.2	2.1×10^{-4}	0.425	2.85	0.82	1.53	72
D_2O	1.10	36,700	0.15	2.4	171	0.97	0.370	12,000
Be	1.85	906	4.3×10^{-3}	2.0	20.8	0.89	0.176	159
Graphite	1.60	2820	1.2×10^{-2}	2.8	50.8	0.93	0.064	170

* From I. Kaplan, *Nuclear Physics*, Addison-Wesley Publishing Co., Reading, Mass., 1955.

The *albedo* γ is the reflection coefficient for neutrons at the interface of two different media, and is a measure of the efficiency of a reflector in a pile. It depends on λ_t and on L; the smaller the first and the larger the second, the more quickly does the albedo approach unity for an infinite thickness of reflector γ_∞. For graphite, for example, $\gamma_\infty = 0.93$, so that 93% of the thermal neutrons are reflected toward the medium in which they were produced, and only 7% of the neutrons which strike the surface are absorbed.

The values in Table 11–14 suggest that hydrogen would be the best moderator, since it requires the smallest number of collisions for thermalization. However, the factors just discussed show that moderation also depends on the scattering and capture cross sections, and on the density of the medium, since the number of collisions increases with the density. To take account of these factors, the efficiency of a moderator is expressed by its *macroscopic stopping power* $\xi n \sigma_d$ and by its *moderator ratio* $\xi \sigma_d / \sigma_c$. The characteristic values for the usual moderators are given in Table 11–15.

11–11 Applications to studies of molecular structure. The cross section (in barns) for the elastic scattering of slow neutrons for a number of nuclides or elements are given in Table 11–16.

The values given in this table are based on scattering by "free" atoms. When the neutron energies are appreciably greater than the chemical binding energies, atoms bound into a molecule or a crystal can be regarded as being "free," but this is not true for neutrons which have energies of the order of 1 ev or less. Theory [68] shows that the scattering cross section of an atom tightly bound into a molecule in the gaseous state is inversely proportional to the square of the reduced mass (i.e., atom + neutron),

$$\sigma = \sigma_0 \frac{1}{[A(A+1)]^2}, \tag{11–51}$$

where σ_0 is the cross section for the free atom. For hydrogen in a heavy molecule, $\sigma = 4\sigma_0$, since the reduced mass is 0.5. These theoretical predictions have been confirmed [69, 70] by measurements on various hydrocarbons; the cross section per proton is in the region of 80 b, compared with $\sigma_0 = 20$ b for the free proton.

TABLE 11-16

CROSS SECTIONS FOR THE ELASTIC SCATTERING OF SLOW NEUTRONS*

Element or Nuclide	σ_d	Element or Nuclide	σ_d	Element or Nuclide	σ_d
H^1	20.36	P^{31}	3.3	Zn	4.1
D^2	3.3	S	1.2	Br	5.9
He^4	1.4	Cl	14.2	Ag	7
Li^7	1.5	Ar	0.8	Cd	5.3
Be^9	6.1	K	2	I	3.7
B	3.9	Ca	3.3	Sm	23
C^{12}	4.7	Fe^{54}	2.1	Gd	26
N^{14}	9.96	Fe^{56}	12.5	Ta	6.9
O^{16}	3.73	Fe^{57}	2	Pt	11.1
Na^{23}	3.3	Ni^{58}	27	Au	9
Mg	3.9	Ni^{60}	1.0	Pb	11.5
Al	1.35	Ni^{62}	9	Bi	9.2
Si	2.2	Cu	7.6	U	8.2

* From Ref. 60.

In fact, atoms are not rigidly bound in molecules, since they may have vibrational and rotational motion, which tend to decrease the scattering cross section [71, 72, 73]. Such a reduction has been observed experimentally with methane and methyl alcohol. For methane, this is attributed to vibrational effects, and in the case of methyl alcohol, to the rotation of the hydroxyl proton about the axis of the C—O bond. Carrol [69] has shown that the cross section of solid cetane ($C_{16}H_{34}$) is more than 10% greater than that for the same compound in the liquid state, in the same way that the cross section for gaseous oxygen is greater than that calculated from the cross section for silica by assuming additivity. The influence of physical and chemical state and deviations from the additivity rule have been reported in several other cases. Beyer and Whitaker [74] have reported the following values for different silica structures:

amorphous silica, $\sigma = 8.0$ b;
polycrystalline silica, $\sigma = 8.8$ b;
single crystal, $\sigma = 4.5$ b.

The same authors found nonadditive behavior with various Mn, Zn, and Cu compounds, and for some alloys in which the degree of order or disorder affects the cross section. This latter finding has been confirmed by measurements on Fe/Ni alloys which had been given various thermal pretreatments [75]; disordering an annealed 75%-nickel alloy by cold-working increased the absorption of thermal neutrons by 20.6%. Working with a velocity selector for neutrons produced in an accelerator by the D + D reaction, Keller [76] has measured the scattering cross section of hydrogen in a number of compounds at neutron energies between 0.003 and 1 ev; significant differences were found between different compounds. In particular, the cross section for water of crystallization in $CuSO_4{\cdot}5H_2O$ is greater than that in free water. The scattering cross section of the proton is also anomalous in KH_2PO_4 crystals, in which it varies with the axis of symmetry [77].

Clearly then, the scattering of neutrons can be used to study problems of molecular structure. Equally, the coherent scattering already mentioned yields crystal structure diagrams which are precisely analogous to those found by x-rays. There are, however, a number of important advantages, due in particular to the fact that the scattering of neutrons is caused by nuclei, whereas x-rays are scattered by electrons. In the latter case, the position of the nucleus can be deduced only by defining the electron cloud. In addition, scattering by electrons increases quickly with atomic number, so that light atoms are masked by heavy atoms, whereas the scattering cross sections for neutrons are of the same order of magnitude for virtually all the elements. This method is especially suitable for identifying the position of hydrogen atoms and various other light constituents of crystals. The small differences between atoms of similar atomic number, and between the isotopes of the same element, allow one to make identifications and localizations which would be impossible with x-rays. Equally, neutron diffraction can be used to reveal the presence of impurities on the surface crystals if these impurities have a high scattering cross section for neutrons. Finally, since the neutron has a magnetic moment, its interactions with paramagnetic atoms or ions depends on the relative orientation of their moments, so that the diffraction of a beam of neutrons by a crystal can be used to study various problems connected with the structure and order of magnetic substances.

One experimental difficulty is the generally low intensity of neutron sources, so that larger crystals are required than in the x-ray method. Neutron beams are not rigorously monoenergetic, and this produces a spreading of the reflections, and a consequent decrease in the accuracy of the intensity measurements. Despite these, and other, experimental difficulties, the neutron diffraction technique has quickly established itself as an efficient method of studying structure, and is certain to continue to develop, especially since higher neutron intensities are now available from more powerful reactors.

Examples* of the use of the neutron diffraction method include the work of Shull and his collaborators [78], who identified the tetrahedral structure of frozen D_2O, in agreement with Pauling's proposed structure for normal ice. The same authors [79] have shown that sodium hydride NaH has the same crystal structure as sodium chloride. The carbides and hydrides of the heavy metals have also been studied, as have allotropic modifications and second-order transitions in the ammonium halides [80, 81]. For

---

* Excellent reviews of the applications of neutron diffraction have been given by G. E. Bacon and K. Lonsdale, *Reports on Progress in Physics,* **16,** 1 (1953); G. E. Bacon, *J. Chim. Phys.,* **51,** D 65 (1954), and D. J. Hughes, *Ann. Rev. Nuclear Sci.,* **3,** 93 (1953).

KHF_2, it was found [82] that the hydrogen is equidistant from the fluorine atoms in the linear HF_2^- ion. Other work which should be mentioned includes studies of the structure of KH_2PO_4 and of spinels, and of order and disorder in magnetic and other alloys. The method has also been applied to the examination of the molecular structure of liquids (Pb, Bi, S [83], N_2, O_2, Ar [84], D_2O [85], amorphous silica [86, 87], and of gases, for example, in measuring the C—F distance in CF_4 [88, 89]).

References

1. D. E. Lea, *Actions of Radiations on Living Cells,* Cambridge University Press, 1955.
2. F. Dessauer, *Z. Physik,* **20,** 288 (1923).
3. S. K. Allison and S. D. Warshaw, *Revs. Modern Phys.,* **25,** 779 (1953).
4. H. Bethe, *Ann. Physik,* **5,** 325 (1930).
5. H. Bethe, *Z. Physik,* **76,** 293 (1932).
6. M. S. Livingston and H. A. Bethe, *Revs. Modern Phys.,* **9,** 245 (1937).
7. F. Bloch, *Z. Physik,* **81,** 363 (1933).
8. F. Bloch, *Ann. Physik,* **16,** 285 (1933).
9. H. A. Bethe and J. Ashkin, in *Experimental Nuclear Physics,* Vol. I, E. Segrè, ed., Wiley and Sons, New York, 1953, p. 166.
10. G. Mano, *Ann. Physik,* **1,** 407 (1934).
11. E. Fermi, *Phys. Rev.,* **57,** 485 (1940).
12. A. Bohr, *Danske Videnskab. Selskab, Mat.-fys. Medd.,* **24,** No. 19 (1948).
13. R. H. Frost and C. E. Nelson, *Phys. Rev.,* **91,** 864 (1953).
14. P. M. S. Blackett and D. S. Lees, *Proc. Roy. Soc. (London),* **A134,** 658 (1932).
15. See R. L. Platzman, *Oberlin College Symposium on Radiobiology,* 1950, p. 139.
16. L. H. Gray, *Proc. Cambridge Phil. Soc.,* **40,** 72 (1944).
17. T. Thompson, *U.S.A.E.C. report UCRL–1910,* 1952, quoted in Ref. 3.
18. W. Michl, *Akad. Wiss. Wien, Abt. IIa,* **123,** 1965 (1914).
19. K. Phillip, *Z. Physik,* **17,** 23 (1923).
20. R. K. Appleyard, *Nature,* **163,** 526 (1949).
21. H. G. de Carvalho and H. Yagoda, *Phys. Rev.,* **88,** 273 (1953).
22. R. H. Ellis, H. H. Rossi, and G. Failla, *Phys. Rev.,* **86,** 562 (1952); **97,** 1043 (1955).
23. H. A. Kramers, *Physica,* **13,** 401 (1947).
24. C. B. Madsen and P. Venkateswarlu, *Phys. Rev.,* **74,** 648 (1948).
25. E. Rutherford, J. Chadwick, and C. D. Ellis, *Radiations from Radioactive Substances,* Cambridge University Press, 1951.
26. R. D. Evans, *Phys. Rev.,* **45,** 29 (1934).
27. G. Finney and R. D. Evans, *Phys. Rev.,* **48,** 503 (1935).
28. R. D. Evans, in *The Science and Engineering of Nuclear Power,* Addison-Wesley Publishing Co., Reading, Mass., 1947, p. 1.
29. M. Perey, *J. phys. radium,* **6,** 28 (1945).
30. N. Feather, *Proc. Cambridge Phil. Soc.,* **34,** 599 (1938).
31. L. E. Glendenin and C. D. Coryell, *U.S.A.E.C. report MDDC–19,* 1946.

32. L. E. GLENDENIN, *Nucleonics,* **2,** No. 1, 12 (1948).

33. G. FOURNIER, *Ann. Physik,* **8,** 205 (1927); see also G. FOURNIER and M. GUILLOT, *Absorption exponentielle des rayons-β* (Actualités Scientifique No. 57), Hermann, Paris, 1933.

34. B. GUILLOT, personal communication.

35. M. HAÏSSINSKY and B. PULLMAN, *J. phys. radium,* **8,** 33 (1947).

36. E. BRODA, W. E. GRUMMITT, J. GUERON, L. KOWARSKI, and G. WILKINSON, *Proc. Phys. Soc. (London),* **60,** 460 (1948).

37. L. WERTENSTEIN, *Ann. Physik,* **1,** 347 (1914).

38. O. HAHN and L. MEITNER, *Physik Z.,* **10,** 697 (1909).

39. S. RUSS and W. MAKOWER, *Proc. Roy. Soc. (London),* **A82,** 205 (1909).

40. C. CHAMIÉ, *J. phys. radium,* **5,** 54, 436 (1934).

41. P. LANGEVIN, *J. phys. radium,* **5,** 57 (1934).

42. C. CHAMIÉ and S. T. TSIEN, *J. phys. radium,* **2,** 46 (1941).

43. P. CURIE and A. LABORDE, *Compt. rend.,* **136,** 673 (1903).

44. E. RUTHERFORD, J. CHADWICK, and C. D. ELLIS, Ref. 25, p. 158.

45. A. DAUVILLIER, *Compt. rend.,* **212,** 1156 (1941); **237,** 1202 (1953).

46. A. F. KAPUSTINSKY, *Nature,* **180,** 1245 (1957).

47. O. KLEIN and G. NISHINA, *Z. Physik,* **52,** 853 (1929).

48. W. HEITLER, *The Quantum Theory of Radiation,* 3rd ed., Oxford University Press, 1957.

49. P. A. CERENKOV, *C. R. Acad. Sci. U.S.S.R.,* **8,** 451 (1934); **20,** 651 (1938); **21,** 116, 339.

50. P. A. CERENKOV, *Phys. Rev.,* **52,** 378 (1937).

51. I. M. FRANK and I. E. TAMM, *C. R. Acad. Sci. U.S.S.R.,* **14,** 109 (1937).

52. I. E. TAMM, *J. Phys. Russe,* **1,** 439 (1939).

53. G. BECK, *J. Phys. Russe,* **74,** 795 (1948).

54. L. H. GRAY, *Proc. Roy. Soc. (London),* **A122,** 647 (1929); **156,** 578 (1936).

55. F. W. SPIERS, *Brit. J. Rad.,* **19,** 52 (1946).

56. See *Brit. J. Rad.,* **27,** 243 (1954).

57. L. H. GRAY, in *Actions Chimiques et Biologiques des Radiations,* Vol. 1, Masson, Paris, 1955, p. 3.

58. N. MILLER, *Actions Chimiques et Biologiques des Radiations,* Vol. 2, 1956, p. 149.

59. Calculated by M. LEFORT, *J. Chim. Phys.,* **47,** 624 (1950).

60. B. FELD, in *Experimental Nuclear Physics,* Vol. 2, E. Segrè, ed., Wiley and Sons, New York, 1953, p. 209.

61. E. AMALDI, *Physik. Z.,* **38,** 692 (1937).

62. E. SEGRÈ, *Revs. Modern Phys.,* **27,** 257 (1955).

63. P. B. MOON and J. R. TILLMAN, *Nature,* **135,** 904 (1935).

64. P. B. MOON and J. R. TILLMAN, *Proc. Roy. Soc. (London),* **A153,** 476 (1936).

65. J. R. DUNNING, G. B. PEGRAM, G. A. FINK, D. P. MITCHELL, and E. SEGRÈ, *Phys. Rev.,* **48,** 704 (1935).

66. See *The Science and Engineering of Nuclear Power,* C. Goodman, ed., Addison-Wesley Publishing Co., Reading, Mass., 1948.

67. S. GLASSTONE and M. C. EDLUND, *Elements of Nuclear Reactor Theory,* Van Nostrand, New York, 1952.

68. R. G. SACHS and E. TELLER, *Phys. Rev.,* **60,** 18 (1941).

69. H. Carrol, *Phys. Rev.*, **60,** 702 (1941).
70. W. B. Jones, *Phys. Rev.*, **74,** 364 (1948).
71. A. M. L. Messiah, *Phys. Rev.*, **84,** 204 (1951).
72. W. Kolos, *Acta Phys. Polon.*, **13,** 67 (1954).
73. J. A. Janik, *1955 Geneva Conference*, P. 941.
74. H. G. Beyer and M. D. Whitaker, *Phys. Rev.*, **57,** 976 (1940).
75. F. C. Nix, H. G. Beyer, and J. R. Dunning, *Phys. Rev.*, **58,** 1031 (1940).
76. H. Keller, *Thesis*, Geneva, 1950.
77. J. Rossel, *Helv. Phys. Acta*, **20,** 105 (1942).
78. E. O. Wollan, W. L. Davidson, and C. G. Shull, *Phys. Rev.*, **75,** 1348 (1949).
79. C. G. Shull, E. O. Wollan, G. A. Morton, and W. L. Davison, *Phys. Rev.*, **73,** 842 (1948).
80. G. H. Goldschmidt and D. G. Hurst, *Phys. Rev.*, **83,** 88 (1951); **86,** 797 (1952).
81. H. A. Levy and S. W. Peterson, *Phys. Rev.*, **86,** 766 (1952).
82. S. W. Peterson and H. A. Levy, *J. Chem. Phys.*, **20,** 704 (1952).
83. O. Chamberlain, *Phys. Rev.*, **77,** 305 (1950).
84. D. G. Henshaw, D. G. Hurst, and N. K. Pope, *Phys. Rev.*, **92,** 1229 (1953).
85. S. J. Czyczak and A. Wartenberg, *Phys. Rev.*, **75,** 1634 (1949).
86. I. W. Ruderman, *Phys. Rev.*, **78,** 317 (1950).
87. W. O. Milligan, H. A. Levy, and S. W. Peterson, *Phys. Rev.*, **83,** 226 (1951).
88. N. Z. Alcock and D. G. Hurst, *Phys. Rev.*, **75,** 1609 (1949); **83,** 1100 (1951).
89. D. G. Hurst and N. Z. Alcock, *Can. J. Phys.*, **29,** 36 (1951).

CHAPTER 12

THE CHEMICAL EFFECTS OF IONIZING RADIATIONS: INTRODUCTION, AND REACTIONS IN THE GAS PHASE

12–1 Historical introduction. Radioactivity was discovered as a result of the reduction of silver bromide by the α-particles from uranium and its daughter elements. Despite this, radiation chemistry was for many years a relatively unexplored part of the whole field of radiochemistry, and it is still true that those phenomena which have been studied are only partially understood. There are at least two principal reasons for this. In the first place, the interest of the radiobiologist in these problems involves either the use of radiation to destroy malignant growths or tissues, or to protect an organism against the undesirable effects of radiation. Now, of course, the series of processes between the primary act of the ionization of water (which is the principal constituent of tissue) and the alteration of a cell, the inactivation of a virus, or a genetic mutation consists of an extremely large number of very complex intermediate steps.

The approach to these problems was necessarily empirical, and for a long period this attitude took precedence over attempts at understanding the true nature and mechanism of the phenomena involved. On the other hand, the interest of radiochemists has been almost exclusively in the ionic aspect of radiation; one of the reasons for this is, of course, the importance of radiometric techniques involving ionization. As a result, virtually all the chemical effort has gone into establishing the quantitative relations between the ions produced by radiation (essentially α-particles and x-rays) and the observed chemical effects, these being regarded as a direct consequence of the formation and neutralization of ions.

The *ionic yield* of such reactions is expressed as the M/N ratio, which is the number of equivalents undergoing reaction divided by the number of ions formed. This relation is obviously similar to the quantum yield of photochemistry. This mode of expression has been extended to solution systems, despite the fact that here the energy absorbed by the solute is normally only a very small fraction of the total energy expended in ionization and despite the fact that only very rarely can the number of ions formed in a liquid be measured (Section 12–2). In liquids, the values of N used are those calculated for ionization in air for equal energy absorption. If the ionic yield is determined in this way for the decomposition of liquid water by the radiations from radium, the value obtained is very close to unity ($M/N = 1.06$), and this provided an apparently decisive argument in favor of the ionic mechanism. From this result, an analogy with electrolysis and Faraday's electrochemical laws was inferred, and the process was spoken of as "electrodeless electrolysis." This idea appealed to the early workers in physical chemistry as much as it did to those in other fields. We shall see that a purely ionic mechanism does not in fact provide a satisfactory interpretation of the experimental results on gases, and still less for aqueous solutions, although it remained in favor until about 1935.

As early as 1914, Debierne [1], who studied the decomposition of water by the radiations from actinium decay products, suggested that the primary products were hydroxyl radicals and hydrogen atoms. A similar hypothesis was advanced by Risse [2] in 1929. At the time, however, these ideas were not seen in their true worth, and it was not until 1935 that the elegant experimental work of Capron [3] on the effect of α-particles on the ortho-parahydrogen conversion demonstrated that the ionic mechanism could not apply to this system. In the following year, Eyring, Hirschfelder, and Taylor [4] gave a theoretical explanation which emphasized the essential part played by atoms or *free radicals* in radiochemical gaseous reactions.

During this same period, Fricke and his collaborators [5, 6, 7] carried out a considerable amount of experimental work on the irradiation of aqueous solutions with x-rays, and reached a number of general conclusions. These experiments provided a good experimental basis for the later development of radiation chemistry. In particular, Fricke introduced the idea of *activated water*, implying that the dissolved materials are not directly changed by irradiation but via some intermediate involving the solvent. Weiss [8, 9] suggested more precisely that the primary physical effect of radiations on water was to give two ions of opposite sign, which are unstable and dissociate to give the free radicals OH and H:

$$H_2O + e \rightsquigarrow H_2O^+ + 2e, \tag{12-1}$$

$$H_2O^+ \rightarrow OH + H^+, \tag{12-2}$$

$$H_2O + e \rightsquigarrow H_2O^-, \tag{12-3}$$

$$H_2O^- \rightarrow H + OH^-. \tag{12-4}$$

The symbol $\rightsquigarrow$, indicating a primary act in radiation chemistry, was introduced by Burton.

Weiss, and subsequently Dainton [10], established kinetic equations for the reactions of these radicals in aqueous solutions. Lea [11] and Gray [12, 13] extended the theory by emphasizing the effect of the ionization density, and were thus able to explain the different effects observed with α-particles and γ-rays.

Parallel to this new theoretical treatment of radiation chemistry came a considerable advance in the scope of experimental methods, with the increasing construction of nuclear reactors and particle accelerators. Similarly, radiation sources with energies and intensities thousands of times greater than those previously used now became available. Numerous problems, involving mechanical, electrical, optical, and related changes in irradiated solids; the choice of appropriate materials for the construction of reactors, such as metals, plastics, semiconductors, etc.; and problems of protection, dosimetry, etc., had to be solved.

In the field of aqueous solution chemistry, the development of radiation chemistry has produced a mass of new systematic precise data, which has led to important modifications to the initial theory.

TABLE 12–1

THE AVERAGE ENERGY FOR ION-PAIR PRODUCTION

Gas	5-Mev α-particles		340-Mev protons [17]	Electrons		Ionization potential
	Po^{210} [14]	Pu^{239} [15]		3–20 kev [17]*	1 Mev [18]	
H	36.3	37.0	35.3	36.3		15.6
He	42.7	46.0		42.3		24.5
Ne	36.8	36.3	28.6	36.6		21.5
Ar	26.4	26.4	25.5	26.4	25.5	15.7
Kr	24.1			24.2		13.9
Xe	21.9			22.0		12.1
N_2	36.6	36.3	33.6	34.9	34.8	15.5
O_2	32.5	32.3	31.5	30.9	30.9	12.5
Air	35.5	35.0	33.5	34.0	33.9	
CO_2	34.5	34.3		33.0	32.6	14.3
CH_4	29.2	29.4		27.3	26.8	14.5
C_2H_4	28.0	28.0		26.2	26.3	12.2
C_2H_2	27.5			25.9		12.3
H_2O		37.6 [20]				

* The values reported by J. M. Valentine, *Proc. Roy. Soc.*, **A211**, 75 (1952), using the β-particles from T and Ar^{37} are much the same, except for a value of 32.5 ev for He.

12–2 The energy required for ion-pair production. Free radicals can be produced by either ionization or excitation, and one of the uncertainties of current theory arises from ignorance of the relative importance of each of these two processes. Measurements of the average energy required to produce a pair of ions in various gaseous media show clearly that a considerable fraction of this energy is used in producing excitation phenomena. The energy required is always greater than the energy corresponding to the ionization potential as determined, for example, mass spectrometrically. Table 12–1 gives the values of these ionization energies in different gases for Po α-particles, 340-Mev protons, and electrons. The ionization potentials are also shown.

Several of the values in Table 12–1 are significantly different from those based on older measurements. In particular, the energy W required to produce a pair of ions in air by electrons was believed to be 32.5 ev, and to decrease slightly with increasing electron energy. More recent measurements have not confirmed this [21]. The differences between the values reported by different authors are due, at least in part, to the presence of impurities in the gas; only very small amounts of impurity are required to bring about considerable changes in the mean ionization energy. Jesse and Sadauskis [14] showed that the addition of 0.01% of argon to helium is

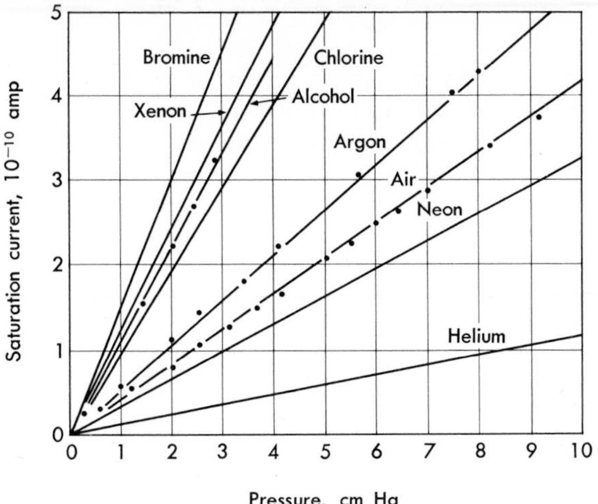

FIG. 12-1. The saturation current as a function of the pressure for different gases (Ref. 27).

sufficient to cause an appreciable decrease in W; an argon concentration of 0.13% brings the value down from 42.7 to 33.0 ev. The addition of Xe, Kr, or CO_2 to helium, or of C_2H_2 to argon has a similar effect. The presence of 1.2% of alcohol in argon produces a 15% increase in the ionization produced by the α-particles from polonium [22, 23], an increase of 21% is found on adding benzene (see also Ref. 24). These effects are partly due to the excitation of the metastable states of the main gas, which causes additional ionization in impurities, which have lower ionization potentials. For example,

$$\mathrm{He}^* + \mathrm{Ar} \rightarrow \mathrm{He} + \mathrm{Ar}^+ + \mathrm{e}^-,$$

$$\mathrm{Ar}^* + \mathrm{C_6H_6} \rightarrow \mathrm{Ar} + \mathrm{C_6H_6^+} + \mathrm{e}^-.$$

Platzman [25] has drawn attention to the role of the so-called *subexcitation electrons*, whose kinetic energy is too small to excite the principal component of the mixture, but is greater than the ionization potential of the impurity.

For hydrogen and the inert gases, the value of W (the energy required to produce an ion-pair) appears to be virtually the same for α-particles and electrons, and to be independent of the particle energy. For other gases, the ratio W_α/W_{el} varies slightly with energy, tending toward unity with increasing E. Table 12-1 shows that W varies only slightly from one gas to another. For very pure gases, the ratio W/I, where I is the ionization potential, is around 1.7 [26].

The values of W for different gases are, however, often sufficiently different that the linear plots of the saturation current as a function of the pressure show distinctly different slopes (Fig. 12-1). A device called the *alphameter* is based upon these differences, which are mainly due to the variation in the stopping power with the mean atomic weight (Sections 11–2 and 11–9). This apparatus can be used either to measure the pressure of a gas by the ionization produced by a source of α-particles (U, Ra, Po, etc.) or to determine the composition of a binary gaseous mixture at a known pressure [27]. This method of analysis is particularly suitable for hydrogen-oxygen mixtures, since there is an appreciable difference in the slopes of the lines for these two gases. A device of this type at the Radium Institute (Paris) uses about 0.5 mc of radium, and measures quantities of $H_2 + O_2$, at a total pressure of 10^{-2} mm Hg, with an accuracy of 1 to 2%; at a pressure of 10^{-5} mm Hg, the accuracy falls to 10% [28]. Mixtures of carbon dioxide and oxygen, and of nitrous oxide and nitrogen, have also been analyzed in this way.

The energy required to produce an ion-pair in water vapor by α-particles is 37.6 ev [22]; see also [29]. The corresponding value in liquids is virtually unknown, since there are difficulties in getting the saturation currents required for the ionization measurements, but it is assumed that the energy is virtually the same as for vapors of the same composition. This appears to have been confirmed in the case of liquid argon [30].

12–3 The spatial distribution of ions and radicals. The specific ionization of electrons (i.e., the linear density of ionization which they produce) is appreciably smaller than that of α-particles or protons (Tables 11–5 and 11–6). Electrons with an energy of 100 ev (range 0.003 μ in water) produce about three times fewer ions per micron than a 1-Mev α-particle (with a range of 5.3 μ), and this ratio increases rapidly with electron energy. The effect of the ionization density on chemical change can be better appreciated by considering two further facts: first, the differences in the distribution of positive and negative ions (and consequently in the radicals derived from them), and second, the diffusion-controlled recombination of ions and radicals. These phenomena have been analyzed by Jaffé [31], and subsequently studied in greater detail by Lea [11, 32], Gray [33], Allen [34], and others.

If at the instant of formation, the ions have a lateral Gaussian distribution, the initial number n_0 of ions of each sign produced per cubic centimeter at a distance r from the axis of the path of an ionizing particle is given by

$$n_0 = \frac{a_0}{\pi r_0^2} e^{-r/r_0^2}, \tag{12–5}$$

where a_0 is the number of ions of each sign produced per centimeter of path, and r_0 is the average radius of the initial cylinder formed by these ions. As the result of diffusion, the density after a time t is

$$n = \frac{a}{\pi(4Dt + r_0^2)} e^{-r/(4Dt+r_0^2)}, \tag{12–6}$$

where D is the diffusion coefficient of the ionic species in question and a the number of ions per centimeter of path at time t. As the result of recombination processes, a_0 has decreased to a, and, according to Lea, one has

$$\frac{a_0}{a} = 1 + \frac{\alpha a_0}{8\pi D} \log_e \frac{4Dt + r_0^2}{r_0^2}, \tag{12-7}$$

where α is the recombination coefficient ($da/dt = -\alpha a^2$).

The value of r_0 depends upon the density of the medium; the figures for air, nitrogen, and carbon dioxide are 1.8, 2.4, and 0.5×10^{-3} cm, respectively. This parameter is much smaller in liquids, but Lea and Gray believe that it is still possible to distinguish between the behavior of α-particles and x-rays. Photographs obtained in a Wilson cloud chamber show that with α-particles the positive ions are concentrated along the geometric axis of the path, with a high linear density, whereas the electrons are scattered over some distance. Experimental work with hexane gives the value of r_0 for electrons as 230 A; allowing for the difference in densities, r_0 for water would then be 150 A. This would be the initial radius of the column formed by the electrons or negative ions, and hence by the H atoms derived from the former by reaction (12-4). The corresponding radius for the column of positive ions, and hence of the OH radicals [Eq. (12-2)], is very much smaller, probably of the order of 8 A. In contrast to this, the ionization produced by x- and γ-rays is approximately uniform, because of the secondary and tertiary electrons, and the two radii are assumed to be the same, of the order of 150 A.

It follows from these arguments that with x- and γ-radiation the probability of encounter and recombination of oppositely charged ions, or between different species of free radicals, is favored compared with the α-particle case. With α-particles, combinations between like radicals (OH + OH, H + H) will predominate before diffusion of the products from the positive column allows these to come in contact with the products of the negative column. Figure 12-2, due to Lea [11], shows that the time

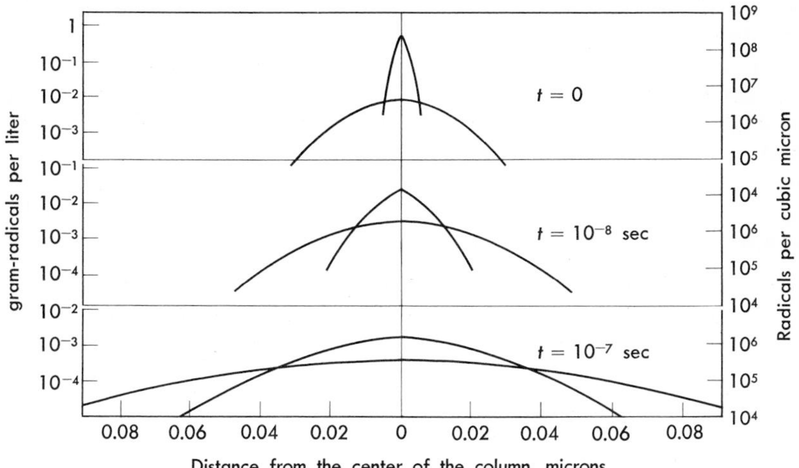

FIG. 12-2. The distribution of radicals around the path of an α-particle. [D. E. Lea, *Brit. J. Rad.*, Suppl. 1 (1947).]

interval necessary for the distribution to become uniform is greater than 10^{-7} sec, a time which is relatively long in terms of chemical reactions.

After a much longer time, depending on the intensity of the radiation, the columns formed by different α-particles or by different primary electrons overlap, and unreacted species can then react with each other, irrespective of their origin. For an intensity of 10 r/sec, Lea has evaluated this time interval at 0.01 sec for x-rays with a linear density of 6×10^5 ion-pairs/cm, and at 0.08 sec for α-particles with a density of 3×10^7 ion-pairs/cm. Kinetic study of the reactions between the radicals themselves, or between the radicals and a solute, as a function of the intensity is in principle a method which in some cases can be used to determine whether the radicals diffuse away from one track sufficiently quickly to allow them to react with those from other tracks [36–40].

Because of such factors, one normally distinguishes between those radiations which produce a dense or heterogeneous ionization, such as α-particles, and those uniform radiations such as x-rays in the energy range from 0.1 to several Mev. It should be remembered, however, that for a given type of radiation, the stopping power, and hence the ionization density, varies with the energy, so that with decreasing energy, an electron tends to behave more like an α-particle, and vice versa. This is particularly the case for δ-rays, which produce ionization as small clusters of ion-pairs, very close together (Fig. 12–2). Allen has emphasized the role of these secondary electrons, which should favor combinations between radicals, as with α-particles. This topic is discussed further in Chapter 13.

In terms of radiation chemistry or radiobiology, one additional feature of radiation which must be considered is the linear density of ionization produced, or better, by the linear energy transfer LET [41, 42]. This latter parameter has the advantage of including excitation effects, and requires no assumption about the energy required to produce an ion-pair.

The theory which has just been described is only approximate, and, as we shall see, only qualitatively successful for aqueous solutions. Criticisms have been made both of some of the detailed reasoning, and of certain fundamental aspects. Thus Read [43] has pointed out that in the case of α-particles, the initial charge separation assumed by Jaffé and Lea should set up a very intense radial electrostatic field; for a density of 1000 ions/micron, this would be of the order of 10^5 v/cm in water at distances relatively far from the axis of the track. Because of this field, electrons produced in the ionization of water should be attracted back toward the positive ions. Measurements by Richards [44] of the ionization produced in hexane by Po α-particles have led this author too to postulate the formation of a very intense electric field (10^7 v/cm) inside the column of ionization. It follows that the rate of recombination should be determined more by this electrostatic field than by diffusion. Only the δ-rays formed beyond the initial track should contribute to the ionization current. We shall return to this question in the following chapter.

12–4 The nature of the primary ions. The principal source of our knowledge of the ions produced by ionizing radiation is mass spectrometry. This method can be used to measure M/e, for the fragments produced in

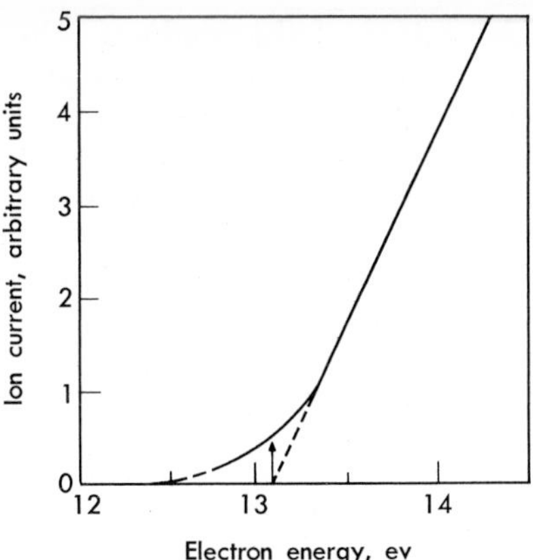

FIG. 12-3. Mass-spectrometric determination of the appearance potential of an ion.

the bombardment of a volatile compound with electrons (energies of the order of 10 ev), so that these species can then be identified. The relative abundances can also be determined, and the *appearance potential* of a given ion R^+ found. For an ion formed in the reaction

$$RX + e^- \rightarrow R^+ + X + 2e^-, \qquad (12\text{–}8)$$

the appearance potential V_R is defined by the equation

$$V_R = D + I_R + E_k + E_{ex}, \qquad (12\text{–}9)$$

where D is the dissociation energy of RX (to R and X), I_R is the ionization potential of R, E_k is the kinetic energy of the fragments and E_{ex} is their excitation energy. It follows that even if the two latter terms are negligibly small, the appearance potential is greater than the ionization potential by an amount equal to the dissociation energy. The appearance potential is determined by measuring the ionization current due to the fragments as a function of electron energy (Fig. 12-3).

If ion current is detected at energies lower than the appearance potential, but above the ionization potential, it is attributed to the formation of a free radical R by chemical or thermal dissociation, rather than by electron bombardment [45, 46]. This method can therefore be used to detect free radicals formed in a gas by chemical processes, and to measure their concentration.

Much caution must, however, be used in applying mass-spectrometric results to radiation chemistry. They are generally obtained at very low pressures (of the order of 10^{-3} to 10^{-5} mm Hg), and the time interval between the molecule-electron collision and the measurement of the current is of the order of 10^{-6} sec. This technique consequently gives no information about the deactivation processes which may occur in a more condensed medium, nor about the nature of the products subsequently formed by charge neutralization. Furthermore, some metastable ions may dissociate in the accelerating field of the mass spectrometer, and hence the deactivation processes may be different from those in an irradiated gas or liquid.

These points will be illustrated in terms of results for the molecules H_2, O_2, H_2O, and H_2O_2, which play a fundamental part in the radiation chemistry of aqueous solutions. Some rules for polyatomic organic molecules are discussed later in Chapter 14.

The experimentally determined appearance potential of the H_2^+ ion in hydrogen gas is around 15.4 v, in agreement with the theoretical value of 15.37 v. The H_3^+ ion appears at 15.9 v, and the H^+ ion at approximately 18 v. The current carried by the latter ion increases rapidly at 26 v, and again at 30 v. The H^- ion is formed in the triple collision process

$$\text{H (atom)} + \text{e} + \text{particle (electron, atom, molecule)},$$

which requires no activation energy.

The first appearance potential of oxygen corresponds to the formation of the O_2^- ion at 3.0 v; the ion O_2^+ appears at 12.3 v. The results on the appearance potential of the ion O^+ are rather discordant, but suggest a value in the neighborhood of 19.2 v.

The first product in the electron bombardment of water vapor [47, 48] is the H^- ion at 5.6 v, probably as a result of the excitation of the H_2O molecule to a repulsive level

$$H_2O + e \rightarrow H^-(^1S\text{-state}) + OH(^2\Pi).$$

The appearance potential of O^- is 7.5 v; this ion is formed by dissociation, either to $2H + O^-$, or to $H_2 + O^-$ [49]. The H_2O^+ ion appears at 13.0 v, followed by H_3O^+ at 13.8 v; the first of these is formed by a simple ionization process, and the second in the secondary reaction

$$H_2O^+ + H_2O \rightarrow H_3O^+ + OH,$$

or

$$H_2O^+ + H \rightarrow H_3O^+.$$

The appearance potential of OH^+ is 18.7 v, very close to that of the O^+ ion (18.8 v), while the H^+ ion does not appear until 19.5 v. At 23 v the H_2 ion appears. At still higher energies, the current carried by O^- and O^+ increases. The relative abundances of some of these ions at 50 ev are

H_2O^+	OH^+	H^+	H_3O^+	O^+	H_2^+
1000	200	200	200	20	5

The H^+ ion is therefore much more abundant than O^+, even though it has the higher appearance potential. Mass-spectrometric studies of hydrocarbons also show that the magnitude of the appearance potential is not a

TABLE 12–2

ELECTRON AFFINITIES, EV

H	0.75	SH	2.61
Li	0.54	HO_2	3.04
Na	0.74	NH_2	1.21
C	1.7	N_3	2.35
P	0.8	CH	~1.65
As	1.0	CH_3	~1.22
O	2.2	CN	3.61
S	2.4	H_2	−0.72
Se	2.0	O_2	0.87
Te	2.1	O_3	2.89
F	3.6	Cl_2	$\leq$1.70
Cl	3.8	SO_2	2.80
Br	3.55	NO	>0
I	3.24	NO_2	1.62
OH	2.17	NO_3	3.89

criterion of the abundance of an ion. It should be noted that the OH^- ion does not figure among the products formed in the gas phase [49].

The hydrogen peroxide molecule ionizes to produce $H_2O_2^+$, HO_2^+, and OH^+, whose appearance potentials are 12.1, 16.1, and 16.0 v respectively [50]. At 30 ev, the relative intensities of these ions are 100, 6, and 200.

Mass spectrometry is not the only method used for studying the experimental conditions under which gaseous negative ions are formed [51]. Bradbury [52, 53, 54] has determined the "electron attachment coefficient" by generating a current of slow electrons at a cathode and passing this through the gas in question toward an anode in a uniform electrical field. By the appropriate siting of "electron filters" (metallic wire grids connected to a radio-frequency oscillator) the electrons can be stopped and the negative ions allowed to reach the anode. These measurements show that diatomic molecules in the $^1\Sigma$-state (zero angular momentum) or atoms in the $^1S_0$-state do not form negative ions. Diatomic molecules with a spin greater than zero, or molecules from the first category in an excited state, can form negative ions, as for example, $O_2(^3\Sigma)$, $OH(^2\Pi)$, $CN(^2\Sigma)$. Symmetrical polyatomic molecules such as H_2O, NH_3, CH_4, CO_2, or N_2O have zero electron affinity, and in these cases the ions are formed in dissociation processes:

$$NH_3 + e \rightarrow H_2 + NH^-, \qquad (12\text{–}10)$$

$$H_2S + e \rightarrow H_2 + S^-. \qquad (12\text{–}11)$$

Other methods for determining electron affinities have been described and discussed by Pritchard and Skinner [55, 56]. Table 12–2 gives some of the values selected by these authors for various atoms, free radicals, and molecules.

Magee and Burton [40] have given a theoretical discussion of the conditions under which negative ions are formed in radiation chemistry, and have concluded that only very low-energy "thermalized" electrons can be captured by neutral molecules.

12–5 Reactions in the gaseous state. Ionizing radiations may bring about a wide variety of chemical changes, including decomposition, synthesis, oxidation, reduction, polymerization, depolymerization, isotopic exchange, etc. Table 12–3 gives the experimental M/N ratios for a number of radiolytic reactions in the gaseous state; unless otherwise indicated, these are taken from the works of Lind [58] and Mund [59].

Mechanisms involving free radicals now form the theoretical foundation of the radiation chemistry of solutions, and the ionic yield is replaced by the "radiochemical yield," expressed as G, the number of molecules reacted or the number of free radicals formed per 100 ev absorbed by the irradiated system. For aqueous solutions, a value given as M/N can be converted to G units by multiplying by 3, since N in the older publications is generally based on the assumption that the energy necessary for ion-pair production by x- or γ-rays is 32.5 ev, and by α-particles 35.0 ev.

It will be seen from the table that there are only small differences between the yields for gaseous reactions caused by α-particles and x-rays. The high yield for the γ-ray polymerization of ethylene was obtained in very long irradiations with an extremely strong source (10 kilocuries of Co^{60}); for a small dose absorbed, M/N falls to a value similar to that found with α-particles. This polymerization is one example of the possible industrial application of radiation.

Wourtzel [80] was the first to draw attention to the fact, self-evident from Table 12–3, that the M/N ratio is far from always being equal to 1, or to any other small whole number, as the simple ionic theory would require; furthermore, the ratio depends on the experimental conditions. To explain the high yields sometimes obtained, Lind proposed the hypothesis that radiolytic transformations in gases, and in solutions, involve ionic *clusters*—groups of neutral molecules associated together around one or more ions by polarization of the molecules by the ions. Two clusters of opposite sign would approach because of electrostatic attraction and would neutralize each other in the same way that ions neutralize each other near electrodes. The dissociation of the unstable complex would lead to the formation of the products which are observed; thus the synthesis of water was attributed to the process

$$(H_2 \cdot O_2 \cdot H_2)^+ + (H_2 \cdot O_2 \cdot H_2)^- \rightarrow 4H_2O \qquad (M/N = 4).$$

The corresponding reaction for the oxidation of methane would be

$$(O_2 \cdot CH_4 \cdot O_2)^+ + (O_2 \cdot CH_4 \cdot O_2)^- \rightarrow 3CO_2 + 4H_2O \qquad (M/N = 4),$$

and for the decomposition of ammonia

$$(NH_3 \cdot NH_3)^+ (-) \rightarrow N_2 + 3H_2 \qquad (M/N = 2).$$

TABLE 12-3

Compound irradiated	Radiation	Products	M/N	Ref.
$H_2 + O_2$	α	H_2O	3.4–4	—
$T_2 + O_2$	β	T_2O	3.2	60
O_2	α	O_3	1–2	—
$Cl_2 + H_2$	α	HCl	$\sim 10^5$	—
$Cl_2 + H_2$	x	HCl	$4\text{–}8 \times 10^4$	61
$Br_2 + H_2$	α	HBr	0.5–2.9	—
$Br_2 + H_2$	x	HBr	2	62
$I_2 + H_2$	α	HI	6	63
HBr	α	H_2, Br_2	~ 3	62
HBr	electrons	H_2, Br_2	4.6	64
HI	α, x	H_2, I_2	8	58, 65
NH_3	α	N_2, H_2	0.9–1.3	66
$N_2 + H_2$	α	NH_3	0.3–0.5	—
N_2H_4	α	NH_3	~ 3	67
N_2O	α	N_2, NO	4.4	68
H_2S	α	H_2, S	2.7	—
$CO + O_2$	α	CO_2	3.9–4.4	—
$CH_4 + O_2$	α	CO_2, H_2O	1.5 CO_2; 3 H_2O	—
$C_2N_2 + O_2$	α	$(CNO)_x$ (solid); CO_2, N_2	7.2	—
$CO + Cl_2$	α	$COCl_2$	8.5×10^4	69
C_2H_4	α	$(C_2H_4)_5$ (liq)	5.1	—
C_2H_4	γ	polyethylene	0.3–1000	70
C_2H_2	α	solid polymer, C_6H_6	20–21	71, 72, 73
C_2H_2	β	polymer	26.6	74
HCN	α	solid polymer	11.3	73
C_4H_8	α	polymer	~ 120	75
$CH_2{=}CHCl$	α	polymer	10–57	76
$H_2 + D_2$	α, β	HD	$2 \times 10^3\text{–}10^4$	77, 78
$H_2 + T_2$	β	HT	1.6×10^3	79
p-H_2	α	o-H_2	700–1000	3

* See the original papers for the exact conditions of irradiation.

This theory took no account of chain reactions, and even the polymerization of acetylene, for which $M/N \approx 20$ was regarded as the result of the improbable intermediate formation of very large ionic clusters.

Some of the other difficulties implicit in this approach were emphasized by Mund [62], who pointed out that the M/N values were often in agreement with the chemical reactivity, which could only be reconciled with the theory with difficulty. Furthermore, radiolytic compounds are often produced in a series of successive reactions rather than in a single act involving the dissociation of an unstable complex. Mund rejected the electrolytic picture of radiolysis, but retained the idea of cluster formation, and like Wourtzel before him, suggested that ions do not necessarily play a direct role in these reactions, which can also be brought about by excitation processes. More recently, Essex and his collaborators have investigated the α-particle decomposition of ammonia, hydrogen sulfide, and gaseous nitrogen oxide in an electric field designed for rapid collection of ions formed, and found that the field has too little effect to support any ionic mechanism [87].

In addition, the theory made no distinction between the effects due to α-particles, with their dense local ionization, and the more uniform ionization produced by electrons and x-rays. We shall see later that for aqueous solutions, these two types of reactions are quite different, sometimes even qualitatively.

The most serious objection against the theory was probably the work of Capron (noted above) on the effect of the Rn α-particles on the $p\text{-H}_2 \rightarrow o\text{-H}_2$ conversion. Under the experimental conditions used, the ionic yields were found to be in the range 700 to 1000, and this result cannot be explained in terms of the formation of gigantic clusters. Capron suggested that the conversion involved a chain reaction propagated by free hydrogen atoms

$$H_2 \xrightarrow{\alpha} 2H, \qquad H + p\text{-H}_2 \rightarrow o\text{-H}_2 + H, \qquad \text{etc.} \qquad (12\text{–}12)$$

The theory of this reaction was subsequently developed by Eyring, *et al.* [4], using mass-spectrometric data on the ions produced from hydrogen by electron bombardment (Section 12–4). These authors showed that the probability of formation of even simple clusters $(H_2H_2)^+$ and $(H_2H_2H_2)^+$) is too low for these species to be the primary species in the radiolytic reactions. They subsequently drew attention to the probable importance of excitation processes, since these take up more than half the energy used in the production of an ion-pair. The transition of hydrogen molecules from the normal $^1\Sigma$ state to $^3\Sigma$ would lead to dissociation into free atoms, and three or four of these would be formed per primary H_2^+ ion:

$$H_2^+ + H_2 \rightarrow H_3^+ + H, \qquad H_3^+ + e \rightarrow H_2 + H \text{ (or } H_3),$$
$$H_3^+ + H^- \rightarrow 4H, \qquad \text{etc.} \qquad (12\text{–}13)$$

The authors thus confirmed the crux of the mechanism (12–9) proposed previously by Capron, and suggested that the chain terminated by collisions on the walls. Similar mechanisms were suggested for the radiolytic synthesis and decomposition of hydrogen bromide:

synthesis

$$H_2^+ + H_2 \rightarrow H_3^+ + H, \text{ etc.,} \quad (12\text{–}14)$$
$$Br_2 \rightsquigarrow Br_2^+ + e \rightarrow Br^+ + Br + e, \quad (12\text{–}15)$$
$$Br^+ + Br_2 \rightarrow Br_3^+,$$
$$Br_2^+ + Br_2 \rightarrow Br_3^+ + Br,$$
$$Br_2 + e \rightarrow Br + Br^-,$$
$$Br^- + Br_3^+ \rightarrow 4\,Br,$$
$$H + Br \rightarrow HBr,$$

decomposition

$$HBr \rightsquigarrow HBr^+ + e, \quad (12\text{–}16)$$
$$HBr^+ + HBr \rightarrow H_2Br^+ + Br,$$
$$HBr + e \rightarrow H + Br^-,$$
$$Br^- + H_2Br^+ \rightarrow 2H + 2Br,$$
$$Br^- + HBr \rightarrow H + 2Br,$$
$$H + H \rightarrow H_2,$$
$$Br + Br \rightarrow Br_2.$$

The chain reaction mechanism suggested for the ortho-parahydrogen conversion also holds for the isotopic exchange reactions

$$H_2 + D_2 \rightarrow 2HD,$$
$$H_2 + T_2 \rightarrow 2HT,$$

for which extremely high ionic yields are reported (Table 12–3), and for the polymerization of acetylene:

$$C_2H_2 \rightsquigarrow C_2H + H, \quad \text{(initiation)}$$
$$C_2H_2 + C_2H \rightarrow C_4H_3, \quad \text{(propagation)}$$
$$C_4H_3 + C_2H_2 \rightarrow C_6H_5,$$
$$C_nH_{n-1} + H \rightarrow C_nH_n. \quad \text{(termination)}$$

Lind and Bardwell [83] showed that when this reaction occurs in mixtures of acetylene and some inert gas (N_2, Ne, Ar, Kr, or Xe), M/N is a function of the total ionization but independent of the nature of the added gas. In these systems, the ionization potential of acetylene is lower than that of any of the inert gases added, and it appears that charge-transfer occurs,

$$C_2H_2 + Ar^+ \rightarrow C_2H_2^+ + Ar,$$

and the reaction proceeds as if C_2H_2 were the only gas being ionized. More recently, Lind and Vanpee [84] have measured the yield for the α-particle induced synthesis of water in the presence of xenon. With mixtures containing 75 to 95% of xenon, the yield is 12 times higher than in the absence of this gas, even though its ionization potential (12.1 ev) is lower than that of either hydrogen and oxygen (15.4 and 12.3 ev). Similar results had previously been reported by Gunther and Holzapfel [85] for the synthesis of water and the decomposition of ammonia by x-rays in the presence of xenon. These reactions probably involve a transfer of energy from a xenon atom in the first excited state (8.3 ev) to a molecule of the reacting gas, which then dissociates. Eyring [86] has pointed out that the Xe^+ ion is isoelectronic with the free iodine atom, and would therefore be very reactive, giving reactions such as

$$Xe^+ + NH_3 \rightarrow (XeH)^+ + NH_2. \qquad (12\text{–}17)$$

From experiments on the irradiation of gases in an electric field (mentioned above) Essex [87] believes that the initiation of radiolytic reactions by electron collision can occur by one of the four following mechanisms.

1. The recombination of oppositely charged species, as suggested by Lind

$$AB^+ + e \rightarrow A + B, \qquad AB^+ + AB^- \rightarrow 2A + 2B.$$

2. The attachment of an electron to a fragment formed in a collision process

$$N_2O + e \rightsquigarrow N_2 + O^-.$$

This mechanism may also occur to a certain extent in the hydrogen-chlorine reaction

$$Cl_2 + e \rightsquigarrow Cl + Cl^-.$$

3. The rupture of a molecule with neither attachment nor ionization

$$N_2O + e \rightsquigarrow N_2 + O + e.$$

The decomposition of azomethane is also probably of this type.

4. Molecular decomposition with ionization

$$C_2H_6 \overset{\alpha}{\rightsquigarrow} C_2H_5^- + H^+.$$

Burton and Magee [88] have also suggested that radiolytic reactions in gaseous mixtures can occur either by the transfer of excitation energy, or by charge-transfer processes via *collision complexes.* The average life of these would depend on the bonding energy of the constituents of the complex, and upon the number of vibrational degrees of freedom. These ionic complexes are in some respects similar to the clusters proposed by Lind.

12–6 Geiger-Müller counters. The operation of Geiger-Müller (or Geiger) counters underlines a number of problems directly connected with radiation chemistry and photochemistry. The basic principle is the amplification of the ionization current produced by ionizing radiation in a gas, or mixture of gases, by an appropriate voltage applied between electrodes.

When ionizing radiation passes through an ionization chamber filled with some gas which has no affinity for electrons, the charge collected at

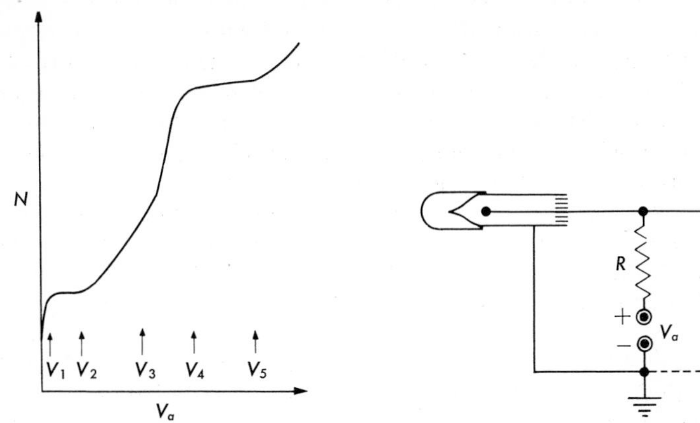

FIG. 12-4. The ionization produced in a gas as a function of applied potential.

FIG. 12-5. Schematic circuit diagram for a Geiger-Müller counter.

the anode initially increases with the applied voltage until a saturation value is reached, corresponding to the plateau V_1 to V_2 of Fig. 12-4. As the voltage is further increased, the electrons acquire sufficient energy to ionize the gas molecules and the current rapidly increases. Up to some voltage V_3, the current amplified in this way is proportional to the number of initial charges, and the voltage range V_2 to V_3 is the so-called *proportional region.* The current subsequently changes more slowly up to V_4, when it becomes virtually independent of the voltage up to V_5; V_4 to V_5 is the *Geiger region.*

A Geiger counter normally consists of two metallic cylindrical electrodes; a tube (brass, copper, nickel) about 1 to 2 cm in diameter serves as the cathode and a coaxial wire (e.g., tungsten) of the order of 0.1 mm in diameter, as the anode. The latter is supported by insulating discs at the ends of the tube. The counter contains a gas at low pressure (5 to 10 cm Hg) and is hermetically sealed. The anode is connected through a resistance of the order of 1 megohm to a stabilized d-c voltage V_a of a few hundred volts or more (Fig. 12-5). As this voltage is gradually increased, the *threshold* of the counter is reached; this is the lowest voltage beyond which the number of impulses or collisions produced by an ionizing particle varies only slightly (or not at all) with the voltage (Fig. 12-4). The *plateau,* which in well-constructed counters will be about 300 v long, has a characteristic slope determined by the various parameters of the apparatus. In this voltage region, electrons arriving at the intense field around the wire ionize further molecules, producing further secondary electrons, which in their turn produce further ionization, and so on. This is the so-called *Townsend avalanche,* in which the amplification of the initial ionization may be as high as 10^9.

Because of their greater mass, the positive ions do not have enough mobility to produce secondary ionization; they form a space charge around the wire, and this lowers the field strength sufficiently to prevent further avalanches. These only become possible again when the sheaf of positive ions has moved some critical distance from the wire. The time required for this corresponds to the *dead time* of the counter; this is normally of the order of 10^{-4} sec, and determines the rapidity of response of the counter. At voltages beyond those of the plateau, the positive space charge is not great enough to delay the discharge, which then becomes continuous.

To get correct stable working conditions, it is necessary to prevent discharges in the counter due to parasitic electrons, caused by particles not arising from the source being measured. When the positive ion reaches the surface of the cathode, it can be neutralized by an electron from the surface; furthermore the neutral gas molecule may be formed in an excited state and detach further electrons from the metal by collision, in an extremely short time interval (of the order of 10^{-2} to 10^{-13} sec). In addition, high-energy photons produced in the recombination of ions or de-excitation processes can remove photoelectrons from the cathode if the work function of the metal is lower than the photon energy. For argon, for example, the first excited state is at 11.6 v, while the work function of the metals normally used is 3.5 to 5 ev. Inert gas atoms in a metastable state can also remove electrons from these metals.

These difficulties exist only in an air-filled counter, or one containing a pure inert gas, and were eliminated in the early counters by using an electrical circuit containing a very high resistance, of the order of 10^8 to 10^9 ohms. After each discharge, the voltage fell to a value below the threshold for a time sufficient for the positive ions to be neutralized. Trost [89] showed that the discharge can be made *self-quenching* if a mixture of argon and ethyl alcohol vapor is used as the filling gas for the counter. The ionization potential of ethanol is 11.5 v and that of argon 15.7 v, so that in multiple collision processes the alcohol molecules will be ionized and the Ar^+ ions neutralized. When $C_2H_5OH^+$ ions are neutralized at the cathode by electron capture, they are left in an excited state, which undergoes dissociation or predissociation in a time comparable to that for a collision of the second kind, but no further electrons are produced. At the same time, alcohol vapor allows the metastable states of argon to decay, absorbing the photons emitted in the neutralization and de-excitation processes, and in this way prevents the emission of photoelectrons from the walls of the counter.

Other polyatomic organic molecules can be used instead of alcohol, provided that they fulfill the energetic and photochemical conditions implicit in the above processes, namely an ionization potential lower than the ionization and excitation potentials of the rare gases, and the ability to absorb photons emitted in the neutralization of the positive ions and in the energy transfer between the inert gas and the organic compound (or else, that these photons should not have sufficient energy to release electrons from the walls of the counter). Finally, the inevitable radiolytic decomposition of the organic molecules in the counter should not give products or radicals which can produce parasitic electrons in any way. Ethane, ethyl formate or acetate, amyl acetate, ether, metaldehyde, toluene, lead tetraethyl, and other polyatomic organic molecules have been used or suggested for filling self-quenching counters.

During the working of the counter, the organic molecules undergo radiolytic and photochemical decompositions and probably form free radicals. Recombination of these may form the initial compound again, but may also give rise to other gases, some of which (for example, H_2, O_2) do not have the quenching properties of the initial compound. Mass-spectrometric measurements [90] have shown that among the species found in alcohol vapor from a counter are such molecules and radicals as CH_2OH, HCO, C_2H_4, C_2H_3, C_2H_2, OH, CH_4, O, C, H_2, and H. Similarly [91] it was found that after 10^{10} counts, a counter filled with argon and ethyl acetate (molecular weight 88) contained appreciable amounts of species with molecular weights of 44 (CO_2), 28 (CO), 16 (CH_4), and others. The overall radiolytic reaction occurring in a counter filled with argon-ethanol has been represented by the stoichiometric equation [92]

$$24C_2H_5OH \rightarrow 16CH_3OH + 15C_2H_4 + CH_4 + 2H_2 + 6H_2O + CO_2. \tag{12–18}$$

In the course of time, the composition of the mixture becomes less favorable for quenching and the changing characteristics of the counter render it useless. Molecules heavier than the initial compound may also form and produce a solid deposit on the walls of the cylinder. The life of a self-quenching counter is therefore limited and depends upon the properties of the filling gas. It has been calculated that 10^{10} alcohol molecules decompose in each discharge, out of a total of 10^{20} molecules in an ordinary counter, so that the counter would be expected to be useless after 10^{10} counts. In practice, however, values 10 to 100 times lower than this are found. The life of a methane-filled counter is even lower [93], between 10^7 and 10^8 events, due to the formation of a carbonaceous deposit on both electrodes, and the simultaneous enrichment of hydrogen in the filling gas (14% after 4×10^8 counts), and of C_2H_4, C_2H_6, and C_2H_2.

The presence of molecules with an appreciable electron affinity is detrimental to the working of counters of the type just discussed. Since the negative ions have a low mobility, they can arrive near the anode between two normal impulses; if the field has then recovered to a sufficiently high value, an electron can be released and a parasitic avalanche can occur. Self-quenching mixtures can, however, be made by replacing the organic vapor by a halogen (Cl_2, or better, the less corrosive Br_2) and pure argon by neon containing a small percentage of argon [94, 95]. Such halogen-filled counters are satisfactorily self-quenching, and in theory have an infinite life, since the halogen molecule is reformed in recombination reactions. A further advantage lies in the very low threshold, between 300 and 400 v, and a negligible temperature coefficient between -50 and 100°C. In practice, however, chlorine or bromine atoms gradually become fixed on the metal cylinder, and the mixture loses its favorable characteristics. An appreciable increase in the useful life of the counter can be achieved by an appropriate pretreatment of the metal, such as electrolytic polishing [96].

References

1. A. Debierne, *Ann. phys.*, **2,** 97 (1914).
2. O. Risse, *Z. physik. Chem.*, **140,** 133 (1929).
3. P. Capron, *Ann. Soc. Sci. Bruxelles*, **55,** 222 (1935).
4. H. Eyring, J. O. Hirschfelder, and H. S. Taylor, *J. Chem. Phys.*, **4,** 479, 570 (1936).
5. H. Fricke, *J. Chem. Phys.*, **2,** 556 (1934).
6. H. Fricke and E. J. Hart, *J. Chem. Phys.*, **3,** 60, 364, 596 (1935).
7. H. Fricke and E. R. Brownscombe, *J. Am. Chem. Soc.*, **55,** 2358 (1933).
8. J. Weiss, *Nature*, **153,** 748 (1944).
9. J. Weiss, *Trans. Faraday Soc.*, **43,** 314 (1947).
10. F. S. Dainton, *J. Phys. Chem.*, **52,** 490 (1948).
11. D. E. Lea, *Action of Radiations on Living Cells*, Cambridge University Press, 1955.
12. L. H. Gray, *Proc. Cambridge Phil. Soc.*, **40,** 72 (1944).
13. L. H. Gray, *J. Chim. Phys.*, **47,** 172 (1950).
14. W. P. Jesse and J. Sadauskis, *Phys. Rev.*, **88,** 417 (1952).
15. T. E. Bortner and G. S. Hurst, *Phys. Rev.*, **93,** 1236 (1954).
16. C. J. Bakker and E. Segrè, *Phys. Rev.*, **81,** 489 (1951).
17. W. P. Jesse and J. Sadauskis, *Phys. Rev.*, **97,** 1668 (1955).
18. J. Weiss and W. Bernstein, *Phys. Rev.*, **98,** 1828 (1955).
19. W. C. Barber, *Phys. Rev.*, **97,** 1071 (1955).
20. W. F. Patton, G. S. Hurst, and T. E. Bortner, *U.S.A.E.C. report ORNL–2352*, 1957.
21. N. Miller, in *Actions Chimiques et Biologiques des Radiations*, Vol. 2, Masson, Paris, 1956, p. 149.
22. G. Bertolini, M. Bettoni, and A. Bisi, *Phys. Rev.*, **92,** 1586 (1953).
23. G. Bertolini, M. Bettoni, and A. Bisi, *Nuovo cimento*, **11,** 458 (1954).
24. C. E. Melton, G. S. Hurst, and T. E. Bortner, *Phys. Rev.*, **96,** 643 (1954).
25. R. Platzman, *Radn. Research*, **2,** 1 (1955).
26. W. P. Jesse, quoted by S. C. Lind, *J. Phys. Chem.*, **58,** 800 (1954).
27. C. Gimenez and J. Labeyrie, *J. phys. radium*, **12,** 64A (1951).
28. M. Lefort, *J. phys. radium*, **17,** 164 (1956).
29. R. K. Appleyard, *Nature*, **163,** 526 (1949).
30. G. W. Hutchinson, *Nature*, **162,** 610 (1948).
31. G. Jaffé, *Ann. Physik*, **42,** 303 (1913).
32. E. Kara-Michailova and D. E. Lea, *Proc. Cambridge Phil. Soc.*, **36,** 101 (1940).
33. L. H. Gray, *J. Chim. Phys.*, **48,** 173 (1951).
34. A. O. Allen, *J. Phys. Chem.*, **52,** 479 (1948).
35. A. O. Allen, *Discussions Faraday Soc.*, **12,** 79 (1952).
36. H. Fricke, *Ann. N. Y. Acad. Sci.*, **59,** 567 (1955).
37. A. H. Samuel and J. L. Magee, *J. Chem. Phys.*, **21,** 1080 (1953).
38. J. L. Magee, *J. Chim. Phys.*, **52,** 528 (1955).
39. R. W. Noyes, *J. Chem. Phys.*, **22,** 1349 (1954).
40. R. W. Noyes, *J. Am. Chem. Soc.*, **77,** 2042 (1955).

41. R. E. Zirkle, *Radiation Biology*, McGraw-Hill, New York, 1954, Vol. 1, Pt. 1, p. 315.
42. L. Gray, in *Actions Chimiques et Biologiques des Radiations*, Vol. 1, Masson, Paris, 1955, p. 3.
43. J. Read, *Brit. J. Rad.*, **22**, 366 (1949).
44. E. W. T. Richards, *Proc. Phys. Soc. (London)*, **A66**, 631 (1954).
45. G. C. Eltenton, *J. Chem. Phys.*, **15**, 455 (1945).
46. G. C. Eltenton, *J. Phys. Chem.*, **52**, 463 (1948).
47. H. D. Smyth and D. W. Mueller, *Phys. Rev.*, **43**, 116 (1933).
48. M. M. Mann, A. Hustrulid, and J. T. Tate, *Phys. Rev.*, **58**, 340 (1940).
49. K. J. Laidler, *J. Chem. Phys.*, **22**, 1740 (1954).
50. A. J. B. Robertson, *Trans. Faraday Soc.*, **48**, 228 (1952).
51. H. S. W. Massey, *Negative Ions*, Cambridge University Press, 1950.
52. N. E. Bradbury, *J. Chem. Phys.*, **2**, 827 (1935).
53. N. E. Bradbury and H. E. Tatel, *J. Chem. Phys.*, **2**, 835 (1935).
54. F. Bloch and N. E. Bradbury, *Phys. Rev.*, **48**, 689 (1935).
55. H. O. Pritchard, *Chem. Revs.*, **52**, 529 (1953).
56. H. O. Pritchard and H. A. Skinner, *Chem. Revs.*, **55**, 745 (1955).
57. J. L. Magee and M. Burton, *J. Am. Chem. Soc.*, **73**, 523 (1951).
58. S. C. Lind, *Chemical Effect of α-particles and Electrons*, Chemical Catalog Co., New York, 1928.
59. W. Mund, *C. R. Congres Nat. Sci. Bruxelles*, 1930.
60. L. M. Dorfman and B. A. Hemmer, *J. Chem. Phys.*, **22**, 1555 (1954).
61. S. Gotzky and P. Gunther, *Z. physik. Chem.*, **B26**, 373 (1934).
62. E. F. Ogg, *J. Phys. Chem.*, **43**, 399 (1939).
63. K. G. Brattain, *J. Phys. Chem.*, **42**, 617 (1938).
64. E. G. Zubler, W. H. Hamill, and R. R. Williams, *J. Chem. Phys.*, **23**, 1263 (1955).
65. P. Gunther and H. Leichter, *Z. physik. Chem.*, **B34**, 443 (1936).
66. C. Smith and H. Essex, *J. Chem. Phys.*, **6**, 188 (1938).
67. A. Van Tiggelen, *Bull. Soc. Chim. Belg.*, **47**, 1 (1938).
68. A. D. Kolumban and H. Essex, *J. Chem. Phys.*, **8**, 450 (1940).
69. H. N. Alyea and S. C. Lind, *J. Am. Chem. Soc.*, **52**, 1853 (1930).
70. J. G. Lewis, J. J. Martin, and L. C. Anderson, *Chem. Eng. Progr.*, **50**, 249 (1954).
71. W. Mund and C. Rosenblum, *J. Phys. Chem.*, **41**, 469 (1937).
72. S. C. Lind, *J. Chem. Phys.*, **7**, 790 (1939).
73. C. Rosenblum, *J. Phys. Chem.*, **52**, 474 (1948).
74. L. M. Dorfman and F. J. Shipko, *J. Am. Chem. Soc.*, **77**, 4723 (1955).
75. W. Mund and P. Huyskens, *Bull. Sci. Acad. Roy. Belg.*, **36**, 610 (1950).
76. W. Mund, M. Van Meersche, and J. Momigny, *Bull. Soc. Chem. Belg.*, **62**, 109 (1953).
77. W. Mund and M. Van Meersche, *Bull. Soc. Chem. Belg.*, **57**, 88 (1948).
78. S. O. Thompson and O. A. Schaeffer, *J. Chem. Phys.*, **23**, 759 (1955).
79. L. M. Dorfman and F. J. Shipko, *J. Phys. Chem.*, **59**, 1110 (1955).
80. E. Wourtzel, *Le Radium*, **11**, 289, 332 (1919).
81. E. Wourtzel, *J. Phys. (U.S.S.R.)*, **6**, 77 (1920).
82. W. Mund, *Bull. Soc. Chem. Belg.*, **36**, 19 (1927); **43**, 100 (1937).
83. S. C. Lind and D. C. Bardwell, *J. Am. Chem. Soc.*, **48**, 1575 (1926).

84. S. C. LIND and M. VANPEE, *J. Phys. Chem.*, **53,** 898 (1949).
85. P. GUNTHER and L. HOLZAPFEL, *Z. physik. Chem.*, **B38,** 211 (1937).
86. H. EYRING, *J. Chem. Phys.*, **7,** 792 (1939).
87. H. ESSEX, *J. Phys. Chem.*, **58,** 42 (1954).
88. M. BURTON and J. L. MAGEE, *J. Phys. Chem.*, **56,** 842 (1952).
89. A. TROST, *Z. Physik,* **105,** 399 (1937).
90. W. SPATZ, *Phys. Rev.*, **64,** 236 (1943).
91. S. S. FRIEDLAND, *Phys. Rev.*, **71,** 377 (1947).
92. R. W. KISER and W. H. JOHNSTON, *J. Am. Chem. Soc.*, **78,** 707 (1956).
93. E. C. FARMER and S. C. BROWN, *Phys. Rev.*, **74,** 902 (1948).
94. S. H. LIEBSON, *Phys. Rev.*, **72,** 181 (1947).
95. S. H. LIEBSON and H. FRIEDMAN, *Rev. Sci. Instr.*, **19,** 303 (1948).
96. A. BENOIST, *Le Vide,* **50,** 1475 (1954).

CHAPTER 13

THE RADIOLYSIS OF WATER AND OF AQUEOUS SOLUTIONS

13–1 The radiolysis of liquid water. More accurate recent work [1, 2] has confirmed the earlier conclusion that the radiolytic behavior of pure water depends on the type of radiation, and also on the presence or absence of oxygen. Alpha-particles from Rn^{222} cause the decomposition of deaereated water to hydrogen peroxide, hydrogen, and oxygen, and for reasonably low-energy absorption ($<2 \times 10^{20}$ ev/cm^3) the radiochemical yield G is 0.95 for H_2O_2, 1.7 for H_2, and 0.4 for O_2. These values are fairly independent of changes in the radiation intensity, of temperature, and are the same in acid and neutral solution. The same results are obtained using the α-particles from Po^{210} in 1 N sulfuric acid solution (acid is necessary to prevent the hydrolysis and precipitation of Po; see Section 7–6), provided that precautions are taken to prevent the introduction of even the smallest amount of impurity into the solution during the preparation of the source [3]. The yield $G(H_2O_2)$ is slightly greater in aereated acid solutions, with a value of 1.15 [4].

In contrast to this, no decomposition of oxygen-free water is observed with x- or γ-radiation. Hydrogen peroxide is formed, however, when oxygen is present; the yield increases with the partial pressure of oxygen, decreases with the length of irradiation and with temperature, and is pH dependent. The initial yield $G(H_2O_2)$ is between 1 and 2, depending on the experimental conditions. Fast (1-Mev) electrons decompose oxygenated water with an initial yield for hydrogen peroxide formation of $G_i = 1.15$. On the other hand, dilute solutions of hydrogen peroxide ($<10^{-2}\,M$) are only slightly decomposed by α-particles, but undergo decomposition by electrons, and by x- and γ-rays. In the absence of oxygen, this decomposition is complete, while with aereated solutions, a stationary state is set up in which decomposition is balanced by formation [5].

Toulis [6] has measured the hydrogen produced on irradiating deaereated water with accelerated helium ions (energy 7 to 40 Mev) and has found that the decomposition is proportional to the dose absorbed, and independent of the particle energy. With accelerated protons or deuterons, however, the yields of hydrogen and hydrogen peroxide decrease with the increasing energy; with 7.4-Mev protons, G_i is three times smaller than with 1-Mev protons, and a stationary state is rapidly set up. Shalek and Bonner [7] report that a stationary state is reached in the production of hydrogen peroxide even with 1-Mev protons.

The radiolytic decomposition of water is extremely sensitive to the presence of impurities. This has been especially observed [8] with irradiations in a nuclear reactor, where the quantities of hydrogen peroxide and hydrogen produced by the total radiation are highly irreproducible. A similar behavior with polonium was noted above; when the radioelement is spontaneously deposited on silver, followed by chemical separation from the support and dissolution in acid, the formation of hydrogen peroxide reaches a stationary state instead of increasing with the dose absorbed [9].

The number of water molecules actually decomposed per 100 ev by x- or γ-rays (i.e., taking no account of molecules reformed by recombination reactions) has been evaluated by indirect methods (Section 13–4) at 3.8 in neutral media, 4.6 in acid solution [10], and 3.3 in alkaline solutions [10a].

13–2 Oxidation-reduction reactions in aqueous solution. The range of radiation-induced reactions in solution is at least as wide as in the gaseous state. The yields vary considerably, not only between different compounds, but also with the physico-chemical conditions of the medium and often with the type of radiation and sometimes with the radiation intensity. The yields may also depend on the presence or absence of air. If the solute is a reducing agent, it is virtually always oxidized; strong oxidants are reduced. Table 13–1 gives the yields G for a number of oxidation reactions, and for most of the inorganic reductions known at present. For those systems in which the yield varies with the length of irradiation, the values given in the table are for the initial yields G_i. In some cases, the values given should be regarded as only approximate, since the yields may vary with the experimental conditions, which are not detailed in the table; it should also be remembered that the results reported by different authors [11] do not always agree. The yields refer to the number of molecules or ions transformed, and not to equivalents.

For all these compounds, oxidation or reduction is complete if a sufficiently large dose is absorbed. For a small number of systems, listed in Table 13–2, a stationary state is reached, which is independent of the initial species irradiated (i.e., whether oxidant, reductant, or a mixture of the two; see Fig. 13–1). Such radiolytic equilibria are not found with α-particles, except for the formation and decomposition of hydrogen peroxide

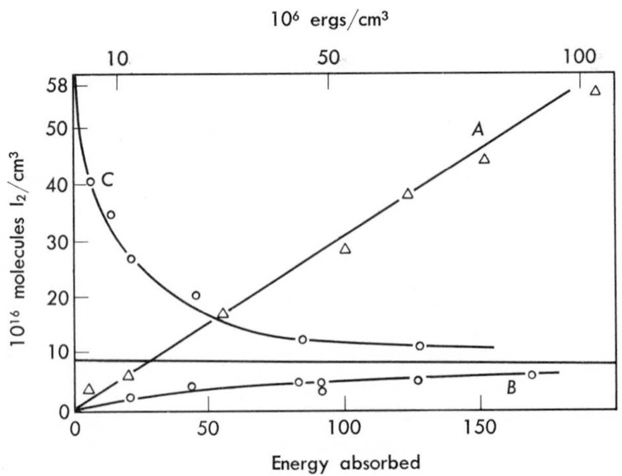

FIG. 13–1. Curve A, total oxidation of KI with α-particles; curve B, 25% oxidation with x-rays at pH 5.6; curve C, 75% reduction of I_2 with x-rays at pH 5.6.

TABLE 13–1

RADIOCHEMICAL YIELDS IN AQUEOUS SOLUTION
(a) Oxidations

Compound or ion	Initial concentration, N	Product	Potential E_h, v, at pH 0	G: α in air	G: α in vacuo	G: x or γ in air	G: x or γ in vacuo	Remarks	Ref.
H_3PO_3	8×10^{-4}	H_3PO_4	−0.27	0.8	0.6	6.9	5.2	0.8 N H_2SO_4; increases with concentration	12, 13
H_2S	$2.4\text{–}6 \times 10^{-3}$	S	−0.14			large			14
$[Fe(CN)_6]^{4-}$	10^{-4}	$[Fe(CN)_6]^{3-}$	+0.41				1.2		15
I^-	10^{-3}	I_2	+0.53		1.6–10	(See Table 13–2)		G_i increases with concentration and with acid	16
AsO_2^-		AsO_4^{3-}	+0.56		0.4–1.8	(See Table 13–2)		G_i increases with concentration and with acid	17
Fe^{2+}	$10^{-4}\text{–}10^{-2}$	Fe^{3+}	+0.77	6	3.7	15.5	6–8	0.8 N H_2SO_4	9, 18, 19, 125
NO_2^-	10^{-3}	NO_3^-	+0.94		0.4	(See Table 13–2)		Neutral solution	16
NH_4OH	0.2	NO_2^-				1.1		pH 12; varies with pH	20
N_2H_4	10^{-3}	N_2, NH_3		0.6–1.0	1.0	2.2–20	2.2	Increases with pH	21, 22
Br^-	0.5	Br_2		2–10				Varies with concentration	23, 24
Ce(III), K_2CO_3	$10^{-2}\text{–}10^{-3}$	Ce(IV)			3		1.6		25, 26, 27
U(IV)(3N H_2SO_4)		UO_2^{2+}	+0.334	3.2		10.5	1.5		28
$N_2 + O_2$		NO_2^-, NO_3^-				0.1		In alkaline solution	29

(Continued)

TABLE 13–1 (*Cont.*)

RADIOCHEMICAL YIELDS IN AQUEOUS SOLUTION
(b) Reductions

Compound or ion	Initial concentration, N	Product	Potential E_h, v, at pH 0	G				Remarks	Ref.
				α		x or γ			
				in air	in vacuo	in air	in vacuo		
$S_2O_8^{2-}$	3×10^{-3}	SO_4^{2-}	+2.05			large			30
Ce^{4+}	10^{-3}	Ce^{3+}	+1.6	3.2	3.2	2.5–3.7	2.5–3.7	Varies with energy	25, 26, 27
MnO_4^-		Mn^{2+}	+1.52		1.6–2.8	2.2–3		Varies with concentration and pH	31, 32
$Cr_2O_7^{2-}$	10^{-3}	Cr^{3+}	+1.36		2	1–1.7	2.5		33, 34
IO_3^-	10^{-3}	I_2, I^-	+1.2	0	0	0.6	0.45	Varies with pH	35, 36
Fe(III)-phenanthroline	10^{-3}	Fe(II)-phenanthroline	+1.15		0.9	10.4	~5.2	Varies with pH	37
$PuO_2^{2+}(SO_4^{2-})$	10^{-3}	Pu^{4+}	+1.04	1.6	1.6	2.4	2.4	Varies with acidity	38
Am(VI), Am(V)	3×10^{-2}	Am^{3+}	+1.69	2.6				α-particles from Am itself	39
Tl^{3+}		Tl^+	+1.25			~4			40

TABLE 13-2

RADIOLYTIC EQUILIBRIA WITH X- OR γ-RAYS

Couple	Potential, E_h, pH = 0	Ratio oxidized form : reduced form at equilibrium	Oxidized form	Ref.
I_2/I^-, pH 5.6	+ 0.53	1 : 3	increases with acid	16
AsO_4^{3-}/AsO_2^-, pH 7	+ 0.56	2 : 1	decreases with acid	17
NO_3^-/NO_2^-, pH 6	+ 0.94	3 : 2	increases with acid	16

(Section 13-1) and perhaps for the nitrate-nitrite couple. Both iodide and arsenite can be completely oxidized by radiation. Radiolytic oxidation is found much more frequently than reduction, especially with α-particles.

The radiochemical yields are often smaller with α-particles than with x- or γ-rays, particularly when the irradiated compound does not react with hydrogen peroxide. An examination of Tables 13-1 and 13-2 shows that reduction occurs only with inorganic compounds with fairly high redox potentials, greater than 0.9 v for α-particles and 0.5 v for x-rays. All the species reduced by α-particles can also be reduced by hydrogen peroxide. (Ferric *o*-phenanthroline is reduced very slowly by this reagent.) The following chapter will show that the radiolytic reactions of organic compounds in aqueous solution are also almost exclusively oxidation or hydroxylation processes.

Coloring matters seem to be a class of compounds with relatively low potentials which can be reduced by x-rays. Conclusions about the nature of these transformations have frequently been based on observations on the decolorization, change of potential, or the protective action of certain substances (Section 13-6), but none of these criteria is reliable in the absence of a precise kinetic study. Furthermore, no valency changes need take place, since the rearrangement of complex molecules can occur via intermediate organic free radicals formed in some primary irreversible oxidation. In the case of methylene blue, which has been carefully examined [42, 43], reduction in the absence of air occurs simultaneously with oxidation. Other examples of such conjugated oxidation-reduction reactions of molecular pairs will be discussed later [Fe(II) + cyclohexane, Section 13-6, and alcohol + pyridine-nucleotide, Section 14-5].

13-3 The free-radical theory. We shall now examine the interpretation of the radiolysis of water itself and of the oxidation-reduction reactions which take place in aqueous solution in terms of the free-radical theory (Section 12-1). By assuming the primary formation of the ions H_2O^+ and H_2O^-, most workers in the field agreed with Weiss that these ions decomposed by Eqs. (12-2) and (12-4),

$$H_2O^+ \rightarrow H^+ + OH, \tag{13-1}$$

$$H_2O^- \rightarrow OH^- + H. \tag{13-2}$$

Reaction between H atoms and some molecule or ion which can be reduced, such as Ce^{4+} or Fe^{3+}, results in the reduction of the latter to a lower valency state; OH radicals have the reverse effect,

$$Fe^{2+} + OH + H^+ \rightarrow Fe^{3+} + H_2O. \tag{13–2a}$$

Depending on which reaction predominates, there will be an overall reduction, oxidation, or a radiolytic equilibrium between the two valency states.

The radicals and free radicals themselves, however, can react with each other in *combination* reactions,

$$H + H \rightarrow H_2, \tag{13–3}$$

$$OH + OH \rightarrow H_2O_2, \tag{13–4}$$

$$OH + OH \rightarrow H_2O + O, \tag{13–5}$$

$$O + O \rightarrow O_2, \tag{13–6}$$

$$O + H \rightarrow OH, \tag{13–7}$$

or in *recombination*,

$$H + OH \rightarrow H_2O, \tag{13–8}$$

or in *back reactions* which regenerate H_2O molecules,

$$H_2O_2 + OH \rightarrow H_2O + HO_2, \tag{13–9}$$

$$O_2 + H \rightarrow HO_2, \tag{13–10}$$

$$HO_2 + H \rightarrow H_2O_2, \tag{13–11}$$

$$2HO_2 \rightarrow H_2O_2 + O_2, \tag{13–12}$$

$$H_2 + OH \rightarrow H_2O + H, \tag{13–13}$$

$$OH + O \rightarrow HO_2, \tag{13–14}$$

$$H_2O_2 + HO_2 \rightarrow O_2 + H_2O + OH, \tag{13–15}$$

$$OH + HO_2 \rightarrow H_2O + O_2, \tag{13–16}$$

$$H_2O_2 + H \rightarrow H_2O + OH. \tag{13–17}$$

Such a theory provides an explanation of the fact that pure degassed water irradiated with α-particles gives hydrogen peroxide, whereas with x-irradiation the H_2O_2 yield is barely measureable. Since α-particles, like protons, produce dense ionization localized around the path of the particle, there is a very large probability of OH + OH reactions between radicals from H_2O^+ ions. Dissociation of the negative H_2O^- ions, which are formed by the capture of an electron some 150 A from the α-particle track, leads to the combination reaction $H + H \rightarrow H_2$. However, since the electrons produced by the absorption of electromagnetic radiation are more uniformly distributed, the OH and H radicals are intermingled and the H + OH recombination predominates. When the water contains oxygen, the O_2 molecule acts as an acceptor of H atoms [reaction (13–10)] and hydrogen peroxide is formed by reaction (13–12) or (13–11). The greater yield often found in oxidation reactions in the presence of oxygen (Section 13–6) is also attributed to the HO_2 radical. If the water contains a solute which does not react with hydrogen peroxide, but will react with one of the free radicals formed, a higher yield would be expected for x-rays than for α-particles, as is in fact found experimentally.

The free radical theory also gives an explanation of the role of chloride and bromide ions in systems involving the formation and destruction of hydrogen peroxide. Even very low concentrations of these ions bring about the formation of small quantities of hydrogen peroxide and hydrogen in the γ-irradiation of degassed water [43, 44], while the hydrogen peroxide yield from aerated water decreases [24, 45, 46]. These observations are attributed to the reactions

$$X^- + OH \rightarrow X + OH^-, \tag{13–18}$$

$$X + H \rightarrow X^- + H^+, \tag{13–19}$$

where X^- is Cl^- or Br^-. In the presence of oxygen, therefore, there is a decrease in the HO_2 radicals and a reduction in the rate of reaction (13–10), which is necessary for the formation of hydrogen peroxide. In the absence of oxygen, reactions (13–9), (13–15), and (13–17), which involve the destruction of hydrogen peroxide, are less important.

It appears that the H atom can sometimes act as an oxidizing agent by removing another hydrogen atom from a molecule. For example, in the γ-ray oxidation of phosphorous acid, the yields imply that the two reactions

$$H_2PO_3^- + OH \rightarrow HPO_3^- + H_2O \tag{13–20}$$

and

$$H_2PO_3^- + H \rightarrow HPO_3^- + H_2 \tag{13–21}$$

are both taking place [12, 13]. The latter reaction is possible because the energy of H—H bond is greater than that of the H—HPO_3^- bond. It has also been suggested that H atoms are involved in the oxidation of Fe^{2+}, although the exact mechanism of this reaction is not very clear at the moment.

It is also possible that the OH radicals, of which hydrogen peroxide is the dimer, can reduce strong oxidizing agents, as does H_2O_2 itself. For such reagents, reactions such as

$$M^{n+} + OH + H_2O \rightarrow M^{(n-1)+} + H^+ + H_2O_2 \tag{13–22}$$

or

$$MO_x^{n-} + OH + H_2O \rightarrow MO_x^{(n+1)-} + H^+ + H_2O_2 \tag{13–23}$$

are exothermic.

Experimental evidence for the free radical mechanism has been obtained by Dainton [47], who induced the polymerization of acrylonitrile in aqueous solution by x- and γ-irradiation. The reaction doubtless requires free radicals to initiate the polymerization chain. It should also be noted that Stein and Weiss [48, 49] have shown that when benzene and other organic compounds are irradiated with x-rays, either as an emulsion with water or in aqueous solution, phenol, benzoic acid, and other oxygenated or hydroxylated derivatives are produced, even in the absence of oxygen. These results appear to be explicable only in terms of some process involving OH radicals.

13–4 Development of the theory. We saw in Section 12–3 that Allen [10, 50] has drawn attention to the importance of the δ-rays which form clusters of ion-pairs close together, and so tend to destroy the uniform distribution assumed by Lea and Gray for x- or γ-rays. Allen suggests that as in the case of the dense ionization from α-particles, but to a lesser degree, the free radicals immediately combine in these clusters to give hydrogen and hydrogen peroxide, so that the radical yields are in principle distinguishable from the "molecular yields." The proportion of the two yields would be determined by the energy of the radiation in question (i.e., by the density of the ionization), and for a given LET (Section 12–3) one can write

$$G_{-\mathrm{H_2O}} + G_{\mathrm{H}} + 2G_{\mathrm{H_2}} = G_{\mathrm{OH}} + 2G_{\mathrm{H_2O_2}}. \qquad (13\text{–}24)$$

If the irradiated solution contains appropriate amounts of solute(s), which can capture one of the radicals, but which are inert toward the molecular species, the G's in Eq. (13–24) can be determined by measuring the yields for the appropriate reaction of the solute. If one of the solutes reacts with hydrogen peroxide or hydrogen, this can be allowed for by suitable changes in the composition of the solution. The two following examples are good illustrations of the method, in both cases for γ-rays.

1. In the presence of excess oxygen, formic acid in aqueous solution reacts only with free OH radicals [51]

$$\mathrm{HCOOH + OH \rightarrow H_2O + CO_2 + H}. \qquad (13\text{–}24a)$$

The H atoms from this reaction, together with those produced directly by the radiolysis of water, react with O_2 to give HO_2 radicals, which eventually give hydrogen peroxide,

$$\begin{aligned} \mathrm{H + O_2} &\rightarrow \mathrm{HO_2}, \\ \mathrm{2HO_2} &\rightarrow \mathrm{H_2O_2 + O_2}. \end{aligned}$$

Molecular hydrogen plays no part in these reactions, and it is therefore easy to show that

$$\begin{aligned} G\,(\mathrm{CO_2}) &= G_{\mathrm{OH}}, \\ G\,(\mathrm{H_2O_2}) &= G_{\mathrm{H_2O_2}} + \tfrac{1}{2}(G_{\mathrm{H}} + G_{\mathrm{OH}}), \\ G\,(-\mathrm{O_2}) &= \tfrac{1}{2}(G_{\mathrm{H}} + G_{\mathrm{OH}}), \\ G\,(\mathrm{H_2}) &= G_{\mathrm{H_2}}. \end{aligned}$$

The yields actually measured experimentally are in parentheses, and the radical and molecular yields being sought as subscripts. From the four equations it is possible to calculate the yields G_{H}, G_{OH}, $G_{\mathrm{H_2O_2}}$, and $G_{\mathrm{H_2}}$, and consequently $G_{-\mathrm{H_2O}}$.

2. Ceric salts are reduced in acid solution by radiation, the yield being the same in the presence or absence of oxygen. This reduction is attributed to hydrogen peroxide, H, or HO_2 (in the presence of oxygen), while OH radicals bring about the back reaction

$$\begin{aligned} Ce^{4+} + H_2O_2 &\rightarrow Ce^{3+} + H^+ + HO^2, \\ Ce^{4+} + HO_2 &\rightarrow Ce^{3+} + H^+ + O_2\ , \\ Ce^{3+} + OH &\rightarrow Ce^{4+} + OH^-. \end{aligned}$$

Proceeding as before, one then has

$$\begin{aligned} G\,(Ce^{3+}) &= G_H + 2G_{H_2O_2} - G_{OH}, \\ G\,(O_2) &= G_{H_2O_2}. \end{aligned}$$

If a thallous salt is added to the solution, it is oxidized by OH [36]

$$\begin{aligned} Tl^+ + OH &\rightarrow Tl^{2+} + OH^-, \\ Ce^{4+} + Tl^{2+} &\rightarrow Ce^{3+} + Tl^{3+}. \end{aligned}$$

Under these conditions, the oxidizing OH is replaced by the reducing Tl^{2+}, and one then has

$$G\,(Ce^{3+})_{Tl} = G_H + 2G_{H_2O_2} + G_{OH}. \tag{13–24b}$$

Other systems, such as the VO_2^+/VO^{2+} couple [52], are equally suitable for these determinations. The following fairly concordant yields have been derived for acid solutions:

$$G_H,\ 3.65;\quad G_{OH},\ 2.95;\quad G_{H_2},\ 0.45;\quad G_{H_2O_2},\ 0.80;\quad G_{-H_2O},\ 4.55. \tag{13–25}$$

For neutral solutions, the values are significantly smaller [53]:

$$G_H,\ 2.9;\quad G_{OH},\ 2.4;\quad G_{H_2},\ 0.45;\quad G_{H_2O_2},\ 0.7;\quad G_{-H_2O},\ 3.8, \tag{13–26}$$

and in basic solution [10a]

$$G_H,\ 2.75;\quad G_{OH},\ 3.15;\quad G_{H_2},\ 0.30;\quad G_{H_2O_2},\ 0.10;\quad G_{-H_2O},\ 3.35.$$

The reasons for these variations are not at present obvious.

It should be noted that with a number of solutes, the yields are no longer constant at high concentrations. When the concentration is sufficiently large, the solute can enter into the clusters and react with the free radicals before they can combine with each other (H + H or OH + OH). The molecular yields therefore fall, and the radical yields increase. Such deviations have been observed in a number of cases, especially for hydrogen peroxide formation in the presence of acrylamide [54] or VO^{2+} [52], both of which are efficient OH radical scavengers. In the same way, G_{H_2} falls off with sufficiently high concentrations of certain solutes.

Analogous measurements for solutions irradiated with α-particles from Po^{210} give results which agree less well than in the case of γ-rays, and which are in some cases contradictory. Pucheault and Ferradini [56] suggest that this is related to the conditions of diffusion of the molecular products and radicals formed along the path of the α-particles. These authors believe that beyond the actual α-track, where the radicals are produced, there may be a second zone, very close to the first, in which back reactions can occur:

$$\begin{aligned} H_2O_2 + OH &\rightarrow H_2O + HO_2, \\ H_2 + OH &\rightarrow H_2O + H, \\ H_2O_2 + H &\rightarrow H_2O + OH. \end{aligned}$$

The experimental values for the molecular and radical yields therefore depend on the nature of the solute. Its ability to act as an acceptor for hydrogen peroxide, or for one of the free radicals involved (H, OH, HO_2), will determine whether or not it will, at a given concentration and intensity of radiation, react inside this zone and so prevent one or the other of the three above reactions. When solutes are classified on the basis of their ability to capture the various primary products, good agreement with the yields is found in each category. For a species which captures both H atoms and OH radicals, the following yields are found:

$$G_{OH},\ 0.70;\quad G_H,\ 0.50;\quad G_{H_2},\ 1.80;\quad G_{H_2O_2},\ 1.70;\quad G_{-H_2O},\ 4.10. \tag{13–27}$$

Despite the apparent success of the theory, there is still some uncertainty over a number of fundamental questions concerning the radiolysis of water, especially in the mechanism of the formation of the radicals. Laidler [57] has put forward the attractive proposition that the H_2O^+ ion is in a dissociative state, and that consequently OH radicals are formed by Eq. (13–1). The mass-spectrometric values, however, do not exclude the possibility that these radicals are formed in some molecule-ion exothermic reaction such as

$$H_2O^+ + H_2O \rightarrow H_3O^+ + OH.$$

There is much greater uncertainty about the mode of formation of H atoms, and as to the reality (or otherwise) of reaction (13–2) ($H_2O^- \rightarrow OH^- + H$). There is as yet no precise value for the electron affinity of the H_2O molecule, but it appears to be very low, or perhaps even zero. It has already been noted that mass spectrometry gives no evidence for the formation of H_2O^- or OH^-.

Laidler [57] has shown that the electronic configuration of these latter two ions makes the dissociation of H_2O^- into $OH^- + H$ rather improbable, and he suggests that the reaction is

$$H_2O + e \rightarrow 2H + O^-. \tag{13–28}$$

A similar hypothesis has been advanced [58] to explain the predominance of oxidation reactions in the radiolysis of aqueous solutions, but assuming the formation of H_2 in Eq. (13–28) rather than 2H. In either case, the O^- ion would subsequently react either with another water molecule

$$H_2O + O^- \rightarrow OH + OH^-, \tag{13–29}$$

or with the H^+ ion from the dissociation of H_2O^+ [Eq. (13-1)]

$$O^- + H^+ \rightarrow OH. \tag{13-30}$$

It is important to note that the dissociation of H_2O^- to $H + OH^-$ is only energetically possible because of the gain of the solvation energy of the negative ion [59]; in fact, in the gaseous state, this reaction is endothermic by about 3 ev. Platzman [60] has, however, pointed out that this process requires at least $\sim 10^{-11}$ sec, whereas dissociation reactions with capture occur in a time of the order of 10^{-13} sec. It therefore follows from the Franck-Condon principle that the electron will not be captured, and can be as much as 50 A away from the positive ion. The electron will lose energy in moving in a dielectric medium such as water by interaction with water molecules, and finally becomes "solvated"; the time for capture would therefore become comparable with that for dissociation. This slowing down of the dissociation process suggested by Platzman could have important effects on recombination reactions, and on reactions with dissolved substances.

A different approach has been developed by Magee and his collaborators [61, 62, 63] to interpret the "molecular yields" suggested by Allen. We have already mentioned the calculation by Read [64] (Section 12-3), which suggests the formation of an intense electric field between the sheath of electrons along an α-particle track and the column of positive ions. Magee, *et al.*, who have extended this idea to all ionizing radiations, believe that the electrons could be attracted by this field toward the positive ions, which would therefore be neutralized in a time of the order of 10^{-12} to 10^{-13} sec. The H_2O molecule thus reformed would be in an highly excited state, and would dissociate into $H + OH$. The principle consequence of this mechanism is the production at the same place of two radicals, which would not be separated because of the geometry of the primary ions. The probability of recombination reactions between OH and H would therefore become as relatively high for x-rays as for α-particles. The authors assume that for each hydrogen peroxide or hydrogen molecule formed, two molecules of water are reformed by combination processes.

It will be obvious from what has been said that the precise mechanism by which H atoms are formed is still uncertain, and that the actual reducing species formed in the radiolysis of water (H atom, solvated electron) is equally unidentified. Finally, we know nothing of the part played in radiolysis by molecules which are excited directly by the secondary electrons, or by some of the ions (such as OH^+) which have been found in the mass spectrometry of water vapor. The free radical theory has, however, made such considerable progress in explaining radiolytic phenomena in a relatively short time that it seems reasonable to expect that these uncertainties and difficulties will be overcome.

13-5 The effect of concentration, and other kinetic factors. It would be expected that the effect of ionization density, which shows up in the different radiolytic effects of α-particles and x-rays, would lead to a dependence of the yield with energy, or with LET (Section 12-3) for the

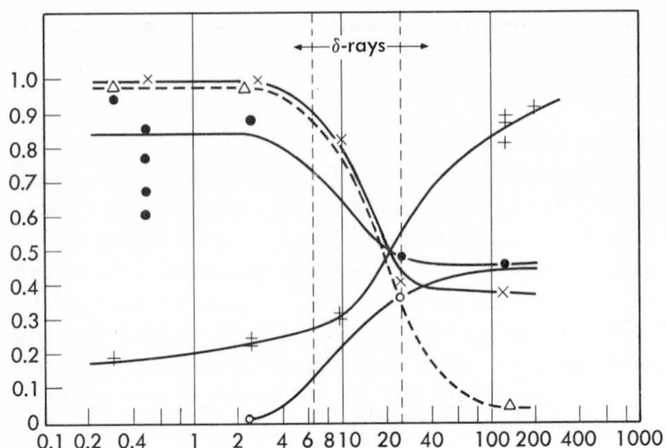

FIG. 13–2. Radiochemical yields as a function of LET (Ref. 67); ○, oxidation of Fe^{2+}; △, inactivation of carboxypeptidase; •, formation of H_2O_2 in the presence of oxygen; ×, formation of H_2O_2 in the absence of oxygen; +, formation of H_2.

same total dose of a given type of radiation (e.g., with x-ray wavelength or with electron velocity). Such variations have in fact been found in radiobiology [65] and bacteriology [66], and for a number of chemical reactions, including the formation of hydrogen peroxide and the oxidation of ferrous sulfate by x-rays or fast electrons, and the reduction of Ce^{4+} by x- and γ-rays.

Gray [67, 68] has suggested that the radiochemical yield and the radiobiological efficiency change appreciably when the LET increases from 6.5 to 24 kev/μ, but vary only a little outside these limits (Fig. 13–2). These calculations are based on the mean LET, obtained by dividing the total energy of all the trajectories by the total length. This is, however, an average of values which vary from 1 to 3 along the path of a ~5-Mev α-particle, and from 1 to 300 for fast electrons. Gray has recently attempted to calculate the yields for a spectrum which expresses the rate of energy loss (dE/dx) as a function of the energy at different points along the path.

The yield is found to be independent of the intensity of the radiation in the oxidation of ferrous sulfate, potassium ferrocyanide, potassium iodide, benzene, and formic acid, and in the reduction of Ce^{4+} and potassium permanganate. On the other hand, the yield varies with the intensity in the decomposition of hydrogen peroxide by x-rays in the absence of air, the formation of H_2O_2 in the presence of air, the oxidation of ferrous sulfate in the presence of organic impurities, and certain other radiolytic reactions. An intensity dependence often shows up in systems which involve chain reaction mechanisms.

If an aqueous solution of some appropriate substance is irradiated at constant intensity, the yield is frequently found to be proportional to the time of irradiation (and hence to the dose absorbed) virtually up to com-

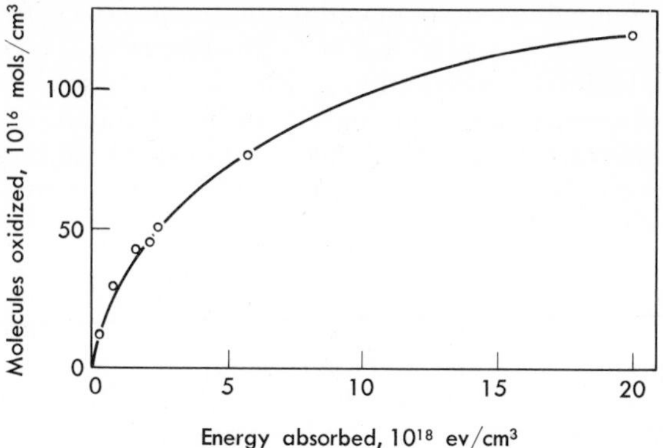

FIG. 13–3. Oxidation of phosphorous acid; dependence on dose absorbed. [M. Cottin, *Thesis*, Paris (1956)]

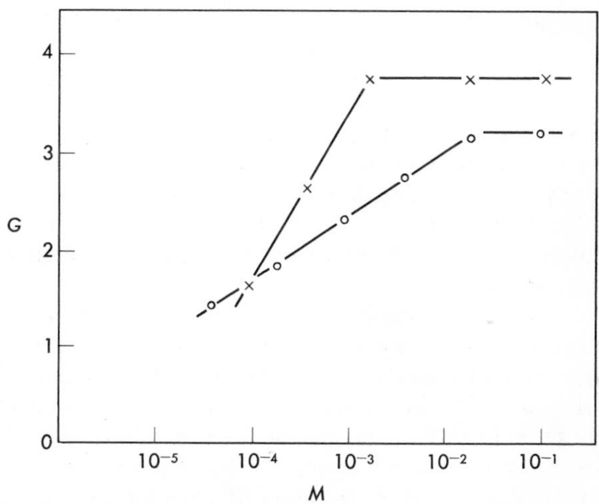

FIG. 13–4. Oxidation of phosphorous acid; dependence of G on concentration; ×, pH 0.0; ○, pH 4.3. [M. Cottin, *op. cit.*]

plete transformation; one example of this is the oxidation of ferrous sulfate. In other cases, the yield decreases as the reaction proceeds (Fig. 13–3). This is always the case for radiolytic reactions which come to some equilibrium state (Fig. 13–1), or when the yield varies strongly with the solute concentration. Care must therefore be taken to distinguish between mean yield and the initial yield G_i.

In very dilute solution, at concentrations below 10^{-3} M, the initial yield generally increases approximately proportionally with concentration, but there is little variation at medium concentrations, up to about 0.1 to 0.2 M (Fig. 13–4). The initial variation with concentration, established by Fricke for the reduction of diochromate and later by Dale, *et al.*

[69], for other compounds and named by him the *dilution effect*, led Fricke to propose the idea of "activated water." The free radical mechanism provides a good qualitative explanation of this; in dilute solution, there is a competition between radical combination and recombination reactions on the one hand and reaction with the solute on the other, and these latter predominate increasingly with concentration. When all the free radicals are used up in reaction with the solute, the yield can no longer vary with concentration.

In this concentration region, one can neglect direct effects due to the action of fast particles on the solute molecules or ions without involving intermediate products and species derived from the solvent in the reaction scheme. In concentrated solution, however, direct absorption of energy by the solute cannot be neglected. This may result either in a further increase of yield, or the setting up of some other reaction which was energetically improbable with radicals. The first established example of this behavior appears to have been the oxidation of potassium iodide [16], for which the initial yield G_i as a function of the concentration at constant pH is given by the relation

$$G_i = A_1 + a_1 e^{-k_1/c_0} + a_2 e^{-k_2/c_0}, \tag{13–31}$$

where c_0 is the initial concentration of iodide, and a_1, a_2, k_1, and k_2 are constants whose value depends upon the type of radiation (that is, α-particles or x-rays). This equation is compatible with the interpretation given above.

A direct effect, which is different from the indirect radiolytic reaction, has been observed [17] in the oxidation of arsenious acid by α-particles from radon. In solutions with $c_0 > 0.2\,M$, the oxidation is accompanied by the formation of elementary arsenic, with a yield which increases with concentration. At concentrations above 60%, the γ-irradiation of sulfuric acid [70] results in decomposition with the formation of sulfur dioxide. Other oxygenated acids, such as perchloric acid [71], release oxygen by direct action at much lower concentrations. Direct effects may be superimposed on the indirect reaction, at very high intensities, even in dilute solution. Platzman [72] has suggested that even in dilute solution the sub-excitation electrons (Section 12–2), which cannot ionize or excite the solvent, may interact directly with the solute.

Equation (13–31) shows that the radiochemical yield depends on the initial concentration c_0 and not on the concentration at any instant. This is also true for the oxidation of arsenite, and for a number of other radiolytic reactions such as the deamination of glycine [73], the oxidation of aminobenzoic acids [74], the oxidation of riboflavine and niacine [75], the inactivation of enzymes [76, 77], etc. In all these cases, the rate constant k varies with the initial concentration c_0 according to the equation

$$kDt = \log_e \frac{c_0}{c}, \tag{13–32}$$

where D is the dose per unit time. This equation can be deduced from a differential kinetic equation established by Weiss [78] and Dainton [79] by assuming that the irradiated substance and the product of the radiolysis have the same probability of reacting with the active radical. For the stationary state of a solution containing a single solute, the differential equation can be written

$$\frac{dn}{dt} = rD - k_1nc - k_2n(c_0 - c) - \sum_i k_inx_i = 0, \qquad (13\text{–}33)$$

where n is the radical concentration, r is the number of radicals formed per unit energy absorbed, and the last term expresses the disappearance of the radical in all other combination, recombination, or back reactions with radicals or molecules of concentration x_i. It follows from this that

$$n = \frac{rD}{k_1c + k_2(c_0 - c) + \sum_i k_ix_i}, \qquad (13\text{–}34)$$

and

$$-\frac{dc}{dt} = k_1nc = \frac{k_1rDc}{k_1c + k_2(c_0 - c) + \sum_i k_ix_i}. \qquad (13\text{–}35)$$

To obtain the first-order equation (13–32), it is only necessary to assume that

$$\frac{k_1}{k_1c + k_2(c_0 - c) + \sum_i k_ix_i} = \text{const} = k_0, \qquad (13\text{–}36)$$

so that one then has

$$-\frac{dc}{c} = k_0rDdt,$$

and on integrating between $t = 0$ and $t = t$,

$$k_0rDt = \log_e \frac{c_0}{c}. \qquad (13\text{–}37)$$

This is identical with Eq. (13–32) apart from the values of the constants.

These approximations are probably valid for the very complex molecules mentioned above, for which it can be assumed that the action of a given radical on all the molecular species present can be properly expressed by a constant such as Eq. (13–36), irrespective of the concentration of the particular species in question. They are not valid for the radiolytic oxidation of arsenite [17], potassium iodide [16], and of leuco-fluorescein [16], or for the liberation of HCl from certain organic chlorides [80]. In these latter reactions, and probably in a number of other cases also, the constant k in Eq. (13–32) is itself a function of c_0,

$$\frac{k'}{c_0} Dt = \log_e \frac{c_0}{c}. \qquad (13\text{–}38)$$

This can be derived from Eq. (13–36) if we neglect the latter term in the denominator and assume $k_1 = k_2$. The first approximation can be reasonably assumed for sufficiently concentrated solutions, but the second hypothesis is ruled out, at least for arsenite and potassium iodide. We saw earlier that the x-ray induced oxidation of these two compounds produces a stationary state condition, which varies with pH, but this never corresponds to

$$\frac{\text{Oxidized form}}{\text{Reduced form}} = 1,$$

as would be required for k_1 and k_2 to be equal.

The stationary state approach again fails to give satisfactory results when it is applied to the effect of radiation intensity on certain radiolytic reactions, such as the x-ray decomposition of hydrogen peroxide [81, 82] or its formation by pile radiation [83]. The reason for these difficulties is probably related to the nonuniform distribution of the radicals in the solution, and the necessity of distinguishing between radical reactions along the same track, and those which are due to diffusion or the crossing of tracks. It seems that this problem should consequently be approached by the considerably more difficult nonstationary state method.

13–6 Competition, and medium effects. If a solution contains two solutes, each of which can react with the solvent radiolysis products, competition will take place for these species, and one of the compounds may consequently undergo virtually no reaction. This *protection effect* was observed by Fricke [84] in the x-irradiation of aqueous solutions of acetic acid; the addition of formic acid considerably decreased the amount of oxidation, even if the concentration of the protective agent was 100 times less than that of the acetic acid. Gallico and Camerino [85] found the same effect for the decoloration of methylene blue by x-rays in the presence of formic acid, malonic acid, gelatin, etc. Saturated compounds such as formaldehyde, ethyl alcohol, and galactose are less efficient than unsaturated compounds [86].

Dale and his co-workers [87, 88, 89] have made a careful study of protection effects in the inactivation of enzymes. They define the protective power P of one compound p upon another i (which they call the *indicator*) by the ratio

$$P = \frac{D_{p+i} - D_i}{D_i} = \frac{q_i}{q_r}, \tag{13–39}$$

where D_{p+i} and D_i are the doses required to produce a given change in i in the presence and absence of p, and q_i and q_p are the weights of the two compounds. The values found for the inactivation of carboxypeptidase by x-irradiation are given in Table 13–3. It will be seen that the protective powers of thiourea and urea differ by a factor of about 5000. Similarly, phenol, allyl alcohol, and ascorbic acid are 10^3 to 10^6 times more efficient in the protection of ovalbumin against denaturization by radiation than is acetic acid [90]. The high protective power of thiourea is probably due to the presence of a sulfur atom, since other sulfur compounds such as cysteine, cystamine (β-mercaptoethylamine), glutathione, sodium thiosulfate, and sulfur itself inhibit various radiolytic and radiobiologic reac-

TABLE 13-3

PROTECTIVE POWER P IN THE INACTIVATION OF CARBOXYPEPTIDASE

Protective agent	P
Thiourea	4.7
Sodium formate	3.1
Dimethyl thiourea	1.9
Glucose	0.79
Dimethylurea	0.4
Ovalbumine	0.24
Alloxane	2.1×10^{-2}
Sodium oxalate	2×10^{-3}
Urea	7.5×10^{-4}

tions such as the inactivation of enzymes [91] or chromosomic aberrations [92]. In Section 14-10, we shall see that a large number of compounds have a protective action on animals irradiated *in vivo*.

The study of protection effects is therefore obviously of both practical and theoretical importance. From the theoretical point of view, the comparison of the protective properties of different compounds gives information about their radiosensitivity, and eventually on the nature of the radical or radicals involved in the competition. Unfortunately, the unambiguous interpretation of the results is always very difficult, since the competition may be not only between the irradiated compounds, but also between these and the various final and intermediate products. It is especially difficult to draw reliable conclusions from competition experiments on complex organic molecules and, *a fortiori*, on enzymes or microorganisms. For example, Forssberg [93] explained the protection effects in the x-irradiation of catalase in terms of the reducing action of the H atom on various organic substances; in particular the protective effect of pyruvic acid was attributed to its reduction to lactic acid. In fact, Bella [94] subsequently showed that it is the reverse reaction (lactic acid → pyruvic acid) which occurs on irradiation.

It should also be noted that the relative protective efficiency of two compounds can vary in different conditions. The protective power of oxalic acid is six times greater than that of methanol in the radiative decomposition of formic acid, but methanol is an efficient protective agent for oxalic acid itself [90]. Moreover, a simple mechanistic treatment of competition, and the definition of protective power [Eq. (13-39)] both show that the latter should remain constant per unit mass, whereas in fact it decreases slightly with increasing concentration; this is especially true for glucose and dimethylurea in the protection of carboxypeptidase [89].

Finally, under certain conditions a protective agent may behave as a *sensitizer*. Clark and Coe [32] have shown that ethanol, benzene, and other organic compounds can accelerate the x-ray reduction of ceric sulfate in acid solution. Similarly, ascorbic acid and methionine sensitize the x-ray

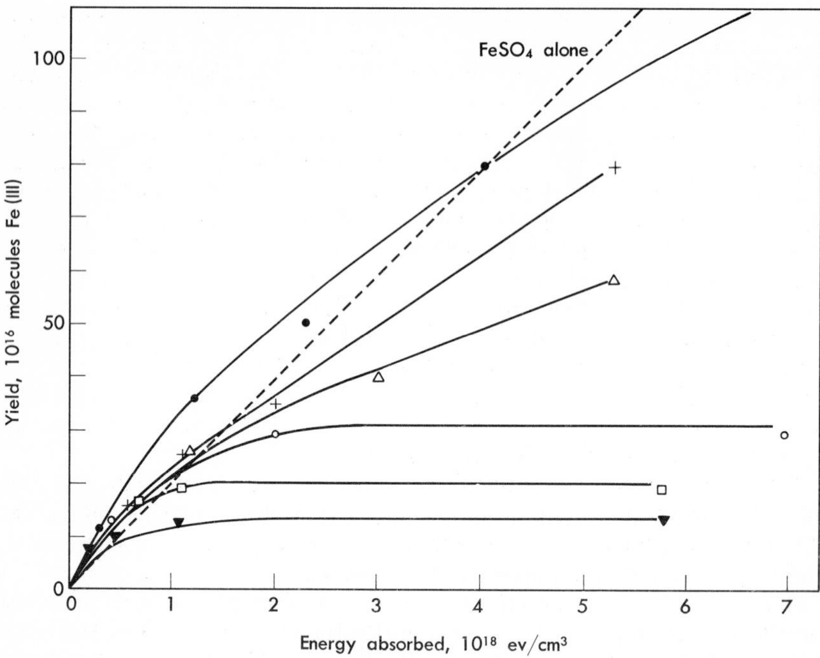

FIG. 13–5. The effect of various alcohols on the oxidation of ferrous sulfate in the presence of air (Refs. 97 and 98).

transformation of nicotinic acid [95, 75]. Dewhurst [96] has reported strong sensitization in the oxidation of ferrous sulfate in air by Co^{60} γ-rays in the presence of various aliphatic alcohols. It was subsequently shown [97, 98] the similar effects are produced by benzene, xylene, cyclohexane, hexane, and other aliphatic hydrocarbons. For all the compounds examined, however, sensitization occurs only with small doses or short irradiations; with long irradiations, the average yield for the formation of Fe^{3+} decreases and drops below the normal value. Taking this as $G = 15.5$, the values found in the presence of cyclohexane with an x-ray intensity of 7400 r/min were $G = 27$ after 1 min and 11.9 after 10 min; with xylene, the figures were $G = 28.5$ after 1 min and 5.7 after 1 hr. Similar results have been obtained with alcohols (Fig. 13–5). The mechanism of these reactions is not yet clearly established, but is very probably a chain reaction involving intermediate organic peroxides. Kolthoff and Medalia [99] have suggested a similar scheme for the reaction between ferrous sulfate and hydrogen peroxide in the presence of organic compounds. The decrease in the yields with the length of irradiation is the result of the competition for the oxygen taken up by the organic products; if oxygen is continually bubbled through the solution gas during the irradiation, the oxidation yield remains virtually constant [100]. In a deaereated solution containing cyclohexane, the ferric ions are reduced; with benzene a stationary ferrous-ferric state is observed [101].

Dewhurst has also noted that sodium chloride acts as an antisensitizer inasmuch as it reduces the yield for the oxidation of ferrous sulfate in the presence of alcohols to the normal value. In sufficiently high concentration, sodium chloride suppresses or decreases the formation of hydrogen peroxide in the irradiation of aereated water with x-rays [102] or α-particles [103]. The chloride itself apparently undergoes no radiolytic reaction. The opposite effect has been observed with "inert" electrolytes such as magnesium sulfate and lithium sulfate which decrease the yield of hydrogen peroxide in pile-irradiated water [104] where the source of the radiation was the nuclear process $Li^6(n, \alpha)T$. These results are no doubt due to the formation of intermediate products (for example, chlorine atoms or unstable peroxides) in reactions with species arising from the radiolysis of the solvent, and the subsequent removal of these in inverse reactions with the same solvent derivatives. The overall result is that the latter species are catalytically decomposed, a phenomenon analogous to the chemically catalysed decomposition of hydrogen peroxide.

The importance of the composition of the medium is particularly illustrated by the effect of oxygen on radiolytic reactions. The considerable influence of this gas on the formation of hydrogen peroxide by x- or γ-irradiation, and on the yields of various reactions has already been discussed (Table 13–1), and will be met again in Chapter 14 in considering the effect of radiation on organic compounds. The oxidation of some organic compounds will occur only in the presence of oxygen, especially in the case of hydroquinone, pyrogallol, gallic acid, tyrosine, etc [105, 106]. In the absence of oxygen, quinone is reduced [107] to hydroquinone.* Some polymers are degraded only in the presence of oxygen (Section 15–6). The aberration of chromosomes [108, 109, 110] and the destruction of micro-organisms [95] are also strongly reduced by lowering the oxygen pressure.

Radiochemical yields are also often affected by the pH of a solution, but the changes are usually in the sense which would be expected from the influence of the acidity on the chemical reactivity of the system, so that the changes in yield are caused by chemical rather than radiolytic phenomena. In some cases, however, especially in the decomposition or formation of hydrogen peroxide at different pH's, the acidic nature of the products of the radiolysis of water should be considered.

At the appropriate pH, a number of oxidation processes, including the oxidation of hydrazine [21], uranous sulfate [28], and phosphorous acid [12, 13] show considerably increased yields in the presence of oxygen. The measured G values (greater than 10 to 20) have been taken as evidence of chain reactions in which the oxygen becomes "activated" and takes part in the oxidation, with the regeneration of the free radicals. This activation is probably due to electron transfer to the O_2 molecule from an unstable radiolytic product, free radical, intermediate oxidation state

---

* New experiments by C. Vermeil and her co-workers show that quinone is reduced to hydroquinone even in the presence of oxygen, and that hydroquinone undergoes degradation, probably by an oxidative mechanism, without producing any quinone.

of the solute, etc. [111]. For hydrazine, for example, the reaction scheme would be

$$N_2H_4 + OH \rightarrow N_2H_3 \rightarrow N_2H,$$
$$N_2H \rightleftharpoons N_2^- + H^+,$$
$$N_2^- + O_2 \rightarrow N_2 + O_2^-,$$
$$N_2H_4 + O_2^- \rightarrow N_2H_3 + HO_2^-, \text{ etc.},$$

and similarly for U(IV)

$$U(OH)^{3+} + OH \rightarrow UO_2^+ + 2H^+,$$
$$UO_2^+ + O_2 \rightarrow UO_2^{2+} + O_2^- (+ H^+ \rightarrow HO_2),$$
$$U(OH)^{3+} + HO_2 \rightarrow UO_2^{2+} + H^+ + OH, \text{ etc.}$$

13–7 Colloidal solutions. There are a large number of reports in the literature, mostly dating from before 1940, on the coagulation and stabilization of colloidal solutions by ionizing radiations. The experiments were mostly performed on three types of negatively or positively charged colloids; (a) metallic hydrosols of elements such as gold, silver, copper, lead, etc.; (b) hydroxides and sulfides such as $Fe(OH)_3$, $Ce(OH)_3$, $Cu(OH)_2$, As_2S_3, etc.; (c) proteins. This is probably the most confused part of radiation chemistry, because of the contradictory results reported by different authors. This is perhaps less surprising when the extremely complex nature of the problem is considered. We shall see in Section 14–6, that the radiolysis of proteins causes fundamental chemical changes, and a number of simpler compounds are eliminated from the parent species. It must also be remembered that neither of the other two groups of colloidal solutions is pure, since the presence of electrolytes is necessary for their stability. The overall result therefore often represents changes in the colloidal species, allied with purely chemical, competition, and protection effects, which are especially sensitive to the method of preparation and the conditions of the medium. In addition, the irradiated solutions are usually polydisperse, that is to say they contain micelles of nonuniform dimensions and of variable stability.

Finally it should be noted that different authors have used different methods to measure the radiolytic changes, including the ultramicroscope, rate of electrophoresis, color change, viscosity, rate of floculation, sensitivity to the addition of electrolytes or other colloids, etc., so that the criteria chosen as a measure of changes in stability are not necessarily always comparable in different experiments.

The differences between different authors show up most clearly in experiments on negative colloids, since there is some general agreement about the behavior of positive colloids, which coagulate or become less stable on irradiation. Clarck and Pickett [112] report, however, that the positively charged hydrosols of lead are stabilized by x-rays. Annetts [113] quotes several pieces of evidence that metallic sols or proteins coagulate at the same rate, independent of their charge, when irradiated with x-rays. Annetts himself reached a similar conclusion from experiments on the

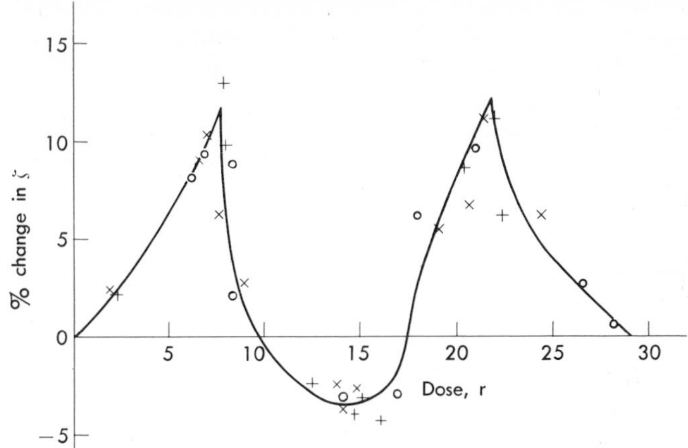

FIG. 13–6. The periodic variation in the stability of colloidal graphite with dose (Refs. 119, 120, 121); +, 0.43 r/sec; ○, 0.15 r/sec; ×, 0.022 r/sec.

cathode-ray bombardment of sols of Pt, Au, Ag, Cu, Bi, Pb, $Fe(OH)_3$, As_2S_3, etc.

In contrast to this opinion, other authors report that negative colloids either undergo a slight stabilization [114, 115] or show no change at all [116, 117]. This conclusion has been confirmed [118] by more recent experiments on the irradiation of colloidal solutions of copper, silver, and gold (prepared by Bredig's method) either with γ-rays from radium, or with neutrons produced in a cyclotron by the D + D reaction, or from a Ra/Be source. The change of stability was followed by photocolorimetric measurements of the optical density. In every case, the positively charged micelles of copper coagulated after an irradiation time which decreased with increasing intensity. Negatively charged silver is stabilized in most cases, the effect being more pronounced for low initial stabilities. The stabilization of the negative gold colloid is less apparent, and is in any case smaller. The stabilization of silver is often preceded by an induction period (of the order of 10 hr with a 400-mc radium source), and practically no change is observed during this period, which is often followed by a decrease in stability, especially in neutron irradiations.

This latter result is probably connected with the curious phenomenon discovered by Crowther and his co-workers [119, 120, 121]. These authors irradiated colloidal solutions of graphite, gold, ferric hydroxide, ovalbumin, etc., with x- or γ-rays. Measurements of the electrokinetic potential ζ, obtained from the rate of electrophoresis, revealed a periodic variation in ζ with the dose. The fluctuations were sinusoidal in character, and for graphite in particular, the maxima and minima were observed with doses as low as 8 to 15 r; the effect still persists with doses as high as 25,000 r. The curve in Fig. 13–6 shows that the changes are independent of intensity (0.43, 0.15, or 0.022 r/sec). The extent of this behavior varies with the dimensions of the particles, with charges of 10% for the largest and 50%

for the smallest. There is an appreciable temperature coefficient, with a 70% increase between 4 and 52°C. The effect appears to be reproducible, as Gray [122] has confirmed by irradiating graphite sols with neutrons from the (D + D) reaction.

Not only has this (perhaps secondary) phenomenon received no explanation, but even the simple and apparently well-established results, namely that positive colloids are coagulated and negative sols are slightly stabilized, have yet to receive interpretation. As early as 1929, Crowther [123] showed that the effects of radiations on colloids are indirect, with the solvent acting as intermediate in some way. Crowther showed in fact that for equal energy absorption by the solvent, β-particles (from the radium active deposit) and x-rays have the same effect on the hydrosols of Cu and $Ce(OH)_4$. He suggested that negative micelles are protected by a sheath of water which prevents the positive ions from penetrating into the double layer, whereas free electrons can reach the positive micelles, neutralize their charge, and so bring about coagulation.

An interpretation of the different behavior of the two colloid species in terms of free radicals is not immediately obvious. However, if it is assumed that H and OH radicals are formed, one could have transfer reactions such as

$$(\text{micelle})^{n+} + m\text{H} \rightarrow (\text{micelle})^{(n-m)+} + m\text{H}^+, \tag{13–40}$$

$$(\text{micelle})^{n-} + m\text{OH} \rightarrow (\text{micelle})^{(n-m)-} + m\text{OH}^-, \tag{13–41}$$

as currently assumed for radiolytic oxidation-reduction processes. On this basis, however, coagulation should always occur, irrespective of the sign of the charge on the micelle. It has therefore been suggested [118] that the OH radicals first undergo a charge-transfer reaction with the ions and molecules of the solution and the double layer, forming OH^- ions. These subsequently cause changes in the double layer, similar to those observed on adding an electrolyte containing a strongly adsorbable anion (i.e., decreased stability for positive micelles, stabilization of negative micelles). If the initial stability of the latter is already rather large, and especially if it is due to OH^- ions as in the case of negatively charged hydroxides, radiation will produce a very small change (or no change at all). This theory therefore predicts a considerable dependence in the medium, and on the method of preparing the sol.

A different view has been advanced by Nanobashvili and Bakh [124], who irradiated various metal hydroxide sols with x-rays and found that the sols of those elements which have only one valency state (Al, Si) are unaffected by radiation. In other cases, the change of the stability could be related to increases or decreases of the charge on the micelles as the result of oxidation-reduction processes. This interpretation does not, however, seem to be of general application; thus thorium hydroxide coagulates on irradiation, and titanium hydroxide is stable. Both elements, however, can form peroxides without a change of valency, and the difference in behavior is therefore attributed by these authors to the insolubility of the thorium peroxide, which makes the particles less stable.

13–8 Chemical dosimetry. The principles of the physical methods of *dosimetry* of the quantity of radiation emitted by a γ- or x-ray source have already been outlined in Section 11–7. For approximate measurements, an air-wall chamber of the Victoreen type is normally sufficient, provided that it has been standardized for the wavelength in question. Other precise methods of determination raise particular experimental difficulties, and introduce uncertainties in the interpretation of the results. Apart from these difficulties, it is *a priori* more desirable that in radiation chemistry the energy absorbed should be directly determined by measuring the radiochemical yield in some appropriate system, which would require only one standardization against some physical dosimeter.

Such a dosimeter should satisfy several conditions, the most important of which is that the yield be independent, over wide limits, of the concentration, of the energy and intensity of the radiation, and of the total dose absorbed. It is also desirable that the system should be relatively insensitive to the presence of impurities and to the nature of the containing vessel. Finally, a relatively simple analytical method should be available to measure the chemical change. The Fe(II) $\rightarrow$ Fe(III) oxidation, which can be easily measured spectro-photometrically, comes closest to fulfilling these requirements. This dosimeter, normally an aereated solution of Mohr's salt, $(NH_4)_2\,Fe(SO_4)_2 \cdot 6H_2O$, at a concentration of 10^{-3} to $10^{-2}\,N$ in $0.8\,N$ (or $0.1\,N$) sulfuric acid is widely favored in radiation chemistry. For some time, different authors reported yields with deviations as large as 30% [125]. With Co^{60} and Ra γ-rays, and x-rays with energies of about 100 kv, several authors found $G \approx 21$, while others reported 15 to 15.6, and a number of intermediate values. Carefully controlled measurements in different laboratories, using different physical methods of calibration (calorimetry, absolute ionization chambers, charge measurements) showed that the disagreements were mainly due to the variation of the yield with energy, and to errors in the physical standardizations. It is now well established that for γ-rays from Co^{60} or Ra, and for electrons with energies between 0.1 and 2 Mev, the correct value of G is 15.6 ± 0.1 [125]. For x-rays from a molybdenum anticathode (i.e., electrons with an average energy of 10 kev), measurements give $G = 14.15$ [126], and from copper (8 kev), $G = 13.4$; for the β-particles from tritium (5.6 kev), $G = 12.8$ [127]. With the Po α-particles, various authors find $G = 5.8 \pm 0.2$. For the corpuscular radiation from the $B^{10}(n, \alpha)Li^7$ reaction occurring in reactors, $G = 4.0 \pm 0.4$.

The oxidation yield is independent of the Fe(II) concentration, at least between 0.1 and 0.01 N, and independent of acidity between 0.1 and 4 N, provided that allowance is made for the effect of electron density on the absorption of the radiation. The temperature coefficient of the reaction is $0.04 \pm 0.03\%$ per degree [128]. To protect the oxidation against sensitization by organic impurities, the additions of small quantities of sodium chloride (about 0.005%) to the solution is sometimes recommended (Section 13–6). This should not, however, be regarded as completely efficient.

Rudstam and Svedberg [129] have claimed that the sensitivity of the ferrous sulfate dosimeter is considerably increased if the ferric ions formed are measured radiometrically. These authors used solutions of $(NH_4)_2\,Fe(SO_4)_2 \cdot 6H_2O$ containing Fe^{59} ($t_{1/2} = 45$ days); after irradiation with

Co^{60} γ-rays, the ferric ion was extracted as the thiocyanate into isoamyl alcohol and the activity of the organic phase measured with a Geiger counter. This technique can be used to measure between 1 and 100 r with a precision of $\pm$2r.

A number of other chemical dosimeters have been proposed. Jerome Weiss [130] suggests that the reduction of ceric sulfate in acid solution is a more appropriate reaction than the oxidation of ferrous sulfate, although many other workers would not agree with this; ceric salts are photosensitive, and rather unstable chemically. The radiolytic hydrolysis of various organic chlorine compounds such as chloroform [131, 132] or chloral hydrate [133] has also been suggested. A chain reaction gives hydrochloric acid in high yield, and this can be measured either colorimetrically or conductimetrically. With this latter method, doses between 50 and 100 r can be measured. Other authors have proposed systems involving the decolorization of methylene blue [134], the transformation of benzene plus water into phenol [135], the polymerization of acrylonitrile (followed dilatometrically) [136], and the decomposition of oxalic acid in aqueous solution [137]. For the last system, the yield is independent of radiation intensity, temperature, initial concentration, and pH (below pH 2) over a wide range of absorbed doses (up to 30% decomposition). It seems that this dosimeter should be particularly suitable for large doses, of more than a megarad.

Day and Stein [138] have reported a method based on the x-ray decolorization of methylene blue incorporated in a gell such as agar-agar or gelatine; this not only measures the dose, but also gives the spatial distribution of the radiation. Proctor and Goldblith [139] used tartrazine or methylene blue dissolved in agar-agar in a similar study of cathode rays. Solid dosimeters based on luminescence are discussed in Chapter 16.

It has been suggested that the total radiation from a nuclear reactor (i.e., neutrons plus γ-rays), can be measured by determining manometrically the gas given off by an aqueous solution of potassium iodide [140]. By adding boric acid to the solution, it should be possible to determine the yield due to the neutrons, which bring about the $B^{10}(n, \alpha)Li^7$ reaction. The γ-radiation from a reactor could be measured to within about 10% by following the reduction of ferric orthophenanthroline ($G_\gamma = 9.7$), taking advantage of the fact that this compound is reduced only slightly by corpuscular radiation ($G_\alpha = 1.1$) [141].

References

1. P. Bonet-Maury and M. Lefort, *Compt. rend.*, **226,** 173 (1948).
2. M. Lefort, *J. Chim. Phys.*, **47,** 624 (1950); **48,** 339 (1951).
3. M. Anta and M. Lefort, *J. Chim. Phys.*, **51,** 29 (1954).
4. M. Anta, *Thesis*, Paris, 1955.
5. M. Ebert and J. W. Boag, *Discussions Faraday Soc.*, **12,** 189 (1952).
6. W. J. Toulis, *U.S.A.E.C. report UCRL–583*, 1950.
7. R. J. Shalek and T. W. Bonner, *Nature*, **172,** 259 (1953).
8. A. O. Allen, C. J. Hochanadel, J. A. Ghormley, and T. W. Davis, *J. Phys. Chem.*, **56,** 575 (1952).
9. M. Anta and M. Haïssinsky, *Compt. rend.*, **235,** 170 (1952).
10. A. O. Allen, *Radn. Research*, **1,** 85, (1954).
10a. M. Haïssinsky and P. Patigry, *J. Chim. Phys.*, **59,** 675 (1962).
11. For further details, see A. O. Allen, *Radiation Chemistry of Water*, New York, 1961.
12. M. Cottin and M. Haïssinsky, *J. Chim. Phys.*, **50,** 195 (1953).
13. M. Cottin, *J. Chim. Phys.*, **51,** 404 (1954).
14. O. Risse, *Z. physik. Chem.*, **A140,** 133 (1929).
15. H. Fricke and E. J. Hart, *J. Chem. Phys.*, **2,** 824 (1934).
16. M. Lefort, *J. Chim. Phys.*, **47,** 179, 624 (1950).
17. M. Haïssinsky and H. Lefort, *J. Chim. Phys.*, **48,** 429 (1951).
18. J. Wilkinson and N. Miller, *Trans. Faraday Soc.*, **50,** 690 (1954).
19. M. Lefort, *Compt. rend.*, **237,** 159 (1953).
20. T. Rigg, G. Scholes, and J. Weiss, *J. Chem. Soc.*, **1952,** 3034.
21. M. Lefort and M. Haïssinsky, *J. Chim. Phys.*, **53,** 527 (1956).
22. H. A. Dewhurst and M. Burton, *J. Am. Chem. Soc.*, **77,** 5781 (1956).
23. C. J. Hochanadel, *J. Phys. Chem.*, **56,** 587 (1952).
24. T. J. Sworski, *J. Am. Chem. Soc.*, **76,** 4687 (1954).
25. M. Haïssinsky, M. Lefort, and H. LeBail, *J. Chim. Phys.*, **48,** 208 (1951).
26. T. J. Hardwick, *Can. J. Chem.*, **30,** 23 (1952).
27. C. J. Hochanadel and J. A. Ghormley, *J. Chem. Phys.*, **21,** 880 (1953).
28. M. Haïssinsky and M. Duflo, *J. Chim. Phys.*, **53,** 970 (1956).
29. V. D. Orekhov, A. I. Chernova, and M. A. Proskurnin, *Symposium on Radiation Chemistry*, Moscow, 1955, p. 69 (English translation).
30. R. Glocker and O. Risse, *Z. Physik*, **48,** 845 (1928).
31. F. C. Lanning and S. C. Lind, *J. Phys. Chem.*, **42,** 1229 (1938).
32. G. L. Clark and W. S. Coe, *J. Chem. Phys.*, **5,** 97 (1937).
33. M. Lefort, P. Radhakrishna, and M. Haïssinsky, *J. Chim. Phys.*, **48,** 435 (1951).
34. C. J. Hochanadel and T. Davis, quoted by A. O. Allen, *1955 Geneva Conference*, P. 738.
35. M. Lefort, *J. Chim. Phys.*, **51,** 351 (1954).
36. N. Todd and S. L. Whitcher, *J. Chem. Phys.*, **20,** 1172 (1952).
37. M. Lefort and J. Pucheault, *J. Chim. Phys.*, **50,** 580 (1953).
38. M. Pagès, *Thesis*, Paris, 1960.
39. L. B. Asprey and S. E. Stephanou, *U.S.A.E.C. report AECU–924*, 1950.
40. T. J. Hardwick, personal communication.

41. E. COLLINSON, *Discussions Faraday Soc.*, **12**, 285 (1952).
42. V. D. OREKHOV, A. I. CHERNOVA, and M. A. PROSKURNIN, Ref. 29, p. 75.
43. C. J. HOCHANADEL, *J. Phys. Chem.*, **56**, 587 (1952).
44. A. M. KOULKÈS-PUJO, *Compt. rend.*, **246**, 1203 (1958).
45. T. J. SWORSKI, *Radn. Research*, **2**, 26 (1955).
46. A. M. KOULKÈS-PUJO, *Compt. rend.*, **245**, 2510 (1957).
47. F. S. DAINTON, *Nature*, **160**, 268 (1947).
48. G. STEIN and J. WEISS, *Nature*, **161**, 650 (1948).
49. G. STEIN and J. WEISS, *J. Chem. Soc.*, **1949**, 3245.
50. A. O. ALLEN, *Discussions Faraday Soc.*, **12**, 79 (1952).
51. E. J. HART, *Radn. Research*, **1**, 53 (1954).
52. J. PUCHEAULT and C. FERRADINI, *J. Chim. Phys.*, **54**, 659 (1957); **55**, 772 (1958).
53. A. O. ALLEN and H. A. SCHWARZ, *1958 Geneva Conference*, P. 1403.
54. E. COLLINSON, F. S. DAINTON, and G. S. MCNAUGHTON, *Trans. Faraday Soc.*, **53**, 357 (1957).
55. J. PUCHEAULT, *Compt. rend.*, **246**, 409 (1958).
56. J. PUCHEAULT and C. FERRADINI, *1958 Geneva Conference*, P. 1232.
57. K. J. LAIDLER, *J. Chem. Phys.*, **22**, 1740 (1954).
58. M. HAÏSSINSKY and M. MAGAT, *Compt. rend.*, **233**, 954 (1951).
59. J. L. MAGEE and M. BURTON, *J. Am. Chem. Soc.*, **73**, 523 (1951).
60. R. PLATZMAN, in *Basic Mechanisms in Radiobiology*, Vol. 2, National Research Council, Washington, 1953, p. 22.
61. J. L. MAGEE, *Basic Mechanisms in Radiobiology*, p. 51.
62. A. H. SAMUEL and J. L. MAGEE, *J. Chem. Phys.*, **21**, 1080 (1953).
63. H. A. DEWHURST, A. H. SAMUEL, and J. L. MAGEE, *Radn. Research*, **1**, 62 (1954).
64. J. READ, *Brit. J. Rad.*, **22**, 366 (1949).
65. H. M. PATT, *Nucleonics*, **12**, No. 12, 42 (1954); see also Section 14–6.
66. S. A. GOLDBLITH, *et al.*, *Food Research*, **18**, 659 (1953).
67. L. H. GRAY, in *Actions Chimiques et Biologiques des Radiations*, Vol. 1, Masson, Paris, 1955, p. 3.
68. L. H. GRAY, *J. Chim. Phys.*, **52**, 519 (1955).
69. W. M. DALE, W. J. MEREDITH, and M. C. K. TWEEDIE, *Nature*, **151**, 280 (1953).
70. C. J. HOCHANADEL, J. A. GHORMLEY, and T. J. SWORSKI, *J. Am. Chem. Soc.*, **77**, 3215 (1955).
71. B. MILLING, G. STEIN, and J. WEISS, *Nature*, **170**, 710 (1952).
72. R. L. PLATZMAN, *Radn. Research*, **2**, 1 (1955).
73. W. M. DALE, J. V. DAVIES, and C. W. GILBERT, *Biochem. J.*, **45**, 93 (1949).
74. M. CORSON, S. A. GOLDBLITH, B. E. PROCTOR, J. R. HOGNESS, and W. H. LANGHAM, *Arch. Biochem. Biophys.*, **33**, 263 (1951).
75. B. E. PROCTOR and S. A. GOLDBLITH, *Nucleonics*, **3**, No. 2, 32 (1948).
76. W. M. DALE, *Biochem. J.*, **34**, 1367 (1940).
77. W. M. DALE, L. H. GRAY, and W. J. MEREDITH, *Phil. Trans. Roy. Soc. (London)*, **242**, 33 (1949).
78. J. WEISS, *Trans. Faraday Soc.*, **43**, 314 (1947).
79. F. S. DAINTON, *Research*, **1**, 486 (1948).
80. W. MINDER, *Radiol. Clinica*, **19**, 277 (1950).

81. J. Weiss, *Discussions Faraday Soc.*, **12,** 161 (1952).
82. E. J. Hart and M. S. Matheson, *Discussions Faraday Soc.*, **12,** 169 (1952).
83. J. Pucheault, M. Lefort, and M. Haïssinsky, *J. Chim. Phys.*, **49,** 286 (1952).
84. H. Fricke, E. J. Hart, and H. P. Smith, *J. Chem. Phys.*, **6,** 229 (1938).
85. E. Gallico and B. Camerino, *Experientia*, **4,** 109 (1948).
86. W. Minder and D. Schoen, *Strahlenther.*, **91,** 126 (1953).
87. W. M. Dale, *Biochem. J.*, **36,** 80 (1942).
88. W. M. Dale, *Brit. J. Rad.*, suppl. 1, 46 (1947).
89. W. M. Dale, J. V. Davies, and W. J. Meredith, *Brit. J. Cancer*, **3,** 31 (1949).
90. H. Fricke, *Symposium on Radiation Dosimetry*, Vol. 1, Army Chemical Center, Maryland, U.S.A., 1950, p. 24.
91. E. S. G. Barron and S. R. Dickman, *J. Gen. Physiol.*, **32,** 595 (1949).
92. K. Mikaelsen, *Science*, **116,** 172 (1952).
93. A. Forssberg, *Nature*, **159,** 308 (1947).
94. S. Di Bella, *Boll. Soc. Ital. Biol. Sper.*, **25,** 1268 (1949).
95. B. E. Proctor and S. A. Goldblith, *Nucleonics*, **5,** No. 3, 56 (1949).
96. H. A. Dewhurst, *J. Chem. Phys.*, **19,** 1329 (1951).
97. C. Vermeil, M. Cottin, and M. Haïssinsky, *J. Chim. Phys.*, **49,** 437 (1952).
98. C. Vermeil, M. Cottin, and M. Haïssinsky, *Compt. rend.*, **235,** 542 (1952).
99. I. M. Kolthoff and A. I. Medalia, *J. Am. Chem. Soc.*, **71,** 3777, 3784 (1949).
100. C. Vermeil, *Thesis*, Paris, 1956.
101. C. Vermeil and M. Cottin, *J. Chim. Phys.*, **51,** 24 (1954).
102. E. S. G. Barron, L. Seki, and P. Johnson, *Arch. Biochem. Biophys.*, **41,** 188 (1952).
103. T. Sworski, *Radn. Research*, **2,** 26 (1955).
104. M. Haïssinsky and J. Pucheault, *J. Chim. Phys.*, **49,** 294 (1952).
105. J. Loiseleur, *Bull. Soc. Chim. Biol.*, **25,** 22 (1943).
106. J. Loiseleur and R. Latarjet, *Compt. rend. Biol.*, **135,** 1534 (1941).
107. N. Waterman and H. Limburg, *Biochem. Z.*, **263,** 400 (1933).
108. J. M. Thoday and J. Read, *Nature*, **160,** 608 (1947).
109. B. Hayden and L. Smith, *Genetics*, **34,** 26 (1949).
110. N. H. Giles and H. P. Riley, *Proc. Natl. Acad. Sci. U.S.*, **35,** 640 (1949); **36,** 337 (1950).
111. M. Haïssinsky, *J. Chim. Phys.*, **53,** 542 (1956).
112. G. L. Clark and L. W. Pickett, *J. Am. Chem. Soc.*, **52,** 465 (1930).
113. M. Annetts, *J. Phys. Chem.*, **39,** 509 (1935).
114. J. A. Crowther and J. A. V. Fairbrother, *Phil. Mag.*, **4,** 325 (1927).
115. F. L. Hopwood and J. T. Phillips, *Nature*, **136,** 1026 (1935).
116. A. Boutaric and M. Roy, *Compt. rend.*, **196,** 1020 (1933).
117. S. S. Bathnager, R. S. Gupta, K. G. Mathur, and K. N. Mathur, *Z. Physik*, **56,** 684 (1929).
118. M. Haïssinsky and W. Gluzbarg, *Compt. rend.*, **233,** 1192 (1951).

119. J. A. Crowther and H. Liebmann, *Nature,* **140,** 28 (1937); **143,** 598 (1939).

120. J. A. Crowther, *Nature,* **141,** 609 (1938); **142,** 569 (1938).

121. J. A. Crowther, H. Liebmann, and R. Jones, *Phil. Mag.,* **26,** 120 (1938); **28,** 64 (1939).

122. L. H. Gray, J. Read, and H. Liebmann, *Brit. J. Rad.,* **14,** 102 (1941).

123. J. A. Crowther, *Phil. Mag.,* **7,** 86 (1929).

124. E. M. Nanobashvili and N. A. Bakh, Ref. 29, pp. 93, 103.

125. See N. Miller in *Actions Chimiques et Biologiques des Radiations,* Vol. 2, Masson, Paris, 1956, p. 149.

126. M. Cottin and M. Lefort, *J. Chim. Phys.,* **53,** 267 (1956).

127. W. R. McDonell and E. J. Hart, *J. Am. Chem. Soc.,* **76,** 2121 (1954).

128. H. A. Schwarz, *J. Am. Chem. Soc.,* **76,** 1587 (1954).

129. G. Rudstam and T. Svedberg, *Nature,* **171,** 648 (1953).

130. Jerome Weiss, *Nucleonics,* **10,** No. 7, 28 (1952).

131. G. V. Taplin, C. H. Douglas, and B. Sanchez, *Nucleonics,* **9,** No. 2, 73 (1951).

132. J. W. Kanwisher, *Nucleonics,* **10,** No. 5, 62 (1952).

133. H. L. Andrews and P. A. Shore, *J. Chem. Phys.,* **18,** 1165 (1950).

134. Y. L. Shekhtman, A. A. Krasnovskii, and I. V. Vereshchinskii, *Doklady Akad. Nauk S.S.S.R.,* **74,** 767 (1950).

135. M. J. Day and G. Stein, *Nature,* **164,** 671 (1949).

136. A. Prevot-Bernas, *Compt. rend.,* **230,** 288 (1950).

137. I. G. Draganic, *J. Chim. Phys.,* **56,** 9 (1959).

138. M. J. Day and G. Stein, *Nucleonics,* **8,** No. 2, 34 (1951).

139. B. E. Proctor and S. A. Goldblith, *Nucleonics,* **7,** No. 2, 83 (1950).

140. E. J. Hart and S. Gordon, *Nucleonics,* **12,** No. 4, 40 (1954).

141. J. Pucheault, *Compt. rend.,* **240,** 772 (1955).

CHAPTER 14

THE RADIOLYSIS OF ORGANIC COMPOUNDS AND THE BIOLOGICAL EFFECTS OF RADIATION

14–1 Hydrocarbons. Since the primary processes involved in the radiolytic decomposition of the relatively simple H_2O molecule are far from understood, it would not be reasonable to expect to find well-established mechanisms for the radiolysis of organic compounds. For one thing, the experimental data are much less numerous and widely dispersed. In addition, these compounds generally contain a large number of atoms, and as a result decomposition frequently produces a considerable number of solid, liquid, and gaseous products, which may be either lighter or heavier than the initial molecule. The analysis of these products, often formed in very small quantities, is extremely difficult (and sometimes impossible), and it is very difficult to establish a mass balance. Finally, the number of ions and neutral intermediates produced in the primary act is incomparably greater than in the case of water; for example, bombardment of benzene with 70-ev electrons results in the formation of 44 ionic species; for cyclohexane the corresponding number is 48 [1].

A knowledge of the structure of molecules and of bond energies suggests *a priori* that certain bonds are more likely to be broken than others, but these predictions are rather unreliable and in many cases not borne out in practice. For example, the probabilities of radiolytic rupture of C—C, C—N, and C—O bonds agree well with the bond energies, whereas the comparatively abundant production of hydrogen in the irradiation of hydrocarbons, acids, and other organic compounds appears to indicate that the C—H bond breaks more easily than the C—C bond, although in fact the latter has the lower bond energy [2]. Similarly, as already noted in Section 13–2, the energy required to produce an ion is an unreliable indication of its relative abundance. The appearance potentials of $C_2H_5^+$ and $C_2H_4^+$ are very similar (12.9 and 12.1 v) but the relative proportion of the two ions in the dissociation of C_2H_6 in a mass spectrometer is about 1:5.

After making allowance for the other reservations mentioned earlier (Section 12–2), Magat and Viallard [3] have been able to deduce a number of very useful general rules for use in radiation chemistry, from the mass-spectrometric data on hydrocarbons. These refer in particular to the probability of the simple ionization process to give the parent ion $RH \rightarrow RH^+$. The main rules are as follows:

1. The percentage of parent ion formed decreases along an homologous series with increasing chain length, going from 46.6 to 0.87% from methane to *n*-dodecane, and from 40.1 to 0.8% from ethylene to *n*-decene-1.

2. The presence of a double or triple bond in a short chain causes an increase in the proportion of parent ions; the reverse is found for long chains. In the ethylene series, the inversion occurs around hexene, and in the acetylenes around butyne-1.

3. Chain-branching lowers the percentage of the parent ion.

4. The percentage of parent ion is higher with saturated cyclic compounds than with the corresponding acyclic compounds. The values are particularly high in the benzene series, being 43.5% for benzene itself. The introduction of aliphatic groups decreases this percentage, the reduction increasing with the aliphatic chain length.

5. For the saturated alkanes, the proportion of ions formed by simple hydrogen atom abstraction decreases with chain length, so that there is a decrease from 84 to 0.015% from ethane to heptane. The introduction of a double bond increases this proportion, so that the value is 22% for C_3H_8 and 63.7% for C_3H_6; the corresponding values for n-C_4H_{10} and C_4H_8-1 are 2.47% and 11.5%, respectively.

6. For ions with the same number of carbon atoms and in the same series, the number of fragments with an odd number of hydrogen atoms is greater than the number of ions with one hydrogen atom more or less. For example, the proportions of C_3 species formed from hexane are

$C_3H_7^+$	$C_3H_6^+$	$C_3H_5^+$	$C_3H_4^+$	$C_3H_3^+$	$C_3H_2^+$	C_3H^+	C_3^+
100	50.4	92.7	4.7	28.1	1.57	0.37	0.0

7. The ease of rupture of the C—H bond in an aliphatic series increases [4] in the order

$$\text{H—C}_{\text{primary}} < \text{H—C}_{\text{secondary}} < \text{H—C}_{\text{tertiary}}.$$

On the other hand, in the aromatic series, the abundance decreases when the number of hydrogen atoms bonded to carbon is increased.

8. The simultaneous rupture of two C—C bonds is very unusual in saturated, unbranched, aliphatic compounds, but does occur in branched or cyclic hydrocarbons.

9. The number of doubly charged ions, and of H^+ or H_2^+ ions, is very small.

The first systematic study of the radiolytic behavior of hydrocarbons was carried out by Lind and Bardwell [5, 6], who bombarded methane, ethane, propane, and butane with α-particles from radon and found that the H_2/CH_4 ratio in the gas phase was of the order of 5. Also formed were higher (and partly unsaturated) hydrocarbons, in which the number of carbon atoms increased with the increasing molecular weight of the initial hydrocarbon. After long irradiation, a liquid and a solid phase were also found. The M/N ratio was always about 2.

Schoepfle and Fellows [7] obtained rather similar results in the *in vacuo* irradiation of saturated C_6 to C_{14} paraffinic hydrocarbons with 170-kv cathode rays. Large quantities of hydrogen were detected, along with light saturated hydrocarbons, and liquid and solid condensation products. As the molecular weight of the target hydrocarbon was increased, the proportion of hydrogen in the gaseous phase rose, but the yield relative to the total decomposition fell. Increasing the number of methyl groups increased the yield of methane. Burton [8] has deduced from these experiments that in a given homologous series, the yield of the various radiolysis products are determined by the nature and relative abundance of the appropriate groups in the molecule, provided that no specific chemical effects affect the decomposition. Much lower yields of gaseous products were obtained from the analogous unsaturated hydrocarbons, a result attributed to the saturation of the double bonds by atoms and free radicals produced in the radiolysis. Unsaturated compounds also have a strong tendency to undergo polymerization.

Aromatic hydrocarbons, and especially benzene itself, are very resistant to the action of radiation, and the yields are very small, both in terms of gas produced (G_g) and of polymer formation (G_p). For example, Burton [9, 10] irradiated benzene with 1.5-Mev electrons and found $G_g = 0.059$, which is some 100 times smaller than the value found for cyclohexane ($G_g = 6$). The resistance of aromatic hydrocarbons to radiolysis has been attributed to the ease with which the energy can be transferred to the benzene nucleus; because of the delocalization of the π-electrons, the acquired energy is rapidly distributed throughout the molecule before any given bond can be particularly affected, and the energy is dissipated by collision before decomposition can occur.

Gordon and Burton [11] investigated the radiolytic behavior of mixtures of $C_6H_6 + C_6D_6$ and found evidence for a self-protection effect. Perdeutero-benzene has a zero-point energy which is 1.1 kcal/mole lower than that of normal benzene, and is even more resistant to radiolysis. When a liquid mixture of the two isotopic molecules was irradiated with 1.5-Mev electrons, the yields of H_2, HD, C_2H_2, and C_2D_2 were found to be lower than the values calculated from the additivity rule, so that there is a mutual protection effect due to dissipation of the excitation energy. Similar effects have been found in the irradiation of mixtures of benzene and toluene, cyclohexane, or cyclohexene [12]. A rather complex transfer of energy to the compound with the lowest ionization potential or excitation potential is observed, and this causes a decrease in the yields.

Transfer by coupling is more important in the condensed state, where it is additionally favored by the "cage effect" first suggested by Franck and Rabinowich. The polymerization yield in irradiation of liquid benzene with accelerated electrons is $G_p = 0.5$ [13]; the value for the irradiation of the vapor (with α-particles) is $G_p = 4$ [14]. A total yield $G = 4.9$ has been reported more recently for irradiation of the vapor with α-particles [15]. The yield for the decomposition of cyclohexene is particularly high ($G = 16.3$). It is, of course, always possible that the type of radiation is significant in such experiments. In fact, pile irradiation (n + γ) of toluene, mesitylene, *iso*propylbenzene, and *t*-butylbenzene gives yields 10 to 30% higher than those found in irradiations with 1.5- to 1.8-Mev electrons [16]. Likewise, the H_2/CH_4 ratio is twice as high in the reactor experiments.

A sensitive method for determining the nature and quantity of the radicals formed in the radiolysis of organic compounds has been described by Williams and Hamill [17], and applied to hydrocarbons by Gevantman and Williams [18]. Before irradiating a gas (CH_4, $C_2H_4 \ldots C_5H_{10}$) with x-rays, γ-rays, or 2-Mev electrons, small quantities of radioactive iodine (scavenger) were added to pick up the radicals formed; subsequent separation and analysis of the products then allowed the radicals to be identified. Gevantman and Williams showed that except for methane, the radicals which arise from the primary decomposition of the parent molecule by hydrogen abstraction (C_2H_5, C_3H_7, etc.) are a relatively small fraction of the total yield. For all the gases irradiated, appreciable quantities of CH_3I (from the CH_3 radical) were found, but very little HI. The effect of molecular structure shows up in the radical yields from the various isomers of pentane:

	CH_3	C_2H_5	n-C_3H_7	n-C_4H_9	n-C_5H_{11}	CH_2
n-pentane	24	30	6	5	22	13
neopentane	80	4	2	6	2	6

The predominant formation of CH_3 from neopentane is probably due to the reaction

$$C(CH_3)_4 \rightsquigarrow C(CH_3)_3^+ + CH_3 + e, \qquad (14\text{–}1)$$

since in the mass spectrometer the maximum intensity corresponds to the $C_4H_9^+$ ion [19, 20]. For the radiolysis of normal pentane the process

$$C_5H_{12} \rightsquigarrow C_3H_7^+ + C_2H_5 + e \qquad (14\text{–}2)$$

must play some considerable part; in mass spectrometry the maximum corresponds to this same $C_3H_7^+$ ion.

Radioactive iodine has also been used [21] to scavenge the radicals formed in the radiolysis of n-heptane, trimethylpentane, and cyclohexane. Magat, Chapiro, and their collaborators [22, 23] have used the compound 1-1-diphenyl-2-picryl-hydrazyl (DPPH)

$$(C_6H_5)_2N\text{—}N\text{—}C_6H_2(NO_2)_3$$

as a radical scavenger in their investigations of the radiolytic behavior of organic compounds. This easily crystallized compound is a stable free radical, and being colored, is easily measurable. Despite its stability, it has the drawback of being sufficiently reactive to undergo capture by excited molecules, ions, double bonds, nonradical products of radiolytic decompositions, or impurities. The reaction with other free radicals is affected by the presence of oxygen. The nature of the products which it forms in capture, or in subsequent decomposition reactions, are not yet clear, so that a good deal of care must be exercised in using this method [24].

In the presence of oxygen, the irradiation of hydrocarbons with 80-kv x-rays or 0.8 to 0.9-Mev electrons results in the formation of peroxides, aldehydes, ketones, and acids [25, 26]. With heptane, iso-octane, and toluene, the peroxides are of the type R_1OOR_2, ROOH, and H_2O_2; cyclohexane gives R_1OOR_2 and ROOH, and benzene R_1OOR_2 and H_2O_2. The yields (G) of peroxides are of the order of 1 to 2, depending on the target material; similarly for carbonyl compounds $G = 0.6$ to 2, and for acids 0.2 to 0.6. Benzene gives no acid, but produces phenol ($G = 0.6$) and benzaldehyde ($G = 0.45$). The mechanism of peroxide formation is further discussed in Section 14–5.

14–2 Alcohols, aldehydes, and acids. McLennan and Patrick [27] bombarded methanol and ethanol vapors with cathode rays and analyzed the gaseous products, which included large quantities of H_2, CO, CO_2, CH_4, plus small quantities of C_2H_4 and C_2H_2. With ethanol, ethane was also found. Formaldehyde and acetaldehyde were also produced. Cathode rays cause these latter two compounds to polymerize, and also to decompose to H_2, CO, CO_2, CH_4, and other gases.

A systematic study of ten different alcohols from methanol to n-decanol, including the four isomeric butanols, was carried out by McDonell, using 28-Mev α-particles [28, 29, 30]. The gaseous products were analyzed mass spectrometrically. In addition to hydrogen and saturated hydrocarbons resulting from reduction of the target material, the primary alcohols gave aldehydes and glycol, the secondary alcohols gave aldehydes, ketones, and glycols, and the tertiary alcohols yielded ketones and small quantities of glycols. Carbon monoxide and water were always found among the products. For all the alcohols investigated, the overall yield (G) of reduced products was between 7 and 8. These results are compatible with the idea that the radiolytic products are formed in fairly simple primary reactions, involving the rupture of the groups around the carbinol function

$$\begin{array}{c} \mathrm{OH} \\ | \\ -\mathrm{C}-\mathrm{CH_3} \\ | \end{array}$$

without any rearrangement or complex chain reactions occurring. The reaction proceeds as if the attack were localized around the electronegative OH group, which would weaken the bonds to neighboring groups by polarization, and hence renders them more easily ruptured. However, the stoichiometric balance shows that increasing the number of carbon atoms increases the tendency for groups far from the carbinol group to be oxidized. The total reactivity decreases in the order

$$\begin{array}{c} | \\ -\mathrm{C}-\mathrm{H} \\ | \\ \mathrm{OH} \end{array} > \begin{array}{c} | \\ -\mathrm{C}-\mathrm{Et} \\ | \\ \mathrm{OH} \end{array} > \begin{array}{c} | \\ -\mathrm{C}-\mathrm{Me}. \\ | \\ \mathrm{OH} \end{array}$$

As with hydrocarbons, C—H bonds are broken more easily than C—C bonds. McDonell attributes this result to the greater ease with which the hydrogen atom escapes from the Franck-Rabinowitch cage in the liquid phase, compared with the heavier fragments formed by the rupture of a C—C bond.

The yield of free radicals in the γ-irradiation of methanol in air has been evaluated at $G = 19.7$ by the DPPH method; for propanol, the value is 24.6. The presence of oxygen brings about a considerable increase in the yield for the decomposition of ethanol [31] by x-rays or fast electrons, going from $G = 9$ to more than 25. The products include acids and peroxides.

Several workers have studied the radiolysis of the fatty acids in connection with the problem of the origin of petroleum. Lind and Bardwell, on the basis of the α-particle experiments mentioned earlier, have suggested that under suitable geological conditions petroleum could be formed by the condensation of light hydrocarbons under α-particle bombardment. This is contrary to the theory widely held by geologists that petroleum was formed from solid or semisolid organic sediments. Bell, Goodman, and Whitehead [32] have consequently suggested that these sediments could have been transformed into light and heavy hydrocarbons by the effect of the α-particles from radon and its daughter products. A number of authors in the United States [33, 34, 35] have subsequently irradiated paraffinic fatty acids, from acetic to melissic (C_{30}), with radon or accelerated deuterons, and have analyzed the various decomposition products. The main reactions observed are dehydrogenation and decarboxylation, which show up in the production of large quantities of H_2, CO_2, and unsaturated acids:

$$CH_3(CH_2)_xCH_2COOH \rightsquigarrow CH_3(CH_2)_xCH_3 + CO_2, \qquad (14\text{–}3)$$

$$CH_3(CH_2)_xCH_2CH_2(CH_2)_yCOOH \rightsquigarrow CH_3(CH_2)_xCH{=}CH(CH_2)_yCOOH + H_2. \qquad (14\text{–}4)$$

The gas phase also contains small quantities of CO, H_2O, and light hydrocarbons from methane to butane. In addition, the heavier acids give higher molecular weight hydrocarbons. The carbon dioxide yield is a linearly decreasing function of the chain length, while the hydrogen yield increases linearly up to C_{16}, decreases up to C_{22}, and then increases once more. The (smaller) yield of H_2O also goes through a maximum at C_{16}. The formation of CO, CO_2, and H_2 in the decomposition of palmitic acid is found to increase with the temperature at which the bombardment is carried out (from -70 to 150°C). On the whole, these results are compatible with the idea that petroleum is of radiolytic origin.

The irradiation of oleic acid with accelerated deuterons gives polymeric acids, heptadecene, and about 2% stearic acid [36]. The formation of this last compound shows that hydrogen produced in the radiolysis of one molecule is able to saturate the double bond of a neighboring molecule. Bombardment of benzoic acid gives only small quantities of gas, 85% of which is carbon dioxide and 1.8% hydrogen.

Unlike the results found with ethanol, the total yield in the radiolytic decomposition of acetic acid is virtually independent of the absence or presence of oxygen ($G = 5.9$ and 6.2 respectively), but with CH_3COOH

TABLE 14–1

YIELDS OF Cl_2 AND Br_2 FROM THE IRRADIATION OF ORGANIC HALOGEN COMPOUNDS [41]

Compound	Total dose, 10^{21} ev	T, °C	G
CCl_4	15.4	−187	0.96
CBr_4	15.4	18	0.14
C_2Cl_6	6.2	18	0.075
C_2Cl_6	6.2	−187	0.075
C_6Cl_6	7.7	18	0.02

the products include peroxides, acetone, and formaldehyde, in addition to carbon dioxide and other gases [37].

14–3 Halogen compounds. The irradiation of carbon tetrachloride with γ-rays from radium was studied as early as 1917 by Kailan [38], who reported that the main reaction was the production of free chlorine. This gas is also produced with x-rays [39, 40], fast electrons, and α-particles from radon [41]. The yield depends on the type of radiation, and also on the total dose, the intensity, and the physical state of the tetrachloride. Carbon tetrabromide CBr_4 is more resistant to radiolysis than is CCl_4; C_2Cl_6 and C_6Cl_6 are more resistant still. Table 14–1 shows the G values found for the irradiation of these compounds with 410-kev electrons. The results for C_2Cl_6 suggest that the temperature has no effect on the yield.

The radiolysis of chloroform, either pure or in petroleum ether or cyclohexane solution, has been studied by Gunther [40]. In the absence of oxygen, HCl is formed in quantities which are proportional to the dose, with a very high yield ($G = 110$). This implies a chain reaction, which may be written as

$$CHCl_3 \rightsquigarrow CHCl_2 + Cl, \qquad (14\text{–}5)$$

$$CHCl_3 + Cl \rightarrow HCl + CCl_3, \qquad (14\text{–}6)$$

$$CHCl_3 + CCl_3 \rightarrow CCl{\cdot}CHCl_2 + Cl_2 + Cl, \text{ etc.}, \qquad (14\text{–}7)$$

or

$$CHCl_3 \rightsquigarrow CCl_3 + H, \qquad (14\text{–}8)$$

$$CHCl_3 + H \rightarrow H_2 + CCl_3, \text{ etc.} \qquad (14\text{–}9)$$

In the presence of oxygen and of moisture, the reactions become more complex, since HClO is formed, and the HCl yield increases several-fold.

Solutions of iodoform in the two solvents mentioned above yield HI on irradiation. Under similar conditions, carbon tetrachloride gives off only small quantities of Cl_2, plus HCl in the presence of moisture.

Schulte, Suttle, and Wilhelm [42] have reported results which are in disagreement with the above findings, since on irradiating chloroform in the absence of oxygen with Co^{60} γ-rays, only traces of HCl were found. No chlorine was detected, but significant amounts of C_2Cl_6 were produced. In the presence of oxygen, these authors obtained Cl_2, HCl, phosgene ($COCl_2$), and peroxides. Furthermore, the nature and quantity of the radiolytic products were found to depend on the temperature, and to show a complex dependence on the length of irradiation. It seems that the first product is a peroxide, such as CCl_3OOH, which decomposes to HCl, Cl_2, and $COCl_2$. As the reaction proceeds, chlorine disappears, probably as a result of the process

$$CHCl_3 + Cl_2 \rightarrow CCl_4 + HCl.$$

The formation of peroxides has also been observed in the irradiation of CH_2Cl_2 in the presence of oxygen, but not with CCl_4 and C_2Cl_4, although these produce Cl_2 and $COCl_2$, as do chloroform and CH_2Cl_2. It was concluded that hydrogen atoms are necessary for peroxide formation, and probably enter into the molecule. This conclusion should not, however, be taken to apply generally to the production of peroxides in all radiolytic processes.

Irradiation of C_2H_5Br, $C_2H_4Br_2$, and C_6H_5Br with x-rays, or with 0.5- to 2-Mev electrons, releases very small quantities of Br_2, the predominant product being HBr. In contrast to this, the iodides CH_3I, C_2H_5I, C_3H_7I, and $C_2H_2I_2$ only produce iodine. The yield for the x-ray radiolysis of C_2H_5I in the air is $G = 5.7$ [44], whereas with α-particles from radon or polonium, $G = 2.4$; the yield is proportional to the time of irradiation. The same is true for irradiation with neutrons from a Ra/Be source [45]. For these compounds, the yield varies slightly with the individual iodide, almost doubling over the series

$$CH_3(CH_2)_3I < C_6H_5I < (CH_3)_2CHCH_2I < CH_3CH_2CHICH_3$$
$$< CH_3I < (CH_3)_2CHI < CH_3CH_2I < CH_3(CH_2)_2I.$$

Gevantman and Williams [18] have studied the radiolysis of aliphatic iodides from CH_3I to C_4H_9I in the presence of radioactive iodine. From measurements of the activity of the initial iodides after the irradiation, it is possible to work out the extent of the recombination reactions; for example,

$$CH_3I \rightsquigarrow CH_3 + I, \qquad CH_3 + I_2^* \rightarrow CH_3I^* + I^*, \qquad (14\text{–}10)$$

where I* is radioiodine. Using the same radiation sources as in the hydrocarbon work (Section 14–1), these authors showed that the predominant radical is that corresponding to the initial molecule, which is a different result from that found with hydrocarbons. In particular, HI, which would arise from the rupture of C—H bonds, is only found in small quantities (about 1%), so that the C—I bond breaks more easily than C—C and C—H bonds. The ratio of C—C/C—I bonds broken is greater in the vapor than in the liquid state, with C_4H_9I an exception. For liquids, the I_2 yield increases with the number of H atoms attached to the carbon next to the carbon of the C—I bond [46].

Minder [47, 48] has used x-rays to irradiate chloroform and other chlorinated compounds (C_2Cl_6, $C_6H_4Cl_2$, $C_6H_6Cl_6$, etc.) in acetone or alcohol solution. The HCl yields are 20% smaller in acetone, but even in alcohol they are only a third of those in aqueous solution. Addition of 25% water to the acetone, or of 50% water to the alcohol, produces no change in the results. In dilute solution, the yields are about three times greater per chlorine atom for aliphatic compounds than for aromatic substances. The rate of the reactions depends upon the initial concentration, and follows a kinetic law similar to Eq. (13–32).

Tunitskii and his colleagues [49] have recently carried out a systematic study of the ionization and dissociation of various aliphatic hydrogen compounds in a mass spectrometer, and have also investigated the effect of electron energy on these processes.

14–4 Radiosynthesis and polymerization. In addition to causing the decomposition of molecules, ionizing radiation may also be used to bring about syntheses. This aspect of radiation chemistry, which has only been investigated over the last few years, is of special importance in connection with the problem of the peaceful utilization of nuclear energy.

The preparation of hydrogen peroxide by the irradiation of pure water is an example of such a synthesis, and although this is not a very economic procedure, it is one method of obtaining very small quantities of this reagent in a very pure state on the laboratory scale. Similarly, Loiseleur [50] has prepared methylene blue by irradiating an aqueous solution of dimethyl-*p*-phenylene-diamine and H_2S in the presence of air with a dose of 100,000 r of x-rays. When *p*-phenylene-diamine was used, Lauth's violet was produced. Loiseleur has also synthesized urea by irradiating a mixture of *m*-phenylene-diamine and ammonia dissolved in methanol.

The γ-ray irradiation of a liquid mixture of ammonia and benzene gives aniline [51], with $G = 0.3$ for an equimolar mixture. The yield increases in the presence of air, and can also be increased by adding C_2Cl_4 or CBr_4; in the latter case, G rises to 1.6. The irradiation of a liquid mixture of $CCl_4 + C_6H_6$ produces $C_6H_5CCl_3$ ($G = 0.45$). The action of γ-rays on benzene, toluene, and other aromatic hydrocarbons in the presence of chlorine either brings about substitution of H atoms by Cl, or else causes saturation of the aromatic nucleus [52, 53]. The yields are enormously high; under some conditions G may be of the order of 400,000 to 800,000.

The prospects in the field of radiolytic polymerization seem encouraging. The condensation of acetylene to give a solid product, with the simultaneous production of benzene, has already been mentioned in Chapter 12, and as already noted, the yields for the polymerization of ethylene are appreciably higher. The physical state of the polymer obtained by irradiation with 1 to 10 kilocurie sources depends upon the temperature of irradiation [52, 53]; a white solid is produced between 6 and 130°C, a white wax at 160°C, and an opaque liquid above this temperature. In some respects, the mechanical properties of the solid polyethylene obtained in this way are better than those of the commercial product.

Hopwood and Phillips [54, 55] have shown that styrene, vinyl acetate, and methyl methacrylate can be polymerized by γ-rays or neutrons from a Ra/Be source. Similarly, Joliot [56] was able to polymerize methyl methacrylate with fast neutrons from a cyclotron.

Magat and his collaborators [57, 58, 59] have studied the kinetics of the radiolytic polymerization of a number of liquid monomers, either in the pure state or in the presence of diluents. These authors have shown that provided the rate constants for the propagation and termination of the free-radical initiated chains are available from other work, the rate of initiation, and hence the number of radicals formed in the radiolysis, can be calculated. Magat [60, 61] has recently discussed the conditions under which this method is applicable. The particular system which has been most thoroughly investigated is the polymerization of styrene with γ-rays or pile radiation, but other monomers including butadiene, vinyl acetate, and acrylonitrile have also been studied. The polymerization must be carried out in the complete absence of oxygen, since this acts as an inhibitor; the presence of even small traces of this gas can be detected by the induction period which is then observed. The fact that radiolytic polymerization involves free radicals has been confirmed by demonstrating the inhibition caused by benzoquinone, which is known to inhibit polymerizations initiated by free radicals, but not by ions.

The rate of polymerization of styrene and other monomers is proportional to the square root of the radiation intensity over a certain intensity range. This corresponds to chain termination by mutual interaction. If small quantities of organic compounds which are more sensitive to radiation than the monomer and its derivatives are added to the monomeric liquids, or to the solutions, the rate of polymerization is accelerated. The rate of polymerization can therefore be used as a measure of the sensitivity of the diluent. As in the case of benzene and deutero-benzene mentioned earlier (Section 14–1), the polymerization yields from mixtures do not obey the additivity rule [62]. Despite the uncertainties in the kinetic constants, which show wide variation between different authors, Chapiro [57] has been able to calculate from such experiments the free-radical yields, relative to benzene, for a number of compounds shown in Table 14–2. The resistance of aromatic compounds to radiolysis, and the sensitizing effect of aliphatic groups, is once more quite obvious.

Schmitz and Lawton [63] used cathode rays with energies up to 800 kev to induce the polymerization of various monomers. They confirmed the inhibiting action of oxygen and benzoquinone, and showed that the rate of polymerization of bifunctional monomers, such as the dimethacrylate of tetra-ethylene-glycol, is about 50 times greater than that of monofunctional monomers. Below −55°C, the dimethacrylate does not polymerize, but the process is initiated on warming the system to room temperature after irradiation, even after several hours at the temperature of solid carbon dioxide. This result appears to suggest a remarkably long life for the free radicals.

Apart from the action of free radicals, some compounds, such as isobutene for example, polymerize on irradiation at low temperatures (−78°C) by an *ionic* mechanism [64]. The yields from such processes are therefore independent of the intensity of the radiation.

The γ-ray degradation of polymers in organic solvents takes place only in the presence of oxygen [65]. It seems probable that the oxygen forms peroxides by combining with free radicals from the solvent, and that these

TABLE 14–2

RELATIVE RADICAL YIELDS IN γ-RADIOLYSIS

Compound	G
Benzene	1
Toluene	1.45
m-xylene	3.8
Ethylbenzene	5.5
Carbon disulfide	1
Styrene	0.9
Methanol	10–20
Propanol	50
Acrylonitrile	1.1–1.4
Methyl acrylate	13.6
Methyl methacrylate	15
Vinyl acetate	18.7
Ether	8.7

subsequently react with the polymer to cause decomposition. The degradation continues for some time (of the order of several hours) after the irradiation, (the aftereffect, see Section 14–5). Those substances which act as protective agents against the degradation in aqueous solution [66] such as mercaptan, thiourea, β-napthol, etc., are generally found to have the same effect and efficiency in chloroform solution [67]. The x-ray degradation of polymethacrylic acid in chloroform solution also requires the presence of oxygen [68]. Unlike this polymer, polyvinyl alcohol, polyvinyl pyrrolidone, and polyacrylamide are degraded only in very dilute solution [69]; at concentrations above 0.5 to 1%, these polymers undergo changes similar to those caused by radiation in the solid state (Section 15–6).

14–5 Aqueous solutions of organic substances. One of the most remarkable features of the radiolytic behavior of aqueous solutions of organic compounds and substances of biological interest is that irrespective of their class or molecular complexity, oxidation and hydroxylation reactions predominate. Thus alcohols are oxidized to aldehydes, aldehydes to acids, acids to peracids or hydroxy-acids, which finally go to carbon dioxide. Similarly aromatic compounds, sterols, thiols, cysteine, glutathione, nucleic acids, and coenzymes are oxidized, or undergo oxidative degradation. Ferricytochrome, which is easily reduced by hydrogen and platinum black, is not reduced by x-rays [70], even at a dose of 100,000 r; above this, the protein is denaturized. Reduction reactions are uncommon, and in those cases where they are observed can often be attributed to the effect of organic free radicals. The yields generally increase in the presence of oxygen, and in some cases different radiolytic products are obtained.

Another important feature of these reactions is that they continue after irradiation has ceased. These *aftereffects* show up as a yield which increases for several hours or even 1 to 2 days after the end of the irradiation. This effect was discovered by Loiseleur [71] in irradiations of tyrosine with x-rays, and has subsequently been reported for a number of other reactions including the oxidation of benzene, gallic and linoleic acid, *o*-phenanthroline, and ferrous sulfate in the presence of formic acid or hydrocarbons; for the degradation of a number of polymers and of desoxyribonucleic acid; and for the deactivation of enzymes and bacteriophages, etc. [72]. Measurements carried out immediately after the irradiation and at the end of the aftereffect often differ by 40 to 60%, and sometimes by a factor of 2 to 4.

In the majority of cases, the presence of oxygen is an essential condition for the aftereffect in aqueous solution. The amount of hydrogen peroxide produced in aereated solution by x-rays has been shown to be insufficient to explain quantitatively the effects observed [73]. For some time it was thought that the effects could be attributed to the HO_2 radical, but it seems unlikely that this species could persist in aqueous solution for several hours, and although it may play some part in the reaction mechanism, it seems more reasonable to assume that the aftereffect is a consequence of the formation of peroxides, which slowly decompose or react with other molecules:

$$RH + OH \rightarrow R + H_2O, \tag{14–11}$$

$$R + O_2 \rightarrow RO_2, \tag{14–12}$$

$$RO_2 + R'H \rightarrow RO_2H + R', \tag{14–13}$$

$$RH + RO_2 \rightarrow RO_2H + R, \quad \text{(aftereffect)} \tag{14–14}$$

$$RO_2 + H_2O \rightarrow ROH + HO_2, \tag{14–15}$$

$$R' + HO_2 \rightarrow R'O_2H, \tag{14–16}$$

$$R + R'H \rightarrow RR' + H, \text{ etc.} \tag{14–17}$$

The aftereffects can be suppressed by adding certain reducing agents which react easily with peroxides (e.g., hypophosphite, thiourea, cysteine, ascorbic acid [69, 74].

Alcohols and aldehydes. X- or γ-irradiation of an aqueous solution of methyl alcohol gives two products, glycol, formed from radicals, and formaldehyde, which could be formed by direct reaction [75, 76]. The yield (G) for acetaldehyde formation in the irradiation of ethanol (0.5 M solution, pH 7.8) is 1.6 in the absence of oxygen, and 5 in the presence of this gas [77]. The yields are smaller in dilute solution, but the ratio between them remains at about three. The ratio between the radiochemical yields in aereated and deaereated solutions of organic compounds are frequently close to this figure; examples include the oxidation of thiols [78], the formation of aldehydes by the irradiation of amino-acids [79], and the formation of ammonia from guanine and adenine [80].

If an oxygen-free solution of ethanol containing diphosphopyridine nucleotide (DPN, coenzyme I) is irradiated, the acetaldehyde yield is the same as in the presence of oxygen, and at the same time DPN is reduced to DPNH (dihydrodiphosphopyridine nucleotide) [79]. The take-up of H atoms by the DPN might conceivably protect the aldehyde from back reactions, which would increase the yield of CH_3CHO, but Swallow [77] has shown that DPN alone in aqueous solution is not reduced radiolytically, either in the absence of oxygen or in the presence of hydrogen. The presence of alcohol is therefore necessary for the reduction, which probably takes place via the CH_3CHOH radical, which undergoes rearrangement to give CH_3CHO. This illustrates the care which must be exercised in attempting to use sensitivity experiments as a method of identifying the radical responsible for the observed phenomenon. The same comment also applies to protection effects, as noted earlier (Section 13–6).

Thiols, mercaptans, and glutathione are decomposed [78] by irradiation with x-rays. The SH group is simultaneously oxidized with a yield (G) which may be as high as 9 in the absence of air, and 30 in its presence.

Formaldehyde, acetaldehyde, and propionaldehyde are converted by x-radiation to the corresponding acids, or to CO_2 in long irradiations [75]. The yields for the oxidation process, and for the simultaneous production of hydrogen, vary with concentration and with pH. At high concentrations, the Cannizzaro reaction occurs:

$$2RCHO + H_2O \rightarrow RCH_2OH + RCOOH. \qquad (14\text{–}18)$$

Acids. At pH 2, γ-rays cause the decomposition of formic acid, giving $CO_2 + H_2$, with $G = 3.2$ [81]. The yield falls off with increasing pH; thus at pH 8, $G_{H_2} = 2$, and no CO_2 formation can be detected. The reaction occurring is probably

$$2HCOOH \rightarrow (COOH)_2 + H_2.$$

A systematic study of the radiolytic behavior of formic acid in aqueous solution has been carried out by Hart [82, 83] using Co^{60} γ-rays, tritium β-particles, and Po α-particles. Experiments were also carried out with the deuterated acid (HCOOD), and in the presence of ferrous sulfate or hydrogen peroxide. In this latter system, a chain reaction brings about a 50-fold increase in the CO_2 yield, corresponding to the process

$$HCOOH + H_2O_2 \rightarrow CO_2 + 2H_2O. \qquad (14\text{–}19)$$

Hart has proposed the following mechanism to interpret his experimental findings:

$$HCOOH + OH \rightarrow H_2O + COOH, \qquad (14\text{–}20)$$

$$HCOOH + H \rightarrow H_2 + COOH, \qquad (14\text{–}21)$$

$$COOH + O_2 \rightarrow HO_2 + CO_2, \qquad (14\text{–}22)$$

$$2HO_2 \rightarrow H_2O_2 + O_2. \qquad (14\text{–}23)$$

In concentrated solution, competition between H_2O and HCOOH would occur:

$$H_2O + e \rightarrow H_2O^- \rightarrow H + OH^-,$$

$$HCOOH + e \rightarrow HCOOH^- \rightleftharpoons HCO + OH^-, \qquad (14\text{–}24)$$

$$HCO + HCOOH \rightarrow HCOH + COOH, \text{ etc.} \qquad (14\text{–}25)$$

The radiolysis of dilute aqueous solutions of aliphatic acids gives different products from those obtained from the pure compound. Direct decarboxylation does not take place; monobasic acids are oxidized to di-acids, and in some cases to peracids, di-acids are hydroxylated, and hydroxy-acids are degraded to give carbon dioxide. It follows that with sufficiently high doses, irradiation of any of these acids in aqueous solution eventually yields CO_2. Thus the effect of 35-Mev α-particles [84, 85] or 18-Mev deuterons on aqueous solutions of acetic acid is to produce succinic acid, H_2O_2, H_2, and small quantities of CH_4, C_2H_6, CO_2, CO; the yields increase with acid concentration up to 1 M. In more concentrated solutions, direct effects are added to the radical reactions and the yields of the gaseous products other than hydrogen increase, while the yields of the other products decrease.

Oxalic acid is decomposed on irradiation with γ-rays in the presence of oxygen, two molecules of CO_2 being formed per molecule of acid decomposed [86]: $G\,(-H_2C_2O_4) = 2.9$, $G\,(CO_2) = 5.6$. In the presence of air, the corresponding values are 4.9 and 7.8. The liquid phase then also contains small quantities of formaldehyde ($G = 0.08$) and glyoxal ($G = 0.004$). The decomposition decreases with increasing pH. The COOH radical and, in the absence of oxygen, the CHO radical, appear to play an essential part in the mechanism of these processes.

Succinic acid on irradiation goes to tricarballylic acid, malic acid, citric acid, and malonic acid, with only a very small yield of CO_2 ($G = 0.07$), but the main product from the x-irradiation of solutions of malonic and succinic acid at pH 3 is hydrogen, with traces of CO_2. Carbon dioxide is also produced in the irradiation of tartaric and hydroxy-isobutyric acids. In the absence of air, lactic acid is converted to pyruvic acid [87, 88]; G changes from 6.6 to 1.4 as the pH is increased from 1.2 to 5. In acid solution, hydrogen peroxide is formed. The presence of oxygen increases the oxidation yield 5-fold at pH 1.2.

When an aqueous solution of benzoic acid is irradiated with x-rays, it undergoes hydroxylation with the formation of three isomers, of which 80% is the para-form [89, 90] (cf. benzene and its derivatives). Diphenyl is also formed, probably through decarboxylation. In a very long irradiation with the γ-rays from radium, Kailan [91] also observed the formation of formic and oxalic acids.

Other compounds. Irradiation of other benzene derivatives, $C_6H_5NO_2$ and C_6H_5Cl, also results in the take-up of a hydroxyl group into the three ortho-, meta- and para-positions [89, 90]. The hydroxylation of phenol takes place preferentially at the ortho-position, and partly at the para-, but never at the meta-position [79]. In the presence of oxygen, *o*-benzoquinone is the only product. Removal of the nitro- and chloro-groups has also been observed, HCl being formed in the latter case. Minder [47, 48, 92, 93, 94] has made a careful study of the kinetics of the radiolytic hydrolysis of both aromatic and aliphatic halogenated compounds.

Carbohydrates are oxidized both by γ-rays [95] and 1-Mev electrons [96]. *D*-glucose, *D*-galactose, and *D*-mannose give uronic acid, with $G = 0.4$ in deaereated solution and 1.9 in the presence of oxygen (these figures are for electron bombardment). The gas given off at the same time consists of hydrogen (87%), CO_2 (10%), and very little CO. Inulin, fructose, and amidon are decomposed, being oxidized to acids or aldehydes; in addition, amidon yields dextrins.

14-6 Biochemical compounds. *Amino-acids.* The main effects of radiation on amino-acids, studied in particular by Dale [97–101] and Weiss [79, 102, 103], consist of deamination and decarboxylation; aldehydes are also formed, along with small amounts of other substances. The yields vary with the particular acid, with pH and with concentration. The presence of oxygen does not alter the yield for the deamination of glycocol and alanine, but changes the ratios between the resulting fatty acids [104].

Dale has found a strong concentration dependence in the deamination yield in the x-irradiation of acid solutions of glycine and *l*-serine (see Fig. 14-1; compare Fig. 13-4). With very concentrated solutions, this may be due to direct action, but chain reactions cannot be excluded. Weiss, *et al.*, find that the hydrogen yield has a sigmoid dependence, and suggest that an intermediate compound is formed which itself dissociates under the effect of the irradiation to give additional hydrogen.

The ammonia yield is smaller for amino-acids with the NH_2 group in the β-position; thus for α-alanine and β-alanine, G is 2.9 and 1.7 respectively. The SH group acts as a self-protective agent, and reduces the deamination considerably. Cysteine is not deaminated, but gives off H_2S, especially in the absence of oxygen, and is oxidized to cystine [99, 105, 106, 107]. The H_2S yield goes through a maximum at pH 6. In the presence of oxygen, G may be as much as 70 at the beginning of the irradiation. Hydrogen peroxide is also formed, in greater quantities than in the absence of cystene. Swallow has explained these results by a chain reaction mechanism,

$$RSH + OH \rightarrow RS + H_2O, \tag{14-26}$$

$$RS + RSH \rightarrow RSSR + H, \tag{14-27}$$

$$H + O_2 \rightarrow HO_2,$$

$$RSH + HO_2 \rightarrow RS + H_2O_2. \tag{14-28}$$

In long irradiations, the yield falls off quickly and cystine itself is oxidized, probably to sulfonic acids and SO_2. The irradiated cystine is deaminated, but reduction to cystene does not take place, and no H_2S is given off. The study of the radiolysis of compounds of this type is of especial interest in radiobiology because of their remarkable protective effect on various biochemical products *in vivo*.

Irradiation with α-particles has been investigated for tyrosine [108, 109], glycine, alanine, leucine, and tryptophan [110]; less decomposition occurs than with x-rays. For glycine, for example, the ratio G_α/G_X is approximately $\frac{1}{5}$ or $\frac{1}{6}$, and for tyrosine in 10^{-4} M solution, the value is $\frac{1}{28}$. With increasing concentration, however, this increases quickly and in a 5×10^{-4} M solution, the ratio is only 0.4. Even with x-rays, G is very small (0.28) due to the protective action of the benzene ring. Low deamina-

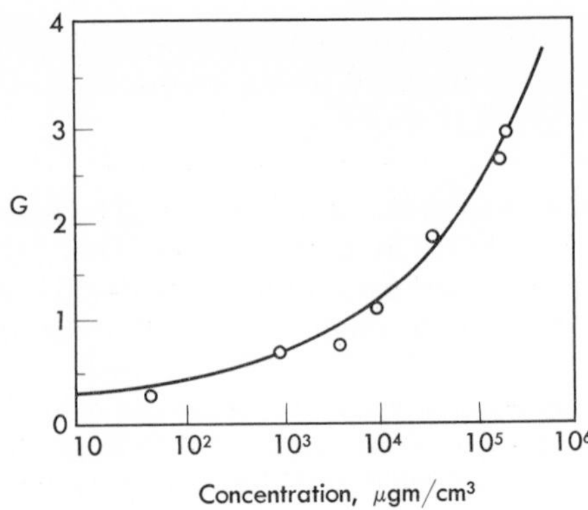

FIG. 14–1. Concentration dependence in the deamination of glycine (after W. M. Dale, Ref. 100).

tion yields are also found in the irradiation of tyrosine, phenylalanine, tryptophane, and amino-benzoic acids with 3-Mev electrons [111, 112]; the yields decrease in the order histidine > cystine > phenylalanine > tyrosine > tryptophan.

Nucleic acids and nucleo-proteins. In view of the complexity of such molecules, it is not possible to give a detailed and complete analysis of their radiolytic behavior. From the results obtained by spectral, chemical, or viscometric methods, mostly on deoxyribonucleic acid (DNA) and ribonucleic acids (RNA) or albumin, serum-albumin, and other proteins, the following general conclusions can be drawn:

1. Relatively small doses cause depolymerization of these compounds, so that the absorption spectra change and the viscosity of solutions decreases.

2. The effect continues for several hours after irradiation has ceased [113] (the aftereffect), and this can only be partly attributed to hydrogen peroxide [73]. A mechanism involving peroxides as intermediates seems highly probable.

3. The effect of dilution, and the protection found with a number of compounds, suggest that the changes in dilute solution are due to indirect effects. For instance, no change is found with DNA in glycol solution after irradiation with x-rays [114], and the same is true of the dry material and of aqueous solutions of DNA irradiated in the frozen state, so that the free radicals produced by the radiolysis of water are necessary for reaction to occur. This is further confirmed by the fact that OH radicals produced by Fenton's reagent (ferrous sulfate plus hydrogen peroxide), or by ultraviolet irradiation of hydrogen peroxide, have similar effects to ionizing radiation [115, 116].

4. The reactions which occur most readily are the oxidation of the SH and OH groups, double bonds, and other groups in the molecule.

5. The effects of sufficiently strong doses on nucleic acids include the production of ammonia, rupture of the glycosidic linkages, ring opening, the formation of inorganic phosphates, and acidification. With pro-

teins, one finds denaturation, precipitation, and rupture of amino, carboxyl, and hydrogen bonds. Denaturation requires doses of the order of 10^5 roentgens.

6. Certain changes in the absorption spectrum are sensitive to the presence of oxygen [117, 118], while other changes measured by the viscosity are not affected by the presence of this gas [119]. Contradictory reports on this subject appear in the literature, however, and the results probably depend to some extent on experimental conditions.

Ephrussi-Taylor and Latarjet [120] have studied the x-ray inactivation of DNA molecules by measuring the changes in the biological activity directly (rather than by measuring changes in physical properties). According to these measurements, the acid is very sensitive to indirect action (i.e., free radicals), so that protection against these effects, by yeast extract for example, requires very high concentrations of protective agent. The presence of oxygen has no great effect on the inactivation.

Enzymes. Because of the importance of enzyme reactions in living cells, a number of authors have studied the conditions needed to suppress their activity (*inactivation*) by radiation. Such work has involved, in particular, carboxypeptidase, catalase, pepsin, trypsin, ribonuclease, urease, and phosphoglyceraldehyde dehydrogenase. Dale [121, 122] was the first to show that pure enzyme preparations in water are extremely sensitive to radiation, and that the high resistance previously reported by various authors was due either to the use of impure preparations, or to working in a natural medium rich in protein and other organic compounds which protect the enzymes. In a systematic study of the dilution and protection effects discussed earlier (Sections 13-5 and 13-6), Dale was able to confirm the indirect action of radiation (via the "activated water" previously postulated by Fricke). Dale's results on the protection effect were confirmed with catalase by Forssberg [123, 124], who showed that in dilute solution the pure enzyme is inactivated by an x-ray dose as small as 15 r, but that when associated with tissue it remains active even after 83,000 r. It was later shown [111, 112] that peroxydase in milk is not completely inactivated by cathode rays even after a dose of 5×10^6 r. Similarly, cytochrome oxidase, succinic dehydrogenase, and invertase are completely protected by the cell constituents up to x-ray doses as high as 2×10^5 r [125].

Measurements by Dale, Gray, and Meredith [97] show that α-particles are 16 times less efficient in bringing about the inactivation of carboxypeptidase than are x-rays ($G = 0.03$ and 0.48 respectively). Barron [117, 118] has reported small differences in the effect of x-rays, γ-rays, and β-particles on phosphoglyceraldehyde dehydrogenase, but these can be attributed at least in part to uncertainties in the dosimetry. Glutathione added before the irradiation has a protective action, while after partial radiolytic inactivation it reactivates the enzyme. In effect therefore the inactivation consists only of the reversible oxidation of the SH group, and the R-S-S-R thus formed can be transformed back to biologically active HSR-RSH. Only after long irradiation, which probably brings about denaturation of the protein, does glutathione have no further measurable effect.

TABLE 14–3

RADIOCHEMICAL YIELDS FOR THE INACTIVATION OF ENZYMES

Enzyme	G
Alcohol dehydrogenase	3.4
Phosphoglyceraldehyde dehydrogenase	2.9
Carboxypeptidase	0.55
d-amino-acid oxidase	0.31
Ribonuclease	0.09
Trypsin	0.077
Lysozyme	0.03
Catalase	0.009

The differing sensitivities of enzymes are illustrated by the G values for x-rays given by Barron (Table 14–3). These values emphasize the sensitivity of enzymes which contain the SH group. The importance of this group in the inhibition of the metabolic activity of phosphoglyceraldehyde dehydrogenase was demonstrated by Barron [118].

The reactivation produced by glutathione after irradiation is a special case of an important type of phenomena in radiobiology, to which the name *restoration* has been given. In particular, restoration is frequently observed with the various biological effects caused by ultraviolet radiation, when it can be brought about by following the primary irradiation with exposure to visible or infrared radiation, by temperature change, or by adding catalase. The only example of restoration by light after irradiation with x-rays is in the synthesis of virus in a culture of lysogenic bacteria, reported by Latarjet [126, 127]. This author suggests that three restoration mechanisms can be distinguished: (a) reversal of some reaction by suppressing an intermediate compound (or other change) produced by the primary irradiation; (b) formation of a constituent which was altered by the primary irradiation; (c) destruction of some normal constituent which is involved in an intermediate step in the series of events which result in damage.

14–7 The biological effects of radiation. The effects of radiation on tissues and living cells are diverse, showing up in histological and physiological changes which may extend to the death of the cell or organism in question. These effects are known as *radiolesions*. In the present discussion we shall be concerned only with a brief summary of the most thoroughly studied topics and shall ignore the extremely complex intermediate physicochemical and biochemical processes which occur between the absorption of the radiation and the production of the lesions. Such processes are in any case far from understood.

The lesions are the result of both direct and indirect action, the mechanisms of which are for the most part similar to those suggested earlier for the isolated constituents of the cell. In addition, there may be functional changes in the cell itself and in the tissues, and effects due to toxic substances produced by radiolysis. As previously emphasized in discussing protection effects with enzymes, there is little justification for extrapolating results obtained *in vitro* to the behavior of the cell *in vivo.*

Some information on the mechanism of radiobiological action can be obtained by investigating whether or not oxygen affects the change under study. The oxygen effect is often very large with x-rays, less pronounced with neutrons, and very small with α-particles [128, 129, 130], an order which suggests that radical interactions are involved. If a virus is irradiated in a sufficiently large volume of medium, which protects it against radical reactions, the inactivation is independent of the presence of oxygen [131]. Genetic changes, retardation of growth, sterility, and lethal changes produced in barley corn by irradiation, are up to 40 times greater with fast (reactor) neutrons than with x-rays, but the efficiency of the latter is considerably increased by the presence of oxygen, although this gas has little effect in neutron bombardment [132, 133, 134]. For equal ionization density, however, different radiations produce the same biological effects [135]. Experiments by Alper [136, 137] on the x- or γ-irradiation of bacteriophages S-13 and T-3 in water in the presence of various gases seem to show that in these systems the inactivation is due to the indirect effects of reduction; the yield doubles when hydrogen is substituted for nitrogen, which Alper suggests is due to the reaction

$$H_2 + OH \rightarrow H_2O + H.$$

The yield decreases in the presence of air, or of a mixture of oxygen and hydrogen. Protection by oxygen has also been found for the phage *coli* T-1 [138].

The sensitivity of biological systems to radiation varies widely (Table 14–4). The minimum dose required to cause different changes varies between 10 and 10^6 r (see, for example, Refs. 139 through 142), but in some cases much smaller doses (a fraction of a roentgen) are sufficient to induce changes in micro-organisms. The rate of mitosis is appreciably affected by a dose of x-rays of the order of a roentgen, whereas the paramecies are apparently able to survive doses up to 500,000 r [143].

As early as 1906, Bergonie and Tribondeau [144] recognized that the radiosensitivity of tissue increases as its degree of differentiation decreases, and that actively growing tissues are especially sensitive. A number of factors can, however, affect the validity of these rules. A classification in order of decreasing sensitivity would be lymphoid tissue, bone marrow, intestinal mucous membrane, sex glands, phaneres, skin, eyes.

The time interval between the absorption of radiation and the response of the organism varies *inter alia* with the dose and with the nature of the lesion. Thus an interval of minutes or hours is involved for chromosome destruction, and months or years for carcinogenesis.

For a dose which is insufficient to have a lethal effect, changes in the cells may show up in anomalies involving division, growth, and differentiation. The nucleus of the cell is apparently more sensitive than the cytoplasm. The chromosomes are broken at one or more points, and the resulting chromatide segments undergo widely different rearrangements and exchanges. These aberrations may appear minutes or hours after the irradiation, although in some cases the latent period is even longer. The frequency and the precise nature of the aberration also depends on the state of division (mitosis), during the irradiation; thus the prophase is more sensitive than the metaphase and the anaphase. The absence of oxygen decreases the number of chromosomic anomalies.

For some types of aberration, the frequency increases linearly with the dose. With electromagnetic radiation, however, the number of aberrations often varies with the $(\text{dose})^n$, where n is between 1 and 2, depending on the wavelength and the intensity. It has been estimated that 15 to 20 ionizations are necessary to produce chromosome rupture in the microspores of *Tradescantia*. Radiations with dense ionization (α-particles or neutrons) are less efficient than electromagnetic radiation. The theoretical implication of these results is discussed in Section 14–8.

Chromosome aberrations are associated with a retardation of mitosis; the extent of this increases with increasing administered dose. Here again, the prophase of the cell division is the period of greatest sensitivity, although there is some disagreement as to whether this sensitivity is at the end or the beginning of the prophase. It could well be that this differs for different types of cells. In other cases, the interphase, which precedes mitosis and in which the synthesis of nucleic acids takes place, is the period of greatest sensitivity [145].

The interval between irradiation and minimum mitotic activity depends on the dose, and is generally of the order of 1 or 2 hours. It has been suggested that the decrease of activity immediately after irradiation is greater in animal tissues than in vegetables. The efficiency of different doses also depends upon the nature of the cell.

As a particular example of lethal effects, let us consider briefly the inactivation of micro-organisms such as viruses or bacteriophages. The viruses are reproducible organisms, some of which can be crystallized, and occupy an intermediate place between living and nonliving matter, or at least represent one of the least complex levels of living matter. Those that are extremely small (a few hundred angstroms) can be inactivated by a single ionization (or rather by the indirect effects of a single ionization). The largest viruses have a structure which can be recognized under the electron microscope, and these are inactivated by only a single ionization if this occurs at a "radiosensitive" point [140]. The yields are higher for dry viruses than for those in the wet state; in the latter case the action is at least partly indirect.

14–8 Genetic effects. Multicellular organisms are able to some extent to repair radiolesions induced in their tissues. For such effects, some sort of *threshold* is believed to exist, and consequently there is a *tolerance dose*. These ideas are not, however, applicable at the level of the individual cell nor to hereditary changes.

It has recently been shown [146] that the frequency of the lyses with bacteriophage production, induced in certain bacteria by x- and γ-rays, is proportional to the dose for doses up to the order of a roentgen. In addition these experiments have shown that for these two radiations there can be no threshold at any dose, no matter how small. This result had already been suggested previously for genetic mutations in *Drosophilia* [147]; the x-ray induction of such mutations was discovered by Müller [148] in 1927. After irradiation, these fruit flies show various structural changes, which can be transmitted to successive generations. As for the inactivation of viruses, it is believed that mutations can be produced by a single ionization if a sensitive region of the chromosome is affected. The yield is independent of the dose (so that there is no threshold), and for x-rays it is probably independent of the wavelength between 1 and 0.01 A. Experiments on *Drosophilia* and mice show that the yield per unit of absorbed dose is independent of the intensity, and is cumulative. Effects brought about by a discontinuous chronic exposure to low-intensity radiations over a long period of time are therefore quantitatively the same as those produced by a very intense source in a very short time, providing that the effective energy absorption is the same in both cases.

If these observations are applicable to human beings, as geneticists believe, very serious consequences could result from a long-term increase in the average level of ionization on the earth following developments in the use of nuclear energy. The current level is estimated at approximately 0.1 r per year at sea level, and a fraction of the "spontaneous" mutations in man and other animals is attributed to the effects of this ionization. The principal feature of such mutations is the almost total predominance of unfavorable modifications, malformations, infirmities, and other congenital defects. Geneticists suggest that as a result of natural selection, an equilibrium is set up in the human race between the freshly acquired undesirable hereditary factors and those which are eliminated by the disappearance of the relevant individual or his family. If this equilibrium were to be seriously disturbed by increasing amounts of radioactivity in the atmosphere or on the earth, not only would the number of infirm and condemned individuals increase, but there would also be a serious threat to the whole human species.

Despite the lack of direct data for man,* it seems that this danger is recognized by all geneticists. The disagreements only appear when it becomes necessary to estimate the imminence and gravity of the situation, or in other words to estimate the average level of permitted radioactivity. Muller [149, 150] and others estimate that the average dose per generation should not exceed 20 to 25 r, a value which corresponds to a multiplication of the present rate of spontaneous mutations by a factor of 1.25. Others are more optimistic, and without minimizing the serious dangers implicit in an excessive increase in the "natural" radioactivity, believe (e.g., Ref. 151) that even doubling the rate would not cause serious problems for the

* In addition to the as yet uncertain observation on the young generations in Nagasaki following the explosion of an atomic bomb in 1945, T. Jodai, *Atom. Sci. J.* (*G.B.*), **4,** 289 (1955) (see Section 14–12) there are reports of a statistical survey of the children of American radiologists, which shows the existence of an increased frequency of congenital defects relative to the rest of the population.

human race. It should be noted in this respect that the natural radioactivity in some granitic regions in Northern Europe are very much greater than normal, apparently without any appreciable increase of genetic changes in the local population.

We may conclude, with Carter [152], that while very little is known about the genetic structure of human populations and about the induction of mutations in man, sufficient is known to recognize the importance of this genetic problem. It does not seem that there need yet be any slowing down in the development of the properly controlled peaceful applications of nuclear energy, but the reckless multiplication of nuclear explosions could constitute a real danger for successive generations, if not for our own. At the individual level, precautions should not only be taken for the protection of persons working with radioactive materials or in frequent contact with such materials, but also in the radioscopic and radiographic examination of human beings.

A very small fraction of the spontaneous mutations may improve the individual with respect to the average population. When this involves plants or animals, with which experiment is possible, it should be possible to use radiation to induce mutations and so produce strains with good agricultural possibilities [133, 134]. We shall return to this point later (Section 25–5).

14–9 Metabolic anomalies, anaemia, carcinogenesis, etc. In higher organisms, "radiation sickness" shows up as a variety of disorders which affect the cells and the tissue. With sufficiently high doses, of the order of 2500 r, more serious and irreversible degeneracies are observed, which involve the nucleus of the cytoplasm and result in the death of the cell. These effects may partly arise from aberrations of the chromosomes. They may also be of chemical origin; Hevesy [153] has shown for example that there is a much lower rate of incorporation of radioactive phosphorus into nucleic acids in the liver, spleen, kidneys, and other tissues of rats irradiated with x-rays than in unirradiated tissues.* Several other metabolic changes due to radiation have been studied, especially those involving carbohydrates and lipids [154].

It is well known that the erythroblasts are among the most radiosensitive cell elements. Radiation affects the erythropoiesis and the assimilation of iron, as has been proven by the use of radioactive iron [155]; inhibition occurs after 24 hours with doses of 5 to 25 r, depending on the particular animal involved. As a result, there is a decrease in the number of red cells (erythrocytes) accompanied by a deficiency in haemoglobin, and eventually haemolysis. The minimum dose necessary to cause anaemia in a rabbit is of the order of 500 r; the figures for the rat and the dog are rather lower (200 to 300 r).

An important alteration is the decrease in the lymphocytes. With a dose of 50 r this occurs after 15 min in a rabbit, reaching a maximum effect after

* For a bibliography, see G. Hevesy, *Strahlentherapie,* **93,** 325 (1954).

24 or 48 hours. The recuperation period depends on the size of the dose, and is of the order of several weeks. The relative proportions of the other constituents of the blood are also changed. X-rays or neutrons produce at least qualitatively the same effects.

The functioning of the central nervous system and of the neuro-endocrinal mechanisms are also to some extent disturbed after irradiation [156, 157]; thus electroencephalogram traces are changed even by small doses. The permeability of the membranes and cell capillaries is also altered.

Changes in the immunological reactions of rabbits were observed following irradiation with γ-rays, or the injection of polonium or radiothorium [158, 159]. With a dose of $\sim$400 r, the number of antibodies in the serum decreased considerably when antigen was injected more than six hours after irradiation.

In the historical introduction to this book (Section 1–8), reference was made to a number of accidents resulting in radiodermatitis and sarcoma in the early years of radioactive study. Since that time, several serious cases of "chronic radiation sickness," producing occupational cancers, have been reported among workmen and technicians in radium industries, those working on luminous dials and x-ray ampoules, and among radiologists, radiochemists, and former invalids treated with radiation. It has been established that the lesions always appear in the regions directly exposed to the radiation [160, 161, 162]. The cancer develops at a site which already shows special alterations of the skin, due, for example, to previous irradiation. The latent period is generally very long, and Lacassagne has quoted periods of 40 and 34 years. It has not been possible to establish any obvious relationship between the malignancy and the age of the invalid, but a close relationship has been noted with the age of the radiodermatitis.

Despite the considerable experimental difficulties involved, the production of cancers in the skin of animals (guinea pig, rabbit, rat, etc.) has been carried out for a long time using x-rays or radon or radium tubes, and more recently γ-rays or β-particles from the radioactive isotopes of calcium, strontium, barium, ytterbium, cerium, etc., have been investigated. This usually involves local irradiations by the subcutaneous or intramuscular introduction of the radioactive material, but in some cases the whole body of the animal is exposed to fairly uniform x- or γ-irradiation. The x-ray doses used are generally thousands or tens of thousands of roentgens, but 1500 to 5000 r is already sufficient to cause the cancer. The latent period in animals depends on the dose, and varies from months to 2 to 3 years. Quantitative measurements of the relationship between dose and effect are extremely difficult, as is any comparison of the efficiency of various radiations. The mechanism of the carcinogenesis by radiation is still as obscure as the origin of natural cancer itself, and the same is true of the destruction of tumors by radiation (Section 14–10). The theories suggested involve the inhibition of the mitosis of certain cells, the differentiation or the death of certain others, restoration processes, and other similar and ill-defined factors.

14–10 Radiotherapy and chemical protection. Radiotherapeutic methods depend basically on the widely differing radiosensitivity of cells, which in its turn depends on their nature and on the accentuated sensitivity of proliferating tissues. The problem is to attack sick or diseased tissue with radiation and to leave healthy tissue unaffected. External radiotherapy (roentgentherapy and curietherapy) utilizes penetrating electromagnetic radiation for this purpose. Internal radiotherapy until recent years has used the natural α-emitting elements, applied in very small quantities by injection, inhalation (radon), or even in the form of radioactive baths.

Initially, external radiotherapy was exclusively concerned with the γ-rays from radium and mesotherium and their daughter products, but such sources are being increasingly replaced by Co^{60} (half-life 5.3 years, γ-ray energy 1.17 and 1.33 Mev) which is available as "bombs" containing kilocurie amounts of activity in a very small volume. Observations made on 2000 patients in the U.S.S.R. [163] suggest that Co^{60} treatment affects the tissues near the neoplasms less than is the case with radium or mesothorium [163]. Radiocaesium (Cs^{137}, half-life 30.4 years) has also been used, although its γ-ray is less penetrating (0.5 Mev). The use of Tm^{170}, with 84-kev γ-ray has also been suggested, since the energy is comparable with the energies of the x-rays produced in the normal generators used in radiotherapy. In some circumstances, it might be advantageous to use the γ-rays from Xe^{133} (81 kev). Other radio isotopes including P^{32}, Sr^{89}, Sr^{90} (in equilibrium with Y^{90}), Ru^{106} (in equilibrium with Rh^{106}), and other high-energy β-emitters have been used (or suggested) for the treatment of accessible surface tissues (for example, in certain skin diseases). Kozlova [163] reports high percentage cures for dermatitis, eczema, and neoplastic affections of certain parts of the eye (eyelid, cornea, conjunctiva) using radiophosphorus. Good results in localized external treatment have been obtained with chromium radiophosphate and colloidal radioactive gold; active isotopes of bromine, arsenic, bismuth, and gallium have also been tried in a number of special medical applications.

Another development, which depends on the fact that radioactive indicators have demonstrated the selective fixation of certain radioelements in various tissues (Sections 24–4 and 24–5), involves the use of artificial β-emitters, especially radiophosphorus and radioiodine, in internal curietherapy. The latter element fixes itself preferentially in the thyroid gland; when it is administered to patients suffering from thyroid cancers, frequent regression of the metastatic tumours is observed, and in some cases a complete cure is achieved. Unfortunately these cures are far from being general or reliable, and the risk of poisoning by radiation cannot be excluded [164]. The principal reason for failure is a decrease in halogen retention by the gland as the cancer advances [165, 166, 167].

Analogous attempts have been made, especially by J. Lawrence and his co-workers [168, 169], to treat leukemia by introducing radiophosphorus into the digestive tract as phosphate. The same treatment has subsequently been attempted by other physicians for different malignant neoplastic conditions. The best results have been obtained in polycythemia, but acute leukemias are completely unaffected. Chronic leukemias show cures and survivals as frequently as in roentgentherapy [164]. Compared with the latter treatment, internal curietherapy using radiophosphorus (when this is possible) has distinct advantages due to the simplicity and ease of the treatment, but it seems doubtful at present whether the fixation is sufficiently selective to have no danger for healthy cells [170].

Encouraging, but so far limited, results have been obtained from a number of studies on chemical protection against radiation, involving attempts to prevent or to cure radiolesions by administering some appropriate chemical reagent to the organism either before or after irradiation. The type of experiments actually attempted tend to depend on the ideas held as to the origin of "radiation sickness." For example, on the belief that the bleeding condition following irradiation is due to the production of an anticoagulant, of the heparin type, substances such as toluidine blue or protamine have been injected into irradiated dogs, since such compounds inactivate the anticoagulant.* The bleeding ceases immediately and the survival of the animal is prolonged, but death cannot be prevented. Similarly, on the assumption that radiolesions of the intestinal mucous permit the passage of bacteria into the blood and so set up septicemia, some workers have tried to overcome the resultant fatal effects by the use of antibiotics. Whatever the cause, such therapeutic agents are very efficient against the infectious syndrome which follows irradiation. There is a decrease in the mortality in rats for doses of less than 600 r. Empirical attempts have also been made, with some degree of success, to use various vitamins, folic acid, cortisone, and other drugs.

A different principle underlies chemical protection, before or during irradiation. In this case the aim is to prevent the indirect effects of the radiation by capturing or destroying the free radicals, oxygen, or peroxides which may cause the lesions. It has been shown by Bacq and Herve [171, 172], Patt [173, 139], Loiseleur [174], and others [175], that sodium cyanide and nitrite, cysteine, mercaptoethylamine, glutathione, various amines, carbon monoxide, glucose, alcohols, etc., have a protective action *in vivo* on animals irradiated immediately after administration of the reagent. The majority of these substances are also efficient in protecting enzymes *in vitro* (Sections 13–6 and 14–6), but this parallelism is far from general. It should be noted that these protective agents are often poisonous, and also that they are effective only for a very limited period. They are therefore of no practical interest at present, but could well help to elucidate the mechanism of the protection effect.

14–11 The target theory. For a number of years, radiobiologists have favored a theory suggested by Blau and Altenburger, and subsequently developed through the work of Lacassagne and Holweck, Crowther, Glocker, Timofeeff-Ressovsky, Lea, and others. This theory attempts to relate radiobiological action to the direct effect caused by ionizations, which are likened to the discreet particles or quanta striking a precise region of the living matter, as a target is struck by a burst of gunfire.

---

* See A. Lacassagne, *Fortsch. Gebiete Roentgenstrahl.*, **75,** 98 (1951), for a bibliography on this topic.

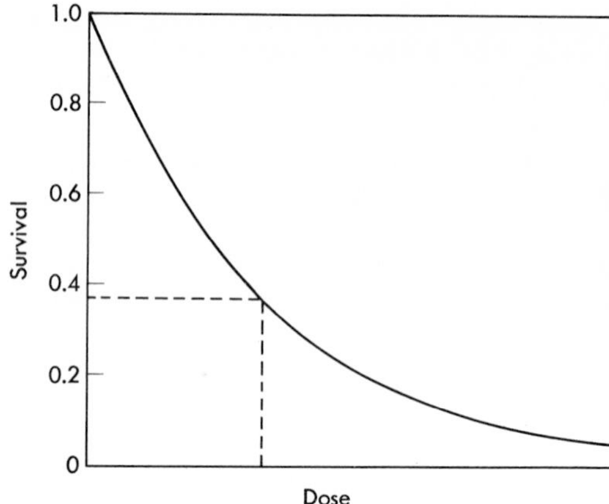

FIG. 14–2. Variation of survival with dose.

Lea [140] has devoted the greater part of the book quoted earlier to a thorough examination of this theory, its application and its limitations.

The theory attempts to interpret certain radiobiological phenomena such as chromosomic rupture, inactivation, or mutation, which occur in the immediate neighborhood of particular structural elements, and in particular to explain the differing radiosensitivity of different biological systems. These differences are illustrated by experimental dose-effect, or survival, curves, which are often exponential in form (see Fig. 14–2).

$$N_D = N_0 e^{-D/D_0}, \tag{14–29}$$

or

$$\log_e \frac{N_D}{N_0} = \frac{-D}{D_0}, \tag{14–30}$$

where N_0 is the number of organisms exposed to irradiation, and N_D the number unaffected or surviving after the administration of a dose D. The coefficient D_0 expresses the probability of the radiolesion in question being produced; for $D = D_0$, $N_D/N_0 = e^{-1} = 0.368$. The radiosensitivity is often expressed as the mean dose required for inactivation, or *the 37% dose*, corresponding to the survival of e^{-1} organisms. Other authors use the 50% dose, written as LD_{50}, as a measure of this sensitivity. It should be noted that in some cases, the survival curve has a sigmoid form, as shown in Fig. 14–3; such curves are obtained for instance for the destruction of yeast cells and bacteria, and for the inhibition of cell division in tissues.

The target theory ascribes the differing radiosensitivities not to intrinsic differences in the cells or organisms of a given species, but to the existence of *sensitive zones*, with fixed geometrical dimensions, which must be affected if a radiolesion is to be produced. Since the radiations act by discreet collisions, or ions, or ionic clusters, the sensitive zone is only injured if it receives an efficient hit, that is to say, sufficient quanta or ions to produce the required effect. Since the spatial distribution of the primary physical

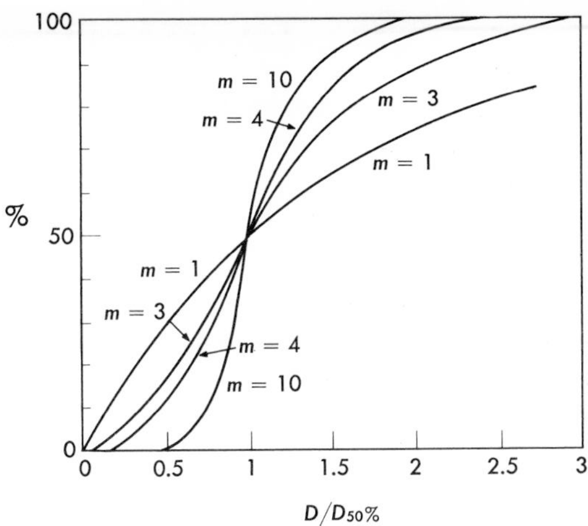

FIG. 14–3. Theoretical survival curves.

events is governed by statistical laws, the production of radiolesions should also obey such laws.

Starting from these hypotheses, it is easy to show that if V is the volume of the sensitive zone and m the number of events (e.g., ionization) necessary to bring about the observed effect, the number N of organisms affected is

$$\frac{N}{N_0} = 1 - e^{-VD}\left[1 + VD + \frac{(VD)^2}{2!} + \cdots + \frac{(VD)^{m-1}}{(m-1)!}\right], \quad (14\text{–}31)$$

and for $m = 1$

$$\frac{N}{N_0} = 1 - e^{-VD}, \quad (14\text{–}32)$$

which is identical with Eq. (14–29) if $N = N_0 - N_D$ and $V = 1/D_0$. Equation (14–31) is illustrated graphically in Fig. (14–3) by curves corresponding to different values of m; for $m = 1$, the curve is exponential in form, and for $m > 1$, implying multiple collisions, the curves are sigmoid.

The experimental survival curves can therefore be used to determine the number of primary acts necessary to produce a given radiolesion, and in addition to determine the radiosensitive volume V. When a single collision is efficient (named by Gray, the *monotopic effect*) the effects observed should be independent of the radiation intensity, and α-particles and protons (or neutrons) should be less efficient than x-rays, since the ionization from x-rays is more uniformly distributed in space, and hence for a given dose, the probability of affecting the target is greater.

According to Lea, a single ionization is sufficient to inactivate a virus provided that it is produced in a genetically important region, which for smaller viruses coincides with their overall size. The virus of the vaccine contains a large number of sensitive zones, each 60 A in diameter; ionization at any of these would lead to inactivation. From the 37% dose, the diameter of the dysentry bacteriophage is estimated at 150 A; the size of the sensitive zone of *Drosophile melanogaster* is 30 A, and of *Bacterium coli* 630 A.

On the other hand, we saw earlier that a simple chromosomic rupture requires 15 to 20 ionizations. The yield shows a complex dependence on dose, depending on the radiation used; it is greater for fast neutrons (Be + D) than for α-particles. For x-rays, there is a maximum as a function of the wavelength, and the yield is independent of the intensity. It has been deduced from this that the lesion is produced by the passage of a single ionizing particle such as an α-particle, proton, or δ-ray, through the sensitive zone. The number of double ruptures (of two segments of the same chromosome, or of neighboring chromosomes) is still independent of the intensity; in the case of α-particles and neutrons, the number is proportional to the dose, but with x-rays it increases with intensity and is proportional to the square of the dose. In the first case then a single particle furnishes sufficient ionizations to produce both ruptures, in a time which must be short so that one shall not be repaired before the other event occurs; with x-rays, which produce less strongly ionizing secondary electrons, two particles are necessary to achieve the same result.

The target theory does not claim to be a complete substitute for the free-radical theory, but rather to interpret a limited number of radiobiological phenomena. Even for such systems, however, it seems to be of limited applicability. A large number of experimental facts, especially in the field of protection effects, show that changes in the chemical medium have a significant influence on the radiolesion production.

Furthermore, radiobiological measurements do not seem to be sufficiently exact to indicate with certainty whether the variations follow an exponential or a sigmoid curve. We saw in Section 13–8 that the exponential curves, which correspond to first-order reactions in chemical kinetics, are frequently found in radiation chemistry even when ions or fairly simple molecules are involved. The same applies to the two other criteria for a simple collision process proposed by Lea, namely independence of the intensity, and a decrease in the efficiency with radiations producing dense ionization. These criteria therefore do not constitute a proof of the target mechanism, but can be used to make it more exact if the theory is assumed to be basically correct. Experiments by Pollard and Forro [176], however, show that the deuteron inactivation of phage can occur at energy depositions which are lower than those corresponding to a single ionization. Nor is the hypothesis of the uniform radioresistance of the various cells of a given species, which is fundamental to the target theory, completely established. Finally, as Franck and Platzman [177] have pointed out, to attribute a biological effect to a simple or multiple collision does not solve the problem of the real mechanism of the observed biological change, which is certainly very complex and involves a large number of elementary processes. For example, the sensitive volume or "sensitive area" may in fact be a fairly complicated average of the cross sections for various elementary physico-chemical processes, and is not necessarily a geometrical area. A complete analysis of these processes, which is as yet still impossible, would possibly show that the indirect effects are not incompatible with certain aspects of the target theory.

TABLE 14–4

LETHAL DOSES (LD_{50})

Organism	LD_{50}, r
Calliphora (eggs)	40
Axolotl (eggs)	50
Drosophilia (eggs)	190
Ascaris (eggs)	1000
Drosophilia (larvae)	1300
Bacterium coli	5100
Mesotaenium	9000
Saccharomices	42,000
Drosophilia (*imago*)	95,000
Bacterium	200,000
Colpidium colpoda	330,000
Guinea pig	250
Pig	350–400
Dog	325
Goat	350
Mouse	500–650
Monkey	500–600
Rat	600–700
Fowl	600–800
Rabbit	800

14–12 Fatal doses and tolerance doses. The extent and gravity of the alterations produced in living matter by ionizing radiations not only vary from one species to another, and from one individual to another in a given species, but also from one organ or tissue to another, depending on the physiological state, stage of development, and a large number of other factors. Table 14–4 gives the approximate doses (in roentgens) necessary to kill 50% of the organisms irradiated, or to reduce their normal growth by half [178, 179, 180]. For mammals the doses shown are lethal after a latent period of several days; immediate death only occurs after absorption of 50,000 r or more. The effects are evidently different depending on whether the same dose is received by a particular organ of the organism or by the whole organism (irradiation *in toto*).

Table 14–5 shows the probable effects of increasing doses of a penetrating radiation in man. Various national and international medical organizations have tried to estimate the maximum doses to which a person can be continually exposed in his work without reasonable fear of any harmful consequences. In general these *tolerances doses* are designed to give a comfortable margin of security; for example the dose of x- and γ-rays has been lowered from 0.1 r per day to 0.3 r per week. The doses, in rep, for corpuscular radiation are 0.3 for β-particles, 0.06 for slow neutrons, 0.03

TABLE 14–5

EFFECT OF PENETRATING RADIATION ON MAN

Dose, r	Probable effect
0–25	No obvious lesion
25–50	Possible changes in the blood
50–100	Lesions, definite changes in the blood
100–200	Lesions, possible illness
200–400	Lesions, illness (possibly fatal)
400	50% fatal
600+	Fatal

TABLE 14–6

MAXIMUM PERMITTED QUANTITIES AND CONCENTRATIONS OF RADIOACTIVE ELEMENTS, IN μc*

Element	Total body burden	Per cm^3 of water	Per liter of air
Po^{210}	0.02	3×10^{-5}	2×10^{-7}
Rn^{222}	7×10^{4}	2×10^{-6}	10^{-8}
Ra^{226}	0.1	4×10^{-8}	8×10^{-9}
Natural U	0.2	7×10^{-5}	1.7×10^{-8}
U^{233}	0.04	1.5×10^{-4}	10^{-7}
Pu^{239}	0.04	1.5×10^{-6}	2×10^{-9}
T	10^{4}	0.2	2
C^{14}	250	3×10^{-3}	10^{-3}
Na^{24}	15	8×10^{-3}	2×10^{-3}
P^{32}	10	2×10^{-4}	10^{-4}
S^{35}	100	5×10^{-3}	10^{-3}
Cl^{36}	200	2×10^{-3}	4×10^{-4}
K^{42}	20	10^{-2}	2×10^{-3}
Ca^{45}	65	5×10^{-4}	3×10^{-5}
$Fe^{55, 59}$	1000	4×10^{-3}	6×10^{-4}
$Sr^{90} + Y$	1	8×10^{-7}	2×10^{-7}
I^{131}	0.3	3×10^{-5}	3×10^{-6}

* From *National Bureau of Standards Handbook*, Washington, D.C., 1952.

for fast neutrons, and 0.015 for α-particles. The maximum quantities of various radioelements which can be tolerated by the body, and the maximum concentrations in air and in water, are shown in Table 14–6. The wide range of the values given is the result of the different types of radiation, half-life, and differing ease of elimination of the element from the body.

It is a tragic fact that most of our knowledge concerning the effect of radiations upon human beings is the result of the deliberate dropping of two nuclear weapons on the Japanese cities of Hiroshima and Nagasaki, and of various subsequent test explosions. The effect of the bombardment on the fate of the population have been soberly described, and illustrated with numerous photographs, by the "Japanese Committee at the World Congress of Medical Workers for the Study of the Current Conditions of Life," in Vienna in June 1953 [181]. We shall summarize here the most salient facts. The book begins as follows: "An atomic bomb was exploded at 8:15 on August 6th, 1945; this was followed by a second bomb dropped on Nagasaki at 11:30 on August 9th. The miseries and the sufferings of the unfortunate men and women who fell victims of the bombs have been described by several writers and artists, and in the writings of those schoolchildren who survived this horror."

We shall not stop here to discuss the destruction and damage caused by the air pressure, the fires, the burnings, and the fall of houses. The number of persons killed immediately in Hiroshima, or who died later as the result of lesions, has been estimated at between 210,000 and 270,000. The proportions killed was 100% up to a distance of 0.5 km from the epicenter (the point of the explosion of the bomb), 30 to 40% at 1.5 km, and 10 to 20% at 2 km. These numbers are (approximately) inversely proportional to the square of the distance; about 10% died more than three weeks after the fatal date. On October 23, 1945, the number dead or missing in Nagasaki was more than 25,000, and the number of persons affected about 112,000. Some 145 deaths were recorded at Hiroshima and 68 at Nagasaki among the medical personnel who helped the victims or who were involved in pathological researches.

The greatest loss of human life was caused by the γ-rays and neutrons emitted in the actual explosion, and to a lesser degree by the fission products and induced radioactivity. At Nagasaki, on October 1, the radioactivity 2 to 3 km from the epicenter was still 200 to 300 times greater than normal, and at one point it rose to a factor of 2000. Among people who were inside a zone 1 km from the site of the explosion, and who were not instantly killed or burned, the blood and internal organs were strongly affected. Such persons showed the typical symptoms of radiation sickness —loss of hair, haemorrhage, fever, diarrhea, vomiting, leukemia, etc. The majority of the victims died within a few days, or a few weeks. The effects on the inhabitants of the zones farther away were less severe and less frequent as the distance from the epicenter increased. The sickness known in Hiroshima as "atomic sickness" therefore showed itself in about 5 to 15 days by a total loss of hair (white hair excepted), haemorrhages in all parts of the body, decrease of the leucocytes below 1000 per mm^3, of the blood platelets to 10,000 to 30,000, and of the erythrocytes to 200,000, and the hemoglobin below 40%. Gingivitis (inflammation of the gums), stomatitis (inflammation of the mouth), gangrenous pharyngitis (inflammation of the throat), production of ulcers, diarrhea, fever, serious disorders of the ear, nose, larynx, and the eyes and the genital organs, and other afflictions accompanied this stage of the sickness, which was fatal in approximately 10% of the cases.

A number of fatal cases were reported at Nagasaki at a later stage characterized by a state of cachexia with loss of weight, oedema, ascites, and persistant diarrhoea. Even now "eight years after the explosion, its effects continue to cause sickness, and many people are still dying" (Kusano, 1953) [181]. The formation of kheloides, leukemia, and cataract are the most characteristic radiolesions which affect the population of the two cities in abnormal proportions. More serious still is the influence of the radiation on the younger generation—delayed physical and mental development, the seriousness of which increases in children exposed when very young, and malformations of newborn children, with some cases of microcephaly. It is as yet too soon to be certain about the hereditary consequences of the explosions; the facts established so far [182] show that genetic anomalies have been detected among the children of persons who suffered radiolesions at a rate of 1.40%, against 1.18% in a normal population.

A further series of tragic events followed the explosion of a thermonuclear weapon on the Bikini atoll on March 1, 1954 [183, 184, 185]. According to a report issued by the United States Atomic Energy Commission, the radioactivity due to *fallout* (Section 6–11) at a point some 125 miles from the atoll was 2000 r 36 hours after the explosion; this is 5 times the lethal dose. Assuming a decay law of the $t^{-1.2}$ type for the decay of the fission products (Section 6–10), we can assume that the total dose received at the distance in question during the first 24 hours was 1625 r [186]; this corresponds to 2985 r during the first week, and the dose after 48 hours was still 15 r/hr. It so happened that a small Japanese tunny boat, the "Happy Dragon," with 23 men on board, was at sea about 100 miles from Bikini at the time of the explosion. According to the fishermen, a fine white powder began to fall about $1\frac{1}{2}$ hours later and covered various parts of the boat for several hours. Chemical and radiochemical analysis of this "Bikini ash" led to the conclusion that it arose from the pulverization of corals; the debris, which was strongly contaminated with fission products, had been drawn upward into the atmosphere along with the "cloud" from the explosion. Those parts of the bodies of the fishermen touched by the powder, such as the face, the neck and the hands, became red and swollen. Other symptoms of radiation sickness, such as fever, leukemia, dermatitis, digestive troubles, loss of hair, etc., appeared gradually throughout the whole crew. The boat reached its home port 13 days after the explosion, when the crew were placed in the hospital, and with the exception of one member who died suddenly seven months later, the exterior lesions of the others were cured, thanks to the remarkably successful efforts of the medical workers. The total dose received by these fishermen is estimated at more than 100 r.

Less seriously affected by the thermonuclear explosion at Bikini and its aftereffects were 236 inhabitants of the Marshall Islands, and 28 Americans who were in the neighborhood. In addition, large quantities of the fish caught a considerable distance (more than 2000 miles) from Bikini were found to be seriously contaminated even several months after the explosion. Finally, for some time afterward the rain water, vegetables, and milk in various parts of Japan had an abnormally high activity.

The whole scientific world, and especially nuclear experts, were alarmed by the events on the "Happy Dragon" with the clear illustration of the terrible repercussions of fallout, even for populations of regions far away from a nuclear explosion [186–191]. It has been estimated that the population in an area of 7000 square miles lying below the radioactive cloud from the Bikini explosion of March 1, 1954, would have completely perished. The pathological and genetic effects obviously would have occurred (or have occurred) over a much wider area. In fact, Libby [192] has estimated that the initial intensity after the explosion of a bomb of the Bikini type would correspond to 67 r/day over an area of the order of 100,000 square miles. It is known that the whole surface of the earth is already contaminated with detectable quantities of fission products, but the activity from this source is as yet of the same order of magnitude as that due to natural radioactivity.

References

1. G. Glocker and S. C. Lind, *The Electrochemistry of Gases*, Wiley and Sons, New York, 1939.
2. I. A. Breger, *J. Phys. Chem.*, **52,** 551 (1948).
3. M. Magat and R. Viallard, *J. Chim. Phys.*, **48,** 385 (1951); see also F. L. Mohler, *J. Wash. Acad. Science*, **38,** 193 (1948).
4. D. P. Stevenson, *Discussions Faraday Soc.*, **10,** 35 (1951).
5. S. C. Lind, D. C. Bardwell, and J. H. Perry, *J. Am. Chem. Soc.*, **48,** 1556 (1926).
6. S. C. Lind and D. C. Bardwell, *J. Am. Chem. Soc.*, **48,** 2335 (1926).
7. C. S. Schoepfle and C. H. Fellows, *Ind. Eng. Chem.*, **23,** 1396 (1931).
8. M. Burton, *Ann. Rev. Phys. Chem.*, **1,** 113 (1950).
9. M. Burton, *J. Phys. Chem.*, **52,** 564 (1948).
10. M. Burton, S. Gordon, and R. R. Hentz, *J. Chim. Phys.*, **48,** 190 (1951).
11. S. Gordon and M. Burton, *Discussions Faraday Soc.*, **12,** 88 (1952).
12. J. P. Manion and M. Burton, *J. Phys. Chem.*, **56,** 560 (1952).
13. J. Flanagan, C. J. Hochanadel, and R. A. Penneman, quoted in Ref. 9.
14. W. Mund and E. Bogaert, *Bull. Soc. Chim. Belg.*, **134,** 410 (1925).
15. V. P. Henri, C. R. Maxwell, W. C. White, and D. C. Peterson, *J. Phys. Chem.*, **56,** 153 (1952).
16. T. J. Sworski, R. R. Hentz, and M. Burton, *J. Am. Chem. Soc.*, **73,** 532, 1998, 3790 (1951).
17. R. R. Williams and W. H. Hamill, *J. Am. Chem. Soc.*, **72,** 1857 (1950).
18. L. H. Gevantman and R. R. Williams, *J. Phys. Chem.*, **56,** 569 (1952).
19. A. Langer, *J. Phys. Chem.*, **54,** 618 (1950).
20. C. C. Schubert and R. H. Schuler, *J. Chem. Phys.*, **20,** 518 (1952).
21. P. F. Forsyth, E. N. Weber, and R. H. Schuler, *J. Chem. Phys.*, **22,** 66 (1954).
22. A. Chapiro, *Compt. rend.*, **233,** 792 (1951).
23. A. Prevot-Bernas, A. Chapiro, C. Cousin, Y. Landler, and M. Magat, *Discussions Faraday Soc.*, **12,** 98 (1952).
24. See the discussion in *J. Chim. Phys.*, **52,** 653 (1955).

25. N. A. BAKH, *Symposium on Radiation Chemistry, Moscow, 1955,* p. 119 (English translation).

26. N. A. BAKH and N. I. POPOV, *Symposium on Radiation Chemistry, Moscow, 1955,* p. 129.

27. J. C. MCLENNAN and W. L. PATRICK, *Can. J. Research,* **5,** 470 (1931).

28. W. R. MCDONELL and A. S. NEWTON, *J. Am. Chem. Soc.,* **76,** 4651 (1954).

29. W. R. MCDONELL, *U.S.A.E.C. report UCRL–1378,* 1951.

30. W. R. MCDONELL and S. GORDON, *J. Chem. Phys.,* **23,** 208 (1955).

31. N. A. BAKH and Y. I. SOROKIN, Ref. 25, p. 135.

32. K. G. BELL, C. GOODMAN, and W. L. WHITEHEAD, *Bull. Am. Assoc. Petroleum Geol.,* **24,** 1529 (1940).

33. C. W. SHEPPARD and V. L. BURTON, *J. Am. Chem. Soc.,* **68,** 1636 (1946).

34. R. E. HONIG, *Science,* **104,** 27 (1946).

35. C. GOODMAN and I. A. BREGER, *J. Chim. Phys.,* **48,** 184 (1951).

36. V. L. BURTON, *J. Am. Chem. Soc.,* **71,** 4117 (1949).

37. N. A. BAKH and V. V. SARAEVA, Ref. 25, p. 145.

38. A. KAILAN, *Monatsh. Chem.,* **38,** 537 (1917).

39. P. GUNTHER, H. HORST, and G. CRONHEIM, *Z. Elektrochem.,* **34,** 616 (1928).

40. G. CRONHEIM and P. GUNTHER, *Z. Physik. Chem.,* **B9,** 201 (1930).

41. A. V. ZIMIN and Z. S. EGOROVA, Ref. 25, p. 207.

42. J. W. SCHULTE, J. F. SUTTLE, and R. WILHELM, *J. Am. Chem. Soc.,* **75,** 2222 (1953).

43. R. H. SCHULER and W. H. HAMILL, *J. Am. Chem. Soc.,* **74,** 6171 (1952).

44. M. LEFORT, P. BONET-MAURY, and M. FRILLEY, *Compt. rend.,* **226,** 1904 (1948).

45. P. SÜE and E. SAELAND, *Bul. soc. chim. France,* **1949,** 437.

46. E. L. COCHRAN, W. H. HAMILL, and R. R. WILLIAMS, *J. Am. Chem. Soc.,* **76,** 2145 (1954).

47. W. MINDER, *Radiol. Clinica,* **19,** 277 (1950).

48. W. MINDER and H. HEYDRICH, *Discussions Faraday Soc.,* **12,** 305 (1952).

49. N. N. TUNITSKII, S. E. KURPIYANOV, and M. V. TIKHOMIROV, Ref. 25, p. 191.

50. J. LOISELEUR, *J. Chim. Phys.,* **52,** 626 (1955).

51. A. V. ZIMIN, S. V. CHURMANTEEV, and A. D. VERINA, Ref. 25, p. 215.

52. L. C. ANDERSON, B. G. BRAY, and J. J. MARTIN, *1955 Geneva Conference,* P. 168.

53. D. E. HARMER, J. J. MARTIN, and L. C. ANDERSON, *J. Chim. Phys.,* **52,** 667 (1955).

54. F. L. HOPWOOD and J. T. PHILLIPS, *Proc. Phys. Soc. (London),* **50,** 438 (1938).

55. F. L. HOPWOOD and J. T. PHILLIPS, *Nature,* **143,** 640 (1939).

56. F. JOLIOT, French patent, No. 451131, 1939.

57. A. CHAPIRO, C. COUSIN, Y. LANDLER, and M. MAGAT, *Rec. Trav. Chim. Pays-Bas,* **68,** 1037 (1949).

58. A. CHAPIRO, *J. Chim. Phys.,* **47,** 747, 764 (1950).

59. Y. LANDLER, *Thesis,* Paris, 1952.

60. M. MAGAT, *Radiochemical Transformations,* Collogue Donegani, Acad. Lincei, Milan-Rome.

61. M. MAGAT, *et al., 1955 Geneva Conference,* P. 363.

62. T. S. Nikitina and Kh. S. Bagdasaryan, Ref. 25, p. 153.
63. J. V. Schmitz and E. J. Lawton, *Science,* **113,** 718 (1951).
64. W. H. T. Davison, S. H. Pinner, and R. Worrall, *Chem. Ind.,* **1957,** 1274.
65. L. A. Wall and M. Magat, *J. Chim. Phys.,* **50,** 308 (1953).
66. P. Alexander and M. Fox, *J. Chim. Phys.,* **50,** 415 (1953).
67. M. Fox, *Compt. rend.,* **237,** 1682 (1953).
68. P. Alexander and M. Fox, *Trans. Faraday Soc.,* **50,** 605 (1954).
69. A. Charlesby and P. Alexander, *J. Chim. Phys.,* **52,** 694 (1955).
70. E. S. G. Barron, *Biochemical Aspects of Radiobiology,* Highland Park Conference, 1954, p. 30.
71. J. Loiseleur, *Bull. Soc. Chim. Biol.,* **25,** 22 (1943).
72. See *Trans. Faraday Soc.,* **49,** 323 (1953).
73. J. A. V. Butler and B. E. Conway, *J. Chem. Soc.,* **1950,** 3418; **1952,** 834.
74. J. Loiseleur, L. Catinot, and P. Morenne, *Compt. rend.,* **237,** 410 (1953).
75. H. Fricke, E. J. Hart and H. P. Smith, *J. Chem. Phys.,* **6,** 229 (1938).
76. W. R. McDonell, *J. Chem. Phys.,* **23,** 208 (1955).
77. A. J. Swallow, *Biochem. J.,* **54,** 253 (1953).
78. E. S. G. Barron and V. Flood, *J. Gen. Physiol.,* **33,** 229 (1950).
79. G. Stein and J. Weiss, *J. Chem. Soc.,* **1949,** 3256.
80. G. Scholes and J. Weiss, *Biochem. J.,* **53,** 567 (1953).
81. H. Fricke and E. J. Hart, *J. Chem. Phys.,* **2,** 824 (1934).
82. E. J. Hart, *J. Am. Chem. Soc.,* **73,** 68 (1951); **74,** 4174 (1952); **76,** 4198, 4312 (1954).
83. E. J. Hart, *J. Phys. Chem.,* **56,** 594 (1952).
84. W. M. Garrison, *et al., J. Am. Chem. Soc.,* **75,** 2459 (1953); **77,** 2720 (1955).
85. W. M. Garrison, *Radn. Research,* **1,** 97 (1954).
86. I. G. Draganic, *J. Chim. Phys.,* **59,** 9, 16, 18 (1959).
87. S. di Bella, *Boll. Soc. Ital. Biol. Sper.,* **25,** 1268 (1949).
88. G. R. A. Johnson, G. Scholes, and J. Weiss, *J. Chem. Soc.,* **1953,** 3091.
89. H. Loebl, G. Stein, and J. Weiss, *J. Chem. Soc.,* **1950,** 2704; **1951,** 405.
90. G. R. A. Johnson, G. Stein, and J. Weiss, *J. Chem. Soc.,* **1951,** 3275.
91. A. Kailan, *Monatsh. Chem.,* **41,** 312 (1920).
92. W. Minder, *Radiol. Clinica,* **16,** 339 (1947).
93. R. Feller, W. Minder, and A. Liechti, *Radiol. Clinica,* **17,** 156 (1948).
94. A. Meister and W. Minder, *Radiol. Clinica,* **19,** 238 (1950).
95. M. A. Khenokh, *J. Gen. Chem. Russ.,* **20,** 1560 (1950).
96. G. O. Phillips, *Nature,* **173,** 1044 (1954).
97. W. M. Dale, L. H. Gray, and W. J. Meredith, *Phil. Trans. Roy. Soc. (London),* **A242,** 33 (1949).
98. W. M. Dale, J. V. Davies, and C. W. Gilbert, *Biochem. J.,* **45,** 93, 543 (1949).
99. W. M. Dale and J. V. Davies, *Biochem. J.,* **48,** 129 (1951).
100. W. M. Dale, *J. Chim. Phys.,* **48,** 245 (1951).
101. W. M. Dale, in *Actions Chimiques et Biologiques des Radiations,* Vol. I, Masson, Paris, 1955, p. 205.
102. G. R. A. Johnson, G. Stein, and J. Weiss, *Science,* **114,** 412 (1951).

103. J. WEISS and G. SCHOLES, *Nature,* **167,** 693 (1951).
104. C. R. MAXWELL, D. C. PETERSON, and N. E. SHARPLESS, *Radn. Research,* **1,** 530 (1954); **2,** 135 (1955).
105. A. J. SWALLOW, *J. Chem. Soc.,* **1952,** 1334.
106. M. ROTHERAM, N. TODD, and S. L. WHITCHER, *Naturwiss.,* **39,** 450 (1952).
107. M. ROTHERAM, N. TODD, and S. L. WHITCHER, *Nucleonics,* **11,** No. 8, 30 (1953).
108. K. STENSTROHM and A. LOHMAN, *J. Biol. Chem.,* **79,** 673 (1928).
109. C. E. NURNBERGER, *Proc. Natl. Acad. Sci. U.S.,* **23,** 189 (1937).
110. J. LOISELEUR, *Compt. rend. Biol.,* **114,** 589 (1933).
111. D. S. BHATIA and B. E. PROCTOR, *Biochem. J.,* **49,** 550 (1951).
112. B. E. PROCTOR and S. A. GOLDBLITH, *U.S.A.E.C. report NYO-337,* 1952.
113. B. TAYLOR, J. P. GREENSTEIN, and A. HOLLAENDER, *Arch. Biochem. Biophys.,* **16,** 19 (1948).
114. G. LIMPEROS and W. A. MOSHER, *Am. J. Roentgen,* **63,** 681 (1950).
115. G. SCHOLES, G. STEIN, and J. WEISS, *Nature,* **164,** 709 (1949).
116. J. A. V. BUTLER and K. A. SMITH, *Nature,* **165,** 847 (1950).
117. E. S. G. BARRON, in Ref. 141, p. 283.
118. E. S. G. BARRON, *Radn. Research,* **1,** 109 (1954).
119. D. B. SMITH and G. C. BUTLER, *J. Am. Chem. Soc.,* **73,** 258 (1951).
120. H. EPHRUSSI-TAYLOR and R. LATARJET, *Biochem. Biophys. Acta,* **16,** 183 (1955).
121. W. M. DALE, *Biochem. J.,* **34,** 1367 (1940); **36,** 80 (1942).
122. W. M. DALE, *J. Physiol. (London),* **102,** 50 (1943).
123. A. FORSSBERG, *Acta Radiol.,* **27,** 281 (1946).
124. A. FORSSBERG, *Nature,* **159,** 308 (1947).
125. W. F. POWELL and E. POLLARD, *Radn. Research,* **2,** 109 (1955).
126. R. LATARJET, *Compt. rend.,* **232,** 1713 (1951).
127. R. LATARJET, *Acta Radiol.,* **41,** 84 (1954).
128. L. H. GRAY and J. READ, *Brit. J. Rad.,* **23,** 300 (1950).
129. L. H. GRAY, *Radn. Research,* **2,** 189 (1950).
130. L. H. GRAY, *1955 Geneva Conference,* P. 899.
131. H. HEWITT and J. READ, *Brit. J. Rad.,* **13,** 416 (1940).
132. L. EHRENBERG, A. GUSTAFSSON, and N. NYBOM, *Arkiv Botan.,* **1,** 557 (1952).
133. L. EHRENBERG and E. SAELAND, *J. Nuclear Energy,* **1,** 150 (1954).
134. R. S. CALDECOTT, *1955 Geneva Conference,* P. 101.
135. C. A. TOBIAS, in *Symposium on Radiobiology,* J. Nickson, ed., Wiley, New York, 1952.
136. T. ALPER, *Brit. J. Rad.,* **27,** 50 (1954).
137. T. ALPER, *Radn. Research,* **2,** 119 (1955).
138. C. S. BACHOFER and M. A. POTTINGER, *Science,* **119,** 378 (1954).
139. H. M. PATT, *Physiol. Rev.,* **33,** 35 (1953).
140. D. E. LEA, *Actions of Radiations on Living Cells,* Cambridge University Press, 1955.
141. A. HOLLAENDER, ed., *Radiation Biology,* McGraw-Hill, New York, 1955.
142. Z. A. BACQ and P. ALEXANDER, *Fundamentals of Radiobiology,* Butterworths, London, 1955.
143. A. HOLLAENDER, *1955 Geneva Conference,* Vol. 16.

144. J. Bergonie and L. Tribondeau, *Compt. rend.*, **143,** 983 (1906).
145. N. H. Giles, in Ref. 141, p. 713.
146. M. Markovitch, *1955 Geneva Conference,* P. 371.
147. W. Spencer and C. Stern, *Genetics,* **33,** 43 (1948).
148. H. J. Müller, *Science,* **66,** 84 (1927); **67,** 82 (1938).
149. H. J. Müller, *Am. Scientist,* **38,** 83 (1950).
150. H. J. Müller, *Acta Radiol.,* **41,** 5 (1954).
151. H. M. Slatis, *Science,* **121,** 817 (1955).
152. T. C. Carter, *1955 Geneva Conference,* P. 449.
153. G. Hevesy, *Revs. Modern Phys.,* **17,** 102 (1945).
154. G. Hevesy, *Radioactive Indicators,* Interscience, New York, 1948, Chapter 12; see also M. N. Meissel, *1955 Geneva Conference,* P. 690.
155. T. G. Hennessy and R. L. Huff, *Proc. Soc. Exptl. Biol. Med.,* **73,** 436 (1950).
156. P. F. Minaev, *Sess. Acad. Sci., U.S.S.R.,* July 1–5, 1955, Biol. Sect., p. 51.
157. A. V. Lebedinsky, *1955 Geneva Conference,* P. 616.
158. G. Gaude and J. Coursaget, *1955 Geneva Conference,* P. 375.
159. I. A. Pigalyev, *1955 Geneva Conference,* P. 692.
160. A. Lacassagne, *Les cancers produits par les rayonnements electromagnetiques,* Hermann, Paris, 1948.
161. A. M. Brues, *Advances in Cancer Research,* **2,** 177 (1954).
162. J. Furth and E. Lorenz, in Ref. 141, p. 1145.
163. A. V. Kozlova, *1955 Geneva Conference,* P. 685.
164. A. Lacassagne, *Acquisitions medicales recentes,* Flammarion, Paris, 1955.
165. J. G. Hamilton, *J. Appl. Phys.,* **12,** 440 (1941).
166. L. D. Marinelli, F. W. Foote, R. F. Hill, and A. F. Hocker, *Am. J. Roentgen,* **58,** 17 (1947).
167. P. J. Fitzgerald and F. W. Foote, *J. Clin. Endocrinol.,* **9,** 1153 (1949).
168. J. H. Lawrence, L. W. Tuttle, K. G. Scott, and C. L. Connor, *J. Clin. Investigation,* **19,** 267 (1940).
169. L. W. Tuttle, L. A. Erf, and J. H. Lawrence, *J. Clin. Investigation,* **20,** 57, 577 (1941).
170. L. G. Lajtha, R. Oliver, and F. Ellis, *Brit. J. Cancer,* **8,** 367 (1954).
171. Z. A. Bacq and A. Herve, *Brit. J. Rad.,* **24,** 617 (1951).
172. Z. A. Bacq, *Experientia,* **7,** 11 (1951).
173. H. M. Patt, *Ann. Rev. Nuclear Sci.,* **1,** 495 (1952).
174. J. Loiseleur and G. Velley, *Compt. rend.,* **231,** 182 (1950).
175. For example E. Graievsky, *Sess. Acad. Sci., U.S.S.R.,* July 1–5, 1955, Biol. Sect., p. 34.
176. E. C. Pollard and F. Forro, *Science,* **109,** 374 (1949).
177. J. Franck and R. Platzman, in Ref. 141, p. 191.
178. A. Sparrow and B. Rubin, *U.S.A.E.C. report BNL–97,* 1951.
179. H. M. Patt and A. M. Brues, in Ref. 141, p. 919.
180. J. Thomson, *Ann. Rev. Nuclear Sci.,* **4,** 377 (1954).
181. N. Kusano, *Atomic Bomb Injuries,* Tsukiji Shokan Cy, Tokyo, 1953.
182. J. C. Bugher, *Nucleonics,* **10,** No. 9, 18 (1952).
183. M. Tsuzuki, quoted by A. Ravina, *Presse medicale,* **62,** 881 (1954).
184. Y. Nichiwaki, *Atom. Sci. J. (G. B.),* **4,** 97 (1954); **4,** 279 (1955).

185. J. ARNOLD, *Bull. Atomic Scientists,* **10,** 347 (1954).
186. R. E. LAPP, *Bull. Atomic Scientists,* **11,** 206, 270 (1955).
187. J. ROTBLAT, *Bull. Atomic Scientists,* **11,** 171 (1955).
188. A. H. ROSENFELD, E. STORY, and S. D. WARSHAW, *Bull. Atomic Scientists,* **11,** 213 (1955).
189. H. J. MÜLLER, *Science,* **121,** 837 (1955).
190. J. B. S. HALDANE, *Nature,* **176,** 115 (1955).
191. A. LACASSAGNE, *Bruxelles medical,* **35,** 184 (1955).
192. W. F. LIBBY, *Bull. Atomic Scientists,* **11,** 256 (1955).

CHAPTER 15

THE EFFECTS OF RADIATIONS ON SOLIDS

15–1 Atomic displacements. The primary interactions between radiations and solids are qualitatively the same as for fluids, namely excitation, ionization, recoil, decomposition, etc. There are two important differences, however. One is the very limited mobility of the constituents of a solid, due to the high density of the medium. Secondly, the particular electronic structure of each type of solid means that the detectable results of these interactions are often very different from the liquid case, and depend on whether the irradiated solid is a metal, semiconductor, ionic crystal, covalent crystal, plastic, etc. Thus in metals, which are good conductors, the effects of ionization disappear rapidly and the alterations observed are mainly due to the effects of recoils from elastic collisions. The displacements of atoms in the lattice increase the degree of disorder in semiconductors and ionic crystals. In addition, in ionic crystals, the release of electrons by ionization, and their subsequent capture after migration to other points of the lattice, causes very complex luminescence and color phenomena. If the ions in the crystal are polyatomic (for example, MnO_4^-, NO_3^-) or can undergo valency changes, changes in the chemical composition of the compound may occur simultaneously (and sometimes preferentially). The same applies to organic substances, in which the molecules may either pass from an excited state to the ground state by the emission of light, or may undergo some more permanent change, such as degradation, rearrangement, etc. The present chapter is devoted to the discussion of these various effects (known generally as *radiation damage*) which result in changes, either in the physical or structural properties of a solid, or in its chemical composition.

```
ABABAB          ABABAB
   B
BABABA          B BABA

A ABAB          ABABA

BABA A          B BABA
  B
ABABAB          ABA AB

  (a)              (b)
```

FIG. 15–1. (a) Frenkel defects. (b) Schottky defects.

Physical and structural damage is governed by the "defects" which are always present in solids. In addition to the fixed imperfections due to foreign atoms or accidental irregularities, two types of "mobile defects" can be recognized in crystals (Fig. 15–1). In Fig. 15–1(a), an atom or an ion has left its normal site to occupy an interstitial position between the regular layers of the lattice; this is a *Frenkel defect.* In Fig. 15–1(b), the atom has left its normal position to migrate toward the surface or some other discontinuity (intercrystalline boundary, dislocation, or impurity), leaving behind a vacant site or *vacancy* in the lattice; this is a *Schottky defect.* When an atom is displaced from its position into an interstitial site, both defects are present simultaneously. The formation of these two types of defect is thermodynamically reversible, and increases with temperature, in agreement with the fact that there is an increase in entropy resulting from the increasing disorder. The number (n) of atoms per cubic centimeter which occupy interstitial positions in equilibrium with N normal sites varies with the temperature according to a Boltzmann distribution:

$$n = Ne^{-E/2kT}, \tag{15–1}$$

where E is the energy required to transfer the atom into the interstitial position. A similar equation applies to Schottky defects:

$$n' = Ne^{-E'/kT}. \tag{15–2}$$

Atomic displacements caused by radiation therefore increase the degree of disorder in a solid by increasing the number of interstitial atoms and vacancies. Qualitatively, both charged particles and neutrons have the same effects. In addition, however, neutron capture by the components of the lattice may produce a new nuclide with a different atomic number and so introduce a chemical impurity into the lattice. Neutralized charged particles (protons, α-particles, etc.) which have come to rest at the end of their tracks constitute a similar source of impurities, and of course when these particles have sufficiently high energy, they too can bring about nuclear reactions which give rise to foreign atoms. Finally, changes can be caused by the rapid temperature change at the "hot spots" created by the movement of the displaced atoms. When the latter have sufficient energy, they can bring about nuclear reactions leading to the production of foreign atoms.

We saw in Chapter 11 that fast neutrons lose their kinetic energy by elastic collisions, while for charged particles this mode of energy loss is extremely small, ($\sim$1 in 1000) as long as the velocity is greater than that of the electrons in the struck atom. Consequently, the slowing down is essentially due to ionization and excitation. At the end of the track, charged particles also lose their energy by elastic collisions. According to Seitz [1, 2], the transition between the two modes of scattering is characterized by the parameter ϵ discussed in Section 11–2:

$$\epsilon = E\frac{m}{A}, \tag{15–3}$$

which gives the energy of an electron of mass m with the same velocity as the particle of mass A and energy E. For an insulator, the transition occurs at energies corresponding to $\epsilon = I_c/8$, where I_c is the lowest excitation potential of the scattered atom. For a given incident particle passing through a metal, the value of ϵ depends on the atomic number and on the number of free electrons per atom, and generally lies between 0.1 and 10 ev.

The effects of elastic collisions can be considered in two parts: first, the displacement of the atoms of the lattice by recoil (the *Wigner effect*), and second, a local increase of temperature, which may be of the order of 10°C for good conductors and hundreds of degrees for poor conductors, such as quartz. The "hot spots" thus formed at the end of the tracks may affect some 10^4 atoms for a very short time interval, of the order of 10^{-11} sec, so that local melting and structural changes may occur.

The rate of loss of energy per unit track length in excitation and ionization processes is governed by an equation analogous to Eq. (11–3) for gases; the corresponding loss due to displacements is given by a relation of the same type [1], namely

$$-\left(\frac{dE}{dx}\right)_d = \frac{2\pi z^2 Z^2 e^4 n_0}{A_2 v^2} \log_e \left(\frac{E}{E_0}\,\frac{4\mu^2}{A_1 A_2}\right), \tag{15–4}$$

where E is the energy and A_1 the mass of the incident particle, E_d is the energy required to displace an atom (mass A_2) of the solid from its normal position into an interstatial position, μ is the reduced mass, and the other terms have the same significance as in Eq. (11–3). The average kinetic energy transferred to the displaced atom is

$$\overline{E} = E_d \log_e \left(\frac{E}{E_d}\,\frac{4\mu^2}{A_1 A_2}\right). \tag{15–5}$$

Experiments described in Sections 15–2 and 15–3 show that the value of E_d is 25 ev for copper [3] and 30 ev for germanium [4].

A displaced atom may have sufficient kinetic energy to displace another atom, and this secondary atom to displace a third, and so on. The total number of atoms displaced by the action of one particle is therefore

$$N_d = N_p N_s = \frac{f E_e}{\sqrt{\overline{E} E_d}}, \tag{15–6}$$

where N_p is the number of atoms displaced directly by the incident particle, and N_s that by secondary displacements; f is the fraction of the energy dissipated in elastic collisions which is used in displacements ($f \approx 0.5$), and E_e is the energy dissipated by the particle in elastic collisions over its whole path.

Table 15–1 gives values of some of the parameters calculated by Seitz for some typical elements. The values of the critical energy ϵ_c have been calculated on the assumption that $E_d = 25$ ev. The number of atoms displaced per particle (N_d) is given for 5-Mev α-particles, 20-Mev protons, and 2-Mev neutrons.

Fast electrons cause appreciable atomic displacement in metals only if their energy is greater than about 0.5 Mev. It appears, however, that electrons or x-rays with energies much lower than this can produce atomic displacements in crystals of the alkali halides. Varley [5, 6] (see also [7]) has

TABLE 15–1

ATOMIC DISPLACEMENTS

Element	ϵ_c	5-Mev α-particles			20-Mev protons			2-Mev neutrons	
		$\overline{E}$, ev	E_e, kev	N_d	$\overline{E}$, ev	E_e, kev	N_d	$\overline{E}$, kev	N_d
Be	0.14	282	4.8	33	298	8.6	56	360	454
Graphite	0.5	280	8.2	55	290	11.1	72	284	1870
Diamond	2.5	280	23.0	154	290	14.8	96	284	—
Al	0.35	280	8.8	59	273	12.9	79	137	6030
Si	0.14	268	7.4	49	272	12.9	81	—	—
Ge	0.10	248	9.2	59	250	13.8	87	55	—

suggested that these arise by indirect action, being due to multiple ionization of the anion; on becoming positively charged in this way, it finds itself in an abnormal position, from which it easily goes to an interstitial site by thermal activation. It could also displace another neighboring positive ion from its normal position.

Huntington [8] has extended the Seitz theory to metals, especially copper, by assuming that the s and p electrons can move freely, whereas the interactions between d electrons and the positive ions, and between the incident particles and the atoms of the metal, are governed by the Born-Mayer law [9]. This states that the lattice energy (E) of an ionic crystal is given by

$$E = -\frac{Ae^2}{r} + Be^{-\alpha r}, \tag{15–7}$$

in which the first term corresponds to the attraction between oppositely charged ions a distance r apart and the second term to the repulsion between the electron shells. Depending on the value chosen for the exponent α (13 or 17), $E_d = 18.5$ or 43 ev for displacement to an interstitial position in the (111) direction, and 17.5 or 34 ev in the (100) direction. A similar calculation of the energy of formation of a vacancy in the same metal gives approximately 1.5 to 1.8 ev; the activation energy for the migration of one vacancy toward another in the lattice is of the order of 1 ev. For interstitial processes, the corresponding values are 5 to 6 ev, and between 0.07 and 0.27 ev.

The disorganization of the crystal lattice as a result of displacements produces varying degrees of change in the mechanical and electrical properties. Generally, the changes induced by radiation show a number of similarities with those produced by cold working, which also increases the degree of disorder. In particular, in both cases there are increases in the hardness and in the electrical resistivity, and changes in density. These can be partially or completely eliminated by annealing at some appropriate temperature, which increases the mobility of the vacancies and the interstitial atoms, and the rate of the recombination processes. For such reasons, changes in these properties produced by irradiation must be investigated at very low temperatures. This is especially important for studies of the resistivity, since it is the residual resistance in particular which is altered. For metals such as aluminum, in which annealing to the normal state occurs even at room temperature, only small changes in these properties are observed. The same is true for cold-worked metals in which the disorder is already close to saturation, since irradiation can produce no further increase.

The significance of this type of research to a proper understanding of the solid state has been emphasized by Slater [10] and Dienes [11, 12] in particular. There is also a considerable practical importance because of the widespread use of solid materials in nuclear reactors.

15-2 Metals and alloys. As might be expected, the most serious damage has been observed in uranium exposed to a high neutron flux and the effects of fission fragments [13, 14, 15]. During the irradiation, the metal becomes strongly plastic and undergoes irregular deformations; thus the thickness of a sheet of uranium, initially 0.28 to 0.34 mm, changed after irradiation with 10^{19} n/cm^2 to between 0.06 and 0.45 mm at different points. Similarly, the metal became twisted and brittle, and the hardness increased, as did the elastic modulus measured at liquid helium temperatures. The density decreased by about 1%, and the thermal conductivity by 10 to 15%; the other mechanical properties and the microcrystalline structure were also affected. The considerable distortion or irradiated uranium is at least partly due to the existence of three allotropic varieties of the metal, and, especially, to its high anisotropy; for example, the coefficients of linear expansion vary with the orientation from slightly negative to strongly positive values. Thorium, and the alloys of uranium with aluminum, beryllium, chromium, and zirconium, are more resistant to irradiation.

Of the other metals, there has been a considerable theoretical and experimental interest in copper. Irradiation with 10- to 20-Mev helium ions [16, 17, 18], deuterons [19, 20, 21], or fast neutrons [22, 23] at liquid nitrogen or liquid helium temperatures causes an increase in the resistivity, hardness, and critical shear stress, and a decrease in the density. The resistance change may be of the order of 30% under certain conditions, and the density decrease about 0.03%; the critical shear stress after neutron irradiation of single crystals of copper increases from 0.24 to 3.5 kg/mm^2. When the sample is allowed to warm up, the recovery of the properties takes place in successive stages, with sharp changes at certain temperatures (for example, 40°K). Annealing is therefore already occurring at very low temperatures, but the residual effects remain even up to temperatures as high as +100°C. From plots of the change in resistivity as a function of temperature, it is possible to determine the activation energies for the recovery processes; these appear to show a spectrum of values between about 0.1 and more than 2 ev. These energies are related to the migration processes of interstitial atoms and vacancies, but their precise significance is not quite clear. According to Seitz and Koehler [2], there is a low-temperature diffusion process, which has an activation energy of approximately 0.7 ev, and which does not increase the degree of order, and another with an energy of 1.2 ev, which occurs at higher temperatures and increases the ordering. The electrical resistivity of copper held below −150°C is also increased on bombardment with 810-kev electrons [4], the increase being a linear function of the dose received. The resistance to shearing is also affected, and is recovered in successive stages up to about 300°C [24].

The behavior of silver and gold on deuteron bombardment is qualitatively the same as that of copper [25]. The ratio of the initial resistivity changes in the deuteron bombardment of two metals is 1.17 for silver/copper, and 1.70 for gold/copper. These values are very close to the ratios $(Z_{Ag}/Z_{Cu})^2$ and $(Z_{Au}/Z_{Cu})^2$, as required by Eq. (15–4).

The effect of crystal structure in such changes has been examined [26] by irradiating iron, nickel, and copper wires with 10-Mev deuterons (10^{18} d/cm^2) at −150°C. The change in the resistivity at −180°C was 50% for iron, and 10% for the other two metals. Wires of iron and nickel were also irradiated for two months at ordinary temperature with pile neutrons; the resistivity change measured at −195°C was 10 times greater for iron. These results appear to suggest that metals with close-packed structures (nickel and cobalt) are more resistant to radiation.

Single crystals of iron, zinc, and lead were irradiated with 10^{18} n/cm^2, and the increase in length subsequently measured [27]. With lead, no change was detected, but the deformation strains of the other two metals increased considerably. Bombardment of iron with 10-Mev protons (22 μA hr/cm^2) caused the thermoelectric potential to become more positive (with respect to unirradiated iron) by 0.3 μv/deg; for constantin, the potential became more negative by 0.1 μv/deg [28].

Aluminum undergoes various radiation-induced changes which are similar to, but smaller than, those described for copper [16, 19, 23]. Molybdenum [29, 30, 31], tungsten [32], and tantalum [19] have also been studied.

The rate of the white tin → grey tin transformation is increased by neutron irradiation at low temperatures [33]. A one-month exposure of black phosphorus to pile neutrons at 50°C also causes a phase change [34].

Beryllium is rather insensitive to fast neutrons [15], but virtually all the physical properties of graphite show considerable changes [35, 36, 37, 38], including resistivity, Hall effect, thermal conductivity, thermal expansion, thermoelectric power, lattice constants, hardness, and various other mechanical properties. Measurements of the heat of combustion show that the internal energy of graphite increases during the irradiation. The damage can be annealed out at temperatures around 100°C, but the process is complete only at much higher temperatures [39].

Bombardment of alloys generally produces more pronounced changes than in pure metals, since the properties of alloys are more sensitive to the degree of ordering. Siegel [40] has irradiated an ordered sample of Cu_3Au (obtained by heating to 400°C, followed by slow cooling) in a reactor with a total fast-neutron flux of 3.3×10^{19} n/cm^2. The resistivity at 15° increased to 4.6×10^6 ohms/cm. This is too large an effect to be explained only by atom displacement, and it is suggested that local temperature increases contribute to the disordering. Considerable disordering is also produced by the fast neutron bombardment of Ni_3Mn [41], and it is estimated that 5000 atoms are displaced per neutron (average energy 1 Mev).

Murray and Taylor have reported [42] large increases in the hardness and resistivity of copper-beryllium alloys on exposure to neutrons ($\sim 2 \times 10^{18}$ n/cm^2). Other alloys of copper (with Zn, Ge, Sn, As, and Mn) also show large increases in hardness, but the resistivity changes are less significant; the effects are similar to those observed on cold working. In addition, changes in the x-ray diffraction pattern and in the density have been found with copper-beryllium alloys. These results are attributed to the formation of precipitation nuclei consequent upon increased diffusion caused by the presence of newly formed vacancies and interstitial atoms.

In the same way, the bombardment of CuAu and Cu_3Au in the ordered state with 33-Mev α-particles brings about disordering of these alloys; the resistivity at -160°C increases 2 to 2.3 times during the bombardment. This is accompanied by a change in the lattice constant; for CuAu, the tetragonal structure of the ordered state changes to face-centered cubic, which is the form of the alloy in the disordered state. If, however, the alloy is disordered, for example, by cold working, irradiation sometimes increases the order, as revealed by a decreased resistivity. This has been observed in the neutron bombardment of CuAu, Cu_3Au [43, 44], and brass [45], and in the bombardment of Cu_3Au with 36-Mev α-particles [46, 47, 48] or 1-Mev electrons [49].

This ordering may either be the result of enhanced migration of interstitial atoms and vacancies, or in gold alloys, of the formation of an amalgam with Hg^{198} produced by neutron capture on Au^{197}, since the presence of mercury increases the resistivity of gold. With Cu_3Au, however, the hardness increases on irradiation irrespective of the initial state of the alloy (i.e., order or disorder), in contrast to the effect of heat treatment. The fact that the order-disorder transformation occurs even with fast electrons seems to imply that this is not caused by "hot spots," since the kinetic energy of the electrons is not very large, although Denney [50] has identified this mechanism in an alloy of copper with 2.4% iron containing precipitated iron in solid solution. This very stable ferromagnetic precipitate is usually transformed to the paramagnetic form only by heating to a high temperature, which makes the alloy homogeneous, but this transformation can also be produced by bombarding the ferromagnetic form with 9-Mev protons from a cyclotron [51]*.

The effect of radiation on the resistance of metals such as aluminum, copper, and steel to corrosive solutions depends on the way these metals behave in the absence of radiation [51]. If they are normally covered with a passive layer (for example, of some oxide), radiation favors the formation of this and the protection is increased; in the opposite case, corrosion is accelerated.

---

* For the effect of radiation on the other properties of steel, and of Co and Ni alloys, see C. Sutton and D. Lesser, *Nucleonics,* **12,** No. 9, 8 (1954), and Ref. 13.

15–3 Semiconductors. Lark-Horowitz and his collaborators [52, 53] have published an extensive series of papers on the effect of radiation on the properties of germanium and silicon, which are the most important semiconducting elements. Semiconductors are described as *n*- or *p*-type depending on whether the impurities which they contain are negatively charged (donor) or positively charged (acceptor). Radioactive transitions which introduce negative impurities (for example, As from the β-decay of Ge) therefore increase the donor character, while those which produce acceptors [for example, Ga from an (n, p) reaction on Ge] lower this donor character. In addition, a vacancy produced by an atom displacement acts as an electron trap, (i.e., as an acceptor), whereas an interstitial atom is analogous to a donor.

If *n*-type germanium is bombarded with α-particles from polonium, deuterons from a cyclotron, or fast (reactor) neutrons [54], the conductivity initially decreases, then passes through a minimum, and subsequently increases. Measurements of the Hall effect show that in the region of this minimum conductivity the *n*-type germanium is virtually transformed into "neutral" or intrinsic germanium. On the average, 58 atoms are displaced by each α-particle. Graphs of conductivity as a function of length of bombardment, and the effect of temperature, suggest [52, 55] that the bombardment produces two types of traps, corresponding to double ionization with the formation of two empty levels. Bombardment of samples of *p*-type germanium produces a slow and continuous increase in the conductivity. Similar changes are caused by bombardment at 87°K with electrons from a Van de Graaf machine [52, 56, 57, 58]. The threshold at 0.63 Mev corresponds to a displacement energy of 30 ev; on the average, a 1-Mev electron displaces 0.058 atoms. The photoconductivity of *n*-type germanium increases during the bombardment, indicating the formation of electron traps.

The conductivity of silicon decreases on bombardment with α-particles, deuterons, or neutrons whether it is *n*- or *p*-type; at the same time, the elastic constants [59] and the infrared absorption [60] show detectable changes.

The damage induced by radiations generally disappears slowly at room temperature, and completely at 450°C, so that it cannot be attributed to nuclear reactions, which produce permanent effects (provided that the initial atoms are not being regenerated), but to vacancies and interstitial sites created by recoil. There does not seem to be any satisfactory explanation at present for the different behavior of germanium and silicon.

The change produced by neutrons in the conductivity of germanium single crystals can be used to measure the neutron flux. A dosimeter of this type, constructed by Cassen and his co-workers, has a linear response in the 200 to 4500 rad range [61, 62].

Irradiation of *p*-*n* junctions of germanium with β-particles from a 50-mc source of $Sr^{90} + Y^{90}$ causes an increase in the electron emission [63]. Under appropriate conditions, an electromotive force is set up, with a maximum value in open circuit of 30 mv; in closed circuit, a current of 2×10^{-5} amp was produced. With a silicon junction, the potential difference was 250 mv, and the current 10^{-5} amp. Depending upon the energy of the β-particles involved, the energy required to produce an electron-hole pair is calculated to be 3.7 ev for germanium, and 4.7 ev for silicon. The same effects can be produced [47] by α-particles from polonium; in this case the calculated energy for formation of the pair in silicon is 3.6 ev. In Chapter 25 we shall see how these phenomena can be used for transforming the kinetic energy of radiation into electrical energy. The rectifying action of junctions of germanium or silicon or other semiconductors deteriorates under the action of fast neutrons, however, which makes them difficult to use in reactors.

15-4 Ionic crystals and insulators. The structural sensitivity of such compounds to radiation depends essentially on their composition, and on the type of chemical bond involved. The lattice constants of diamonds, carbon, silicon, quartz [65, 66], zircon, and beryl [67] increase on fast neutron bombardment. It has been shown by x-ray methods that after irradiation of quartz with an integral flux of 6.6×10^{19} n/cm^2 at 100°C, a_0 for α-quartz increases from 4.903 to 5.01 A [65, 66], and c_0 from 5.393 to 5.41 A. A flux of 2×10^{20} n/cm^2, caused a 14.7% decrease in the density. Changes in the rotary power and the refractive index occur at the same time. The thermal conductivity decreases by about a tenth after a moderate radiation, and its temperature variation becomes similar to that for vitrious silica, to which form the irradiated quartz eventually goes [68, 69]. Recovery occurs only at temperatures in the neighborhood of 1000°C.

It is possible to draw up an order of decreasing radiation stability $Al_2O_3 > BeO > ZrO_2 > SiO_2$ [67], which corresponds to the order of increasing covalency in the chemical bonding. Primak [66] found no change in the x-ray diffraction pattern of corundum, GeO_2, or TiO_2 after pile neutron irradiation, and only small changes for MgO and CaF_2. With this latter compound, as with $CaCl_2$, NaF, Ma_2CO_3, and HgS, no change was observed after irradiation with α-particles from radon [70].

Differing sensitivities to radiation are also found on examining the *metamict state* of minerals which contain radioactive impurities (Section 10-9). Certain rare earth, Nb, Ta, and U minerals such as allanite, fergusonite, smarskite, gadolinite, zircon, and to a lesser degree, thorite, all have a crystalline structure at the surface, but are amorphous in the bulk interior. This condition is attributed to the recoil of atoms from the initially regular lattice due to the action of α-particles emitted by the radioactive constituents of the minerals. Minerals rich in these elements, such as autunite, carnotite, monazite, etc., do not show the metamict state. This may be explained either by the stronger ionic character and hence higher resistance of the compounds involved, by a more tightly packed and hence more stable lattice structure [71, 72], or by the greater ease with which the lattice is able to recrystallize after disorganization [66].

Irradiation of crystals of sodium chloride or potassium chloride with γ-rays [73, 74], helium ions, protons, or fast electrons [75, 76, 77] changes their mechanical properties in such a way that the hardness and elastic limits increase, and the density decreases. Similar effects have been observed in the irradiation of silver chloride crystals with 50-kv x-rays [78].

Crystals of LiF are especially sensitive to neutrons, since large numbers of high-energy helium ions and tritons are produced in the $Li^6(n, \alpha)T$ nuclear reaction, which has a very high cross section. Binder and Sturm [79] have measured gravimetrically the density change in pile-irradiated crystals, and have also determined the lattice constants using x-rays. The difference in the results from these two methods is about 6%, from which these authors have concluded that at least 94% of the defects are Frenkel defects. Theory predicts that the introduction of such defects, characterized by equal numbers of vacancies and interstitial atoms, should give the same relative change in both the gravimetric density and the lattice constants, while for Schottky defects, which are associated with the movement of displaced atoms toward the surface, the gravimetric change should be the greater.

In addition to atom displacements, ionic crystals and other solid compounds undergo significant optical and electrical changes connected with excitation and ionization phenomena. These effects are more conveniently examined in the following chapter.

15–5 Chemical decomposition. Solid water irradiated at —196°C with γ-rays shows an electron paramagnetic resonance spectrum from which the presence of H and OH radicals can be inferred [80]. The yield (G) of radical pairs is 0.14.* At the same temperature heavy water is decomposed to D and OD. Only OH and OD radicals can be identified in the irradiation of H_2O_2 in H_2O, and of D_2O_2 in D_2O. The disappearance of H and D atoms is attributed either to the reaction

$$H + H_2O_2 \rightarrow H_2O + OH, \qquad (15\text{–}8)$$

which assumes that the H atom is formed in the immediate vicinity of an H_2O_2 molecule, or to the process

$$e + H_2O_2 \rightarrow OH^- + OH. \qquad (15\text{–}9)$$

When the irradiated ice is warmed, the H atoms disappear completely around 115 ± 10°K, but the OH radicals persist to a slightly higher temperature.

The irradiation of ice between —196 and 0°C with α-particles from radon [81] gives hydrogen peroxide with a temperature-independent yield which is about one-half that found for liquid water ($G = 0.48$). With γ-rays too, oxygen-saturated ice forms hydrogen peroxide between 0 and —269°C. The initial yield increases with temperature between —200 and 0°C, at which there is a sharp increase [82]. Minder and Liechti [82] observed no

* More recent experiments by the same technique [L. H. Piette, R. C. Rempel, and H. E. Weaver, *J. Chem. Phys.* **30**, 1623 (1959)] detected no H atoms at —196°C, but at 4.2°K a value of $G \approx 0.5$ was found for their formation.

oxidation on irradiating frozen, very dilute, aqueous solutions of ferrous sulfate with x-rays at $-78°C$. On the other hand, Lefort [84] has reported appreciable oxidation of frozen KI solutions with both x-rays and α-particles from radon, even at $-196°C$. For concentrated solutions, the yields are not very different from those obtained by this same author for concentrated (liquid) solutions (80 to 90%). Similar results have been obtained for the oxidation of arsenite [85]. These results suggest that the primary radiolytic act, the formation of radicals, is virtually unaffected by the physical state and the temperature of the system. In the course of warming up and melting to the liquid state, these radicals react with each other, and with solute molecules, as in irradiated liquids, at relative rates which depend on the temperature.

On bombarding crystals of barium nitrate with 1.2-Mev electrons in a Van de Graaf accelerator, Allen and Ghormley [86] observed a slight decomposition of the salt, with the formation of nitrite and oxygen. The gas is trapped in the crystal in the molecular or atomic form, and can be liberated by dissolving or heating. A similar result was obtained by pile irradiation of solid potassium and sodium nitrate [87]; the radiochemical yield of gas (G) is 0.3 for $NaNO_3$ and 0.8 for KNO_3. The quantity of nitrite ion formed is equivalent to the oxygen produced. Similar yields have been obtained with 49-kv x-rays, showing that the effects of pile irradiation on the salts is essentially due to ionization and excitation, and not to atom displacements. Irradiation of $NaNO_3$ with γ-rays changes the absorption spectrum of the salt [88] due to the formation of NO_2^- and color centers.

Values of G between 2 and 3 have been obtained for the pile decomposition of $KClO_3$, but with $KBrO_3$, prolific formation of gas takes place. Crystals of K_2SO_4, Li_2SO_4, and $CaCO_3$ become colored, but no decomposition is observed [87], and the same is true for K_2CrO_4 irradiated in a reactor for six weeks [89].

Heal [90] has shown that the irradiation of $KClO_4$ with 50-kv x-rays causes decomposition to $KClO_3$ and KCl, with $G = 5$. The ClO_3^- ion subsequently gives Cl^- and O_2. After five hours irradiation, the crystal is converted to a fine powder, but shows no coloration, and for this reason Heal rejects the idea that the primary act is

$$ClO_4^- \rightarrow ClO_4 + e^-,$$

since this would produce coloration due to electron capture in crystal defects. It is suggested instead that the excited species migrates to a crystal defect at which it dissociates. This would result in the accumulation of $KClO_3$ and KCl at the crystal imperfections, and in a corresponding increase in the pressure of the oxygen released at the same sites, which eventually causes the crystal to rupture.

Radiolytic decompositions of varying violence have been observed with a number of explosive salts. Examples include barium azide exposed to x-rays [91, 92] or bombarded with 100 to 200-v electrons [93], sodium azide with 11.6-v electrons [94], and nitrogen iodide with fission fragments (actually neutron irradiation of a powdered mixture with uranium oxide)

[95] or with α-particles from polonium [96]. A deposit of as little as 1 esu of Po (1/1340 mc) on a metal sheet causes explosion of the dried powdered iodide after a sufficiently long period [97]; in this case, the explosion is attributed to the effect of local heating. This mechanism has also been proposed for the explosion of lead, silver, and cadmium azides, and silver acetylide, with fast electrons [98].

The decomposition of NaN_3 with x-rays has been reexamined by Heal [99]. Ammonia and nitrogen were formed on dissolving the irradiated crystals in water, and the resultant solution was alkaline. The decomposition yield at 51°C is $G = 4.0$, and at 102°C, $G = 5.2$. The suggested mechanism is

$$N_3^- \rightsquigarrow N_2 + N^-,$$

$$N^- + H_2O \rightarrow NH + OH^-,$$

$$NH + N_3^- \rightarrow NH_2^- + \tfrac{3}{2}N_2,$$

$$NH^- + H_2O \rightarrow NH_2 + OH^-,$$

$$NH_2 + N_3^- \rightarrow NH_2^- + \tfrac{3}{2}N_2,$$

$$NH_2^- + H_2O \rightarrow NH_3 + OH^-.$$

Walton and Croall [100] have studied the radiolytic decomposition of KIO_3 by fission fragments by reactor bombardment of a finely powdered mixture of the salt and uranium oxide. The yield (G) for the reduction to I_2 and I^- varies between 2 and 6 depending on the conditions.

15–6 The action of radiation on polymers. The irradiation of polymers causes either varying degrees of structural modification, or brings about degradation, and in some cases both these phenomena are observed. A considerable amount of the work in this field is due to Charlesby, working with polyethylene, polystyrene, rubber, and other polymers [101, 102, 103].

Polyethylene (or polythene), C_nH_{2n}, is essentially a linear chain polymer containing upwards of 2000 carbon atoms and on the average 1 vinylidene group

```
           CH2—
          /
  —CH=C
          \
           CH2—
```

per molecule. At room temperature, the compound is about 70% crystalline; between 70 and 115°C, it goes slowly to the amorphous state, or melts to a viscous liquid. Exposure to pile neutrons changes it to a new transparent plastic state, which is less crystalline, more elastic, and more chemically resistant, and which does not melt even at 300°C. The appreciable solubility of unirradiated polythene in organic solvents above 70° decreases; this effect increases as the length of irradiation is increased. In addition, a change in the weight (M) of the polymer is observed. This is related to the surface area A and the dose absorbed D by the parabolic relation

$$\Delta M = -\alpha_1 MD + \alpha_2 MD^2 + \beta_1 AD + \beta_2 AD^2. \qquad (15\text{–}10)$$

This weight change is the result of the liberation of gas (consisting mainly of hydrogen, but also containing small quantities of CH_2, C_2H_6, etc.) and to surface oxidation. The changes in the physical properties are attributed mainly to bridging or *cross linking*—the formation of new C—C bonds between neighboring molecules, at the expense of C—H bonds, to form a stronger three-dimensional lattice.

```
      |             |                  |  |
      C             C                  C  C
      |             |                  |  |
  —C—C—H  +  H—C—C—   →   —C—C—C—C—
      |             |                  |  |
      C             C                  C  C
      |             |                  |  |
```

These changes are analogous to those produced in rubber by vulcanization. A flux of 10^{17} slow neutrons/cm^2, plus the associated pile radiation, produces an average of one cross linking per 100 monomers.

Cross linking can also be produced by exposing polyethylene to fast electrons, to Co^{60} γ-rays, or to x-rays [104]. On the basis of their effect on various hydrocarbon polymers, 50×10^6 roentgens of electromagnetic radiation are equivalent to a flux of 10^{17} neutrons/cm^2 plus the associated pile radiation. In addition to cross linking, chain rupture or fracture occurs, and a fraction (2.4 to 2.8%) soluble in organic solvents is obtained. The ratio of ruptures to cross linking is about 1:5.

When other paraffinic hydrocarbons from heptane to hexatriacontane ($C_{36}H_{74}$) are irradiated with neutrons [101], they undergo changes which increase with the dose, and which are related to a decreased fusibility. After a given dose (D), the hydrocarbon will no longer melt, being transformed into a cross-linked insoluble gell. The product $Dn\rho$, where n is the number of carbon atoms and ρ is the density, is constant between $n = 7$ and 36. This relationship also applies to polythene when $n = 2000$, but not for $n = 250$. These results imply that the energy needed to produce cross linking is independent of the chain length; the actual energy required is 24 ev, compared with the estimated bond energy of 12 ev for the C—H bond. Higher unsaturated hydrocarbons containing either double or triple bonds, are also cross linked by neutron bombardment [105]. The energy required to cause cross linking does vary in these systems with the chain length; if the unsaturated bond is at the end of the chain, the energy is lower than in the case of the saturated hydrocarbons.

Polystyrene [106] too is cross linked by radiation, but the yield is much lower than that for polythene; 3000 to 5000 ev are absorbed per cross linkage. The pile radiation associated with a flux of 10^{17} n/cm^2 produces one cross linkage per 1000 to 1500 monomers, compared with the figure of 100 in the polythene case. The resistance of polystyrene is due to the presence of benzene rings. According to Feng and Kennedy [107], the cross linking or increased polymerization of polystyrene by β-particles or deuterons only takes place in the absence of air; in the presence of air degradation occurs. Neoprene, nylon (polychlorbutadiene), polyvinyl chloride, polymethylsiloxane, and rubber are also cross linked by pile radiation [108]. The molecular weight of rubber increases at the same time as does the proportion of *gel* insoluble in organic solvents [109].

Dole and his co-workers [110] have reported results with polythene slightly different from those of Charlesby. Infrared spectroscopy was used to investigate cross linking, and bromination to detect unsaturated bonds. The polymer, in powdered form, or as a thin sheet, was irradiated in a pile. The first effect observed was the production of hydrogen, corresponding to the disappearance of vinylidene group, but despite this the degree of unsaturation of the polymer was increased by the formation of vinyl groups (RCH=CHR′); 70 to 80% of the hydrogen released corresponds to the formation of these unsaturated bonds, and the remainder to cross-linking processes. From the amount of gas given off, the authors estimate that C—C bonds are broken less frequently along the main chains than in the side chains, where the ratio of C—C : C—H ruptures is about 1:2. In order to explain the rapid disappearance of the very small number of vinyl groups, they suggest that the free radicals which are initially formed throughout the polymer migrate along or across the chains until they reach a vinyl group, where they are fixed until cross linking occurs. The infrared spectra, which have also been investigated by other authors, has given evidence of the formation, not only of new double bonds, but also of groups such as —OH, $\rangle$CO, —COO, etc., [111].

Cross-linked products with molecular weights up to 35,000 have been obtained by irradiating polyethylene with doses of electrons (maximum energy 800 kv) up to 2×10^8 r [112, 113]. The extent to which the mechanical properties (stretching, breaking strength, etc.) are changed depends on the initial molecular weight of the polymer, and on the total dose received.

The solid compound acrylamide polymerizes as the result of γ-irradiation [114, 115]. The crystals become turbid and yellow in color, without undergoing any change in exterior form. After extracting the residual monomer with methanol, the polymer showed optical properties obviously different from those of the initial product.

Certain polymers, notably polymethylmethacrylate (perspex, plexiglass), polytetrafluorethylene (teflon), polyisobutylene, and cellulose, behave quite differently from the plastics discussed above [116, 117, 118]. On irradiation, the main chains rupture, and the side chains decompose with the evolution of gas. This degradation results in a decrease in the average molecular weight; with polyisobutylene a very viscous fluid is produced, and with cellulose a powder results [119]. On the average, the deposition of 61 ev is required for each main chain rupture in cellulose.

According to Miller, Lawton, and Balwit [120], whether a polymer cross links or undergoes degradation on irradiation is determined by its chemical structure. The first group includes those polymers which contain at least one hydrogen atom in the α-position for each carbon in the chain, and so contain the structural units $(\text{—}CH_2CH_2\text{—})_n$ or $(\text{—}CH_2CHR\text{—})_n$, where-

TABLE 15-2

AVERAGE GAS YIELDS IN THE γ-IRRADIATION OF POLYMERS

Polymer	G
Teflon (polytetrafluoroethylene)	0.051
Polystyrene	0.069
Polybutadiene	0.25
Rubber	0.44
Polyisobutylene	0.79
Polyvinyl alcohol	0.96
Polymethylmethacrylate	1.11
Polyethylene	2.03
Polymethacrylic acid	2.89

as polymers which undergo degradation have the general formula

$$\left(-CH_2C \begin{matrix} CH_3 \\ / \\ \\ \backslash \\ R- \end{matrix} \right)_n .$$

The relative resistance of various plastics and elastomers to pile radiation, γ-rays from Co^{60} or Au^{197}, etc., has been studied by Bopp and Sisman [121], who have established the following order of decreasing stability, which depends on the nature of the characteristic chemical group of the polymer: polystyrene, aniline-formaldehyde resin, rubber, polyethylene, nylon, silicones, phenol-formaldehyde resin, polyallyldiglycol, thiokol, ethyleneglycol polyterephthalate (dacron, terylene), polyvinyl chloride, cellulose, teflon, plexiglass.

Karpov [118] has measured the average yields for the production of gas in the irradiation of various polymers with total doses of 80 to 100 $\times$ 10^6 r of Co^{60} γ-rays. The results are shown in Table 15–2. If the co-polymer formed between styrene and isobutylene is irradiated, the latter is partially protected against degradation by the former to an extent which depends on the relative proportions of the two components [122, 123]. This protection can also be achieved by incorporating substances such as aniline, di-*m*-tolylthiourea or allylthiourea (10%) into the polymer (e.g., polymethylmethacrylate). The energy required for rupture of the main chain increases in these conditions from 61 to 152, 297, and 143 ev, respectively.

In normal co-polymers, the monomer groups are randomly distributed in the main and side chains. Chapiro, *et al.* [124], have established methods by which it is possible to "graft" by irradiation the lateral chains of one polymer upon another, which constitutes the principal chain (for example, acrylonitrile upon polyvinyl chloride). Such polymers combine the properties of the constituents, depending on the conditions chosen for their production, and may well have considerable practical importance.

It is worth noting finally that although it seems evident from the results discussed that free radicals or macro-radicals formed by radiation play an essential part in cross linking and degradation of polymers, there is as yet no general theory which explains the mechanism of these actions satisfactorily [125].

References

1. F. Seitz, *Discussions Faraday Soc.*, **5,** 271 (1949).
2. F. Seitz and J. S. Koehler, *1955 Geneva Conference*, P. 749.
3. D. T. Eggen and M. J. Laubenstein, *Phys. Rev.*, **91,** 238 (1953).
4. E. E. Klontz and K. Lark-Horovitz, *Phys. Rev.*, **82,** 763 (1951); see also W. Kohn, *Bull. Am. Phys. Soc.*, **29,** No. 3, 11 (1954).
5. J. H. O. Varley, *Nature*, **174,** 886 (1954).
6. J. H. O. Varley, *J. Nuclear Energy*, **1,** 130 (1954).
7. D. E. McLennan, *Can. J. Phys.*, **29** 122 (1951).
8. H. B. Huntington, *Phys. Rev.*, **91,** 1092 (1953); **93,** 1414 (1954).
9. M. Born and J. E. Mayer, *Z. Physik*, **75,** 1 (1932).
10. J. C. Slater, *J. Appl. Phys.*, **22,** 237 (1951).
11. G. J. Dienes, *J. Appl. Phys.*, **24,** 666 (1953).
12. G. J. Dienes, *Ann. Rev. Nuclear Sci.*, **2,** 187 (1953).
13. S. T. Konobeevsky, N. F. Pravdyuk, and V. I. Kutaitsev, *1955 Geneva Conference*, PP. 680, 681.
14. S. F. Pugh, *1955 Geneva Conference*, P. 443.
15. D. S. Billington, *1955 Geneva Conference*, P. 744.
16. A. B. Martin, *et al.*, *Phys. Rev.*, **81,** 664 (1951).
17. R. R. Eggleston, *Acta Met.*, **1,** 679 (1953).
18. D. Bowen and G. W. Rodeback, *Acta Met.*, **1,** 649 (1953).
19. J. W. Marx, H. G. Cooper, and J. W. Henderson, *Phys. Rev.*, **88,** 106 (1952).
20. A. W. Overhauser, *Phys. Rev.*, **94,** 1551 (1954).
21. W. R. McDonell and H. A. Kierstead, *Phys. Rev.*, **93,** 247 (1954).
22. A. W. McReynolds, W. Augustyniak, M. McKeown, and D. Rosenblatt, *Phys. Rev.*, **98,** 418 (1955).
23. J. K. Redman, R. R. Coltman, and T. H. Blewitt, *Phys. Rev.*, **91,** 448 (1953).
24. D. Kiekamp, *Bull. Am. Phys. Soc.*, **30,** No. 2, 8 (1955).
25. H. G. Cooper, J. S. Koehler, and J. W. Marx, *Phys. Rev.*, **94,** 496 (1954); **97,** 599 (1955).
26. D. Wruck and C. Wert, *Phys. Rev.*, **94,** 1417 (1954).
27. F. W. Kuntz and A. N. Holden, *Phys. Rev.*, **94,** 1417 (1954).
28. A. Andrew and C. R. Davidson, *Phys. Rev.*, **89,** 876 (1953).
29. B. W. Randolph, *Bull. Am. Phys. Soc.*, **26,** No. 1, 14 (1951).
30. I. G. Geib and R. E. Grace, *Bull. Am. Phys. Soc.*, **27,** No. 2, 10 (1952).
31. C. A. Bruck, W. E. McHugh, and R. W. Hockenbury, *Acta Met.*, **2,** 355 (1954).
32. E. Pearlstein, H. Ingham, and R. Smoluchowski, *Phys. Rev.*, **98,** 1530 (1955).
33. J. Fleeman and G. J. Dienes, *J. Appl. Phys.*, **26,** 652 (1955).

34. D. L. Chipman, B. E. Warren, and G. J. Dienes, *J. Appl. Phys.*, **24,** 1251 (1953).

35. W. K. Woods, L. P. Bupp, and J. F. Fletcher, *1955 Geneva Conference,* P. 746.

36. G. R. Hennig and J. E. Hove, *1955 Geneva Conference,* P. 751.

37. G. H. Kinchin, *1955 Geneva Conference,* P. 442.

38. G. H. Kinchin, *J. Nuclear Energy,* **1,** 124 (1954).

39. G. Mayer, P. Perio, J. Gigon, and M. Tournaric, *1955 Geneva Conference,* P. 362.

40. S. Siegel, *Phys. Rev.*, **75,** 1823 (1949).

41. L. R. Aronin, *J. Appl. Phys.*, **25,** 344 (1954).

42. G. T. Murray and W. E. Taylor, *Acta Met.*, **2,** 52 (1954).

43. L. G. Cook and R. L. Cushing, *Acta Met.*, **1,** 539, 549 (1953).

44. T. H. Blewitt and R. R. Coltman, *Phys. Rev.*, **85,** 384 (1952).

45. D. B. Rosenblatt, R. Smoluchowski, and G. J. Dienes, *Phys. Rev.*, **94,** 1417 (1954).

46. C. E. Dixon, C. J. Meechan, and J. A. Brinkmann, *Phil. Mag.*, **44,** 449 (1953).

47. C. E. Dixon, C. J. Meechan, and J. A. Brinkmann, *Acta Met.*, **2,** 38 (1954).

48. C. E. Dixon and D. B. Bowen, *Phys. Rev.*, **94,** 1418 (1954).

49. J. Adam, A. Green, and R. A. Dugdale, *Phil. Mag.*, **43,** 1216 (1952).

50. J. M. Denney, *Phys. Rev.*, **94,** 1417 (1954).

51. F. Hittman and O. A. Kuhl, *Nucleonics,* **13,** No. 7, 62 (1955).

52. K. Lark-Horovitz, *et al.*, *Phys. Rev.*, **73,** 1256 (1948); **76,** 442 (1949); **83,** 312 (1951); **84,** 861 (1951).

53. H. M. James and K. Lark-Horovitz, *Z. physik. Chem.*, **198,** 107 (1951).

54. W. H. Brattain and G. L. Pearson, *Phys. Rev.*, **80,** 846 (1950).

55. J. W. Cleland, J. H. Crawford, and J. C. Pigg, *Phys. Rev.*, **98,** 1742 (1955).

56. W. L. Brown, R. C. Fletcher, and K. A. Wright, *Phys. Rev.*, **92,** 591 (1953).

57. E. E. Klontz, *U.S.A.E.C. report AECU-2664,* 1953.

58. E. E. Klontz, *Bull. Am. Phys. Soc.*, **30,** No. 2, 12 (1955).

59. W. P. Binnie and A. M. Liebschutz, *Bull. Am. Phys. Soc.*, **29,** No. 3, 12 (1954).

60. M. Becker, H. Y. Fan, and K. Lark-Horovitz, *Bull. Am. Phys. Soc.*, **26,** No. 6, 34 (1951).

61. B. Cassen, T. Crough, and H. Gass, *U.S.A.E.C. report UCLA-309,* 1954.

62. B. Cassen, *1955 Geneva Conference,* P. 60.

63. P. Rappaport, *Phys. Rev.*, **93,** 246 (1954).

64. K. G. McKay and K. B. McAfee, *Phys. Rev.*, **91,** 1079 (1953).

65. W. Primak, L. H. Fuchs, and P. Day, *Phys. Rev.*, **92,** 1064 (1953).

66. W. Primak, *Phys. Rev.*, **95,** 837 (1954); **98,** 1854 (1955).

67. J. H. Crawford and M. C. Wittels, *1955 Geneva Conference,* P. 753.

68. R. Berman, *Proc. Roy. Soc. (London),* **A208,** 90 (1954).

69. M. Wittels and F. A. Sherrill, *Phys. Rev.*, **93,** 1117 (1954).

70. B. Stech, *Z. Naturforsch.*, **7b,** 175 (1952).

71. A. FAESSLER, *Z. Krist.*, **104,** 81 (1942).
72. P. PELLAS, *Compt. rend.*, **233,** 1369 (1951); **234,** 538 (1952).
73. V. D. KUZNETZOV and V. A. SEMENTZOV, *J. Phys. Russe*, **2,** 199 (1932).
74. M. N. PODASHEVSKI, *Phys. Z. Sowjetunion*, **8,** 8 (1935).
75. D. R. WESTERVELT, *Acta Met.*, **1,** 755 (1953).
76. W. H. VAUGHAN, W. J. LEIVO, and R. SMOLUCHOWSKI, *Phys. Rev.*, **91,** 245 (1953).
77. W. LEIVO and R. SMOLUCHOWSKI, *Phys. Rev.*, **93,** 1415 (1954).
78. Y. LI, *Acta Met.*, **1,** 455 (1953).
79. D. BINDER and W. J. STURM, *Phys. Rev.*, **96,** 1519 (1954).
80. M. S. MATHESON and B. SMALLER, *J. Chem. Phys.*, **23,** 521 (1955).
81. P. BONET-MAURY and M. LEFORT, *Compt. rend.*, **226,** 1445 (1948).
82. A. C. STEWART and J. A. GHORMLEY, *Radn. Research*, **1,** 230 (1954).
83. W. MINDER and A. LIECHTI, *Experientia*, **2,** 410 (1946).
84. M. LEFORT, *J. Chim. Phys.*, **47,** 776 (1950).
85. M. HAÏSSINSKY and M. LEFORT, *J. Chim. Phys.*, **48,** 368 (1951).
86. A. O. ALLEN and J. A. GHORMLEY, *J. Chem. Phys.*, **15,** 208 (1947).
87. G. HENNIG, R. LEES, and M. S. MATHESON, *J. Chem. Phys.*, **21,** 664 (1953).
88. P. PRINGSHEIM, *J. Chem. Phys.*, **23,** 369 (1955).
89. J. H. GREEN, G. HARBOTTLE, and A. G. MADDOCK, *Trans. Faraday Soc.*, **49,** 1413 (1953).
90. H. G. HEAL, *Can. J. Chem.*, **31,** 91 (1952).
91. P. GUNTHER, L. LEPIN, and K. ANDREW, *Z. Elecktrochem.*, **36,** 218 (1930).
92. W. E. GARNER and C. H. MOON, *J. Chem. Soc.*, **1933,** 1398.
93. J. M. GROOCOCK and F. C. TOMPKINS, *Proc. Roy. Soc.* (*London*), **A223,** 267 (1954).
94. R. H. MULLER and G. C. BROUS, *J. Chem. Phys.*, **1,** 482 (1933).
95. E. FEENBERG, *Phys. Rev.*, **55,** 980 (1939).
96. G. H. HENDERSON, *Nature*, **109,** 749 (1922).
97. M. HAÏSSINSKY and R. J. WALEN, *Compt. rend.*, **208,** 2067 (1939).
98. F. P. BOWDEN and K. SINGH, *Proc. Roy. Soc* (*London*), **A227,** 22 (1955).
99. H. G. HEAL, *Can. J. Chem.*, **31,** 1153 (1952).
100. G. N. WALTON and I. F. CROALL, *J. Inorg. Nuclear Chem.*, **1,** 149 (1955).
101. A. CHARLESBY, *Proc. Roy. Soc.* (*London*), **A215,** 187 (1952); **A222,** 60 (1953).
102. A. CHARLESBY and M. ROSS, *Proc. Roy. Soc.* (*London*), **A217,** 122 (1953).
103. A. CHARLESBY and N. H. HANCOCK, *Proc. Roy. Soc.* (*London*), **A218,** 245 (1953).
104. A. C. BASKETT and C. W. MILLER, *Nature*, **174,** 364 (1954).
105. A. CHARLESBY, *Radn. Research*, **2,** 96 (1955).
106. A. CHARLESBY, *J. Polymer Sci.*, **11,** 521 (1953).
107. P. Y. FENG and J. W. KENNEDY, *J. Am. Chem. Soc.*, **77,** 847 (1955).
108. J. W. RYAN, *Nucleonics*, **11,** No. 8, 13 (1953).
109. A. CHARLESBY, *Atomics*, **5,** 12 (1954).
110. M. DOLE, C. D. KEELING, and D. G. ROSE, *J. Am. Chem. Soc.*, **76,** 4304 (1954).
111. N. A. SLOVOKHOTOVA and V. L. KARPOV, *Symposium on Radiation Chemistry, Moscow, 1955*, pp. 165, 175 (English translation).

112. D. S. Ballantine, G. J. Dienes, B. Manowitz, P. Ander, and R. B. Mesrobian, *J. Polymer Sci.*, **13,** 410 (1954).

113. E. J. Lawton, J. S. Balwit, and H. M. Bueche, *Ind. Eng. Chem.*, **46,** 1703 (1954).

114. A. Henglein and R. Schulz, *Z. Naturforsch.*, **9b,** 617 (1954).

115. R. B. Mesrobian, P. Ander, D. S. Ballantine, and G. J. Dienes, *J. Chem. Phys.*, **22,** 565 (1954).

116. P. Alexander, A. Charlesby, and M. Ross, *Proc. Roy. Soc.* (*London*), **A223,** 392 (1954).

117. K. Little, *Nature,* **173,** 680 (1954).

118. V. L. Karpov, *Sess. Acad. Sci., U.S.S.R.*, Chem. Sect., July 1–5, 1955, p. 3.

119. A. Charlesby, *J. Polymer Sci.*, **15,** 263 (1955).

120. A. A. Miller, E. J. Lawton, and J. S. Balwit, *J. Polymer Sci.*, **14,** 503 (1954).

121. C. D. Bopp and O. Sisman, *Nucleonics,* **13,** No. 10, 51 (1955).

122. P. Alexander and A. Charlesby, *Proc. Roy. Soc.* (*London*), **A230,** 136 (1955).

123. P. Alexander and A. Charlesby, *Radiobiology Symposium, Liege,* 1954, p. 49.

124. A. Chapiro, *et al.*, French patents Nos. 692735 and 692736 (1955).

125. A. Chapiro, *et al.*, *J. Chim. Phys.*, **53,** 306 (1956).

CHAPTER 16

FLUORESCENCE AND COLORATION PRODUCED BY RADIATION

16–1 The transfer of excitation energy. In a monotomic gas, the atoms are normally sufficiently far apart that they do not interact with each other, and the separations between electronic energy levels correspond to discreet energy differences. In a gas which contains diatomic molecules, the energy spectrum already has a band structure because of the broadening of the levels due to vibrational and rotational motion. This broadening is even more pronounced in the spectra of solids, since interactions between neighboring atoms or ions may lead to the splitting of each electronic level into several components. Normally, all the fundamental levels are filled, in agreement with the Pauli principle, and are therefore so close together (or even overlapping) (Fig. 16–1) that these bands can be regarded as being quasi-continuous *filled bands.* Above these are other bands of allowed energy, separated from the former by forbidden energy regions. With increasing temperature, or due to the action of a photon or a charged particle, an electron in a solid can "jump" to an unoccupied higher level, leaving behind a "hole" in the filled band. This hole is eventually filled by another electron, and the replacement of this creates another hole, so that the successive migrations of the electron in a given direction can be regarded as the movement of "positive holes" in the opposite direction. In an alkali halide, for example, the movement of an electron is associated with that of a neutral halogen atom. The highest allowed excitation level, the energy of which is close to that required to remove the electron completely from the solid, is the *conduction band.*

If the electron returns directly from the excited state to the initial state with the emission of an energy quantum $h\,(\nu_2 - \nu_1)$, equal to the energy difference between the two levels, the process is known as resonance emission. In such a case, the lifetime of the excited state is of the order of 10^{-7} to 10^{-8} sec, to be compared with a time of 10^{-14} to 10^{-15} sec for the light-emission process (in the visible region). The resonance therefore effectively consists of two distinct successive processes, absorption and re-emission. The electron may, however, also end up in some intermediate state, in which case two possibilities can be identified:

(a) The electron returns to the ground state, with the emission of a quantum of energy lower than that required for excitation; this is *fluorescence* (Fig. 16–2).

(b) The probability of the above transition (a) may be very low, as is particularly the case if the transition is between two states of unequal multiplicity, such as, for example, from a singlet state to a doublet state. The life of the intermediate state, the so-called *metastable state,* then becomes

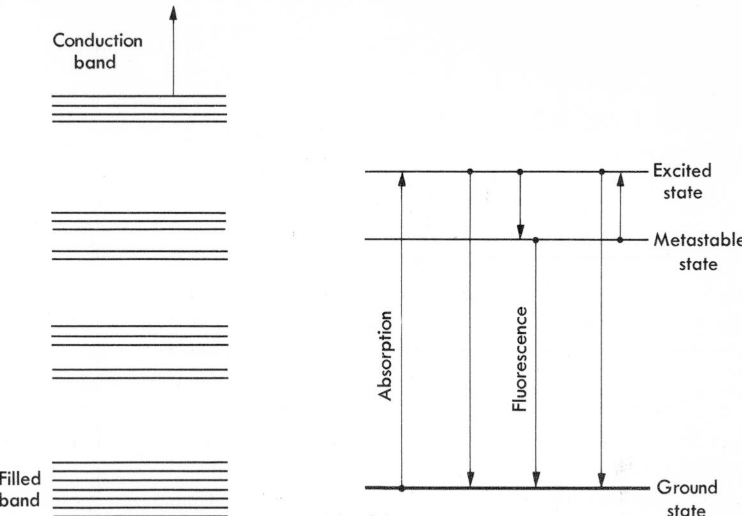

FIG. 16–1. Schematic representation of the energy levels in a solid.

FIG. 16–2. Electronic transitions in an excited molecule.

sufficiently long for the electron to acquire extra energy, for example, by thermal agitation, and so return to the original excited level, from which it goes to the ground state with the emission of a quantum of *phosphorescence*. At one time these phenomena were subdivided by designating very short-lived luminescent processes ($\sim 10^{-8}$ sec) as luminescence, and delayed emissions as phosphorescence. The classification more generally adopted today is that just described, and originally proposed by F. Perrin [1].

The decay of the intensity of the phosphorescence with time (i.e., after cutting off the exciting radiation) does not follow a simple law. In some cases there is evidence for an exponential law of the type

$$I = \frac{I_0}{\tau} e^{-t/\tau}. \tag{16–1}$$

In other cases a hyperbolic law is obeyed:

$$I = I_0(1 + t/\tau)^{-2}, \tag{16–2}$$

where τ is the half-life of the *decay*. In phosphorescent phenomena which obey Eq. (16–1), τ is a function of temperature

$$\tau = \tau_0 e^{\epsilon/kT}. \tag{16–3}$$

The first equation corresponds to first-order kinetics, and can be interpreted by assuming that the process is controlled by the rate at which electrons leave the excited levels. Equation (16–2), which is a second-order equation, can be regarded as being valid for processes whose overall rate is determined by recombination between free electrons and positive holes.

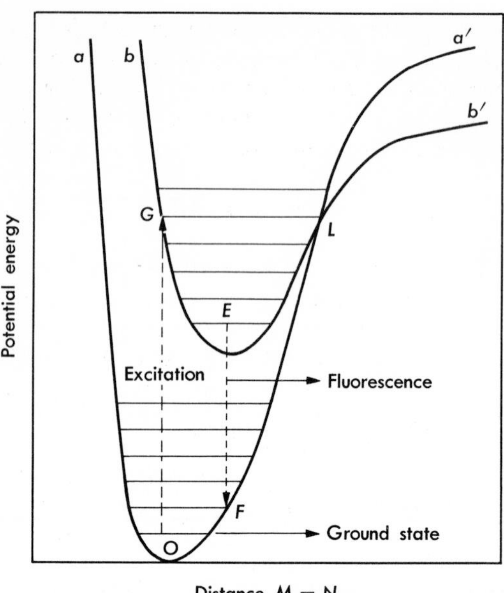

FIG. 16–3. Potential energy diagram for a diatomic molecule.

In practice, however, one often finds changes from one law to the other, or multimolecular decay processes with the order $n > 2$.

The well-known potential energy diagram showing energy as a function of the distance between atoms illustrates clearly the phenomenon of luminescence. The curves in Fig. 16–3 refer to a diatomic molecule MN. The curve aOa' represents the normal vibrational state of the molecule in the electronic ground state, and bGb' is the corresponding curve for an excited state. When it acquires energy, an electron can be raised from O to G, and this transition follows a vertical line because of the Franck-Condon principle, according to which the movement of the much heavier nuclei does not immediately follow the excitation of the electron. If G is above b', which is the stability limit of the molecule, the molecule will dissociate; in the opposite case, it will pass from G to E and dissipate the excess vibrational energy as heat. A stable molecule subsequently passes to the ground state along EF with the emission of fluorescent radiation. This cannot occur if the two curves aOa' and bGb' have a common point (L), or lie very close to one another at a point L on one of the curves, since vibration in the excited state GL allows the molecule to pass from L to the ground state and dissipate its excess excitation energy thermally along LO without emitting light.

The potential energy diagrams for a polyatomic molecule, or for a solid, are very much more complex because of the considerably larger number of vibrational levels, but the principles of energy transfer between the levels are the same as for diatomic molecules. With increasing molecular complexity, however, the probability of "quenching" the luminescence by intramolecular processes also increases. The efficiency of such processes increases with temperature, as does energy degradation by intermolecular collisions, so that fluorescent phenomena are favored by low temperature.

Sensitized fluorescence in gases has been known for some time [2]; in this an excited molecule or atom transfers its energy to another molecule, which dissipates the energy by emission of a quantum of lower energy:

$$A + B + h\nu \rightarrow A^* + B \rightarrow A + B^* \rightarrow A + B + h\nu', \qquad (16\text{–}4)$$

where the asterisk identifies the excited atom. Kallmann and Furst [3, 4] have shown this transfer can also occur in the liquid phase, in which a solvent excited by high-energy radiation transfers the energy to the solute, which emits fluorescence in high yield. Ageno and his collaborators [5] subsequently claimed that not only in solution, but even in crystals of transstilbene, excitation of fluorescence by polonium α-particles may take place over distances of several millimeters. This migration of energy may occur by different mechanisms [6, 7], although it is rather difficult to decide which of these is responsible in each particular case.

1. In liquids, as in gases, sensitized fluorescence can be propagated by collision between the molecules of different species if the absorbing molecule has a resonance level slightly higher than one of the excited states of the fluorescent molecule [8]. Förster [9] suggests that this type of energy transfer can take place in liquids by the interaction of molecular dipoles.

2. In an insulating solid, electrons raised to the conduction band do not belong to any particular atom but to the whole lattice, so that an electron can move easily throughout the lattice, until it meets a positive hole, with which it recombines with the emission of light or heat. The electron can also be captured by a "trap," such as an impurity or vacant anionic site (Schottky defect), or by any sort of crystal imperfection which can act as an electron acceptor. These traps constitute the characteristic absorption *centers* or *color centers*. The release of an electron from a trap by thermal activation, or by irradiation with light of the appropriate wavelength, can also give rise to luminescence by recombinations with "holes."

3. In a lattice of strongly bound ions or atoms, instead of the electron moving independently of the "hole," it may combine with it to form a pair of the hydrogenoid type, the so-called *exciton*, proposed by Frenkel [10, 11, 12], which migrates rapidly from one ion to another, remaining with each for a time interval which is very short relative to the elastic vibrations. In this way, energy can be propagated by excitation waves until the wave meets a defect or lattice impurity [13]. Following the work of Masakuso and Kasuku [14], and Gross and Currier [15], various authors have recently reported absorption spectra in crystals explicable in terms of excitons.

4. According to Birks [16, 17], most of the high-energy photons produced in fluorescent organic crystals by the action of ionizing particles are absorbed, re-emitted, re-absorbed, and re-emitted several times within the same crystal. When such processes follow photofluorescence, some of the energy of the primary quantum could be dissipated in transitions between vibrational and rotational levels, so that only the quanta corre-

sponding to decay from the first excited electronic state to the ground state would be finally emitted by the crystal. A similar mechanism of energy transfer by absorption and re-emission had already been proposed for dilute organic solutions by Ageno [5].

16–2 Luminescence and coloration. The luminescent properties of radioactive compounds were observed by Pierre and Marie Curie in their first experiments with radium [18, 19]. Radium bromide and radium chloride, and anhydrous barium salts containing radium, spontaneously emit an intense luminescence, which is visible in daylight if the source contains more than about 0.1 gm of radium. This luminescence falls off in time due to the alteration of the salt, which gradually becomes colored, but the initial luminescence can be restored by recrystallization and dessication. Similarly, if a solution containing millicurie amounts of a polonium salt (chloride, nitrate, etc.) freed from other materials is evaporated to dryness in a quartz crucible, a strong luminescence can be seen at the bottom of the crucible in darkness; this is again visible in daylight with quantities of polonium some ten times greater. Actinium and ionium compounds are also luminescent.

These effects are due to the radiation exciting the fluorescence of the compounds containing the radioelements, or the supporting materials (quartz), or some other suitable surrounding material. The fluorescence of layers of zinc sulfide by α-particles, and of $Ba[Pt(CN)_6]$ or $CaWO_4$ by β-particles, which take the form of *scintillations* produced by the passage of individual particles, are classical examples of this phenomena.

When water is bombarded with α-particles from polonium [20], or when ice is irradiated with 50-kv x-rays at a low temperature, ultraviolet radiation is emitted [21]. The α-particles from polonium [22, 23, 24, 25] also cause emission in the ultraviolet and visible regions with a number of gases, including air, oxygen, nitrogen, hydrogen, helium, neon, argon, carbon dioxide, and methane; for nitrogen the yield in the 300 to 400 mμ region is 1000 quanta per α-particle. The intensity is found to be additive for mixtures of hydrogen and oxygen, but not for nitrogen-oxygen or hydrogen-nitrogen mixtures. We shall see later, however, that these fluorescent emissions are much more significant with many solids and liquids. The coloration of radioactive substances, and of materials exposed to the action of their radiations (see Ref. 26), are closely related to the luminescence. Examples of these effects were noted above in the aging of radium salts. Radioactive minerals, or those containing traces of a radioactive element, such as rock salt, fluorite, mica, quartz, etc., are often strongly colored. Diamond, alumina, various types of glass, and ceramics color up progressively when exposed to the action of α-particles, β-particles, γ-, or x-rays, going brown, violet, green, etc., according to their composition. A 1-cm thick sample of borosilicate glass retains only 4% of its initial transmission at 450 mμ after irradiation with 10^6 r of x-rays [27]; a dose of 10^{10} r shatters the glass. Even small amounts of coloration may be undesirable, as for example in optical instruments required to be close to intense sources. Kreidl reports that this coloration can be prevented by adding 1% Ce_2O_3 to the glass [27].

The color can be removed from the materials mentioned by raising the temperature; this phenomena is often associated with luminescence. Various authors have studied the kinetics of the coloration and decoloration processes in vitreous silica, and it seems that the mechanism is similar to that in the alkali halides (see, for example, Refs. 28, 29, 30) which are dealt with below.

16–3 Ionic crystals. When an alkali halide is irradiated with x- or γ-rays, or with α-particles, deuterons, or other charged particles, the electrons attached to the anions (Cl^-, Br^-) are excited and go into the conduction band, so that they move through the lattice until they meet some sort of trap. In the crystals under consideration, the traps are especially Schottky vacancies, which fix these electrons to form *F-centers* [31, 32]. These have characteristic absorption bands whose maximum intensity depends on the particular solid; the maximum is at 465 mμ for NaCl, which is colored yellow, 560 for KCl (violet), 620 for rubidium and caesium chlorides (blue), etc. The intensity of the coloration is proportional to the number (n_0) of centers per cubic centimeter; n_0 can be calculated from an equation derived by Smakula [33]

$$n_0 = k\alpha_m W, \tag{16–5}$$

where α_m is the absorption coefficient at the maximum of the band, W is the width of the band at midheight (expressed in ev); k is a dimensionless number, of the order of 10^{16}, which depends only slightly on the nature of the crystal, and in particular is dependent on the refractive index.

For small doses of radiation, the density of centers is proportional to the energy absorbed. Alger [34] has investigated this by irradiating NaCl, KBr, and LiF with x-rays with energies between 0.03 and 3 Mev, or with 1-Mev cathode rays. For a dose of 25,000 r of 3-Mev x-rays, he finds 4 to 6×10^{16} F-centers per cubic centimeter, depending on the previous thermal history of the salt. With increasing dose, n_0 tends toward a limiting value, which is of the order of 10^{18} to 10^{19} F-centers per cubic centimeter. This density is too high for the number of Schottky defects present in a well-formed crystal, and it was concluded that a certain number of vacant sites is produced during the radiation itself. This should result in a small but measurable decrease in the bulk density, and this has been confirmed by irradiating single crystals of KCl with x-rays [35, 36]. An elegant method was used, based on the following principle: the coefficient of expansion of a crystal is much lower than that of a liquid, and it is therefore possible to find a temperature at which the crystal of KCl remains suspended in some appropriate inert liquid (which in this case was 1-3 dibromopropane). The difference between this temperature for the initial crystal and that irradiated for 85 hours was 0.09°, corresponding to a density change of 1.4×10^{-4} gm/cm^3. A decrease of 5×10^{-5} gm/cm^3 was found after irradiating a crystal with 10^{15} 360-Mev protons per square centimeter. We saw earlier (Section 15–4) that density measurements on neutron bombarded LiF lead to the conclusion that fast neutrons produce Frenkel defects.

Along with the F-band, a V-band of comparable intensity appears in the ultraviolet. The maximum of this band corresponds to a frequency (ν_m) 2 to 2.4 times greater than that for the F-band, being 228 mμ for NaCl, 235 for KCl, and 267 for KBr. The two bands show a number of analogies [37], and in particular the relation derived by Mollwo [38] $\nu_m d^2 =$ constant (where d is the lattice constant of the crystal) is obeyed. The origin of the V-band is not yet quite clear; it may be due to the capture of a positive hole in a trap or in a cationic vacancy, which would give a neutral halogen atom [39] in the same way that the F-centers can be regarded as being neutral alkali metal atoms (e + Na^+ close to the trap). From a chemical point of view then, the formation of an $F + V$ pair corresponds to a photochemical reaction of the type NaCl $\rightarrow$ Na + Cl. The V-band has a rather more complex structure than the F-band, and three components V_1, V_2, and V_3 have been identified [40], but Dorendorf [41] has reported that in addition there are four others.

Molnar [42] has discovered that irradiation of alkali halides produces yet a third band, appearing at 720 mμ in NaCl and 820 mμ in KCl. If a crystal which already contains F-centers is illuminated with light of the same wavelength as the F-band, the latter is partially transformed into the M-band reported by Molnar, and vice versa. In both cases, a fraction of the light intensity is utilized in forming another two-component band (R_{I} and R_{II}), which in the case of KCl is at the red end of the spectrum. According to Seitz [39], an M-center consists of the combination of a neutral pair of vacancies with an F-center. An R-center would be the association of two F-centers, or of two F-centers which have lost one electron, so forming an F-center plus an anionic vacancy. If the above illumination of the F-band is carried out at a sufficiently low temperature (below 25°C for NaCl and below −75°C for KCl), the band disappears and gives place to an F'-band which is shifted about 200 mμ to the red end of the spectrum. At the same time, the intensity of the V-band decreases. According to Seitz, an F'-center is an F-center which has captured a second electron, and is therefore rather like an anion.*

The intensity of the color due to F-centers decreases spontaneously with time. This decrease occurs more rapidly with the heavier halides, for which production of the color itself is also more difficult. The time for half-decoloration is a few seconds for KCl and KBr, several weeks for NaCl and about one year for LiF (although Joffé [43] has reported a residual coloration in a NaCl crystal irradiated with x-rays and then kept in darkness for 21 years). The thermal instability of F-centers is due to the migration of electrons toward the V-centers, where the initial anions are re-formed, so that this instability increases with temperature; it is also dependent on the temperature at which the centers are produced [44].

During irradiation with x-rays, NaCl crystals emit a fluorescence in the neighborhood of 2450 A [45]. After the irradiation, a very weak phosphorescence is observed in the visible region [46] and this decreases with a half-life of several days; the decay of another more intense phosphorescence

* For further discussion of color centers, see Refs. 26 and 39, and F. Seitz, *Revs. Modern Phys.*, **26,** 7 (1954).

which appears in the ultraviolet follows a first-order law (Eq. 16–1), with a half-life of 186 sec. Glasser and Beasley [47] have examined this phosphorescence, using excitation by both x- and γ-rays, and report that the decay rate depends on the length and intensity of irradiation. The other alkali halides show similar effects, which are generally attributed to the release of electrons from the various traps, followed by recombination with positive holes. This temporary storing of energy, which is re-emitted as luminescence, is strongly enhanced if the crystal contains electron traps due to impurities, which often need only be present in trace quantities; these are known as *activators*. The addition of 1 mole percent of AgCl into a crystal of NaCl increases the phosphorescence produced by x-rays by a factor of 100 to 1000 [48]. Thallium is an excellent activator for NaI and other alkali iodides; Cu^{2+}, Ni^{2+}, Mn^{2+}, or Pb^{2+} ions also increase the ultraviolet luminescence of the alkali halides. The high scintillation efficiency of ZnS or of (Zn, Cd)S is brought about by traces of Cu, Ag, or Mn. Certain phosphorescent materials such as strontium sulfide are more active in the presence of a principal activator (Eu) and a *co-activator* (Sm).

The effect of the activator is either to make the metastable states of activator itself available to the electrons, or to facilitate the passage of electrons to the metastable states of the main components of the lattice by modifying the potential energy-distance relationships (Fig. 16–3). The activator may either intensify the luminescence of the pure crystal (for example, Cu in ZnS, Li in Zn_2SiO_4), or produce a new luminescence [49]. It may therefore also act as a "poison" relative to the luminescence of the pure crystal (as does MnO_2 in Zn_2SiO_4), or not disturb it at all (co-activation of $Ca_2SiO_4 + MnO_2$ by PbO_2). Finally, impurities can sometimes "kill" the phosphorescence, as in the case of Mn in $CaWO_4$. The luminescence of activators at the trace level is a good illustration of the rapid propagation of excitation through solids.

Another means of stimulating the luminescence of a crystal is to release electrons from the traps, either by raising the temperature and so increasing their kinetic energy, (*thermoluminescence*) or by irradiation with light of an appropriate wavelength [50]. Crystals of LiF are especially suitable for studies of thermoluminescence. Figure 16–4, due to Daniels [51, 52], shows the emission as a function of temperature (the *glow curve*) of LiF crystals after 115 hours irradiation with Co^{60} γ-rays. As can be seen, the threshold temperature is around 100°C; for NaCl it is about 50°. The various maxima, which are even more numerous in the case of fluorite, correspond to emissions from the different color centers. The thermoluminescence increases with the length of exposure to γ-rays, implying that the irradiation produces further traps. All the alkali halides are thermoluminescent; here again the addition of AgCl (1%) increases the intensity by a factor of 100. Similarly, the thermoluminescence of mixed crystals of NaCl + KBr is much greater than that of either of the separate components. Crystals of LiF, NaCl, KCl, and CsBr become thermoluminescent even after irradiation with soft x-rays with energies of a few kev [53].

Other thermoluminescent substances include ice, calcium and mercury carbonates, calcium sulfate, alumina, MgO, SiO_2, various glasses, ceramics, feldspars, and various other natural minerals. Each substance shows

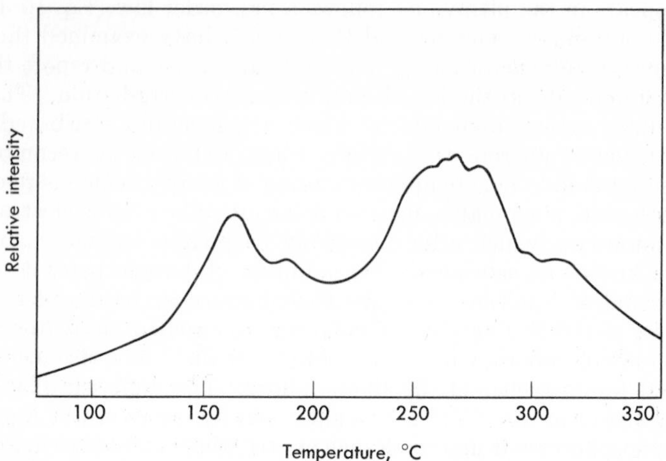

FIG. 16–4. The thermoluminescence curve for LiF (Ref. 51).

its own characteristic temperature-dependent glow curve, which is extremely sensitive to the presence of impurities, and to the thermal history of the sample. Thermoluminescence cannot therefore serve as a precise analytical method, but it can be used to identify and classify minerals, clays, and ceramic materials [54]. The color emitted is itself often characteristic of the nature of the emitting substance; limestones for example give a yellow light, and dolomites an orange color. Since thermoluminescence is sensitive to lattice imperfections, it can also be used to test certain catalysts whose activity shows the same sensitivity to lattice properties.

Finally, thermoluminescence has been suggested as a means of measuring radiation dose. Daniels was the first to suggest lithium fluoride for this purpose, since in this case the intensity of the thermoluminescence is approximately proportional to the γ-ray dose absorbed over a wide energy range, so that a simple apparatus can be used to measure the dose between at least 1 and 1000 r. Unfortunately the crystals may pick up a parasitic thermoluminescence in the course of preparation, and Daniels [55] has preferred to use fused alumina containing silver chloride, used in the form of a capsule covered by a thin sheet of metallic silver.

Rapid but less precise measurements can also be carried out by measuring the coloration of specially prepared glasses. One such method [56] uses a glass containing 50% $Al(PO_3)_3$, 25% $Ba(PO_3)_2$, and 25% of KPO_3, to which is added 8% of $AgPO_3$. The optical density varies linearly (within ~5%) with the dose up to 2×10^6 rep, independent of the radiation intensity.

16–4 Radiophotoluminescence. The stimulation of the luminescence of crystals previously exposed to ionizing radiations by exposure to light is also a common phenomenon. If crystals of LiF, NaCl, or KCl are illuminated at 77°K in the *F*- or *M*-band after irradiation by Co^{60} γ-rays, a complex fluorescent spectrum extending into the infrared is observed [57].

Similarly, if a crystal of NaCl + AgCl is irradiated with γ-rays and then exposed to visible light after decay of the phosphorescence, there is a strong emission in the ultraviolet [58]. Equally the x-ray induced phosphorescence of quartz between 610 and 385 mμ reappears, after extinction, on exposure to light in the 550 to 220 mμ region, and this cycle can be repeated a large number of times [59].

This phenomenon was named *radiophotoluminescence* by Przibram [60], who discovered it in 1921 in experiments with the mineral kunzite, a double aluminum-lithium silicate. If this mineral, which is colored pink by the presence of traces of Mn, is exposed to the radiation from radium, it becomes dark green and emits an intense orange light after illumination. The radiophotoluminescence disappears on heating and can be regenerated by further exposure to ionizing radiation. This is found in a number of other natural crystals, among which rock salt and fluorite in particular have been studied by Przibram and his co-workers [61, 62, 63]. Natural rock salt is often colored blue or violet (less frequently yellow) and the authors were able to show that the optical and thermal behavior of the colors is often identical with that of the F-, M-, and R-color centers produced by radiation. The colors disappear on heating to 200 to 300°C, and this is often accompanied by thermoluminescence.

The behavior of natural fluorite is similar; its very varied colors are partly due to traces of the divalent rare earth elements Eu^{2+}, Sm^{2+}, Yb^{2+}(Tm^{2+}?). The blue radiophotoluminescent band of fluorite is due to Eu^{2+}, the yellow-green band to Yb^{2+}, and the red to Sm^{2+}. These minerals also contain traces of the radioactive elements U, Th, and K, and Przibram has attributed the optical properties just described to the radiations from these elements. Rock salt also contains traces of helium (10^{-7} cm^3/gm), which Hahn and Born [47] suggest originates from the coprecipitation of NaCl + $PbCl_2$ ($RaDCl_2$) in the radium-rich salt deposits of the Tertiary period. Decay of RaD to the α-emitting Po^{210} would set up an extra source of radiation and of helium. The relationship between the He content of rock salt and the color has recently been confirmed by Thomson and Wardle [65]. Weininger [66] has examined a large number of samples of natural sodium chloride from various sources, and has concluded from their optical properties that the coloration is normally due either to color centers (F, M, R) alone, or to both color centers and colloidal aggregates of sodium atoms, depending on the sample. The coloration of one particular sample may have been purely colloidal. Using the Smakula equation [Eq. (16–5)], Weininger estimates that there are 10^{15} to 10^{16} color centers per cubic centimeter in those crystals whose color is predominantly noncolloidal in origin. If, however, it is assumed that the colloidal particles have also been produced by the aggregation of color centers due to the effect of the radiations, the author evaluates the concentration of primary color centers in those crystals with colloidal inclusions at 10^{18}/cm^3.

A much more intense coloration of rock salt by radiation occurs if the crystal is submitted to very high pressures (2000 to 10,000 kg/cm^2) [67, 68], so that a dose which under normal conditions is sufficient to impart a yellow color to the crystal produces an almost black color when pressure is applied. In particular the R_{II} band appears under these circumstances, and this is one of the most frequent components of the spectrum of natural blue NaCl crystals. Since in the course of geological time these crystals have probably been subjected to considerable pressures, it is possible that this has contributed to the intensification of the color by the formation of colloidal clusters.

We shall also note two other mechanisms which have been proposed to explain certain luminescent phenomena. When LiF or NiCl was irradiated at liquid helium temperature (4°K) with Co^{60} γ-rays, Ghormley and Levy [57] observed a phosphorescence occurring as the crystals warmed up at 66 or 135°K. This they attribute to a "self-trapping" of the electron, as previously suggested by Landau [69]; at very low temperatures an electron moving in a solid can displace neighboring ions by polarization, and thus become immobilized in its own trap. The luminescence would then be associated with the release of the electron at some higher temperature. The different spectra observed by these authors show features which vary with the temperature of the measurement, and which correspond to the different activation energies required to release the electron from different traps. Part of the luminescent spectra of LiF is, however, independent of temperature, and the authors attribute this to the recombination between an F-center and a hole, produced by a "tunnelling effect" which requires no activation energy; this mechanism was suggested by Seitz [39] to explain the high density of centers.

16–5 Organic compounds. Organic compounds which show a marked ability to fluoresce generally have a very stable electronic structure and are chemically resistant to radiation. In particular this group includes aromatic molecules with their conjugated system of π-electrons, such as benzene, naphthalene, anthracene, naphthacene, triphenyl

$$C_6H_5—C_6H_4—C_6H_5,$$

and transstilbene

$$C_6H_5—CH{=}CH—C_6H_5.$$

The mechanism of luminescence in these molecules is essentially the same as that described for inorganic compounds, and can be discussed in terms of a potential energy diagram of the type shown in Fig. 16–3. Since the fluorescent spectrum is generally independent of the mode and energy of excitation, it must be assumed either that the electrons are raised to the lowest excitation level by the passage of an ionizing particle or high-energy photon, or, if the excitation is to a higher level, that the excess energy is degraded by transfer to vibrational and rotational states.

Sensitization (activation) is also observed with organic crystals. The addition of one part of anthracene in 10^5 parts of naphthalene, or of naphthacene to anthracene, is sufficient to suppress the emission of the "solvent," and give rise to an intense fluorescence characteristic of the solute [13]. Polystyrene itself is only weakly fluorescent, but the addition (in solid solution) of only a few percent of p-triphenyl [70], or more especially of pyrene or of tetraphenyl-1-1-4-4-butadiene-1-3 (2%), increases the fluorescent yield [71, 72] to the same order as that of anthracene, regarded as being the best scintillator.

Fluorescent liquid solutions, like the solid solutions, show the following characteristic features:

1. nonadditivity of yields;
2. sensitivity to impurities, which may either cause a large increase in the fluorescence or extinguish it completely; in particular oxygen is a poison for liquid scintillators;
3. the spectrum is that of the solute, not of the solvent;
4. energy transfer can occur over some distance; this has already been considered above.

A solution of p-triphenyl ($C_{18}H_{14}$) in xylene or some similar solvent, at a concentration of 5 gm/liter, shows the typical properties of fluorescent solutions. According to Kallmann and Furst [3, 73, 74], other efficient solutions include anthranilic acid, α-naphthylamine, phenyl-α-naphthylamine, and diphenylhexatriene in solvents such as xylene, toluene, benzene, phenylcyclohexane, or phenyl ether. The phenyloxazoles [75], which are very soluble in organic solvents, and which can be employed at low temperatures, are also efficient scintillators. The efficiency of a weakly fluorescent solution can be considerably increased [73, 74] by adding considerable amounts of some appropriate third component. For example, the fluorescent intensity of 2-5-diphenyloxazole in trimethylborate is only 5% of that given by the same concentration (3 gm/liter) of the solute in xylene; if, however, the trimethylborate is diluted with an equal volume of xylene, the relative yield increases to 79%. Equally, the addition of naphthalene (30%) to n-butyl phosphate containing diphenyloxazole increases the relative yield from 9% to 72%.

The structural conditions which are necessary for an organic molecule to have good fluorescent properties are not as yet completely established, but it appears [76] that it must have a high degree of symmetry and no steric hindrance. The efficiency is increased by hydroxyl, amine, and alkoxy groups, whereas substituent groups such as halogen, nitro, and carboxyl reduce the yield. Furthermore, the yield is generally better in solutions in which the absorption spectrum of the solvent and the fluorescent spectrum of the solute are fairly similar.

The variation of the yield I with the solute concentration c obeys the equation

$$I = \frac{Pc}{(Q + c)(R + c)}, \tag{16–6}$$

in which P, Q, and R are parameters which depend on the solvent, the solute, and the type of radiation, respectively. This, and other similar equations which have been proposed, account for the fact that with increasing concentration the yield goes through a maximum, and then decreases at relatively high concentrations due to self-extinction processes arising from molecular interactions with the solute. Since extinction is due to the dissipation of energy by modes other than phosphorescence, it depends on the specific energy loss dE/dx (Section 11–2) and hence on the nature and energy of the radiation. Experiment shows in fact that the light yield per unit energy from organic scintillators is smaller for α-particles than for β-particles and γ-rays ($\sim$10%). Birks [77] has established a theoretical formula for the dependence of the specific yield dI/dE with the concentration (or with the stopping power dE/dn, which is proportional to the concentration)

$$\frac{dI}{dE} = \frac{q}{w}\left(\frac{1}{1 + kc}\right), \tag{16–7}$$

where q is the quantum yield of the emission, w the excitation energy of the fluorescence, and k the extinction coefficient. A slightly different relationship has been proposed by Wright [78].

The spectral composition of the light emitted by fluorescent crystals is displaced toward the red end of the spectrum relative to the spectrum of the same substance in solution. The average life of the fluorescence is 2 to 3 times longer than that of the excited electronic states of the isolated molecule.

16–6 Changes in electrical properties. If an electric field is applied across an insulating crystal, such as an alkali halide or diamond, during irradiation with ionizing particles or high-energy photons, a current can be shown to flow. This is due to electrons in the filled band being transferred to the conduction band and moving toward the positive electrode, while at the same time the mobile positive holes migrate in the opposite direction. Measurements of the Hall effect show that this conductivity is electronic, not ionic. The only difference between this and the conductivity induced by radiation in semiconductors (Section 15–3) lies in the fact that the latter already contain a large number of free electrons before irradiation. Movement toward the electrodes is, however, hindered by the presence of traps, which can capture electrons and holes in spite of the kinetic energy acquired from the applied field. The greater the intensity of this field, the faster can the electrons move, so that the chance of capture by the traps is reduced. Each electron does not therefore contribute its effective total charge to the current, but only a fraction which is proportional to the average distance δ traveled before capture [79]. The relation between the field intensity E, the electron mobility m, and δ, is given by

$$\delta = mE\tau, \tag{16–8}$$

where τ is the average time for which an electron is free (i.e., untrapped). The total effective charge transferred by n_0 electrons excited into the conduction band by each impulse is

$$Q_{\text{eff}} = \frac{\delta n_0 e}{d}\,(1 - e^{-d/\delta}), \tag{16–9}$$

where d is the thickness of the crystal. For weak fields the exponential term is negligibly small, so that

$$Q_{\text{eff}} = \frac{\delta n_0 e}{d}. \tag{16–10}$$

At 77°K, the value of δ is 0.28 cm for KCl, 0.07 for KBr, 0.60 for NaCl, and more than 10 cm for LiF ($E = 10^4$ v/cm), 2.1 for AgBr, 6.2 for TlBr, and 11 cm for AgCl ($E = 5 \times 10^3$ v/cm). At 300°K, for $E = 10^4$ v/cm, δ is only 0.03 for KCl and 0.11 for LiF.

It follows that the silver and thalium halides are good photoconductors, and this property is utilized in the so-called "crystal counters," in which the radiation intensity is measured by the induced electrical conductivity. Such counters are operated at low temperatures, since at room temperature they possess an ionic conductivity of their own; zinc and cadmium sulfides, and diamond, can, however, be used at ordinary temperatures.

The high-temperature conductivity of the alkali halides is also changed by the action of radiations such as Co^{60} γ-rays, fast neutrons from a reactor [80], and 350-Mev protons [81]. With small doses, the conductivity decreases because of the capture of holes at lattice vacancies, but there is an increase in a long irradiation, which increases the number of vacancies. Annealing at some appropriate temperature tends to restore the initial resistance, but the conditions are then so complex that a precise analysis is not possible. The self-diffusion of Na^+ ions in NaCl crystals decreases during irradiation with 48-kv x-rays [82].

The conductivity of plastics increases considerably on irradiation, but the precise change observed depends on the nature and origin of these electric materials. Thus for example the conductivity of certain types of polyvinyl chloride shows a very rapid initial increase on exposure to 2.5-Mev x-rays, but eventually reaches a limiting value which depends on the intensity of the dose [83]. With a dose of 400 r/min, this limiting conductivity is some 30 times greater than the initial value. When the radiation is cut off, half of the resistance is recovered in 30 min, and 90% after 16 hr. The conductivity of irradiated polystyrene increases by a much greater factor, which probably varies with the nature of the sample, since different authors [83, 84, 85] report values extending from 2×10^3 to 10^7.

The current (i) induced in plastics by x-irradiation is related to the dosage rate (I) [85, 86] by a relation of the type $i = aI^b$, where the value of the exponent b is 0.6 for polystyrene, 0.8 for polythene, and 1 for perspex. In this latter case, the induced conductivity is independent of the temperature between 20 and 90°C, but with polythene it varies exponentially with temperature, with an activation energy of 0.35 ev. These results imply a uniform energy distribution of the electron traps in perspex, and an exponential distribution in polythene.

Kinderman and Carson [87, 88] have examined the behavior of various electrodes left in contact with strongly radioactive solutions (~0.5 curie/liter of P^{32}) for long periods. The stability of a calomel electrode and a silver chloride electrode was unaffected over periods of 3 to 6 hours, but an antimony electrode was only reliably useful for less than 15 hours exposure under the conditions used by these authors. Radiations from various very intense sources (Pu^{239} α-particles, P^{32} β-particles, fission products up to 40 curies/liter, and Co^{60} γ-rays up to 60,000 r/hour, etc.) have no effect on pH measurements with a glass electrode [88]. Other electrodes, however, such as platinum and graphite, and especially tungsten and mercury, are directly affected by interaction with the radiolytic products in the solution.

16–7 Scintillation counters. The fluorescence produced in substances which are sensitive to α-particles (ZnS) or β-particles ($Ba[Pt(CN)_6]$) has been utilized for the detection and counting of such particles in various laboratories since the beginning of the century. The visual observation of scintillations with a microscope is, however, imprecise, and in the long run extremely tedious. Curran and Baker [89] in 1944, and Blau and Dreyfus [90] in 1945 suggested that the naked eye could be replaced by a photomultiplier tube, which transforms the scintillations into electrical impulses. This provides a highly sensitive technique, which under the appropriate conditions is highly efficient, and rapid developments have led to the widespread use of this method in many nuclear physics and radiochemical investigations.

A scintillation counter consists essentially of some fluorescent crystal which is placed opposite the emitting source. The photons strike the photocathode of the photomultiplier (Fig. 16–5) in which the photoelectrons produced are multiplied successively by a series of secondary emission electrodes (dynodes). The current is amplified in this way, and then registered and counted by an electrical circuit. The photocathode generally consists of an alkali metal alloy, the most widely used being caesium-antimony.

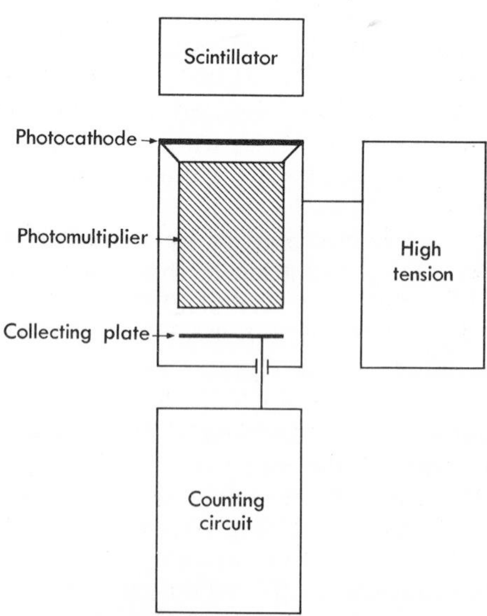

FIG. 16–5. Diagram of a scintillation counter.

The main properties which one looks for in a good scintillator are the following:

1. Transformation of the incident energy into light energy in high yield.
2. For a given type of particle, this yield must be constant over wide limits of energy variation.
3. The frequency of the emitted light should be concentrated in a region which corresponds to the maximum sensitivity of the photocathode.
4. The length of emission must be very short, in order to achieve a satisfactory resolving time for the whole setup.
5. The light emitted should not be re-absorbed by the fluorescent substance itself (i.e., high transparency).
6. To measure γ-rays, the crystal should have an atomic number and a density high enough to ensure that a significant fraction of the radiation is usefully absorbed.

Generally speaking, none of the scintillating materials known at present fulfill all these conditions completely, but there is a large number of substances from which a satisfactory and appropriate choice can be made for measurements in particular circumstances. The best phosphorescent inorganic crystals appear to be NaI or CaI_2 (Tl activated), ZnS (Cu or Ag activated), CdS (Ag), Zn_2SiO_4 (Mn), $CdWO_4$, $MgWO_4$, and $CaWO_4$. Organic crystals frequently have a much shorter decay period ($\sim 10^{-8}$ sec) than inorganic salts (10^{-4} to 10^{-6} sec), and a rather higher yield for β-particles, but not for α-particles. The most widely used are stilbene, anthracene, pure naphthalene (or naphthalene containing 0.1 to 1% anthracene), and diphenylacetylene (tolan). Liquid solutions of organic fluorescent materials in an appropriate solvent (see Section 16–5) have an efficiency which can approach that of crystals under favorable conditions. In addition solid solutions of anthracene, stilbene, triphenyl, or tetraphenylbutadiene in plastic materials such as polystyrene, polymethylmethacrylate, or polyvinylbutyltoluene have been employed.

Slow neutrons can be detected with scintillation counters by counting the α-particles from lithium or boron in the Li^6 $(n, \alpha)H^3$ or B^{10} $(n, \alpha)Li^7$ nuclear reactions. For this purpose crystals of LiF, or LiI containing TlI or SnI_2, Li_2SnO_3 activated with TiO_2, $Li_2B_4O_7$, molten H_3BO_3 + ZnS, or liquid scintillants can be used; other suitable materials include solutions of borazole and triphenyl in xylene, or phenyloxazole compounds in toluene containing methyl borate. For fast or medium energy neutrons, a screen of boron, cadmium, or mercury placed between the source and the scintillator emits α-particles or γ-rays which can then be detected. Another method is to detect the recoil protons produced in some fluorescent organic crystal. For neutrons with energies greater than 20.4 Mev, the reaction C^{12} $(n, 2n)C^{11}$ can be used in, say, anthracene or stilbene [91, 92]; the C^{11} produced emits positrons ($E_{\text{max}} = 0.97$ Mev) which excite the crystal. According to Wouster [93], a scintillator in front of the cathode is not necessary for the detection of fast neutrons, since the recoil nuclei formed cause sufficient local heating to evaporate several hundred electrons within the space of a few millimicroseconds, and these are subsequently amplified in the photomultiplier tube.

Very long irradiation of organic scintillators with excessive doses results in the accumulation of secondary products, and in damage which alters the luminescent properties of the crystal. Birks and Black [94] have reported that the irradiation of anthracene with a strong polonium source does not reduce the number of scintillations, but does decrease their amplitude.

Inorganic phosphorescent materials also undergo damage on bombardment with corpuscular radiations by the *Wigner effect*. Thus the bombardment of copper-activated zinc sulfide with neutrons from a pile or from a nuclear reaction results in a decrease in its luminescent power as an exponential function of the length of irradiation, and also changes in its other properties [95]. These effects are attributed to an increased copper concentration due to the nuclear reaction Zn (n, p) Cu. The coloration of NaCl produced by α-particles or electrons is not completely removed by light exposure (as in the case of the F-centers) but only by heating; this residual effect is due to the formation of interstitial atoms by recoil processes [96].

In some nuclear physics problems involving high-energy particles, counters based on the Cerenkov effect have been used (Section 11–6)*. Combinations of Cerenkov counters with liquid scintillation counters [97], or with Wilson cloud chambers [98], have been particularly successful in studying the properties of heavy mesons.

16–8 Autoradiography and nuclear emulsions. Although the discovery of radioactivity was a consequence of the effect of radiation on a photographic plate, the present wide applicability of photographic techniques is the result of long combined efforts by both experimentalists and technologists. Before the introduction of the "nuclear emulsions," the applications of *autoradiography* depended on the blackening of the plate. The material being studied was left in close contact with the photographic plate for a fixed time; after the plate was developed, an image was obtained with black spots, visible to the naked eye, corresponding to the active parts of the object studied. With an emulsion of a given composition, the blackening is greatest where the radiation is most intense, so that the points of emission can be localized, and the relative intensities of the radiation measured by microphotographic methods.

One of the first applications of this method was the development of *autohistoradiography* by Lacassagne and Lattès [99]. These authors injected polonium into animals which were subsequently slaughtered; certain organs were then removed and the selective localization of the radioelement investigated by the photographic examination of histological sections. The photographic method was also used by C. Chamié [100], and later authors, in the study of the colloidal behavior of certain radioactive

---

* For further details of scintillation counters, see S. C. Curran, *Luminescence and the Scintillation Counter*, Butterworths, London, 1953; R. K. Swank, *Nucleonics*, **12,** No. 3, 14 (1954); idem., *Ann. Rev. Nuclear Sci.*, **4,** 111 (1954). For neutron scintillation counters, see L. M. Bollinger, *1955 Geneva Conference*, P. 580. For Cerenkov counters, see J. Marshall, *Ann. Rev. Nuclear Sci.*, **4,** 141 (1954); and A. D. Kantz and R. Hofstadter, *Nucleonics*, **12,** No. 3, 36 (1954).

compounds, and Tammann [101] used it in examining aggregates of radioactive lead in certain alloys. Numerous examples of the use of autoradiography in a wide variety of physico-chemical problems are discussed in later chapters.

However, these autoradiographs, in which the traces produced by particles are ill defined, are far from satisfactory for nuclear research, where one wishes not only to detect *each* particle which passes through the emulsion, but also to determine its mass, charge, and energy. With the modern nuclear emulsions developed to meet these requirements, individual particles produce their own autoradiographic tracks, which can be subsequently identified by microscopic examination. These emulsions are quite thick [102] ($\geq 500\ \mu$), and have a high silver bromide concentration, up to 90% AgBr [103], so that the whole energy can be absorbed in the emulsion. The grains are finer and closer together, so that the track is better defined and can be followed almost to its origin. In addition, the method is considerably more sensitive than that involving detection from the overall blackening.

Further progress was made in 1944 when various industrial laboratories, encouraged by Powell and Occhialini [104, 105], produced a series of special emulsions with a wide range of sensitivities. A large number of the fundamental observations and discoveries described in the earlier chapters of this book are the result of the use of such plates. Their sensitivity was, however, not sufficient to detect weak ionizing particles such as protons, fast mesons, or electrons. Various research workers [106, 107, 108] and industrial laboratories were able to fill this gap by preparing nuclear emulsions of still higher sensitivity, and with increased grain size. A more recent advance was the preparation of emulsions "without support," which are very useful in the study of high-energy particles in cosmic radiation. To prepare these, the liquid emulsion is spread on glass, allowed to set, removed and cut into sections ($600 \times 400 \times 0.6$ mm) which are then mounted one upon another. After exposure to the radiation, the sections are remounted on glass, and then developed and examined in the usual way. An event occurring on one section can then be followed over a long path into the other sheets which were in contact with the first.

In such autoradiographs, the nature and characteristics of the particle are determined by a careful examination of the length, width, and density of the blackened grains, the number of δ-rays along the track, and the shape of the track itself. Jdanov [103] has shown that for a given ionizing particle, the average density of the grains (n) is related to the average grain diameter d, to the range R and to the AgBr concentration (c) by the equation

$$n = kR\frac{c}{d}; \qquad (16\text{–}11)$$

$k = 0.23$ when the concentration is expressed in grams per cubic centimeter and the range in microns.

The rate of energy loss by ionizing particles passing through the emulsion is given by the theoretical equation developed by Bohr and Bethe (Eq. 11–2). With increasing particle velocity, there is an initial decrease, and after passing through a minimum, the energy loss is proportional to the logarithm of the energy. Various authors [109, 110] have pointed out that at very high energies the Cerenkov radiation must contribute to the formation of the latent image. If the exact composition of the emulsion and the stopping power of its constituents are known, it is possible to calculate the total stopping power, and hence the range, from the Bohr-Bethe equation and the additivity rule. Following Cüer [111, 112] and others (e.g., Ref. 113), Vigneron [114, 115] has carried out such calculations for Ilford C2 plates, and has established energy-range relationships for protons with energies between 0.1 and 8 Mev, for α-particles with energies between 0.3 and 28 Mev, and for deuterons and tritons.

The photographic method can be used for neutron detection by incorporating into the emulsion a compound containing a light element with a high capture cross section for some reaction involving α-particle emission (e.g., Li, B, Be). Variations in neutron density in a pile can be measured by the autoradiography of thin sheets of some metal which is activated by neutrons (Mn, Ag, Au, In) [116]. To investigate other specific nuclear processes, particular compounds can be introduced into the sensitive layer; for example, a uranium salt could be used for studies of fission fragments.

The photographic method cannot be applied directly to γ-radiation, since the silver bromide grains are then developed essentially via secondary electrons. However, the overall blackening caused by γ-radiation can be usefully employed in the *radiography* of solids for detecting structural faults, impurities, porosities, and other irregularities. The density of the photographic image depends on the density of absorbing material between the source and the photographic plate, so that if, for example, a cast metal sample containing a bubble of gas is placed between a source of x-rays, γ-rays, or electrons and a photographic plate, the radiograph will reveal the site of the bubble as a black spot resulting from the lesser absorption of radiation at this point. Radiography can be carried out with neutrons, again using the secondary particles produced by the disintegration of elements incorporated into the sensitive layer [117]; this includes α-particles from lithium or boron, β-emission following (n, γ) reaction (e.g., Ag, In, Gd), γ-rays from capture (e.g., Cd), and recoil protons.

The mechanism by which the latent image is formed in a silver bromide emulsion by the action of ionizing particles is believed to be essentially the same as that which occurs with light, apart from the primary act itself; the Br^- ion loses its electron by electrostatic interaction with a charged particle, or by the photoelectric effect in the case of a photon. According to Gurney and Mott [118], electrons raised into the conduction band (by any mechanism) migrate through the crystal to the surface, where they are captured by electron traps. The interstitial Ag^+ ions which move by ionic conductivity are attracted by the negative charge of the traps, and neutralized. Each crystallite has only a limited number of traps, so that the silver atoms concentrate at these and form centers at which the latent image can develop. At the same time the bromine atoms diffuse toward the surface, where they are released. The nature of the electron traps involved is still the subject of some controversy [119, 120].

16-9 Development, desensitization, and fading. The use of the photographic method in nuclear research has raised a number of delicate problems of technique, which are also of considerable interest in the study of the chemistry of the latent image. For example, the appreciable thickness of nuclear emulsions makes uniform development throughout the whole mass difficult because of the slow rate of diffusion of the reagents into the emulsion from the surface. This difficulty can be overcome by using a very slow developer which has an induction period, but frequent use is now made of a method of development at two temperatures, introduced by Occhialini and his group [121, 122]. A developer is used which has a greater temperature coefficient for chemical reaction than for diffusion. After being soaked in distilled water in order to soften the gelatine, the emulsion is treated with the developer in the cold (4 to 5°C) for a time which depends on the thickness of the emulsion, and in this process the developer penetrates deeply into the sensitive layer without having any chemical effect. After being rinsed, the plate is slowly warmed in a humid atmosphere to the temperature at which the developer becomes active. The developer currently favored is based on amidol (the hydrochloride of 2, 4-diaminophenol), for which the "hot stage" requires 30 min to 1 hr at 28°C, or several hours at $\sim$10°C.

Another important problem is that of fogging by parasitic tracks from secondary electrons from cosmic radiation, and from the γ-radiation associated with corpuscular radiation. Only a few roentgens are sufficient to make a nuclear emulsion opaque and unusable. This problem, in a more general form, was met by Blau and Wambacher [123] in attempting to discriminate between tracks from Po^{210} α-particles and those from fast recoil protons on a photographic plate. These authors made the curious observation that pynacryptol green and yellow, which act as desensitizers in the photon irradiation of ordinary emulsion, behave as sensitizers for proton tracks; the effect of these substances on the tracks produced by α-particles is less pronounced. Similarly, mercury vapor, which sensitizes panchromatic emulsion to light, partially destroys the latent image due to α-particles [124]. More recent work by Demers [125], however, has shown that the effect of pynacryptol yellow on proton tracks in silver bromide-rich nuclear emulsions is less marked, so that the effect depends on the type of emulsion used. According to this author, coloring matters can be generally divided into three groups: sensitizers, desensitizers, and inerts. Fluorescein, erythrosine, methyl violet, and (especially) eosin belong to the first group; neutral red, rhodamine B and rhodamine 6 G, phenolsafranine, and tartrazine are desensitizers, while other organic nitrogen compounds such as acetonitrile, aniline, diethylamine, and α-naphthylamine sensitize the tracks of particles without increasing the background fogging. Traces of hydrogen peroxide vapor [125], or of permanganate and chromic acid in dilute solution [126, 127], eliminate the fog without affecting the tracks. By increasing the concentration of this latter reagent, it is possible to discriminate between protons and α-particles, and between α-particles and fission fragments from uranium [104, 128, 129].

Loading the emulsion with uranyl nitrate has its own desensitizing effect [129], which is probably due to hydrolysis of the salt and the resultant change in the pH of the developer; in fact, desensitization does not occur at any uranyl nitrate concentration if the solution added is at pH 7. The effect of pH has been confirmed by Broda and Jenkner [130] by examining the influence of adding acetic acid (desensitization) and ammonia (sensitization) to the emulsion, and by Picciotto [131], who loaded emulsions with borax.

The effect of all these reagents are observed on treatment of the emulsion either before irradiation, or after irradiation and before development, depending on the particular system. Desensitization can also be achieved by decreasing the reducing power of the developer by the appropriate direct change of pH, or by some other method of underdevelopment, such as lowering the temperature of the developer or decreasing the contact time for development [122, 132, 133, 134].

Because of the desensitizing effect of chromic acid, hydrogen peroxide, and other oxidizing agents, it is generally believed that all desensitizing agents act by partial destruction of the latent image by oxidation. The action of the sensitizers would result in an increased number of sites at the crystal surface, and hence an increase in the number of electrons captured. An increase of pH would have much the same effect.

A problem closely connected with desensitization is that of the spontaneous *fading* (or regression) of the latent image. This phenomena, first observed for charged particles by Blau [136] with tracks produced by Po^{210} α-particles, consists in a decrease in the number of developable grains in the track when the emulsion is left for some time before being developed. This becomes an increasing nuisance when long exposures are necessary, as is especially the case in cosmic ray work (and in other experiments with low-intensity sources).

Lauda [136], using the old type of emulsion with x-rays and α-particles, showed that immediately after the exposure the blackening increases with the time interval between exposure and development; after an interval of about 10 hours, however, the linear density of grains and the number of tracks decreases with time. This fading is more marked with higher energy particles, and in the presence of a desensitizer; it increases with decreasing intensity of irradiation, and is favored by oxygen, the humidity of the air, and by a temperature decrease. The influence of these three latter factors has been confirmed by Albouy and Faraggi [137], who carried out a systematic study of the fading of the tracks produced by α-particles from Po^{210} and Th(C + C′) in Ilford C2 emulsions. Without going into the details of the chemical mechanism of the process, the authors suggest that the fading is due to the oxidation of silver,

$$2Ag + \tfrac{1}{2}O_2 + H_2O \rightarrow 2Ag^+ + OH^-.$$

This reaction is compatible with Yagoda's suggestion that the fading can be regarded as a desensitization due to hydrogen peroxide produced radiolytically [124]. It is also possible that the gelatine itself enters into the process in some way.

More recently, Demers and his collaborators [138] have studied the fading in various types of emulsions, using α-particles and fast protons.

These authors conclude that oxygen is not essential for the fading of tracks, but that the humidity plays a dominant role. From the way in which the latent image decreases with time, they postulate the existence of various types of development centers and electron-acceptor centers. They suggest that a silver atom can be ionized by thermal agitation at 300°K so that an electron passes into the conduction band. A water molecule then acts as acceptor and is decomposed

$$\mathrm{Ag} \rightarrow \mathrm{Ag}^+ + \mathrm{e} \qquad (16\text{–}12)$$

$$\mathrm{H_2O} + \mathrm{e} \rightarrow \mathrm{H} + \mathrm{OH}^- \qquad (16\text{–}13)$$

$$\overline{\mathrm{H_2O} + \mathrm{Ag} \rightarrow \mathrm{Ag}^+ + \mathrm{H} + \mathrm{OH}^-.}$$

This mechanism is, however, rather unlikely, not only because of the hypothesis which is fundamental to process (16–12), but also because it implies that water would be decomposed by atomic silver, which from thermochemical data would involve a free energy increase of 32 kcal/mole and is endothermic by 22 kcal/mole.*

References

1. F. Perrin, *Ann. phys.*, **12,** 119 (1929).
2. G. Cario and J. Franck, *Z. Physik,* **17,** 202 (1923).
3. H. Kallmann and M. Furst, *Phys. Rev.*, **78,** 621 (1950); **79,** 857 (1950); **81,** 853 (1951); **85,** 816 (1952).
4. M. Furst and H. Kallman, *J. Chem. Phys.*, **23,** 607 (1955).
5. M. Ageno and R. Querzoli, *Nuovo cimento,* **9,** 196, 282 (1952).
6. J. Franck and R. Livingston, *Revs. Modern Phys.*, **21,** 505 (1949).
7. See M. Ageno in *Actions Chimiques et Biologiques des Radiations,* Vol. 2, Masson, Paris, 1956, p. 67.
8. H. Kallmann and F. London, *Z. physik Chem.*, **B2,** 207 (1928).
9. T. Förster, *Ann. Physik,* **2,** 55 (1948).
10. J. Frenkel, *Phys. Rev.*, **37,** 17, 1276 (1931).
11. R. Peierls, *Ann. Physik,* **13,** 905 (1932).
12. J. Franck and E. Teller, *J. Chem. Phys.*, **6,** 861 (1938).
13. E. J. Bowen, E. Mikiewicz, and F. W. Smith, *Proc. Phys. Soc.* (*London*), **A62,** 26 (1949).
14. H. Masakusu and K. Katsuki, *J. Phys. Soc. Japan,* **7,** 599 (1952).
15. E. F. Gross and N. A. Karryiev, *Doklady Akad. Nauk S.S.S.R.*, **84,** 471 (1952); see also Sept. 1958 issue of *J. Chim. Phys.*, **55,** especially the papers by H. Haken, S. Nikitin, E. Grillot, and others.
16. J. B. Birks, *Scintillation Counters,* Pergamon Press, London, 1953.
17. J. B. Birks and W. A. Little, *Proc. Phys. Soc.* (*London*), **A66,** 921 (1953).
18. Marie Curie, *Traité de Radioactivité,* Hermann, Paris, 1935, p. 339.

---

* Excellent reviews of the use of nuclear emulsions have been given by H. Yagoda, Ref. 124, J. Rotblat (in *Progress in Nuclear Physics,* O. Frisch, ed., Vol. 1, 1950, p. 37), A. Beiser, *Revs. Modern Phys.*, **24,** 273 (1952); and Y. Goldschmidt-Clermont, Ref. 110.

19. MAURICE CURIE, *Fluorescence et Phosphorescence*, Hermann, Paris, 1946.
20. E. W. T. RICHARDS, *Proc. Phys. Soc. (London)*, **A67,** 922 (1954).
21. L. I. GROSSWEINER and M. S. MATHESON, *J. Chem. Phys.*, **22,** 1514 (1954).
22. R. AUDUBERT and L. LORMEAU, *Compt. rend.*, **228,** 318 (1949).
23. L. LORMEAU, *Compt. rend.*, **230,** 956 (1950); **240,** 768 (1955).
24. A. E. GRUN and E. SCHOPPER, *Z. Naturforsch.*, **6a,** 698 (1951); **9a,** 134 (1954).
25. A. WARD, *Proc. Phys. Soc. (London)*, **A67,** 841 (1954).
26. K. PRZIBRAM, *Verfarbung und Lumineszenz*, Springer, Vienna, 1953.
27. N. J. KREIDL, *Ind. Eng. Chem.*, **46,** 170 (1954).
28. G. MAYER and J. GUERON, *J. Chim. Phys.*, **49,** 204 (1952).
29. F. S. DAINTON and J. ROWBOTTOM, *Trans. Faraday Soc.*, **50,** 480 (1954).
30. M. LEVY and J. H. O. VARLEY, *Proc. Phys. Soc. (London)*, **B68,** 223 (1955).
31. R. W. POHL, *Physik. Z.*, **39,** 36 (1938).
32. N. F. MOTT and R. W. GURNEY, *Electronic Process in Ionic Crystals*, Oxford University Press, 1940.
33. A. SMAKULA, *Z. Physik*, **59,** 603 (1930); **63,** 762 (1930).
34. R. S. ALGER, *J. Appl. Phys.*, **21,** 30 (1950).
35. I. ESTERMANN, W. J. LEIVO, and O. STERN, *Phys. Rev.*, **75,** 627 (1949).
36. W. J. LEIVO, *Phys. Rev.*, **91,** 245 (1953).
37. J. ALEXANDER and E. E. SCHNEIDER, *Nature*, **164,** 653 (1949).
38. E. MOLLWO, quoted in Ref. 26.
39. F. SEITZ, *Revs. Modern Phys.*, **18,** 384 (1946).
40. R. CASLER, P. PRINGSHEIM, and P. YUSTER, *J. Chem. Phys.*, **18,** 1564 (1950).
41. H. DORENDORF, *Z. Physik*, **129,** 317 (1951).
42. J. MOLNAR, quoted in Ref. 39.
43. A. F. JOFFÉ, *The Physics of Crystals*, McGraw-Hill, New York, 1928, p. 128.
44. J. J. MARKHAM, R. T. PLATT, and I. L. MADOR, *Phys. Rev.*, **92,** 597 (1953).
45. J. O. PERRINE, *Phys. Rev.*, **22,** 48 (1923).
46. M. N. DIACHENKO, *Physik. Z. Sowjetunion*, **13,** 55 (1938).
47. O. GLASSER and I. W. BEASLEY, *Phys. Rev.*, **47,** 570 (1935).
48. A. M. POLONSKI, *Doklady Akad. Nauk S.S.S.R.*, **31,** 543 (1941).
49. H. W. LEVERENZ, in *Colloid Chemistry*, Vol. 7, A. E. Alexander, ed., Reinhold, New York, 1950, p. 125.
50. F. URBACH, *Akad. Wiss. Wien, Abt. IIa*, **139,** 353, 363 (1930).
51. F. DANIELS, C. A. BOYD, and D. F. SAUNDERS, *Science*, **117,** 343 (1953).
52. F. DANIELS, *Symposium on Radiation Dosimetry*, Army Chemical Center, Maryland, U.S.A., 1950, p. 148.
53. S. P. KELLER and J. J. CLEMMONS, *J. Chem. Phys.*, **23,** 586 (1955).
54. M. DÉRIBÉRÉ, *Rev. Scient.*, **76,** 383 (1928).
55. F. DANIELS, personal communiçation.
56. J. H. SCHULMAN, C. C. KLICK, and H. RUBIN, *Nucleonics*, **13,** No. 2, 30 (1955).
57. J. A. GHORMLEY and H. A. LEVY, *J. Phys. Chem.*, **56,** 548 (1953).
58. M. FURST and H. KALLMANN, *Phys. Rev.*, **91,** 1356 (1953).
59. R. AUDUBERT, M. BONNEMAY, and M. LAUTOUT, *Compt. rend.*, **230,** 1771 (1950).
60. K. PRZIBRAM, *Akad. Wiss. Wien, Abt. IIa*, **130,** 265 (1921).

61. K. Przibram, *Z. Physik,* **20,** 196 (1923); **41,** 833 (1927); **68,** 403 (1931); **102,** 331 (1936); **130,** 269 (1951).
62. K. Przibram, *Doklady Akad. Nauk S.S.S.R.,* **56,** 359 (1947).
63. K. Przibram, *Geochim. Acta,* **1,** 299 (1951).
64. O. Hahn and H. J. Born, *Naturwiss.,* **23,** 739 (1935).
65. S. J. Thomson and G. Wardle, *Geochim. Acta,* **5,** 169 (1954).
66. L. Weininger, *Akad. Wiss. Wien, Abt. IIa,* **160,** 147 (1951).
67. K. Przibram, *Akad. Wiss. Wien, Abt. IIa,* **136,** 43 (1927).
68. L. Weininger, *Akad. Wiss. Wien, Abt. IIa,* **159,** 381 (1950).
69. L. Landau, *Physik. Z. Sowjetunion,* **3,** 664 (1933).
70. M. G. Schorr and F. L. Torney, *Phys. Rev.,* **80,** 474 (1950).
71. L. Pichat and Y. Keochlin, *J. Chim. Phys.,* **48,** 225 (1951).
72. L. Pichat, P. Pesteil, and J. Clément, *J. Chim. Phys.,* **50,** 26 (1953).
73. H. P. Kallmann and M. Furst, *Nucleonics,* **7,** No. 7, 69 (1951); **8,** No. 3, 32 (1951).
74. H. P. Kallmann and M. Furst, *Phys. Rev.,* **97,** 583 (1955).
75. F. N. Hayes, *Nucleonics,* **11,** No. 3, 27 (1954).
76. R. C. Sangster, *M.I.T. Technical Report No. 55,* 1952.
77. J. B. Birks, *Phys. Rev.,* **84,** 364 (1951); **86,** 569 (1952).
78. G. T. Wright, *Phys. Rev.,* **91,** 1282 (1953).
79. R. Hofstadter, *Nucleonics,* **4,** No. 4, 2 (1949); No. 5, 29.
80. C. M. Nelson, R. L. Sproull, and R. S. Caswell, *Phys. Rev.,* **90,** 364 (1953).
81. E. Pearlstein, *Phys. Rev.,* **92,** 881 (1953); **94,** 1409 (1954).
82. D. E. Mapother, *Phys. Rev.,* **89,** 1231 (1953).
83. F. C. Armistead, J. C. Pennock, and L. W. Mead, *Phys. Rev.,* **76,** 860 (1949).
84. F. T. Farmer, *Nature,* **150,** 521 (1942).
85. J. F. Fowler and F. T. Farmer, *Nature,* **171,** 1020 (1953); **174,** 800 (1954).
86. S. Mayburg and W. L. Lawrence, *J. Appl. Phys.,* **23,** 1006 (1952).
87. E. Kinderman and W. N. Carson, *U.S.A.E.C. report HW-16079,* 1950.
88. W. N. Carson and C. E. Michelson, *U.S.A.E.C. report HW-26763,* 1953.
89. S. C. Curran and W. R. Baker, *Rev. Sci. Instr.,* **19,** 116 (1948).
90. M. Blau and B. Drefus, *Rev. Sci. Instr.,* **16,** 245 (1945).
91. J. Sharpe and G. H. Stafford, *Proc. Phys. Soc. (London),* **A64,** 211 (1951).
92. P. S. Baranov and V. Goldanskii, *J. Phys. Russe.,* **28,** 621 (1955).
93. L. F. Wouters, quoted in W. H. Jordan and P. R. Bell, *Nucleonics,* **5,** No. 4, 30 (1949).
94. J. B. Birks and F. A. Black, *Proc. Phys. Soc. (London),* **A64,** 511 (1951).
95. A. W. Smith and J. Turkevich, *J. Chem. Phys.,* **21,** 367 (1953).
96. D. R. Westervelt, *Bull. Am. Phys. Soc.,* **27,** No. 2, 10 (1952).
97. L. Mezzetti and J. W. Keuffel, *Phys. Rev.,* **95,** 858 (1954).
98. P. R. Barker, *et al., Phil. Mag.,* **46,** 300, 307 (1955).
99. A. Lacassagne and J. Lattès, *Compt. rend.,* **178,** 488 (1924).
100. C. Chamié, *J. Phys. (U.S.S.R.),* **10,** 44 (1929).
101. G. Tammann, *Z. Elektrochem.,* **38,** 530 (1932).
102. L. Myssovsky and P. Tschishov, *Z. Physik,* **44,** 408 (1927).
103. A. Jdanov, *J. phys. radium,* **6,** 233 (1935).

104. C. F. POWELL, G. P. S. OCCHIALINI, D. L. LIVESEY, and L. V. CHILTON, *J. Sci. Instr.*, **23,** 102 (1946).

105. C. F. POWELL, *Reports on Progress in Physics,* **13,** 350 (1950).

106. R. W. BERRIMAN, *Nature,* **161,** 432 (1948); **162,** 992 (1948).

107. R. H. HERZ, *Phys. Rev.*, **75,** 478 (1949).

108. B. ZAJAC and M. A. S. ROSS, *Nature,* **164,** 311 (1949).

109. H. MESSEL and D. M. RITSON, *Phil. Mag.*, **41,** 1129 (1950).

110. M. SCHONBERG, *Nuovo cimento,* **8,** 159 (1951); see also Y. GOLDSCHMIDT-CLERMONT, *Ann. Rev. Nuclear Sci.*, **3,** 141 (1953).

111. P. CÜER, *Compt. rend.*, **223,** 1121 (1946).

112. C. M. G. LATTES, P. H. FOWLER, and P. CUER, *Proc. Phys. Soc.* (*London*), **59,** 883 (1947).

113. J. ROTBLAT, *Nature,* **165,** 387 (1950); **167,** 550 (1951).

114. L. VIGNERON, *J. phys. radium,* **14,** 145 (1953).

115. M. BOGAARDT and L. VIGNERON, *J. phys. radium,* **11,** 652 (1950).

116. A. ERTAUD and P. ZALESKI, *J. phys. radium,* **14,** 191 (1953).

117. H. KALLMANN, *Research,* **6,** 234 (1953).

118. R. W. GURNEY and N. F. MOTT, *Proc. Roy. Soc.* (*London*), **A164,** 151 (1938).

119. J. M. HEDGES and J. W. MITCHELL, *Phil. Mag.*, **44,** 357 (1953).

120. J. W. MITCHELL, in *Fundamental Mechanisms of Photographic Sensitivity,* Butterworth, London, 1951, p. 242 (and other papers in this volume).

121. C. C. DILWORTH, G. P. S. OCCHIALINI, and R. M. PAYNE, *Nature,* **162,** 102 (1948).

122. C. C. DILWORTH, G. P. S. OCCHIALINI, and L. VERMAESEN, in Ref. 120, p. 297.

123. M. BLAU and H. WAMBACHER, *Akad. Wiss. Wien, Abt. IIa,* **143,** 285 (1934); **145,** 609 (1936).

124. H. YAGODA, *Radioactive Measurements with Nuclear Emulsions,* Wiley and Sons, New York, 1949.

125. P. DEMERS, *Can. J. Research,* **25,** 223 (1947).

126. H. WAMBACHER, *Akad. Wiss. Wien, Abt. IIa,* **140,** 271 (1931).

127. N. A. PERFILOV, *Doklady Akad. Nauk S.S.S.R.*, **42,** 258 (1944); **43,** 14 (1944).

128. E. BRODA, *Nature,* **158,** 872 (1946).

129. L. L. GREEN and D. L. LIVESEY, *Phil. Trans. Roy. Soc. London,* **A241,** 323 (1948).

130. E. BRODA and K. JENKNER, *Experientia,* **7,** 121 (1951).

131. E. PICCIOTTO, *Compt. rend.*, **228,** 173, 247 (1949).

132. M. MORTIER and L. VERMAESEN, *Bull. Centre Phys. Nucl. Bruxelles,* No. 5 (1948).

133. G. W. W. STEVENS, *Nature,* **162,** 526 (1948).

134. M. GAILLOUD and C. HAENNY, *Mem. Soc. Vaudoise Sci. Nat.*, **10,** 271 (1952).

135. M. BLAU, *Akad. Wiss. Wien, Abt. IIa,* **140,** 623 (1931).

136. J. LAUDA, *Akad. Wiss. Wien, Abt. IIa,* **145,** 707 (1936).

137. G. ALBOUY and H. FARAGGI, *J. phys. radium,* **10,** 105 (1949).

138. P. DEMERS, J. LAPALME, and J. THOUVENIN, *Can. J. Phys.*, **31,** 295 (1953).

CHAPTER 17

THE CHEMICAL EFFECTS OF NUCLEAR TRANSFORMATIONS

17–1 The Szilard-Chalmers effect. Apart from the chemical effects discussed in the last few chapters, some nuclear transformations which involve the emission of radiation must necessarily be accompanied by significant molecular change. Consider, for example, the bombardment of the relatively simple molecules CH_3Cl with slow neutrons. Each of the three atomic species concerned (C, H, and Cl) consists of two stable isotopes with different neutron capture cross sections, but for the sake of simplicity the discussion will be limited to the transmutations involving the isotope Cl^{35}, for which three possible nuclear reactions may occur:

$$Cl^{35} + n \rightarrow \begin{cases} Cl^{36} + \gamma, \\ S^{35} + p, \\ P^{32} + \alpha. \end{cases}$$

An important problem is the chemical state of each of the three new atoms Cl^{36}, S^{35}, and P^{32}; for example, will the Cl^{36} remain in the molecule by substituting itself for the parent Cl^{35} atom, or will it be thrown out of the molecule in the nuclear change as a free atom? Similarly, since sulfur and phosphorus have different valences from chlorine, what valency will the S^{35} and P^{32} atoms have? Similar questions arise for spontaneous disintegration processes, since, for example, the α-particle disintegration of the chemically neutral radon atom, with 86 extra nuclear electrons, gives an atom of radium-A, which has only 84 electrons and which normally exists in solution in the tetravalent state.

The study of these chemical changes accompanying nuclear interaction is an important part of nuclear chemistry, often called "hot-atom chemistry," which in its widest sense includes chemical reactions involving ions, atoms, or free radicals with high kinetic energies. In addition to their theoretical interest, such researches have considerable practical application, since when a nuclear reaction results in the formation of an isotopic nuclide, as in (n, γ), (γ, n), (d, p) reactions, this isotope can be separated from the parent by a simple and elegant method. In other cases, the chemical effects associated with nuclear transformations can be used to prepare "labeled" materials (i.e., mixtures of active and inactive isotopic molecules in the same physical and chemical state).

Let us consider the neutron irradiation of a chemical compound $BC_mD_n \ldots$, and assume that B is the only atom to undergo any detectable nuclear change:

$$_ZB^{A-1} + {}_1n^0 \rightarrow {}_ZB'^A + \gamma.$$

As the result of the emission of the photon, the atom B' undergoes Compton recoil (Section 11–7) and acquires a momentum p, given by

$$p = Av = \frac{E_\gamma}{c} = \frac{h\nu}{c}, \tag{17–1}$$

where A is the mass of B′, v is its velocity after the recoil, E_γ is the energy of the photon of frequency ν, and c is the velocity of light. The recoil energy E_r of B′ is then

$$E_r = \frac{Av^2}{2} = \frac{(Ap)^2}{2A} = \frac{E_\gamma^2}{2Ac^2}. \tag{17–2}$$

On introducing the actual value of c and the mass number A of the recoiling atom, and putting E_γ in Mev, we find

$$E_r = \frac{536E_\gamma^2}{A}\, ev = \frac{12{,}360\, E_\gamma^2}{A}\, \text{kcal/mole}. \tag{17–3}$$

Thus, for a 5-Mev photon and $A = 80$ (i.e., a bromine atom), the recoil energy $E_r = 167.5$ ev $= 3860$ kcal/mole, an energy which is more than ten times that necessary to break any chemical bond. Even for a photon of only 2 Mev energy and $A = 200$, the recoil energy is still about 250 kcal/mole. Since the binding energy of a neutron is the order of 6 to 8 Mev, a polyatomic molecule will normally be expected to dissociate when one of its constituents becomes radioactive by neutron capture.

The *Szilard-Chalmers effect* (or Szilard effect) is based on such arguments. These authors [1] irradiated ethyl iodide with neutrons and subsequently treated the compound with water containing a small quantity of ordinary iodine, which was then reduced with sodium bisulfite. A significant fraction of the radioiodine (half-life 25 min) formed in the I^{127} (n, γ) I^{128} process was found in the aqueous phase as inorganic iodide, which could be separated from the organic liquid. The addition of iodine simplifies the "carrying" of very small quantities of radioactive iodine as, for example, precipitated silver iodide. Instead of adding sulfite, the radioiodine can be extracted equally well with aqueous solutions of $Na_2S_2O_3$, NaOH, HCl, KI, or on powdered AgI, Al_2O_3, active charcoal, or deposited on a sheet or metallic powder of silver, copper, zinc, or aluminum [2, 3, 4]. The same methods can be applied with equal success to the separation of other radioactive halogens formed by neutron capture from other organic or organometallic target materials (see below).

In the study of the Szilard-Chalmers effect, two important parameters must be considered: the *enrichment factor* and the *retention*, a concept first introduced by Libby [5]. The enrichment factor is defined as the ratio of the specific activity of the final product to the specific activity of the irradiated material. The retention expresses, as a percentage, the fraction of the activity retained by the irradiated species and which is not extracted by the physical or chemical methods used; we shall see that this is not necessarily the same as the fraction of molecules which have undergone transformation. These two parameters are related to each other, but are quite distinct. Thus even when the retention is very small, the enrichment factor may be poor if the method of separation requires the use of a considerable quantity of carrier material. Conversely, the enrichment may be excellent if carrier-free separation is possible by some method such as extraction into a volatile solvent, electrolytic deposition, or chromatography with a volatile eluant, even though a significant fraction of the activity may remain with the target compound.

Very long or very intense irradiations bring about a decrease in the enrichment factor. If, for example, macroscopic quantities of ethyl iodide are irradiated for a long period in a reactor, the ionizing radiation may cause radiolysis to give inactive iodine, which mixes with the radioactive iodine from the Szilard-Chalmers process and so lowers the enrichment. Decreases of this sort have been observed in long pile irradiation (followed by dissolution and carrying with some appropriate reagent) in the Szilard-Chalmers reaction with radioactive antimony, using crystals of NH_4SbF_6 or $Sb(C_6H_5)_3$ [6], radioactive iron from $K_4[Fe(CN)_6]$ [7], radioactive chromium from K_2CrO_4 [8], and radioactive bromine from $KBrO_3$ [9, 10]. In all these, and other similar systems, then, there is an optimum length and intensity of irradiation. Adamson and Williams [11] have established quantitative expressions giving the specific activity and the enrichment factor as a function of the neutron flux, irradiation time, capture cross section, and the rate constants of the radiochemical reactions.

Another important condition in obtaining a good enrichment is the absence of any significant isotopic exchange between the irradiated compound and the compound in which the active species is to be concentrated. For example, if manganese dioxide is irradiated with neutrons, the radioactive Mn^{56} atoms may initially be formed as Mn^{2+} by recoil action, and Mn^{2+} can be separated chemically, in principle, but since Mn^{2+} exchanges with the dioxide, most of the activity will finally remain on the dioxide after the separation process. If, however, potassium permanganate is irradiated, the radioactive manganese is found as MnO_2, which can be simply separated from the bulk permanganate by filtration [12].

Since isotopic exchange in aqueous solution between heteropolar compounds is generally quite fast (Section 19–3), separation by the Szilard-Chalmers process is not always possible with electropositive metals. It is most easily applied to elements with a high electronegativity (such as the metalloids), the noble metals, or polyvalent elements in a high oxidation state, in which its compounds have a very small or zero probability of isotopic exchange.

17–2 Experimental separations. The factors discussed above frequently dictate the type of compound which must be irradiated to get good separations, namely *organic molecules*, *stable complex ions*, or *oxygenated anions*. Thus several organic halogen compounds give good yields for the Szilard-Chalmers effects, including CH_3Cl, CCl_4, $C_2H_4Cl_2$, C_6H_5Cl, CH_3Br, C_2H_5Br, C_4H_9Br, CH_2Br_2, $CHBr_3$, CH_3I, CH_2I_2, C_4H_9I, and C_6H_5I. In all these cases, the radioactive halogen atoms go into the aqueous phase, but the retention often depends on the experimental conditions. Chlorates, perchlorates, bromates, iodates, and periodates [2, 3, 13, 14, 15, 16] are reduced to chloride, bromide, and iodide.

Selenites, selenates, and tellurates are reduced to the element or to the tetravalent state [16]. The tellurites show no Szilard effect, probably because of the fast isotopic exchange with tellurium (Section 20–2). Chromates are reduced to Cr^{3+} [8]. Irradiation of triphenyl phosphate, $(C_6H_5O)_3PO$, in benzene, followed by extraction with water, gives very high enrichment factors [17]. The alkali phosphates are transformed to phosphites, with a retention of ~50% [5]. The same is true for the arsenates [16, 18], but the yield appears to be better with cacodylic acid, $(CH_3)_2AsOOH$, which probably gives arsenious acid [12, 19, 20]. Gaseous arsine (AsH_3) is decomposed by recoil; the charged atoms of radioarsenic can be collected on metal electrodes at a potential of 1000 v [21, 22].

The antimonates apparently do not give any Szilard effect, but the compounds NH_4SbF_6 and $Sb(C_6H_5)_3$ mentioned earlier can be used, as can the pentafluoride [6]; 60% of the activity produced by neutron bombardment of SbF_5, which is a volatile liquid, is fixed in a solid residue, which is very probably SbF_3.

The yield from the bombardment of sodium meta-vanadate ($NaVO_3$) is virtually zero. Very small yields have been obtained with the vanadium compounds examined; for example, 7% with the cupferron complex, and 3.5% with the oxinate [23].

Other organo-metallic compounds successfully used include $As(C_6H_5)_3$ [24], $Bi(C_6H_5)_3$, $Pb(C_6H_5)_4$ [25], and $Sn(C_6H_5)_4$ [26]; an enrichment factor of 2800 was obtained with this last compound.

Several separations have been achieved with complexes of the transition group elements, including the following.

Iron. $K_4[Fe(CN)_6]$ [6] and $H_4[Fe(CN)_6]$ [27]; the activity was carried down on $Al(OH)_3$, or extracted into ether.

Cobalt. $[Co(NH_3)_6](NO_3)_3$, $[Co(NH_2CH_2CH_2NH_2)_3](NO_3)_3$, and $[Co(NH_2CH_2CH_2NHCH_2CH_2NH_2)_2](NO_3)_3$ [28, 29]; when these complexes are irradiated in aqueous solution, extraction of radiocobalt as the hydroxide gives a virtually 100% yield. If the crystals are irradiated for 24 hours and are then dissolved in water, the yield is about 80% for the first two complexes, and 95% for the third. The cobalticyanide complexes $Na_3[Co(CN)_6]$ and $Cu[Co^{II}Co^{III}(CN)_6]_2$ [30, 31, 32] also give very good results; when the latter compound is irradiated in the solid state the enrichment factor is better than 10^6. The Co^{60} atoms are ejected from the complex ion into the crystal lattice, so that they can be separated by electrolysis after extraction with some appropriate ionic solution; the yield is of the order of 50 to 65%. Similar yields have been obtained with the extraction of radioactive iron from neutron-bombarded $Cu[CuFe(CN)_6]_2$. This same procedure has been applied, with comparable results, to basic double salts such as $4Co(OH)_2 \cdot M(OH)Cl$, where M = Co, Zn, or Mn; $4Zn(OH)_2 \cdot Ni(OH)Br$; or $4MnO_2 \cdot M(OH)_2 \cdot xH_2O$, where M = Mn, Zn, or Cu, which give very good enrichments, with yields in the range 10 to 45%.

Nickel. The diethyldithiocarbamate, $Ni[CS_2N(C_2H_5)_2]_2$ has been used [33].

Iridium, rhodium, platinum, osmium, and palladium. Steigman [29] has obtained appreciable enrichments by irradiating the ethylenediamine complexes of the first three elements. The ethylenediamino-, ammino-, diam-mino-, and chlorammino-complexes of platinum $[Pten_3]Cl_4$, $[Pten_2]Cl_2$, $[Pt(NH_3)_4]Cl_4$, $[Pt(NH_3)_4]Cl_2$, trans-$[PtenCl_2]Cl_2$, etc., give yields between 93 and 100% [34]. The last-mentioned complex is particularly suitable for the preparation of very high specific-activity radioactive platinum. Herr [35, 36, 37] achieved separations with enrichment factors of more than 1000 with phthalocyanine or sodium phthalocyanine-disulfonate complexes of platinum, iridium, osmium, and palladium. Phthalocyanines can also be used for the separation of active isotopes of *copper*, *molybdenum*, *tungsten*, *vanadium*, *indium*, and *gallium*, and even for metals as electropositive as *zinc* and the *rare earths*. The yields are of the order of 90% for the light and medium elements, but only 12% for platinum and iridium. The latter element can also be bombarded as $Na_3[IrCl_6]$ [38].

Gold and copper. It appears to be difficult to use the Szilard-Chalmers reaction with organic gold complexes because of their strong tendency to decompose to the metal. Herr [39] has, however, succeeded by irradiating the complex $[(C_6H_5{\cdot}CO{\cdot}C\text{–}OH{:}C{\cdot}C_6H_5)_3Si]AuCl_4$. Small enrichments can also be obtained by irradiating sodium gold hyposulfite, followed by extraction of the activity with mercury, or by irradiating auric chloride and concentrating the activity on traces of colloidal gold [40]. For copper, the ethylacetylacetonate complex [41], or the condensation product of a copper salt with salicylaldehyde-*o*-phenylenediamine [42] have been used.

Uranium. Condensation of the latter reagent with uranyl acetate gives a product which has been used to separate U^{239} and U^{237} [42, 43, 44]. The isotope U^{239} has also been obtained by irradiating the benzoylacetonate [45], uranyl dibenzoylmethane [46], or the double acetate $UO_2Na(CH_3CO_2)_3$ [47]. Manganese benzoylacetonate and acetylacetonate do not show the Szilard-Chalmers effect because of the fast isotope exchange with Mn^{2+} ions [48].

Rhenium. In all the cases quoted so far, when the Szilard effect involves a valency change, the final oxidation state is lower than the initial state, as in

$$Au(III) \rightarrow Au, \qquad As(III) \rightarrow As, \qquad Se(VI) \rightarrow Se,$$
$$Cl(VII) \rightarrow Cl^-, \qquad Mn(VII) \rightarrow Mn(IV).$$

An important exception to this rule is provided by the compounds of rhenium. The perrhenates give no Szilard-Chalmers reaction, but the tri- and tetravalent salts, $ReCl_3$ and K_2ReCl_6, give radioactive rhenium (VII), with a yield very close to 100% in the irradiation of solutions, and about 30% for irradiations in the solid state [49]. This behavior is the opposite of that found with compounds of manganese (the homologue of rhenium), showing that the electrochemical potential of the irradiated compound/product couple is an important factor in the Szilard-Chalmers effect, as it is in radiation chemistry. However, in contrast to the predominance of oxidation processes in radiolysis, the Szilard-Chalmers effect apparently most frequently results in reduction.

In order to understand this difference, it is necessary to realize firstly that the necessity of avoiding isotopic exchange means that the compounds used for Szilard-Chalmers reactions are often those with a high redox potential, so that they are also reduced by ionizing radiations (e.g., permanganates, chromates, periodates, etc.). It should also be realized that recoil effects in inorganic compounds are analogous not to the indirect action of free radicals produced by solvent radiolysis but rather to the direct effects of radiation on concentrated solutions which can also result in reduction, such as $AsO_2^- \rightarrow As$, or $ClO_4^- \rightarrow ClO_3^-$ (Section 13–2). We shall see below that atoms or ions produced by recoil can also cause solvent decomposition. It is therefore possible that in some cases the secondary reactions resulting from recoil are similar to those produced by ionizing radiations.

It is worth noting in this connection that Muller and Broda [50] found on irradiating solutions of arsenious acid or sodium arsenite that about 85% of the radioarsenic produced was in the trivalent state, and 15% as arsenate. The same distribution was found on irradiating solutions of Na_2HAsO_4, to which 1% As_2O_3 was added to "protect" the very small traces of radioarsenic against radiolytic oxidation. This distribution of valency states is exactly the same as that obtained by the x-irradiation of either arsenates or arsenites at pH 10.5 [51]. Platinum(II) compounds also appear to be at least partially oxidized to radioactive Pt(IV) by slow neutron bombardment [34]. Lastly, by choosing the appropriate conditions for irradiation [52, 53], it is possible to bring about slight oxidation of radioactive chromium from the III- to the VI-state (up to 10 to 20%), even though the Szilard-Chalmers effect usually causes the reverse change. These examples and the behavior of the compounds of rhenium emphasize the importance of the careful study of recoil effect in inorganic compounds of elements in their lower valency states.

17–3 Nuclear reasons for retention. Yields from the Szilard-Chalmers reaction rarely reach 100%, especially in the condensed phase, and for a given capture process, the yield often varies with the compound irradiated, and with the physico-chemical state during irradiation; for a solid, the medium in which it is subsequently dissolved may also affect the yield. The reasons for retention are numerous, and frequently far from clear. If the retention is independent of the physico-chemical conditions over fairly wide limits, it seems reasonable to seek its origin in the recoil process itself.

It was tacitly assumed in deriving Eq. (17–3) that the recoil energy exceeds the bond energy sufficiently that there is no need to consider the recoil energy of the molecule as a whole, since the molecule is broken up. However, if the energy available is of the same order of magnitude as that required for bond rupture, some of it can be dissipated as translational energy (E_t) of the whole molecule, and bond rupture can be prevented. For example, in a diatomic molecule of mass $(A + A')$, E_t is given by [54, 55]

$$E_t = \frac{536E_\gamma^2}{A + A'}, \qquad (17\text{–}4)$$

[cf. Eqs. (17–2) and (17–3)], so that the remaining recoil energy E_r' of the liberated atom is

$$E'_r = E_r - E_t = 536E_\gamma^2\left(\frac{1}{A} - \frac{1}{A + A'}\right) = E_r\left(\frac{A'}{A + A'}\right), \quad (17\text{–}5)$$

where, as before, E_r is the total available recoil energy. If A' is very small (for example, a hydrogen atom in a compound such as HBr), E_r is then multiplied by $1/(A + 1)$, a factor which considerably reduces the energy available for bond rupture. For HBr^{80}, E'_r is 2.4 ev, while the energy of the HBr bond is 3.7 ev, so that a high retention would be predicted.

Suess [55] has attempted to verify this conclusion by irradiating gaseous HBr in the presence of acetylene, which is a bromine atom acceptor, so that the retention can be measured. Although completely unambiguous conclusions were not possible, a kinetic study of the reaction appeared to indicate zero retention. These experiments were repeated by Hamill and Williams [47], using ethylene instead of acetylene, and using a more intense neutron source. By comparing results obtained with HBr and with C_2H_5Br, these authors concluded that only about 10% of the molecules did not undergo dissociation.

A further assumption in Eq. (17–3) is that the γ-photon is emitted as a single quantum of energy E_γ. It is now known, however, that the excitation energy of (n, γ) capture processes for nuclei with Z between 11 and 72 is generally emitted as 2 to 6 photons in cascade. If the time interval between two successive emissions is shorter than the time required for the atom to separate itself from the molecule ($\sim 10^{-14}$ sec), the recoil energy will be the resultant of the vectorial addition of the two impulses, and dependent upon the angular distribution of the consecutive photons. For two photons with energies E_1 and E_2 emitted at an angle θ, the momentum is

$$p = \frac{1}{c}\sqrt{E_1 + E_2 + 2E_1E_2\cos\theta}. \quad (17\text{–}6)$$

For $E_1 = E_2$, and $\theta = 180°$, p, and hence the recoil energy, are both zero. It can be shown [48, 49] that for an isotropic distribution, the recoil energy lies between the two limiting values

$$536(E_1 + E_2)^2/A \qquad \text{and} \qquad 536(E_1 - E_2)^2/A \text{ ev}.$$

If E_1 and E_2 have similar values, the energy is too small to break some chemical bonds, and a fraction of the initial molecules which become radioactive will be chemically unchanged.

Various authors have used this mutual compensation of recoil effects to explain low retentions which are unaffected by changes in the physicochemical conditions. It does not, however, seem that this is a very important factor in the Szilard-Chalmers effect. Cobble and Boyd [10] have calculated that the proportion of the atoms which acquire a recoil energy lower than 10 ev from the Br^{81} (n, γ) Br^{82} reaction are 1.5%, 3%, and 5% for the emission of 3, 4, and 6 photons, respectively, in cascade.

It does not follow, however, that increasing photon energy necessarily results in a smaller retention. If the kinetic energy of the recoiling atom is sufficiently high, the atom may leave the initial molecule only to break a bond in an identical neighboring molecule, and so replace a nonradioactive isotopic atom. This sort of process raises the retention by *repenetration:*

$$RX^* \to R + X^*, \quad RX + X^* \to RX^* + X. \tag{17-7}$$

We shall see later, in discussing isomeric transitions, that the emission of electrons due to internal conversion of low energy γ-rays (Section 4–7) leads to a build-up of charge at the surface of the atom, and hence to the dissociation of the parent molecule. The probability of internal conversion increases with decreasing γ-ray energy. Wexler and Davies [59] irradiated C_2H_5Br and C_2H_5I at a pressure of 3 μ with a flux of 10^{12} n/cm$^2\cdot$sec in vessels which contained collecting electrodes, and were able to show that a significant proportion of the radioactive atoms formed are positively charged—12% for Br^{80} ($t_{1/2}$, 4.4 hours) and 50% for I^{128}. An analogous result has been reported for neutron-bombarded indium and gold surfaces [60].

Finally, as we see again below, the retention can be increased by raising the temperature of the crystal after irradiation. Libby [58, 61] has suggested that the passage of a recoiling atom in a solid causes a local rise in temperature, which increases the retention, so that retention would be favored by increasing the recoil energy.

17–4 Retention in organic compounds. For any given compound, retention in the condensed state is generally greater than that in the gaseous phase; it also decreases with decreasing gas pressure, or for solutions with increasing dilution. In the experiments mentioned above by Wexler and Davies using ethyl bromide at very low pressures, the retention was less than 1%. Libby found a retention of 4.5% with the same gas at a partial pressure of 30 mm [58]. Irradiation of n-C_4H_9Cl vapor at low pressure resulted in less than 2% of the Cl^{38} remaining in the original target molecules, and a similar result has been reported for $CBrF_3$ [62, 63, 64]. In contrast to this, the retention (R) is 75% for liquid C_2H_5Br and 100% for CBr_4 [58], but if the latter compound is dissolved in alcohol (concentration 1.15 mole percent), R falls to 28%, and is virtually zero at concentrations below 0.4%. This is also the case for a 4% solution of CBr_4 in CS_2. This *dilution effect* (which should not be confused with the identically named effect in radiation chemistry; see Section 13–5), has also been observed with C_2Cl_6 [65]; if this compound is irradiated in the solid state, only 8% of the radiochlorine can be extracted by water, but if a benzene solution is irradiated, the extractable fraction is now 50%.

Lu and Sugden [4] have reported that the addition of 1% aniline to bromobenzene before neutron bombardment reduces R from 70 to 37%; with 4 to 6% of aniline, R is 24%. Addition of aniline to n-C_4H_9Br lowers R from 60 to 26%.

An important series of experiments has been reported by Glueckauf and Fay [66, 67]. When CH_3I was bombarded with slow neutrons, 11% of the radioiodine formed appeared as $CH_2I_2^*$, which was identified by fractional distillation with inactive methylene iodide. With $CHBr_3$, 19% of the activity was found as CBr_4, together with a true retention (i.e., as $CHBr_3$) of 47%. Similarly, the total retention of C_6H_5Cl was 50%, but 15% of the chlorine activity was in the form of $C_6H_4Cl_2$. It has been shown [68] that the addition of very small quantities of free iodine (<0.007%) to CH_3I before bombardment significantly changes the distribution of radioiodine between the different chemical forms (CH_3I, CH_2I_2, I_2), and that in general this distribution is extremely sensitive to the presence of impurities, even at virtually undetectable levels. The considerable influence of the purity of the organic reagents on the retention has also been demonstrated in a number of other cases [64].

These experiments show firstly that the retention by organic compounds does not exactly express the fraction of molecules which have escaped Szilard-Chalmers rupture, since the nonaqueous phase may contain radioactive molecules which are chemically different from the initial molecule. They also show that labeled molecules can be conveniently synthesized by means of the Szilard-Chalmers effect. This *radiosynthesis* can also be achieved by the addition, to the irradiated compound, of a scavenger, a substance which is able to react with the fragments arising from the recoil. Glueckauf and Fay were able to obtain bromobenzene labeled with radioactive bromine by bombarding mixtures of CH_3Br and C_6H_6. Reid [69] has prepared $C_5H_{11}I^*$ by bombarding iodine dissolved in pentane; 38% of the activity was in the amyl iodide fraction. Similar results were obtained with bromine dissolved in pentane [70], with iodine dissolved in hexane, heptane, octane, or mixed with methane in the vapor state [71, 72], and with Cl_2 or CCl_4 in cyclohexane or benzene [73]. The bombardment of bromo-olefins in C_2H_5Br or C_6H_5Br solution results in isomerization; 2-bromopropene is partially transformed into 1-bromopropene and allyl bromide, and vice versa [74].

This technique, based on catching the free radicals (*scavenging*), has been widely used in research on the mechanism of the Szilard-Chalmers effect. In effect, the scavengers react with molecular fragments only after these have lost their excess kinetic energy (i.e., when they have been *thermalized*), so that scavenging can be used as a criterion to distinguish between "hot reactions" and thermal reactions. A further point is that reactions of the first class are independent of the temperature at which the experiment is carried out.

An important aspect of organic radiosynthesis by the Szilard-Chalmers reaction is the production of active "polymers" with high molecular weights and high boiling points. In the neutron bombardment of Br_2 in CCl_4, Willard and his collaborators [62] found 55% of the "organic yield" was as CCl_3Br, 20% as CCl_2Br_2, and 25% as a mixture of heavy compounds, including CBr_4. The presence of this latter compound, produced by the rupture of four C—Cl bonds in the initial molecule, is a significant indication of the high-energy activations and bond ruptures which can be brought about by recoiling atoms.

Libby [61, 70] has obtained interesting results by bombarding *n*- and *iso*propyl bromides in either the liquid or solid state at various temperatures. Irrespective of the target isomer, the yield of active *n*-C_3H_7Br was always 2.5 to 3 times greater than that of *iso*-C_3H_7Br. For a given physical state, the temperature has little effect on the yields of the various active products, but the change from liquid to solid phase, which has no significant effect on the retention by the initial compound, causes a considerable increase in the yields of a number of the synthetic products, especially of the polymer fraction.

The addition of Br_2 decreases the retention, especially for the monobromides. This effect has also been observed with C_2H_5Br, CCl_3Br, and C_2H_5I; the addition of 0.5% Br_2 to the bromides, or of I_2 to the iodide, decreases the "organic yields" to 15 to 20% [77, 78]. Chlorine decreases this yield to 30 to 35% in the Cl^{37} (n, γ) Cl^{38} reaction in CCl_4, whereas with allyl chloride there is an increase to 53% [79].

17–5 The mechanism of retention. In order to explain the high retention of the halogens by organic compounds in the condensed state, and the various radiosynthetic phenomena, Libby [58] made use of the "cage" theory, originally proposed by Franck and Rabinowitch. According to Libby, a recoiling halogen atom initially loses its high kinetic energy by elastic collision with other halogen atoms of similar mass, in agreement with the laws of conservation of momentum. In a collision between an atom of mass A_1 and initial energy E_0, and an atom of mass A_2, the energy ΔE given up by the first atom to the second is

$$\frac{\Delta E}{E_0} = \frac{4A_1A_2}{(A_1 + A_2)^2} \cos\theta, \tag{17–8}$$

where θ is the angle between the paths of the atoms after the collision. In a head-on collision ($\theta \approx 0$) with $A_1 = A_2$, the transfer of energy is practically complete, and the radioactive atom, now deprived of its energy, remains imprisoned within the solvent "cage." The energy transfers in collisions with light atoms (hydrogen, carbon) are much smaller, and so do not prevent the "hot atoms" from continuing with their "billiard-ball" collisions, rather as if they were moving through an assemblage of free atoms. At this stage, in fact, the energy losses by the rupture of chemical bonds and other inelastic processes are comparatively unimportant. However, at some point the recoiling atom has "cooled" sufficiently as to be no longer able to escape from the cage, even though it may still possess sufficient kinetic energy to cause molecular dissociations.

In contrast with elastic collisions of "hot atoms," which are independent of temperature, Libby has named "epithermal" those reactions which occur in the later stages of the dissipation of the recoil energy. Before the thermal region then there is a small energy region, around 10 ev, in which a halogen atom can be substituted for an atom of hydrogen, break C—C bonds, or bring about other chemical changes. The temperature will not have a very large effect on these epithermal reactions.

Summarizing then, retention due to reactions of the type

$$C_2H_5Br + Br^* \rightarrow C_2H_5Br^* + Br \tag{17–9}$$

will be restricted to the "hot" stage, while the synthesis of new molecules will be effected by atoms which are incompletely "cooled" in the epithermal stage:

$$C_2H_5Br + Br^* \rightarrow C_2H_4BrBr^* + H. \qquad (17\text{-}10)$$

The lowering of the retention in the gaseous phase, and on dilution with a solvent containing lighter atoms, is explained on this basis by the cage effect, and by the decreasing probability of elastic collisions.

The low sensitivity of the retention to a change from the liquid to the solid phase, which has been demonstrated for the propyl bromides, is attributed to local heating along the track of the "hot" atom in the solid. Since the temperature rise would be greater at the beginning of the track than at the end, the molten region would be pear-shaped in form, with a volume estimated at about 1000 molecules. Retention due to elastic processes would therefore be the same as in the liquid phase, while epithermal reactions between free radicals, whose diffusion would be more restricted in the solid state, would be more important in crystals.

In all these arguments, Libby assumed that free radicals and ions produced by ionizing radiations from the neutron source played no part in the reactions of hot atoms in the epithermal stage. In order to check this hypothesis, Rowland and Libby [80] irradiated n-C_3H_7Br with neutrons from a cyclotron, and from Ra/Be or Po/Be sources; in each case, the measured retention was the same (84%) within the limits of experimental error. The γ-intensity from the cyclotron was 700 r/hr, and that from 30 curies of Po/Be only 0.1 r/hr, so that the γ-flux from normal neutron sources is not sufficient to cause any appreciable change in the behavior of the recoiling atoms in the irradiated media. With very high intensities, however, there will eventually be sufficient radiolytic products formed to affect the retention, as was in fact observed [81] in the irradiation of pure degassed propyl bromide with γ-rays (10^5 to 10^6 r/hr) either during or before neutron bombardment. The abnormally high retention of radiobromine is then probably due to reaction of HBr and Br_2 (produced by the Szilard-Chalmers effect) with unsaturated compounds formed by radiolysis.

There are, however, some results on retention by organic compounds which do not seem to receive a satisfactory explanation in Libby's theory. In particular, a long series of experiments by Willard [62, 63, 64, 74, 77, 78] on the scavenging effect of molecular halogens has shown that some of the reactions which result in retention occur *after* the "hot" atom stage. Furthermore, halogens can remove hot atoms from organic molecules, contrary to the Libby hypothesis. In addition, experiments by Miller and Dodson [73], which are in reasonable agreement with the theory as far as retention in CCl_4-$SiCl_4$ mixtures is concerned, show serious deviations for mixtures of CCl_4^* with C_6H_6 or C_6H_{12}. In the latter case in particular the quantity of Cl^{38} fixed in the diluent as $C_6H_{11}Cl$ is independent of the composition of the mixture (between 1 and 99%). Although the increase in the epithermal reactions in the solid state observed for the propyl bromides has been confirmed in several other cases, it is not general; the yields of organic compounds from C_2H_5I, *iso*-C_4H_9I, and *sec*-C_4H_9I vary only slightly with phase change.

Finally, the model of billiard-ball collisions followed by epithermal reactions neglects the effect of chemical properties and molecular structure on the yield, although there is good evidence for this in some cases. For example the yields of organic compounds from the similar molecules C_2H_5Cl, C_2H_5Br, and C_2H_5I at 0°C are respectively 23, 32, 40%, and at −190°C, 62, 77, and 41%. The yields from the alkyl chlorides vary little with chain length between CH_3Cl and $C_5H_{11}Cl$, being of the order of 20%, but the *t*-butyl and *t*-amyl chlorides give yields close to 35%. On the other hand, for the iodides at ordinary temperatures, the yields are CH_3I 56%, C_2H_5I 40%, *n*-C_3H_7I 41%, *i*-C_3H_7I 27%, *n*-C_4H_9I 40%, *i*-C_4H_9I 43%, and *s*-C_4H_9I 27%. According to experiments by Karamian [82] on the alkyl bromides from CH_3Br to $C_6H_{13}Br$, the radiosynthesis yields are greater for compounds which have an even number of carbon atoms than for those with an odd number.

This collection of data led Willard to suggest that the modes of energy transfer in a condensed phase are not the same as those in collisions between isolated molecules in the gaseous phase. In a liquid or a solid, an atom cannot continue along its path after striking a stationary molecule even if the moving atom is hot, because the struck molecule is surrounded by a rigid assemblage of other molecules which contribute to the energy dissipation by the random breaking of bonds. When the recoiling atom has cooled sufficiently, it recombines with one or other of the radicals or atoms formed around it in a very high local concentration. The probability and type of recombination reactions depend on the chemical properties, density and structure of the medium, and on the activation energies for reaction with stable molecules. If the conditions in the thermal region do not favor reaction, the atom can diffuse through the system until it encounters some species with which thermal reaction is possible. In a pure alkyl bromide or iodide, in which all the reactions between the solvent and the free halogen atom have high activation energies, the atom ends up by combining thermally with the radicals or atoms formed during the dissipation of the kinetic energy.

From these arguments, Willard and other authors [73, 79] have suggested that the reactions which result in the formation of organic compounds can also take place in the "hot" region. Examples of these reaction would be

$$\mathrm{Br} + \mathrm{Br}^* \rightarrow \mathrm{BrBr}^*, \tag{17–11}$$

$$\mathrm{RH} + \mathrm{Br}^* \rightarrow \mathrm{R} + \mathrm{HBr}^*, \tag{17–12}$$

$$\mathrm{RBr} + \mathrm{Br}^* \rightarrow \mathrm{R} + \mathrm{BrBr}^*. \tag{17–13}$$

It seems that this theory provides a better explanation of the complex series of chemical processes which give such a wide variety of synthetic products, some of which could only be formed in reactions requiring a very high activation energy. The formation of amyl iodide by the bombardment of $C_5H_{12} + I_2$, mentioned above, is an example of this latter point.

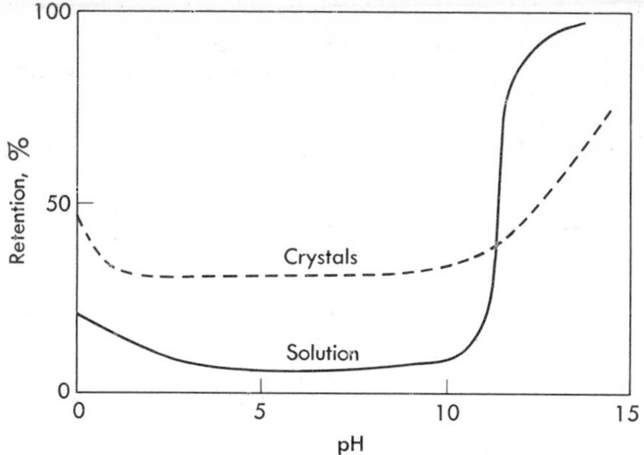

FIG. 17-1. The retention of radiomanganese in $KMnO_4$ as a function of pH (Ref. 5).

17-6 Retention in oxygenated anions. Libby [5] studied the retention (R) of Mn^{56} as a function of pH in the neutron bombardment of potassium permanganate solutions, and found that R was very low in almost neutral solution, reached about 20% in very acid solution, and was nearly 100% in alkaline media (Fig. 17-1). If crystals were bombarded, the measured retention varied in a similar fashion with the pH of the medium in which the crystals were subsequently dissolved. The retention was zero in acetone solution. McCallum and Maddock [83] later showed that the pH dependence of the retention is approximately the same for other permanganates (Li, Na, K, Ag, Ca, Ba). Experiments by Broda [84, 85] showed that in neutral solution the retention increases with the concentration; this author also found that slow neutrons and 1-Mev neutrons gave the same retention, despite the considerable difference in the resultant recoil energies.

In order to explain the pH effect, Libby assumed that the recoil causes the MnO_4^- ion to lose one or more O^{2-} ions to give the MnO_3^+, MnO_2^{3+}, MnO^{5+}, or Mn^{7+} states; the first of these would probably be the most important. These very unstable radical ions may then undergo either oxidative or hydrolytic reaction, depending on the pH. In weakly acid or neutral solution, the ion will be reduced

$$2Mn^*O_3^+ + OH^- \rightarrow 2Mn^*O_2 + \tfrac{3}{2}O_2 + 2H^+, \qquad (17\text{-}14)$$

but in alkaline conditions, on the other hand, retention would occur by the process

$$Mn^*O_3^+ + OH^- \rightarrow Mn^*O_4^- + H^+. \qquad (17\text{-}15)$$

The slight increase in the retention in highly acidic solutions could be due to the exchange reaction

$$Mn^*O_3^+ + MnO_4^- \rightarrow MnO_3^+ + Mn^*O_4^-, \qquad (17\text{-}16)$$

although it is not clear why acid conditions should favor this reaction.

Broda has pointed out that the isotopic exchange can be used to explain the residual retention in neutral solutions. According to Jordan, reduction of the Mn(VI) state takes place via a lower valency state, Mn(II) or Mn(III) [86].

The partial retention observed with phosphates can be attributed to the competition

$$PO_4^{3-} \rightarrow O^{2-} + PO_3^- \xrightarrow{\text{hydrolysis}} PO_4^{3-}, \qquad (17\text{–}17)$$

$$PO_4^{3-} \rightarrow O + PO_3^{3-}, \qquad (17\text{–}18)$$

but very probably other reactions accompany these changes, since hypophosphate and pyrophosphate are always found among the active products [87, 88, 89]. A similar mechanism can be envisaged for the arsenates, but the constant distribution between As(V) and As(III) found by Müller and Broda [50] suggests rather some intermediate common to both arsenate and arsenite, such as an unstable As(IV) compound. For both arsenic and phosphorus pentavalent anions, the retention is independent of pH.

This pH independence is also found with K_2ReCl_6 [49]. Provided that certain analytical complications are avoided, the retention in crystals of K_2CrO_4 is also independent of pH, and of the concentration, ionic strength, and temperature of the dissolving medium [90]. The first two factors have no influence on the retention of radioactive iodine in iodates and periodates [91], but the retention varies with both pH and concentration when chromate is irradiated in solution. It is therefore clear that the mechanism proposed by Libby to explain the retention in permanganates cannot be applied to other oxygenated ions without a strict examination of the properties of the ion itself and of the intermediates which may be formed by recoil action.

Such a study of iodates and periodates has been carried out by Cleary, Hamill, and Williams [91] (see above). The retention of iodates in solution is normally 20%, but this is lowered to 6% by the addition of a reducing agent (I^-, CH_3OH), and increased to a limiting value of 40% by the presence of an oxidizing agent, periodate. Retention of periodate is 6% independent of the composition of the medium; the distribution of the remaining 94% of the radioactive iodine between IO_3^- and I^- depends on the conditions in a way similar to that described above for iodate. From these results, the authors conclude that the invariable 6% residual retention is nuclear in origin, that a fraction of the activity is produced in a reduced form (I^-, IO^-), and that a further fraction is as ions of intermediate valency state which may be oxidized or reduced, depending on the composition of the medium:

Iodate		Periodate	
$I^*O_3^-$	6%	$I^*O_4^-$	6%
$I^*O_2^- + O$	34%, variable	$I^*O_3^-$	28%
$I^*O^- + 2O$	60% (bracketed)	I^*O_2	60%
$I^*O^- + 3O$		I^*O^-	6%

TABLE 17-1

RETENTIONS IN INORGANIC ANIONS

Permanganates	R	Chromates	R	Iodates	R	Re(IV) salts	R
$LiMnO_4$	8.8	Li_2CrO_4 $Li_2Cr_2O_7$	66.0 54.5	$LiIO_3$	66	K_2ReCl_6	30
$NaMnO_4$	9.1	Na_2CrO_4 $Na_2Cr_2O_7$	73.6 79.9	$NaIO_3$	67	Rb_2ReCl_6	30
$KMnO_4$	22.5	K_2CrO_4 $K_2Cr_2O_7$	60.8 89.9	KIO_3	67		
$AgMnO_4$	8.0	$(NH_4)_2CrO_4$ $(NH_4)_2Cr_2O_7$	17.5 31.9	NH_4IO_3	22		
$Ca(MnO_4)_2$	6.0	$Na_2CrO_4 \cdot 4H_2O$	87.8	HIO_3	60		
$LiMnO_4 \cdot 3H_2O$	4.0	$K_2Cr_2O_7 \cdot 2H_2O$	72.7				
$NaMnO_4 \cdot 3H_2O$	6.9	$MgCrO_4$ $ZnCrO_4$	55.3 34.6				
$Ca(MnO_4)_2 \cdot 5H_2O$	6.0	CrO_3	78.0				

When solid iodates are bombarded, the nature of the cation may influence the retention, which is particularly small with ammonium salts. A similar result has been reported for chromates. The retentions in a number of permanganates [83], chromates [90], iodates [91], and two rhenium(IV) salts [49] are shown in Table 17–1. It will be seen that there are often considerable differences between the retentions for different cations, without there being any obvious reason for the small retention of $KMnO_4$, for instance. The low retention in ammonium salts is perhaps explained by the decomposition of the polyatomic cation, followed by diffusion of the hydrogen atoms from their original site, so that reconstitution of the original molecule would then be impossible. Maddock [90, 92] has emphasized the parallelism between the retention in crystals containing oxygenated anions, and the redox potential of the anion relative to a lower valency state; the higher the potential, the smaller the retention. Examples of this rule include $KMnO_4$, $KReO_4$, and the halates. This correlation is explained by the greater tendency of intermediates from a strong oxidizing agent to be reduced to a lower valency state by the solvent. However, this rule will not be valid if other competitive reactions prevail over the reduction. Thus although the potential of the Sb_2O_5/SbO^+ couple is slightly greater than that for AsO_4^{3-}/AsO_2^- (0.58 and 0.56 v respectively), the retention by the antimonate is complete; it may be as low as 15% in the arsenate.

We saw that the composition of the medium affects the retention in liquids; it can also have some influence with solids. For example, in the bombardment of mixed crystals of $KMnO_4$ and $KClO_4$, the retention of radiomanganese increases with the $KClO_4$ concentration from 20% for pure $KMnO_4$ to about 50% at mole fraction 0.5 [84]. Adding K_2SO_4 to K_2CrO_4 increases the retention slightly [90], but the retention decreases considerably in K_2CrO_4/K_2BeF_4 solid solutions. These results apparently imply that re-formation of the initial oxygenated ion is favored by the presence of other oxygenated ions which can provide replacements for oxygen atoms or ions lost in the recoil,

$$Mn^*O_3^+ + ClO_4^- \rightarrow Mn^*O_4^- + ClO_3^+, \qquad (17\text{–}19)$$

or

$$Mn^*O_3^- + ClO_4^- \rightarrow Mn^*O_4^- + ClO_3^-. \qquad (17\text{–}20)$$

When these two reactions are compared with the exchange reaction (17–16), which makes only a slight contribution to the retention, it appears that reaction (17–20) is more probable than (17–19), which results in the formation of the unstable ClO_3^+. Reaction (17–20) implies the formation by recoil of ions such as MnO_3^- with the loss of *atomic* oxygen.

Retention in crystals can also be increased by heating to 100°C or more after neutron bombardment, or by exposure to fairly intense γ-radiation. Such effects have been reported for $KMnO_4$ [93], K_2CrO_4 [90], Co-triethylenediamine [30], $KBrO_3$ [10], $NaIO_3$ and NH_4IO_3 [91], and copper phthalocyanine [49], and are attributed either to the acceleration of isotopic exchanges, such as (17–16), or to some electronic mechanism, such as ionization ($CrO_3^- \rightarrow e + CrO_3$) or the transport of a free electron to a trap ($CrO_3^+ + e \rightarrow CrO_3$); a temperature rise would accelerate the rate of diffusion of the recoiling fragments, and so favor their recombination.

An increase in the retention due to the subsequent γ-irradiation could already have occurred during neutron bombardment if the neutron source emits γ-rays. We saw earlier in fact that long irradiation in a reactor can produce a considerable decrease in the Szilard-Chalmers effect for $KBrO_3$, and for antimony and iron compounds.

17–7 Isomeric transitions. Certain nuclear isomers can be chemically separated by procedures similar to those already described in Section 17–2 for isotopes. Most of the work on such separations, or in studies of the mechanism of the phenomenon, have involved the isomers of Br^{80}, whose disintegration scheme is shown in Fig. 17–2. The method consists in preparing the metastable parent isomer by neutron activation (Br^{80m}, $t_{1/2}$, 4.4 hr), or the mixture of the isomers, in some chemical state suitable for a Szilard-Chalmers reaction (i.e., organic compound, oxy-anion, complex, etc.). After time for a sufficient accumulation of the lower isomer (the ground state) the separation procedure is carried out; separation can be achieved if the nuclear process by which this isomer is formed is accompanied by sufficiently profound chemical effects.

Segrè, Halford, and Seaborg [94], who were the first to achieve separation of the isomers of Br^{80}, synthesized *t*-butyl bromide from active NaBr, and hydrolyzed this with a mixture of water and methyl alcohol to give HBr, which was found to be considerably enriched in the 18-min Br^{80}. De Vault and Libby [95] obtained a better separation with the bromate ion, rupture of which gave the 18-min isomer in a pure form after precipitation as AgBr. Fairbrother [96] later showed that if $SbBr_3$ or other inorganic bromides are left in contact with active C_2H_5Br, the activity of the 18-min isomer is concentrated in the inorganic bromide, while the 4.4-hr isomer and the 36-hr isotope (Br^{82}) remain with C_2H_5Br.

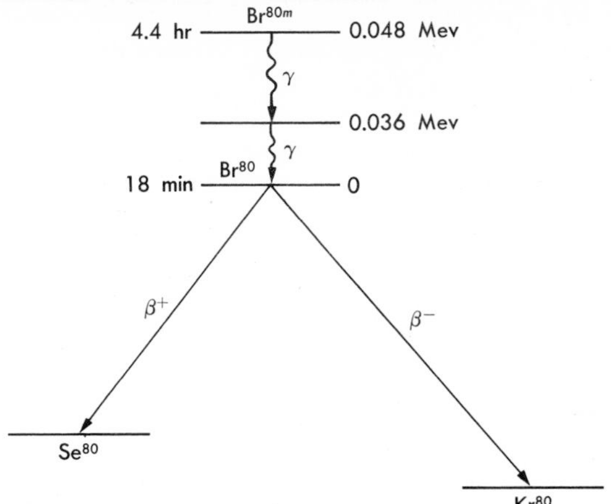

FIG. 17–2. The disintegration scheme of Br^{80}.

Similar chemical separation of the isomers of tellurium and selenium [97, 98] have been achieved, starting with telluric or selenic acids; the lower isomer is found as tellurous or selenous acid, which can be reduced to the corresponding element by SO_2; under the conditions chosen, the higher valency state containing the metastable isomer is not reduced. Isomers of Rh^{104}, as the phthalocyanine complex [99], and of In^{112}, as the hydroxyquinoline complex [100], have also been separated.

In the (n, γ) reaction, the recoil energy is more than sufficient to break the chemical bonds involved, but this is not the case in isomeric transitions. For example, it can be calculated from Eq. (17–2) that for recoil of the 18-min Br^{80}, $E_\gamma = 48.9$ kev, so that the recoil energy is only 370 cal/mole. Similarly for $Te^{129m} \rightarrow Te^{129}$, the transition energy of 100 ev corresponds to a recoil energy of 920 cal/mole. However, the γ-rays emitted in these transitions are strongly converted in the K- or L-shells, and the probability of conversion increases with decreasing transition energy. The energy E_e of the emitted electrons is given by

$$E_e = E_\gamma - E_K \text{ (or } E_L\text{)}, \tag{17–21}$$

where E_K is the energy required to remove an electron from the K-shell. As we shall see below in discussing β-recoil, the recoil energy of a recoiling atom of mass A after electron emission is

$$E_r = \frac{548E_e}{A} + \frac{536E_e^2}{A}. \tag{17–22}$$

Consequently the recoil energy of Br^{80} after K-conversion is 5.9 kcal/mole; in the case of tellurium the recoil energy is 9.2 kcal/mole for Te^{127} and 6.6 kcal/mole for Te^{129}, values which are still insufficient for bond rupture. For instance, in the experiments by Fairbrother mentioned above, the breaking of the C—Br bond in C_2H_5Br requires at least

60 kcal/mole, and energies of the same order are necessary for the synthesis of organic molecules by "hot" atoms from isomeric transitions. For example, when Br^{80m} (as Br_2) was mixed with liquid CCl_4, after a certain time 30% of the 18-min isomer was found to have reacted with the tetrachloride to give substitution compounds of the type CCl_3Br, CCl_2Br_2, etc. [101]. This isomer also reacts with toluene to give a mixture of *o*-, *m*-, and *p*-bromotoluenes and benzyl bromide [102]. Several other radiosynthetic organic reactions involving isomeric transitions of Br^{80} have been reported; these are qualitatively the same as those described earlier for neutron capture, and which as noted above require considerable activation energies.

In addition to the recoil energy, however, the ejection of a conversion electron from the *K*-shell is followed by a rearrangement of the electrons in order to fill the hole created. As a consequence of this, one or more electrons are removed from the valence shell, resulting in the formation of an excited state which is several ev above the ground state. Willard [101], and De Vault and Libby [95], suggested a precise mechanism for these processes by invoking the Auger effect (Section 11–7), which involves the multiple ionization of the atom following the removal of an electron from a low-lying shell. The accumulation of positive charge at the surface of the atom builds up electrostatic repulsions which are sufficiently strong to break any chemical bond. The time for electron emission is always very short compared with the electronic and molecular rearrangements which follow, so that the configuration of atoms in the molecule no longer corresponds to the minimum potential energy of the system, and the molecule therefore dissociates, in agreement with the Franck-Condon principle.

De Vault and Libby estimated that at least 15% of the Br^{80} conversions lead to a total loss of seven valency electrons, more than 60% of them to the loss of four or more electrons, less than 10% to the loss of only two electrons, and less than 2% result in the loss of only one electron. Cooper [103] has calculated that the average positive charge corresponding to each isomeric transition is 4.7. In the first experimental attempts to obtain evidence for this charge, using an applied electric field [104, 105, 106, 107], the isomer of Br^{80} (itself present as an organic bromide) was found on both electrodes, and even preferentially deposited on the anode. This was no doubt due to the extreme instability of Br^+ ion, which reacts rapidly with neighboring molecules to pick up the necessary electrons to go to the stable Br^- state. This chemical reactivity also explains the fact that the 18-min isomer from $C_2H_2Br_2$ or $C_2H_4Br_2$ can be taken up on *anion* exchange resins [108]. Only by working in the gaseous phase at very low pressures does the mean free path of the positive ions become sufficiently long to prevent collisions with molecules or ions which can give up electrons; in these circumstances, the formation of Br^- should be very low.

Such conditions were achieved by Wexler and Davies [109, 110] who worked with very high specific activity C_2H_5Br at a pressure of a few microns in an electric field between two concentric electrodes at a potential of 1000 to 4000 v, but even so, all the atoms of the 18-min isomer were not collected at the cathode. In one series of experiments, the positively charged fraction was 50% of the total, and in another series only 18%;

nearly all the remainder was in the neutral state. The average charge on the isomer was +10.2, rather than the +4.7 predicted by Cooper [103]. This difference can be explained by the fact that the isomeric transition occurs in two stages (Fig. 17–2), so that the isomer acquires an average charge of +5 in each transition. Wexler [111] has also measured the average charge in the isomeric transition of Kr^{83} and finds a value of +7.7. The average charge for the Xe^{137} isomer is +8.5 [112].

Adamson and Grunland [113] suggested that if the isomer Br^{80m} ($t_{1/2}$, 4.4 hr) is part of some complex ion, the retention of the 18-min daughter should depend on the sign of the ion. If this is positive, the electrostatic repulsion will be stronger, favoring dissociation, so that the retention should be less than for a negative ion. They found in fact that R is zero for $[Co(NH_3)_5Br]^{2+}$ in solution and $R = 14\%$ for crystalline $[Co(NH_3)_5Br](NO_3)_2$, while $R = 53\%$ for $[PtBr_6]^{2-}$ in solution and 100% for $(NH_4)_2[PtBr_6]$ in the solid state. The complexes examined are, however, too different to be able to draw the definite conclusion that the charge is the only cause of the difference in the measured retentions.

The importance of internal conversion in the chemical effects associated with isomeric transitions is proved [114] by the fact that the isomers of Te^{127} as $Te(C_2H_5)_2$ can be separated, while those of Zn^{69} [also as $Zn(C_2H_5)_2$] cannot. The difference in the energy between the isomeric levels of Zn^{69} is 440 kev, and that for the Te isomers is of the order of 90 kev, but in the latter case the γ-rays are strongly converted, whereas for Zn^{69} there is no conversion.

Imre [115] has pointed out that even if the direct effects of recoil in isomeric transitions are insufficient to dissociate the molecules, they can at least lead to a partial separation of isomers in processes such as adsorption. Imre showed that when silver chloride powder is shaken with an aqueous solution containing Br^{80} ions, the radiobromine adsorbed by the powder was richer in the 4.4-hr isomer, and that the solution mostly contained the lower isomer.

Interesting results on the retention following the isomeric transitions in Te^{127}, Te^{129}, and Te^{131} have been reported by Williams [116]. This author prepared the three metastable isomers as either tellurite or tellurate and showed that the former is partially oxidized in the isomeric transition, and the latter is reduced. The yields vary with pH; in acid solution, there is 55% reduction and no oxidation, while in alkaline solution, up to 6 N NaOH, one has 40% reduction and 15% oxidation. With caustic soda solutions above 6 M, the ions behave in the same way as in acid. The retention in gaseous TeF_6 is 50%. As in the case of neutron capture by arsenates and arsenites, these experiments suggest the formation of some intermediate common to both anions. The results also suggest that the maximum chemical efficiency of these transitions is of the order of 55%, and that the γ-rays are not completely converted.

With Br^{80}, on the other hand, experiments by Willard [101] on CCl_4/Br_2 (mentioned above) imply complete conversion, although cloud-chamber studies [117] indicate only 47% conversion. Willard's result was confirmed in another way by measurements of the absorption of the radiation carried out by Berthelot [118], and by retention measurements reported by Hamill and Young [119]. These authors showed that each isomeric transition in gaseous CH_3Br^{80m} results in the breaking of a C—Br bond, as evidenced by the fixation of the 18-min isomer by a scavenger such as CHBr = CHBr, or $CH_2 = CH—CH_2Br$. In contrast to this, only 75% of HBr^{80} and 85% of DBr^{80} molecules undergo dissociation under the same conditions. From the potential energy curves calculated by Magee and Gurnee [120], incomplete dissociation in these two cases could be related to the stability of the complex HBr^{n+} and DBr^{n+} ions (when n has values between 1 and 4); the CH_3Br^{n+} ion would, on the contrary, be unstable.

Generally speaking, virtually the same products are obtained in Szilard-Chalmers reactions in neutron capture and in isomeric transitions, although quantitative differences between the two have been reported in a few cases.

17–8 (γ, n) reactions. The recoil energy in (γ, n) reactions is given by Eq. (17–23), which is generally valid for processes involving particle emission:

$$E_r = \frac{m}{A} E_m, \tag{17–23}$$

where m is the mass and E_m the energy of the particle (in this case $m = 1$) and A is the mass of the nucleus.

Bothe and Gentner [121] (see also Ref. 122) irradiated ethyl bromide with 17.2-Mev γ-rays from the (Li + H) reaction, and separated the three active bromine nuclides formed by the usual Szilard-Chalmers technique. Similarly the oxalate $K_3[Co(C_2O_4)_3]\cdot 3H_2O$ has been irradiated with 68-Mev x-rays [123] and the Co^{58} isomers (half-lives 9.2 hours and 72 days) separated by ion exchange, with an overall yield of practically 100%.

Holmes and McCallum [124] have compared the yields for the separation of Cu^{62} and Cu^{64} obtained from (γ, n) and (n, γ) reactions on Cu^{63}-salicylaldehyde-*o*-phenylene-diamine, either in the solid state or in pyridine solution. The recoil energy in the photonuclear reaction is ~100 kev, and that in the neutron capture reaction only of the order of tens of ev. Despite this, the retention is virtually the same in both cases: 35 to 48% for the solid, and 18% for the pyridine solution. The same authors found small differences, however, in the retentions in the Cl^{35} (n, γ) Cl^{36} and Cl^{35} (γ, n) Cl^{34} processes [125]. Neutron bombardment of $NaClO_3$ crystals gave 98.5% of the active chlorine as Cl^- ions after dissolutions, but with approximately 20-Mev x-rays, 91% of the Cl^{34} was as Cl^-, 2% as ClO_2^-, and the rest as ClO_3^-.

In contrast to this, the same retentions of radioactive iodine were found for the (γ, n), (n, γ), (d, p), and (n, 2n) reactions using liquid CH_3I or C_2H_5I as target materials [126]. The retention of active antimony by $Sb(C_6H_5)_3$ in the Sb^{121} (n, γ) Sb^{122} and Sb^{123} (n, γ) Sb^{124} processes is also the same in both cases [127]. These results suggest that provided the initial recoil energy is sufficiently high, the actual energy has no influence on the chemical effects.

Rowland and Libby [128] irradiated solid CO_2 in a betatron at −78°C, as a liquid at 25°, and as alkali carbonates in aqueous solution, and measured the distribution of the C^{11} [formed in the $C^{12}(\gamma, n)C^{11}$ reaction] between CO_2 and CO. In the liquid state or in solution, 95 to 100% of the activity appeared as CO, but in the solid state only one-half of the activity was in this form. It seems that in the first two cases the radiocarbon formed in the atomic state can diffuse through the medium and react

$$C + CO_2 \rightarrow 2CO, \qquad C + H_2O \rightarrow CO + H_2, \tag{17–24}$$

whereas in the solid state carbon monoxide would be formed because of the high local concentration of strongly excited free atoms, and this would subsequently exchange carbon with CO_2

$$C^{11}O + C^{12}O_2 \rightarrow C^{12}O + C^{11}O_2 \tag{17–25}$$

despite the high activation energy.

The C^{11} distribution from the (γ, n) reaction has also been investigated with both anhydrous and aqueous solutions of Na_2CO_3 [129]; the radioactive products include CO_2 (22%), $(COOH)_2^=$ (39%), HOOC·CH$_2$OH (24%), HOOC·CHO (10%), and very small quantities of CO and HCOOH. If, however, the crystals are heated to between 100 and 500°C before dissolving, the percentage of CO_2 increases at the expense of the other products by an amount which depends on the temperature used. The radiocarbon must therefore be present in the solid as various radicals or excited states which can react with each other in different ways depending on the activation energy provided.

The same radioisotope (C^{11}) has been prepared [130] by recoil by irradiating aquadag, which is an aqueous colloidal solution of graphite, with 70-Mev x-rays. After precipitation of the colloid, 80% of the activity was found in the filtrate. The colloidal particles have a diameter of the order of 0.1 μ, which is less than the recoil range of C^{11} in graphite. A similar technique [131] has been used to prepare carrier-free P^{30} from the $P^{31}(\gamma, n)P^{30}$ reaction by betatron irradiation of a suspension of red phosphorous in tetralin. In the same way, radiocopper formed in the $Cu^{63}(\gamma, n)Cu^{62}$ process has been obtained by irradiating a very fine powder of $CuSO_4$ mixed with $CaCO_3$, which acts as a "catcher"; since the carbonate is insoluble, it can subsequently be easily separated from the target material. The yields from this procedure are of the order of 20%.

17–9 Alpha particle emission. The recoil energy E_r of a nucleus produced by α-disintegration can be derived from Eq. (17–23) by putting $m = 4$. In natural radioactive disintegration processes, E_α is of the order of several Mev, so that E_r is extremely high; thus for the $U^{238} \rightarrow Th^{234}$ transition, calculation gives $E_r = 1.6 \times 10^6$ kcal/mole. The effects of α-recoil are often utilized in the preparation of sources of the natural radioelements, especially for those with very short half-lives (Section 11–8). There is, however, little information on the changes which occur in molecules containing the parent atom after α-emission.

The only experiments reported in this field have been on the $U^{238} \rightarrow Th^{234}$ (UX-1) transformation mentioned above. Uranium freed of

UX-1 was converted to the uranyl complex with either (a) benzoylacetone or (b) dibenzoylmethane [132]:

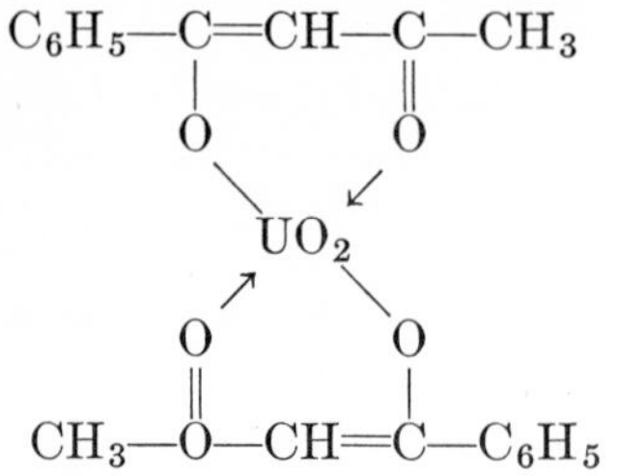

$$\begin{array}{ccc} C_6H_5\text{—}\underset{\displaystyle |}{C}\text{=}CH\text{—}\underset{\displaystyle \|}{C}\text{—}CH_3 & \qquad & C_6H_5\text{—}\underset{\displaystyle |}{C}\text{=}CH\text{—}\underset{\displaystyle \|}{C}\text{—}C_6H_5 \\ O \searrow \quad \swarrow O & & O \searrow \quad \swarrow O \\ UO_2 & & UO_2 \\ O \nearrow \quad \searrow O & & O \nearrow \quad \searrow O \\ CH_3\text{—}\overset{\displaystyle \|}{C}\text{—}CH\text{=}\overset{\displaystyle |}{C}\text{—}C_6H_5 & & C_6H_5\text{—}\overset{\displaystyle \|}{C}\text{—}CH\text{=}\overset{\displaystyle |}{C}\text{—}C_6H_5 \\ \text{(a)} & & \text{(b)} \end{array}$$

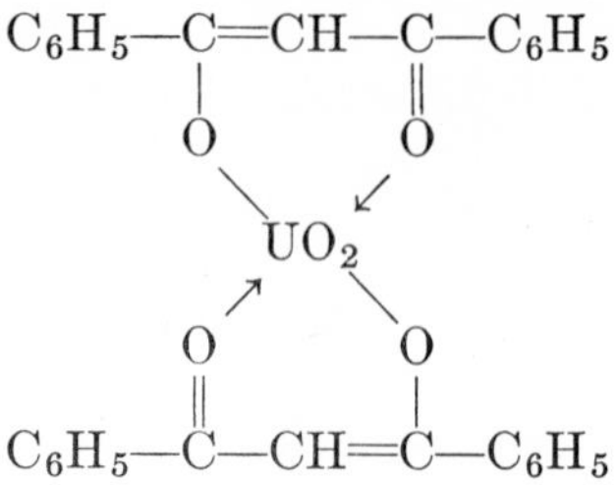

The Szilard-Chalmers effect in these compounds following neutron capture was discussed earlier (Section 17–2). Thorium forms analogous complexes, with similar properties. The two complexes were left in acetone solution, or in the solid state, to allow the thorium daughter to accumulate. After some time the material was treated with an aqueous paste of $BaCO_3$, which picks up those Th^{234} atoms released by the recoil process. The retention is 20 to 50% in acetone solution, and 80 to 90% for the solid complex.

Govaerts and Jordan [133] showed that 90% of the Th^{234} atoms liberated by α-disintegration of the uranyl salicylaldehyde-*o*-phenylenediamine complex in pyridine solution can be deposited at the cathode, and 10% at the anode. Uranium-239 formed by neutron capture does not deposit at either electrode if all traces of electrolyte are previously removed from the solution.

The applications of α-recoil effects in the study of surface phenomena are discussed in Chapter 21.

17–10 Beta disintegrations. The energy of a nucleus recoiling after the emission of an electron can be calculated with the aid of the relativistic equations relating mass and energy (since the β-particles usually have very high velocities). The fundamental equations

$$E_\beta = (m - m_0)c^2 \tag{17–26}$$

and

$$m = \frac{m_0}{\sqrt{1 - (v/c)^2}} \tag{17–27}$$

combined with the relationships $Av_A = mv$ and $E_r = Av_A^2/2$ lead to the equation

$$E_r = \frac{m_0 + m}{2A} E_\beta = \frac{548E_\beta}{A} + \frac{536E_\beta^2}{A}\ \text{ev}, \tag{17–28}$$

in which E_β is the electron energy in Mev, and, as before, A is the mass number of the atom formed [57, 58]. For a given β transition, however, the recoil energy does not have a single fixed value but has a *spectrum* of energies, and to take this into account, the mass of the neutrino and the relative directions of emission of the two particles must be known. If they are assumed to be emitted in the same direction, the recoil energy

$$E_r = 536/A\,(\sqrt{E_\beta^2 + 1.02E_\beta} + E_\nu)^2;$$

for emissions in the opposite sense

$$E_r = 536/A\,(\sqrt{E_\beta^2 + 1.02E_\beta} - E_\nu)^2.$$

For isotropic emission, neglecting the mass of the neutrino,

$$E_r = \frac{536}{A}\left(E_\beta^2 + 1.02E_\beta + E_\nu^2 + 2E_\nu\sqrt{E_\beta^2 + 1.02E_\beta}\cos\theta\right), \quad (17\text{–}29)$$

where the subscript ν refers to the neutrino and θ is the angle of emission. On the further assumption that the maximum intensity of the β-spectra occurs at $E_{\text{max}}/2$, and taking the average angle of the isotropic distribution as 90° ($\cos\theta = 0$), Eq. (17–29) reduces to

$$E_r = 274\frac{E_{\text{max}}}{A} + 268\frac{E_{\text{max}}^2}{A}. \quad (17\text{–}30)$$

In the emission of a negative electron, the balance of charges should lead to an increase of +1 unit in the valency of the product atom

$$Z^{A(n+)} - e \rightarrow (Z+1)^{A(n+1)+}. \quad (17\text{–}31)$$

As in the case of recoil following neutron capture, measurement of the charge due to β-emission is hindered by considerable experimental difficulties because of the low mobility of the recoiling nuclei, and of recombination and neutralization reactions, and even changes in sign caused by impurities. Experiments by Wexler and Davies [109, 110] give average values close to +1 for the H^3 β-emission (in H_2^3) and C^{14} (in CO_2); for K-capture in $Ar^{37} \rightarrow Cl^{37}$, the average value is +3, or +3.4 [112].

If the daughter nuclide $(Z+1)^A$ is itself radioactive, the overall valency change can eventually be detected chemically by the use of appropriate carriers. Coryell and his collaborators [134] have used this technique to show that the greater part of Ce^{143} ($t_{1/2}$, 33 hr) produced by β-emission from La^{143} ($t_{1/2}$, 19 min) is in the tetravalent state, as predicted by Eq. (17–31). If, however, the β-emitting nuclide Ce^{144} ($t_{1/2}$, 275 days) is prepared as the trivalent acetylacetonate complex, either in the solid state or in CS_2 or anhydrous CCl_4 solution, the daughter element Pr^{144} ($t_{1/2}$, 17 min) appears to remain in the same molecule. The complex does not therefore undergo appreciable dissociation, at least if the possibility of extracting the daughter nuclide with water or depositing it on the surface of the vessel is regarded as the criterion of rupture. Only if water is present in the organic solvent during the disintegration, and if excess free acetylacetone is present, can the Pr^{144} be removed from the organic phase [135].

To explain these results, Edwards and Coryell assumed that the undissociated acetylacetonate molecule has a charge of +1 after the β-emission (that is, $Pr^{144}A_3^+$). In the absence of any other acceptor molecule, this oxidizes a molecule of Ce(III) acetylacetonate, but in the presence of water and excess acetylacetone other reactions could take place, such as

$$PrA_3^+ + HA \rightarrow PrA_4 + H^+, \qquad (17\text{–}32)$$

$$PrA_4 + 3H_2O \rightarrow PrO^+ + OH^- + OH + 4HA. \qquad (17\text{–}33)$$

Coryell and his group have also made a careful study of the chemical form of radiobromine and radioiodine produced by β-emission from fission product radioselenium and radiotellurium. The latter were prepared as the oxygenated anions, in the tetra- or hexavalent states (SeO_3^{2-}, SeO_4^{2-}, etc.). In the transition $Se^{83} \rightarrow Br^{83}$, the radiobromine was always found in the proportion of 40% bromate and 60% lower valency state, whether the parent atom was present as selenite or selenate. For I^{132} from the disintegration of Te^{132}, the ratios between periodates, iodate, and lower valency states are 11:14:75 from the tellurite and 12:28:60 from the tellurate.

Finally, Edwards and Coryell [135] determined the proportion of molecules decomposed in the natural radioactive transition RaD → RaE (Bi^{210}) when the parent atom (Pb^{210}) is as $Pb(CH_3)_4$, either in the gaseous state or in C_6H_6, CCl_4, or C_8H_{18} solution. Since $Bi(CH_3)_3$ is volatile, the criterion of rupture of the initial molecule was the detection of bismuth in an involatile form [136]. It was found that in the presence of an inert gas in the vapor state only 5 to 10% of the molecules are ruptured, whereas in solution the fraction of molecules dissociated increases from 50 to 82% as the concentration is changed from 1 to 0.05 *M*. In still more dilute solution, the yield falls sharply to about 10%. The high proportion of the molecules dissociated in fairly dilute solution is probably the result of the Auger effect, and to excitation caused by conversion electrons; 63% of the 46-kev γ-rays associated with the β-emission from RaD are converted in the *L*-shell, and 11% in the *M*-shell [137, 138]. The reasons for the anomalous behavior at low dilutions, and in the gaseous state, are not at all clear.

Kenesha and Kahn [139] bombarded $TeCl_4$, dissolved in benzene, in a reactor, and examined the chemical form of the radioiodine produced by β-emission in the Te^{131} formed

$$Te^{130} + n \rightarrow Te^{131} \xrightarrow[25\text{ min}]{\beta-} I^{131} \xrightarrow[8\text{ d}]{\beta-} \cdot \qquad (17\text{–}34)$$

When the benzene was washed after the bombardment with H_2SO_4 containing NaI or Na_2SO_3, 87% of the radioiodine went into the aqueous phase, 10% distilled with C_6H_5I, and the remaining fraction had a high boiling point. The yield of iodobenzene increased if chloro- or iodobenzene was added to the solution before bombardment; in pure chlorobenzene the organic yield was 40%. The authors suggest that radiotellurium formed by neutron capture remains as $TeCl_4$, so that the reactions of radioactive iodine are those occurring in the β-emission.

Burgus and Kennedy [140] have studied the chemical changes in the

$$Mn^{51} \xrightarrow{\beta+} Cr^{51}$$

transition. If the manganese is in the divalent state, a simple charge balance would lead to Cr^+, but in fact in an aqueous solution of a Mn(II) salt, containing Cr^{3+} and CrO_4^{2-} as carriers, more than 97% of the radiochromium is carried by the trivalent salt, independent of the pH. In water-acetone or water-dioxane solution, this fraction is only 5 to 15%. With solid $MnCO_3$, 30% of the radiochromium is found as chromate. With a permanganate, the charge balance should give CrO_4^{2-}, but with MnO_4^- in solution one finds approximately equal activities as Cr(III) and Cr(VI). With solid $CsMnO_4$, all the radiochromium is carried down by chromate ion (i.e., after dissolving in water). It is believed that the recoiling atom in the crystal is strongly ionized after emission of the positron, and is in an oxidation state higher than III, which exchanges in solution with Cr(VI). If the disintegration occurs in solution, the excited Cr^{6+} ions are reduced by H_2O, going in part to the trivalent state.

17–11 Reactions involving the capture and emission of particles. In nuclear processes such as (n, p), (n, α), (p, n), (p, α), (d, n), etc., the energy balance is expressed by the equation

$$E_2 + E_r = E_1 + Q, \qquad (17\text{–}35)$$

where the subscripts 1, 2, and r refer to the incident particle, the emitted particle, and the product nucleus respectively. The relative values of E_2 and E_r depend upon the mass of the emitted particle and of the recoiling nucleus, and on the angular correlations between the captured and emitted particles. But in general the recoil energy is very high, and sufficient not only to break chemical bonds but also to detach several extranuclear electrons from the atom.

This "hot" chemistry has been especially studied in terms of the Cl^{35} (n, p) S^{35}, Cl^{35} (n, α) P^{32}, S^{32} (n, p) P^{32} reactions, and of the active isotopes of carbon. The recoil energy of the radioactive sulfur atoms produced in the first of these processes is 14.8 kev. Using a CCl_4 target, 30% of the S^{35} is found in the elementary state, but most of it probably reacts with the solvent to give volatile compounds such as $CSCl_2$ [141]. In the presence of CS_2, radiosulfur exchanges with this compound, although this exchange does not normally occur at room temperature [142].

When crystals of KCl or some other alkali chloride are bombarded with neutrons in the air and then dissolved in water, the S^{35} is found as SO_4^{2-} (coprecipitation) [143]. With carefully degassed crystals, Koski [144, 145] found 35% of the S^{35} as sulfide. If the crystals are heated for 5 hr in an atmosphere of oxygen at 600°C after the bombardment, all the radiosulfur can again be carried down by sulfates, and Koski concludes from this that the formation of SO_4^{2-} is due to occluded oxygen in the crystal. In agreement with this, Milham [146] obtained yields of 90% of S^{2-} by using crystals sublimed under vacuum and degassed solutions, and dissolving the crystals in water already containing sulfide carrier. If this carrier is added to the water after dissolving the irradiated crystals, only 30% of the activity is carried down, and the remainder appears as SO_4^{2-}. It seems that this fraction may initially be in some highly active form (perhaps atomic S) which is oxidized by the water in the absence of sulfide carrier.

TABLE 17–2

THE CHEMICAL FORMS OF RADIOPHOSPHORUS

S^{32}(n, p)P^{32}		Cl^{35}(n, α)P^{32}	
Crystal	Reduced P: total P	Crystal	Reduced P: total P
$Na_2SO_4 \cdot 10H_2O$	0.02	Hydrated $MgCl_2$	0.07
$Na_2SO_3 \cdot 7H_2O$	0.5	$KClO_3$	0.01
K_2SO_4	0.1	$KClO_4$	0.01
Hydrated Na_2S	0.64–0.93	NaCl	0.65

The chemical form of P^{32} produced in the Cl^{35} (n, α) or S^{32} (n, p) reactions also depends upon the amount of available oxygen. Table 17–2, taken from a paper by Aten [147], gives the ratio of phosphite + hypophosphite to total phosphorus for the bombardment of various crystals. The proportion of reduced phosphorus is very small in crystals containing oxygenated anions or water of hydration, but the chemical nature ($Na_2SO_3 \cdot 7H_2O$) and the crystal structure (K_2SO_4) also appear to influence the degree of oxidation. In agreement with these results, Caillat and Sue [148] have shown that the yield of reduced radiophosphorus in pile bombardment is of the order of 50% for solid LiCl, NaCl, or KCl, but that with saturated solutions of these salts only phosphate is formed. If a crystal of NaCl is heated after bombardment and before dissolution to remove the coloration produced by the pile radiation, the fraction of phosphate is reduced to about 28%. This decrease is attributed to the reduction of P(V), preformed in the crystal by electrons released from the *F*-centers by heating.

Whitmore [149] has found that irradiation of Na_2S with fast neutrons in the dry state, or of crystals of thiourea in an atmosphere of argon, followed by dissolving in degassed water, gave all the radiophosphorus as phosphate. With CS_2 as the target material, about 50% is as elementary phosphorus and the remainder as substitution products of CS_2. Radiophosphorus can be separated from CS_2 by irradiation in an electric field, since up to ~95% is deposited on electrodes immersed in the liquid [150].

Separation techniques based on recoil, similar to those used for (n, γ) reactions, have been successfully applied to the separation of radioactive sodium from a suspension of a very fine powder of MgO in water [151], [the reaction being Mg^{24} (n, p) Na^{24}], of radioaluminum on kieselguhr [86] [Si^{28} (n, p) Al^{28}], and of P^{32} formed by neutron bombardment of powdered sulfur suspended in water [152]. Measurements of the yields of these processes can be used to determine the range of the recoiling atoms.

Chemla [153, 154] has observed that S^{35} and P^{32} formed in solid NaCl diffuse to the surface and accumulate in a very thin surface layer if the crystal is heated to ~650°C (Fig. 17–3). When an electric field is applied across the crystal, the radiosulfur migrates toward the anode. If hydrogen

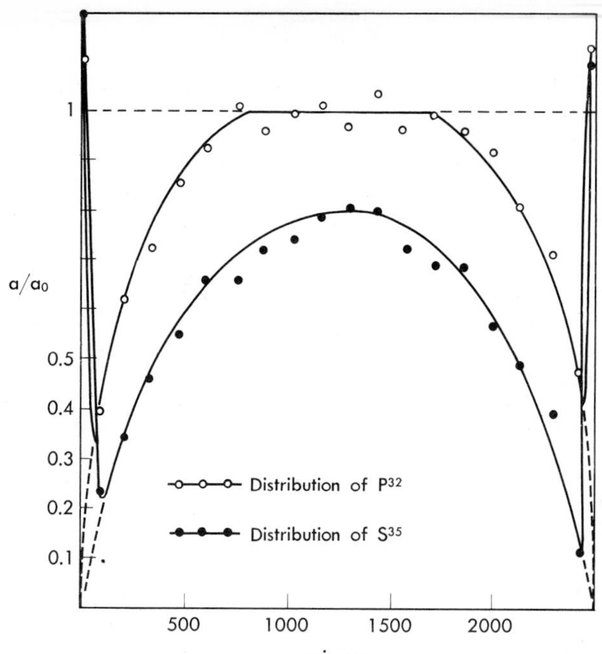

FIG. 17–3. Diffusion of active species in neutron-bombarded NaCl after heating to 660°C for 4 hr 10 min in an atmosphere of nitrogen; a = specific activity of heated sample, a_0 = specific activity of unheated crystal.

gas is circulated over the surface of the crystal after heating, the gas picks up H_2S^{35}; pure radiosulfur can be separated by bubbling this through bromine water. The yield may be as high as 95% if the crystal is gound to a fine powder before treatment with hydrogen.

In neutron bombardment of a finely divided mixture of $LiCO_3$ and glucose, formed in the Li^6 (n, α) T^3 reaction, about 10% of the tritium is fixed on the glucose by substitution of ordinary hydrogen [155]. With a mixture of Li_2SO_4 and benzoic acid, 25% substitution in the benzene ring occurs.

The chemical transformations associated with the (p, n) reaction have been examined with targets of crystalline K_2SO_4 and $K_2S_2O_8$ [156]. Practically all the radiochlorine produced in the S^{34} (p, n) Cl^{34} process is as the Cl^- ion, or some form which can exchange with this. This result does not necessarily imply that these ions have already been formed in the solid, since they can also be produced during the dissolving process, for example, by

$$Cl + H_2O \rightarrow HCl + OH,$$

or

$$Cl^+ + H_2O \rightarrow Cl^- + 2H^+ + \tfrac{1}{2}O_2.$$

The radionitrogen formed in the O^{16} (p, α) N^{13} process appears partly as NH_4^+ and partly in the form of oxygenated anions.

TABLE 17–3

THE DISTRIBUTION OF C^{14} FROM THE N^{14} (n, p) REACTION, % YIELD

Product	Target compound		
	$(NH_4)_2SO_4$	NH_4Br	Be_3N_2
CO_2	39.5	1.7	13.5
CO	2.0	1.3	0.06
CH_4	0.5	7.5	25.4
HCN	3.9	2.0	
CH_3NH_2	16.1	79	6.3
HCOOH	15.5	1.3	3.8
HCHO	13.2	5.8	8.0
CH_3OH	0.7	0.4	0.1
$CO(NH_2)_2$	7.3	0.4	6.5
$CNH(NH_2)_2$	—	—	18.2
H_2NCN	—	—	4.5
CH_3NHNH_2	—	—	10.7

The influence of oxygen, and the general influence of the medium on the products formed during nuclear reactions, also shows up in the formation of radioactive carbon isotopes. When amorphous boron is bombarded, C^{11} is obtained from the B^{10} (d, n) reaction as a mixture of CO and CO_2 [133], but if the target is B_2O_3, only CO_2 is formed [158].

The chemical state of C^{14} produced by the bombardment of nitrogen compounds in the N^{14} (n, p) C^{14} reaction has been the subject of considerable research. The first results by Yankwich and his co-workers [159] for crystals or saturated solutions of ammonium nitrate, hydrazine, and urea already gave evidence for the formation of several radioactive products including CO_2, CO, CH_4, HCN, CH_3OH, HCHO, and HCOOH, etc. The distribution of C^{14} between these various compounds depends on the physical state of the target, and on its oxygen and hydrogen contents. Table 17–3, taken from more recent publications [160, 161, 162] shows the percentages of the various products formed by the bombardment of crystals of $(NH_4)_2SO_4$, NH_4Br, and Be_3N_2. In order to interpret these results qualitatively, it must be assumed that at the end of its track the hot carbon atom produces excited free radicals CH*, CO*, CN* (where the asterisk here implies the excited state), and that the preponderance of any one of these is determined by the chemical composition of the medium. The final fate of the radicals would then depend on the competition between hydration and oxidation reactions. For example, the production of CH_4 from Be_3N_2 could be the result of the hydrolysis of Be_2C formed in the course of the deactivation of BeC radicals. Similarly, methanol could be produced by the hydration of the CH_2 radical, and formic acid by the hydration of CO, etc.

It follows from these results that this nuclear process can be used to prepare simple organic molecules labeled with C^{14}. Thus by bombarding quinoline, radioactive naphthalene and α-naphthol are obtained [163], and pyridine oxalate gives benzene and phenol [164]:

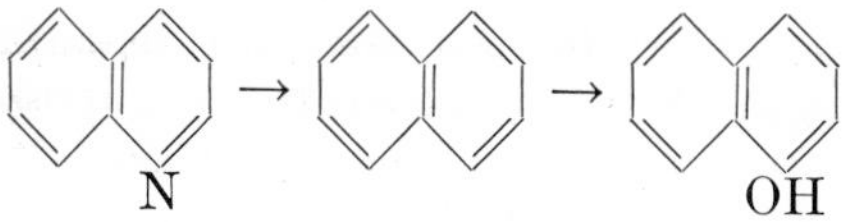

Bombardment of acridine gives C^{14}-labeled anthracene [165]. At the same time, active molecules of the target are produced by repenetration of radiocarbon, and by exchange with inactive atoms. In experiments with acridine, 0.2% of the activity was found as radioanthracene and 3.5% as radioacridine, corresponding to a ratio of 1:17.5, where as a statistical distribution between the 14 positions in the ring system of the molecule would have given a ratio of 1:13. Recent work on the neutron bombardment of quinoline, isoquinoline, etc., shows, however, that the distribution is not purely statistical, but also depends on the nature of the bonds which are broken [166].

Much better radiosynthesis yields are obtained by bombarding aniline dissolved in *n*-pentane; 26% of the activity appears as pentane, 12% as *n*-hexane, 6% as isomers of hexane, and 39% as heavier hydrocarbons [167].

Two-thirds of the radiophosphorus produced in the bombardment of aluminum with 100-Mev N^{14} (6+) ions comes off as PH_3 on dissolving the metal; the remainder is as oxygenated anions of lower valency state, probably H_3PO_2 [168]. It is suggested that the phosphorus formed in the Al^{27} (N, 4p5n) P^{32} process (Section 5–6) is in the atomic state, but that on dissolving this reacts either with the solvent, or with H atoms from the reaction of water with aluminum:

$$P + 3H \rightarrow PH_3, \tag{17–36}$$

$$P + 2H_2O \rightarrow H_3PO_2 + H. \tag{17–37}$$

The extraction of fission product radioiodine from metallic uranium by organic solvents gives evidence of its neutral state [169]. It is probably formed as a positive ion, but in the direct extraction of the crystalline powder, it picks up an electron from the crystal to go to the atomic state, and subsequently to the I_2 molecule.

References

1. L. Szilard and T. A. Chalmers, *Nature,* **134,** 462 (1934).
2. S. Roginskii and N. Gopshtein, *Physik. Z. Sowjetunion.*, **7,** 672 (1935).
3. O. Erbacher and K. Philipp, *Ber.*, **69,** 893 (1936).
4. C. S. Lu and S. Sugden, *J. Chem. Soc.*, **1939,** 1273.
5. W. F. Libby, *J. Am. Chem. Soc.*, **62,** 1930 (1940).
6. R. R. Williams, *J. Phys. Chem.*, **52,** 603 (1948).
7. E. R. Tompkins, W. E. Cohn, A. W. Adamson, and R. R. Williams, in *Radiochemical Studies: The Fission Products* (N.N.E.S. IV-9), McGraw-Hill, New York, 1951, Book 1, p. 199.

8. G. Harbottle and A. G. Maddock, *J. Chem. Phys.*, **21,** 1686 (1953).
9. G. E. Boyd, J. W. Cobble, and S. Wexler, *J. Am. Chem. Soc.*, **74,** 237 (1952).
10. J. W. Cobble and G. E. Boyd, *J. Am. Chem. Soc.*, **74,** 1282 (1952).
11. A. W. Adamson and R. R. Williams, Ref. 7, p. 176.
12. O. D'Agostino, *Gazz. Chim. Ital.*, **65,** 1071 (1935).
13. E. Amaldi, O. D'Agostino, E. Fermi, B. Pontecorvo, F. Rasetti, and E. Segrè, *Ricerca sci.*, **2,** 467 (1934).
14. E. Amaldi, O. D'Agostino, E. Fermi, B. Pontecorvo, F. Rosetti, and E. Segrè, *Proc. Roy. Soc. (London)*, **A149,** 522 (1935).
15. E. Berne, *Acta Chem. Scand.*, **6,** 1106 (1952).
16. R. Daudel, *Compt. rend.*, **213,** 479 (1941); **214,** 547 (1942).
17. O. Erbacher and K. Philipp, *Z. physik. Chem.*, **A179,** 263 (1937).
18. P. Süe, *J. Chim. Phys.*, **45,** 177 (1948); see Ref. 50.
19. K. Starke, *Naturwiss.*, **28,** 631 (1940).
20. H. Laurent and P. Simonnin, *J. phys. radium*, **14,** 294 (1953).
21. F. A. Paneth and J. W. J. Fay, *Nature*, **135,** 820 (1935).
22. F. A. Paneth and J. W. J. Fay, *J. Chem. Soc.*, **1936,** 384.
23. P. Süe and T. Yuasa, *J. Chim. Phys.*, **41,** 160 (1944).
24. A. G. Maddock and N. Sutin, *Trans. Faraday Soc.*, **51,** 184 (1955).
25. W. Maurer and W. Ramm, *Z. Physik*, **119,** 602 (1942).
26. H. Spano and M. Kahn, *J. Am. Chem. Soc.*, **74,** 568 (1952).
27. A. W. Kenny and W. R. E. Maton, *Nature*, **162,** 567 (1948).
28. P. Süe and G. Kayas, *J. Chim. Phys.*, **45,** 188 (1948).
29. J. Steigman, *Phys. Rev.*, **59,** 498 (1941).
30. S. Chatterjee and P. Ray, quoted by G. B. Cook and J. F. Duncan, *Modern Radiochemical Practice*, Oxford University Press, 1952, p. 224.
31. W. Buser and U. Imobersteg, *Experientia*, **9,** 288 (1953).
32. W. Buser, P. Graf, and U. Imobersteg, *Z. Elektrochem.*, **58,** 605 (1954).
33. M. Guillot, M. Haïssinsky, and G. Scoffier, unpublished results.
34. B. C. Haldar, *J. Am. Chem. Soc.*, **76,** 4229 (1954).
35. W. Herr and H. Götte, *Z. Naturforsch.*, **5a,** 629 (1950).
36. W. Herr, *Z. Naturforsch*, **7b,** 201, 265 (1952).
37. W. Herr, *Angew, Chem.*, **65,** 303 (1953).
38. U. Croatto, G. Giacomello, and A. G. Maddock, *Ricerca sci.*, **21,** 1788 (1951); **22,** 265 (1952).
39. W. Herr, *Z. Naturforsch.*, **3a,** 645 (1948).
40. V. Majer, *Naturwiss.*, **25,** 252 (1937).
41. M. Goldhaber and B. C. Saunders, quoted by F. G. Mann, *Nature*, **142,** 709 (1938).
42. R. B. Duffield and M. Calvin, *J. Am. Chem. Soc.*, **68,** 1129 (1946).
43. L. Melander, *Acta Chem. Scand.*, **1,** 169 (1947).
44. L. Melander and H. Slatis, *Phys. Rev.*, **74,** 709 (1948).
45. K. Starke, *Naturwiss.*, **30,** 577 (1942).
46. H. Götte, *Z. Naturforsch.*, **1,** 377 (1946).
47. J. W. Irvine, *Phys. Rev.*, **55,** 1105 (1939).
48. U. Drehmann, *Z. physik. Chem.*, **B53,** 227 (1943).
49. W. Herr, *Z. Elektrochem.*, **56,** 911 (1952).
50. H. Müller and E. Broda, *Monatsh. Chem.*, **82,** 48 (1951).

51. M. Haïssinsky and M. Lefort, *J. Chim. Phys.*, **48,** 429 (1951).
52. L. M. Fishman and G. Harbottle, *J. Chem. Phys.*, **22,** 1088 (1954).
53. N. Ivanoff and M. Haïssinsky, *J. Chim. Phys.*, **53,** 400 (1956).
54. H. Suess, *Z. physik. Chem.*, **B45,** 297, 312 (1940).
55. H. Steinwedel and J. H. D. Jensen, *Z. Naturforsch.*, **2a,** 125 (1947).
56. W. H. Hamill and R. R. Williams, *J. Chem. Phys.*, **16,** 1171 (1948).
57. R. R. Edwards and T. H. Davies, *Nucleonics*, **2,** No. 6, 44 (1948).
58. W. F. Libby, *J. Am. Chem. Soc.*, **69,** 2523 (1949).
59. S. Wexler and T. H. Davies, *J. Chem. Phys.*, **20,** 1688 (1952).
60. S. Yosim and T. H. Davies, *J. Phys. Chem.*, **56,** 599 (1952).
61. M. S. Fox and W. F. Libby, *J. Chem. Phys.*, **20,** 487 (1952).
62. J. C. W. Chien and J. E. Willard, *J. Am. Chem. Soc.*, **75,** 6160 (1953).
63. W. E. Rice and J. E. Willard, *J. Am. Chem. Soc.*, **75,** 6156 (1953).
64. J. E. Willard, *Ann. Rev. Nuclear Sci.*, **3,** 193 (1953).
65. J. K. Major and P. Sue, *Compt. rend.*, **232,** 52 (1951).
66. E. Glueckauf and J. W. J. Fay, *J. Chem. Soc.*, 390 (1936).
67. E. Glueckauf, R. B. Jacobi, and G. P. Kitt, *J. Chem. Soc.*, S 330 (1949).
68. T. Brustad and J. Baarli, *J. Chem. Phys.*, **22,** 1311 (1954).
69. A. F. Reid, *Phys. Rev.*, **69,** 530 (1949).
70. L. Friedman and W. F. Libby, *J. Chem. Phys.*, **17,** 647 (1949).
71. J. F. Hornig, G. Levey, and J. E. Willard, *J. Chem. Phys.*, **20,** 1556 (1952).
72. S. Goldhaber, R. S. H. Chiang, and J. E. Willard, *J. Am. Chem. Soc.*, **73,** 2271 (1951).
73. J. M. Miller and R. W. Dodson, *J. Chem. Phys.*, **18,** 865 (1950).
74. R. R. Williams, W. H. Hamill, H. A. Schwarz, and E. J. Burrell, *J. Am. Chem. Soc.*, **74,** 5737 (1952).
75. E. G. Bohlmann and J. E. Willard, *J. Am. Chem. Soc.*, **64,** 1342 (1942).
76. J. F. Hornig and J. Willard, *J. Am. Chem. Soc.*, **75,** 461 (1953).
77. S. Goldhaber and J. E. Willard, *J. Am. Chem. Soc.*, **74,** 318 (1952).
78. G. Levey and J. E. Willard, *J. Am. Chem. Soc.*, **74,** 6161 (1952).
79. W. H. Hamill and R. R. Williams, *J. Chem. Phys.*, **22,** 53 (1954).
80. F. S. Rowland and W. F. Libby, *J. Chem. Phys.*, **21,** 1495 (1953).
81. J. C. W. Chien and J. E. Willard, *J. Am. Chem. Soc.*, **77,** 3441 (1955).
82. A. S. Karamyan, *Doklady Akad. Nauk S.S.S.R.*, **69,** 787 (1949).
83. K. J. McCallum and A. G. Maddock, *Trans. Faraday Soc.*, **49,** 1150 (1953).
84. E. Broda, *J. Chim. Phys.*, **45,** 196 (1948).
85. W. Rieder, E. Broda, and J. Erber, *Monatsh. Chem.*, **81,** 658 (1950).
86. P. Jordan, *Helv. Chim. Acta*, **34,** 699, 715 (1951).
87. J. G. A. Fiskel, *Science*, **113,** 244 (1951).
88. J. G. A. Fiskel, W. A. DeLong, and W. F. Oliver, *Can. J. Chem.*, **30,** 9 (1952).
89. A. H. W. Aten, H. van der Straaten, and P. Riesebos, *Science*, **115,** 267 (1952).
90. J. H. Green, G. Harbottle, and A. G. Maddock, *Trans. Faraday Soc.*, **49,** 1413 (1953).
91. R. E. Cleary, W. H. Hamill, and R. R. Williams, *J. Am. Chem. Soc.*, **74,** 4675 (1952).

92. A. G. MADDOCK, *Radiochemical Transformations, Colloque Donegani*, Acad. Lincei, Milan-Rome, 1953.

93. A. H. W. ATEN and J. B. M. VAN BERKUM, *J. Am. Chem. Soc.*, **72,** 3273 (1950).

94. E. SEGRÈ, R. S. HALFORD, and G. T. SEABORG, *Phys. Rev.*, **55,** 321 (1939).

95. D. C. DE VAULT and W. F. LIBBY, *Phys. Rev.*, **55,** 322 (1939).

96. F. FAIRBROTHER, *Nature*, **145,** 307 (1940).

97. G. T. SEABORG, J. W. KENNEDY, and J. J. LIVINGOOD, *Phys. Rev.*, **55,** 410 (1939); **57,** 363 (1940).

98. A. LANGSDORF and E. SEGRÈ, *Phys. Rev.*, **57,** 105 (1940).

99. W. HERR, *Z. Naturforsch.*, **9a,** 180 (1954).

100. G. J. GOLDSMITH and E. BLEULER, *J. Phys. Chem.*, **54,** 717 (1950).

101. J. E. WILLARD, *J. Am. Chem. Soc.*, **62,** 256, 3161 (1940).

102. G. GAVORET and N. IVANOFF, *Bull. soc. chim. France*, **1952,** 166.

103. E. COOPER, *Phys. Rev.*, **61,** 1 (1942).

104. P. P. CAPRON, G. STOKKINK, and M. VAN MEERSCHE, *Nature*, **157,** 806 (1946).

105. P. P. CAPRON, E. CRÈVECOEUR, and M. FAES, *J. Chem. Phys.*, **17,** 349 (1949).

106. L. I. RUSINOV and A. S. KARAMYAN, *Doklady Akad. Nauk S.S.S.R.*, **55,** 599 (1947); **58,** 573 (1947).

107. W. S. KOSKI, *J. Am. Chem. Soc.*, **70,** 4251 (1948).

108. G. KAYAS, *Ann. phys.*, **7,** 802 (1952).

109. S. WEXLER and T. E. DAVIES, *J. Chem. Phys.*, **18,** 376 (1950).

110. S. WEXLER and T. E. DAVIES, *Phys. Rev.*, **88,** 1203 (1952).

111. S. WEXLER, *Phys. Rev.*, **93,** 182 (1954).

112. M. L. PERLMAN and J. A. MISKEL, *Phys. Rev.*, **91,** 899 (1953).

113. A. W. ADAMSON and J. M. GRUNLAND, *J. Am. Chem. Soc.*, **73,** 5508 (1951).

114. G. T. SEABORG, G. FRIEDLANDER, and J. W. KENNEDY, *J. Am. Chem. Soc.*, **62,** 1309 (1940).

115. L. IMRE, *Naturwiss.*, **28,** 158 (1940).

116. R. R. WILLIAMS, *J. Chem. Phys.*, **16,** 513 (1948).

117. R. E. SIDAY, *Proc. Roy. Soc. (London)*, **A178,** 189 (1941).

118. A. BERTHELOT, *Ann. phys.*, **19,** 117, 219 (1944).

119. W. H. HAMILL and J. A. YOUNG, *J. Chem. Phys.*, **20,** 888 (1952).

120. J. L. MAGEE and E. F. GURNEE, *J. Chem. Phys.*, **20,** 894 (1952).

121. W. BOTHE and W. GENTNER, *Z. Physik*, **106,** 236 (1937).

122. W. H. BARKAS, P. R. CARLSON, J. E. HENDERSON, and W. H. MOORE, *Phys. Rev.*, **58,** 577 (1940).

123. D. CHRISTIAN and D. S. MARTIN, *Phys. Rev.*, **80,** 1110 (1950).

124. O. G. HOLMES and K. J. MCCALLUM, *J. Am. Chem. Soc.*, **72,** 5319 (1950).

125. K. J. MCCALLUM and O. G. HOLMES, *Can. J. Chem.*, **29,** 691 (1951).

126. R. H. SCHULER, *J. Chem. Phys.*, **22,** 2026 (1954).

127. M. KAHN, *J. Am. Chem. Soc.*, **73,** 479 (1951).

128. F. S. ROWLAND and W. F. LIBBY, *J. Chem. Phys.*, **21,** 1493 (1953).

129. L. J. SHARMAN and K. J. MCCALLUM, *J. Am. Chem. Soc.*, **77,** 2989 (1955).

130. H. MORINAGA and D. J. ZAFFARANO, *Phys. Rev.*, **93,** 1422 (1954).

131. J. PAULY and P. SÜE, *Compt. rend.*, **240,** 2226 (1955); **241,** 197 (1955).

132. M. Haïssinsky and M. Cottin, *J. Chim. Phys.*, **45,** 270 (1948).
133. J. Govaerts and P. Jordan, *Experientia*, **6,** 329 (1950).
134. W. H. Burgus, T. H. Davies, R. R. Edwards, H. Gest, C. W. Stanley, R. R. Williams, and C. D. Coryell, *J. Chim. Phys.*, **45,** 165 (1948).
135. R. R. Edwards and C. D. Coryell, *U.S.A.E.C. report BNL-C7*, 1948, p. 52.
136. R. A. Mortensen and P. A. Leighton, *J. Am. Chem. Soc.*, **56,** 2397 (1934).
137. L. Cranberg, *Phys. Rev.*, **77,** 155 (1950).
138. D. K. Butt and W. D. Brodie, *Proc. Phys. Soc. (London)*, **A64,** 791 (1951).
139. F. J. Keneshea and M. Kahn, *J. Am. Chem. Soc.*, **74,** 5254 (1952).
140. W. H. Burgus and J. W. Kennedy, *J. Chem. Phys.*, **18,** 97 (1950).
141. M. Kamen, *Phys. Rev.*, **60,** 537 (1941).
142. R. R. Edwards, F. B. Nesbett, and A. K. Solomon, *J. Am. Chem. Soc.*, **70,** 1670 (1948).
143. U. Croatto and A. G. Maddock, *J. Chem. Soc.*, **1949,** S351.
144. W. S. Koski, *J. Am. Chem. Soc.*, **71,** 4042 (1949).
145. W. S. Koski, *J. Chem. Phys.*, **17,** 582 (1949).
146. R. Milham, quoted by Willard, Ref. 64.
147. A. H. W. Aten, *Phys. Rev.*, **71,** 641 (1947).
148. R. Caillat and P. Süe, *Compt. rend.*, **230,** 1666, 1864 (1950).
149. F. E. Whitmore, *Nature*, **164,** 240 (1949).
150. J. Govaerts, *J. Chim. Phys.*, **36,** 130 (1939).
151. E. Bleuler and W. Zunti, *Helv. Phys. Acta*, **20,** 195 (1947).
152. J. Pauly, *Compt. rend.*, **240,** 2415 (1955).
153. M. Chemla, *Compt. rend.*, **232,** 1553, 2424 (1951); **234,** 2064 (1952).
154. M. Chemla and P. Süe, *Compt. rend.*, **233,** 247 (1951); **238,** 1502 (1954).
155. R. Wolfgang, F. S. Rowland, and C. N. Turton, quoted by J. E. Willard, *Ann. Rev. Phys. Chem.*, **6,** 141 (1955).
156. D. J. Meier and C. S. Garner, *J. Chem. Phys.*, **17,** 1344 (1949).
157. S. Ruben, W. Z. Hassid, and M. D. Kamen, *J. Am. Chem. Soc.*, **61,** 661 (1939).
158. R. Caillat and P. Süe, *Bull. soc. chim. France*, **1947,** 687.
159. P. E. Yankwich, G. K. Rollefson, and T. H. Norris, *J. Chem. Phys.*, **14,** 131 (1946).
160. P. E. Yankwich and J. D. Vaughan, *J. Am. Chem. Soc.*, **76,** 5851 (1954).
161. P. E. Yankwich and W. R. Corman, *J. Am. Chem. Soc.*, **77,** 2096 (1955).
162. W. Corman, *Diss. Abs.*, No. 1, 47 (1955).
163. U. Croatto, G. Giacomello, and A. G. Maddock, *Ricera sci.*, **21,** 1598 (1951).
164. G. Giacomello, *Ricerca sci.*, **21,** 1211 (1951).
165. A. P. Wolf and R. C. Anderson, *J. Am. Chem. Soc.*, **77,** 1608 (1955).
166. C. Brunello and R. Muxart, *Bull. soc. chim. France*, **1960,** 16.
167. A. G. Schrodt and W. F. Libby, *Bull soc. chim. France*, **76,** 3100 (1954).
168. G. A. Chackett and K. F. Chackett, *Nature*, **174,** 232 (1954).
169. G. N. Walton, B. Bowles, and I. F. Croall, *1955 Geneva Conference*, P. 436.

CHAPTER 18

RADIOACTIVE INDICATORS

18–1 The principle of the method. The principle of the radioactive indicator method, already outlined briefly in Section 6–10, can be understood in terms of the general scheme

$$S(xAyA') \rightarrow \begin{cases} M \rightarrow N \;\ldots\; Y \rightarrow Z(x'Ay'A'), \\ M' \rightarrow N' \;\ldots\; Y' \rightarrow Z', \\ M'' \rightarrow N'' \;\ldots\; Y'' \rightarrow Z'', \end{cases} \tag{18–1}$$

in which $S(xAyA')$ is the initial chemical system containing x atoms of species A (generally in macroscopic amounts) and y atoms of the radioactive isotope A'. It is assumed that everything observed for A' also applies to A, so that if, for example, it is found that there are y' atoms of A' in Z, which is one of the products of the process or reaction, then an equivalent number (x') of atoms of A, given by $x' = xy'/y$, will also be found in the same state. Similarly if at time t a fraction x''/x of A' atoms are detected as some intermediate N, then this will also contain at the same instant $x'/x = y''/y$ of A, and so on.

This argument implies identical physico-chemical behavior for the various isotopes of a given element, or in other words, isotope effects are neglected. Other assumptions include the absence of appreciable radiolytic effects in the system *labeled* with the indicator, at least as far as the property under investigation is concerned. For certain light elements, an alternative approach is to use as the indicator stable isotopes with a different mass from the principle isotope concerned, but this technique is less convenient from a practical point of view than that involving radioactive indicators. Both the assumptions just mentioned are, however, only approximately true. The first, the absence of isotope effects, can be accepted almost without reservation for most work involving elements of medium or heavy atomic weight (see Tables 9–5 and 9–7), but the validity of this assumption must be carefully examined in quantitative tracer studies with light elements, and especially hydrogen and carbon. Radiolytic effects can be neglected provided that the intensity of the radiation or the specific activity of the product is very low.

From the radiochemical yields quoted in Chapters 12 through 15, it can be seen that the order of activity normally used in tracer work (rarely above microcuries per gram) will not generally bring about appreciable change in the chemical state of a compound during the normal time span of an experiment. More care is necessary, however, in biological research, since the substances involved are often much more sensitive to radiation. The same is also true for colloidal systems (Section 13–7) and for organic compounds rich in tritium or C^{14}, for which a number of cases of *autoradiolysis* have been reported. For example, methanol containing 8 to 10 millicuries of C^{14} per millimole decomposes on standing, and in a closed vessel generates a pressure of several atmospheres of permanent gas (H_2, CH_4), plus a radioactive oil [1]. The radiochemical yield (G) for the decomposition is 5.4, which is not very different from that reported for the irradiation of methanol with an external source. Similarly, labeled CH_3I (activity 0.2 millicuries of C^{14} per millimole) liberates iodine, with $G \approx 3$ [2]. Appreciable autoradiolysis has also been reported [3, 4] for choline, valine, leucine, cholesterol, calcium glycollate, and others. The effect of radiation in a labeled system can be checked by varying the specific activity over wide limits, and observing whether or not this produces any change in the results.

The precision which is possible in radiochemical work using counting or photographic methods is generally lower than that which can be achieved with other modern physico-chemical techniques, except by using special apparatus or carrying out a very large number of measurements. To compensate for this, however, the tracer method has two advantages which make it highly efficient and extremely suitable for investigating and solving problems which are not accessible by any other technique. These two advantages are the *sensitivity* and the *specificity*. Under favorable conditions it is possible to detect and determine quantities of material as low as 10^{-19} gm or less, representing only thousands of atoms.* This makes radiochemical methods particularly suitable for the detection and analysis of impurities at the tracer level (for example, in substances which are already "spectroscopically pure"), or for the measurement of the solubility product of so-called "insoluble" substances or the vapor pressure of involatile compounds, and similar purposes.

Along with this, the specificity, which is the direct result of the individual nuclear characteristics of each nuclide, such as the half-life and the type and energy of radiation, allow the changes and movement of labeled species in both time and space to be followed unambiguously. In chemical kinetics in particular, the reaction path can be "traced" directly by examining the chemical or physical fate of radioactive or stable isotopic atoms incorporated in the substance being studied, or added to the reaction system at a suitable moment. Examples of this were discussed in connection with the radiolysis of organic compounds (Section 14-1) and other examples will arise in discussing the identification of unstable intermediate products (Chapter 23). Isotopic exchange reactions and the study of self-diffusion (Chapter 19) are typical applications of the tracer method in experiments for which there is virtually no other method of investigation.

The spatial *localization* of atoms is a particularly precise use of radiographic methods. The type of phenomena which can be most advantageously studied in this way include crystallization and recrystallization, isolation, crystal inclusions, the structure and properties of surfaces, electro-

---

* The discovery of mendelevium was achieved with only 17 atoms [A. Ghiorso, *et al.*, *Phys. Rev.*, **98**, 1518 (1955)].

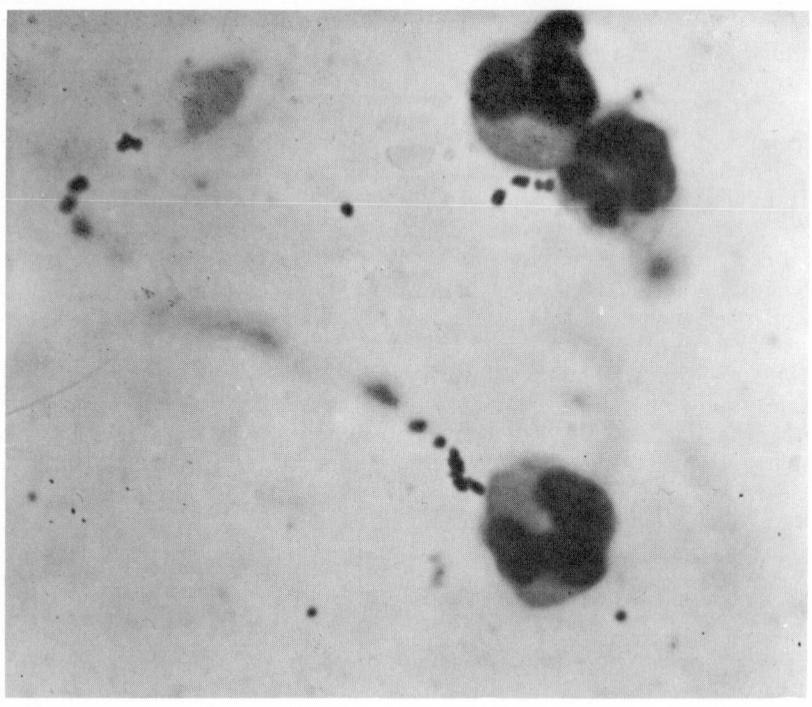

FIG. 18–1. An autoradiograph showing the incorporation of labeled glycine into bone marrow cells (Ref. 5).

lytic deposition, and metabolic processes in vegetable and animal organs. The autoradiograph shown in Fig. 18–1 as an example was obtained with an emulsion suitable for detecting the tracks of individual β-particles, and illustrates the localization of glycine labeled with radiocarbon in three polynuclear leucocytes [5].

The use of tracers in chemical analysis is becoming increasingly widespread, not only because of the advantages outlined above, but also because, as will be seen in Chapter 22, they lend themselves to *nondestructive* analytical methods, which do not require chemical attack on the substance under analysis, being carried out by a simple measurement of the radioactivity induced on exposure to radiation (the *activation* method).

Using the term in its widest sense, the tracer method includes a number of techniques concerned not with the *atomic* properties of isotopes, but with the ionizing properties of *radiations* and the effect of the properties of some absorbing material on the absorption and scattering of radiation; γ-ray radiography, and analysis by neutron transmission, are examples of this. Methods based on the ability of solids to release a radioactive gas formed in the solid itself (the *emanating power*) are another of these applications.

18–2 Choosing a tracer. The possibility of using a radioactive indicator depends on two essential conditions being fulfilled; first there must be a radioactive isotope with a half-life sufficiently long to be compatible with the time necessary for the experimental operations and measurements involved, and second the radiation intensity after incorporating the indicator into the system must be sufficient to be measurable, and sufficient to be able to determine (if necessary quantitatively) changes in the distribution of the activity between a number of different compounds or phases. These two conditions, a reasonably long half-life and a reasonably high intensity, are often mutually contradictory. Thus for a given activation period in a reactor or an accelerator, the number of radioactive atoms produced generally increases as the half-life decreases, and the same applies to the accumulation of a nuclide in a family of natural radioactive elements. When an element has several radioactive isotopes, one would normally choose the one most easily prepared and with the most advantageous overall nuclear properties. It is, for example, preferable to use C^{14} ($t_{1/2}$, 5568 years) rather than C^{11} ($t_{1/2}$, 20 min); on the other hand, in most cases, thorium-B with a half-life of 10.6 hours is the most useful indicator for lead, rather than radium-D with a half-life of 22 years, since the latter emits only very soft β-particles.

The properties of the radiation emitted is a third factor which must be considered in choosing an indicator. Radiation which is very easily absorbed, such as that emitted in electron capture processes, can be measured with normal Geiger counters only with difficulty, so that scintillation counters must be used. On the other hand, penetrating γ-radiation is a drawback in measurements designed to give the spatial distribution of the emitting atoms, as in self-diffusion measurements (Section 19–8), or in electrolytic deposition in the presence of the radioactive solution being electrolyzed (Section 20–4). Beta-emitters are most easily measured with ordinary counters; α-emitters are the most suitable for autoradiography.

A very long-lived radioelement which emits soft radiation can be labeled by a more active natural or artificial isotope, so that natural uranium can be traced by using U^{237}, natural protactinium by Pa^{233}, thorium by RdAc or UX-1, radium by ThX, etc. In purely qualitative experiments it is even possible to label an element with its homologue, such as tagging barium with a radium isotope, or bromine with radioiodine.

The intensity of the radioactive indicator should not be too high, first to avoid introducing errors in the counting techniques, and second to prevent radiolytic effects, and the contamination of apparatus or of individuals handling the materials. From this latter point of view, the use of an indicator with a short half-life has some advantages, since any contamination disappears rapidly as the nuclide decays away. For convenience of measurement, intensities at least 5 to 20 times greater than the "background" of the counter are used, but quite accurate results may still be obtained with much lower intensities by making a larger number of measurements.

For experimental simplicity and reliability, the radioactive indicator itself must be quite pure, so that nonisotopic radioactive atoms must be

TABLE 18–1

RADIOACTIVE ISOTOPES USED AS TRACERS

Element	Mass number	Half-life	Principal radiation	Energy,* Mev	Produced by†	Specific activity per gm‡
H	3	12.46 yr	β^-	0.019	n	
Be	7	53.6 d	γ	0.48	p	cf
Be	10	2.4×10^6 yr	β^-	0.56	n	μc
C	14	5568 yr	β^-	0.155	n	12 c
F	18	112 min	β^+	0.65	p	
Na	22	2.6 yr	β^+	0.54	p	1 c
Na	24	15.06 hr	β^-	1.39	n	2 c
Mg	27	9.6 min	β^-	1.8	n	
Al	26	8×10^5 yr	β^+	1.16	p	
Si	31	2.6 hr	β^-	1.47	n	
P	32	14.3 d	β^-	1.7	n	cf
S	35	87.1 d	β^-	0.167	n	cf
Cl	36	4.4×10^5 yr	β^-	0.71	n	0.6 mc
Cl	38	37,3 min	β^-	4.81	n	
Ar	37	34.1 d	x	—	n	cf
K	42	12.4 hr	β^-	3.6	n	150 mc
Ca	45	152 d	β^-	0.25	n	60 c
Sc	46	85 d	β^-	0.36	n	6.5 c
V	48	16 d	β^-	0.72	p	cf
Cr	51	27.8 d	γ	0.32	n, p	4c
Mn	54	290.7 d	γ, x	0.84	p	cf

Mn	56	2.57 hr	β^-	2.86	n	
Fe	55	2.94 yr	x		n, p	5 c
Fe	59	45.1 d	β^-	0.46	n, p	5 c
Co	57	270 d	γ, x	0.13	p	cf
Co	60	5.27 yr	γ	1.17, 1.33	n	8 c
Ni	63	85 yr	β^-	0.067	n	0.5 c
Cu	64	12.8 hr	β^-, β^+, γ	β^- 0.57; β^+ 0.65	n	6.5 c
Zn	65	250 d	γ, x	1.12	n, p	cf
Ga	72	14.3 hr	β^-	3.15	n	2 c
Ge	71	11.4 d	x		n	
As	76	26.8 hr	β^-	3.04	n	8 c
Se	75	127 d	γ	0.405	n	
Br	82	35.9 hr	β^-, γ	β^- 0.46; γ 1.31		
Rb	86	19.5 d	β^-	1.8	n, f	cf
Sr	89	53 d	β^-	1.46	f	cf
Sr	90	27.7 yr	β^-	0.61	f	cf
Y	90	2.54 d	β^-	2.18	f	cf
Zr	95	65 d	β^-	0.39	f	cf
Nb	95	35 d	β^-	0.16	f	cf
Mo	99	67 hr	β^-	1.23	f, p	

* For β-particles, this is $E_{\max}$, and for γ-rays the hardest component; the x-rays are from electron capture processes.

† n–neutron bombardment
p–accelerated particle reaction
f–fission product
nat.–natural radioelement

‡ These specific activities are for production in the Oak Ridge reactor, and are taken from A. F. Rupp and F. T. Binford, *J. Appl. Phys.*, **24,** 1069 (1953), with corrections kindly supplied by Dr. Rupp. (c = curies, cf = carrier-free.)

(Continued)

TABLE 18–1 (*Continued*)

Element	Mass number	Half-life	Principal radiation	Energy,* in Mev	Produced by†	Specific activity per gm‡
Tc	99	2.1×10^5 yr	β^-	0.30	f	cf
Ru	103	39.6 d	β^-	0.22	f	5 c
Ru	106	1 yr	β^-	0.04	f, n	5 c
Rh	105	36.5 hr	β^-	0.57	f, p	
Pd	103	17 d	x		n	
Ag	110	270 d	β^-	0.088	n	1 c
Cd	115	43 d	β^-	1.6	n	210 c
In	114	49 d	β, γ	β^- 1.98; γ 1.27	n	1 c
Sn	113	112 d	γ	0.393	n	20 mc
Sb	124	60 d	β^-	2.29	n	2.7 c
Te	127	115 d	β^-, γ	β^- 0.7; γ 0.085	f	cf
I	129	1.7×10^7 yr	β^-	0.13	f	cf
I	131	8.1 d	β^-	0.815	f	cf
Xe	133	5.3 d	β^-	0.34	f, n	cf
Cs	137	30.4 yr	β^-	0.52	f	cf
Ba	140	12.8 d	β^-	1.02	f	cf
La	140	40 hr	β^-	2.26	f, n	cf
Ce	144	275 d	β^-	0.30	f	cf
Pr	143	13.7 d	β^-	0.93	f	cf
Nd	147	11.3 d	β^-	0.825	f	cf
Pm	147	2.6 yr	β^-	0.223	f	cf
Sm	151	73 yr	β^-	0.076	f	cf
Eu	152, 154	13–16 yr	β^-	1.9	n	5 c

Eu	155	1.7 yr	β^-	0.154	f	cf
Gd	153	236 d	γ	0.102	n	
Hf	181	45 d	β^-	0.408	n	cf
Ta	182	115 d	β^-	0.53	n	1.7 c
W	185	73.2 d	β^-	0.43	n	cf
Re	186	92 hr	β^-	1.07	n, p	
Os	191	16 d	β^-	0.14	n	
Ir	192	74.37 d	β^-	0.67	n	>10 c
Pt	197	18 hr	β^-	0.67	n	
Au	198	2.7 d	β^-	0.96	n	30 c
Au	199	3.15 d	β^-	0.46	n	
Hg	203, 5	47.9 d	β^-	0.208	n	830 mc
Tl	204	3.5 yr	β^-	0.78	n	0.6 c
Pb	212 (ThB)	10.6 hr	β^-	0.355	nat.	cf
Bi	210 (RaE)	5 d	β^-	1.165	nat., n	cf
Ra	224 (ThX)	3.64 d	α	5.68	nat.	cf
Ac	228 (MsTh-2)	6.13 hr	β^-	2.03	nat.	cf
Th	234 (UX-1)	24.1 d	β^-	2.32 (UX-2)	nat.	cf
Pa	233	27.4 d	β^-	0.530	n	
U	237	6.7 d	β^-	0.231	n	

* For β-particles, this is $E_{\max}$, and for γ-rays the hardest component; the x-rays are from electron capture processes.

† n–neutron bombardment
p–accelerated particle reaction
f–fission product
nat.–natural radioelement

‡ These specific activities are for production in the Oak Ridge reactor, and are taken from A. F. Rupp and F. T. Binford, *J. Appl. Phys.*, **24,** 1069 (1953), with corrections kindly supplied by Dr. Rupp. (c = curies, cf = carrier-free.)

absent; even the presence of two isotopes of the same elements with different half-lives and radiations may be a considerable nuisance. It is often difficult to satisfy this condition with natural radioelements, and with some fission products produced by the decay of other nuclides. If the parent isotope has a relatively short half-life, it is only necessary to wait for it to decay away, but in other cases it may be necessary to separate the two chemically. It is also possible to eliminate the radiation of one isotope by absorption if it is appreciably the softer; for example, there is no difficulty in using the β-emitter RaE as a tracer for bismuth in spite of the presence of Po^{210}, since the α-particles from the latter can be easily absorbed. In fact, in certain cases the existence of a radioactive daughter element may facilitate the measurements. Thus the concentration of RaD can be easily measured by determining the β-activity of RaE after the two nuclides have been allowed to come to radioactive equilibrium; similarly the measurement of Ru^{106} is made considerably easier by the formation of Rh^{106}, which emits 3.55- and 2.3-Mev β-particles.

Radioactive isotopes prepared by activation with slow neutrons or other relatively low-energy accelerated particles are generally purer than those obtained in high-energy reactions, in which multiple simultaneous nuclear processes may occur.

The necessity for an appreciably long half-life virtually excludes (or renders extremely difficult) the use of radioactive indicators for a number of light elements, including He, Li, B, or O. For oxygen, the stable isotope O^{18} can be used if a mass spectrometer is available, and for nitrogen the stable N^{15} is more frequently used than the radioactive N^{13}. Similarly compounds containing hydrogen and carbon are often labeled with D or C^{13}. Table 18–1 contains a list of the isotopes normally used as tracers for various elements.

In addition to radium, a number of radioelements are used for industrial or medical radiography, including [6]

$$Na^{24},\ Co^{60},\ Xe^{133},\ Cs^{127},\ Ce^{144},\ Eu^{154},\ Tm^{170},\ Ta^{182},\ Ir^{192},\ Au^{198}.$$

18–3 Labeling molecules. The scheme set out in Eq. (18–1), which is fundamental to the tracer method, is valid only if the atoms A and A' are initially in the same physical and chemical state. If this is not the case, the reactions of one species can obviously differ from those of the other. Suppose, for example, that an organic acid labeled with C^{14} is partially oxidized and 50% of the C^{14} is found as $C^{14}O_2$; one can only conclude that 50% of the acid has combusted (even neglecting isotope effects) if the method of preparation (i.e., the labeling) of the active acid did not allow any other labeled organic compound to be produced or to remain after the purification process.

Similarly, if a mixture of active CrO_4^{2-} and inactive Cr^{3+} ions are electrolyzed, deposition of radiochromium at the cathode only indicates the reduction of the former type of ion. This conclusion is justified by the fact that isotopic exchange between CrO_4^{2-} and Cr^{3+} is very slow compared with the time taken for electrolysis (Section 19–3). On the other hand, if a mixture of Fe^{2+} and Fe^{3+} is partially electrolyzed, with only one of these species labeled, the radioiron content of the deposit gives no information about the relative rate of discharge of the two ionic species, since the isotopic exchange between them is rapid and the indicator is distributed between them very rapidly in the ratio of their concentrations. Quite generally, if a radioactive indicator appears in a product Z after having been originally in a compound S, reliable conclusions about the reaction $S \rightarrow Z$ can only be drawn if the system contains no compound S' which could rapidly exchange with S. This condition is especially important in using tracer techniques to study biochemical metabolism.

When a labeled compound S^* is diluted with the isotopic inactive compound S, it is absolutely necessary to be certain of the *physical homogeneity* of the mixture. For this reason, it is necessary to convert the mixture completely to the fluid state, at least for a very short period. If one of the components is crystalline, the homogeneity can sometimes be achieved by slow recrystallization. A simple mechanical mixing of powders, no matter how intimate the final mixture, will obviously not be sufficient to achieve isotopic homogeneity inside the grains themselves.

In order to get the tracer into the desired molecular form, some appropriate synthesis must be carried out. If this involves relatively simple compounds, normal chemical methods will usually suffice, but it is sometimes necessary to use specific radiochemical procedures such as isotopic exchange or Szilard-Chalmers reactions. Aromatic halogen compounds in particular can be labeled by exchange with active $AlCl_3$ or $AlBr_3$, or by the use of these compounds as catalysts for transfer reactions between organic halides. Other syntheses utilizing exchange reactions can be carried out at room temperature or on heating. The Szilard-Chalmers effect can sometimes be a hindrance; thus in attempting to prepare an active compound directly by neutron bombardment, some of the activity may end up in a form chemically different from the initial molecule due to recoil effects. This is the case (despite earlier claims) in attempts to label vitamin B_{12} ($C_{63}H_{90}N_{14}O_{14}PCo$) with radiocobalt by neutron bombardments, which gave negative results since the retention of radiocobalt is practically zero [7, 8, 9].

The synthesis of complex organic molecules labeled with H^2, H^3, C^{14}, N^{15}, P^{32}, S^{35}, etc., is less straightforward, first because losses of the rather expensive indicators must be avoided, and second because of the risk that the tracer may concentrate in some impurity or by-product. The purity of the required compound can be checked by chemical degradation, followed by comparison of the specific activity of the products with the specific activity of the initial molecule. This degradation also gives information on the position of the tracer atom in a synthetic molecule, which is frequently a most important point in solving certain problems.*

In some cases, it is necessary to place two identical tracer atoms in different positions, or two chemically different atoms, in the same molecule. For example, acetic acid doubly labeled with C^{14} has been synthesized

---

* For the synthesis of labeled organic molecules, see H. R. V. Arnstein and R. Bentley, *Quart. Revs.*, **4**, 172 (1950), and S. L. Thomas and H. S. Turner, *Quart. Revs.*, **7**, 407 (1953).

from active barium carbonate [10]:

$$BaC^{14}O_3 \xrightarrow{Mg + H_2} BaC_2^{14} \xrightarrow{H_2O} C_2^{14}H_2 \xrightarrow{KOH} C^{14}H_3{\cdot}C^{14}OOH. \quad (18\text{-}2)$$

By using this acid as a starting point for further reactions, it is possible to prepare ethyl iodide, ethylene, and other doubly labeled compounds [10]:

$$\begin{aligned} C^{14}H_3C^{14}OOH &\xrightarrow{C_6H_5COCl} C^{14}H_3C^{14}OCl \xrightarrow{LiAlH_4} C^{14}H_3C^{14}H_2OH \\ &\xrightarrow{HI} C^{14}H_3C^{14}H_2I \xrightarrow{(CH_3)_3N} (CH_3)_3C^{14}H_3C^{14}H_2NI \\ &\xrightarrow[NaOH]{AgNO_3} (CH_3)_3C^{14}H_3C^{14}H_2NOH \\ &\xrightarrow{heat} C^{14}H_2{=}C^{14}H_2 + (CH_3)_3N + H_2O. \end{aligned} \quad (18\text{-}3)$$

An organic compound can be labeled with both C^{14} and D or T at the same time, or with N^{15}; similarly in an inorganic sulfate both the metal and the sulfur can be labeled. Double labeling is particularly important in metabolic studies, since the debris from the degraded molecules may undergo differing fates; examples of this are discussed in Chapter 24. In synthesizing radioactive organic molecules, microbiological and enzymatic methods are often used, as is photosynthesis with $C^{14}O_2$.

A large and continually increasing number of radioactive compounds have been synthesized (see previous footnote). These include high molecular weight amino-acids, carbohydrates, coloring matters, silicones, steroids (including cortisone), vitamin B_1, alkaloids, penicillin and streptomycin, and hormones such as thyroxine (with radioactive iodine) and insulin (radiozinc). The tobacco mosaic virus has been labeled with P^{32} or C^{14} by growing the infected plants either in a medium containing radiophosphorus, or in an atmosphere containing $C^{14}O_2$ [12].

18-4 Experimental conditions and radiometric techniques. The determination of the absolute intensities from natural radioelements is a relatively simple matter because of the relationships between the members of each radioactive family at equilibrium, which makes it possible to prepare standards with known rates of disintegration. The absolute measurement of artificial β-emitters is much more difficult [13] because of the energy dependence of the various factors which affect the response of the counter (e.g., absorption, scattering, back-scattering, etc.). Fortunately, in experiments with tracers, the measurement of absolute activities is only rarely important; more frequently one wishes either to follow changes in the specific activity of a reacting substance relative to a standard sample of the same substance (*internal standardization*), or to measure the distribution of the activity between various derivatives, fractions, or phases. For such relative measurements, it is sufficient to ensure that the various products are in the same chemical and physical state, and to place them in the counting apparatus under identical geometrical conditions.

Specific activities are expressed either in curies (or millicuries) per gram, or as a number of counts per unit time and per unit mass or volume. The relative specific activities can be obtained directly from counting rates if these are measured on "thick layers" (Section 11–4) (i.e., on layers of material which are sufficiently thick that further increase in the thickness causes no increase in the measured activity). The quantity of material required to achieve such conditions depends essentially on the nature and the energy of the emitted radiation. For the very soft β-particles from C^{14} or S^{35}, 20 to 30 mg/cm^2 already constitutes a thick layer [14]. The specific masses required for harder β-particles are indicated in Fig. 11–8. If the radiation is highly penetrating, or if insufficient material is available to form a thick layer, it is still desirable to carry out the comparative measurements on the thickest possible layers since changes in the measured intensity with the superficial mass decrease as the mass increases. In certain cases, however, it is more advantageous to do the measurements with thin layers, as when studying electrolytic deposition from extremely dilute solutions, or isotopic exchange between a (solid) metal and its ions.

The handling of labeled products, and especially of concentrated radioactive sources, requires special precautions because of the necessity of avoiding contamination. These precautions depend on the nature of the materials and on the experiment being carried out, especially on the possible presence of substances which are volatile under the experimental conditions. The precautions also depend on the nature of the radiation (i.e., whether penetrating or not), and on the amount of activity being used, since obviously the precautions necessary for working at the microcurie level will differ from those used when dealing with curies of activity.

In principle, a laboratory for working with very low activities should be separate, and if possible completely removed, from one designed for average or high activities. The laboratory must be equipped to give efficient protection to the workers, by the use of installations by which experiments can be carried out behind a screen of metal or lead glass, by a suitable ventilation system, and by the use of fume cupboards and glove boxes. The equipment of "hot" laboratories, that is to say, those designed for working with activities of $\sim$1 curie or more, require remote-control installations, handling facilities, and specially designed controls which cannot be fully discussed here (see Refs. 15, 16, 17). Although less hazardous, contamination of the substances being handled and of the counting apparatus can also be a great nuisance. There is always a risk of introducing errors if substances labeled with different radioelements are handled in the same laboratory. The successive use of vessels for different active species should be avoided, since even careful cleaning cannot prevent the almost inevitable spread of the activities due to several different radioelements in these circumstances. In particular it should be noted that radioactive compounds of metals in the higher valency states are easily, and to some extent irreversibly, adsorbed as either ionic or colloidal species on the surfaces of solids at the tracer level.

The storage of highly active substances also raises several delicate problems. Vessels of fused silica or quartz are preferred for concentrated solutions, since glass vessels may crack on standing; plastics do not have good chemical resistance to radiation. Another difficulty is that electric charges build up inside sealed ampoules containing highly radioactive powders, and there is an especially strong risk of discharge and breakage when such an ampoule is being opened. To guard against this danger, a platinum wire is normally sealed into the vessel; this helps to dissipate the charge through the end which projects from the vessel.

18–5 Tracer-level chemistry. It is not always an advantage to dilute a tracer with inactive isotopic atoms, and in fact there are a large number of physico-chemical problems at the "tracer level" which can be studied only by using the tracer in the purest possible state without "carriers." The term "tracer level" then implies unweighable quantities of material, lower than the microchemical scale. These quantities are invisible even to the microscope, and are generally below the sensitive level of normal detection methods; roughly speaking, this means less than 10^{-7} gm, corresponding to concentrations below $10^{-7}\,M$ in solution, or to surface coverages of less than a monomolecular layer.

The fundamental question here is whether the already known properties of macroscopic quantities can be directly extrapolated to the tracer level, and vice versa, whether conclusions about the tracer-level behavior of an element are valid for its macroscopic properties. In other words, it is necessary to find out whether the normal physico-chemical laws apply to almost infinitely small quantities of material, or whether these laws possibly lose their validity or require some modification, in the same way that some of the properties of the permanent gases are changed at extremely low pressures at which the mean free path of the molecules becomes greater than the distances between the walls of the containing vessel. This question is of considerable theoretical and practical importance, especially in the separation and purification of radioelements which do not occur naturally or which can only be prepared in extremely high dilution or in tracer quantities. Information from the study of extremely small quantities is also of considerable interest in analytical chemistry, in relation to the removal or concentration of traces of contaminants, and an understanding of their importance (or interference) in various procedures.

In considering these questions, it must first be remembered that although a change in scale in using quantities several powers of ten lower than normal may lead to results which are *apparently qualitatively different*, these may still be governed by the same laws as are valid on the macroscopic scale. Let us take an example from chemical kinetics and consider a mixture of three substances, A, B, and C, in which A may react with either B or C:

$$A + B \xrightarrow{k_1} X, \tag{18–4}$$

$$A + C \xrightarrow{k_2} Y. \tag{18–5}$$

Let k_1, the rate constant for reaction (18–4) be much larger than k_2; for example, let $k_1/k_2 = 10^6$. Suppose also that the reaction product X can react with some other substance present (M) to set up the equilibrium condition

$$X + M \rightleftharpoons XM, \qquad \text{with } \frac{[XM]}{[X][M]} = K. \tag{18–6}$$

If the concentrations of B and C are comparable, allowing for the ratio k_1/k_2, then X will be essentially formed at the expense of Y, and reaction (18–6) will proceed from left to right. If, however, B is present at the tracer level, (e.g., concentration $10^{-12}\,M$), and the concentration of C (which might for example be the H^+ ion) is of the order of 1 N, then the formation of Y will take place. Under these conditions, the substance XM, if it is present, will undergo dissociation, according to Eq. (18–6), from right to left. However, note that both sets of results, which are in the opposite sense, result from the same law, expressed by the equilibrium constant.

Another case in which a change in the relative quantities can produce seemingly different results is the formation of complexes by a cation in the presence of an excess of anions. The stability of such complexes increases with the anion : cation concentration ratio, so that a complex whose formation cannot be detected under macroscopic conditions at which the concentration of the positive and negative components is similar may well be formed at the tracer level. This is the case with Pb^{2+} ions; complexing with Cl^- ions gives the slightly soluble simple compound $PbCl_2$, but with ThB ions (Pb^{212}) at a concentration of 10^{-10} to $10^{-12}\,M$ in sufficiently concentrated HCl solution, migration of most of the ThB to the anode suggests the formation of complex anions of the type $[PbCl_n]^{(n-2)-}$.

A last example comes from electrochemistry. In Section 20–7 a discussion is given of the conditions under which the Nernst electrochemical equation,

$$E = E_0 + \frac{RT}{zF} \log_e a, \tag{18–7}$$

is valid at the tracer level. Let us assume for the moment that it describes the displacement of one metal by another which is more electropositive, such as, for example, the displacement of radiocopper by zinc in very dilute solution. Consider the situation when zinc has been bombarded with neutrons to give radiocopper, Zn^{64} (n, p) Cu^{64}. The normal potential of Cu/Cu^{2+} is 0.34 v and that of Zn/Zn^{2+} − 0.76 v, and it is therefore easy to see that the Zn^{2+} ions will tend to remain in solution to a much greater extent than Cu^{2+}, even if their respective concentrations are 10^{-2} and $10^{-16}\,N$. Under these conditions, the potential for zinc would be

$$E = -0.76 - \frac{0.058 \times 2}{2} = -0.82 \text{ v},$$

and for copper

$$E = +0.34 - \frac{0.058 \times 16}{2} = -0.12 \text{ v},$$

so that if the radiozinc powder is treated with dilute HCl solution until only about 10 mg remains, this residue retains the radioactive copper in high yield. It is possible to go even further [18]; the zinc residue can be dissolved in a small volume of more dilute HCl, and a sheet of lead placed in this. This metal dissolves slightly in the solution to give a concentration of Pb^{2+} ions of the order of 10^{-4} N, so that its potential is

$$E = -0.13 - \frac{0.058 \times 4}{2} = -0.24 \text{ v},$$

so that the radiocopper now deposits on the surface of the lead.

Suppose instead the zinc powder had been bombarded with α-particles, giving the nuclear reaction Zn^{64} (α, p) Ga^{67}. Assuming again a concentration of 10^{-16} N for radioactive Ga^{3+} and 10^{-2} for Zn^{2+}, we find that the relative potentials would be —0.83 and —0.82 v, and the radiogallium would remain in solution. If, however, a drop of very dilute ordinary $GaCl_3$ is added to the radioactive solution, the Ga concentration becomes, say 10^{-10} N, and the potential is then approximately —0.72 v, favoring deposition of the gallium on the zinc.

It will become apparent later, however, that the Nernst equation is far from being generally valid for the electrolysis of extremely dilute solutions when deposition on the electrodes is not sufficient to give a monatomic layer (assuming that the surface is perfectly planar). Many examples discussed in later chapters will demonstrate that in the presence of a solid phase, surface effects, adsorption, diffusion, the slow rate at which some true thermodynamic equilibria are established, and other factors make the phenomena very complex and difficult to predict. The same laws hold, but their analysis and interpretation becomes more unreliable. In contrast to this, the experimental facts show that for phenomena in homogeneous systems, and especially in aqueous solutions, the principles and laws of macroscopic chemistry can apparently be applied, provided that account is taken of the qualitative changes which may be caused by the relative proportions of the species present. The best illustration of this is the chemistry of plutonium and its compounds; the physico-chemical properties were first established at the tracer level, subsequently confirmed on the microgram scale, and finally proven with milligram or gram quantities of the element. The same is also largely true for the chemistry of polonium.

References

1. J. W. Scraba, J. G. Burr, and N. D. Hess, *J. Chem. Phys.*, **21,** 1296 (1953).

2. C. D. Wagner and J. V. Guinn, *J. Am. Chem. Soc.*, **75,** 4861 (1953).

3. R. M. Lemmon, *et al.*, *J. Am. Chem. Soc.*, **75,** 1867 (1953).

4. R. M. Lemmon, *et al.*, *Nucleonics*, **11,** No. 10, 44 (1953).

5. A. Ficq, F. Gavosto, and M. Errera, *Exptl. Cell Res.*, **6,** 69 (1954).

6. See W. S. Eastwood, *Research*, **5,** 399 (1952).

7. P. Numerof and J. Kowald, *J. Am. Chem. Soc.*, **75,** 4350 (1953).

8. D. T. Woodbury and C. Rosenblum, *J. Am. Chem. Soc.*, **75,** 4364 (1953).

9. A. G. Maddock and F. Pinto Coelho, *J. Chem. Soc.*, **1954,** 4702.

10. R. Abrams, *Experientia*, **3,** 488 (1947).

11. G. H. Wood, *J. Biol. Chem.*, **194,** 905 (1952).

12. G. Wüstinger, E. Broda, and H. Schönfellinger, *Monatsh. Chem.*, **86,** 131 (1955).

13. See, for example, W. J. Whitehouse and J. L. Putnam, *Radioactive Isotopes*, Oxford University Press, 1953.

14. W. F. Libby, *Ind. Eng. Chem., Anal. Ed.*, **19,** 2 (1947).

15. G. N. Yakovlev, *et al.*, *1955 Geneva Conference*, P. 672.

16. P. R. Fields and H. Youngquist, *1955 Geneva Conference*, P. 725.

17. A. F. Rupp, *1955 Geneva Conference*, P. 315.

18. M. Haïssinsky, *Nature*, **136,** 141 (1935).

CHAPTER 19

ISOTOPIC EXCHANGE

19–1 Introduction. Isotopic exchange reactions were discussed in Chapter 9 as a special case of thermodynamic isotope effects. The kinetic study of such processes, which is a typical example of the use of radioactive indicators (or of isotopic indicators in general) approaches this topic from a very different point of view, and in fact in such work isotope effects are neglected completely, and a system labeled with a radioactive or stable isotope is regarded as being chemically homogeneous, so that the isotope is simply used as an indicator. In other words, the rates of exchange are assumed to be the same for all the isotopic atoms, irrespective of their mass. For example, if the initially labeled species contains x radioactive atoms, and a atoms of the inactive isotope, and if after exchange x' radioactive atoms are found to have exchanged, it can be concluded that $a'(=ax'/x)$ inactive atoms have also exchanged. This approach has been most successful in using exchange reactions to study problems of chemical bonding, structure, reaction mechanisms, and the like.

From this point of view, then, *isotopic exchanges* are regarded as being *spontaneous reciprocal substitutions of an atom (electrically neutral or charged, radioactive or stable) in a molecular entity by another atom of the same atomic number and of equal or different mass, arising from another (or the same) molecular entity.* The two species may differ either in their chemical constitution, or in their physical state, or in both of these. It follows from the above definition that for a given system the rate of the process is independent of the species marked by the tracer isotope, so that if k_1 and k_2 are the rates for the exchange processes $A^* \rightarrow B$ and $B^* \rightarrow A$ (where the asterisk indicates the initially marked species), k_1 should be equal to k_2, and it is essential to verify this condition in kinetic studies of exchange processes.

Isotopic exchanges often require an activation energy, which may be considerable, but they result in a very small decrease in the free energy, due to the increase in the entropy of the system due to the redistribution of the tracer. The internal energy of the system undergoes virtually no change, since the initial and final states of the system are identical [1]

$$\Delta G = T\,\Delta S, \qquad \Delta H \approx 0. \tag{19–1}$$

All other free energy changes in the system should in principle be zero, which is another way of saying that the exchange should not be accompanied by the transfer of matter in only one direction, and hence that it should not be associated with a chemical change. Suppose, for instance, a sheet of radioactive copper is placed in a solution of $CuSO_4$, which becomes radioactive after a certain contact time; this does not necessarily mean that an exchange has taken place, since the transfer of activity to the solution may be due to chemical attack on the metal. Alternatively, if the solution itself is labeled, the appearance of active atoms in the metallic sheet may possibly be due to some adsorption effect. To be certain that exchange is taking place, it is necessary to verify that $k_1 = k_2$ (see above). In some cases, chemical changes associated with the exchange are inevitable, in which case due allowance must be made for these effects in the kinetic study.

Isotopic exchange reactions are usually *thermal* processes; that is to say, the activation energy necessary for the process to take place is provided by thermal agitation. In some cases, however, exchange reactions are accelerated by the action of light or of ionizing radiations, or may occur only through "hot atom" reactions (Chapter 17).

Exchange reactions can be catalyzed both homogeneously and heterogeneously. For example, arsenious acid does not exchange with arsenic acid at room temperature, but exchange does occur if a trace of iodide is added to the solution [2], since the iodine acts as an intermediate for the redox process

$$H_3AsO_3 + I_3^- + H_2O \underset{k_2}{\overset{k_1}{\rightleftharpoons}} H_3AsO_4 + 3I^- + 2H^+. \qquad (19\text{–}2)$$

In a similar way, chloride ions often catalyze exchanges between ions such as Eu^{2+}/Eu^{3+} and Tl^+/Tl^{3+}.

The latter exchange shows another catalytic effect, also found in other systems, and which may be a considerable nuisance in kinetic studies. The chemical separation of the two constituents, which is generally achieved by precipitating one species from aqueous solution, *induces* additional exchange, which depends on the conditions, and which may be quite appreciable in magnitude. Thus if the Tl(I) ion is precipitated as Tl_2CrO_4, the induced exchange is between 2 and 8%, whereas that induced by precipitating $Tl(OH)_3$ may exceed 65%; precipitation of TlBr or Tl_2PtCl_6 gives values between these two extremes [3]. If the overall exchange (i.e., induced plus homogeneous) is incomplete after a certain contact time, this catalytic effect can be allowed for in establishing the kinetics, by correcting for the exchange found at time $t = 0$. If, however, complete exchange is found when the two constituents are mixed and then separated immediately, it is not possible to decide whether this is due to instantaneous homogeneous exchange or to catalytic processes in the separation.

Various attempts have been made to get over this difficulty, either by using a physical method of separation such as diffusion through a glass sinter, or by extraction into an organic solvent, or by complexing one of the constituents with some appropriate reagent which halts the exchange immediately. For example, if α-α'-dipyridyl is added to an aqueous Fe(II)/Fe(III) solution containing one labeled ionic species, the Fe(II) ions are "blocked" by the formation of a very stable complex and so can undergo no further exchange [4]. The two constituents can then be separated by a suitable chemical procedure without any possibility of induced exchange occurring.

The exchange between the cobalto-triethylamine and cobalti-triethylamine ions is catalyzed by silica and platinum [5]. Catalysis on the surface of solids is particularly important in exchange between H_2 or O_2 and their compounds.* The $H_2 + D_2 \rightleftharpoons 2HD$ homogeneous exchange, originally studied at high temperatures in the classical work of A. and L. Farkas [6, 7], goes with a measurable velocity on Cr_2O_3 at temperatures as low as 190°, and the reaction is complete after a few minutes contact with a nickel catalyst at 450°C. The kinetics of the process are very similar to those for the ortho-parahydrogen conversion (Section 7–5), and it seems that the mechanism involves dissociation to hydrogen atoms in both cases. The H_2 + liquid D_2O exchange proceeds only in the presence of platinum or other metals, or of certain fermenting agents. The exchange of H_2 with unsaturated hydrocarbons is fairly rapid on catalysts, such as nickel or copper at 100°; for paraffins, exchange is complete after a few hours on nickel at 180°C for CH_4, at 110° for C_2H_6, and at 30° for *n*-hexane. Nickel also catalyses the $C_6H_6 + D_2O$ exchange, which is about 10% complete after 24 hr at 80°, and 100% after 2 hr at 200°C.

The exchange of oxygen between H_2O^{18} and carboxylic ions is catalyzed by specific enzymes [8]. The $O_2^{16} + H_2O^{18}$ exchange is catalyzed by a number of surfaces, being 50% on MgO at 530°, on CaO at 510°, on BaO at 400°, on Al_2O_3 at 650°, on TiO_2 at 690°, on V_2O_5 or MoO_3 at 630°, on WO_3 at 50°, and on CuO at between 500 and 730° depending on the method of preparing the catalyst [9]. This exchange is also catalyzed by asbestos impregnated with NaOH or KOH, obtained by calcination of the carbonate.

In some cases, negative catalysis is also observed, as for example, in the already slow Mn^{2+}/MnO_4^- exchange, which is still further slowed down by the presence of MnO_2 [10].

19–2 Exchange by association. Kinetic studies of exchange processes show that they may have extremely fast, medium, or zero rates depending on the particular system and on the experimental conditions. The aim of such studies is to establish precisely the dependence of the velocity on the various factors involved, and if possible to deduce the mechanism of the process. From this point of view, exchange reactions can be conveniently divided into two groups, associative and dissociative. The first type can be represented by the general equation

$$AB + A^*C \rightleftharpoons ABA^*C \rightleftharpoons A^*B + AC. \qquad (19\text{–}3)$$

An example of this is the $N^{14}O + N^{15}O_2$ exchange, in which atom transfer occurs via the intermediate compound N_2O_3 [11]:

$$N^{14}O + N^{15}O_2 \rightleftharpoons N^{14}N^{15}O_3 \rightleftharpoons N^{15}O + N^{14}O_2. \qquad (19\text{–}4)$$

In other cases, the intermediate complex is very unstable and cannot be isolated. We shall see (Section 20–1) that electron transfer exchanges between the ions of different valency states of a metal, such as

* The examples which follow are taken from A. I. Brodsky, *Isotope Chemistry*, Academy of Sciences, Moscow, 1957.

Fe^{2+}/Fe^{3+}, Mn^{2+}/Mn^{3+}, MnO_4^-/MnO_4^{2-}, very probably involve the formation of short-lived complexes between oppositely charged ions. Hughes, *et al.* [12, 13, 14], have shown that exchange between organic halides and LiBr in acetone or alcohol solution proceeds through unstable compounds whose existence can be demonstrated by the optical inversion associated with the exchange when the organic molecule contains an assymetric carbon atom. This shows that the mechanism is the same as that proposed for the Walden inversion:

$$X^{*-} + R\!-\!\overset{\displaystyle R'}{\underset{\displaystyle R''}{C}}\!-\!X \rightarrow \left[X^{*}R\!-\!\overset{\displaystyle R'}{\underset{\displaystyle R''}{C}}\!-\!X\right]^{-} \rightarrow X^{*}\!-\!\overset{\displaystyle R'}{\underset{\displaystyle R''}{C}}\!-\!R + X^{-}. \tag{19-5}$$

In agreement with this, the rates of substitution for octyl iodide, α-phenylethyl bromide, and α-bromopropionic acid obtained from exchange experiments and from measurements of the rates of racemization agree within experimental error.

For such a mechanism, the probability of formation of the intermediate complex, and hence the rate of exchange, should decrease with increasing steric hindrance by the organic molecule. This conclusion has been confirmed on the $RI + I^{*-} \rightleftharpoons RI^* + I^-$ exchange in ethanol, for which the rates decrease in the order $CH_3 > C_2H_5 > C_3H_7 > C_4H_9$ [15, 16].

If an associative mechanism requires a considerable reorganization of the intermediate compound, the probability of exchange becomes very small, or even zero. Thus $[Pt(NH_3)_2]^{4+}$ and $[PtCl_6]^{2-}$ do not exchange platinum, since this process would require the removal of six chloride atoms from platinum.

19–3 Exchange by dissociation. To some extent, dissociative and associative mechanisms are related by the necessity for the dissociation of an addition complex. A dissociative exchange is represented by the general equation

$$A^*B + A \rightleftharpoons A^* + B + A \rightleftharpoons AB + A^*. \tag{19-6}$$

The H_2/D_2 exchange mentioned earlier is of this type, as is the exchange between PCl_5 and Cl_2,

$$PCl_5 \rightleftharpoons PCl_3 + Cl_2.$$

Dissociative exchange may take place by the intermediate formation of ions, followed by atom transfer. According to Brodsky (see previous footnote), H/D exchange between certain organic molecules and water is an example of this ionization mechanism (Section 19–5)

$$RH + HDO \rightarrow \begin{cases} RHD^+ + OH^- \rightarrow RD + H_2O, \\ R^- + HDOH^+ \rightarrow RD + H_2O. \end{cases} \tag{19-7}$$

An essential factor governing the rate of dissociative exchange reactions is the nature of the chemical bond to the labeled atom. In general, if the bond is essentially heteropolar, exchange in aqueous solution is fairly rapid, but with covalent bonds, exchange does not take place, or is very slow. Long [17] has reported a convincing example of this rule in the exchange of chromium, cobalt, aluminum, and iron oxalates with oxalic acid. Using C^{14}, it was found that the first two oxalates did not exchange, but that the rate of exchange was measurable for the aluminum and iron compounds. It is known from rates of racemization and from magnetic measurements that the bond between the metal and the oxalate group is covalent in the chromium and cobalt oxalates and electrovalent in the two others. Another example [18] is the case of diphenyliodonium iodide $(C_6H_5)_2I_2$; only one iodine atom exchanges in alcohol solution, the one which dissociates in the ionization of the molecule into $[(C_6H_5)_2I]^+$ and I^-.

This latter example introduces the concept of the *nonequivalence* of identical atoms within a molecule. Thus the sulfur atoms in the $S_2O_3^{2-}$ ion do not exchange with each other [19] and only one, that which can be precipitated with HCl, exchanges (at 100°C) with HS^- [20]. On the other hand, all four iodine atoms in $[HgI_4]^{2-}$ exchange with I_2 or I^- in solution, and are therefore all equivalent [21]. Similar experiments on the intramolecular exchange in alkaline pyrosulfates have shown that the sulfur atoms are equivalent in $Li_2S_2O_7$, in which exchange is rapid in the molten salt at 150°C, and nonequivalent in the cesium salt, in which the exchange is very slow. Similar experiments have shown the equivalence of the tungsten atoms in the isopolytungstates $Na_2W_2O_7$ and $Na_2W_4O_{13}$ [22].

In attempting to explain exchange phenomena in terms of the nature of the chemical bond, the precise influence of the bond must not be wrongly emphasized. In the first place there are no purely homopolar or heteropolar compounds, since bonds generally involve a mixing of both types. Following Pauling [23], the difference in the electronegativities of the bonded atoms can be taken as a measure of the ionic character of the bond; the greater this difference, the greater is the ionic character of the bond, and the stronger the bond.

If in spite of this, heteropolar molecules exchange more easily than homopolar molecules in aqueous solution, it is because interaction with the high dielectric solvent lowers the dissociation energy. In the absence of this effect, covalent molecules exchange more readily. A good example is CBr_4, which exchanges with $AlBr_3$ at room temperatures, whereas $SiBr_4$ does not exchange with $AlBr_3$ at all [24]. The electronegativities of Br and C are 2.8 and 2.5 (difference 0.3), and for Br and Si 2.8 − 1.8 (= 1.0), so that $SiBr_4$ has more ionic character than CBr_4, in agreement with the energies of formation, which are 90 and approximately zero kcal/mole respectively (see also Refs. 25 and 26).

The structural complexity of the molecule is also an important factor in dissociative exchange processes. Although steric hindrance may make the temporary release of one of the periphery atoms of the molecule easier, and hence facilitate exchange, it can also completely prevent exchange of an atom from the interior of a molecule. Thus both CrO_4^{2-} and MnO_4^- ions exchange oxygen fairly readily with water, but exchange of the central atoms with Cr^{3+} or Mn^{2+} is extremely slow. Equally the $[PtBr_6]^{2-}$ and $[PtBr_4]^{2-}$ ions exchange bromine slowly [27], but do not exchange platinum at all, and a similar result has been reported for $[PtCl_6]^{2-}$ and $[PtCl_4]^{2-}$ [28]. The chloride exchange is catalyzed by Ce^{4+}, and exchange of the metal atoms by light; this latter catalysis is attributed to the formation of an intermediate Pt(III)-chloro complex, which can react with the Pt(II) and Pt(IV) complexes. In contrast to the platinum complexes, $[OsCl_6]^{2-}$ does not exchange with Cl^- [29]. There is a rapid exchange of iridium between the complex $[IrCl_6]^{2-}$ and $[IrCl_6]^{3-}$ ions, since this merely involves electron transfer, but the exchange of chlorine between these two is very slow [30, 31].

In general, the barrier to the exchange of a constituent of a complex molecule increases with the coordination number. The $[Ni(CN)_4]^{2-}$ and $[Pd(CN)_4]^{2-}$ ions, for example, rapidly exchange with the CN^- ion, but $[Fe(CN)_6]^{3-}$ and $[Cr(CN)_6]^{3-}$ exchange slowly with this ion, and only under certain acidity conditions. Similarly, no exchange is found between CN^- and $[Mo(CN)_8]^{4-}$ in the absence of light [32].

Steric hindrance can be used to explain some of the exceptions to the correlation between ionic bonding and rate of exchange. Chlorophyll, which is a magnesium porphyrin, does not exchange with Mg^{2+} in acetone solution although the Mg—N bond in this molecule is probably heteropolar in nature [33], and equally iron haemoglobin and copper phenophytin do not exchange with Fe^{3+} or Cu^{2+} [34], despite the ionic character of the bonds involved. The structure of these molecules is too complex, and the number of bonds which must be broken too high, for exchange to depend only on the type of bonds involved.

19–4 The kinetics of homogeneous exchange reactions. From the kinetic point of view, exchange reactions can be further divided into two groups, homogeneous and heterogeneous. Each of these can be used to investigate different types of problems.

Various authors [35, 36] have shown that homogeneous exchange reactions are always first order with respect to *time*, irrespective of the mechanism of the process. Consider a system involving two molecular species AX and BX in dynamic equilibrium; let the first of these be labeled with an isotopic tracer

$$AX^* + BX \rightleftharpoons AX + BX^*. \tag{19–8}$$

Let a be the total number of AX molecules (i.e., both active and inactive) per unit volume, and y_0 the initial number of active molecules AX^*; equally let b be the number of BX molecules, and x the number of molecules of BX^* formed after a time t, so that the specific activities of the two compounds at this time are y/a and x/b. These will become equal (neglecting isotope effects) when the exchange is complete, so that at equilibrium the distribution of the tracer between the two species gives $x = x_\infty$ and $y = y_\infty$:

$$x_\infty/b = y_\infty/a. \tag{19–9}$$

There will also be the obvious relation

$$y_0 = y + x = y_\infty + x_\infty. \tag{19–10}$$

Let R be the rate of exchange, defined by the equation

$$\frac{dx}{dt} = R\frac{y}{a} - R\frac{x}{b} = R\left(\frac{y}{a} - \frac{x}{b}\right). \tag{19–11}$$

Note that R depends on the *order* of the reaction in terms of each component of the system, being a function of the macroscopic concentrations of these components, and possibly of other molecules or ions which may be present

$$R = k'[a]^m[b]^n[\mathrm{H}^+]^p[c]^r \ldots. \tag{19–12}$$

The equation corresponding to a first-order reaction (in terms of time) is then easily established:

$$-Rt = \frac{ab}{a+b}\ln\left(1 - \frac{x}{x_\infty}\right), \tag{19–13}$$

or, for given values of a and b

$$-kt = \log\left(1 - \frac{x}{x_\infty}\right) = \ln(1 - F). \tag{19–14}$$

The fraction exchanged is written as $F = x/x_\infty$, so that $(1 - F)$ is the fraction which has not exchanged up to time t. If the second species BX already contains x_1 atoms of the tracer per unit volume at $t = 0$, F is given by the expression

$$F = \left(\frac{x - x_1}{x_\infty - x_1}\right),$$

which must be used when working with stable isotopic tracers such as C^{13} or N^{15}, since in such cases the unlabeled compound initially contains a small proportion of the tracer isotope. In the same way it is easy to show [37] from Eqs. (19–9) and (19–10) that

$$F = \left(1 + \frac{b}{a}\right)\frac{x}{y_0} = \frac{y_0 - y}{y_0 - y_\infty} = 1 - \left(\frac{\overline{y} - \overline{x}}{\overline{y}_0}\right), \tag{19–15}$$

where $\overline{x}$ and $\overline{y}$ are the specific activities.

If one of the constituents is present in large excess over the other, one has

$$F = \frac{x}{y_0} = 1 - \frac{y}{y_0} = \frac{a}{b}\frac{\overline{x}}{\overline{y}_0}, \qquad \text{for } a > b,$$

$$F = \frac{b}{a}\frac{x}{y_0} = \frac{b}{a}\left(1 - \frac{y}{y_0}\right) = \frac{\overline{x}}{\overline{y}_\infty}, \qquad \text{for } b > a.$$

The ratio x/x_∞, which appears in Eqs. (19–13) and (19–14) can be expressed

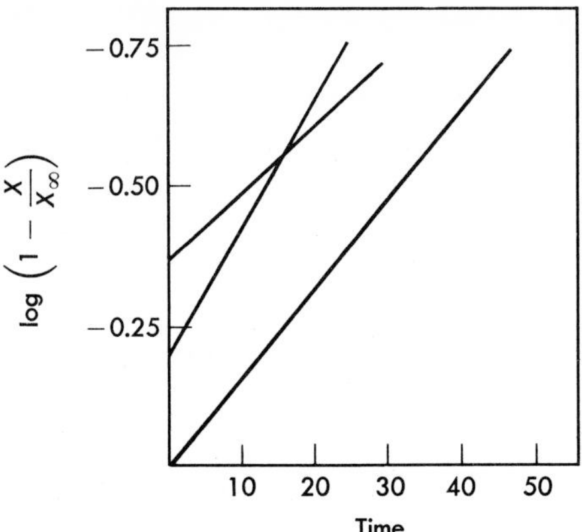

FIG. 19–1. The time dependence of isotopic exchange reactions.

in any units which are proportional to the concentration, such as number of gram atoms exchanged, number of counts per minute in some suitable counter, percentage exchange, etc.

If the logarithm of the fraction $(1 - F)$ is plotted against time, a straight line passing through the origin should be obtained, and from this R can be derived if a and b are known. If the line cuts the ordinate, it may be that the exchange is catalyzed in some way, or more generally, that the exchange proceeds by two different mechanisms, the first of which is faster than the second (Fig. 19–1). An example of this is the exchange between PCl_5 and Cl_2 in carbon tetrachloride [38]. The structure of PCl_5 is a trigonal bypyramid, in which the five chlorine atoms are not all equivalent [39]; three of these exchange immeasurably quickly, while the rate of exchange of the other two gives a straight line for $\log (1 - F)/t$, starting above the origin. There is no *a priori* reason for excluding the possibility that the line would cut the abscissa; this would imply the existence of an induction period which would slow up the start of the exchange reaction.

As in any kinetic study, a necessary step in identifying the actual exchange mechanism is to find the order of the process in terms of each of the exchanging species, and possibly of the other components of the system, or in other words to establish the factors affecting R in Eq. (19–12). When the exchange involves ionic species, it is necessary either to work at constant ionic strength, or (better) to examine the effect of changes in ionic strength on the rate of the reaction. It is often necessary to express a and b in the thermodynamic activities, rather than in formal concentrations.

The equations given are valid for molecules containing one isotopic atom, but are still valid for molecules containing two or more nonequivalent atoms if only one takes part in the exchange and the others are completely inert from this point of view. This is the case, for example, in $S_2O_3^{2-}$ (see above) in which only one sulfur atom exchanges with sulfide ions. For a molecule which contains chemically equivalent isotopic atoms, as for example in the PCl_3/HCl exchange, the equations are only valid if the concentrations are expressed in atoms per gram and not in molecules per gram. In all other cases of nonequivalence, the kinetic equations become more complex.*

A useful parameter which expresses the rate of exchange is $t_{1/2}$, the time required for half of the equilibrium distribution of the tracer to be attained (the time of half-exchange):

$$t_{1/2} = \frac{ab}{(a+b)R} \ln_e 2 = \frac{0.693}{k}. \tag{19–16}$$

Like R, $t_{1/2}$ is a function of the concentration, and only characterizes the rate of exchange precisely if the concentrations are given.

If the rate constant k is measured at several temperatures, the Arrhenius equation

$$k = \mathrm{A}e^{-E/RT} \tag{19–17}$$

can be used to get the activation energy E for the exchange being studied. This parameter is important for clarifying the mechanism of the exchange, and for characterizing the type of bonds involved in the primary processes. In a more refined study, the entropy of activation $\Delta S^{\ddagger}$ can be obtained by identifying E with $\Delta H^{\ddagger}$, the enthalpy of activation, and using the relation given by the absolute rate theory

$$\begin{aligned} k = \frac{\boldsymbol{k}T}{h} \exp - \left[\frac{\Delta F^{\ddagger}}{RT}\right] &= \frac{\boldsymbol{k}T}{h} \exp - \left[\frac{\Delta H^{\ddagger}}{RT}\right] \exp\left[\frac{\Delta S^{\ddagger}}{R}\right] \\ &= \frac{\boldsymbol{k}T}{h} \exp - \left[\frac{E}{RT}\right] \exp\left[\frac{\Delta S^{\ddagger}}{R}\right] \end{aligned} \tag{19–18}$$

where $\Delta F^{\ddagger}$ is the activation free energy, $\boldsymbol{k}$ the Boltzmann constant, and h Planck's constant.

Although the verification of the first-order law [i.e., Eqs. (19–13) and (19–14)] is essential, it is not sufficient in itself to ensure that the processes examined are in fact isotopic exchange reactions, since there are several other physico-chemical processes which obey a similar law.

19–5 Exchange reactions involving hydrogen atom transfer. The importance of the distinction between the associative and dissociative mechanisms is clearly shown when the exchange behavior of hydrogen compounds is examined [40, 41]. With only a few exceptions, hydrogen atoms bonded to halogens, oxygen, sulfur, or selenium undergo rapid and complete exchange, but the hydrogen of a C—H group exchanges either very slowly or not at all. Thus in

$$\overset{1}{\mathrm{H}}\mathrm{COO}\overset{2}{\mathrm{H}},$$

the hydrogen [2] of the carboxyl group exchanges instantaneously with

* This is discussed by C. A. Bunton, D. P. Craig, and E. A. Halevi, *Trans. Faraday Soc.*, **51,** 196 (1955), who also consider isotope effects; see also G. M. Harris, *Trans. Faraday Soc.*, **47,** 716 (1951).

TABLE 19-1

ENERGIES OF BONDS INVOLVING HYDROGEN

Bond	Energy, kcal/mole	Electronegativity of atom bonded to H
C—H	87.3	2.5
N—H	83.7	3.0
S—H	87.5	2.5
Cl—H	102.7	3.0
O—H	110.2	3.5

D_2O, whereas there is only 10% exchange of hydrogen atom [1] after a few days at room temperature. These differences cannot be attributed to the bond energies, since the energy of the C—H bond is lower than the energy of most of the other bonds, as shown in Table 19-1.

Table 19-1 shows that the electronegativities of carbon and sulfur are the same. The rate of exchange is often affected by the properties of the compound which contains the relevant group. According to Brodsky [41], the ease with which a group H—X can exchange is determined by the presence or absence of electron pairs on the atom X. If a pair of electrons is available, the atom or ion D^+ (or H^+) from another molecule can easily form an addition compound, and no activation energy is necessary:

$$\begin{matrix} \mathrm{H} \\ \cdot\cdot \\ \mathrm{H:S:} \\ \cdot\cdot \end{matrix} + \mathrm{D^+} \rightarrow \left[\begin{matrix} \mathrm{H} \\ \cdot\cdot \\ \mathrm{H:S:D} \\ \cdot\cdot \\ \mathrm{H} \end{matrix}\right]^+ \rightarrow \begin{matrix} \mathrm{H} \\ \cdot\cdot \\ \mathrm{:S:D} \\ \cdot\cdot \end{matrix} + \mathrm{H^+}.$$

In the opposite case, especially with a saturated carbon atom

$$\begin{matrix} \mathrm{H} \\ \cdot\cdot \\ \mathrm{R:C:H}, \\ \cdot\cdot \\ \mathrm{H} \end{matrix}$$

such a mechanism is not possible and the exchange can only take place by dissociation, which requires a considerable activation energy, or the presence of strong donors, acids, or bases, or other catalysts. The same is true for the Si—H group in $(C_2H_5)_3SiH$, $(C_6H_5)_3SiH$, or $(C_2H_3O)_3SiH$, which do not exchange with D_2O, C_2H_5OD, or $(CH_3)_2ND$ even at 100 or 115°C [42].

A very rapid exchange occurs between D_2O and NH_3, in which the nitrogen has a lone pair of electrons, but exchange is slow with the NH_4^+ ion in which the electron pair is not available. The hexammine and tetrammine complexes of Co, Pd, or Pt, in which the lone pair on the nitrogen is bonded, do not exchange (or only very slowly), provided that the pH does not favor hydrolysis. Very rapid H/D exchange is found [43] between ethylamine and *n*-heptylamine, between ethylamine and *t*-amyl alcohol, between *t*-butyl alcohol and di-*t*-butylcarbinol, and in general between primary and secondary aliphatic or aromatic amines and the OH group of alcohols, phenols, and carbohydrates. The hydrogen bonded to oxygen in phosphoric and phosphorus acids, and in their acid salts, exchanges spontaneously with D_2O, but not the hydrogen which is bonded to the phosphorus atom. The exchange is very slow with KH_2PO_2, in which the phosphorus atom has no available free electrons (a), but it is very fast with free hypophosphorus acid due to the availability of an electron pair in the tautomeric form (b):

$$\left[\begin{array}{c} \text{H} \\ \cdot\cdot \\ \text{O}:\text{P}:\rightarrow\text{O} \\ \cdot\cdot \\ \text{H} \end{array}\right]^- \qquad\qquad \begin{array}{c} \cdot\cdot \\ \text{HO—P—OH} \\ \cdot\cdot \\ \text{H} \end{array}$$

(a) (b)

We have already noted that the aliphatic hydrocarbons do not exchange with D_2O in the absence of catalysts. This exchange will, however, take place with concentrated D_2SO_4 if the hydrocarbon contains a tertiary carbon atom, going via an ionic mechanism involving the formation of a carbonium ion. Acetylene exchanges slowly with D_2O at room temperature in alkaline solution. Since this compound has a weak acidic character, it is reasonable to suppose that this exchange also goes by an ionization process

$$C_2H_2 + \text{B (base)} \rightleftharpoons C_2H^- + BH^+. \tag{19–19}$$

The same mechanism no doubt applies to the alkali-catalyzed deuterium-hydrogen exchange between D_2O and the C—H groups in nitroparaffins, acetonitrile, acetamide, etc. The rate of exchange decreases with the acidity of the substituent in the order

$$NO_2 > CO > CN, \quad CONH_2 > COO^-, \quad SO_3^- > Cl.$$

Acetone also exchanges rapidly with D_2O in acid solution, and even faster in alkaline solution. The hyperconjugation introduced into the molecule by the strongly electronegative oxygen atom weakens the C—H bond by making the hydrogen more positive, so that exchange in alkaline medium involves an ionization mechanism [25]

$$CH_3COCH_2^- + D^+ \rightleftharpoons CH_3COCH_2D. \tag{19–20}$$

This effect is accentuated in acetylacetone $CH_3COCH_2COCH_3$, due to the presence of two carbonyl groups, and this compound exchanges rapidly in alkaline, neutral, or acid solution.

Electronegative substituents also favor hydrogen exchange in the ortho- or para-position in aromatic compounds in alkaline solution; benzene itself does not exchange under these conditions. These compounds can, however, also exchange by an associative mechanism, which is therefore favored by acid conditions. This exchange is an electrophilic substitution [44, 45] by reagents which tend to remove electrons and which therefore attack the organic molecule at the points of high electron density. The two isotopic atoms occupy equivalent positions in the association complex formed; for example, the exchange between benzene and highly concentrated H_2SO_4 solution probably involve the formation of an intermediate complex in which the two isotopic atoms occupy equivalent positions:

$$C_6H_5H + D\text{-}OSO_3H \rightarrow C_6H_5^- \genfrac{}{}{0pt}{}{H^+}{D^+} {}^-OSO_3H \rightarrow \begin{cases} C_6H_6 + HDSO_4, \\ C_6H_5D + H_2SO_4. \end{cases} \tag{19–21}$$

The rate of exchange decreases with the nature of the substituent in the order

$$O^- > NR_2 > OR > H > Cl, \quad SO_3H, \quad NO_2,$$

while the effect of electrophilic reagents as deuterating agents decreases in the order

$$H_2SO_4 > H_2SeO_4 > H^+ > C_6H_5OH > H_2O > OH^-,$$

in which H^+ signifies dilute acid solutions.

19–6 Other atom-transfer exchange reactions. Alcohols and phenols do not generally exchange oxygen with O^{18}-labeled water, and the same is found for acetamide, benzamide, nitrobenzene, urea, and glycol, but the oxygen in $\rangle C{=}O$ groups in aldehydes and ketones exchanges fairly readily, the exchange being catalyzed by acids and bases. In sugars, the carbonyl group oxygen will exchange, but not those of the OH groups. Exchange between a carboxyl group and D_2O is slow, and is catalyzed by acids; thus neither acetic acid nor the alkali acetates exchange, but exchange does take place on the addition of strong acid to the aqueous solution. Substitution enhances the rate of exchange considerably, so that monochloro-acetic acid exchanges slowly, and trichloro-acetic acid more rapidly. Certain enzymes, especially the lipids, also catalyze this exchange process [46]. For the aliphatic acids, the rate decreases in the order acetic > formic, propionic > butyric.

The exchange of oxygen between water and oxygenated anions has been studied by numerous authors, but the results obtained are not quantitative, and are in some cases contradictory. The exchange is fairly rapid with neutral solutions of the anions periodate, MoO_4^{2-}, WO_4^{2-}, tellurate, SeO_3^{2-}, SO_3^{2-}, AsO_2^-, AsO_4^{3-}, SiO_3^{2-}, BO_2^-, and $B_4O_7^{2-}$. It is slower with MnO_4^-, BrO_3^-, CrO_4^{2-}, $Cr_2O_7^{2-}$, SeO_4^{2-}, and CO_3^{2-}, and very slow or zero with ClO_4^-, ClO_3^-, SO_4^{2-}, and PO_4^{3-}. Acidity favors the exchange with NO_3^-, SO_4^{2-}, and PO_4^{3-}, and alkalinity that with ClO_3^- and IO_3^-. It has been shown [25, 26] that the probability of exchange bears a simple relation to the difference between the electronegativity of oxygen and that of the central atom of the anion; the exchange is fairly rapid with anions in which the central atom has an electronegativity equal to or less than 2.5 (that of oxygen being 3.5):

Si	As	B	W	Mo	Cr	P	Mn	Se	C	S
1.8	2.0	2.0	2.1	2.1	2.1	2.1	2.3	2.3	2.4	2.5

The electronegativity is not the only factor involved, however, since for a given central atom, the rate of exchange varies with the constitution of the anion. The following series have been established [40, 41]:

$$H_2SO_3 > H_2SO_4 > HSO_4^- > SO_4^{2-},$$
$$H_3PO_2 > H_3PO_3 > H_3PO_4,$$
$$H_2CO_3 > HCO_3^- > CO_3^{2-}.$$

Some authors suggest that these exchange processes occur by a dissociative mechanism such as

$$CrO_4^{2-} + H_2O \rightleftharpoons CrO_3 + 2OH^-. \qquad (19\text{–}22)$$

Brodsky, however, prefers a hydrolytic mechanism,

$$2CrO_4^{2-} + H_2O \rightleftharpoons Cr_2O_7^{2-} + 2OH^-, \qquad (19\text{–}23)$$
$$Cr_2O_7^{2-} + H_2O \rightleftharpoons 2CrO_4^{2-} + 2H^+, \qquad (19\text{–}24)$$

which is justified by the fact that anions of weak acids exchange more rapidly than those of strong acids. Exchange by a reaction such as (19–22) is probable in concentrated acid solution.*

As noted earlier, the central atoms of oxygenated anions exchange much more slowly than does the oxygen. This exchange can occur, but it is generally very slow, since it can only be brought about by a series of reversible oxidation-reduction reactions (IO_3^-/I_2, MnO_4^-/Mn^{2+}, etc.). However, the exchange between $C^{13}O_2$ and $NaHC^{12}O_3$ in aqueous solution is complete at room temperature within a few minutes. A kinetic study of this reaction [47] has shown that it involves the reaction

$$C^{12,13}O_2 + H_2O \underset{k_2}{\overset{k_1}{\rightleftharpoons}} HC^{12,13}O^- + H^+. \qquad (19\text{–}25)$$

It has further been shown that within experimental error the rate constant k_1 for the isotopic exchange is the same as the ordinary chemical hydration rate constant of CO_2 (0.021 sec^{-1} at 25°C), the kinetics of both reactions being governed by the equation

$$\frac{[CO_2]}{dt} = k_1[H_2O][CO_2] - k_2[H^+][HCO_3^-]. \qquad (19\text{–}26)$$

---

* Brodsky has also suggested another mechanism involving the formation of an ortho-acid as an intermediate.

A similar result was obtained in a kinetic study of the iodine-catalyzed isotopic exchange between H_3AsO_3 and H_3AsO_4 [48]. This is of particular interest, since it gave a direct confirmation of the well-known relationship between the equilibrium constant of a reversible reaction and the ratio of the rate constants for the forward and backward reactions, namely

$$K = k_1/k_2. \tag{19–27}$$

With normal physico-chemical methods this relation can be verified only by measuring the rates of reactions in systems far from equilibrium. Radioactive tracers can be used to show the dynamic nature of chemical equilibria, and to prove that equilibria are in fact the result of reactions continually occurring in opposite directions with equal velocities.

No exchange is found between the central atoms of the SO_3^{2-} and SO_4^{2-} anions at 100°C [20], nor between H_3PO_4, H_3PO_3, $H_4P_2O_7$, and H_3PO_2 or their ions [49, 50]. For the phosphorus oxy-anions, this negative result refers to solutions sealed in quartz ampoules and heated to 280°C for several hours.

Wilson [51] synthesized hypophosphoric acid $H_4P_2O_6$ by the condensation of labeled H_3PO_4 with inactive H_3PO_3, and then hydrolyzed the product

$$H_3P^*O_4 + H_3PO_3 \rightleftharpoons H_4P_2O_6 + H_2O. \tag{19–28}$$

All the activity was found in the initially marked product, showing the nonequivalence of the two phosphorus atoms in $H_4P_2O_6$.

The ClO_3^- and ClO_4^- anions do not exchange with Cl_2 or Cl^- in neutral or acid solutions at room temperature [52, 53]. Lee [54] found no exchange between ClO_3^- (labeled with Cl^{36}) and ClO_4^- in neutral aqueous solution after 2 years; no exchange was detected in acid or alkaline solution after 19.5 hours. On the other hand, complete exchange is observed between IO_3^- and I_2 in acid solution; although slow at room temperature, equilibrium is reached after 35 minutes at 100°C [55]. Myers and Kennedy [56] have studied the kinetics of this exchange, and find for R (see Eq. 19–12) the relationship

$$R = k[I_2]^{0.6}[IO_3^-]^{0.8}[H^+]^{1.8}[A^-], \tag{19–29}$$

in which $[A^-]$ is the concentration of anions other than IO_3^- (ClO_4^-, NO_3^-, etc.). The activity coefficients of the ions are taken into account in the constant k. The presence of fractional exponents in this equation led the authors to suggest that it could be modified by considering the probable mechanism of the exchange, and by assuming that the exchange takes place via an intermediate dynamic equilibrium between IO_3^- and I_2:

$$IO_3^- + 5I^- + 6H^+ \rightleftharpoons 3I_2 + 3H_2O. \tag{19–30}$$

The concentration of I_2 in Eq. (19–29) can then be replaced by the concentrations of I^-, IO_3^-, and H^+ given by the equilibrium constant

$$K = \frac{[I_2]^3}{[IO_3^-][I^-]^5[H^+]^6}. \tag{19–31}$$

Equation (19–29) shows that foreign anions (A^-) can substitute for IO_3^- in the exchange mechanism, and by taking account of this contribution one finally obtains

$$R = k_1[I^-][IO_3^-][H^+]^3(k_2[IO_3^-] + k_3[A^-]). \tag{19–32}$$

The authors suggest the following series of consecutive reactions as a possible mechanism:

$$IO_3^- + 2H^+ + A^- \rightarrow IO_2^+A^- + H_2O \qquad \text{(fast)}$$

$$I^- + H^+ \rightarrow H^+I^- \qquad \text{(fast)}$$

$$IO_2^+A^- + H^+I^- \rightarrow (HI_2O_2A) \rightarrow IO_2^- + I^+ + H^+ + A^- \qquad \text{(slow)}$$

$$IO_2^- + 4H^+ + 3I^- \rightarrow 2I_2 + 2H_2O \qquad \text{(fast)}$$

$$I^- + I^+ \rightarrow I_2 \qquad \text{(fast)}$$

$$IO_3^- + 5I^- + 6H^+ \rightarrow 3I_2 + 3H_2O$$

A similar mechanism has been proposed by Adamson [10] to explain the MnO_4^-/Mn^{2+} exchange, in which the Mn^{3+}, MnO^+, and MnO^{2+} ions are assumed to be involved.

The halogens, Cl_2, Br_2, and I_2, exchange very rapidly both with the halide ions Cl^-, Br^-, and I^- in aqueous solution, and with HCl, HBr, and HI in the gaseous phase or in chloroform solution. In contrast to this, there is no exchange between F_2 and HF in the gaseous state above 200°C [57]. It therefore seems that for the heavier halogens the exchange goes via the X_3^- or HX_3 species; even the transitory existence of HF_3 is unlikely for energetic reasons.

Exchanges between the halogens (or their ions) and organic halogen compounds are generally very slow at room temperature in the absence of catalysts, but the rates are considerably increased by the presence of $AlCl_3$ and $AlBr_3$ [58]. The exchange between S (or H_2S) and a number of organic sulfur compounds has recently been studied in connection with the mechanism of the action of accelerators in the vulcanization of rubber [59, 60].

There have been several recent reviews of atom-transfer exchange reactions [26, 61, 62, 63, 64]. Exchanges involving electron transfer are discussed later in connection with electrochemical phenomena (Section 20–1).

19–7 Heterogeneous exchange reactions. The rate of an isotopic exchange between two phases may be controlled by the exchange process itself, by the rate of diffusion of one of the exchanging species in one of the phases, or by a resistance to transfer at the interface between the two phases. If one of the phases is a solid, the transport of the exchanging material to the surface from the interior (i.e., the rate of self-diffusion in the solid) generally controls the overall rate of exchange. This case has been discussed by Wagner [65], and subsequently by Zimens [66] and

Berthier [67]. Wagner has given a solution of Fick's second equation

$$\frac{\partial c}{\partial t} = D\frac{\partial^2 c}{\partial x^2}, \tag{19–33}$$

which is applicable to this problem (D is the self-diffusion coefficient). The solution is considerably simplified for those systems in which the number of exchanging atoms in the fluid phase (n_l) is in a very large excess over the number of the same atoms in the solid (n_s);

$$s = \frac{n_s}{n_l + n_s} \ll 1.$$

The logarithm of the fraction which has not exchanged at a time t, $(1 - F) = (1 - x/x_\infty)$, is then a complex decreasing function of time, which, however, tends to become linear with increasing t and x. In other words, as the system moves toward equilibrium (complete exchange) an equation similar to (19–14) is again valid, but in this case also containing a constant term

$$-kt = \log\left(1 - \frac{x}{x_\infty}\right) + \text{const.} \tag{19–34}$$

The constant k is a function of D, and of the form and dimensions of the solid. If the solid is a flat plane of thickness d with a single face in contact with the solution,

$$k = \pi^2 D/4d^2. \tag{19–35}$$

If both faces are in contact with the liquid, the denominator of Eq. (19–35) is divided by a factor of 4. Similarly for a sphere of radius r, one has

$$k = \pi^2 D/r^2, \tag{19–36}$$

and for a cylinder whose radius r is small with respect to the height

$$k = 5.78D/r^2. \tag{19–37}$$

Berthier has extended Wagner's calculation and introduced a new parameter, the reduced time $\tau = Dt/r^2$. The variation of log $(1 - F)$ with τ, for a given ratio n_s/n_e, is a parabolic function for small values of τ, tending toward an asymptotic linear dependence as τ increases. Graphs given by Wagner and by Zimens, and numerical tables calculated by Berthier, give the value of $(1 - F)$ as a function of τ for sheets, spheres, and cylinders and for different n_s/n_e ratios. A single measurement of the quantity not exchanged at a time t allows τ, and hence the self-diffusion coefficient D, to be calculated. It is, however, necessary to be certain that the process whose rate is measured is in fact diffusion-controlled.

Experiments on the exchange between monoclinic sulfur and polysulfide ions S_x^{2-} ($x = 4 - 7$) [68], and between crystals of Ag_2S and Ag^+ or S^{2-} ions [69], show that a plot of t against log $(1 - F)$ does in fact give a straight line even over very short times. It follows from this that the kinetic equation is virtually the same in both cases (diffusion and exchange controlled mechanism), apart from the constants. The fact that the straight line corresponding to Eq. (19–34) does not pass through the origin is not in itself sufficient to distinguish between an exchange governed by diffusion and an exchange obeying Eq. (19–14), since even for a homogeneous exchange the straight line may cut the ordinate when there are two different mechanisms, one of which is considerably faster than the other. To differentiate between the two types of exchange with certainty, the effects of the dimensions of the solid on the rate constant must be investigated. If the same value is always obtained for D using Eqs. (19–34) to (19–37) when the dimensions are varied, one can be sure that the measured rate depends on self-diffusion. If, however, the rate varies with the concentration of one of the constituents of the solution, it is unlikely that self-diffusion is the rate-controlling process.

The use of solution-solid exchange experiments to determine self-diffusion coefficients is of course limited to systems in which the rate of self-diffusion is sufficiently high at temperatures compatible with the existence of aqueous or other solutions. The application of the method is considerably more difficult, or excluded, if the exchange is accompanied by recrystallization phenomena, since the overall rate is then no longer controlled by self-diffusion. A particular example of this is the exchange between metallic selenium and polyselenide ions in alkaline solution [70]. Even at room temperature, the exchange between amorphous selenium and polyselenide ions, or SeO_3^{2-} ions in very acid solution (which are in equilibrium with Se^{4+} ions),

$$SeO_3^{2-} + 6H^+ \rightleftharpoons Se^{4+} + 3H_2O,$$

is accompanied by the allotropic transformation of the amorphous to the metallic form [71].

The exchange method has also been applied to the determination of the self-diffusion coefficients of monoclinic sulfur and molten sulfur [68], although the values found in the first case are a hundred times lower than those obtained by direct measurements (see Table 19–2). Interesting results have, however, been obtained by Peschanski [69] on the exchange between solid silver sulfide and its ions (in aqueous solution). Two separate series of experiments were performed, using Ag^{110} as a tracer for Ag^+ ions (with a solution of $AgNO_3$) and S^{35} for sulfur ions (with a solution of Na_2S). The silver sulfide was in the form of a crystalline powder, a sheet, or a wire. By investigating the dependence of the rate on the dimensions, it was possible to show from Eqs. (19–34) through (19–37) that the slowest process was the diffusion of ions in the solid. Measurements carried out over a series of temperatures gave the following values for the self-diffusion coefficients:

$$D_{Ag^+} = 93.1\, e^{-9100/RT}\ \text{cm}^2\cdot\text{sec}^{-1}, \tag{19–38}$$

$$D_{S^{2-}} = 0.237\, e^{-24,500/RT}\ \text{cm}^2\cdot\text{sec}^{-1}. \tag{19–39}$$

At 18°C, then,

$$D_{Ag^+} = 1.4 \times 10^{-9}\ \text{cm}^2\cdot\text{sec}^{-1} : D_{S^{2-}} = 1.1 \times 10^{-19}\ \text{cm}^2\cdot\text{sec}^{-1}, \tag{19–40}$$

so that the ratio $D_{Ag^+}/D_{S^{2-}}$ is very high, being of the order of 10^{10} at 18°C. These experiments gave a direct proof of the predominance of cationic diffusion in an ionic solid, in agreement with the ideas of Wagner on the mechanism of oxidation, sulfuration, and the corrosion of metals in general.

This theory has been further confirmed by work by Castellan and Moore [72], who used active copper to measure the activation energy for the self-diffusion of copper in copper oxide between 800 and 1000°C; the value found (37 kcal/mole) is very close to the activation energy for the oxidation of crystalline copper (39 kcal/mole). Lindner [73] has also found an agreement between experiment and theory for the oxidation of zinc, and for the formation of zinc-iron spinels, although for the oxidation of lead and the high-temperature formation of silicates, the cationic diffusion mechanism in itself did not give a complete explanation, and the diffusion of oxygen had to be invoked.

In contrast with the results obtained with Ag_2S, Langer [74] found from heterogeneous exchange experiments that the diffusion of silver in silver bromide is only six times greater than that of bromine. The exchange between Ag^+ ions and freshly precipitated silver bromine was complete in 24 minutes, but complete exchange with Br^- ions required 3 hours at 18°C. The rapid diffusion of Br^- ions is most surprising, since the radius (1.95 A) is greater than the ionic radius of sulfur (1.74 A). It seems very likely that the fast exchange is due to recrystallization; the importance of this in the $AgBr/Br^-$ and $AgCl/Cl^-$ exchanges has been demonstrated by Polessitsky and Murin [75], and by Kolthoff and O'Brien [76]. Measurements by Murin [77] show that the rate of the $AgBr/Ag^+$ exchange is in fact determined by the self-diffusion of Ag^+ in the crystal, but that for Br^- recrystallization is the rate-controlling process.

Whatever the mechanism, these fast exchanges with halides may have considerable analytical usefulness. It has been suggested [78], for example, that traces of radioactive silver can be removed from solution by treatment with precipitated AgCl. In another application, labeled bromine can be prepared by exchange between radioactive AgBr and Br_2 in a sealed tube at 160°C [79].

The movement of atoms in a solid at room temperature is essentially governed by the degree of disorder of the solid, that is to say, by the presence and extent of Schottky and Frenkel defects (Section 15–1). Isotopic exchanges whose rates are determined by the rate of diffusion can therefore be used to get information on the reactivity of a solid. With this point in view, Buser has studied the exchange between aqueous solutions of Co^{2+} and Mn^{2+} ions and various insoluble cobalt and manganese compounds in order to obtain information on the effect of structure, degree of order, and stability [81, 82] (see also Ref. 83).

A type of exchange which is essentially heterogeneous is that already discussed in Section 19–1 between two gases on the surface of a solid. The study of these processes is of considerable interest in investigating the structure of catalysts and the mechanism of catalytic reactions. Work of this type has been carried out in particular by Taylor [84] on the H_2/D_2 exchange, catalyzed on the surface of various metals and alloys, and by

Kemball on the exchange of deuterium with ammonia, methane, and benzene on metallic films obtained by vaporization, and on metallic oxides [85, 86] (see also Ref. 87). The deuterium-ammonia exchange on an iron catalyst has also been studied by Weber and Laidler [88] and that between N_2^{14} and N_2^{15} on the same surface by Kummer and Emmett [89].

Similar studies have been carried out on the exchange of O^{18}-labeled oxygen between O_2, H_2O, CO_2 and various metallic oxides such as V_2O_5 [90]. Winter and his co-workers [91, 92, 93] have shown that the exchange between O_2 and Al_2O_3, Cr_2O_3, ZnO, MgO, etc., at relatively low temperatures ($< 400°C$) require activation energies of the order of 25 to 40 kcal/mole, but that at higher temperatures, the activation energy never exceeds 8 kcal/mole, and may even be zero. These low activation energies are thought to represent the energy required for the migration of adsorbed oxygen atoms over the surface. The activation energy at low temperatures refers to the exchange process itself, the substitution of atoms in the solid by those from the gaseous phase, which requires dissociation of the oxygen molecule.

19–8 Self-diffusion in metals. With a few exceptions, the melting points of metals are too high for the movement of atoms in these solids to be detectable at room temperature, or even at 100°C, so that measurements of the self-diffusion coefficients of metals are carried out by direct radioactive methods. These consist in depositing a thin layer of tracer on the end of a rod or disc of inactive metal, and measuring the spread of the activity through the solid which is held for a suitable time at a sufficiently high temperature. The measuring techniques are varied, but all require the appropriate solution of the Fick equation (19–33). We shall note here the two most important techniques.

1. The concentration (N_2) of the indicator is measured in successive layers which are a *distance* x from the initial radioactive layer. For a very thin original deposit, the solution of Eq. (19–33) gives

$$N_2 = \frac{N_1}{2\sqrt{\pi\, Dt}} \exp\left[-\frac{x^2}{4\, Dt}\right], \tag{19–41}$$

in which N_1 is the concentration of indicator in the initial deposit and t is the time of the diffusion experiment. The slope of a plot of log N_2 against x^2 gives D quite simply. This method has been applied to gold [94] and to silver [95] (see Table 19–2). The indicator was deposited electrolytically; in the case of silver, it was compressed into a sandwich between two discs of inactive metal, so that the diffusion could be followed in two directions at once (Fig. 19–2). The concentration of the indicator at various distances was determined by dissolving off successive layers of the metal with acid. Hevesy [96] was the first to use this method, which he tried to apply to lead using RaD as tracer. The sample was kept at 250°C for 14 months, but diffusion in lead is still extremely slow at this temperature, and Hevesy could only conclude that the self-diffusion coefficient was less than 10^{-9} cm^2·sec^{-1}.

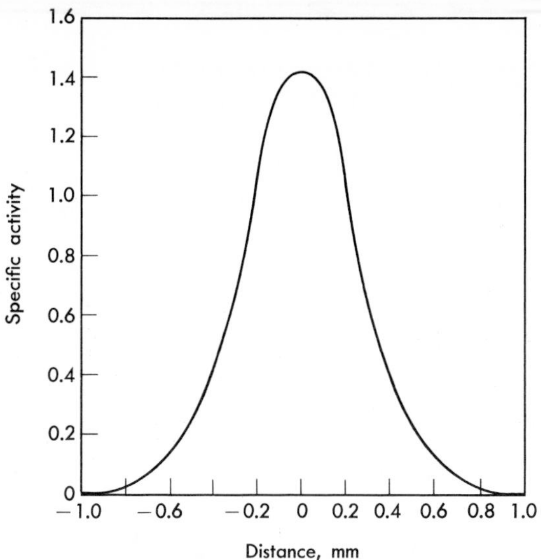

FIG. 19–2. The measurement of self-diffusion in a solid.

2. In the second method, which is also due to Hevesy [97, 98], the sample is held in a fixed position relative to a counter, and the change of the activity with *time* is followed. The change in the counting rate is then due to the increase (or decrease depending on the geometrical conditions) in the distances between the counting apparatus and the point of emission of the ionizing particles, which have a definite range. The sensitivity of the method increases with decreasing range of the particles, and is therefore much higher for α-emitting tracers than for β-emitters; a considerable increase in sensitivity is obtained by measuring the recoiling atoms. The solution of the diffusion equation for these experimental conditions gives an integral, which in the case of α-particle emitters is of the form

$$\frac{N_2}{N_1} = \int_0^x \frac{1}{\sqrt{\pi\, Dt}}\left(1 - \frac{x}{a}\right) \exp\left[-\frac{x^2}{4\, Dt}\right], \qquad (19\text{–}42)$$

in which a is the range of the α-particles. The integration is usually performed graphically. The method has been subsequently applied to bismuth [99], copper [100], iron [101, 102], and a number of other metals. By measuring D over a series of temperatures, the activation energy (E) can be determined, together with the frequently coefficient D_0 from the relation

$$D = D_0 e^{-E/RT}. \qquad (19\text{–}43)$$

Values of D_0 and E for various metals and metaloids are given in Table 19–2 (columns 5 and 6). In the 4th column are given the measured self-diffusion coefficients at one of the experimental temperatures (column 3).

TABLE 19–2

SELF-DIFFUSION COEFFICIENTS AND ACTIVATION ENERGIES FOR SELF-DIFFUSION

Element	Melting point, °C	Experimental result		D_0, cm²·sec⁻¹	E, kcal/gm-atom	Ref.
		Experimental temperature, °C	D_t, cm²·sec⁻¹			
Na	97.8	39.6	1.31×10^{-8}	0.242	10.45	103, 104
Cu	1083	839	1.05×10^{-10}	0.468	47.14	105
Ag	960	936	4.6×10^{-9}	0.72	45.5	106, 107
Au	1063	941	1.5×10^{-7}	126	51	94, 108, 109
Mg	650	551	3.6×10^{-9}	1	32	110
Zn, $\|\|^l$ c-axis	420	—	—	0.13	21.8	111, 112
Zn, $\perp^r$ c-axis		—	—	0.58	24.3	111, 112
In	156	150	6.6×10^{-10}	1.02	17.9	113
Ge	959	—	—	7.8	68.5	114
Sn, $\|\|^l$ c-axis	232	180	7.8×10^{-9}	8.4×10^{-4}	10.5	115
Sn, $\|\|^l$ a-axis		180	5.5×10^{-11}	3.7×10^{-8}	5.9	115
Pb	327	304.4	1.94×10^{-10}	0.28	24.21	116
Bi, $\|\|^l$ c-axis	271	269	10^{-15}	10^{-3}	31	99
Bi, $\perp^r$ c-axis		269	10^{-10}	2.4×10^{46}	140	99
α-Fe	1535	800	3.1×10^{-13}	2300	73.2	101, 102
γ-Fe	~1520	1058	4.3×10^{-12}	5.8	74.2	101, 102
Co	1495	1150	2×10^{-11}	0.367	67	117
Tl, $\|\|^l$ c-axis	303.5	—	—	0.4	22.9	118
Tl, $\perp^r$ c-axis		—	—	0.4	22.6	118
Cd, $\|\|^l$ c-axis	320.9	—	—	0.05	18.2	119
Cd, $\perp^r$ c-axis		—	—	0.10	19.1	119
Se	220.2	175	8.5×10^{-12}	2.75×10^{-7}	13.3	70
S, $\|\|^l$ c-axis	112.8	87.5	5.7×10^{-13}	1.78×10^{36}	78.0	120
S, $\perp^r$ c-axis		—	—	8.3×10^{-12}	3.1	120
α-P	44.1	18.7	1.07×10^{-10}	1.07×10^{-3}	9.4	121
Liquids						
Na	97.8	134.3	5.39×10^{-5}	1.1×10^{-3}	2.43	122
Hg	−38.9	23	1.79×10^{-5}	1.26×10^{-4}	1.16	123
In	156	250	4.62×10^{-5}	1.76×10^{-5}	1.35	124
Ga	29.8	60	1.97×10^{-5}	1.07×10^{-4}	2.12	125

The results for zinc, tin, and bismuth and others show that self-diffusion in noncubic metals is anisotropic. If D_θ is the diffusion coefficient in a direction at an angle θ to the axis of symmetry, and $D_{||}$ and $D_\perp$ are the coefficients parallel to and perpendicular to the axis, one then has [126, 127]

$$D_\theta = D_{||} \cos^2 \theta + D_\perp \sin^2 \theta. \tag{19–44}$$

For cubic metals, the activation energy is related to the elastic constants and cell constants of the metal, and is of the order of $\frac{2}{3}$ of the energy of sublimation [114]. These facts are compatible with the idea that self-diffusion takes place by the movement of atoms between the vacancies in the lattice, and that the activation energy is necessary to produce these vacancies. This mechanism is valid for the diffusion in a crystal grain, or in a single crystal. This *volume diffusion* must be distinguished from *grain boundary diffusion*, which predominates in polycrystalline metals at low temperatures; volume diffusion becomes increasingly important with increasing temperatures. Equations (19–41) and (19–42) are valid either for a pure volume self-diffusion or pure grain boundary diffusion; if both take place without either mechanism predominating, log N_2 is a linear function of x instead of x^2 [128, 129].

Self-diffusion is sensitive to structural effects, to imperfections in the crystal, to the presence of impurities, and to mechanical and thermal pretreatment. To a large extent, these factors explain the disagreements between the results reported by different authors for the same metal. For example, the following results have been given for self-diffusion in copper:

		Ref
$D = 11\, e^{-57.2/RT}$		100
$D = 0.468\, e^{-47.14/RT}$		105
$D = 47\, e^{-61.4/RT}$		130
$D = 0.34\, e^{-46.8/RT}$		131
$D = 0.6\, e^{-49/RT}$	(single crystal)	132
$D = 0.1\, e^{-45.1/RT}$	(polycrystalline)	132

The values given in Table 19–2 are generally from the most recent determination.

Nachtrieb and Handler [133] have proposed a mechanism in which the rate of diffusion in solid metals is limited by the movement of atoms in small disordered regions of the crystal. These regions contain, on the average, 12 to 14 atoms clustered around a vacancy; this energy would be approximately the same as that of an equivalent number of atoms in the liquid state.

Self-diffusion in graphite has been studied by Feldman, *et al.*, [134] (see also Ref. 135) using C^{14} over the temperature range 1835 to 2370°C. The activation energy for volume diffusion was found to be 90 kcal/gm-atom, and for grain boundary diffusion 75.4 kcal/gm-atom. Kanter, however, finds an activation energy of 170 kcal/gm-atom for the volume self-diffusion [136].

Several measurements have also been made with radioactive indicators on the diffusion of one metal into another, or into an alloy, and of ions into their own or other salts in the solid or molten state (e.g., Refs. 137, 138, 139). The diffusion coefficients in ionic crystals can be simply related to the conductivity, and a knowledge of one allows the other to be calculated.

19–9 Diffusion in the liquid phase. Values are given at the end of Table 19–2 for the self-diffusion coefficients of four metals in the liquid state. Naturally the techniques used for liquids differ from those for solids. The most convenient method appears to be the capillary method, originally devised by Anderson and Saddington [140]. A capillary tube a few centimeters long and 0.05 to 0.06 cm in diameter is sealed at one end, filled with liquid labeled with a suitable tracer, and placed in a much larger volume of the same, inactive, liquid. It can be shown that for relatively large values of Dt/l^2 (>0.2), where l is the length of the tube, the solution of the Fick equation gives

$$\frac{N_2}{N_1} = \frac{\pi^2 Dt}{4l^2} \log_e \frac{8}{\pi^2}. \tag{19–45}$$

A simpler procedure [141, 142, 143, 144] consists in using a vertical tube, widened in the middle, with the inactive liquid in the lower compartment and the labeled liquid in the upper. To prevent mixing due to vibrational and convection effects, the two compartments are separated by a sintered glass disc. If the composition in each compartment is constant, so that diffusion through the sinter governs the overall rate, it can be shown that

$$\ln \frac{\Delta c}{\Delta c_0} = -\frac{S}{l}\left(\frac{1}{v_1} + \frac{1}{v_2}\right) Dt, \tag{19–46}$$

in which Δc and Δc_0 are the differences in the specific activities in the two compartments at time t and 0, v_1 and v_2 are the volumes of liquid, S is the total area, and l the average length of the capillaries in the sinter. These two latter factors must be determined by calibrating the cell with a liquid whose diffusion coefficient is known, and this is one of the disadvantages of the method.

Wang [145, 146, 147] has used these methods to measure the self-diffusion coefficient of water, using deuterium, tritium, and O^{18} as tracers. Experiments carried out between 0 and 55°C gave a value of 4.6 kcal/mole for the activation energy, and showed that the ratio $D\eta/T$ is constant, where η is the viscosity and T the absolute temperature. These results are incompatible with older ideas on the existence of associated molecules $(H_2O)_n$, but do confirm the semicrystalline structure of liquid water in which each molecule is hydrogen-bonded to four other molecules in a tetrahedral arrangement. Diffusion occurs by the displacement of isolated molecules which are in equilibrium with the "lattice," and the activation energy is essentially the energy required to break a hydrogen bond.

Wang [148, 149], Adamson [141, 142], and a number of other authors (e.g., Ref. 150) have used one or other of these techniques to measure the self-diffusion coefficients of the ions of various alkali halide and other salts in water, and to determine the activation energy for these processes. Measurements of the diffusion of radioactive ions in extremely dilute solution was used by Hevesy [151] to determine the valency of the ion concerned. For a cation of valency z and mobility u diffusing in the presence of a large excess of anions, the Nernst diffusion theory gives the relationship

$$z = 0.0242\, u/D \tag{19–47}$$

at 18°C. Since the mobility of several cations is only slightly dependent on their nature, and is usually around 55 $cm^2 \cdot day^{-1}$, an empirical relation can be deduced from Eq. (19–47), namely that

$$z = 1.25/D \text{ cm}^2\cdot\text{day}^{-1}. \tag{19–48}$$

It should be realized that the value of z determined in this way refers to the ion in the solution, (i.e., whether simple, complex, or partially hydrolyzed) and not to the valency of the element. Thus Hevesy found $z = 2$ for both RaE, which is an isotope of trivalent bismuth, and for tetravalent polonium.

19–10 Surface measurements. If self-diffusion in a crystal is extremely slow, and recrystallization phenomena can be neglected, isotopic exchange between a solid and its saturated solution is limited to the surface. Paneth [152, 153] was the first to suggest that measurement of the quantities exchanged after a short contact time could be used to evaluate the area of a powder, or a solid of ill-defined geometrical form. For the total number of atoms or ions N_{sur} in the surface layer, one should have

$$\frac{N^*_{\text{sur}}}{N_{\text{sur}}} = \frac{N^*_{\text{sol}}}{N_{\text{sol}}}, \tag{19–49}$$

in which N_{sol} is the number of inactive atoms in solution (which can be determined chemically), and the same symbols with asterisks refer to the number of active atoms. If the interatomic or intermolecular distance d is known, measurements of N^*_{sur} and N^*_{sol} can then be used to calculate the surface area S, given approximately by $S = N_{\text{sur}}\, d^2$. The distance d can be obtained by measuring the density ρ, since

$$d = \left(\frac{M}{nN\rho}\right)^{1/3}, \tag{19–50}$$

in which M is the molecular weight, N is Avogadro's number, and n is the number of atoms concerned in the molecule (i.e., for PbI_2, $n = 2$).

The validity of the method rests on the assumption that *only* the surface takes part in the exchange, and that *all* of the surface is involved. These conditions are, however, difficult to achieve in practice. If the exchange takes too long, particles from the bulk interior of the solid can take part in the reaction as the result of diffusion, and the results are equally falsified by recrystallization. Kolthoff and his co-workers [76, 154, 155, 156, 157] have investigated a large series of exchanges of this type with ionic crystals, in particular insoluble lead salts, and have shown that recrystallization is particularly important with freshly prepared precipitates. To overcome this, the exchange was measured as a function of time and subsequently extrapolated to zero time; at least 30 min of contact between the solid and the solution are necessary for the surface exchange to be complete. These authors also point out that corrections must be made in some cases to take account of the adsorption of ions on the surface. Recrystallization can be prevented if the solid is pretreated with a solution of some appropriate dyestuff, such as methylene blue, in which case the exchange is limited to a single monomolecular layer. On the other hand, if crystals which are too aged are used, the surface exchange may not be complete. Thus Paneth found that with certain naturally occurring minerals, such as galena (PbS), crocoite ($PbCrO_4$), and celestite ($SrSO_4$), only part of the surface exchanges with ions in solution. Paneth regards this fraction as being the "active surface," and estimates that 3 min are sufficient for the complete exchange of this fraction. These partially active surfaces can be prepared by appropriate thermal pretreatment (annealing), and autoradiographs show that with such crystals the exchange is restricted to the edges.

In a partial surface exchange, the amount of "active surface" measured can vary with the tracer ion used (i.e., whether cation or anion). Since cations diffuse much more rapidly through solids than anions (Section 19–8), diffusion may be much more important for cations than is the case for anions. This may be the explanation of the results reported by Stow and Spinks [158], who measured the surface area of a strontium sulfate powder; exchange with a solution containing Sr^{90} gave a value 1.5 times higher than that obtained with a solution labeled with S^{35}. It will be clear from what has been said that the method can give only an approximate measure of the surface area, and that it can be used only after investigating the most suitable conditions for the system in question. There are, however, useful applications in the study of surface *changes*, the aging of precipitates, their degree of aggregation, etc.

The area of a powdered oxide can also be determined by exchange with O^{18} at a sufficiently high temperature [159]. The method used is similar to that suggested by Kolthoff for solid-solution exchanges, involving back-extrapolation of the slow diffusion-controlled exchange to zero time; subtraction of this from the total exchange gives the exchange between the gas and the surface atoms.

Another radioactive technique for surface measurement is based on the fact that radioactive gases (in particular radon isotopes) formed in solids as the result of radioactive decay processes tend to escape from the solid. Quantitatively, this *emanating power* [160, 161, 162] is defined as that fraction of the radioactive inert gas atoms formed in the bulk of a solid which escape. If, for example, n atoms of radon are formed per unit time in a mixed crystal of $BaCO_3 + RaCO_3$, and n' atoms escape, the emanating power is the ratio n'/n. It depends essentially upon two factors, radioactive recoil and diffusion. If the parent atom (radium) is near the surface of the solid, the gaseous daughter atom can escape by recoil, and it can be shown that for sufficiently large particles (greater than 10^{-4} cm) the emanating power from this cause is given by

$$E_R = \frac{RS}{4M}\rho, \tag{19–51}$$

where R is the range of the recoiling atom in the solid, ρ the density, S the surface area, and M the mass of the particle concerned. Atoms from the bulk interior can still reach the surface by diffusion if their average life is sufficiently long, so that this contribution to the emanating power (E_D) depends on the decay constant λ of the gas. If the diffusion coefficient D of the gas is small,

$$E_D = \rho\frac{S}{M}\sqrt{\frac{D}{\lambda}}. \tag{19–52}$$

The total emanating power for the conditions stated is therefore given by

$$E = E_R + E_D = \rho \frac{S}{M}\left(\frac{R}{4} + \sqrt{\frac{D}{\lambda}}\right). \tag{19-53}$$

All the parameters in Eq. (19–53) necessary to determine S are generally known, or can be easily measured, with the exception of D. This difficulty can, however, be overcome in various ways [163]:

1. E_D is dependent on time, whereas E_R is not, so that measurements of E as a function of time can be used to deduce E_R, and hence S.
2. The same argument applies to the temperature variation of E_D, since E_R is temperature independent.
3. The emanating power can be measured for two gaseous isotopes (e.g., radon and thoron) which have the same D, giving two equations with two unknowns, S and D.
4. The emanating power of a solid sample of known dimensions can be measured, from which one can obtain the coefficient $(R/4 + \sqrt{D/\lambda})$; Eq. (19–53) can then be used to determine S for other powders of the same substance.

It should be realized, however, that surface measurement by the emanation method is a difficult technique, and like the methods described earlier can give only approximate values.

References

1. S. Z. Roginski, *Acta Physicochim. U.R.S.S.*, **14,** 1 (1941).
2. J. N. Wilson and R. G. Dickinson, *J. Am. Chem. Soc.*, **59,** 1358 (1937).
3. G. Harbottle and R. W. Dodson, *J. Am. Chem. Soc.*, **70,** 880 (1948).
4. J. Silverman and R. W. Dodson, *J. Phys. Chem.*, **56,** 846 (1952).
5. W. B. Lewis, C. D. Coryell, and J. W. Irvine, *J. Chem. Soc.*, **1949,** S 386.
6. A. Farkas and L. Farkas, *Nature*, **132,** 894 (1933).
7. A. Farkas and L. Farkas, *Proc. Roy. Soc.* (*London*), **A152,** 124 (1935).
8. R. Bentley and D. Rittenberg, *J. Am. Chem. Soc.*, **76,** 4883 (1954).
9. N. Morita, H. Tanaka, and T. Titani, *Bull. Chem. Soc. Japan*, **14,** 9, 520 (1939); **15,** 1, 47, 71, 119, 166, 226, 298 (1940).
10. A. W. Adamson, *J. Phys. Chem.*, **55,** 293 (1951).
11. E. Leifer, *J. Chem. Phys.*, **8,** 301 (1940).
12. E. D. Hughes, F. Juliusberger, S. Masterman, B. Topley, and J. Weiss, *J. Chem. Soc.*, **1935,** 1525.
13. E. D. Hughes, F. Juliusberger, A. D. Scott, B. Topley, and J. Weiss, *J. Chem. Soc.*, **1936,** 1173.
14. W. Cowdrey, E. D. Hughes, T. P. Nevell, and C. L. Wilson, *J. Chem. Soc.*, **1938,** 209.
15. F. Juliusberger, B. Topley, and J. Weiss, *J. Chem. Phys.*, **3,** 437 (1935).
16. H. A. C. McKay, *J. Am. Chem. Soc.*, **65,** 702 (1943).
17. F. A. Long, *J. Am. Chem. Soc.*, **61,** 571 (1939); **63,** 1353 (1941).
18. F. Juliusberger, B. Topley, and J. Weiss, *J. Chem. Soc.*, **1935,** 1295.
19. E. Buch Andersen, *Z. physik. Chem.*, **B32,** 237 (1936).

20. H. H. VOGE, *J. Am. Chem. Soc.*, **61**, 1032 (1939).

21. A. E. POLESSITSKI, *Doklady Akad. Nauk S.S.S.R.*, **24**, 540 (1939).

22. V. I. SPITSYN, *Rocz. Chem.*, **29**, 209 (1955).

23. L. PAULING, *The Nature of the Chemical Bond*, Cornell University Press, Ithaca, 2nd ed., 1948.

24. Y. A. FIALKOV and Y. P. NAZARENKO, *Doklady Akad. Nauk S.S.S.R.*, **73**, 727 (1950).

25. M. HAÏSSINSKY and R. DAUDEL, *Bull. soc. chim. France*, **1947**, 552.

26. M. HAÏSSINSKY, *J. Chim. Phys.*, **47**, 957 (1950).

27. A. A. GRINBERG and F. M. FILINOV, *Doklady Akad. Nauk S.S.S.R.*, **23**, 912 (1939).

28. R. L. RICH and H. TAUBE, *J. Am. Chem. Soc.*, **76**, 2608 (1954).

29. L. L. LARSON and C. S. GARNER, *J. Am. Chem. Soc.*, **76**, 2180 (1954).

30. E. N. SLOTH and C. S. GARNER, *J. Am. Chem. Soc.*, **77**, 1440 (1955).

31. A. A. GRINBERG, *Sess. Acad. Sci., U.S.S.R.*, July 1–5, 1955, Chem. Sect., p. 238.

32. A. W. ADAMSON, J. P. WELKER, and M. VOLPE, *J. Am. Chem. Soc.*, **72**, 4030 (1950).

33. S. RUBEN, A. W. FRENKEL, and M. D. KAMEN, *J. Phys. Chem.*, **46**, 710 (1942).

34. S. RUBEN, M. D. KAMEN, M. B. ALLEN, and P. NAHINSKY, *J. Am. Chem. Soc.*, **64**, 2297 (1942).

35. N. E. BREZHNEVA and S. Z. ROGINSKI, *Acta Physicochim. U.R.S.S.*, **14**, 1 (1941).

36. H. A. C. MCKAY, *Nature*, **142**, 997 (1938).

37. T. H. NORRIS, *J. Phys. Chem.*, **54**, 777 (1950).

38. J. J. DOWNS and R. E. JOHNSON, *J. Chem. Phys.*, **22**, 143 (1954).

39. H. MOUREUX, M. MAGAT, and G. VETROFF, *Compt. rend.*, **205**, 276 (1937).

40. A. I. BRODSKY, *Doklady Akad. Nauk S.S.S.R.*, **93**, 847 (1953).

41. A. I. BRODSKY, *Sess. Acad. Sci., U.S.S.R.*, July 1–5, 1955, Chem. Sect., p. 210.

42. I. G. KHASKIN, *Zhur. Obshchei Khim.*, **23**, 32 (1953).

43. J. HINE and C. H. THOMAS, *J. Am. Chem. Soc.*, **76**, 612 (1954).

44. C. K. INGOLD, C. G. RAISIN, and C. L. WILSON, *J. Chem. Soc.*, **1936**, 915, 1643.

45. S. K. HSU, C. K. INGOLD, C. G. RAISIN, E. DE SALAS, and C. L. WILSON, *J. Chim. Phys.*, **45**, 232 (1948).

46. R. BENTLEY and D. RITTENBERG, *J. Am. Chem. Soc.*, **76**, 4883 (1954).

47. G. A. MILLS and H. C. UREY, *J. Am. Chem. Soc.*, **62**, 1019 (1940).

48. M. D. KAMEN, J. W. KENNEDY, and O. E. MYERS, *J. Chim. Phys.*, **45**, 199 (1948).

49. D. E. HULL, *J. Am. Chem. Soc.*, **63**, 1269 (1941).

50. V. D. IONIN, A. F. LUKOVNIKOV, M. B. NEIMAN, and A. N. NESMEYANOV, *Doklady Akad. Nauk S.S.S.R.*, **67**, 463 (1949).

51. J. N. WILSON, *J. Am. Chem. Soc.*, **60**, 2697 (1938).

52. H. W. DODGEN and H. TAUBE, *J. Am. Chem. Soc.*, **71**, 2501 (1949).

53. D. J. MEIER and C. S. GARNER, *J. Chem. Phys.*, **17**, 1344 (1949).

54. D. A. LEE, *J. Am. Chem. Soc.*, **76**, 2590 (1954).

55. M. COTTIN and M. HAÏSSINSKY, *Compt. rend.*, **224**, 1636 (1947).

56. O. E. Myers and J. W. Kennedy, *J. Am. Chem. Soc.*, **72**, 897 (1950).
57. H. W. Dodgen and W. F. Libby, *J. Chem. Phys.*, **17**, 951 (1949).
58. N. E. Brezhneva and S. Z. Roginski, *Uspekhi Khim.*, **7**, 1503 (1938).
59. G. P. Miklukhin, *Sess. Acad. Sci., U.S.S.R.*, July 1–5, 1955, Chem. Sect., p. 251.
60. E. N. Gur'yanova, V. N. Vasileva, and L. S. Kuzina, *Sess. Acad. Sci., U.S.S.R.*, July 1–5, 1955, Chem. Sect., p. 270.
61. A. C. Wahl and N. A. Bonner, *Radioactivity Applied to Chemistry*, Wiley and Sons, New York, 1951.
62. R. R. Edwards, *Ann. Rev. Nuclear Sci.*, **1**, 301 (1952).
63. A. I. Brodsky, *Isotope Chemistry*, Academy of Sciences, Moscow, 1957.
64. D. R. Stranks and R. G. Wilkins, *Chem. Revs.*, **57**, 743 (1957).
65. C. Wagner, unpublished work.
66. K. E. Zimens, *Arkiv Kemi*, **20A**, No. 18 (1945); **21 A**, No. 16 (1946).
67. G. Berthier, *J. Chim. Phys.*, **49**, 527 (1952); **52**, 41 (1955).
68. M. Haïssinsky and D. Peschanski, *J. Chim. Phys.*, **47**, 191 (1950).
69. D. Peschanski, *J. Chim. Phys.*, **47**, 933 (1950).
70. D. G. Tuck and M. Haïssinsky, *J. Chim. Phys.*, **51**, 577 (1954).
71. M. Haïssinsky and A. Pappas, *J. Chim. Phys.*, **47**, 506 (1950).
72. G. W. Castellan and W. J. Moore, *J. Chem. Phys.*, **17**, 41 (1949).
73. R. Lindner, *J. Chem. Phys.*, **23**, 410 (1955).
74. A. Langer, *J. Chem. Phys.*, **10**, 321 (1942); **11**, 11 (1943).
75. A. E. Polessitsky and A. Murin, *Doklady Akad. Nauk S.S.S.R.*, **45**, 254 (1944).
76. I. M. Kolthoff and A. S. O'Brien, *J. Am. Chem. Soc.*, **61**, 3409, 3414 (1939).
77. A. N. Murin, *Doklady Akad. Nauk S.S.S.R.*, **74**, 650 (1950).
78. D. N. Sunderman and W. W. Meinke, *Science*, **121**, 777 (1955).
79. N. Davison and J. H. Sullivan, *J. Chem. Phys.*, **17**, 176 (1949).
80. W. Buser, W. Feitknecht, and U. Imobersteg, *Helv. Phys. Acta*, **25**, 619 (1952).
81. W. Buser and U. Imobersteg, *Helv. Chim. Acta*, **37**, 2345 (1954).
82. W. Buser and D. Graf, *Helv. Chim. Acta*, **38**, 810 (1955).
83. D. B. Broughton, R. L. Wentworth, and M. E. Farnsworth, *J. Am. Chem. Soc.*, **71**, 2346 (1949).
84. R. J. Mikovsky, M. Boudart, and H. S. Taylor, *J. Am. Chem. Soc.*, **76**, 3814 (1954).
85. C. Kemball, *Proc. Roy. Soc.* (*London*), **A214**, 413 (1952); **A217**, 376 (1953).
86. J. R. Anderson and C. Kemball, *Proc. Roy. Soc.* (*London*), **A223**, 361 (1954).
87. J. R. Gutmann, *J. Phys. Chem.*, **57**, 309 (1953).
88. J. Weber and K. J. Laidler, *J. Chem. Phys.*, **19**, 381 (1951).
89. J. T. Kummer and P. H. Emmett, *J. Chem. Phys.*, **19**, 289 (1951).
90. W. C. Cameron, A. Farkas, and L. M. Litz, *J. Phys. Chem.*, **57**, 229 (1953).
91. E. R. S. Winter, *J. Chem. Soc.*, **1950**, 1170, 1175; **1954**, 1522.
92. G. Houghton and E. R. S. Winter, *J. Chem. Soc.*, **1954**, 1509.
93. J. A. Barnard, E. R. S. Winter, and H. V. A. Briscoe, *J. Chem. Soc.*, **1954**, 1517.

94. A. Zagrubski, *Physik. Z. Sowjetunion,* **12,** 118 (1937).
95. W. A. Johnson, *Trans. Am. Inst. Met. Eng.,* **143,** 107 (1941).
96. J. Groh and G. Hevesy, *Ann. Physik,* **65,** 216 (1921).
97. G. Hevesy and W. Seith, *Z. Physik,* **56,** 79 (1929); **57,** 869 (1929).
98. G. Hevesy, *Trans. Faraday Soc.,* **34,** 841 (1938).
99. W. Seith, *Z. Elektrochem.,* **39,** 538 (1933).
100. J. Steigman, W. Shockley, and F. C. Nix, *Phys. Rev.,* **56,** 13 (1939).
101. C. E. Birchenall and R. F. Mehl, *J. Appl. Phys.,* **19,** 217 (1948).
102. C. E. Birchenall and R. F. Mehl, *J. Metals,* **188,** 144 (1950).
103. N. H. Nachtrieb, E. Catalano, and J. A. Weil, *J. Chem. Phys.,* **20,** 1185 (1952).
104. R. E. Meyer and N. H. Nachtrieb, *J. Chem. Phys.,* **23,** 405 (1955).
105. A. Kuper, H. Letaw, L. Slifkin, E. Sonder, and C. T. Tomizuka, *Phys. Rev.,* **96,** 1224 (1954).
106. L. Slifkin, D. Lazarus, and C. T. Tomizuka, *J. Appl. Phys.,* **23,** 1032 (1952).
107. R. E. Hoffman and D. Turnbull, *J. Appl. Phys.,* **22,** 634 (1951).
108. H. A. C. McKay, *Trans. Faraday Soc.,* **34,** 845 (1938).
109. H. Hatos and A. Kurtz, *J. Metals,* **6,** 616 (1954).
110. P. Shewan and F. Rines, *J. Metals,* **6,** 1021 (1954).
111. G. A. Shirn, E. S. Wajda, and H. B. Huntington, *Acta Met.,* **1,** 513 (1953).
112. P. H. Miller and F. R. Banks, *Phys. Rev.,* **61,** 648 (1942).
113. R. E. Eckert and H. G. Drickamer, *J. Chem. Phys.,* **20,** 13 (1952).
114. H. Letaw, L. Slifkin, and W. M. Portnoy, *Phys. Rev.,* **93,** 892 (1954); **98,** 1536 (1955).
115. W. Boas and P. J. Fensham, *Nature,* **164,** 1127 (1949).
116. N. H. Nachtrieb and G. S. Handler, *J. Chem. Phys.,* **23,** 1569 (1955).
117. F. C. Nix and F. E. Jaumot, *Phys. Rev.,* **82,** 72 (1951).
118. G. A. Shirn, *Acta Met.,* **3,** 87 (1955).
119. E. S. Wadja, G. A. Shirn, and H. B. Huntington, *Acta Met.,* **3,** 39 (1955).
120. R. B. Cudderback and H. G. Drickamer, *J. Chem. Phys.,* **19,** 790 (1951).
121. N. H. Nachtrieb and G. S. Handler, *J. Chem. Phys.,* **23,** 1187 (1955).
122. R. E. Meyer and N. H. Nachtrieb, *J. Chem. Phys.,* **23,** 1851 (1955).
123. R. E. Hoffman, *J. Chem. Phys.,* **20,** 1567 (1952).
124. G. Careri, A. Paoletti, and F. L. Salvetti, *Nuovo cimento,* **11,** 399 (1954).
125. J. Petit and N. H. Nachtrieb, *J. Chem. Phys.,* **24,** 1027 (1956).
126. F. S. Buffington and M. Cohen, *Acta Met.,* **2,** 660 (1954).
127. J. C. Fisher and R. E. Hoffman, *Nucl. Sci. Abs.,* **4,** 842 (1950).
128. J. C. Fisher, *J. Appl. Phys.,* **22,** 74 (1951).
129. R. E. Hoffman and D. Turnbull, *J. Appl. Phys.,* **22,** 634 (1951).
130. B. V. Rollin, *Phys. Rev.,* **55,** 231 (1939).
131. C. L. Raynor, L. Thomassen, and L. J. Rouse, *Trans. Am. Soc. Metals,* **30,** 313 (1942).
132. M. S. Maier and H. R. Nelson, *Trans. Am. Inst. Met. Eng.,* **147,** 39 (1942).
133. N. H. Nachtrieb and G. S. Handler, *Acta Met.,* **2,** 797 (1954).

134. M. H. Feldman, W. V. Goeddel, G. J. Dienes, and W. Gossen, *J. Appl. Phys.*, **23,** 1200 (1952).

135. G. J. Dienes, *J. Appl. Phys.*, **23,** 1194 (1952).

136. M. A. Kanter, *Phys. Rev.*, **98,** 1563 (1955).

137. R. M. Barrer, *Diffusion in Solids*, Cambridge University Press, 1951, Chapter 6.

138. W. Jost, *Diffusion in Solids, Liquids, Gases*, Academic Press, New York, 1955, Chapter 4.

139. G. V. Kurdiumov, *1955 Geneva Conference*, P. 702.

140. J. S. Anderson and K. Saddington, *J. Chem. Soc.*, **1949,** S 381.

141. A. W. Adamson, *J. Chem. Phys.*, **15,** 762 (1947).

142. A. W. Adamson, J. W. Cobble, and J. M. Nielsen, *J. Chem. Phys.*, **17,** 740 (1949).

143. A. W. Adamson, J. W. Cobble, and J. M. Nielsen, *J. Am. Chem. Soc.*, **74,** 446 (1952).

144. J. H. Wang and J. W. Kennedy, *J. Am. Chem. Soc.*, **72,** 2080 (1950).

145. J. H. Wang, *J. Am. Chem. Soc.*, **73,** 510, 4181 (1951).

146. J. H. Wang, *J. Phys. Chem.*, **58,** 686 (1954).

147. J. H. Wang, C. V. Robinson, and I. S. Edelman, *J. Am. Chem. Soc.*, **75,** 466 (1953).

148. J. H. Wang, *J. Am. Chem. Soc.*, **74,** 1182, 1612 (1952).

149. J. H. Wang and S. Miller, *J. Am. Chem. Soc.*, **74,** 1611 (1952).

150. C. J. Krauss and J. W. T. Spinks, *Can. J. Chem.*, **32,** 71 (1954).

151. G. Hevesy, *Physik. Z.*, **14,** 49 (1913).

152. F. A. Paneth and W. Vorwerk, *Z. physik. Chem.*, **101,** 445, 480 (1922).

153. F. A. Paneth, *J. Chim. Phys.*, **45,** 205 (1948).

154. I. M. Kolthoff and C. Rosenblum, *J. Am. Chem. Soc.*, **55,** 2656, 2664 (1933); **56,** 1264, 1658 (1934).

155. I. M. Kolthoff and H. C. Yutzy, *J. Am. Chem. Soc.*, **59,** 1634 (1937).

156. I. M. Kolthoff and F. T. Eggertsen, *J. Am. Chem. Soc.*, **62,** 2125 (1940); **63,** 1412 (1941).

157. I. M. Kolthoff and R. C. Bowers, *J. Am. Chem. Soc.*, **76,** 1503, 1510 (1954).

158. R. M. Stow and J. W. T. Spinks, *J. Chem. Phys.*, **17,** 744 (1949).

159. E. Whalley and E. R. S. Winter, *J. Chem. Soc.*, **1950,** 1175.

160. O. Hahn, *Applied Radiochemistry*, Cornell University Press, Ithaca, 1936.

161. O. Hahn, *J. Chem. Soc.*, **1949,** S 259.

162. S. Flugge and K. E. Zimens, *Z. Physik. Chem.*, **B42,** 179 (1939).

163. A. C. Wahl, in Ref. 63.

CHAPTER 20

ELECTROCHEMICAL APPLICATIONS

20–1 Isotopic exchange by electron transfer. This topic includes both exchanges between two ions of the same element differing only in their charge (e.g., Mn^{2+}/Mn^{3+}), and between an element and one of its ions (S/S^{2-}, Ag/Ag^{+}). Exchange between the halogens (or other metaloids) and their negative ions have already been discussed in the previous chapter, and those between metals and their ions are examined in Section 20–2. It should be noted immediately that the higher oxidation states of elements, that is, above (IV), are not present as "naked" ions in aqueous solution, but are complexed by oxygen or some other electronegative elements (MnO_4^-, $SbCl_6^-$), so that exchange between such species and a simple ion of lower valency generally requires an atom transfer. Even tetravalent cations, and to a lesser extent cations of lower valency, are frequently complexed or partially hydrolyzed in solution. For this reason, exchange by simple charge transfer is probably much rarer than the usual ionic formulae would suggest, and an absence of sufficient information on the actual state of ions in solution is one of the main difficulties involved in considering such problems, especially since the complexing, etc., varies considerably with the composition of the medium.

The mechanism of exchanges of this type is of considerable importance in any theoretical treatment of the kinetics of oxidation-reduction reactions, since they involve only very small free energy or entropy changes, and are therefore the simplest examples of this class of reactions. Furthermore, since the number of electrons lost by one ion is equal to that gained by the other, the principle of *equivalent change*, which is one of the conditions necessary for rapid charge transfer [1] is always fulfilled. There may, however, be other reasons why these exchanges should not be rapid. One important factor is the electrostatic repulsion, which means that two ions of the same sign cannot approach one another very closely without sufficient activation energy. It is difficult to calculate this energy exactly by applying Coulomb's law, because the magnitude of the microscopic dielectric constant ϵ on which the electrostatic interaction between ions at very small distances depends is considerably smaller than ϵ_0, the macroscopic dielectric constant (ϵ_0 for water is 80). The estimated repulsion energy for a pair of ions with charges 1 and 2 respectively is at least 15 to 20 kcal/mole, and some three times larger for two ions with charges of 2 and 3.

Franck [2] has drawn attention to the necessary delay in the displacement of the heavy hydration sphere of the ions relative to the movement of the electron during charge transfer (the Franck-Condon principle). If the two ions have different hydration shells, there must be a rearrangement after electron transfer, requiring an extra activation energy and causing a consequent slowing down of the process [3].

These theoretical considerations can now be compared with the experimental facts, summarized in Table 20–1 for cations and Table 20–2 for

TABLE 20-1

ISOTOPIC EXCHANGE BETWEEN CATIONS

Cationic pair	$t_{1/2}$	at concentration, M	Activation energy, kcal/mole	Conditions	Ref.
Cu^+/Cu^{2+}	fast			bromides	4
NpO_2^+/NpO_2^{2+}	97 sec	10^{-4}	8.3	$1M$ $HClO_4$, 10°C	5
Hg_2^{2+}/Hg^{2+}	fast			$HClO_4$, HNO_3	6, 7, 8
Tl^+/Tl^{3+}	7–12 d	2×10^{-4}	14.7	$HClO_4 + NaClO_4$	9, 10
Tl^+/Tl^{3+}	25 min	2×10^{-4}	14.7	$1.5M$ HCl	9, 10
V^{2+}/V^{3+}	<1 min			$HClO_4$, 2°C	11
Cr^{2+}/Cr^{3+}	2 min	0.1		HCl; slower in H_2SO_4	12, 13
Cr^{2+}/Cr^{3+}	14 hr	0.1	22	$HClO_4$	14
Mn^{2+}/Mn^{3+}	10–20 sec	10^{-2}		$HClO_4$	15
Fe^{2+}/Fe^{3+}	2–4 min	$\sim 10^{-4}$	9.5	$HClO_4$; catalyzed by HCl	16
Co^{2+}/Co^{3+}	fast			0°C	17
Eu^{2+}/Eu^{3+}	30–60 min	0.1	20.3	HCl; very slow in $HClO_4$ at 39.4°	18, 19
$[Co(NH_3)_6]^{2+}/[Co(NH_3)_6]^{3+}$	>80 d	0.09			17, 20
[Co *en*$_3$]$^{2+}$/[Co *en*$_3$]$^{3+}$	10–50 hr	0.02–0.09	14.3		20
[Os *dipy*]$^{2+}$/[Os *dipy*]$^{3+}$	<5 sec	5×10^{-4}		$HClO_4$; catalyzed by NO_3^-	21
Sn^{2+}/Sn^{4+}	7 min	0.1	10.8	$9M$ HCl	22
Ce^{3+}/Ce^{4+}	11.2 min	2×10^{-3}	7.7–11.7	$HClO_4$, HNO_3; strongly catalyzed by F^-	23, 24

en = ethylenediamine; *dipy* = α,α'-dipyndyl.

TABLE 20-2

ISOTOPIC EXCHANGE BETWEEN ANIONS

Anionic pair	$t_{1/2}$	at concentration, M	T, °C	Ref.
MnO_4^-/MnO_4^{2-}	5 sec	4×10^{-4}	0	15, 25, 26
$[IrCl_6]^{2-}/[IrCl_6]^{3-}$	30 sec	10^{-5}	1–50	27
$[Fe(CN)_6]^{3-}/[Fe(CN)_6]^{4-}$	2–5 sec	10^{-4}	0	28
$[Mn(CN)_6]^{3-}/[Mn(CN)_6]^{4-}$	<5 sec			29
$[Mo(CN)_6]^{3-}/[Mo(CN)_6]^{4-}$	fast		2	30

anions. Provided that the exchange is not too fast to be measurable, the rate is given in these tables as the time for half exchange ($t_{1/2}$) for the particular concentration shown. Exchanges involving ions with valencies above (IV) are not given. Unless otherwise indicated, the results refer to room temperature.

It will be seen from Tables 20–1 and 20–2* that all the electron transfer exchanges between anions investigated so far are very fast, with rates which are either immeasurable or barely measurable. The same is true for mono- and divalent cations, and even for some di- and trivalent pairs $t_{1/2}$ does not exceed 1 to 2 minutes, but exchanges between polyvalent cations are usually slow or very slow, and require activation energies of the order of 10 to 20 kcal/mole. The Cr^{2+}/Cr^{3+} couple is especially interesting because of the fact that the solvated trivalent ion has a six-coordinate hydration shell. Measurements with radioactive chromium show that the exchange is very slow in perchlorate solution, but much more rapid in chloride.† It has been shown [37, 38] using O^{18} that exchange between the hydrate water of Cr^{3+} and the bulk solvent is very slow in perchlorate solution ($t_{1/2} = 40$ hr), but that exchange of the solvation water of the Co^{2+}, Co^{3+}, Fe^{3+}, Al^{3+} ions, etc., is complete during the 2 to 3 min required to separate a small fraction of the solvent by distillation. If, however, Cr^{2+} or Cl^- ions are added to the Cr(III) perchlorate solution, the rate of exchange is considerably increased [39]; in the presence of both of these species, the time for half exchange may be as low as 7 min. It seems therefore that electron transfer is not strongly hindered by the hydration shell, and that in addition electron transfer facilitates exchange between the hydration shell and the bulk solvent. This is not true, however, when the coordinated H_2O is replaced by NH_3, since there is no exchange between Co^{2+} and $[Co(NH_3)_6]^{3+}$ in 0.01 M chloride solution at 25° after 7 days, and less than 1% after a much longer period at 50°C.

The relative ease of exchange between simple ions corresponds to the thermodynamic reversibility of their redox potentials. This parallelism is also found in exchanges between metals and their ions (see below). A striking example of this is given by the AsO_2^-/AsO_4^{3-} couple, which as we saw earlier (Section 19–1) exchanges only in the presence of iodide; equally, the potential becomes reversible only on the addition of this catalyst [40]. The potential of the iodate/periodate couple changes reversibly with changes in the thermodynamic activities [30], but it is established very slowly [41] and, in agreement with this, exchange between these two ions is very slow [42, 43].‡

Table 20–1 also illustrates the great influence of the anion on the rate of exchange, especially in terms of the catalytic effect of chloride and fluoride ions. Kinetic study of these exchanges leads to the conclusion that they occur (at least in part) not between the "naked" ions but between species such as $FeCl^{2+}$, $FeCl_2^+$, $TlOH^{2+}$, etc. This lowering of the total charge carried by the ions results in a decreased electrostatic potential barrier, but these "chemical" species do not appear sufficient to account for every case of rapid exchange and relatively low activation energy. It

---

* For further details of exchange experiments, see Refs. 31 through 36.

† It should be noted, however, that Anderson and Bonner (Ref. 14) did not observe any catalysis of this exchange by chloride ions in perchlorate media.

‡ For further examples, see Refs. 31 through 36.

has therefore been suggested [44] that the role of oppositely charged ions is more general; the ideas of Bronsted and Bjerrum on weak ionic association in solution suggest the formation of short-lived "collision complexes," which may be neutral or charged, e.g.,

$$\begin{matrix} \text{Cl} & & & & \text{Cl} \\ & \diagdown & & \diagup & \\ & \text{Mn}^*(\text{III}) \cdots \text{Cl} \cdots \text{Mn}(\text{II}) & & & \\ & \diagup & & \diagdown & \\ \text{Cl} & & & & \text{Cl} \end{matrix}$$

This can subsequently dissociate either to give the original ions [Mn*(III) + Mn(II)], or to "activate" the initially inactive ion [Mn*(II) + Mn(III)], depending on the way in which this short-lived complex breaks up.

Association between cations should be more likely with small anions, which will have a greater tendency both for partial neutralization of the cations ($FeCl_2^+$)* and for the formation of stable anionic complexes ($FeCl_6^{3-}$). In the latter case, if the lower valency ion remains cationic, the electrostatic force becomes an attraction and the exchange will be easier, provided that the stability of the negative complex is not too high. With highly stable complex anions, extra activation energy will be required for rupture of the covalent bonds implicit in the exchange. In the limiting case, highly stable complexes which do not react with chemical reagents do not exchange at all ($Fe^{3+}/[Fe(CN)_6]^{4-}$).

Exchange induced by chemical precipitation of one of the species concerned may also be the result of unstable intermediate states formed by one of the cations with the precipitating reagent. If this is the case, the catalysis should be greater if the cation precipitated is the one most likely to form complexes, which will generally be the higher oxidation state. For example, the precipitation of $Tl(OH)_3$ induces an exchange 5 to 20 times greater than that found in the precipitation of Tl_2CrO_4 or TlCl [10].

The formation of short-lived ionic associations complexes has been confirmed by the work of Davidson and his collaborators [47, 48], who observed nonadditive, increased absorption of light by mixtures of aqueous solution of $CuCl/CuCl_2$, $FeCl_2/FeCl_3$, and $SnCl_2/SnCl_4$. For the copper chlorides, the effect is already measurable at low chloride concentrations (0.2 to 0.4 M). From the way in which this extra absorption depends on the cation concentrations, the authors attribute this effect to the formation of "interaction complexes" of the type suggested above for the manganese chlorides.

The idea of such complexes has been retained by various authors, especially Taube [12] and Libby [3], who suggest that a small anion can act as a bridge between two cations in a linear symmetrical activated complex $(Mn\text{-}Cl\text{-}Mn)^{4+}$. In this way the positive ions can approach each other sufficiently to allow an easier rearrangement of the hydration shells, so that the electron transfer requires less activation energy. Marcus, Zwolinski, and Eyring [49, 50] (see also Ref. 51) have applied the absolute rate theory

* See Refs. 45 and 46 for discussions of the formation of ion-pairs of this type.

to this problem, and have advanced the hypothesis that the transfer is facilitated by the tunnelling effect (Section 4–5). The probability k_e of an electron passing through a potential barrier of height V is given by

$$k_e = \exp\left[-\frac{8\pi r_t}{3h}\{2m(V - W)\}^{1/2}\right], \tag{20–1}$$

in which r_t is the tunnelling distance at the height at which the electron passes; m is the mass of the electron, W its kinetic energy, and h Planck's constant. The value of r_t can be evaluated semiempirically. Since the rate constant for the exchange (k), which depends on the enthalpy $\Delta H^{\ddagger}$ and entropy of activation $\Delta S^{\ddagger}$ according to Eq. (19–18), is proportional to k_e, the theory can be tested by measuring the three parameters k, $\Delta H^{\ddagger}$, and $\Delta S^{\ddagger}$. The agreement between theory and experiment is satisfactory in some cases, but less satisfactory in others.

The extremely slow exchange between the cobalt hexammines (see Table 20–1) is surprising, especially since large ions of this type are generally considered to be relatively weakly hydrated, and contrasts with the behavior of the iron hexacyanides. It is very possible that the difference lies in the different electronic structure of these compounds. According to Pauling [52] the residual positive or negative charge of the complex ions is distributed over the outer surface of the complex, so that the transfer requires the extraction of an electron from the interior of the $[Co(NH_3)_6]^{2+}$ ion and its passage across the positive exterior. This would require a higher activation energy, which would moreover depend on the nature of the complexing ligand. On the other hand, this theory assumes that for anions such as

$$[Fe(CN)_6]^{3-}/[Fe(CN)_6]^{4-} \qquad \text{or} \qquad [Mn(CN)_6]^{3-}/[Mn(CN)_6]^{4-},$$

the excess electrons are at the periphery, and the transfer mechanism will be effectively the same as between the simple ions. From this point of view, exchange between cations may sometimes be more difficult than between anions, a distinction also made by Cobble and Adamson [37] on other grounds. However, certain steric factors may hinder exchange in both anion and cation systems.*

20–2 Exchange between metals and their ions. The most striking fact observed in exchanges of this type is the relatively large number of atomic layers of the metal which participate in the process, even though the self-diffusion of solid metals is negligible at room temperature (Section 19–8). Hevesy [54, 55] demonstrated this effect in the first experiments on the $Pb/Pb(NO_3)_2$ exchange, and it has been confirmed subsequently by Rollin [56] and Coffin and Tingley [57] on the $Ag/AgNO_3$ system, and by a series of systematic measurements [58] on exchange between lead, bismuth, copper, antimony, manganese, tellurium, and lanthanum and their ions as a function of time, concentration, pH, temperature, and the state of the

* For recent work in this field, see *Discussions Faraday Soc.*, **29** (1960).

TABLE 20–3

EXCHANGE BETWEEN METALS AND THEIR IONS
(Number of monatomic layers exchanged)

Time	Pb/0.1 M $Pb(NO_3)_2$ pH 5.1	Mn/0.5 M $MnSO_4$ pH 2.9	Bi/0.1 N $Bi(NO_3)_3$ 1 M HNO_3
2 sec	61	—	—
5 sec	88	—	—
10 sec	94	5.9	—
30 sec	122	22	15
2 min	231	66	57
5 min	306	120	209
19 min	663	282	—
30 min	914	421	1003
60 min	1654	626	1020

surface. The most important conclusions which can be drawn from these experiments are the following:

1. For most metals examined, with 0.001 M solution, tens of atomic layers have participated in the exchange after about 10 min, increasing to hundreds of layers if the solutions are 100 times more concentrated. Table 20–3 shows this for lead, bismuth, and manganese. After the initial exchange, the process slows down and the results become irregular and irreproducible. A decrease in the rate of exchange after a time of this order has also been observed with the $Zn/ZnSO_4$ system [59].

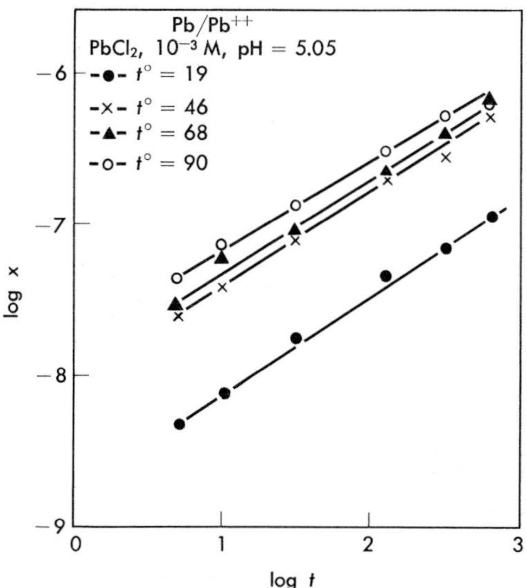

FIG. 20–1. The rate of the Pb/Pb^{2+} exchange at different temperatures (Ref. 58).

TABLE 20–4

EXCHANGE BETWEEN Pb AND VARIOUS LEAD SALTS
(Salt concentration 0.001 M, pH 5.1)
(Number of monatomic layers exchanged)

Time	$PbCl_2$	$Pb(NO_3)_2$	$Pb(CH_3COO)_2$
10 sec	6.3	3.1	3.4
30 sec	9.8	4.8	5
2 min	23.7	10.7	7
5 min	25.3	21.3	9.6

2. The time dependence of the exchange does not follow a kinetic equation such as (19–34); instead, over a period of 1 to 2 hours, the exchange obeys the empirical equation (Fig. 20–1)

$$\log x = a \log t + b, \tag{20–2}$$

in which a and b are constants which depend on the nature of the system.

3. The anion has a considerable effect on the rate of exchange, as shown by Table 20–4 for lead salts, and by Fig. 20–2 for bismuth salts. Furthermore, the order of the rates may vary considerably with the anion concentration. The exchange is faster in the presence of those anions which can

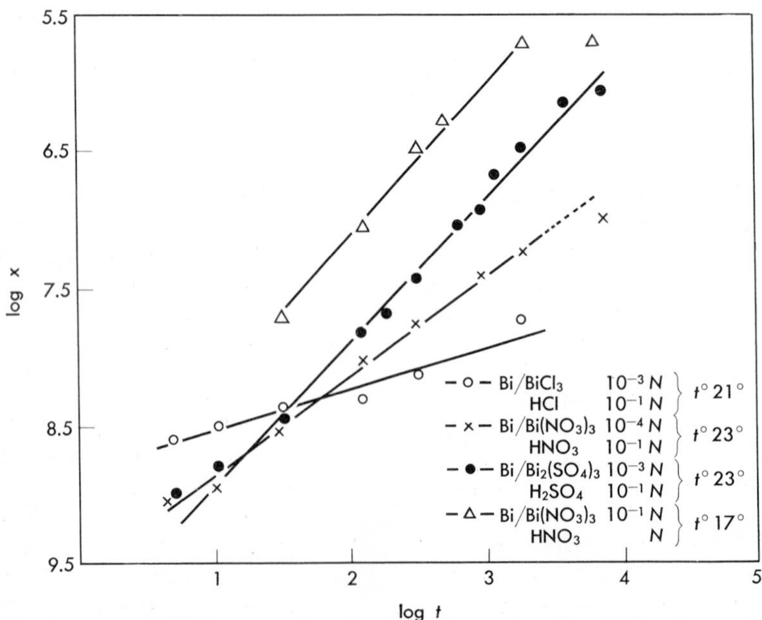

FIG. 20–2. The effect of the anion on the Bi/Bi^{3+} exchange (Ref. 58).

TABLE 20–5

EXCHANGE BETWEEN Pb AND $Pb(NO_3)_2$ SOLUTION AT DIFFERENT pH
(Numbers of monatomic layers)

Time	pH 0.9	pH 2.85	pH 4.7
10 sec	226	117	41
30 sec	416	166	78
2 min	718	279	144
5 min	1419	321	207

TABLE 20–6

EXCHANGE BETWEEN Au AND 0.1 *M* AQUEOUS SOLUTION OF Au(III) CHLORIDE*
(Number of monatomic layers exchanged in 2 min)

T, °C	pH 0.97	pH 1.41
19	83	56
53	169	110
68	264	185
91	346	264

* More recent experiments by J. P. Pérolat and M. Cottin [*J. Chim. Phys.*, **58,** 330 (1961)] show that the true exchange is much less than the values shown in this table, and that it is masked either by adsorption of ions or by dissolution of the metal, depending on the conditions.

interact chemically with the metal, so that the measured exchange is higher if the metal rather than the solution is labeled; the average represents approximately the true exchange. For example, after 1 min, the exchange between Cu* and 0.27 *M* $CuBr_2$ at pH 3.4 corresponds to 2670 layers, and that between Cu and Cu^*Br_2 to 1034 layers; after 5 min the values are 6340 and 5820 respectively.

4. Even with inert metals, the rate generally increases with acidity (see Tables 20–5 and 20–6). From experiments on the exchange of lead with lead nitrate and lead chloride, Hevesy and Biltz [55] concluded that corrosion of the metal is not a necessary condition for exchange. The later results shown above confirm this conclusion, but show that corrosion does enhance the exchange by disrupting the surface of the metal.

5. If a proportionality is assumed between the exchange and time over very short periods, an initial activation energy can be obtained by measuring the exchange at various temperatures and applying the Arrhenius equation. This procedure gives activation energies which depend somewhat on the anion, being 3 to 5.5 kcal/mole for chlorides and around 7 to 8 kcal/mole for nitrates.

6. The rate of exchange is not related to the electrochemical potential; for example, with the same anion and at equal concentrations, manganese ($E^0 = +1.05$ v) exchanges at almost the same rate as copper ($E^0 = -0.34$ v).

The behavior of typical inert metals, such as cobalt and tantalum, has been examined by Cottin [60]; cobalt has also been studied by Simnad and Ruder [61, 62]. The rate of exchange (for Co/Co^{2+}) is much smaller than for the other metals quoted above, and depends strongly on the anion, being measurably fast with chloride and sulfate, but slowing down fairly quickly with nitrate, acetate, and perchlorate. The Ta/TaF_7^{2-} exchange is slower than the dissolution of the metal even in conditions under which this system appears to give a reversible electrochemical potential.

The effect of the state of the surface has been studied by Erbacher and others [56, 63, 64]. According to Erbacher, the exchange is restricted to a single monatomic layer if the metal is previously placed in a solution identical with that used for the exchange, except for the absence of tracer. The experiments described above, however, show that this pretreatment may either increase or decrease the exchange, depending on the conditions [58]. Rollin [56] has reported that the exchange between Ag and $AgNO_3$ involves 150 layers in 24 hours, even after pretreatment of the metal in a solution of inactive $AgNO_3$.

Coffin and Tingley [57] have reported that silver exchanges not more than about 20 layers with 0.1 *M* $AgNO_3$ solution and that the exchange is practically complete in a few seconds, but that polished silver exchanges a hundred layers, and 24 hours are required for the total exchange to be 90% complete. According to Cottin [60], electrolytic polishing of lead and cobalt reduces the rate of exchange, and makes the results rather irreproducible. Silver powder prepared by reduction with NaH_2PO_2 exchanges 7500 layers in 20 hours with an 0.2 *M* $AgNO_3$ solution, whereas a powder obtained by electrolysis exchanges only 30 layers under the same conditions (100°C, nitrogen atmosphere) [65]. The powder prepared by reduction recrystallizes during the exchange, and changes its appearance; recrystallization of metallic bismuth during exchange with its ions has also been reported [58]. The allotropic transformation of selenium during exchange was mentioned earlier (Section 19–8).

The overall conclusion from these observations [60] is that even in the absence of any detectable corrosion the surface of the metal does not remain unaltered in contact with a solution of its own ions. Hevesy and Biltz suggested [55] that the heterogeneity of the surface, and the formation of local cells as a result of this, is of fundamental importance in such exchanges. Simnad and Ruder [61] have calculated the current from such cells in the case of cobalt from the rate of exchange in the presence and absence of oxygen. According to measurements made by Miller and Pleskov [67], the exchange current between zinc, lead, and bismuth amalgams and solutions of their (radioactive) ions is of the order of 0.04 to 0.1 amp/cm^2.

Since the exchange involves dissolution and equivalent precipitation, it causes disorganization of the surface layers of the crystal and makes them more permeable to penetration by ions of either sign. The recrystallization is one of the results of these processes. The measured rate of exchange will therefore depend on the ability of the metal surface to develop in contact with solutions under different conditions, and will therefore be determined by the structural properties of the metal, and by its cohesive energy. It can be sensibly assumed that the actual electron transfer between a metal and its ions is relatively fast and virtually reversible, as in the case of metaloids and the majority of exchange reactions involving ions of lower valency.

20-3 Corrosion and passivity. The effect of the state of the surface and of local cells on isotopic exchange reactions between metals and their ions suggest that these phenomena are closely related to corrosion and passivity. Autoradiography provides an excellent method of investigating these effects, since it can be used to unambiguously localize points of attack or of surface oxidation. One example of the use of this method is the work of Bacon [68] on the corrosion of iron. Radioactive iron was deposited electrolytically on a polished iron surface; the extent and location of the blackening of photographic plates placed in contact with the surface after corrosion showed directly where metal had been dissolved off, or oxygen had been fixed. Autoradiography of a Sb/Sn/Pb alloy after immersion in a solution containing ThB showed that only those regions rich in lead pick up this isotope, and that the antimony-tin phases were virtually free of the tracer [69]. In a Zn/Al/Pb alloy, lead labeled with ThB was found to be localized around the grains of the Zn/Al eutectic [70]. Corrosion by water vapor at 95° occurs mainly at points rich in lead.

Simnad [62] has immersed various metals (silver, platinum, aluminum, titanium, copper, nickel, iron, steel, and other alloys) in aereated or oxygen-free solutions containing labeled Co^{2+}, Cr^{3+}, or CrO_4^{2-} and subsequently examined the distribution of the active species by autoradiography. Evidence was obtained of the effect of local cells in the surface fixation of radioactive cobalt, which was found to be fixed at the cathodic sites. The effect of oxygen depends on the nature of the oxide surface which is formed. If this oxide is a strong protective agent, the surface acquires less activity, since the area available for electrolysis is reduced, but if the oxide is a weak protective agent the oxygen acts as a depolarizer, and a greater quantity of radiocobalt is picked up. Autoradiographic study of metals rendered passive by chromate solutions indicate that radiochromium is concentrated at the anodic sites of the surface. These experiments corroborate the theory of Hoar and Evans [71], who ascribed the passivity of iron in these solutions to chromate oxidation of iron at the anodic sites, with the formation of Fe^{3+} and Cr^{3+} compounds, which slow down the attack on the metal.

Powers and Hackerman [72, 73] have also studied the passivity of steel and chromium by chromate ions labeled with Cr^{51}. According to these authors, the passivity is due to the irreversible adsorption of ions rather than to the formation of new products. In agreement with this, the fixation of radiochromium, and hence the passivity, is pH dependent. At pH 11 or greater, the chromate ions are not adsorbed; the passivity in such solutions may be due to OH^- ions. The maximum pick-up of anions appears to correspond to the formation of a monomolecular layer.

The corrosion pitting of Al/Fe/Si alloys (0.5% Fe, 3% Si) in solutions containing active cobalt and lead has been studied by Aziz [74]. Autoradiography showed that in this case the site of the pitting is surrounded by a cathodic ring, around which is another ring of passive surface which prevents the point of attack from spreading; the remainder of the surface is cathodic. The same technique showed that the oxide layers formed on the metal in air break up when the metal is placed in an aqueous corrosive solution, and are then built up again by reaction with the solution.

The corrosion of brass by CCl_4 containing small quantities of $CHCl_3$ + C_2H_5OH (a mixture which is used in fire extinguishers) is inhibited by the addition of CS_2. Experiments were carried out to clear up the mechanism of this phenomena [75], using carbon disulfide labeled with S^{35} and ethanol labeled with C^{14}. The liquid containing one or both of these isotopically labeled compounds was left in contact with the alloy for several months; subsequent radiometric measurements showed the formation on the surface of an extremely thin layer (50 to 80 molecular layers) which contained both tracers, and which could not be removed either by evacuation or by ion exchange with an inactive solution. It is believed that this layer is sufficient to protect the alloy against corrosion. In the case of CS_2, reaction with the brass probably gives copper and zinc sulfides; with alcohol, xanthic acid is formed, which subsequently gives the xanthates of these two metals.

Rabinowicz [76] immersed various metals in a solution of amyl iodide labeled with I^{131} for a period of 15 sec, and then determined radiographically the number of molecular layers attacked. This number turns out to be 150 to 200 for Ag, Cu, and Pb, 50 for In and brass, 10 to 15 for Al, Bi, Ni, Sb, Sn, Cd, and steel, and only 3 for Zn and Ti.

To examine the effect of the residual water held by a metal during treatment for protection against rusting, Summer [77] immersed samples in an aqueous solution containing Na^{24} or S^{35} before proceeding with the usual treatment. The measured activity was inversely proportional to the efficiency of the protection. The protective power of electroplating against corrosion has been studied by Bonnemay, Makram, and Royon [78, 79]. These authors neutron-activated a piece of copper, and subsequently electroplated a deposit of chromium onto this, and immersed it in a solution containing inactive Cu^{2+} ions. The solution acquired activity after a time which depended on the thickness and porosity of the electrodeposited chromium. These authors showed that the logarithm of this time is a linear function of the thickness of the chromium, and that the slope of the corresponding line depends on the composition of the chromium bath.

20–4 Electrolytic studies with tracers. Radioactive indicators can be used to investigate a number of electrolytic problems where other physicochemical methods break down. For example, electrochemists have been interested for a long time in whether the cathodic deposition of chromium in the electrolysis of chromates occurs via Cr(III) or is a direct discharge process. Ogburn and Brenner [80] found the answer to this by electrolyzing a solution containing both CrO_4^{2-} and Cr^{3+} ions, of which only one species was labeled with radiochromium. It was shown that an active deposit was obtained only when the CrO_4^{2-} ion was the labeled species, so that direct discharge of the hexavalent ions must occur. This work of course depended on the fact that isotopic exchange between Cr(VI) and Cr(III) is extremely slow at room temperature; obviously if this had not been the case, an active deposit would have been obtained in both cases.

Using radioactive ruthenium, Griess [81, 82] was able to establish the conditions under which brilliant and adherent cathode deposits of this metal could be obtained by the electrolysis of very dilute solutions of the nitroso salt (5×10^{-3} to 5×10^{-5} M). In more dilute solution, deposition is complete only on platinized platinum. The rate of deposition increases on increasing the temperature of electrolysis, but the quality of the deposit is not improved. The results in noncomplexing media were irreproducible and unsatisfactory. On the other hand, experiments by Guebely with labeled Ru^{4+} or Ru^{3+} sulfate, nitrate, or fluoride, gave very good cathodic deposits on gold, platinum, nickel, or copper by the electrolysis of these "simple" salts when temperatures above 75° were used [83].

The measured current intensity during cathodic deposition can be regarded as the resultant of two opposing processes, deposition and dissolution. Audubert [84] has measured the rate of this latter process by using a labeled copper electrode immersed in a solution of copper sulfate, and held at a constant potential with respect to a reference electrode. Over a certain potential range, the rate of dissolution (given by the activity passing into the solution) was a linear function of the applied potential. The same author [85] has shown that a similar method can be used under certain conditions to determine the partial current intensity corresponding to the discharge of one ion during the discharge of another.

Houtermans and his collaborators [86] have used radioactive sulfur in attempts to work out the conditions under which sulfur is incorporated into copper deposited electrolytically from sulfate solution. These authors conclude that during electrolysis the surfaces of both electrodes are covered with a monomolecular layer of sulfate ions. The quantity of sulfur incorporated varies between 10^{-8} and 10^{-5} atoms per Cu atom deposited, depending on the conditions. A similar result was obtained [75] in experiments on the electrodeposition of silver from Ag^+ solutions, to which ammonium thiosulfate is added to increase the brilliance of the deposit. Radiosulfur incorporated into the thiosulfate was found both at the cathode and at the silver anode, despite the continuous anodic dissolution of silver. The proportion of sulfur atoms in the cathodic deposit is again of the same order of magnitude as in the work discussed above.

The conditions for the anodic formation of bismuth peroxide have been established by experiments with the isotope RaE (Bi^{210}) [87]. It was shown that in potassium tartrate solution, the deposit initially formed dissolves during the electrolysis due to oxidation of the tartrate ion, giving products which are stronger reducing agents than the initial ion. In nitrate media, the formation is preceded by an induction period, the length of which depends on the acidity, the concentration, and the current intensity.

A final example is provided by the electrolysis of acetic and propionic acids in heavy water. In the first case, deuterium is formed at the cathode, and C_2H_6 containing no deuterium produced at the anode [88]:

$$2CH_3COOD \rightarrow CH_3{\cdot}CH_3 + 2CO_2 + D_2, \tag{20–3}$$

showing that the C—H bonds are not broken. On electrolyzing

$$\overset{3}{C}D_3{\cdot}\overset{2}{C}H_2{\cdot}\overset{1}{C}OOH \quad \text{or} \quad CH_3CD_2COOH,$$

one obtains $CD_2{=}CH_2$, so that here the C—C bond is preserved:

$$\overset{3}{C}D_3\overset{2}{C}H_2\overset{1}{C}OOH \rightarrow \overset{3}{C}D_2{=}\overset{2}{C}H_2 + \overset{1}{C}O_2 + HD. \tag{20–4}$$

20–5 Electrochemical displacement. Isotopic exchange between a metal and its ions can be regarded as a special case of the electrochemical displacements which are often found at the tracer level. When a sheet or wire of a metal is immersed in an extremely dilute aqueous solution containing ions of a radioelement which is electrochemically more noble, the ions deposit spontaneously on the metal. Thus polonium and astatine deposit on Cu, Fe, Bi, Te, and Ag from chloride, nitrate, sulfuric, or acetate solution, and in chloride solution radiocopper ions discharge on lead or zinc, and ions of radioactive antimony on tin, etc.

Apart from the electrochemical potential, the rate of deposition and the yield in a given system depend on the concentration of the ions in question (Section 18–5), on the nature and concentration of other ions and molecules in the solution, on the state of the metal surface, and on the temperature, etc. For example, appreciable quantities of radioactive ruthenium will deposit spontaneously on lead from sulfate solution if the metal has been cathodically polarized under appropriate conditions [83].

On the other hand, certain ions can inhibit spontaneous deposition. Thus for example, the deposition of polonium on silver is prevented by the presence of ferric ions, but if a reducing agent such as SO_2 or hydrazine is added to the solution, deposition occurs readily [89]. Addition of alkali in high concentrations to a Po solution can also decrease or prevent deposition. On the other hand, if thiourea is added to a chloride solution of polonium, deposition occurs even on gold (the more noble metal) due to the formation of the complex ion $[((NH_2)_2CS)_2Au]^+$, which lowers the potential of the gold [90]. Even in the absence of this complexing agent, very small quantities of Po deposit on gold to an extent which depends on the previous mechanical and thermal history of the gold [91]. This deposition is probably the result of adsorption phenomena.

Although it is therefore difficult to achieve an absolute separation of two different radioelements, the degree of separation which is possible is often sufficient for practical purposes. The following experiments by Erbacher and Philipp [92] are a good illustration of the method. These authors rotated a sheet of nickel in a chloride solution containing 1.47×10^{-5} mg RaE and 0.77 mg RaD. The RaE was completely deposited, but only 3.2×10^{-4} mg RaD was removed from the solution (RaD is an isotope of lead, which is less noble than nickel). The nickel with its deposit was then dissolved, and deposition effected on a new sheet of nickel. This cycle of operations was then repeated twice, at the end of which the quantity of RaD deposited was reduced to 4×10^{-7} mg; the deposition of RaE was always of the order of 100%.

The radioactive displacement laws (Section 1–3) can be used to predict possible separations of natural radioelements by spontaneous deposition. Decay is by either α- or β-emission; in the first case the radioelement formed is displaced two places to the left in the periodic system relative to the mother element (Io $\rightarrow$ Ra) and is more electropositive than the latter, and in the second case it is displaced one place to the right, and a more noble element is obtained (RaD $\rightarrow$ RaE). This relationship between electropositivity and displacement in the periodic system is not a general one, but it happens to be valid for elements with atomic numbers between 81 and 92 (Tl–U). The artificial radioelements which exist throughout the whole of the periodic table are formed in a variety of reactions, and the electro-affinity relationships between the initial and product element do not obey any such general rules. To illustrate this, radioactive nickel formed by the (n, p) reaction on copper is more electropositive than the target material, but radiocopper produced by this same reaction (on zinc) is more noble than zinc. A similar inversion is found on comparing the (α, p) reactions of Mg($\rightarrow$ Al) and Cr($\rightarrow$ Mn).

In some cases, electrochemical displacement can be used to determine roughly the position of an element in the table of normal potentials. For example, by studying the rates of spontaneous deposition of protactinium from fluoride solution on Be, Mn, Zn, Cr, Ta, Pb, Cu, and Ag copper and silver, it was concluded that the electrochemical potential of the Pa/PaF_7^{2-} couple lies between those of Cr/Cr^{2+} and Ta/TaF_7^{2-} [94].

In the case of the spontaneous deposition of Pa on lead, the fraction of protactinium deposited at equilibrium was measured at various concentrations between 3×10^{-5} and 10^{-3} M. It was found that partition between the solution and the metal obeyed the Langmuir isotherm

$$a_d = \frac{a_m b a_s}{1 + b a_s}, \tag{20–5}$$

in which a_d is the maximum quantity which can be deposited (per square centimeter), a_s the quantity per milliliter remaining in solution at equilibrium, a_m the quantity corresponding to a monatomic layer, and b a constant. In very dilute solution (at concentrations below 10^{-9} M), Pa deposits spontaneously from sulfate solution on platinized platinum if the latter has been previously anodically polarized. This deposition is probably due to peroxide formation by reaction with oxygen adsorbed during the polarization [95]. Under these conditions, the partition follows the logarithmic isotherm proposed by Williams and Temkin [96];

$$a_d = k + k' \log_e a_s, \tag{20–6}$$

in which k and k' are constants.

More frequently, however, both spontaneous and electrolytic deposition are governed by the Freundlich isotherm

$$a_d = ka_s^{1/n}. \tag{20-7}$$

Such isotherms are obtained for the spontaneous deposition of polonium on Au, Pt, and Pd [91] and of active Pb and Bi isotopes on Ag, Au, and Ni [97, 98]. The theoretical significance of these results is discussed later.

20–6 Critical deposition potentials. For ionic solutions, a concentration of $\sim 10^{-7}$ N is about the lower limit at which static measurement of electrochemical potentials can be carried out, provided that the conditions are very carefully chosen [99, 100, 101]. Such a concentration generally corresponds to the formation of a *formal* "monatomic layer" when virtually all the ions present in 5 to 10 cm^3 of solution are deposited on an electrode 1 to 2 cm^2 in area. "Formal" implies a (presumably) uniform layer calculated on the basis of the geometrical dimensions of the support, ignoring any surface heterogeneity (Section 19–10). Dynamic electrochemical methods, conductimetric methods, or plots of voltage-current curves are also impossible below the concentration quoted, since the current is then carried by ions other than those under investigation, and in particular by H^+ and OH^- from dissociation of the solvent.

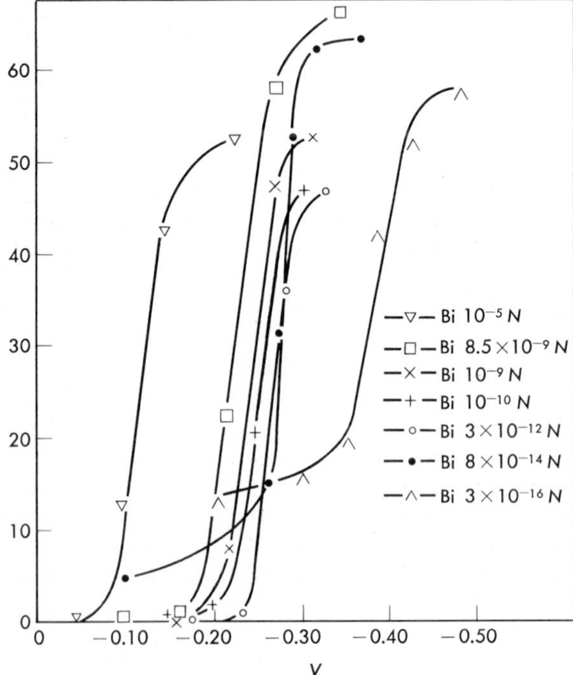

Fig. 20–3. Critical deposition potentials for the cathodic deposition of Bi in the 10^{-5} to 10^{-16} N concentration range.

The electrochemical behavior of extremely dilute solutions can, however, be investigated by means of special polarization curves obtained with radioactive indicators, a method first introduced by Hevesy and Paneth in 1914 [102, 103]. Subsequent developments of this method have resulted in two different experimental procedures. In the first of these, one measures the quantity deposited in a given time on an electrode held at a constant potential with respect to a reference electrode, using a classical potentiometric apparatus or potentiostat. A plot of the rate of deposition against potential under these conditions is usually of sigmoid form, with a fairly easily detectable point of inflection (e/V curves) from which a *critical deposition potential* can be obtained. In the second, and more thermodynamically correct approach, the quantities deposited at equilibrium are plotted as a function of the potential, so that this method requires that sufficient time be allowed for deposition at a given potential to be complete (plot of e/E). The curve is of the same form as in the previous case (see Fig. 20–3 which shows results for the deposition of bismuth), and in most cases the two methods give virtually the same value for the critical potential [104]. The nature of the deposit being studied (i.e., cathodic or anodic) obviously determines which of these electrodes is held at constant potential.

An extremely convenient way of carrying out such experiments is to use the apparatus designed by Joliot [104]. A glass cell has two lateral openings, to each of which is applied a metal sheet which is sufficiently thin to allow the radiation emitted by the deposit formed on the inside surface to pass through the metal into an ionization chamber or counter placed immediately opposite the electrode. Figure 20–4 shows a cell of this type in current use in the Laboratoire Curie. This cell is machined from a block of perspex; the cathode is held in position at C by a metallic ring M which carries the electrical contacts. The letters A, S, and B indicate holes through which the anode wire, a stirrer, and an electrolyte bridge are inserted.

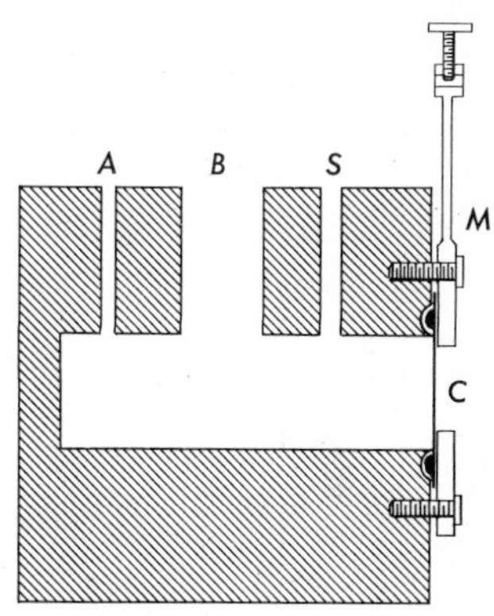

Fig. 20–4. The electrolytic cell designed by F. Joliot.

The experimental curves obtained with such an apparatus show the amount deposited as a function of time at a given constant potential; the example in Fig. 20–5 refers to the cathodic deposition of polonium on gold from 10^{-9} N solution in 0.5 M HNO_3 [104]. The method can also be used to investigate some of the chemical properties of the radioelement being deposited. Suppose, for example, that a reducing agent or some reagent which forms an insoluble compound with polonium is added to a polonium solution in the course of electrolysis at a given potential. Deposition will then cease, and the corresponding curve, instead of continuing to rise, will become a straight line parallel to the axis (Fig. 20–6). If the reagent dissolves a deposit which is already formed, the curve will decrease

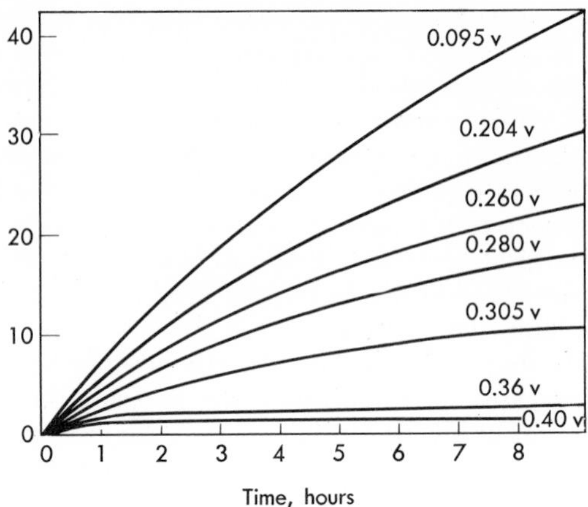

FIG. 20–5. The rate of the cathodic deposition of Po from nitrate solution (Ref. 104).

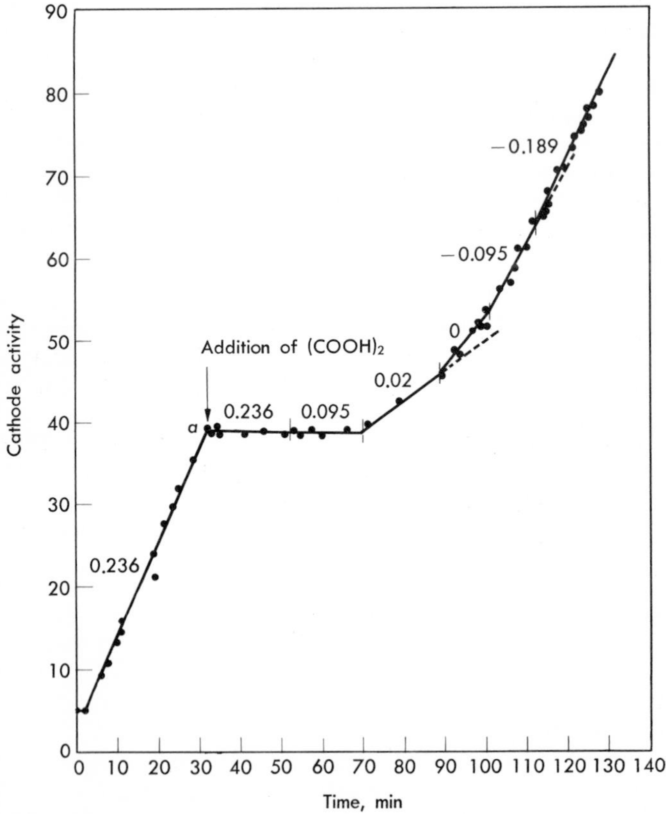

FIG. 20–6. Cathodic deposition of Po from nitrate solution arrested by the addition of oxalic acid (Ref. 104).

instead of rising. This technique has given evidence of the reduction of Po(IV) to a lower valency state by hydrogen peroxide [104] or hydrazine [105, 106], for the formation of an insoluble polonium pyrogallate [107], and for the reduction of anodic deposits of polonium and bismuth by oxalic and tartaric acids. In interpreting the experimental results, possible changes to the added reagent itself due to the effect of the current must always be considered.

Electrode processes can also be studied by following the kinetics of the dissolution of a preformed deposit at constant potential. If the process is reversible, the amount remaining on the electrode at each potential is the same as that obtained by deposition, although the two processes, deposition and dissolution, may go on at different rates.

The curves in Fig. 20–5 correspond to a first-order kinetic equation

$$\frac{dx}{dt} = \alpha(x_0 - x) - \beta x, \tag{20–8}$$

in which dx/dt is the rate of deposition, x_0 is the initial number of disposable ions in solution, and α and β are constants which refer to the probability of discharge of ions and redissolution of already deposited atoms [104]. Similar curves have been obtained for the cathodic deposition of polonium in alkaline solution, for anodic deposition in acid solution [108], and for cathodic deposits of technetium [109], RaE [110], radiozinc [111], and protactinium [112]. It is of course necessary to make corrections to the curves for radioactive decay if the experiment is long compared with the half-life of the isotope. For the very electropositive metal zinc, the values of the coefficients α and β in Eq. (20–8) change during the electrolysis.

20–7 Comparison with the Nernst equation. The fundamental problem relating to these critical potential measurements is the relationship between the critical potential obtained under the conditions described and the thermodynamic potential determined for the same macrochemical process at equilibrium. For example, the normal potential of the Bi/Bi^{3+} electrode is $E_h^0 = +0.226$ v; we must ask whether it is then justifiable to conclude that the critical potential for the discharge of $ThC(Bi^{212})$ at a concentration of 10^{-12} N will be that calculated using the Nernst electrochemical equation

$$E = E_0 + \frac{RT}{zF} \ln a, \tag{20–9}$$

which gives

$$-0.226 + \frac{0.058 \times 12}{3} = +0.006 \text{ v.}$$

Hevesy and Paneth gave implicitly an affirmative answer to this question from measurements with Pb and Bi isotopes, but Herzfeld [113] suggests from simple kinetic arguments that when the deposit does not completely cover the electrode, Eq. (20–9) should be replaced by another relation which in modern notation is written as

$$E = E_0 + \frac{RT}{zF} \ln \frac{a_d}{a_0 - a_d}, \tag{20–10}$$

where a_0 is the initial thermodynamic activity of the ions in question in solution, and a_s the activity in the solution after the deposition is complete, so that $a_d(= a_0 - a_s)$ is the corresponding activity removed from the solution by deposition. This equation implies that:

1. There is no unique critical potential as such, but at each potential there is an equilibrium distribution between ions in solution and deposited atoms.
2. Equation (20–10) is of the same form as that established by Heyrovsky and Ilkovic [114] for the "polarographic wave," and in particular implies that the potential at which half the ions are deposited at the electrode (the *half-wave potential*, $E_{1/2}$, of polarography) is independent of the initial concentration, all other conditions being equal.
3. The equation does not involve the properties of the electrode, which has no effect on the equilibrium distribution, and consequently, no effect on the value of $E_{1/2}$, or more generally, on the position of the deposition curve. This comment also applies to the determination of the critical potential from Eq. (20–9).

This last conclusion is perhaps the most surprising. The electrode potential corresponds to the free energy change in a process such as

$$\mathrm{M^+_{aq}} + \mathrm{e} \rightarrow \mathrm{M_{solid}}.$$

The overall energy change is made up of the desolvation energy of the ion, the energy required to neutralize the ion and the energy to fix the atom on the support, which is equal to the sublimation energy for macroscopic deposits. For a given ion, the first two parameters are independent of the nature of the electrode, but for monatomic deposits, the third term should depend *a priori* on the properties of the electrode and will not necessarily be equal to the sublimation energy of the element being deposited.

It has, however, been believed for a long time from experiments on polonium [104, 108] and lead and bismuth isotopes [102, 103, 115] that the critical deposition potential at the tracer level is independent of the properties of the support. Furthermore, for Pb and Bi, the critical potentials agreed, within the limits of experimental error, with the potentials calculated from the Nernst equation. This conclusion is illustrated in Table 20–7, and by the curves in Fig. 20–3 for a very dilute solution of bismuth; this element has been thoroughly studied down to 10^{-13} N using both e/E and v/E curves [110, 115], and down to 3×10^{-16} N by the latter method only [116]. It should, however, be noted that the results are reproducible for 10^{-12} to 10^{-16} N solution, but that the Nernst law is only valid for the deposition of Bi^{3+} on gold at 3×10^{-16} N if the electrode

TABLE 20–7

CRITICAL DEPOSITION POTENTIAL FOR Bi WITH RESPECT TO THE CALOMEL ELECTRODE

Electrode	Bi concentration, N	Experimental value, V	Calculated value, V
Au or Ag	10^{-5}	—0.120	—0.114
Au or Ag	8.5×10^{-9}	—0.172	—0.163
Au or Ag	10^{-9}	—0.212	—0.197
Au or Ag	10^{-10}	—0.215	—0.216
Au or Ag	3×10^{-12}	—0.250	—0.251
Au or Ag	8×10^{-14}	—0.265	—0.277
Au, polarized	3×10^{-16}	—0.32	—0.323
Au, unpolarized	3×10^{-16}	—0.26	—0.323
Ag, polarized	3×10^{-16}	—0.25	—0.323
Ag, unpolarized	3×10^{-16}	—0.1	—0.323

has been cathodically polarized for some time (2 to 3 hours) before the radioactive ions are added to the solution. Without this previous polarization, deposition begins at a more positive potential (i.e., there is an undervoltage) (see Table 20–7). A small undervoltage persists in the deposition of silver even after previous polarization. It will also be seen from Fig. 20–3 that significant quantities are deposited at this dilution before the critical potential is reached, at rates which vary slightly with the potential. The Nernst law has also been verified for the deposition of bismuth on platinum down to 10^{-12} N, although in this case the results are less reproducible. On the other hand for deposition on tantalum an overvoltage of 0.18 v is found.

Coche has shown that the Nernst law is less generally valid in the case of lead than had been previously believed. The critical potentials obtained on various cathodes with ThB^{2+} (6×10^{-11} N) in acetate solution using the e/E method are as follows (relative to a calomel electrode):

Au	Ag	Cu	Bi	Ni	Ta
—0.67	—0.655	—0.655	—0.675	~ —0.65	—0.85 v

Since the calculated potential is —0.67 v, the equation is valid for Au, Ag, Cu, and Bi, and approximately valid for Ni, but on Ta there is an overvoltage of 0.18 v (cf. the Bi results discussed above). The critical deposition potential on Pt agrees with the theoretical value at a concentration of 10^{-6} N, and does not increase as the concentration is reduced to 6×10^{-11} N; the undervoltage therefore increases with dilution, since the potential ought to become more negative.

The critical deposition potential of polonium on gold is also independent of the concentration between 10^{-8} and 10^{-10} N [96, 118]. This may be due to experimental uncertainty, since the theoretical change in the potential for a tetravalent element is only 0.014 v, but the critical deposition potential on Au or Ag at 10^{-13} N is more positive than at 10^{-9}, instead of being more negative [119]. A 10^{-9} N polonium (IV) solution gives an overvoltage on Ta or W (i.e., with respect to gold) [120]. On platinum or molybdenum cathodes, irregular deposition is observed at all potentials. Despite these variations, one can conclude from the general electrochemical behavior of polonium that its electrode potential is approximately that obtained by extrapolating the critical deposition potential on gold from Po(IV) nitrate solution (10^{-9} N), that is to say, $E_h^0 = +0.77$ v. This conclusion has recently been confirmed by direct measurements of the electrode potential in 10^{-5} to 10^{-4} M solution, which gave +0.76 v [121].

For some of these deposits, previous polarization alters the value of the critical potential. This is also an important factor in the electrolysis of radiotellurium [122] and radioruthenium [83]. In the former case, previous polarization shifts the cathodic deposition potential to a more negative value, but in the other systems it favors the deposition.

The critical deposition potential for protactinium on gold and platinum cathodes from fluoride solution varies with the concentration between 10^{-12} and 10^{-4} M in accordance with Eq. (20–9), if the electrode is assumed to be PaF_7^{2-}/Pa; with a 10^{-12} M solution on Ni, there is an undervoltage with respect to deposition on the other metals, and the deposition potential changes with increasing concentration in the opposite sense to that required by this equation [112, 123, 124].

The electrochemical behavior of radioactive silver has been studied by Rogers and his collaborators [125, 126]. In 10^{-7} and 10^{-9} M solution, the deposition is characterized by a strong undervoltage, which is about 0.4 v at pH 4, and greater in perchloric acid solution. Undervoltages have also been observed on Au, W, and Rh, but on tantalum there is again an overvoltage. The v/E curves at 10^{-9} M depend strongly on the nature and "history" of the electrode. Finally, Haenny and Reymond have shown that the critical deposition potential for radioactive zinc on lead is independent of the concentration between 10^{-5} and 10^{-9} M; on nickel, at 10^{-7} M, there is a strong undervoltage [111].

This review of the experimental results shows that the Herzfeld equation is obeyed qualitatively, but not quantitatively [104]. Equation (20–10) predicts that log a_d/a_s should vary linearly with the potential, with a slope of RT/zF. This linearity is in fact found in the experimental values for polonium [127, 128], RaE [110], and zinc [111], but the valencies (z) calculated from this slope are always lower than the actual values for the elements, being 0.37 for polonium (instead of 4), 0.4 to 0.9 for bismuth (instead of 3), and 0.66 for zinc (instead of 2).

20–8 The heterogeneity of electrode surfaces. One of the most striking results of the electrochemical work discussed above is the fact that for certain surface conditions, the concentration dependence of the critical deposition potential for bismuth obeys the Nernst equation down to 3×10^{-16} N. This systematic agreement with the Nernst law cannot be a fortuitous coincidence. It shows that in terms of their thermodynamic activity, the ions behave normally at this extremely low dilution, at which each cubic centimeter of solution contains only 6×10^4 ions. This is an extremely significant result in the interpretation of a large number of potentiometric, polarographic, and conductimetric measurements. If, as is often found, there are deviations from the macroscopic physico-chemical laws in heterogeneous systems involving very dilute ionic solutions, a prime consideration is to inquire if this is due to the presence of a solid body. Another factor which must be considered is that a large excess of anions favors complex formation, and in extremely dilute homogeneous solution of a given cation, can lead to results which are not found in more concentrated solutions (Section 18–5).

We have seen, however, that the Nernst equation is not generally valid. Often either an overvoltage or an undervoltage is found, and in some cases a critical potential cannot be defined. The energy conditions for the formation of monatomic layers involve not only the nature of the support, but also the state of the surface and its "history," and the importance of these factors usually increases as the concentration is reduced. When the concentration is less than about 10^{-10} M, the results tend to become irregular, but an undervoltage (or an increase in the undervoltage) is usually detected. Mills and Willis [129] have also reached this conclusion from nonradiometric experiments on the formation of the first atomic layers in the cathodic deposition of lead and bismuth on gold and silver.

A review of the experimental results [127, 130] shows that the surface of the electrode must be regarded as being heterogeneous with respect to energy, as currently favored in the theory of adsorption and catalysis. We shall assume that the whole surface of an electrode has a variable activity, which obeys a definite statistical distribution law which depends on the metal surface and on the atoms being deposited. This nonuniformity may have various chemical, physical, or mechanical causes, including faults in the microscopic structure, or at a still lower scale, deformation and disorder phenomena (see Ref. 131). On such a surface, the adhesion or adsorption energy of the atoms deposited on a certain number of sites or "active centers" may be very close to the cohesive energy of these atoms in their own lattice (measured by the heat of sublimation). The free energy change in the formation of a microdeposit on these centers will then be approximately the same as for macrodeposition, and the critical potential will therefore be given by Eq. (20–9). This agreement should be observed at dilutions such that the discharge of a small fraction of the radioactive ions in solution could be detected with the apparatus described earlier. When these surface sites are saturated, successively greater amounts of energy will be required to discharge the ions at other, less active, sites of the surface. When sufficient energy is available to fix the atoms on the whole surface, the amount deposited will no longer depend on the applied potential, and the rate of the process will be determined only by the rate of diffusion of ions to the electrode.

The shape of the e/E curves can therefore be explained by the heterogeneity of the surface. The energy difference between the critical potential and the plateau of the sigmoid curve is generally of the order of 0.1 to 0.2 v, equivalent to 3 to 4 kcal/gm-atom, which would be a reasonable energy

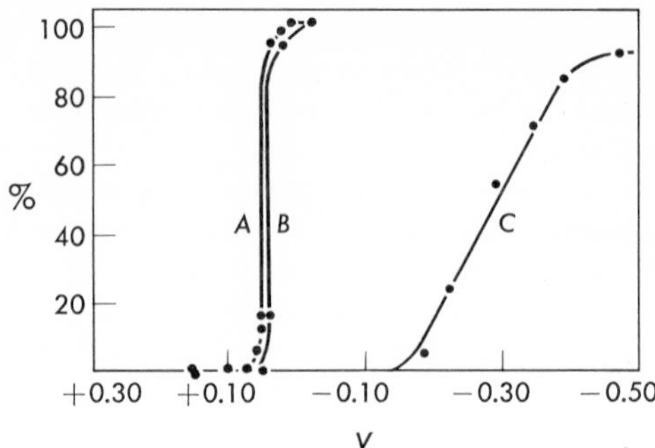

FIG. 20–7. Curve A, electrolytic deposition of RaE on Hg from 10^{-10} N solution; curve B, the same for 10^{-6} N solution; curve C, deposition on Au from 10^{-8} N solution (Ref. 132).

difference between the most active and least active surface sites (for coverages between about 1/1000 and 1/10 of a monatomic layer). For a homogeneous surface, deposition cannot occur until a certain critical potential is reached, but at this (and higher) potentials, practically all the available ions will be deposited, which is in fact observed for the deposition of Bi^{3+} on mercury from 10^{-6} to 10^{-10} N solution [132] (see Fig. 20–7).

The exact mode of deposition on a solid electrode, and its concentration dependence, will depend on the law governing the energy distribution on the surface. The fact that the Herzfeld equation is qualitatively obeyed suggests that this distribution is often exponential, of the type

$$N_{(q)} = Ae^{-q/RT}, \tag{20–11}$$

in which q is the energy of fixation at a given site, and $N_{(q)}$ the number of sites with energy lower than or equal to q; A is a constant at a given temperature.

If the dilution is increased (and a more sensitive measuring technique is used to follow deposition on the less numerous but more active sites), the adsorption energy may exceed the sublimation energy sufficiently to bring about discharge, in spite of the decrease in the concentration [see Eq. (20–9)]. Deposition should therefore occur at an undervoltage, as is in fact often found.

For some systems, this situation may arise at all dilutions corresponding to incomplete coverage of the electrode. This would therefore always give an undervoltage, which could be constant or vary with the dilution, depending on the distribution. If on the other hand, the energy of adsorption is lower than the sublimation energy at all surface coverages, there will always be an overvoltage.

The exponential distribution of sites has been confirmed by measuring the equilibrium distribution of bismuth between extremely dilute nitrate solutions and a silver cathode in the region of the critical potential [116]. As early as 1934, Zeldowitch [133] showed that the Langmuir isotherm for a homogeneous adsorbent transforms to a Freundlich isotherm with

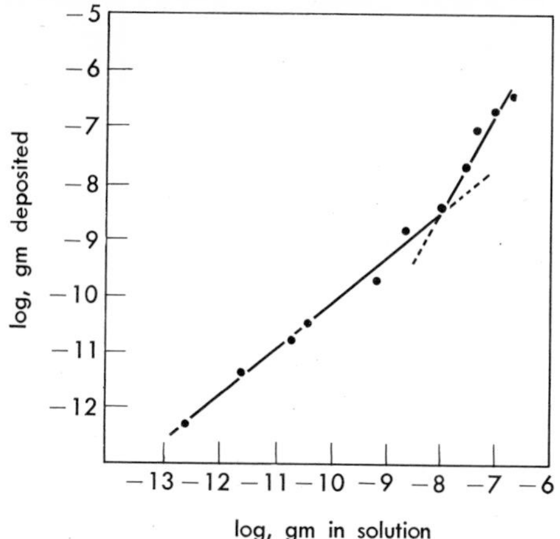

FIG. 20–8. Isotherm for the deposition of Bi on Ag (Ref. 116).

$1/n < 1$ if one assumes a heterogeneous surface with an exponential distribution of active centers [Eq. (20–11)]. This result was subsequently obtained by other authors [134–139], especially Cremer [140, 141], who gave an interpretation on this basis of the measurements (discussed earlier) by Erbacher on the spontaneous deposition of ThB on silver.

It should be noted, however, that the form of the isotherm (with $1/n < 1$) is not in itself sufficient to lead to an unambiguous conclusion about the heterogeneity of an adsorbing surface. In fact, the statistical theory of adsorption shows [135, 136, 137, 142] that this type of isotherm corresponds either to a heterogeneous surface with no interaction between the adsorbed atoms or molecules, or to a homogeneous surface on which there are repulsive forces between the adsorbate atoms. If this interaction is an attractive one, the Freundlich isotherm will still apply, but with $1/n > 1$.

The partition of bismuth at concentrations between 10^{-12} and 8×10^{-7} N, at 0.05 v of the critical potential, is shown in Fig. 20–8, in which the logarithm of the amount remaining in solution is plotted against the quantity deposited (in grams). If the Freundlich isotherm is valid, this plot should give a straight line whose slope gives the value of the exponent in Eq. (20–7). It will be seen that at very low surface coverages (θ), a straight line with $1/n = 0.84$ is obtained, but that at higher coverages (between $\theta = 3/200$ and 1.3), another straight line, with $1/n = 1.7$ appears. From the previous discussion, this latter isotherm is due to attractive forces between the deposited atoms, which tend to form the metallic bismuth lattice. If this is the case, the lower isotherm with $1/n = 0.84$ cannot be attributed to a repulsive interaction, and is necessarily due to the heterogeneous surface structure, with an exponential distribution of energies.

The deposition of bismuth on gold also gives two isotherms, with $1/n = 0.8$ and 1.3, but on platinum only a single isotherm, with $1/n =$

0.95, is found [117]. The same applies for a palladium cathode ($1/n = 0.91$), but with a gold/palladium alloy (60% Au) there are again two isotherms, with $1/n = 0.92$ and 1.40 [143]. For a detailed interpretation of these results, it is necessary to consider the increase in the interaction between the deposited atoms (e.g., Bi) and the unsaturated intermetallic forces of the surface of the support. The greater the energy of this latter interaction, the smaller will be the attractive interaction between those Bi atoms already deposited and the atoms tending to be deposited on the electrode. The intermetallic forces increase in the order Ag < Au < Pt < Pd. These arguments explain the decreased exponent in the second isotherm, in the case of gold, and its disappearance with platinum and palladium, in which the surface effects mask the weaker interactions between the deposited atoms.

Two isotherms are also obtained for the cathodic deposition of protactinium on gold from fluoride media ($1/n = 0.9$ and 2.0). We saw earlier that the spontaneous deposition of this element from sulfate solution on platinized platinum (after previous anodic polarization) obeys the Temkin isotherm, corresponding to a linear distribution of adsorption energy

$$N = k(q_0 - q). \tag{20–12}$$

The form of the isotherms, and the equilibrium distribution, therefore, depend on the particular system in question. One of the chief interests of such electrochemical experiments is in fact to get information on the structure of metallic surfaces, and on the role of the surface in the formation and early development of a new metallic phase.

It has been shown [127] that the heterogeneity of electrode surfaces can also explain the shape of the *kinetic curves*, by establishing a potential energy diagram for the solvated ions and deposited atoms, and making allowance for the different activation energies of the various sites.

Apart from the statistical heterogeneity expressed by equations such as (20–11), the surface may have other, more random defects or disordering, such as chemical impurities, mechanical deformations, crevices, microcracks, dislocations, and other microscopic or ultramicroscopic imperfections. At such points, the energy between the atoms of the support will be less than normal, and the bonds between the atoms will be weaker, so that these sites serve as "traps" for the deposited atoms; at these traps, the density of deposition will be locally increased, or the atoms will penetrate more deeply into the support. Evidence for this has been obtained by autoradiography of the cathodic deposits obtained in the electrolysis of extremely dilute nitrate solutions of polonium [120, 144]. The normal range of the Po α-particles in Ilford C-2 nuclear emulsion is 21.5 μ. Figure 20–9(a) shows the distribution of ranges obtained from the deposit on a gold cathode from a 10^{-9} M Po solution; the maximum corresponds quite well to the value of 21.5 μ, although some significant statistical fluctuations are noted. If, however, a very short electrolysis is carried out on the same solution, so that only about 0.01% of the polonium is deposited, the autoradiograph shows a skewed distribution (Fig. 20–9b) with a flatter and slightly altered maximum (19.5 μ).

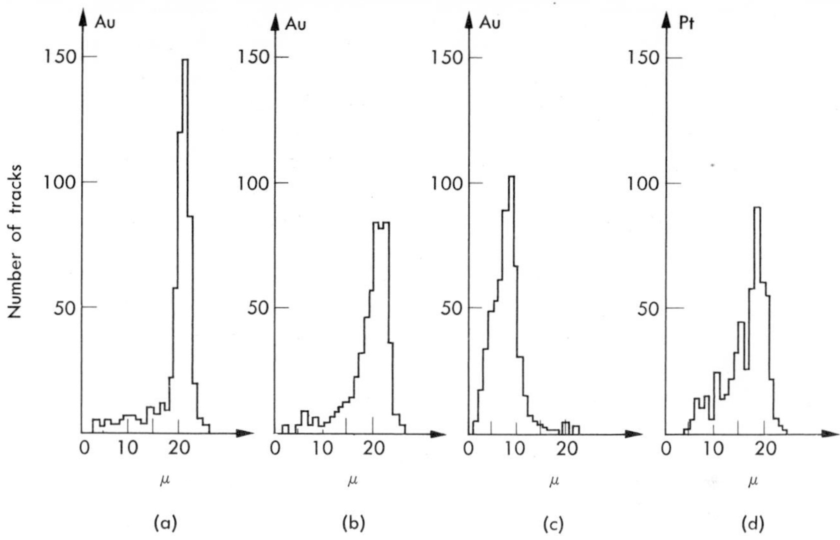

FIG. 20–9. Distribution of α-particle ranges from Po electrolytically deposited on gold; (a) 4.4×10^{-10} N solution, 0.06 esu deposited, (b) 1.1×10^{-10} N solution, 6.7×10^{-5} esu deposited, (c) 10^{-13} N solution, 6.8×10^{-5} esu deposited, (d) same solution, same amount deposited, but on an electrode with a different history (Ref. 144).

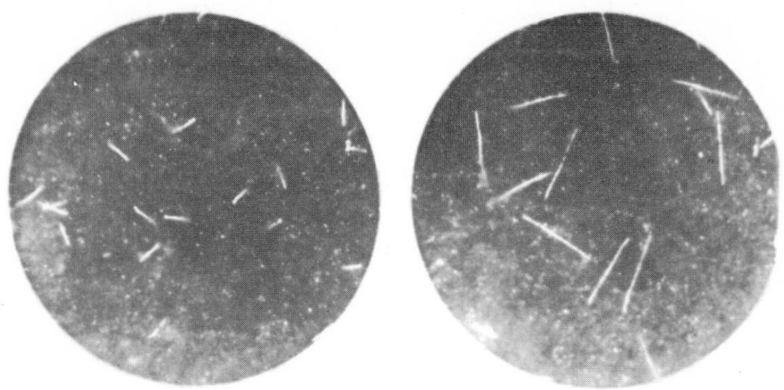

FIG. 20–10. Autoradiograph of α-tracks from a cathodic deposit of Po (Ref. 144).

Still greater differences are found with deposits from 10^{-13} to 10^{-14} M polonium solutions (see Figs. 20–9c and 20–9d, and Fig. 20–10); the results now vary with the origin and history of the electrode. With a silver electrode, the range distribution appears normal, but platinum shows a behavior between that of gold and silver. Since intermetallic diffusion is normally completely negligible at room temperature, it is difficult to explain these anomalies other than by a partial penetration of the deposited

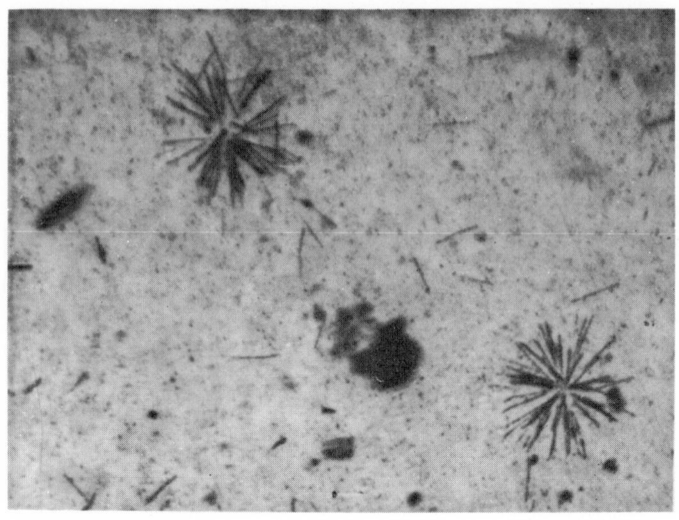

FIG. 20–11. "Star" formation from a deposit of Po on gold.

atoms into some very rare surface sites, of which only about $1/10^6$ were covered by polonium in these experiments. Occasionally an autoradiograph of a deposit obtained with more concentrated solution shows that stars are formed (Fig. 20–11) due to the aggregation of hundreds or thousands of deposited polonium atoms on selective "centers," or on impurities in the electrode surface.

It will be obvious from this review that these techniques will give information on the electrochemical behavior of elements in extremely dilute solution, and are also extremely useful in investigating the structure of metallic surfaces at an ultramicroscopic level.

References

1. P. A. Shaffer, *J. Phys. Chem.*, **40,** 1021 (1936).
2. J. Franck, quoted in Ref. 3; see also Ref. 44.
3. W. F. Libby, *J. Phys. Chem.*, **56,** 863 (1952).
4. R. Daudel, *Compt. rend.*, **215,** 301 (1942).
5. D. Cohen, J. C. Sullivan, and J. C. Hindman, *J. Am. Chem. Soc.*, **76,** 352 (1954).
6. M. Haïssinsky and M. Cottin, *J. Chim. Phys.*, **46,** 476 (1949).
7. E. L. King, *J. Am. Chem. Soc.*, **71,** 3553 (1949).
8. R. L. Wolfgang and R. W. Dodson, *J. Phys. Chem.*, **56,** 872 (1952).
9. G. Harbottle and R. W. Dodson, *J. Phys. Chem.*, **70,** 880 (1948).
10. R. J. Prestwood and A. C. Wahl, *J. Phys. Chem.*, **71,** 3137 (1949).
11. W. R. King and C. S. Garner, *J. Phys. Chem.*, **74,** 3709 (1952).
12. H. Taube and E. L. King, *J. Phys. Chem.*, **76,** 4053 (1954).
13. M. Haïssinsky, *J. Chim. Phys.*, **49,** C 133 (1952).
14. A. Anderson and N. A. Bonner, *J. Am. Chem. Soc.*, **76,** 3826 (1954).
15. A. W. Adamson, *J. Phys. Chem.*, **55,** 293 (1951).
16. J. Silverman and R. W. Dodson, *J. Phys. Chem.*, **56,** 846 (1952).
17. S. A. Hoshowsky, O. G. Holmes, and K. J. McCallum, *Can. J. Research*, **27B,** 258 (1949).
18. D. J. Meier and C. S. Garner, *J. Am. Chem. Soc.*, **73,** 1894 (1951).
19. D. J. Meier and C. S. Garner, *J. Phys. Chem.*, **56,** 853 (1952).
20. W. B. Lewis, C. D. Coryell, and J. W. Irvine, *J. Chem. Soc.*, **1949,** S 386.
21. F. P. Dwyer and E. C. Gyafras, *Nature*, **166,** 481 (1950).
22. J. E. Whitney, C. I. Browne, H. M. McConnell, and N. Davidson, *U.S.A.E.C. report BNL-C-8* (1948).
23. J. W. Gryder and R. W. Dodson, *J. Am. Chem. Soc.*, **71,** 1894 (1949).
24. H. C. Hornig and W. F. Libby, *J. Phys. Chem.*, **56,** 869 (1952).
25. N. A. Bonner and H. A. Potratz, *J. Am. Chem. Soc.*, **73,** 1845 (1951).
26. J. C. Sheppard and A. C. Wahl, *J. Am. Chem. Soc.*, **75,** 5133 (1953).
27. A. A. Grinberg, *Sess. Acad. Sci., U.S.S.R.*, July 1–5, 1955, Chem. Sect., p. 238.
28. A. C. Wahl and C. F. Deck, *J. Am. Chem. Soc.*, **76,** 4054 (1954).
29. A. W. Adamson, *J. Phys. Chem.*, **56,** 858 (1952).
30. R. L. Wolfgang, *J. Am. Chem. Soc.*, **74,** 6144 (1952).
31. M. Haïssinsky, *J. Chim. Phys.*, **47,** 957 (1950).
32. A. C. Wahl and N. A. Bonner, *Radioactivity Applied to Chemistry*, Wiley and Sons, New York, 1951.
33. R. R. Edwards, *Ann. Rev. Nuclear Sci.*, **1,** 301 (1952).
34. A. I. Brodsky, *Isotope Chemistry*, Academy of Sciences, Moscow, 1952.
35. C. B. Amphlett, *Quart. Revs.*, **8,** 219 (1954).
36. D. R. Stranks and R. G. Wilkins, *Chem. Revs.*, **57,** 743 (1957).
37. J. P. Hunt and H. Taube, *J. Chem. Phys.*, **18,** 757 (1950); **19,** 602 (1951).
38. H. L. Friedman, H. Taube, and J. P. Hunt, *J. Chem. Phys.*, **18,** 759 (1950).
39. R. A. Plane and H. Taube, *J. Phys. Chem.*, **56,** 33 (1952).
40. L. Loimaranta, *Z. Elektrochem.*, **13,** 33 (1907).

41. E. Abel and O. Smetana, *Monatsh. Chem.*, **60,** 81 (1932).
42. M. Cottin and M. Haïssinsky, *Compt. rend.*, **224,** 1636 (1947).
43. M. Cottin, M. Haïssinsky, and D. Peschanski, *Compt. rend.*, **48,** 500 (1951).
44. M. Haïssinsky, *J. Chim. Phys.*, **48,** C 11 (1951).
45. E. Rabinowitch and W. H. Stockmayer, *J. Am. Chem. Soc.*, **64,** 335 (1942).
46. N. Uri, *Chem. Revs.*, **50,** 376 (1952).
47. J. E. Whitney and N. Davidson, *J. Am. Chem. Soc.*, **71,** 3809 (1949).
48. H. McConnell and N. Davidson, *J. Am. Chem. Soc.*, **72,** 3168, 5557 (1950).
49. R. J. Marcus, B. J. Zwolinski, and H. Eyring, *J. Phys. Chem.*, **58,** 432 (1954).
50. R. J. Marcus, B. J. Zwolinski, and H. Eyring, *Chem. Revs.*, **55,** 157 (1955).
51. J. Weiss, *Proc. Roy. Soc. (London)*, **A222,** 128 (1954).
52. L. Pauling, *J. Chim. Phys.*, **45,** 142 (1948).
53. J. W. Cobble and A. W. Adamson, *J. Am. Chem. Soc.*, **72,** 2276 (1950).
54. G. Hevesy, *Z. Physik,* **16,** 52 (1915).
55. G. Hevesy and M. Biltz, *Z. physik. Chem.*, **B3,** 271 (1929).
56. B. V. Rollin, *J. Am. Chem. Soc.*, **62,** 86 (1940).
57. C. C. Coffin and I. I. Tingley, *J. Chem. Phys.*, **17,** 502 (1949).
58. M. Haïssinsky, M. Cottin, and B. Varjabedian, *J. Chim. Phys.*, **45,** 212 (1948).
59. C. Haenny and P. Mivelaz, *Helv. Chim. Acta,* **31,** 633 (1948).
60. M. Cottin, *Compt. rend.*, **231,** 697 (1950).
61. M. T. Simnad and R. C. Ruder, *J. Electrochem. Soc.*, **98,** 301 (1951).
62. M. T. Simnad, *Properties of Metal Surfaces,* Institute of Metals, London, 1953.
63. O. Erbacher, *Z. physik. Chem.*, **A 166,** 23 (1933); **A178,** 43 (1937).
64. A. Baerg and C. A. Winkler, *Can. J. Chem.*, **31,** 319 (1953).
65. M. Anta and M. Cottin, *Compt. rend.*, **234,** 1686 (1952).
66. M. Haïssinsky, *J. Chim. Phys.*, **45,** 224 (1948).
67. N. B. Miller and V. V. Pleskov, *Doklady Akad. Nauk S.S.S.R.*, **74,** 323 (1950).
68. C. G. Bacon, *Gen. Elec. Rev.*, **52,** No. 5, 7 (1949).
69. T. Westermark and L. G. Erwall, *Research,* **4,** 290 (1951).
70. K. Lohberg, *Metalforsch.*, **2,** 230 (1949).
71. T. P. Hoar and U. R. Evans, *J. Chem. Soc.*, **1932,** 2476.
72. N. Hackerman and R. A. Powers, *J. Phys. Chem.*, **57,** 139 (1953).
73. R. A. Powers and N. Hackerman, *J. Electrochem. Soc.*, **100,** 314 (1953).
74. P. M. Aziz, *J. Electrochem. Soc.*, **101,** 120 (1954).
75. S. E. Eaton and A. D. Little, *1955 Geneva Conference,* P. 146.
76. E. Rabinowicz, *Nature,* **170,** 1029 (1952).
77. W. Summer, *Atomics,* **5,** 297 (1954).
78. M. Bonnemay, H. Makram and J. Royon, *Compt. rend.*, **235,** 955 (1952).
79. H. Makram, *Compt. rend.*, **237,** 1086 (1953).
80. F. Ogburn and A. Brenner, *J. Electrochem. Soc.*, **96,** 347 (1949).
81. J. C. Griess, *J. Electrochem. Soc.*, **100,** 429 (1953).

82. M. H. LIETZKE and J. C. GRIESS, *J. Electrochem. Soc.*, **100,** 434 (1953).
83. M. HAÏSSINSKY and M. EL GUEBELY, *J. Chim. Phys.*, **53,** 742 (1956).
84. R. AUDUBERT, *Compt. rend.*, **238,** 1997 (1954).
85. R. AUDUBERT, J. PERANO, and T. MALLET, *Compt. rend.*, **238,** 1881 (1954).
86. F. G. HOUTERMANS, D. H. VINCENT, and G. WAGNER, *Z. Elektrochem.*, **56,** 944 (1952).
87. M. HAÏSSINSKY and A. SANIELEVICI, *J. Chim. Phys.*, **36,** 54 (1939).
88. P. HOLEMANN and K. CLUSIUS, *Z. physik. Chem.*, **B35,** 261 (1937).
89. M. D. WHITAKER, W. BJORKSTED, and A. C. G. MITCHELL, *Phys. Rev.*, **46,** 629 (1934).
90. O. ERBACHER, *Z. physik. Chem.*, **163,** 196 (1933).
91. G. TAMMANN and C. WILSON, *Z. anorg. Chem.*, **173,** 137 (1928).
92. O. ERBACHER and K. PHILIPP, *Z. physik. Chem.*, **150,** 214 (1930).
93. O. ERBACHER and K. PHILIPP, *Z. Physik*, **51,** 309 (1928).
94. M. CAMARCAT, G. BOUISSIÈRES, and M. HAÏSSINSKY, *J. Chim. Phys.*, **46,** 153 (1949).
95. C. FERRADINI and M. HAÏSSINSKY, *J. Chim. Phys.*, **53,** 714 (1956).
96. M. I. TEMKIN, *J. Phys. Chem.*, **15,** 296 (1941).
97. O. ERBACHER, *Z. physik. Chem.*, **A163,** 215 (1933); **A182,** 243 (1938).
98. O. ERBACHER, W. HERR, and W. WIEDENMANN, *Z. Naturforsch.*, **3a,** 637 (1938).
99. M. ANDAUER and E. LANGE, *Z. physik. Chem.*, **B,** Bodenstein-Festband, 247 (1931).
100. A. SCHMID, P. VOGELE, and W. WINKELMAN, *Helv. Chim. Acta,* **15,** 1393 (1932).
101. F. MÜLLER and W. DURICHEN, *Z. physik. Chem.*, **A182,** 233 (1938).
102. G. HEVESY and F. A. PANETH, *Akad. Wiss. Wien, Abt. IIa,* **123,** 1618 (1914).
103. G. HEVESY and F. A. PANETH, *Physik. Z.*, **15,** 801 (1914).
104. F. JOLIOT, *J. Chim. Phys.*, **27,** 119 (1930).
105. M. HAÏSSINSKY and M. GUILLOT, *J. phys. radium.*, **5,** 419 (1934).
106. M. HAÏSSINSKY and M. GUILLOT, *Bull. soc. chim. France,* **1935,** 239.
107. M. HAÏSSINSKY, *Compt. rend.*, **192,** 1645 (1931).
108. M. HAÏSSINSKY, *J. Chim. Phys.*, **29,** 453 (1932); **30,** 27 (1933).
109. J. F. FLAGG and W. E. BLEIDNER, *J. Chem. Phys.*, **13,** 209 (1945).
110. A. COCHE, *J. Chim. Phys.*, **48,** 135 (1951); **49,** C 110 (1952).
111. C. HAENNY and P. REYMOND, *Helv. Chim. Acta,* **37,** 2067 (1954).
112. C. FERRADINI, *Thesis,* Paris, 1955.
113. K. HERZFELD, *Physik. Z.*, **14,** 29 (1913).
114. J. HEYROVSKY and D. ILKOVIC, *Coll. Czech. Chem. Comm.*, **7,** 198 (1935).
115. M. HAÏSSINSKY, *J. Chim. Phys.*, **32,** 116 (1935).
116. M. HAÏSSINSKY and J. DANON, *J. Chim. Phys.*, **48,** 106 (1951); **49,** C 123 (1952).
117. A. COCHE, J. DANON, and M. EL GUEBELY, *J. Chim. Phys.*, **49,** 363 (1952).
118. M. WERTENSTEIN, *Compt. rend. Soc. Sci. Warsaw,* **10,** 771 (1917).
119. A. COCHE, H. FARAGGI, P. AVIGNON, and M. HAISSINSKY, *J. phys. radium,* **10,** 312 (1949).
120. A. COCHE and M. HAISSINSKY, *J. Chem. Soc.*, **1949,** S 397.
121. K. W. BAGNALL and J. H. FREEMAN, *J. Chem. Soc.*, **1956,** 2770.

122. A. S. GHOSH-MAZUMDAR, *Thesis*, Paris, 1956.
123. J. DANON and C. FERRADINI, *Compt. rend.*, **234,** 1361 (1952).
124. C. FERRADINI, *J. Chim. Phys.*, **50,** 589 (1953).
125. L. B. ROGERS, D. P. KRAUSE, J. C. GRIESS, and D. B. EHRLINGER, *J. Electrochem. Soc.*, **95,** 33 (1949).
126. J. C. GRIESS, J. T. BYRNE, and L. B. ROGERS, *J. Electrochem. Soc.*, **98,** 447 (1951).
127. M. HAÏSSINSKY, *Electrochimie des Substances Radioactives,* Hermann, Paris, 1946.
128. M. HAÏSSINSKY, *J. Chim. Phys.*, **43,** 21 (1946).
129. T. MILLS and G. M. WILLIS, *J. Electrochem. Soc.*, **100,** 452 (1953).
130. M. HAÏSSINSKY, *Experientia,* **8,** 125 (1952).
131. F. F. WOLKENSHTEIN, *Zhur. Fiz. Khim.*, **15,** 296 (1941); **23,** 917 (1949).
132. A. S. GHOSH-MAZUMDAR and M. HAÏSSINSKY, *J. Chim. Phys.*, **51,** 296 (1954).
133. Y. ZELDOVICH, *Acta Physicochim. U.R.S.S.*, **1,** 961 (1934).
134. S. Z. ROGINSKI, *Doklady Akad. Nauk S.S.S.R.*, **45,** 206 (1944).
135. S. Z. ROGINSKI, *Adsorption and Catalysis,* Academy of Sciences, Moscow, 1949.
136. F. WOLKENSHTEIN, *Zhur. Fiz. Khim.*, **21,** 163 (1947).
137. G. HALSEY and H. S. TAYLOR, *J. Chem. Phys.*, **15,** 624 (1947).
138. G. HALSEY, *J. Chem. Phys.*, **16,** 931 (1948).
139. R. SIPS, *J. Chem. Phys.*, **16,** 490 (1948); **18,** 1024 (1950).
140. E. CREMER and S. FLUGGE, *Z. physik. Chem.*, **B41,** 453 (1939).
141. E. CREMER, *J. Chim. Phys.*, **46,** 411 (1949).
142. Y. M. GOLDFELD and N. I. KOBOZEV, *Zhur. Fiz. Khim.*, **15,** 257, 275 (1941).
143. A. COCHE, *J. Chim. Phys.*, **51,** 286 (1954).
144. M. HAÏSSINSKY, H. FARAGGI, A. COCHE, and P. AVIGNON, *Phys. Rev.*, **75,** 1963 (1949).

CHAPTER 21

THE DISTRIBUTION OF A MICROCOMPONENT BETWEEN TWO PHASES

21–1 Coprecipitation. A substance in contact with two phases, which may be either chemically identical or chemically different, tends to distribute itself between them so as to have the same chemical potential in both phases. Certain qualitative and quantitative distribution laws follow from this; the importance of these at the tracer level has already been discussed (Section 18–5). In the previous chapter we discussed the distribution of a microcomponent between an electrode and a solution. The practical problem of distribution, in its most general form, arose in the earliest days of chemical research on radioelements, since techniques were required for "carrying" these elements, either by coprecipitation or mixed crystallization with a macrocomponent, or by adsorption on an already existing solid. For a long time, there was considerable discussion and controversy over the mechanism of these processes, but it now seems that except for a few special exceptional cases, there is no serious difficulty in the interpretation. Paneth [1, 2, 3] and Fajans [4, 5] have proposed qualitative rules, which have been put on a more exact footing by Hahn [6, 7]. The apparently contradictory quantitative results obtained with distributions between crystals and solutions have been cleared up by the work of Khlopin [8] and Hahn [9] and their co-workers.

The fundamental qualitative rule for the carrying of a microcomponent is the following; *a microcomponent is always carried down by a solid formed by crystallization or precipitation if it enters into the normal lattice formation,* that is to say, if it forms crystals which are isomorphous with those of the macrocomponent. The rule is valid even for large crystals with relatively small surface areas where the microcomponent is uniformly distributed throughout the whole mass. Thus in the mixed crystallization of $Ra(NO_3)_2$ (the microcomponent) and $Sr(NO_3)_2$, 60% of the latter carries down 76% of the radium at 34°C, but at 4°, 55% of $Sr(NO_3)_2{\cdot}4H_2O$ carries only 3% of the $Ra(NO_3)_2$, which at this temperature forms anhydrous crystals. Similarly, at 4°C, 71% $SrCl_2{\cdot}6H_2O$ carries only 2% $RaCl_2{\cdot}2H_2O$.

If isomorphous crystals are not formed, carrying may still be achieved by ion exchange, or by other chemical or physical adsorption processes, or by the formation of radiocolloids (Section 21–5). The following approximate rule can therefore be used: the *microcomponent is adsorbed on a solid, or is coprecipitated with it, if it forms an insoluble compound with the oppositely charged ion of the macrocomponent* (Paneth, Fajans). Adsorption or coprecipitation is favored if the solid has a large surface area and carries an electrical charge of the opposite sign to that of the ions of the microcomponent (Hahn). Thus ThB^{2+} ions are carried by Ag_2S, even though this is not isomorphous with PbS, because the latter is insoluble. Equally, ThB is carried by Hg_2I_2, as would be expected from the insolubility of

PbI_2, but not by Hg_2Cl_2 since $PbCl_2$ is fairly soluble. Polonium (IV) compounds are carried by $Fe(OH)_3$ in slightly acid solution, in which hydrolysis gives rise to insoluble basic salts or hydroxide. As heavy metal salts are generally hydrolized to insoluble compounds in slightly acid solution, ferric hydroxide is often used as a carrier in the separation of medium or heavy radioelements.

We shall now examine the various factors which affect the phenomena in question, in order to define exactly the applicability and limitations of the Paneth-Fajans rule. We shall begin with carrying or coprecipitation due to ion exchange, or to adsorption effects, and establish criteria which distinguish this from mixed crystal formation.

21–2 Adsorption. Table 21–1 shows the conditions under which Ra^{2+} is carried down in the precipitation of $CaCl_2$ by H_2SO_4. It can be seen that the coprecipitation increases with excess acid, which increases the negative charge of the solid sulfate due to adsorption of sulfate ions, and that it is decreased by an excess positive charge due to Ca^{2+} ions. Coprecipitation is, however, only significant if the sulfate is present as a very fine powder; large crystals of $CaSO_4$ produced by the slow cooling of a very hot solution carry down very little $RaSO_4$, despite the latter's low solubility.

Table 21–1

Carrying of Ra^{2+} by $CaSO_4{\cdot}2H_2O$

% $CaSO_4{\cdot}2H_2O$ precipitated	% Ra^{2+} carried	Conditions
70	30.1	10% excess of H_2SO_4
85	65.0	100% excess of H_2SO_4
95	92.0	200% excess of H_2SO_4
70	5.2	10% excess of $CaCl_2$
40	2.0	50% excess of $CaCl_2$

Table 21–2

Carrying of ThB^{2+} by Silver Salts

Adsorbent	Solubility of corresponding Pb salt, wt %	% adsorbed
AgBr	2×10^{-2}	1.8
AgI	10^{-3}	2.1
$AgIO_3$	5×10^{-5}	43.1
$Ag_2(COO)_2$	3×10^{-5}	81.1
Ag_2CrO_4	2×10^{-7}	97.9

In some cases, there is a parallelism between insolubility and adsorption. This is illustrated by the results in Table 21–2 for the carrying of ThB^{2+} by insoluble silver salts in the absence of excess of the component ions.

Adsorption is markedly affected by the valency of the microcomponent. Under given conditions, negatively charged silver sulfide adsorbs only 7.4% Ra^{2+}, but 75% Ac^{3+} and 100% Th^{4+} [10]; it is probable that the carrying of Th is facilitated by hydrolysis of the thorium, and should be therefore pH dependent. Conversely, the adsorption of a microcomponent can be easily reduced by displacement with polyvalent ions such as Tl(III), Th(IV), Zr(IV), etc. Thus potassium sulfate crystals formed in a saturated solution containing Ra^{2+} ions adsorb up to 97% of the radium, but the addition of 0.1% of a thorium salt lowers the adsorption of radium to 2%. Similarly the adsorption of Ra^{2+} on $PbSO_4$ crystals is reduced by the presence of $Al(NO_3)_3$, provided that recrystallization is prevented. Surface-active substances, such as the coloring matter Ponceau 4R, or humic acid, also reduce this adsorption, to an extent which increases as their concentration is increased [11]. Finally, despite the low solubility of PbI_2, the adsorption of ThB^{2+} on silver iodide depends more on the ThB^{2+}/H^+ ratio than on the concentration of the microcomponent alone [12].

To sum up, then, these are ion exchange processes which depend *inter alia* on competition with other ions in the solution. Consequently solubility and valency are not the only properties which govern coprecipitation, and the other factors which are involved in ion exchange (e.g., size and polarizability of the ion) must also be considered.* Some of the anomalies which result from this restrict the general applicability of the rules set out above. For example, the adsorption of a microcomponent on a neutral surface may sometimes occur, as shown in Table 21–3 for the adsorption of ThB^{2+} on silver iodate. It will be seen that there is still 43% adsorption when

TABLE 21–3

ADSORPTION OF ThB^{2+} ON $AgIO_3$

Electrolyte	Concentration, millimolar	% adsorbed
KIO_3	2.0	98.9
KIO_3	1.0	94.1
KIO_3	0.5	70.9
KIO_3	0	43.1
$AgNO_3$	0.16	26.8
$AgNO_3$	0.5	13.3
$AgNO_3$	1.6	0.0
$AgNO_3$	16.0	0.0

* For a thermodynamic treatment, see Ratner, Refs. 13 and 14.

the solution contains no electrolyte, conditions under which the surface of the solid is assumed to have no charge. Traces of radioactive material in aqueous solution are also strongly adsorbed on the surface of nonionic precipitates or powders, such as silica, titanium dioxide, charcoal, parchment, etc. The study of the adsorption of tracer lead and bismuth on glass shows that in addition to ion exchange, these species are also fixed more strongly on the surface by chemical bonding [15]. A comparable kinetic study of the adsorption and desorption of sodium ions from glass, using the two indicators Na^{22} and Na^{24}, also lead to the conclusion that ion exchange alone could not explain the experimental results [16].

As is usually found, the adsorption is affected by the thermal treatment and structure of the surface of the adsorbent. The adsorption of radium ions on glass obeys the Freundlich isotherm over wide concentration limits, with $1/n = 0.6$ [17]. A similar result has been reported for the adsorption of active Ba^{2+} and Sr^{2+} ions on $Fe(OH)_3$ at pH 8, at concentrations between 5×10^{-6} and 10^{-8} mole/cm^3, with $1/n = 0.63$ [18]. In more dilute solution, Henry's law becomes valid, so that adsorption is then proportional to the concentration. The two ions do not behave identically, however, since the adsorption of Ba^{2+} ions is reversible, whereas the desorption of Sr^{2+} is very slow, and only partially complete. The adsorption of Po on different substances generally obeys the Freundlich isotherm [19], and as in the previous examples depends on the pH of the solution [20]. Since the coverage of the surface by the adsorbed ions is very small in the cases discussed, interaction between the adsorbed ions can be neglected, implying that the Freundlich isotherm is a consequence of the surface heterogeneity. However, in the concentration region between 10^{-6} and 10^{-15} M the adsorption of lead ions (labeled with ThB) on paper and glass follows the Langmuir isotherm, corresponding to uniform coverage [21] (see also Ref. 22). In this system, however, adsorption is due to ion exchange with the carboxylic groups of the cellulose of the paper, or the silicate groups on the glass, which are uniformly distributed over the whole surface.

An elegant method for investigating the nonuniformity of adsorbing surfaces has been proposed by Roginski and his co-workers [23, 24, 25]. The principle of this so-called *differential isotope method* is as follows: unlabeled gas is adsorbed so as to cover only part of the surface, and the adsorption is then completed with labeled samples of the same gas. Desorption of the gas is finally brought about by gradual heating, which fractionates the gas into a number of successive portions. If the surface is homogeneous, these fractions will all have the same composition (i.e., the same specific activity if a radioactive isotope is used, or the same molecular weight if the labeling involved a heavy stable isotope such as H^2 or C^{13}). For a heterogeneous surface, however, the unlabeled gas which is adsorbed first would fix itself on the most active sites and would be removed with greater difficulty, so that the first portions would then have a composition closer to that of the gas adsorbed in the second operation. It is also possible to do the experiment the other way round, first of all adsorbing the labeled gas and then the unlabeled material. The method requires certain experimental precautions; the adsorption must be shown to have no significant isotope effect of its own, and the pressure in the gas phase must be low enough that isotopic exchange between the two phases can be neglected.

Keier and Roginski [24] carried out experiments with H_2/D_2 mixtures, adsorbed and desorbed on metallic nickel in the manner just described. Emmett and Kummer [26] have carried out similar experiments with $C^{14}O$ on the surface of an iron catalyst. In each case, the isotopic composition of the first fractions desorbed was that of the second gas adsorbed, labeled or otherwise, and the composition of the later fractions was very close to that of the first gas. In Chapter 23, some related applications of tracers in the study of the mechanism of catalytic reactions are described.

Radioactive indicators have also been used in order to distinguish between physical adsorption and chemisorption [27]. A metallic sheet is allowed to stand for some time in a benzene solution of stearic acid, ethyl stearate, or octadecyl alcohol, and the adsorbed monomolecular layer subsequently removed from the surface of the metal by refluxing with benzene. In the case of platinum and gold, removal of this layer carries no trace of the metal with it, but the material desorbed from copper, zinc, and cadmium surfaces contains a certain quantity of the metal. It is concluded from these results that adsorption on the two first metals is purely physical, but that with the other metals the adsorption involves chemical interaction, with the formation of soaps.

Some of the properties of mono- and multimolecular layers formed by the adsorption of surface active compounds at an air-liquid interface can be studied by using an isotope which emits α-particles or very soft β-particles [28, 29, 30]. If the compound is labeled with such a radioactive tracer, the activity measured close to the surface is the sum of two fractions, a_i arising from the bulk interior of the solution, and a_s from the adsorbed layer. The bulk activity can be determined independently by dissolving a surface-inactive compound labeled with the same indicator; the difference then gives a_s, and hence the quantity adsorbed. The ratio a_s/a_i is larger for softer radiations; Anianson [31, 32] has calculated a ratio of 3.6×10^{-2} for a molar solution of a compound labeled with C^{14}, whose β-particles have a range of $300\,\mu$ in water, or S^{35} ($340\,\mu$), adsorbed at 10^{-10} moles/cm^2, and values of 1.8 for a tritiated compound ($6\,\mu$), and 20 for the recoil atoms from ThC (ThC$''$).

This procedure has been used to establish the adsorption isotherms on water of various aerosols (di-*n*-octyl sulfosuccinate, sodium octadecylsulfate, etc.) labeled with S^{35}, using solutions of sodium sulfate, which is not adsorbed, for comparison. The kinetics of the formation and surface diffusion of monomolecular layers (for instance, of C^{14}-labeled stearic acid on water [33]) can also be studied by this technique.

21–3 Mixed crystals. Coprecipitation due to isomorphous mixed crystal formation can be distinguished from that due to adsorption by the following criteria:

1. In mixed crystallization, the microcomponent is distributed homogeneously throughout the whole mass, whereas in the case of adsorption it is concentrated on the surface. This difference is easily revealed by autoradiography. If, however, a precipitate containing the microcomponent is

allowed to "ripen" for a long time in contact with the mother liquor, recrystallization can give an apparently homogeneous distribution, but this process in fact involves adsorption, which Hahn has therefore named "internal adsorption" [9].

2. Carrying by adsorption depends critically on recrystallization, and on the age of the precipitate, whereas isomorphous mixed-crystal formation is independent of these factors.

3. More generally, the formation of mixed crystals is fairly insensitive to external conditions, and in particular to the charge on the solid and to the presence of other ions, whereas adsorption is strongly affected by these factors. In other words, the adsorption isotherm changes easily from one system to another, but the distribution of a microcomponent between a solution and the isomorphous crystals of the macrocomponent is constant at a given temperature, and varies with the composition of the solution only to the extent that the thermodynamic activities of the components are affected.

The law governing the distribution between the two phases at equilibrium is similar to the Henry law for gases, and is known as the Berthelot-Nernst law

$$\frac{a_{\text{cr}}}{a_{\text{sol}}} = K, \tag{21–1}$$

in which a_{cr} and a_{sol} are the thermodynamic activities of the microcomponent in the crystals and in the solution. The activity coefficient of the solid is generally assumed to be unity, so that a_{cr} coincides with the formal concentration, and the same approximation can be made for fairly dilute solutions. Henderson and Kracek [34] have expressed this law in the form

$$\frac{x}{y} = D\frac{a - x}{b - y}, \tag{21–2}$$

in which a and x are the initial quantity and the quantity which has crystallized for the microcomponent, b and y are the same parameters for the macrocomponent, and D is the recrystallization or *fractionation coefficient*. It can be shown that D is related to K by the relation

$$D = Kc/\rho \tag{21–3}$$

in which c is the concentration of the macrocomponent in the saturated solution, in gm/cm^3, and ρ is the density of the crystals. For values of D greater than 1, the microcomponent concentrates in the crystals; for values lower than 1, the solution is enriched in the microcomponent. In practical separations, one is interested in getting enrichment in the crystal phase, so that impurities present in the solution may be eliminated as much as possible.

In some cases it is found experimentally that instead of Eq. (21–2), an equation proposed by Doerner and Hoskins [35] is obeyed:

$$\log\frac{a}{a - x} = \lambda \log\frac{b}{b - y}, \tag{21–4}$$

in which λ is a constant.

Considerable research has gone into attempts to establish the conditions under which these two relations are applicable [8, 9, 36, 37, 38]. Khlopin, Hahn, and their co-workers have definitely shown that the theoretical law (21–2) is always obeyed if the two phases are allowed to reach true thermodynamic equilibrium, and a constant value of D is obtained, independent of the procedure used to reach the equilibrium state. Khlopin has suggested several techniques which can be used to reach this equilibrium.

1. A very fine powder of the pure macrocomponent (e.g., a Ba salt) is introduced into an already saturated solution which contains a small quantity of the microcomponent (Ra), and the crystals are made to dissolve on a water bath. The solution is then placed in a thermostat set at the temperature at which the initial solution was saturated, and it is stirred vigorously for several hours until the supersaturation has disappeared.
2. The powdered macrocomponent is placed in contact with the saturated solution containing the two components in a thermostat, and is strongly stirred until the concentration of the microcomponent in the solution is constant. This will require 2 to 4 weeks, depending on the temperature and the nature of the salt.
3. A procedure analogous to 2, except that the microcomponent is not initially present in the saturated solution but is incorporated into the powder.
4. A procedure similar to 1, but instead of the supersaturated solution being stirred after the dissolution of the inactive powder, the supersaturation is removed by very slow crystallization in a thermostat.

All these methods result in a true state of equilibrium being reached by diffusion and recrystallization, and the coefficient D in Eq. (21–2) is constant for different ratios of the components, whereas the coefficient λ from Eq. (21–4) is not constant (see Fig. 21–1).

If, however, a saturated solution of the macrocomponent (containing microcomponent) is allowed to evaporate very slowly at the temperature at which saturation was produced, with only slight stirring, it is found that the Doerner and Hoskins equation is obeyed, with λ a true constant.

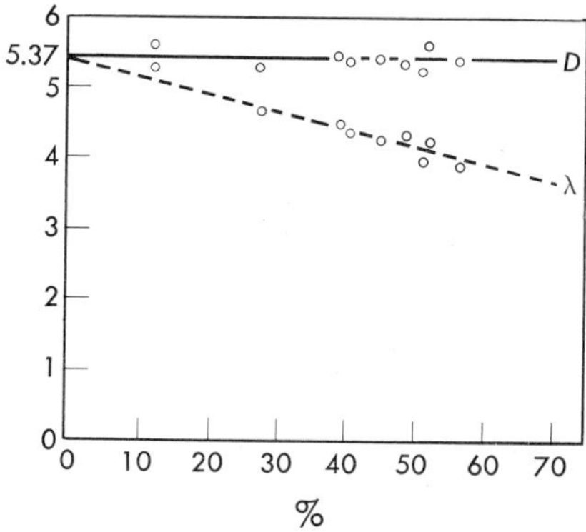

Fig. 21–1. Distribution of Ra between crystals and a solution of $BaCl_2$ (slow crystallization).

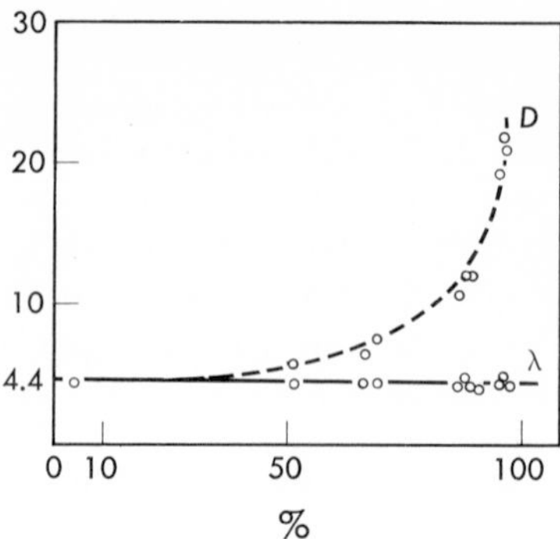

FIG. 21–2. Distribution of Ra between crystals and a solution of $BaCl_2$ (evaporation).

This is also found if instead of removing the supersaturation by a long digestion of the crystals (method 4), the crystals are separated after a few minutes very rapid stirring (Fig. 21–2). In both these procedures, equilibrium is not established between the *whole mass* of the crystals and the solution; instead, each very thin layer of the crystal can be regarded as being in equilibrium at the instant of its formation with the solution, whose composition changes continually due to continued removal of material in the crystallization. It can be shown that under these conditions the Berthelot-Nernst law transforms into the Doerner-Hoskins law, and in fact for each infinitely thin layer, Eq. (21–2) can be written

$$\frac{dx}{dy} = D\frac{a - x}{b - y}. \tag{21–5}$$

Integration of this gives Eq. (21–4), with $D = \lambda$. This equality is not always found experimentally, however, since D is a true thermodynamic constant, whereas λ is a kinetic constant which depends not only on the system and on the temperature, but also on the experimental conditions, and in particular on the rate of recrystallization.

With increasing temperature, the value of D decreases, so that the concentration of the microcomponent in the solution increases. For example, in the mixed crystallization of barium and radium nitrates,

$$D = 2.31 \text{ at } 6°, \quad 1.5 \text{ at } 15°, \quad 0.54 \text{ at } 101.8°,$$

and for the chromates of these elements

$$D = 20.2 \text{ at } 34.5°, \quad 14 \text{ at } 56.1°, \quad 2 \text{ at } 100.4°.$$

For the nitrates of lead and barium, however, D increases slightly with temperature.

The value of D changes continuously with temperature, provided that the composition of the solid phase does not change in any way, such as the formation of a new hydrate. If this is not the case, D can vary sharply.

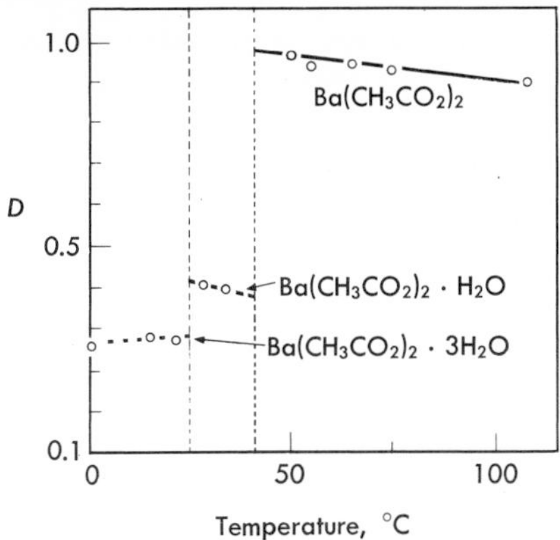

FIG. 21-3. Discontinuities in D with increasing temperature (Ref. 36).

Figure 21-3 illustrates such behavior for barium and radium acetates, in which the crystals have transition points at 25° (trihydrate → monohydrate) and 40°C (monohydrate → anhydrous salt).

A parallelism is sometimes found between the values of D and the solubilities of the microcomponent; the greater the tendency of the latter to go into the solid state, the larger is D.* This is not, however, a general rule, and exceptions to it are known. For instance, the ratio of the solubilities of radium and barium and nitrate at 20° is 0.83, but the radium concentrates in the crystals, with $D = 1.6$.

If the system contains two microcomponents which are isomorphous with the macrocomponent [e.g., Ra and RaD in $Ba(NO_3)_2$], each distributes with its own coefficient, independent of the presence of the other, even if their concentrations are in a ratio of $1 : 10^4$ [40].

Finally, Goldschmidt [38] has shown that the coefficient for the partition of radium between crystals of $Ba(ClO_3)_2 \cdot H_2O$ and their solution is constant ($2.888 \pm 0.3\%$ at 30°C) when the $Ra^{2+} : Ba^{2+}$ ratio varies between 10^{-5} and 10^{-11}. This result explains the success of fractionation methods in the separation and purification of two components.

21-4 "Abnormal" mixed crystals. In some mixed crystallizations, the distribution coefficients (D) are constant and unaffected by the addition of electrolytes, and the microcomponent is homogeneously distributed throughout the whole solid, even though the two components have different chemical formulas and are not isomorphous on the macroscopic scale. A good example of this is the case of ThB forming mixed crystals with Ag_2CrO_4, with $D = 1.4$, independent of kinetic factors, despite the fact that Ag_2CrO_4 and $PbCrO_4$ are not isomorphous. Lead isotopes also form mixed crystals with $BaCl_2 \cdot 2H_2O$ ($D = 10.6$ at 0°C) and with NaCl, KCl, and KBr, despite the absence of isomorphism.

---

* See Ratner, Ref. 39, for a thermodynamic treatment of this point.

Hahn [9] has discussed these examples of the formation of "abnormal" mixed crystals at the tracer level, and without being able to give any satisfactory explanation, he has distinguished them from "internal adsorption." More recent work by Booth, however, on the incorporation of ThB and other microcomponents into NaCl crystals, seems to show that adsorption may well be involved [41]. In particular, the microcomponent can be displaced by excess of Cd^{2+} ions, and by using autoradiographic methods Booth was able to detect a localized distribution. It is probable that this system only appears to obey the Berthelot-Nernst law, as a result of value of $1/n$ in the Freundlich isotherm being very close to unity.

Another apparent anomaly in the opposite sense at the trace scale is found with the mixed crystals prepared by Grimm [42]. This author succeeded in preparing mixed crystals, in all proportions, of salts as different as $BaSO_4$ and $KMnO_4$, $CaCO_3$ and $NaNO_3$, $BaCrO_4$ and KBF_4, PbS and NaBr, etc. This is due to the compensation of changing ionic charge by changes in the atomic radii. An increase in the charge causes increased electrostatic attraction between the ions, which decreases the lattice distances, but increasing the atomic or ionic radii works in the opposite direction, so that the double substitution of small monovalent ions by larger divalent ions (K^+, Ba^{2+}; MnO_4^-, SO_4^{2-}) balances the lattice constants, making mixed crystal formation possible.

Khlopin and Nikitin [44] have shown that the pairs $RaSO_4/RbClO_4$, $RaSO_4/CsClO_4$, $RaSO_4/KMnO_4$, and $PbSO_4/KClO_4$ also form mixed crystals of the type described by Grimm, provided that the concentration of one component (Ra, Pb) is more than 10^{-5} to 10^{-6}% of that of the other. These authors explain this concentration limitation by the fact that to achieve the compensation in this type of crystal, whole molecules rather than ions ($RaSO_4/KMnO_4$) are replaced. The oppositely charged ions of each component must therefore have a sufficient probability of encounter; at very low concentrations, there will be too few encounters to make any contribution to building up the lattice.

21–5 Radiocolloids. This is the name given to colloidal solutions containing radioactive products in unweighable and invisible quantities. Their existence was discovered by Paneth [45] in research on the separation of natural radioelements. Paneth noticed that in slightly acid, neutral, or ammonia solution, RaE and Po do not diffuse through a parchment membrane, and behave like colloids; ThB behaves in this way, but only in ammonia solution. Godlewski [46] drew similar conclusions from experiments on the migration in an electric field of the radon active deposit dissolved in water or aqueous solutions. Since the discovery of artificial radioelements, and especially since the intense research on fission products, radiocolloid formation has been demonstrated for a large number of other elements, including Sc, Y, Ti, Zr, Sn, Ce, Co, Nb, Ag, Mn, Pu, etc. Radiocolloidal behavior is not, however, a common property of all radioactive compounds; for example, the alkali and alkaline earth metals (except $BaSO_4$ and $RaSO_4$ under certain conditions) always show molecular behavior.

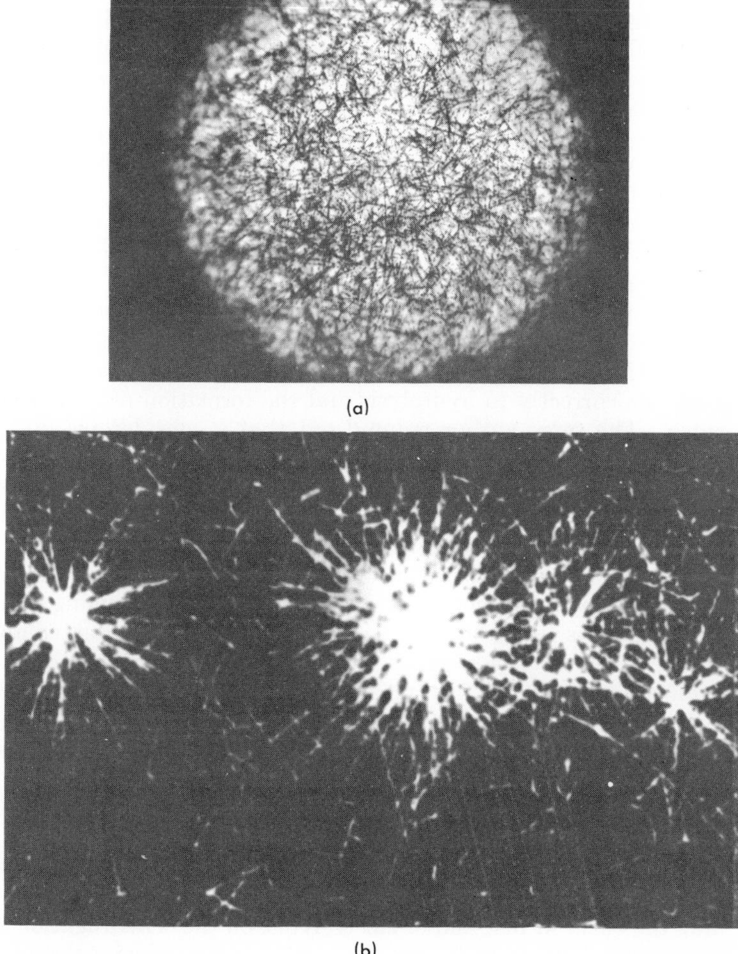

FIG. 21-4. Colloid formation by Po in water, but not in acetone; (a) acetone, (b) water (Ref. 50).

In addition to dialysis and electrophoresis, a number of other methods have been used to investigate the properties of radiocolloids. Simple filtration is often sufficient to show whether a compound is in the colloidal or molecular state. For example, Broda and Erber [47], studying the Szilard-Chalmers reaction in potassium permanganate, found that Mn^*O_2 did not pass through filter paper; the quantities retained depended on the presence of polyvalent cations and anions, and agreed with the known relations for the coagulation of a positively charged colloid. Radioscandium can also be separated in 10^{-9} M solution from 10^{-3} M Ca^{2+} at pH 8.5 by simple filtration [48]. More efficient methods are ultrafiltration and centrifugation, and although the latter method is only semiquantitative, it has been a most useful tool. The slower diffusion of colloidal micelles compared with ions, the absence (or decrease) of electrochemical displacements, and the influence of electrolytes on ion exchange (Section 21–8) or on adsorption have also been profitably applied.

Finally, the autoradiographic method, first applied to radiocolloids by C. Chamié [49], is very sensitive. Figure 21–4 shows the homogeneous distribution of α-particles tracks from a polonium compound (believed to be an oxychloride) (a) dissolved in acetone, and (b) the formation of stars when the same compound is dissolved in neutral water, in which it is almost certainly colloidal [50].

The nature of radiocolloids was for a long time rather obscure, and the subject of some controversy. Paneth observed that the extent of radiocolloid formation with Pb, Bi, and Po compounds increased with pH, and attributed this correctly to hydrolysis and the formation of basic salts or hydroxides. The same author pointed out that a considerable difficulty arose when the minimum concentration necessary for precipitation is calculated from the solubility product. Thus for $[Bi^{3+}][OH^-]^3$, the solubility product is 10^{-31}. Since the OH^- concentration at pH 4 is about 10^{-10}, precipitation should only occur at $[Bi^{3+}] \geq 1\ M$, whereas in fact colloid formation is observed at concentrations below $10^{-10}\ M$. The difference is so large that the difficulty cannot be resolved by assuming that the solubility product is 10^3 to 10^6 times greater than the value quoted above.

Zsigmondy [51] therefore suggested that under the conditions described these radioelements are in fact present as ions, which are adsorbed on invisible impurities such as silica, iron hydroxide, aluminum hydroxide, etc. This point of view has been extended by Hahn [52], who pointed out that colloid formation is easier for compounds with a tendency to form insoluble compounds; the lower the solubility of a given compound on the macroscopic scale, the more strongly it will be adsorbed on impurities at the tracer scale, and consequently the more pronounced will be its *pseudocolloidal* properties. Werner [53] attempted to confirm this theory by examining the effect of pH, and of electrolytes, on the centrifugation of Bi and Pb isotopes. The curve in Fig. 20–5 shows schematically the amount of ThC which can be centrifuged from solution as a function of the pH. Werner has interpreted these results by assuming that bismuth in solution is anionic, which will therefore be adsorbed on either positively charged or negatively charged impurities, depending on the pH, concentration, and type of electrolytes present in the solution.

It has been shown, however [54, 55], that this interpretation does not agree with the properties of bismuth. In fact the colloidal behavior of weighable quantities (2.5 millimoles) of bismuth chloride and nitrate is practically the same as that of ThC; nephelometric measurements of changes in the opalescence of the solution as a function of pH and of the concentration of various salts gave similar results to those found for the centrifugation of the radioactive isotope. Such results cannot of course be attributed to invisible impurities, and can in fact be satisfactorily interpreted from the known laws governing the coagulation and peptization of positively charged $Bi(OH)_3$ micelles.

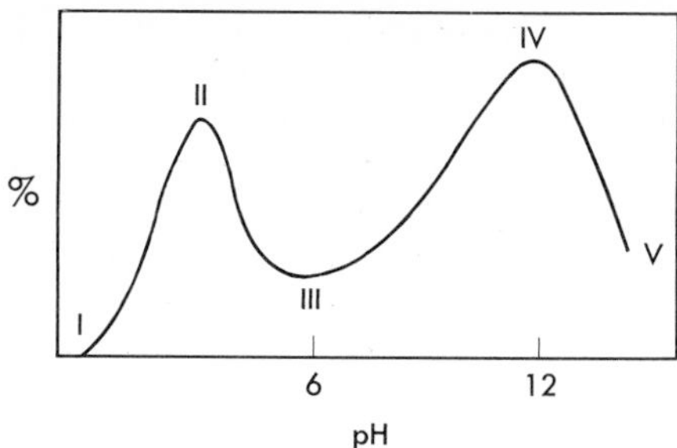

Fig. 21-5. Schematic diagram of the change in the colloidal character of tracer Bi with pH.

Experiments on the colloidal behavior of polonium equally do not agree with the pseudo-colloid theory. The variation in the quantity of polonium salts centrifuged from solution as a function of pH follows a curve similar to that shown in Fig. 21-5, going through a maximum around pH 5 [56]. Starik [20] has found that polonium is more strongly adsorbed in acid media. The effects of age and polonium concentration on the quantities centrifuged from solution are difficult to explain if adsorption on impurities is the only factor operating [57]. Finally, in acid solution, adsorbed polonium will desorb from powders or precipitates and deposit spontaneously on silver, irrespective of the charge and adsorbing power of the solid (silica, TiO_2, AgCl, Se) [40, 43], but at a pH above 3, no deposition occurs in the absence of any visible adsorbant. It is difficult to see why an unweighable quantity of impurity should have a much greater effect on the displacement than a weighable amount of a strong adsorbent in pH conditions less favorable for adsorption.

It has been shown more recently [59, 60] that the colloidal behavior of thorium and zirconium compounds in 10^{-4} M solution, examined by coagulation in the presence of electrolytes and at various pH's, is similar to that of their radioactive isotopes in 10^{-2} to 10^{-13} M solution. Schweitzer and Jackson [61] found no direct relationship between the adsorption of radioactive Y, Sb, and Ag and centrifugation from extremely dilute solution, and it was therefore concluded that adsorption on impurities is not a factor which governs the properties of radiocolloids. Equally, Adler and Steigman [62] have studied the adsorption of UX-1 and RaE on colloidal graphite, and the precipitation of UX-1 by different ions, and find results which imply a true colloidal behavior by these radioelements in some conditions (see also Section 21-7).

The genuine existence of colloidal species is further proved by autoradiographs, in which the "stars" frequently have a blackened center with radii corresponding to the range of the particles in gelatin; if adsorption on inactive impurities were occurring, the tracks would begin some distance from the center [63]. Counting the tracks formed in a given time from different stars gives values for the minimum number of radioactive atoms in a micelle; values as high as 10^6 atoms have been obtained [50]. This number of atoms should be large enough to form centrifugible aggregates, without any need for invoking carrying by impurities. It is, however, clear that impurities do influence the relative extent of radiocolloid formation, and equally that the complete elimination of all trace of foreign material from a solution is extremely difficult, and perhaps impossible. Nevertheless the impurities play a secondary part, and do not decide whether the phenomenon occurs. Finally, it may be that radiation, without actually causing radiocolloid formation, has some effect upon the behavior (Section 13–7).

If, then, radiocolloidal formation is determined by the properties of the compounds and the physico-chemical conditions of the medium, there still remains the apparent contradiction between this conclusion and the relatively high solubilities obtained on the macroscopic scale. A careful examination of the solubility products given in the literature for very insoluble hydroxides and sulfides [64, 65] shows that although fairly concordant values are generally obtained for a given substance by the same method, the results obtained by different methods frequently disagree strongly, with differences sometimes as high as several powers of 10. However, the numerical values for such substances are so small (sometimes below 10^{-30}) that the question arises as to their precise physical significance.

It seems therefore that solutions of these compounds cannot be considered in the normal terms of solubility and solubility product, which implies the possibility of a complete separation of the solid phase from a liquid phase containing only ions and simple molecules. These solutions are rather polydisperse systems, which are not in thermodynamic equilibrium, and which contain colloidal particles of variable dimensions in addition to simple and complex ions, the whole system being in a state of more or less slow evolution. In time, the particles agglomerate and the ions are adsorbed, so that the degree of separation of the two phases will depend on the methods and apparatus used. For similar reasons, the solubility will vary with the method of measurement, with the method of preparation, with the way the solution is stored, and with its age, etc. The values obtained by any given method can certainly be used to evaluate roughly the degree of insolubility of compounds of this type, but they cannot be treated as thermodynamic constants.

It should be noted that under some conditions, insoluble radioactive compounds which normally separate from solution in the crystalline state may show colloidal behavior in highly diluted saturated solutions. For example, $RaSO_4$ is a crystalline substance like $BaSO_4$, but when crystals are separated from the mother liquor by filtration or decantation, the liquor may contain a suspension of microcrystals which can be centrifuged out and which show up on photographic plates as stars. Effects of this type can affect the determination of solubilities, for example (see Ref. 66).

The formation of radiocolloids of $RaSO_4$ in some uranium minerals has been reported by Yagoda [67], who demonstrated this by the photographic method. It is also known that the more soluble $BaSO_4$ precipitates as a colloid under certain conditions on the macroscopic level. Measurements of the rate of diffusion of tracer amounts of barium in sulfate solution show that here too it is in the colloidal state, whereas the homologous radiostrontium is in true solution [68].

The practical consequences of radiocolloid formation are considerable. In particular, in the chemical separation of radioactive compounds, conditions must be chosen to favor either the ionic or the radiocolloidal state depending on the method being used (i.e., electrolysis, centrifugation, ion exchange, etc.).

21-6 Radioactive aerosols. In the same way that some radioelements form colloidal micelles in solution (see previous section), radioactive atoms in the air or in any other gaseous atmosphere can form aerosols although the mechanism involved is quite different. As early as 1906, Madame Curie [69] reported that in a vessel containing air or other gases, the active deposit formed aggregates which were sufficiently large to settle out under the effect of gravity. Direct evidence of the existence of these aggregates was obtained by C. Chamié [70, 71], who found that a mixture of radon and air gave rise to α-particle tracks, in the form of stars, on photographic plates. This conclusion was later confirmed by Harrington [72, 73] by ultramicroscopic and centrifugation experiments. Harrington also showed that aerosol formation is made easier by the presence of polar molecules, such as water vapor, HCl, SO_2, nitrotoluene, ethyl acetate, etc., in the gaseous phase, whereas in dry air, or in air containing the nonpolar molecule CCl_4, the agglomerations were smaller.

The mechanism of the formation of radioactive aerosols has been investigated recently by Labeyrie [74, 75], using the active deposit of radon. Various highly sensitive methods were established for determining the absolute concentrations by α-counting, and systematic measurements showed that the initial aggregates of the active deposit were "ultrafine," and highly mobile. In a vessel with a volume of several liters, filled with filtered air, each aggregate contained only one radioactive atom, at concentrations below 10^{-5} mc/liter; these aggregates disappeared rapidly by fixation on the walls of the vessel. In the normal atmosphere, they are also rapidly absorbed on the normal aerosols present, these being large particles with diameters of the order of 10^{-6} cm or more. In consequence, the fate of the ultrafine aerosols is related to that of the normal aerosols. The concentration of a few micrograms per liter of these aerosols is sufficient to immobilize the radioactive aerosols. This total fixation is independent of the concentrations of the two species in question between wide limits. The time required to reach this state depends on the concentration of the supporting aerosol.

A knowledge of the properties of radioactive aerosols has acquired special practical importance because of the rapid increase in the industrial extraction of uranium from radioactive minerals, and in the construction of nuclear reactors and radiochemical laboratories. In handling active products, suspensions are often formed in the atmosphere, and these may be both a health hazard for human beings and a considerable nuisance in counting measurements. The tolerance levels for various α- or β-emitters in the form of aerosols are given in Table 14-6.

21–7 Distribution between immiscible solvents.* Extraction into organic solvents is a well-established technique in handling radioactive isotopes, but there has been a considerable increase in the application of this method in recent years. In fact, the close relationship between radiochemistry and solvent extraction arises for two reasons. First, it is a clean and neat separation method, by which radioactive isotopes can be obtained, if necessary, carrier-free; second, the use of radioactive tracers has been of the greatest importance in studying the mechanism of the solvent extraction process. We shall see examples below of the relatively simple theoretical conditions necessary for good separations, the experimental convenience of the method, and the wide range of applications of solvent extraction techniques.

At a given temperature, the *partition coefficient* P for the distribution of any substance between two immiscible solvents is given by the Henry-Nernst law

$$\frac{a_1}{a_2} = \frac{c_1 f_1}{c_2 f_2} = P, \tag{21–6}$$

in which a_1 and a_2 are the thermodynamic activities, c_1 and c_2 the concentrations, and f_1 and f_2 the activity coefficients in each phase. In very dilute solution $f \approx 1$, and a becomes equal to c. This is the well-known partition law, first found empirically by Berthelot and Jungfleisch [76] and later derived thermodynamically by Nernst [77]. This equation is valid only for systems in which the extracted species has the same chemical and molecular form in both solvents. The quantity which is most easily obtained experimentally is the *extraction coefficient* D

$$D = \frac{\text{total concentration of species A in all chemical forms in the organic phase}}{\text{total concentration of species A in all chemical forms in the aqueous phase}}$$

$$= \frac{[\mathrm{A}_1]_o + [\mathrm{A}_2]_o + \cdots + [\mathrm{A}_i]_o}{[\mathrm{A}_1] + [\mathrm{A}_2] + \cdots + [\mathrm{A}_j]}, \tag{21–7}$$

where $[\ ]_o$ and $[\ ]$ are the concentrations in the organic and aqueous phases respectively. Obviously D reduces to P for the conditions stated above. Equally one can define a *separation factor* β for two compounds, given by

$$\beta = D_{\mathrm{I}}/D_{\mathrm{II}}. \tag{21–8}$$

The number of inorganic compounds which obey the simple Nernst partition law is of course fairly limited; examples include I_2, Br_2, $HgCl_2$, HgI_2, InI_3, $GeCl_4$, $AsCl_3$, $AsBr_3$, SbI_3, RuO_4, and OsO_4 [78].

The extraction of ionic compounds into organic solvents from aqueous solution is prevented by the large loss of solvation energy which would

---

* By M. Haïssinsky and D. G. Tuck.

be involved, as can be shown from the Born equation [79]. Obviously one way to get over the electrostatic energy barrier against the extraction of ions into low dielectric solvents is to destroy the charge on the ion, which can be done by combining it with some appropriately charged form of a neutral molecular species. The conditions for the formation of such *chelate* complexes are well established. Some examples of chelating complexes are shown here as their anions.

dithizonate:

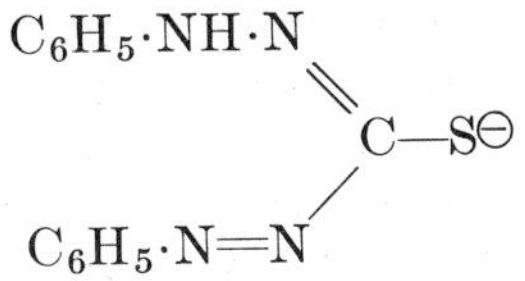

$$C_6H_5 \cdot NH \cdot N{=}C(S^{\ominus})\text{—}N{=}N \cdot C_6H_5$$

acetylacetonate:

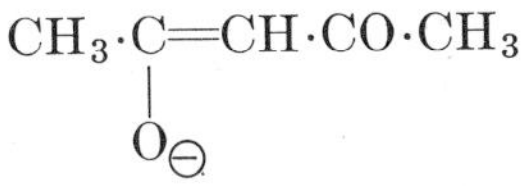

$$CH_3 \cdot C(O^{\ominus}){=}CH \cdot CO \cdot CH_3$$

8-hydroxyquinolate:

(quinoline ring with N, and $O^{\ominus}$ at position 8)

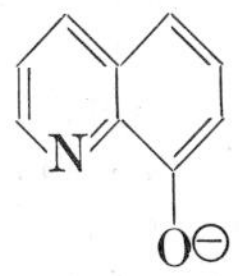

thenoyltrifluoracetone (TTA):

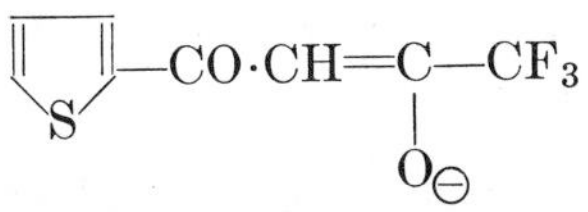

$$(C_4H_3S)\text{—}CO \cdot CH{=}C(O^{\ominus})\text{—}CF_3$$

The resultant complexes are nonelectrolytes, and because of their large molecular size are not solvated and virtually insoluble in water. The acid alkyl phosphates and phosphinates, and the dialkyl pyrophosphates, behave similarly, and have been widely used for extracting the UO_2^{2+} ion. In every case, the polar part of the molecule, around the metal atom, is "buried" in the center of a large hydrophobic organic molecule, as for example, in

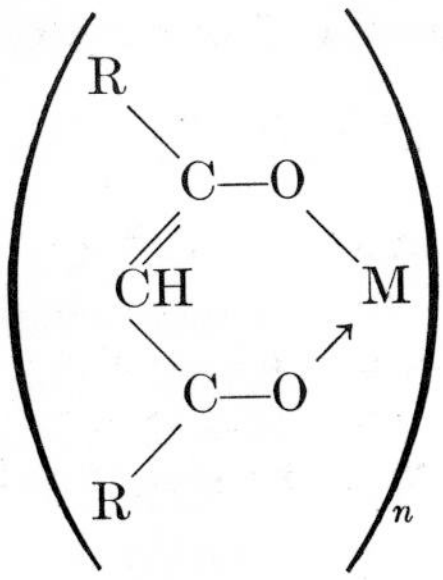

$$\left(\begin{array}{l} R \\ \quad \backslash \\ \quad\; C\text{—}O \\ \;/\!/ \qquad\; \backslash \\ CH \qquad\quad M \\ \quad \backslash \qquad\; \nearrow \\ \quad\; C\text{—}O \\ \;\;/ \\ R \end{array} \right)_n$$

where n is the charge on the original ion.

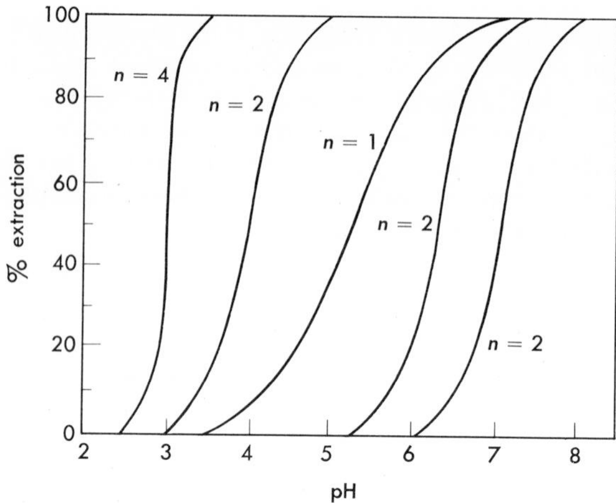

FIG. 21-6. Influence of pH on extraction of a chelate complex into an organic solvent.

The extraction depends upon the equilibrium (see Ref. 80)

$$M^{n+}_{(aq)} + n\,HR_{(org)} \overset{K}{\rightleftharpoons} MR_{n\,(org)} + n\,H^{+}_{(aq)}, \tag{21-9}$$

and the extraction coefficient can be written as

$$D = K\left\{\frac{[HR]_o}{[H+]}\right\}^n, \tag{21-10}$$

in which $[HR]_o$ is the equilibrium concentration of free chelating agent in the organic solvent, and $[H^+]$ that of the hydrogen ions in the aqueous phase. It is easy to show from this that

$$\log D = \log K + n \log [HR] + n\,\mathrm{pH}. \tag{21-11}$$

The sigmoid curves in Fig. 21-6, which show the percentage extraction $x = 100D/(1 + D)$ as a function of pH, depend on the valency n, with a point of inflexion at $x = 50\%$. If the pH corresponding to $x = 50\%$ for given HR is $\mathrm{pH}_{1/2}$, then

$$\mathrm{pH}_{1/2} = -1/n \log K - \log [HR]. \tag{21-12}$$

These relationships, which have been verified using radioactive tracers, emphasize the highly specific separations which can be obtained by appropriate adjustment of the pH [80, 81]. The separation factor β is of course larger as the difference in valency increases.

Many examples of separations of radioactive elements by this method are to be found in the literature; another use is in the investigation of complex formation in solution. A typical application as a separation

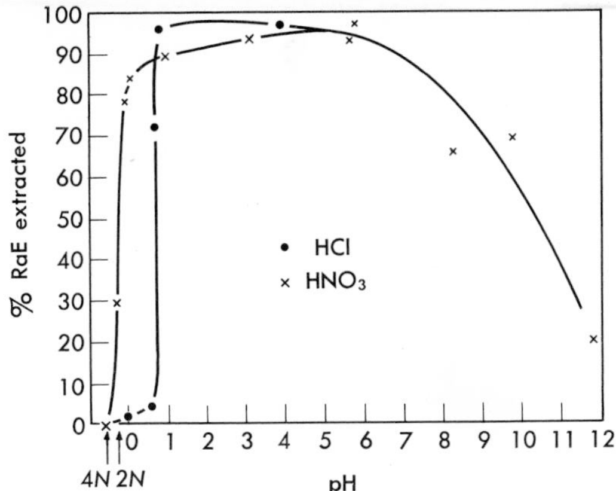

FIG. 21–7. Percentage yield as a function of pH in the dithizone extraction of RaE (Ref. 83).

method is in obtaining ^{227}Ac produced by neutron bombardment of radium:

$$^{226}\text{Ra}\ (\text{n}, \gamma)\ ^{227}\text{Ra} \xrightarrow{\beta} {}^{227}\text{Ac}. \qquad (21\text{–}13)$$

Actinium is extracted from the target with TTA in benzene at pH 6, back-extracted into the aqueous phase with 6 M acid, and subsequently separated from any Th and Po produced by TTA extraction at pH 1 [82]. An example of studying complex formation is in the RaE/RaD separation, by extracting Bi from nitrate or chloride solution into a chloroform solution of dithizone [83]. The extraction coefficients are virtually constant over the concentration region 4×10^{-5} to 10^{-10} M. Graphs of percentage extraction against pH (Fig. 21–7) show that a sharp fall occurs at a lower acidity in the chloride system, due to complexing by Cl^- ions, and in fact the presence of sufficient quantities of NaCl suppresses the extraction altogether, even at pH 3. The decrease at high pH is due to radiocolloid formation.

Another way in which an ion can be removed from aqueous solution is by causing it to form an ion-pair with an oppositely charged ion which is so large that it has no coordinate solvation in the aqueous phase. Suitable ions include Ph_4As^+, Ph_4P^+, Bu_4N^+, and Ph_4B^-, so that both cations and anions can be extracted in this way. A systematic treatment of these extraction systems has been given by Tribalat [84]. Amine extraction has been proposed for commercial separation of uranium from its ores.

Basic organic solvents can extract acids from aqueous solution [85], but in terms of the separation and study of radioactive tracers, it is more interesting to consider the complex halo-acids formed by a number of elements, including Ga(III), Au(III), Fe(III), In(III), Tl(III), and others [78]; these extract as the hydrated acids HMX_4. The way in which the extraction coefficient varies with the concentration of the element involved and with the concentration of added acid shows a number of interesting features, which have been elucidated by the work of Diamond [86] and of Coryell, *et al.* [87]. Some of these acids have extremely high extraction coefficients, so that these systems are of considerable importance in the separation of radioactive elements from bombarded targets.

In addition to the extraction of acids, some salts can be coordinately solvated either by water or by organic solvents [88]. In particular, the extraction of uranyl nitrate into a large number of basic solvents involves coordinate solvation of $UO_2(NO_3)_2$ by the organic solvent; there has been some discussion as to the exact implication of this in terms of structure of the UO_2^{2+} ion (Section 8–8). The extraction of uranyl nitrate has of course been investigated in considerable detail because of its importance in the industrial purification of uranium, and in the separation of uranium (and subsequently plutonium) from fission products. Here again this type of extraction can be used for the separation of radioactive isotopes, for extracting elements from fission products, and for separating the transuranium elements from each other.

21–8 Chromatography. One of the most striking and fruitful successes of modern experimental chemistry has been the application of radioactive tracer methods in chromatography. A good illustration of this is that several years of careful work were previously required to separate the various rare earths by fractional crystallization or precipitation, whereas with chromatography products containing less than $1/10^5$ impurities can now be obtained in a few days.

The efficiency of the chromatographic method is markedly increased by utilizing complex formation in elution from columns of synthetic ion exchange resins (see Refs. 89–91). Figure 21–8 shows an example in the form of a chromatogram or elution curve (i.e., the specific activity measured as a function of the volume of eluant, or of the elution time) for a mixture of radioactive rare earth isotopes fractionated on the resin Dowex-50 at 100° [92].

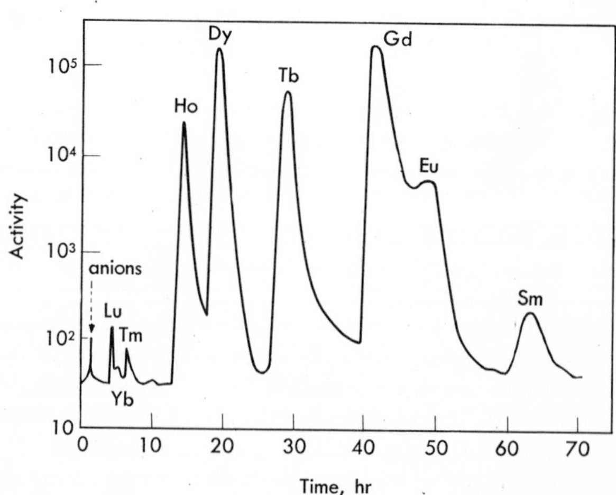

FIG. 21–8. Chromatographic separation of rare earths (Ref. 92).

Chromatographic separations can be treated theoretically as a succession of adsorptions and desorptions obeying the Freundlich or Langmuir isotherms, as a series of Donnan equilibria, or as a series of chemical processes to which the mass action law can be applied. In this latter treatment, cation exchange resins, which are generally organic polymers containing sulfonic, carboxylic acid, phenolic or other groups, are regarded as binary compounds MR, in which R is the insoluble anionic radical and M a displacable cation (often the hydrogen ion). Equally, anion resins can be given the general formula RX, with R the insoluble cation. In the wet state, both behave as electrolyte solutions whose properties are defined by the nature of the terminal groups. Measurements of electrical conductivity, membrane potentials, and the self-diffusion coefficients of ions support this point of view [93].

Following the work of other authors on unlabeled electrolytes, Spiegler and Coryell [94] applied an electrical potential to two metallic electrodes placed in a column of some resin, such as Dowex-50, containing a band of radioactive Na^+ ions, and observed the migration of radioactive sodium towards the cathode. The electrode reactions are

cathode:

$$2NaR + 2H_2O + 2e \rightarrow 2Na^+ + 2R^- + 2OH^- + H_2, \tag{21–14}$$

or

$$2HR + 2e \rightarrow 2R^- + H_2;$$

anode:

$$2R^- + H_2O \rightarrow 2HR + \tfrac{1}{2}O_2 + 2e. \tag{21–15}$$

The combination of this electromigration with normal chromatographic techniques has resulted in several useful analytical applications.

In order to understand the mechanism of the elution, let us assume that a resin, with $M = Na^+$, is contacted with an aqueous solution of a polyvalent ion, for example, La^{3+}. The following equilibrium is then established:

$$La^{3+} + 3NaR \overset{K_e}{\rightleftharpoons} LaR_3 + 3Na^+, \tag{21–16}$$

with Na^+ being displaced from the resin by La^{3+}. The role of the eluant is now to remove the La^{3+} ions from the resin; for example, if the eluting solution contains citrate ion, a complex with La^{3+} is formed:

$$La^{3+} + 3H_2Cit^- \overset{K_c}{\rightleftharpoons} La(H_2Cit)_3. \tag{21–17}$$

The equilibrium distribution coefficient K_p of the lanthanum, at a given ratio of mass of resin : volume of eluant, is given by

$$K_p = \frac{[LaR_3]}{[La(H_2Cit)_3]} = K_e K_c \left\{\frac{[NaR]}{[Na^+][H_2Cit^-]}\right\}^3, \tag{21–18}$$

in which K_e is the exchange constant for reaction (21–16) and K_c that for complex formation in (21–17). If the dissociation constant K_d of citric acid (to give H^+ and H_2Cit^-) is now introduced, one has

$$K_p = \frac{K_e K_c}{K_\alpha^3} \left\{ \frac{[NaR]}{[Na^+]} \frac{[H^+]}{[H_3Cit]} \right\}^3, \tag{21–19}$$

an equation which emphasizes the effect of acidity on the distribution. For two cations with the same valency (e.g., La^{3+} and Ce^{3+}) the separation factor α can be defined as

$$\alpha = K_p^{La}/K_p^{Ce} = \frac{K_e^{La} K_c^{La}}{K_e^{Ce} K_c^{Ce}}. \tag{21–20}$$

The separation factor is therefore independent of the concentrations (taken as being equal to the thermodynamic activities) of the various ions; the efficiency of the separations is due to differences in the equilibria in solution, governed by equations such as (21–17), or to differences in absorbability. In general, the order of elution goes in the same sense as that for the fixation of ions on the resin, so that the most easily adsorbed ion is eluted with the greatest difficulty (although this is not necessarily a general rule since Yang [95] reports that the MoO_4^{2-} ion is adsorbed better than WO_4^{2-} on the anion resin Amberlite-4B, but is eluted more easily by alkali).

Equation (21–19) shows that for anion exchange, an increase in the concentration of the eluting electrolyte reduces take-up by the resin. In contrast to this, the sorption of a radiocolloid is often favored by the addition of an electrolyte, due to the coagulation which results [96, 97]. Conversely, Eq. (21–19) shows that increasing acidity does not favor the passage of ions into the complexing solution, but acidity has the reverse effect on a radiocolloid formed by hydrolysis.

Table 21–4 shows values of K_e for Eu^{3+} at different pH in citric acid solution for three different resins, together with the separation factor α for Eu^{3+} and Pm^{3+}. The values of α do not differ greatly for other complexing eluants, as is shown by Table 21–5.

Even when the separation factor is very small, elution separation is efficient because the flow of the eluant down the column is equivalent to a very large number of decomposition and re-formation steps for the resin-ion

TABLE 21–4

DISTRIBUTION COEFFICIENTS FOR Eu^{3+}, AND SEPARATION FACTORS FOR Eu^{3+}/Pm^{3+}

Dowex-50			Duolite-C			Amberlite IR-1		
pH	K_p(Eu)	α(Eu-Pm)	pH	K_p(Eu)	α(Eu-Pm)	pH	K_p(Eu)	α(Eu-Pm)
2.9	92	1.45	2.40	230	1.65	2.42	39	1.32
3.08	18.8	1.41	2.80	27	1.62	2.58	19	1.34
3.25	5.2	1.41	3.00	3.1	1.52	2.85	8.3	1.30

Table 21–5

Separation Factors

(with Dowex-50)

Eluant	α(Eu-Pm)
Citric acid	1.45
Citric acid in 50% alcohol	1.31
Tartaric acid	1.94
Lactic acid	1.71
Thiosalicylic acid	1.49
Ethyl acetylacetonate	1.33
Oxalic acid	1.32
Acetylacetone	1.41

complexes (or adsorption and desorption) in the successive layers of solid. In this respect, the chromatographic column behaves like a distillation column with a very large number of theoretical plates.

Experiment shows that the behavior of tracer quantities of various ions in exchange columns is not generally very different from that of macroscopic amounts. This technique can therefore be applied to the separation of mixtures in which all or some of the components are at the tracer level, when they can only be detected radiometrically. With a fairly simple apparatus of the type outlined in Fig. 21–9 [95] the separation of two or more components labeled with the appropriate indicators can be monitored continuously.

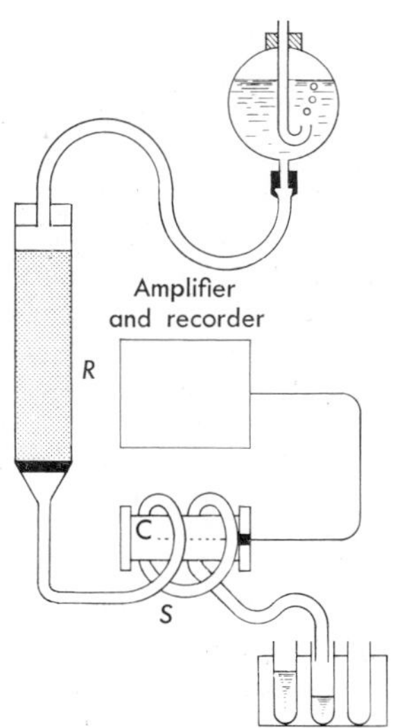

Fig. 21–9. Apparatus for continuous monitoring of eluant in chromatographic separation of radioactive mixtures.

These then are the advantages of the method, efficiency, simplicity, and wide range of application, which have led to its successful use in radiochemical work. In addition to its application in the identification of fission products and in the discovery of promethium (Section 7–4) we also owe much of our knowledge of the properties of the transplutonium elements and the identification of the heaviest elements at present known in the periodic system to the use of ion exchange chromatography (Chapter 8).

Ion exchange methods can also be applied to the study of various physico-chemical phenomena at the tracer level. For instance, Eqs. (21–18) and (21–19) are based on the identification of thermodynamic activities with concentrations, although a more rigorous treatment would include the activity coefficients, so that for the exchange reaction

$$\mathrm{HR} + \mathrm{Na}^+ \overset{K_e}{\rightleftharpoons} \mathrm{NaR} + \mathrm{H}^+ \tag{21–21}$$

the thermodynamic equilibrium constant K_e is given by

$$K_e = g\frac{[\mathrm{NaR}][\mathrm{H}^+]\gamma\mathrm{H}^+}{[\mathrm{HR}][\mathrm{Na}^+]\gamma\mathrm{Na}^+} \tag{21–22}$$

in which the γ's are the activity coefficients of the ions in solution and g is the activity coefficient of the solid. It has been shown [99, 100, 101] that measurements of the distribution of an ion between the two phases in some process such as (21–21) can be used to obtain the activity coefficients in extremely dilute solutions. This method has been used [102] to get the activity coefficients for the alkali chlorides at zero concentration in 0.005 to 1.5 M HCl solutions. Schubert has also used ion-exchange reactions to determine the equilibrium constants for complex formation [as in (21–17)] between citrates, tartrates, and other organic ligands and the alkaline earths (including radium), rare earths, etc.

As can be seen from Eq. (21–19), the change of the distribution coefficient K_p with eluant concentration depends strongly on the valency of the eluted ion. By measuring this change, then, it is possible to determine the actual charge on an ion at the tracer level. One example of this has been the confirmation of the existence of the PaO_2^+ ion [103].

It is worth mentioning that some success has been obtained in separating fission products and the natural radioelements on columns of alumina [104, 105, 106] although this practice has been virtually abandoned in radiochemical work since the introduction of synthetic resins.

21–9 Paper chromatography. This method, which can be regarded as a variant of partition chromatography [107], has also developed rapidly, and has found useful application in radiochemistry. The substances to be separated are distributed between two solvents, one of which is the mobile phase (acetone, butanol, chloroform, etc.), and the other the stationary phase, such as a column of silica gel impregnated with water (especially useful in organic separations), or paper saturated with water. The separation is due to the different rate of travel of the molecules or ions on the paper when the mobile solvent is introduced. The separation is defined by the differences in the characteristic parameter R_f:

$$R_f = \frac{\text{distance traveled by the substance from the starting point}}{\text{distance traveled by the solvent front}}.$$

The parameter R_f depends on the distribution coefficient between the two solvents, and for a given substance may vary with the quality of the paper, the nature of the solvent, the temperature, and other factors. Some authors [108, 109] suggest that this distribution is not the only mechanism governing separations in paper chromatography, and that adsorption, exchange, and other phenomena may also be involved.

Experiments by Lederer [110] have revealed the striking fact that in a number of cases the R_f value remains constant as the concentration is lowered to about $10^{-12}\,M$. This has been demonstrated for ions of Zn, Sn(II), In, Ni, La, Fe(III), Pd, Rh, and Mn treated with butanol or acetone mixed with aqueous HCl solution; R_f is also independent of concentration for Na^+ ions (as NaCl) in alcohol–20% water solution. On the other hand, tracer concentrations of Ce, Y, and Th(UX-1) (as the acetates) chromatographed on paper with butanol containing water and acetylacetone gave R_f values which differed from those found on the macroscopic level; R_f for weighable quantities of these compounds (under given conditions) was 0.38, 0.59, and 1.0 respectively, while the tracers did not move from the point at which they were applied, or only "tailed off." Similarly Zn^{65} in acetate plus butanol solution gives an R_f value different from that of macroscopic zinc [111]. These results are very probably due to adsorption effects; for example, UX-1 is known to be carried by $Fe(OH)_3$ at pH conditions at which weighable quantities of Th are not precipitated.

Electromigration in paper chromatography can be used for analytical separations (Section 23–1) and for studying the state of ions in solution [112].

21–10 The condensation and vaporization of molecular films. The condensation of a molecular beam on a cooled surface is in some ways comparable to electrolytic deposition, the critical potential in the latter case being analogous to the critical temperature below which molecules striking the surface are fixed, and above which they are reflected. The variation of the critical potential with concentration can also be compared with the variation of the critical temperature with the density of the molecular beam. Radioactive methods are particularly convenient for the study of condensation phenomena, since the optical techniques previously used are applicable only to studies of deposits which already contain several atomic layers, and these must mask, at least in part, any effect of the nature and state of the surface.* Ribaud and Devienne [114] and Frauenfelder [115] have used either Geiger-Müller counters or photographic methods for this work.

---

* For a bibliography, see Ref. 113.

TABLE 21–6

CONDENSATION FACTORS FOR RADIOANTIMONY

Cu		Al	
Thickness, A	α	Thickness, A	α
1.9	0.40	6.6	0.26
4.9	0.46	23.5	0.42
40	0.61	59	0.58
24	0.64	81	0.61
210	0.77	393	0.64
438	0.77		

The first authors measured the condensation of antimony vapor on copper and aluminum, defining the condensation factor as

$$\alpha = \frac{\text{condensed atoms}}{\text{atoms striking the surface}}.$$

Devienne [116, 117], who extended this work, pointed out that the idea of a critical temperature should not be taken too strictly, since the condensation factor for Sb or Cd on various metals (Cu, Zn, Al) is never zero and never equal to unity, since a fraction of the atoms are reflected. The condensation factor depends on the nature of the support, the state of the surface, and the thickness of deposit already formed. As this thickness increases, any effect due to the support decreases and a value is reached which is close to that for self-condensation (i.e., Sb on Sb). Table 21–6 gives values of α obtained for the condensation of Sb on Al and Cu at 25°C. Devienne also observed exchange between a molecular beam of inactive antimony and radioactive antimony previously deposited on a metallic support, so that some of the atoms fixed on the surface are re-emitted under the effect of further bombardment.

Similar measurements were carried out by Frauenfelder [115] using carrier-free radioactive isotopes of Cu, Ag, Cd, and Hg. This author also determined the diffusion coefficients of radioactive Cu on Ag, finding $D = 8 \times 10^{-7}$ cm^2·sec^{-1} at 750°C. The migration of polonium on a platinum surface was previously studied by Jedrzejowski [118], and that of radioactive silver on silver by Johnson and Watanabe [119].

The reverse of condensation, namely the vaporization of monatomic layers, was the subject of a number of earlier studies with the natural radioelements Po, RaE, ThB, etc. [120, 121, 122]. Curves showing the rate of volatilization, or the fraction which can be volatilized, as a function of temperature, have a sigmoid shape, and this is almost certainly for the same reason as for electrolytic deposition curves, namely nonuniform bond strengths between the atoms evaporated and the support. The "critical temperature" of vaporization depends naturally on the support; vaporization of polonium begins around 350° on platinum, at a slightly lower temperature on gold, and between 500° and 560°C on palladium. Conversely, if polonium is distilled in a quartz tube in current of carrier gas to the cold end of the tube, where a sheet of Pt or Pd is placed, virtually all the polonium condenses on this sheet, although its surface may only be a small fraction of the total surface available [123]. If sheets of Cu or Ni are placed near the Pt or Pd, they pick up only a small fraction of the activity. This strong affinity of platinum and palladium for polonium also shows up in electrochemical experiments (Section 20–7).

The vaporization temperature of polonium increases with the age of the source, and also depends on the gaseous atmosphere in which the operation is carried out. The rate of vaporization also varies with the method of preparation of the sources. If polonium is deposited on Ni or Pt by some electrochemical method, the curves showing the fraction vaporized as a function of temperature have the normal sigmoid shape, but if the deposit is obtained by distillation and condensation, vaporization begins already below room temperature. The vaporization curve shows a "step," at about 200°C for Ni, and then rises much more rapidly. All this is what would be found if the polonium contained two fractions with different bonding. According to Bonet-Maury, the most volatile fraction can be condensed on a layer of gas previously adsorbed on the metal.

Slightly different results have been obtained by Schwarz [124] for the vaporization of a polonium deposit from silver. The activity of the surface decreases from 100°C, but this decrease is independent of temperature up to 350°C, at which the true vaporization begins. The initial loss has been attributed to Po atoms being projected out of the surface layer when a neighboring atom undergoes disintegration.

The vapor pressure of a number of very involatile compounds have been measured using radioactive tracers; typical examples include yellow phosphorus [126] between −23° and 41°C (10^{-4} to 10^{-1} mm) and thorium acetylacetonate [127] at 100°C (3.2×10^{-4} mm). The vapor pressures of silver [128, 129], of gold and gold alloys [130], and of antimony [131] have also been measured in this way.

21–11 Emanating power. The ability of solids to release radon or other radioactive gases formed in their bulk interior can be expressed as the emanating power (Section 19–10). This property is closely related to the adsorbing power; Fig. 21–10 shows how both of these change with increasing hydration for a zeolite [132]. The adsorption of radon increases as the emanating power decreases, since the greater the tendency of a solid to fix an external gas on its surface, the lower is its power of releasing occluding gases.

The emanating power depends on the surface condition of the solid [9]; freshly prepared precipitates, including certain metal hydroxides such as $Fe(OH)_3$, $Th(OH)_4$, etc., have high emanating powers, which may exceed 90%. Aging produces surface contraction, and so reduces the emanating power. The humidity of the atmosphere in which the precipitate (or more

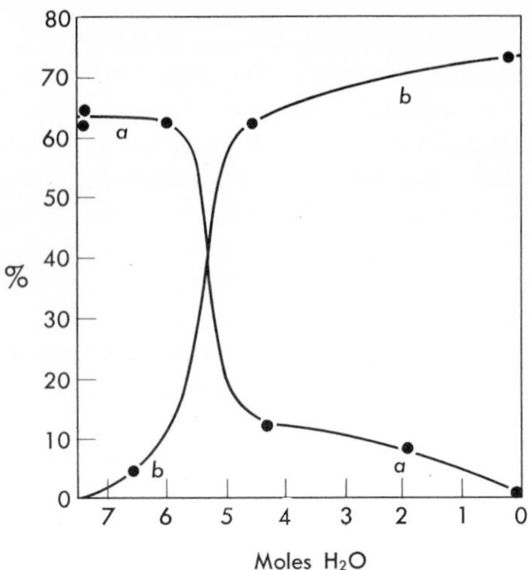

FIG. 21–10. Adsorbing power (a) and emanating power (b) of zeolite for radon (Ref. 132).

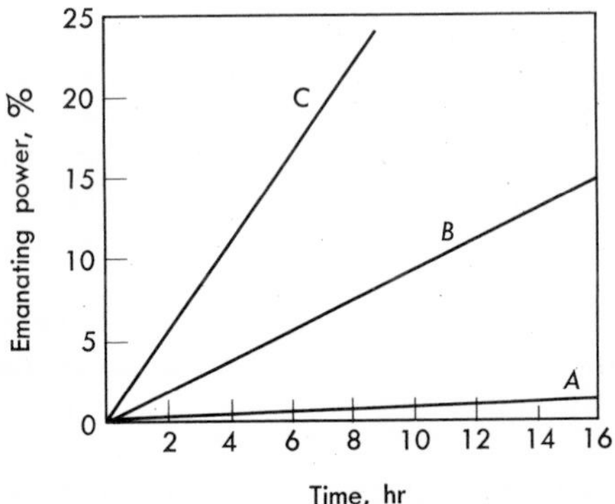

FIG. 21–11. Change in emanating power with time; *A*, Jena glass in moist atmosphere; *B*, barium glass in dry atmosphere; *C*, barium glass in moist atmosphere.

generally the solid) is kept also has considerable influence on the emanating power. In Fig. 21–11 [133] curve *A* shows the time change in the emanating power of Jena glass kept in a humid atmosphere, curve *C* refers to barium glass under the same condition, and curve *B* to barium glass kept in a dry atmosphere. In addition to the influence of humidity, these results show the effect of texture; the Jena glass is less porous and more resistant to attack.

The emanating power is in fact very sensitive to structural factors, and can be used as a means of studying structural changes. Figure 21–12 shows plots of the emanating power against temperature for two allotropic varieties of calcium carbonate, calcite, and aragonite, as measured by

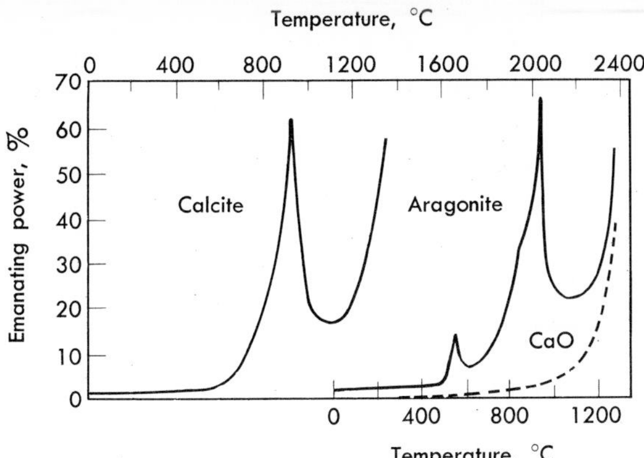

FIG. 21-12. Change in emanating power of calcium carbonate with temperature (Ref. 132).

Zimens [134] after incorporating $ThX(Ra^{224})$ into the solid

$$(ThX \xrightarrow{\alpha} Tn).$$

Both curves show a sharp maximum at 920°C and sharp increases around 600 and 1100°C, but the aragonite curve also has another maximum at 530°C, the allotropic transition temperature. The existence of this last maximum suggests that there is a "loosening" of the lattice at this transformation point, and that this facilitates the escape of the gas. The maximum at 920° is due to thermal decomposition of the carbonate to CO_2 and CaO. Zimens relates the sharp increases at 600° and at 1100° to the "loosening temperature" of the carbonate and of the oxide respectively. Tammann [135] has suggested that the crystal lattices of salts and metal oxides undergo a considerable "structural loosening" at a temperature equal to approximately half the melting point (in °K).

Similar changes in emanating power have been observed at the dehydration, phase change, or decomposition point for various compounds of barium [136, 137], iron [138], aluminum [139], zinc [140], and others. Werner [141] has used this method to study mechanical deformation in Zn, Al, and Zn/Ba alloys.

Some reactions between two solids can also be studied by the emanation method; an emanating element (RdTh, Ra) is incorporated into one of the two reactants, and the mixture is then heated to increasingly higher temperatures. Emanation curves similar to those for decomposition reactions are obtained, with a discontinuity at the temperature at which reaction starts. In this way isothermal curves as a function of time for the mixture and for the active component alone can be compared. Techniques of this sort have been applied to the formation of spinels ($BeAl_2O_4$, $CdFe_2O_4$, $ZnFe_2O_4$, Cu_2FeO_4) [142, 143], and of lead silicate $PbSiO_3$ [144].

When a radioactive gas with a very short half-life such as thoron is used, it must be carried to the measuring instrument by nitrogen or some other inert gas. Gregory [139] has shown that if the carrier gas contains

TABLE 21–7

THE EMANATING POWER OF BARIUM SALTS OF ORGANIC ACIDS

Salt	Number of C atoms	Emanating power, %
Acetate	2	3–4
Propionate	3	17–18
Butyrate	4	60–65
Iso-butyrate	4	70
Caproate	6	96
Laurate	12	100
Palmitate	16	100

traces of oxygen and 5% hydrogen, considerable changes in the emanating power of alumina are found above 1400°C. This effect, which is partially irreversible, is attributed to changes in the concentration of lattice defects, which depend on the partial pressure of oxygen.

Interesting results, whose significance is not at the moment always clear, have been obtained with various organic compounds [140, 145]. The emanating power of the barium salts of monobasic long-chain fatty acids increases with the number of carbon atoms, as shown in Table 21–7. It has been shown that this increase in the emanating power with chain length is not due to the density or the hardness of the salts. A study of the effect of temperature [146, 147] suggests that the very high values for the long chain salts are due to the very high rate of diffusion of the gas through the crystal lattice, and not to surface effects. The emanating power of sodium stearate is also very high, and Bjerge [148] has utilized this in the release of radioactive neon formed in the salt by the nuclear reaction Na^{23} (n, p) Ne^{23} ($t_{1/2}$, 40 sec).

The emanating power of the dibasic acids (oxalic, succinic, adipic) is very low, of the order of 1 to 3% [145], but adding a methyl group to barium adipate

$$\begin{array}{l} CH_2—CH_2—COO \\ \qquad\qquad\qquad\quad \diagdown \\ \qquad\qquad\qquad\qquad Ba \\ \qquad\qquad\qquad\quad \diagup \\ CH_3—CH—CH_2—COO \end{array}$$

brings an increase to 80%. Similarly, substituting hydrogen in the adipate by hydroxide groups to give the saccharate

$$\begin{array}{l} CHOH—CHOH—COO \\ \qquad\qquad\qquad\quad \diagdown \\ \qquad\qquad\qquad\qquad Ba \\ \qquad\qquad\qquad\quad \diagup \\ CHOH—CHOH—COO \end{array}$$

increases the emanating power to 20%, but the analogous substitution in

TABLE 21–8

THE EMANATING POWER OF ISOMERIC BARIUM SALTS

Compound	Emanating power, %
o-amino-benzoate	0.3
m-amino-benzoate	8.2
p-amino-benzoate	16
o-xylo-sulfonate	50
m-xylo-sulfonate	99
p-xylo-sulfonate	4
o-nitro-benzoate	14.0
m-nitro-benzoate	1.5
p-nitro-benzoate	0.4

the caproate, to give the gluconate

$$\begin{array}{l} CH_2OH{-}(CHOH)_4{-}COO \\ \qquad\qquad\qquad\qquad\quad \searrow \\ \qquad\qquad\qquad\qquad\qquad Ba \\ \qquad\qquad\qquad\qquad\quad \nearrow \\ CH_2OH{-}(CHOH)_4{-}COO \end{array}$$

lowers it from 96 to 1.5%.

The significance of the results obtained with different isomeric barium salts is also far from clear. The values given in Table 21–8 show that the emanating power may increase, decrease, or go through a maximum on going from ortho- to meta- and para-compounds.

References

1. K. Horovitz and F. A. Paneth, *Z. physik. Chem.*, **89**, 513 (1915).
2. F. A. Paneth and W. Thimann, *Ber.*, **43**, 1215 (1924).
3. K. Horovitz and F. A. Paneth, *Akad. Wiss. Wien, Abt. IIa*, **123**, 1819 (1914).
4. K. Fajans and K. Beckerath, *Z. physik. Chem.*, **97**, 478 (1921).
5. K. Fajans and T. Erdey-Grüz, *Z. physik. Chem.*, **A158**, 97 (1932).
6. O. Hahn, *Ber.*, **59**, 2014 (1926).
7. O. Hahn, *Naturwiss.*, **14**, 1197 (1926), and papers by O. Hahn, H. Kading, L. Imre, R. Mumbrauer, and N. Riel, in *Z. physik. Chem.* (1929–1935).
8. V. G. Khlopin, *Trav. Inst. Rad. Leningrad*, **4**, 34 (1938), and papers by V. G. Khlopin, A. E. Polesitski, B. A. Nikitin, P. I. Tolmachev, and A. P. Ratner in *Z. anorg. Chem.* (1929–1935).
9. O. Hahn, *Applied Radiochemistry*, Cornell University Press, Ithaca, 1936.
10. L. Imre, *Z. physik. Chem.*, **A153**, 127 (1931).
11. V. G. Khlopin and M. S. Merkulova, *Izvest. Akad. Nauk, Otdel Khim.*, **1949**, 460.
12. E. J. W. Verwey and H. R. Kruyt, *Z. physik. Chem.*, **A167**, 149, 312 (1933).
13. A. P. Ratner, *Acta Physicochim. U.R.S.S.*, **4**, 889 (1936); **11**, 475 (1939).
14. A. P. Ratner, *J. Chem. Phys.*, **1**, 789 (1933).
15. T. Schönfeld and S. Neumann, *Monatsh. Chem.*, **85**, 921 (1954).
16. A. O. Long and J. E. Willard, *Ind. Eng. Chem.*, **44**, 916 (1952).
17. B. A. Nikitin and V. M. Vdovenko, *Trav. Inst. Rad. Leningrad*, **3**, 256 (1937).
18. M. H. Kurbatov, F. Yu, and J. D. Kurbatov, *J. Chem. Phys.*, **16**, 87 (1948).
19. J. Brennen, *Ann. Chim.*, **4**, 126 (1925).
20. I. Starik, *Z. physik. Chem.*, **A157**, 269 (1951).
21. T. Schönfeld and E. Broda, *Mikrochem.*, **36**, 537 (1951).
22. H. Leng, *Akad. Wiss. Wien, Abt. IIa*, **136**, 19 (1927).
23. S. Z. Roginski and O. M. Todes, *Acta Physicochim U.R.S.S.*, **21**, 519 (1946).
24. N. P. Keier and S. Z. Roginski, *Doklady Akad. Nauk S.S.S.R.*, **57**, 157 (1947).
25. N. P. Keier and S. Z. Roginski, *Izvest. Akad. Nauk, Otdel Khim.*, **1950**, 51.
26. P. H. Emmett and J. T. Kummer, *J. Chim. Phys.*, **47**, 67 (1950).
27. E. P. Bowden and A. C. Moore, *Trans. Faraday Soc.*, **47**, 900 (1951).
28. D. J. Salley, A. J. Weith, A. A. Argyle, and J. K. Dixon, *Proc. Roy. Soc. (London)*, **A203**, 42 (1950).
29. C. M. Judson, A. A. Argyle, D. J. Salley, and J. K. Dixon, *J. Chem. Phys.*, **18**, 1302 (1950); **19**, 378 (1951).
30. N. H. Steiger and G. Aniansson, *J. Phys. Chem.*, **58**, 228 (1954).
31. G. Aniansson and O. Lamm, *Nature*, **165**, 357 (1950).
32. G. Aniansson, *J. Phys. Chem.*, **55**, 1286 (1951).
33. D. E. Beischer, *J. Phys. Chem.*, **57**, 134 (1953).
34. L. M. Henderson and F. C. Kracek, *J. Am. Chem. Soc.*, **49**, 738 (1927).
35. H. A. Doerner and W. M. Hoskins, *J. Am. Chem. Soc.*, **47**, 662 (1925).

36. H. Kading, R. Mumbrauer, and N. Riehl, *Z. physik. Chem.*, **A161**, 362 (1932).

37. B. Marques, *J. Chim. Phys.*, **33**, 1 (1936).

38. B. Goldschmidt, *Ann. Chim.*, **13**, 88 (1940).

39. A. P. Ratner, *Trav. Inst. Rad. Leningrad*, **2**, 67 (1933).

40. A. E. Polesitski, *Trav. Inst. Rad. Leningrad*, **2**, 73 (1933).

41. A. H. Booth, *Trans. Faraday Soc.*, **47**, 633, 640 (1951).

42. H. G. Grimm, *Z. Elektrochem.*, **30**, 467 (1924).

43. H. G. Grimm and G. Wagner, *Z. physik. Chem.*, **132**, 131 (1928).

44. V. G. Khlopin and B. A. Nikitin, *Z. physik. Chem.*, **A145**, 137 (1929).

45. F. A. Paneth, *Akad. Wiss. Wien, Abt. IIa*, **121**, 2193 (1912); **122**, 1079, 1637 (1913).

46. T. Godlewski, *Kolloid-Z.*, **14**, 229 (1914).

47. E. Broda and J. Erber, *Monatsh. Chem.*, **81**, 53 (1950).

48. J. E. Duval and M. H. Kurbatov, *J. Am. Chem. Soc.*, **75**, 2246 (1953).

49. C. Chamié, *J. phys. radium*, **10**, 44 (1929).

50. G. Bouissières, R. Chastel, and L. Vigneron, *Compt. rend.*, **224**, 43 (1947).

51. R. Zsigmondy, *Kolloid-Z.*, **6**, 304 (1913).

52. O. Hahn and L. Imre, *Z. physik. Chem.*, **A144**, 161 (1929).

53. O. Werner, *Z. physik. Chem.*, **A156**, 89 (1931).

54. M. Haïssinsky, *Compt. rend.*, **198**, 580 (1934).

55. M. Haïssinsky, *Les Radiocolloides*, Hermann, Paris, 1935.

56. A. Korvezee, *J. Chim. Phys.*, **30**, 130 (1933).

57. C. Chamié and M. Haïssinsky, *Compt. rend.*, **198**, 1229 (1934).

58. M. Haïssinsky, *J. Chim. Phys.*, **34**, 94 (1937).

59. M. H. Kurbatov and J. D. Kurbatov, *J. Chem. Phys.*, **13**, 208 (1945).

60. M. H. Kurbatov, H. B. Webster, and J. D. Kurbatov, *J. Phys. Chem.*, **54**, 1239 (1950).

61. G. K. Schweitzer and W. M. Jackson, *J. Am. Chem. Soc.*, **76**, 941, 3348 (1954).

62. I. Adler and J. Steigman, *J. Phys. Chem.*, **56**, 493 (1952).

63. G. K. Schweitzer and W. M. Jackson, *J. Chem. Educ.*, **29**, 513 (1952).

64. M. Haïssinsky, *J. Chim. Phys.*, **31**, 43 (1934).

65. M. Haïssinsky, *Acta Physicochim. U.R.S.S.*, **3**, 517 (1935).

66. O. Erbacher and B. A. Nikitin, *Z. physik. Chem.*, **A158**, 216 (1932).

67. H. Yagoda, *Am. Mineral.*, **31**, 462 (1946).

68. J. Schubert, *U.S.A.E.C. report AECD-1910*, 1948.

69. M. Curie, *Traite de Radioactivité*, Vol. 1, Gauthier-Villars, Paris, 1910, p. 371.

70. C. Chamié, *Compt. rend.*, **184**, 1243 (1927); **185**, 770, 1277 (1927).

71. C. Chamié, *J. Chim. Phys.*, **29**, 242 (1934).

72. E. Harrington, *Phil. Mag.*, **6**, 685 (1928).

73. E. L. Harrington and O. A. Gratias, *Phil. Mag.*, **11**, 285 (1931).

74. J. Labeyrie, *Thesis*, Paris, 1953.

75. G. Delibrias and J. Labeyrie, *J. phys. radium*, **14**, 407 (1953).

76. M. Berthelot and J. Jungfleisch, *Ann. chim. et phys.*, (4), **26**, 396 (1872).

77. W. Nernst, *Z. physik. Chem.*, **8**, 110 (1891).

78. R. M. DIAMOND and D. G. TUCK, *Progress in Inorganic Chemistry*, **2**, 109, 1960.
79. M. BORN, *Z. Physik*, **1**, 45 (1920).
80. H. M. IRVING, *Quart. Revs.*, **5**, 200 (1951).
81. E. BRODA and T. SCHÖNFELD, *Radiochemische Methoden der Mikrochemie*, Springer, Vienna, 1955.
82. F. HAGEMANN, *J. Am. Chem. Soc.*, **72**, 768 (1950).
83. G. BOUISSIÈRES and C. FERRADINI. *Anal. Chim. Acta*, **4**, 611 (1950).
84. S. TRIBALAT, *Anal. Chim. Acta*, **3**, 113 (1949); **4**, 228 (1950); **5**, 115 (1951).
85. D. G. TUCK and R. M. DIAMOND, *J. Phys. Chem.*, **65**, 193 (1961).
86. R. M. DIAMOND, *J. Phys. Chem.*, **61**, 69, 75, 1522 (1957).
87. A. M. POSTKANZER, R. J. DIETZ, E. RUDZITIS, J. W. IRVINE, and C. D. CORYELL, *U.N.E.S.C.O. Conference on Radioisotopes*, Paris, 1957, No. 30.
88. L. I. KATZIN, *J. Inorg. Nuclear Chem.*, **4**, 187 (1957).
89. A. W. ADAMSON, G. E. BOYD, C. D. CORYELL, R. KUNIN, J. SCHUBERT, F. H. SPEDDING, E. R. TOMPKINS, *et al.*, *J. Am. Chem. Soc.*, **69**, 2769–2881 (1947).
90. F. C. NACHOD, *Ion Exchange*, Academic Press, New York, 1949.
91. E. LEDERER and M. LEDERER, *Chromatography*, Elsevier, Amsterdam, 2nd edition, 1957.
92. B. H. KETELLE and G. E. BOYD, *J. Am. Chem. Soc.*, **73**, 1862 (1951).
93. K. S. SPIEGLER, *J. Electrochem. Soc.*, **100**, 303 C (1953).
94. K. S. SPIEGLER and C. D. CORYELL, *Science*, **113**, 546 (1951).
95. T. YANG, *Thesis*, Paris, 1953.
96. J. SCHUBERT, *Anal. Chem.*, **22**, 1359 (1950).
97. J. SCHUBERT and J. W. RICHTER, *J. Colloid Sci.*, **5**, 376 (1950).
98. E. R. TOMKINS and S. W. MAYER, *J. Am. Chem. Soc.*, **69**, 2859 (1947).
99. A. P. VANSELOW, *J. Am. Chem. Soc.*, **64**, 1307 (1942).
100. J. SCHUBERT, *J. Phys. Chem.*, **52**, 340 (1948).
101. J. SCHUBERT and J. W. RICHTER, *J. Phys. Chem.*, **52**, 350 (1948).
102. R. H. BETTS and A. N. MACKENZIE, *Can. J. Chem.*, **30**, 146 (1952).
103. G. A. WELCH, *Nature*, **172**, 458 (1953).
104. R. LINDNER, *Z. physik. Chem.*, **194**, 51 (1944).
105. R. LINDNER, *Z. Naturforsch.*, **2a**, 329, 333 (1947).
106. R. LINDNER, *Z. Elektrochem.*, **54**, 421 (1950).
107. A. J. P. MARTIN and R. L. M. SYNGE, *Biochem. J.*, **35**, 1358 (1941).
108. C. S. HANES and F. A. ISHERWOOD, *Nature*, **164**, 1107 (1949).
109. L. C. CRAIG, *Anal. Chem.*, **22**, 1346 (1950).
110. M. LEDERER, *Anal. Chim. Acta*, **8**, 134 (1953).
111. W. J. FRIERSON, S. L. HOOD, I. B. WHITNEY, and C. L. COMAR, *Arch. Biochem. Biophys.*, **38**, 397 (1952).
112. M. LEDERER, *Paper Electrophoresis*, Elsevier, Amsterdam, 1957.
113. M. DEVIENNE, *Mem. Sci. Phys.*, No. **53**, 1, 1952.
114. G. RIBAUD and M. DEVIENNE, *Compt. rend.*, **230**, 1811 (1950); **231**, 740 (1951).
115. H. FRAUENFELDER, *Helv. Phys. Acta*, **23**, 347 (1950).
116. M. DEVIENNE, *J. phys. radium*, **13**, 52 (1952); **14**, 257 (1953).
117. M. DEVIENNE, *Compt. rend.*, **239**, 1202 (1954).
118. P. JEDRZEJOWSKI, *Acta Phys. Polon.*, **2**, 137 (1953).
119. G. W. JOHNSON and T. WATANABE, *Phys. Rev.*, **76**, 588 (1949).

120. P. Bonet-Maury, *Ann. physik.*, **11,** 253 (1929).
121. E. Rona, *Akad. Wiss. Wien, Abt. IIa,* **141,** 533 (1932).
122. E. Rona and M. Hoffer, *Akad. Wiss. Wien, Abt. IIa,* **144,** 397 (1935).
123. F. A. Paneth and G. Hevesy, *Akad. Wiss. Wien, Abt. IIa,* **122,** 1049 (1913).
124. K. Schwarz, *Z. physik. Chem.,* **A168,** 241 (1934).
125. K. Schwarz, *Z. Elektrochem.,* **45,** 712 (1939).
126. F. S. Dainton and H. M. Kimberley, *Trans. Faraday Soc.,* **46,** 912 (1950).
127. R. C. Young, C. Goodman, and J. Kovitz, *J. Am. Chem. Soc.,* **61,** 876 (1939).
128. A. P. Lyubimov and A. A. Granovskaya, *Zhur. Fiz. Khim.,* **27,** 473 (1953).
129. H. M. Schadel and C. E. Birchenall, *J. Metals,* **188,** 1134 (1950).
130. L. D. Hall, *J. Am. Chem. Soc.,* **73,** 757 (1951).
131. A. N. Nesmeyanov and B. Z. Iofa, *Doklady Akad. Nauk S.S.S.R.,* **98,** 993 (1954).
132. H. Müller, *Z. physik. Chem.,* **A149,** 257 (1930).
133. O. Hahn and H. Müller, quoted in Ref. 9.
134. K. E. Zimens, *Z. physik. Chem.,* **B37,** 231, 241 (1937).
135. G. Tammann and A. Sworykin, *Z. anorg. Chem.,* **176,** 46 (1928).
136. F. Strassmann, *Naturwiss.,* **19,** 502 (1931).
137. C. Lieber, *Z. physik. Chem.,* **A182,** 153 (1938); **B42,** 240 (1939).
138. K. E. Zimens, *Z. physik. Chem.,* **A192,** 1 (1943).
139. J. N. Gregory and S. Moorbath, *Trans. Faraday Soc.,* **47,** 844 (1951).
140. O. Hahn, *J. Chem. Soc.,* **1949,** S 259.
141. O. Werner, *Z. Metallkunde,* **26,** 265 (1934).
142. W. Schroder, *Z. Elektrochem.,* **52,** 133–166 (1948).
143. W. Schroder and H. Schmals, *Z. Elektrochem.,* **48,** 241, 301 (1942).
144. R. Jagitsch, *Z. physik. Chem.,* **B33,** 196 (1936).
145. F. Strassmann, *Z. physik. Chem.,* **B26,** 362 (1934).
146. J. N. Gregory and S. Moorbath, *Trans. Faraday Soc.,* **47,** 1064 (1951).
147. J. N. Gregory, J. Hill, and S. Moorbath, *Trans. Faraday Soc.,* **48,** 643 (1952).
148. T. Bjerge, *Nature,* **139,** 757 (1936).

CHAPTER 22

APPLICATIONS OF RADIOACTIVITY IN ANALYTICAL CHEMISTRY

22–1 The separation of radioactive elements. The applications of radioactivity in analytical chemistry can be classified under six main headings:

(a) research into the analytical behavior of tracer components in homogeneous or heterogeneous mixtures;

(b) the purification and separation of radioactive compounds, generally in unweighable quantities, from other active materials or from inactive substances; the preparation of radioactive sources for research in nuclear physics, or for the study of physico-chemical behavior at the tracer level;

(c) the measurements of physico-chemical constants of interest in analytical chemistry, such as solubility, partition coefficient, etc.;

(d) the checking and improvement of known analytical methods, and research into new methods;

(e) those techniques which utilize radiation to detect or to determine quantitatively either natural or artificially produced radioelements;

(f) the measurement of those substances which can be detected or measured by virtue of the fact that they alter the intensity of radiation passing through them.

The two previous chapters were devoted to a discussion of the topics outlined in (a), and of the theoretical principles fundamental to (b). From a practical point of view, separation methods which require the use of carriers can be differentiated from those which do not. Mixed crystallization, coprecipitation, adsorption on a precipitate or some surface-active material, and chromatography with an involatile eluant are methods which involve carriers. Filtration and ultrafiltration, the centrifugation of a radiocolloid, spontaneous deposition or electrolysis, adsorption on surfaces, distillation, volatilization, and extraction into a volatile solvent are all procedures which under the appropriate conditions can be used for carrier-free separations. Ion exchange techniques involving elution with some organic compound may also be made a carrier-free process, since the organic compound can be subsequently eliminated by heating. The products obtained from paper chromatography are often used directly without further treatment, but in some cases it is necessary to burn the paper and the residual ash may then be regarded as negligibly small for most purposes.

The choice of procedure is often determined by the nature of the separation problem itself, depending, for example, on whether separation from a more or less electropositive element is involved, whether or not it forms compounds insoluble in water or in organic solvents, whether a chelate complex can be formed, whether the relevant compounds have high vapor pressures, etc. The use of carriers is generally best avoided where possible, especially in the later stages of the separation. In many cases, the efficiency of a carrier depends on the similarity between the chemical properties of the carrier and those of the compound being carried, but of course the greater this similarity, the more difficult is the final definitive separation of carrier and isotope.

Centrifugation has been successfully used to separate polonium and other natural or artificial radioelements [1, 2]. For instance, radioactive iron produced by deuteron bombardment of cobalt, Co^{59} (d, 2p) Fe^{59}, has been separated by dissolving the target in 12 *M* HCl, neutralizing with NH_4OH to pH 9, and centrifuging or filtering off the iron, which forms a radiocolloid under these conditions [3]. Other applications of this technique include the separation of active Mg after dissolving bombarded Al in NaOH [4], radioactive Sc from Ti (dissolution in H_2SO_4, neutralization by NH_4OH and addition of H_2O_2), and of radioactive Bi from Pb [5].

We have already quoted examples of the separation of radioactive elements by partition between two solvents (Section 21–7; see also Ref. 16). Differences in the solubility of various compounds in organic solvents can also be used for this purpose. For example, the actinium isotope MsTh-2 is naturally mixed with its parent MsTh-1 (Ra^{228}), and its own daughter products RaTh (Th^{228}) and ThX (Ra^{224}). Of these elements, the nitrates of Ac and Th are easily soluble in absolute ethanol and that of Ra is not, and similarly thorium nitrate is precipitated by pyridine and actinium nitrate is not, so that a complete and rapid separation of these three elements as their nitrates is easily accomplished [7].

The high efficiency of ion exchange methods for separations of fission products, rare earths, and transuranium elements has already been discussed (Section 21–8). This technique has also been used in the separation of the alkali metals (elution with HCl or $HClO_4$) [8, 9, 10], of Ba and Ra (elution with HCl or citric acid) [11, 12], and of La and Ac (elution with ammonium citrate) [13, 14]. This latter eluant can also be used for the difficult separation of UX-1(Th) and UZ(Pa) [15]. Anion exchangers have been used for separating radioactive isotopes of the halogens, Nb and Ta [16, 17], Ta, Zr and Pa [18, 19], Zr and Hf [20, 21, 22], Re and Tc [23], and many others.

Paper chromatography has been used by Lederer [24, 25] for the separation of Na^{22}-Mg, Zn^{65}-Cu, Rh^{102}-Ru, Pd^{103}-Rh, Sn^{113}-In, Cs^{131}-Ba, UX-1-UZ, U^{233}-Pa, of the rare earths (Fig. 22–1), and also for the detection of radioactive impurities in radiocaesium and radiothalium sources.

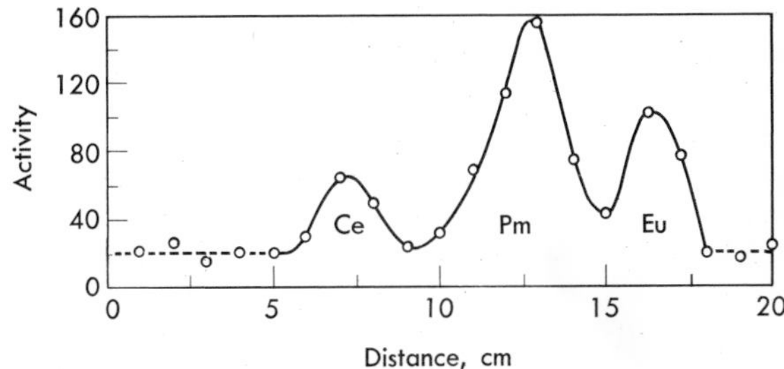

Fig. 22–1. The separation of Ce, Pm, and Eu by paper chromatography, using 0.2 *M* HCl in ethanol as eluant (Ref. 24).

Garrison, Haymond, and Maxwell [26] were the first to apply electromigration on paper to the separation of radioelements. These authors evaporated a solution of the radioelement onto a filter paper, which was then placed in the middle of several layers of paper impregnated with the appropriate electrolyte. A voltage sufficient to give 20 to 40 m amp/cm^2 was applied then between two electrodes. Depending upon the electrolyte composition, the radioelement moved toward the cathode, or toward the anode, or remained in the original spot. For example, if MnO_2 + active Nb was dissolved in oxalic acid, and the paper saturated with ammonium oxalate, the Mn^{2+} ions migrated toward the cathode and niobium oxalate complex moved toward the anode. In chloride media, Mn^{2+} again moved to the cathode, but the radioactive niobium remained in its initial position. Similarly, after carrying down radioactive As on $Cu(OH)_2$, the precipitate was dissolved in 3 M HCl, and the paper electrophoresis again carried out; the As did not move at all, but Cu^{2+} moved to the anode. Various modifications of this method have subsequently been applied to the separation of fission products, especially the rare earths, and of Ac from La [27, 28, 29].

Electrolytic methods involving spontaneous deposition or electrolysis have already been discussed at length (see Chapter 20 and Section 18–5). Some radioelements, including polonium, lead, and manganese, will form anodic peroxides. Even very electropositive metals can sometimes be deposited, either by forming an amalgam at a mercury cathode, or as hydroxides or oxides as the result of the production of alkali in the solution close to the cathode, causing hydrolysis of the salt. Amalgamation has been used to extract Na^{22}, produced by deuteron bombardment of magnesium, by electrolysis at a continually renewed mercury cathode [30]. Mesothorium-2 (Ac) has been deposited by electrolyzing a boiling, neutral aqueous solution at a silver cathode [31], and very similar conditions can be used for thorium isotopes [32]. These two elements can also be obtained as cathodic deposits by electrolysis of the nitrates or chlorides in alcohol solution, or better in a solution of ethanol plus 15 to 20% acetone [33]. Even a metal as electropositive as Ra can be deposited in this way on Pt, Au, Ag, Ni, or Cu by electrolyzing the iodide or thiocyanate in acetone or pyridine solution [34]. Thin layers of these deposits are very adherent, and are probably the metal hydroxide formed by interaction with traces of water in the solvent. Plutonium, americium, curium and any other transuranium element can also be deposited from aqueous solution in a similar form (Section 8–2).

The great advantage of electrochemical methods is that they give very high specific activity sources, in which there is practically no absorption of the emitted radiation. The same advantages apply to volatilization and distillation methods. Volatilization is generally carried out by heating the element, or one of its compounds, previously deposited on some appropriate support, in a stream of carrier gas. Intense sources of polonium have been prepared in this way [35, 36, 37]. In favorable cases, distillation can be carried out at temperatures close to ambient. For example, the radioactive isotopes of ruthenium formed by bombarding Mo with 40-Mev α-particles can be separated from the target by distilling off RuO_4 after fusion with $KOH + KNO_3$ at 400°C and oxidation by chlorine [38].

Similarly, osmium isotopes prepared by the α-bombardment of platinum can be distilled off after conversion to OsO_4 with aqua regia.

Radiophosphorus is sometimes prepared by cyclotron bombardment of iron phosphide with accelerated deuterons P^{31} (d, p) P^{32}, but radioactive copper and a number of other nuclides are formed at the same time in reactions involving iron. To purify the products, the phosphide is heated in a current of chlorine, when PCl_5 and $FeCl_3$ distill out of the target. After reduction with a current of hydrogen, further distillation separates $FeCl_2$ from PCl_3, which is then absorbed in water to give H_3PO_4 [39].

In some cases, it is convenient to volatilize the target or support instead of the radioelement. For example, silver isotopes produced by the deuteron bombardment of Pd are dissolved, with the target, in *aqua regia* and then carried down on Hg_2Cl_2; this can be subsequently separated by distillation at 450°C [40].

When it is necessary to separate a mixture containing several radioelements, a series of different methods must be used, always taking into account the half-life and amount of each nuclide present. In the separation of fission products from uranium, Wilkinson and Grummitt [41], for example, used precipitation methods for Rb, Sr, Y, Zr, Nb, Rh, Pd, Cd, Th, Te, Cs, Ba, La, Ce, and the other rare earths, distillation methods for Ge, As, Se, Ru, Tc, Sn, and Sb, solvent extraction for Mo, I, and Br, and electrolysis for Ag and Sb. Other combinations of methods are naturally also possible; thus Lee and Cook [42] preferred to deposit Sb, Ag, Rh, Sn, Te, and Cd electrolytically.*

In the separation of radioelements from very high intensity sources, as in the treatment of nuclear fuels, possible radiolytic changes to the reagents must be considered in choosing a separation method. In particular, organic solvents and ion exchange resins may suffer damage which can prove a hindrance in the chosen methods [44].

22-2 The investigation of analytical methods. Because of their extremely high sensitivity, radioactive methods are especially useful for investigating the applicability of analytical methods. In particular they can be used for checking the quantitative aspects of precipitation, the coprecipitation of undesirable products, and losses during analytical operations.

Erbacher and Philipp [45] used radioactive gold to show that the separation of Pt, Ir, and Au by dissolving in *aqua regia*, followed by reaction with H_2O_2 in alkaline solution, is not complete, since the gold contains both the other metals as impurities, and the latter in their turn are contaminated with gold. Flagg and Wiig [46] confirmed that labeled Sn(II) is completely precipitated by $K_3[Fe(CN)_6]$ in the presence of NH_4Cl. Phosphorus-32 has been used to show that the double precipitation of ammonium phosphomolybdate from nitric acid solution is more complete when the HNO_3 concentration for the second precipitation is only 1 to 1.75%, rather than the 3.6% normally used.

---

* For other separation and analytical applications of tracers, see Ref. 43.

Cobalt can be determined in chloride solution by precipitation at 70°C with either β-nitroso-α-naphthol or α-nitroso-β-naphthol. Experiments with radioactive cobalt showed that the filtrate contains 0.17 mg/liter of cobalt in the first case, and 1.5 mg/liter in the second, so that the first reagent is to be preferred for this determination [47, 48].

Other similar work includes the investigation of the precipitation of lead as oxychloride; the separation of calcium and magnesium as their oxalates [49, 50]; the precipitation of zinc as phosphate, sulfide, oxinate, or anthranilate [51]; the precipitation of germanium as the quinolinium germanododecamolybdate [52]; the carrying of magnesium by calcium oxalate [53]; coprecipitation of cobalt zinc, and iron sulfides [54, 55]; coprecipitation of Sr by $BaCrO_4$ and $BaCl_2$ [56]; coprecipitation of zinc, copper, and iron hydroxides by $Be(OH)_2$ [57]; the losses which occur on washing precipitated K_2PtCl_6 [58]; the carrying of zinc [59] and sulfur [60] by electrolytic deposits of copper (Section 20–4); and many others.

The determinations of the solubility of almost insoluble compounds by the tracer method is also of great analytical importance. This method was first used in 1912 by Hevesy and Paneth [61], who measured the solubility of $PbCrO_4$ and PbS labeled with RaD. In subsequent work, the solubility of several other compounds of Pb, Mo, Th, Hf, Ta, Ag, Cu, Co, Mg, etc. have been determined by this technique (see Ref. 43 for a bibliography). The solubility of water in benzene has been measured using tritium-labeled H_2O [62]. The solubility of dithizone in water has been measured by adding a labeled Ag salt and extracting the complex formed into chloroform [63].

22–3 Radiometric methods of analysis. Chemical methods of analysis for the natural radioelements are often replaced by measurements of intensity of radiation, even when working with weighable quantities of the element in question. If the absolute rate of disintegration is known, a simple calculation involving the decay constant of the active species gives the weight of material, making allowance if necessary for the isotopic composition of the element. Radiometric analysis can also be used for the determination of a stable element if the latter can be made to combine with a radioelement to give an insoluble compound [64]. Suppose for example, that it is necessary to measure sulfate in solution, and a labeled soluble lead salt of known specific activity is available (labeled with ThB or RaD); $PbSO_4$ can then be precipitated by an excess of the soluble lead salt, and a comparison of the activity of the filtrate with that of the initial solution gives the quantity of lead which has combined, and hence the original concentration of SO_4^{2-}. Similarly, an inactive cation such as Ba^{2+} can be measured by adding a solution containing a known excess of anion, such as sulfate or chromate; after the precipitate formed is removed, a further precipitation of uncombined anion from the solution is carried out with radioactive lead as before. The difference between the initial quantity of anion and that precipitated as the lead salt can be used to calculate the quantity of Ba^{2+}.

The method is also applicable to the determination of those anions which form soluble compounds with lead but insoluble compounds with some other cation. Thus for example, chloride can be precipitated with excess Ag^+, and the remaining Ag^+ subsequently precipitated from the filtrate with excess chromate, and the excess chromate finally precipitated with radioactive lead. In this way the amounts of lead, chromate, and silver ion used up can be related to the amount of chloride. Naturally if labeled chromate or silver salt of known specific activity is available, the number of operations necessary is reduced. This technique has been used to measure Cr, V, and Mo as silver chromate, metavanadate, and molybdate using $Ag^{110}NO_3$ [65].

Süe [66] measured traces of Mg^{2+} by adding Na_2HPO_4 labeled with P^{32} to the solution, and carried the magnesium phosphate formed on a precipitate of inactive magnesium ammonium phosphate. Isotopic exchange between this solid and the Na_2HPO_4 remaining in solution was negligible in the course of the experiment, so that measurement of the activity carried down gave the quantity of the magnesium present. Süe used a similar technique for small quantities of Ag^+, adding NaI labeled with radioactive iodine, and carrying AgI with $Fe(OH)_3$. The natural activity of thorium is too small for direct measurements, but the element can be determined by precipitation with P^{32}-labeled pyrophosphate of known activity and measuring the activity remaining in the filtrate [67].

Langer [68, 69] has used a volumetric technique for the radiometric determination of Mg^{2+}. A solution of a Mg salt, containing NH_4OH and NH_4Cl, is efficiently stirred in a beaker, into which small quantities of active Na_2HPO_4 solution are added from a burette. After each addition and precipitation, the activity of the supernatant liquid is measured with a thin-walled liquid counter. When the precipitation is still incomplete, the measured activity is only that of the background, but when the first excess of phosphate is added, the activity rises sharply (Fig. 22–2a). Conversely, if the active phosphate is placed in the beaker and magnesium solution is added from the microburette, the measured activity gradually decreases, and finally falls to the background level (Fig. 22–2b). Silver,

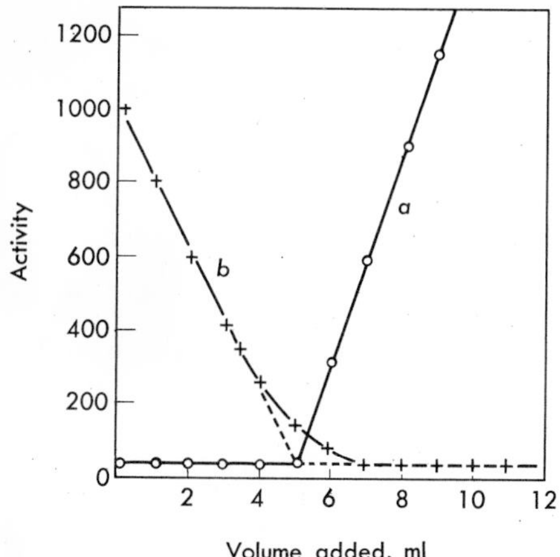

FIG. 22–2. The determination of Mg using radiophosphorus (Ref. 69).

lead, thorium, and uranyl have also been measured in this way by using the appropriate labeled anions. Similarly, the acidity of a solution can be measured radiometrically by making use of the formation of insoluble hydroxides or carbonates with lead or other appropriate radioactive cations; excess alkaline carbonate is added to the solution, and the unused excess is precipitated with radioactive lead [64].

Radiometric methods [64] can also be used for acidimetric measurements by techniques similar to the above, utilizing the formation of insoluble hydroxides or carbonates of lead or other (radioactive) cations; excess alkaline carbonate is added to the solution, and the excess precipitated with the radiolead.

The nitrogen content of an organic substance can be measured by conversion to ammonia by the Kjeldahl method; the ammonia solution is neutralized with excess acid, which is then determined radiometrically as before. Other determinations on organic compounds can be carried out by the radiometric method. For example, carbon can be converted to CO_2 by combustion, collected in excess barium hydroxide, and the unused excess of this measured with active lead nitrate.

Amino-acids can be measured by means of the soluble complexes which they form with labeled copper salts [70]. In fatty acids the iodine number, corresponding to the number of double bonds, has been determined using labeled iodine monobromide [71], and the CO groups in polysaccharides have been measured by conversion into cyanhydrins, using labeled cyanide [72].

22–4 Isotopic dilution analysis. The isotopic dilution method is based on the fact that the isotopic composition of an element remains constant throughout a series of chemical reactions if the isotopes are initially in the same physico-chemical state. Let us suppose that a solution contains P grams of an inactive element A, which is to be determined. A quantity p of the same labeled element in the same chemicals state, with a specific activity a, is added to the solution. The specific activity a' of the mixture then becomes

$$a' = \frac{ap}{P + p}. \tag{22–1}$$

Only a fraction of P need be used in the measurement of a', and P can obviously be found when p and a have also been measured

$$P = p\left(\frac{a}{a'} - 1\right). \tag{22–2}$$

A stable isotope may be used instead of a radioactive isotope, in which case the concentration must be determined by mass spectrometry or by some other appropriate procedure (see Ref. 73). The great advantage of the method lies in the fact that it can be used even when the procedure involves loss of material, or does not allow a complete separation of the element or compound in question. It is therefore particularly useful in measurements of the rare earths, fission products, or complex mixtures of organic or biochemical compounds.

Hevesy and Hobbie [74] first introduced the method for determining traces of lead present in a mineral in about one part in 10^6; Pb was measured by adding RaD and then depositing PbO_2 anodically. Süe used a similar technique for measuring potassium in the presence of other alkali metals [75]; similarly S^{35} can be used to analyze a mixture of benzyl derivatives of sulfides, sulfones, and sulfoxides [76]. Other measurements reported in the literature include naphthalene in coal tar [77], γ-hexachlorobenzene [78], penicillin [79], vitamin B_{12}, and other organic compounds. In the case of penicillin, the molecule was labeled with C^{13}.

The application of stable isotopes in isotopic dilution analysis is due to Rittenberg [80], who determined palmitic acid in a mixture of fatty acids by adding a sample of this acid enriched in deuterium. Similarly heavy nitrogen (N^{15}) has been used for measuring leucine and other amino-acids [81, 82]. The useful results obtained in biochemical research by using isotopic indicators and isotopic dilution analysis are discussed in Chapter 24.

With the development of mass spectrometry, and the availability of separated stable isotopes in high purity, the isotopic dilution method has found several applications in the determination of geological ages (Chapter 10), fission yields, branching ratios in radioactive decay, and other problems of nuclear physics (see Ref. 83 for a bibliography).

Reverse isotopic dilution consists in adding a known quantity of an inactive compound to a mixture of active products; the specific activity is then measured after separating a fraction of the homogeneous mixture. This procedure is used when the activity of the compound in question is too diluted by the rest of the mixture for precise measurements, and there is too little of it for chemical separation. The added inactive substance therefore acts as a carrier, and can be used to get a high specific activity product. Several amino-acids, present in a milligram of mixed proteins, were determined in this way [84] after conversion into labeled iodine derivatives by reaction with p-I^{131}-phenyl-sulfonyl chloride.

If the initial specific activity a of the product (i.e., before adding the carrier) is known, or can be easily measured, the quantity present is determined by an equation analogous to (22-2). If this is not the case, it is sufficient to carry out two dilutions, either using the same quantity of active product with two different amounts of carrier, or using two different activities with the weight of carrier. In this way, the unknown a in the equation can be eliminated (double isotopic dilution) [85].

22-5 Activation analysis. The measurement of extremely small traces of materials, which cannot be determined by the normal analytical techniques, becomes possible, and even relatively rapid and simple, if the element can be made radioactive by the action of sufficiently fast particles, neutrons, or γ-rays. These *activation methods* have the additional advantages that in many cases no chemical treatment of the sample is necessary, and that it can be activated in any form and subsequently measured.

Let us consider the simple case in which the element to be measured contains only one isotope which under the action of a neutron flux Φ acquires an activity, with a decay constant λ; for the sake of simplicity, we shall assume this to be a β-disintegration process. If n_0 is the number of atoms of this element which can be activated, assumed to be virtually constant throughout the irradiation for a time t, then the number n of active atoms formed during this time is given by

$$n = \frac{n_0 \Phi \sigma}{\lambda}(1 - e^{-\lambda t}), \tag{22-3}$$

in which σ is the capture cross section, expressed in cm^2/atom, for the nuclear reaction in question. The activity of the sample, that is to say, the number of disintegrations per unit time, immediately after irradiation is

$$a = \lambda n = n_0 \Phi \sigma (1 - e^{-\lambda t}), \tag{22-4}$$

and that at a time t_1 from the end of this irradiation

$$a_t = n_0 \Phi \sigma e^{-\lambda t_1}(1 - e^{-\lambda t}). \tag{22-5}$$

In practice the counting apparatus will have a certain efficiency f, so that the actual counting rate recorded is $a' = af$. The element may of course have several isotopes, but we shall assume that only one of these, with a relative abundance $r\%$, is activated under the conditions chosen, or (better) that the radiation emitted by the other isotopes or elements present can be eliminated by absorption. It is then easy to show that the relation between the weight p of the element and the activity a' measured immediately after irradiation is

$$p = \frac{(a'/f) M \cdot 100}{N \Phi \sigma r (1 - e^{-\lambda t})}, \tag{22-6}$$

in which M is the atomic weight and N Avogadro's number. For a given neutron flux and time of irradiation, the sensitivity of the method increases with the capture cross section σ, and the isotopic abundance r; it decreases with increasing half-life, and increasing atomic weight.

The capture cross sections of the elements were given earlier in Table 5–2. For an element like Dy, which has an extremely high cross section ($2620 \times 10^{-24}\ \text{cm}^2$ for the isotope Dy^{164}), Eq. (22–6) shows that after irradiation with a 0.5-c source of Ra/Be/paraffin ($\sim 10^4\ \text{n/cm}^2 \cdot \text{sec}$) for 2.5 hours (equal to one half-life), 0.1 mg of this element can be determined if the counter efficiency is 10%. In modern reactors, the flux may be 10^9 to 10^{10} times greater than the value quoted, and it is therefore not surprising that this method can be used to detect 5×10^{-6} gm of Mn in alumina [86]; 10^{-5} gm of Tm in spectroscopically pure Er_2O_3 [87]; 4×10^{-6} gm of Na and 2×10^{-6} gm of Cu in 99.998% pure Al; 10^{-5} to 10^{-6} gm of Cu, Mn, Ni, Co, and As in high purity iron [88]; 10^{-5} to 10^{-6} gm of Re in meteorites* [89]; and less than 10^{-9} gm of Ir in a sample of extremely pure platinum [90]. This list illustrates only some of the many striking examples of the use of this technique which can be found in the literature [43].

* For a discussion of the use of radioactivation analysis in geochemistry, see Ref. 91, and references therein.

TABLE 22–1

LIMITS OF DETECTION IN NEUTRON ACTIVATION ANALYSIS*

Element and isotope	Limit of determination, gm
Eu(152), Dy(165), In(116)	10^{-10}–10^{-11}
Ho(186), Lu(177), Ir(194), Sm(153), Mn(56), Re(188)	10^{-9} –10^{-10}
Sc(46), As(76), I(128), Br(82), Cu(64), Ga(72), Au(198), La(140), Pd(108), Na(24), Pr(142), Ta(182), Tb(160), Tm(170), W(187), Yb(175)	10^{-8} –10^{-9}
Ba(139), Cd(115), Cs(134), Cl(38), Co(60), Er(171), Gd(159), Ge(75), Hf(181), Ni(65), Os(193), P(32), K(42), Rb(88), Se(81), Y(90), Zn(69), Pt(197)	10^{-7} –10^{-8}
Ce(143), Cr(51), Hg(203), Mo(99), Sr(89), Te(127), Tl(204), Nd(147), Ru(105), Ag(110), Sn(121), Zr(97)	10^{-6} –10^{-7}
Bi(210), Ca(45), Fe(59), S(35), Si(31)	10^{-5} –10^{-6}

* Based on Ref. 4; Smales [95] gives values about 10 times lower for activation in the Harwell reactions.

When lithium and boron are bombarded with neutrons, they disintegrate with the emission of α-particles, so that these two elements can be measured very conveniently, either by counting these particles, or by autoradiographic methods. This latter method has found other uses in analytical chemistry (see the end of the section).

Table 22–1 shows the limiting quantities of various elements which can be determined by activation, based on a flux of 5×10^{11} n/cm^2·sec for a month for those nuclides with long half-lives, or to saturation for shorter-lived species. The mass number of the isotope actually measured is given in parentheses.

It will be seen from Table 5–2 that the commonly occurring elements H, O, F, N, C, Mg, Si, Fe (and some others) have very small cross sections. This is an advantage when measuring other elements with higher cross sections in the presence of these elements, but for these elements themselves the neutron activation method can naturally only be used with more difficulty. Equally, some elements are difficult to determine in this way because of the short half-lives of the radioactive products. This difficulty can, however, be overcome if the bombardment is carried out close to the analytical laboratory itself. For this purpose, a pneumatic tube has been used to transfer the target from the source to the counting apparatus, and to synchronize these two operations [96]. This technique has been used to measure hafnium, using the isotope Hf^{165} ($t_{1/2}$, 19 sec) and fluorine by F^{20} ($t_{1/2}$, 12 sec).

In some cases successful activation methods have been based on charged particle or very high-energy photon irradiation. Thus boron, fluorine, and aluminum can be determined by the reactions $B^{10}(\alpha, n)N^{13}$,

F^{19} (α, n) Na^{22}, and Al^{27} (α, n) P^{30} [97]. Oxygen can be measured, using either deuterons, O^{17} (d, n) F^{18} [98], or x-rays from a betatron, O^{16} (γ, n) O^{15} [99]. Although the half-life of O^{15} is some 60 times less than that of F^{18} (118 sec and 112 min), the second method is to be preferred because of the low isotopic abundance of O^{17}, plus the low penetrating power of deuterons compared with the photons from a betatron. The threshold of the nuclear reaction which gives rise to O^{15} is 15.5 Mev. Activation in a betatron can also be applied to the determination of nitrogen (giving N^{13}, with a threshold at 10.5 Mev) and of carbon (C^{11}, threshold 18.77 Mev). These two elements can also be activated with accelerated ions. Nitrogen has been determined either via C^{11} produced by accelerated protons [100], or by O^{15} formed in the process N^{14} (d, n) O^{15} [101]. The limit of sensitivity of this latter method is estimated at 1 μgm. Carbon in iron can be determined either by the (p, n) reaction [102, 103] or by (d, n) [102, 103, 104] to give N^{13}. If conditions are such that the iron itself is little activated, 0.05% C can be measured. Also, autoradiography can be used to examine the spatial distribution of the carbon in the sample. If the radionitrogen is subsequently reduced to NH_3, which can be chemically separated, the sensitivity of measurement is increased to 10^{-4}% [105].

Traces of phosphorus in paper have been detected by bombarding with deuterons and measuring the P^{32} formed in the P^{31} (d, p) P^{32} reaction [106]. Traces of copper in silver have been measured by activation with α-particles Cu^{63} (α, n) Ga^{66}, followed by chemical separation of the radiogallium [107].

22–6 Measurements involving absorption and scattering of particles. The considerable numerical differences in total thermal-neutron cross sections (σ_t) (for capture and scattering) can be utilized in nondestructive quantitative determinations of an element with a high σ_t, mixed or combined with other elements which do not absorb neutrons. A comparison of the values of σ_t with the capture cross sections σ_c in Table 5–2 show that some elements have large total thermal-neutron cross sections, even if their capture cross sections are very small. In particular, this is the case for H, Li, B, C, Cd, Gd, and some others, so that these elements can be rapidly measured by a simple determination of the neutron absorption by the sample. In practice, the intensity I_0 of a flux of thermal neutrons is first measured with no absorber present, using either a BF_3 counter or measuring the activity induced in an "indicator" element such as In, Ag, or Dy. The intensity I of the same flux after passage through the sample is then determined; the ratio $I/I_0 = t_n$, the *transmission*, is related to the density μ (in gm/cm^2) of the absorbing element by the relation [108]

$$\mu = \frac{(-\ln t_n)M}{N\sigma_t}, \tag{22–7}$$

where M is the atomic weight and N Avogadro's number.

This method has been applied to the measurement of hydrogen in fluorcarbon oils [109]; of boron and silicates; cadmium in zinc [110]; and a number of rare earths in minerals [111], etc. It has also been suggested

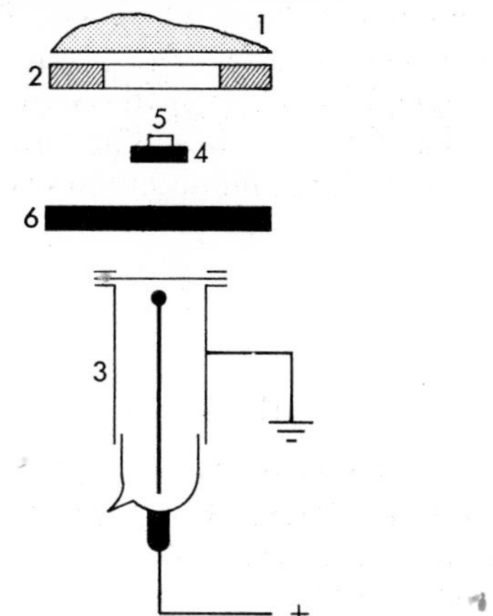

Fig. 22–3. Apparatus for analysis by back-scattering of β-particles (Ref. 114).

[108] as a method of measuring the thickness of electrolytic deposits of Au, Ag, Rh, Cd, Mn, etc., on supports which are transparent to neutrons, and for the measurement of indium in tin, hafnium in zirconium, tantalum in niobium, and hydrogen dissolved in metals. The transmission method becomes specific for elements which have resonances for the capture or scattering of slow neutrons (see Table 5–1); in these circumstances, the absorption at the resonance energy is compared with that at other energies beyond this. This procedure is, however, fairly sensitive, and has so far found no practical application (see Refs. 112 and 108).

The fact that the absorption of β-particles depends on the Z/A ratio of the absorbant (Section 11–4) has been used in the determination of the H/C ratio in hydrocarbons [113]. The Z/A ratio for H is twice that for C, so that for equal weights, H will absorb β-particles twice as efficiently. Measurements of the absorption of β-particles (for example, from Sr^{90}) and of the density provide a rapid method of determining the hydrogen content of a pure hydrocarbon, with a precision of 0.02% (in the weight).

An analytical method which is important because of its simplicity and speed is based on the back-scattering of β-particles. The maximum energy and the intensity of the reflected electrons is known to increase with the atomic number of the reflector (Section 11–4). This has been utilized [114] to determine the niobium content of a Nb/Cr alloy, using the apparatus shown in Fig. 22–3. The alloy (1) is placed on perspex (2) opposite the window of a counter (3); the radioactive source (Tl^{204}) is in position (5), and a disc of lead (4) protects the counter from direct β-particles. An aluminum filter (6) absorbs the radiation reflected by the chromium, and allows the particles scattered by the niobium to pass through. It was shown that the measured counting rate varied linearly with the niobium content of the alloy. The method can be used for rapid determination of 3% or more of this element in the alloy, with a precision of ±2%. It has also been applied to the determination of tungsten in Fe/W alloys.

Finally, it can be noted that the elastic scattering of monokinetic protons by thin layers can be used for the detection of light elements. For a given scattering angle, the energy of the scattered particles depends only on the mass of the scattering species. This procedure has been applied in research on traces of beryllium and aluminum [115].

References

1. C. Chamié and M. Guillot, *Compt. rend.*, **190**, 1187 (1930).
2. M. Guillot, *J. Chim. Phys.*, **28**, 14, 92 (1931).
3. H. R. Haymond, J. Z. Bowers, W. M. Garrison, and J. G. Hamilton, *J. Chem. Phys.*, **18**, 1119 (1950).
4. H. R. Haymond, R. D. Maxwell, W. M. Garrison, and J. G. Hamilton, *J. Chem. Phys.*, **18**, 756 (1950).
5. J. D. Gile, W. M. Garrison, and J. G. Hamilton, *J. Chem. Phys.*, **18**, 1685 (1950); **19**, 256 (1951).
6. G. H. Morrison and H. Freiser, *Solvent Extraction in Analytical Chemistry*, Wiley and Sons, New York, 1957.
7. M. Haïssinsky, *Compt. rend.*, **196**, 1788 (1933).
8. W. E. Cohn and H. W. Kohn, *J. Am. Chem. Soc.*, **70**, 1986 (1948).
9. G. Kayas, *J. Chim. Phys.*, **47**, 408 (1950).
10. G. Kayas, *Compt. rend.*, **228**, 1002 (1949).
11. A. F. Reid, *Ind. Eng. Chem.*, **40**, 76 (1948).
12. E. R. Tompkins, *J. Am. Chem. Soc.*, **70**, 3520 (1948).
13. J. Yang and M. Haïssinsky, *Bull. soc. chim. France*, **1949**, 549.
14. J. Yang, *J. Chim. Phys.*, **47**, 805 (1950).
15. F. Barendregt and S. Tom, *Physica*, **17**, 817 (1951).
16. K. A. Kraus and G. E. Moore, *J. Am. Chem. Soc.*, **71**, 3855 (1949).
17. D. L. Douglas, A. C. Mewherter, and R. P. Schuman, *Phys. Rev.*, **92**, 369 (1953).
18. K. A. Kraus and G. E. Moore, *J. Am. Chem. Soc.*, **73**, 2900 (1951).
19. J. Yang, *Compt. rend.*, **231**, 1059 (1950).
20. K. Street and G. T. Seaborg, *J. Am. Chem. Soc.* **70**, 4268 (1948).
21. R. S. Hansen and K. Gunnar *J. Am. Chem. Soc.*, **71**, 4958 (1949).
22. E. H. Huffman and R. C. Lilly, *J. Am. Chem. Soc.*, **71**, 4147 (1949).
23. R. W. Atteberry and G. E. Boyd, *J. Am. Chem. Soc.*, **72**, 4805 (1950).
24. M. Lederer, *Anal. Chim. Acta*, **8**, 134 (1953); **11**, 528 (1954).
25. M. Lederer, *Nature*, **176**, 462 (1955).
26. W. M. Garrison, H. R. Haymond, and R. D. Maxwell, *J. Chem. Phys.*, **17**, 665 (1949).
27. T. R. Sato, H. Diamond, W. P. Norris, and H. H. Strain, *J. Am. Chem. Soc.*, **74**, 6154 (1952).
28. T. R. Sato, W. P. Norris, and H. H. Strain, *Anal. Chem.*, **26**, 267 (1954).
29. M. Lederer, *Paper Electrophoresis*, Elsevier, Amsterdam, 1957.
30. M. Chemla and J. Pauly, *Bull. soc. chim. France*, **1953**, 432.
31. L. Meitner, *Physik. Z.*, **12**, 1094 (1911).

32. O. Baeyer, O. Hahn, and L. Meitner, *Physik. Z.*, **15,** 659 (1914); **16,** 6 (1915).
33. S. Cotelle and M. Haïssinsky, *Compt. rend.*, **206,** 1644 (1938).
34. M. Haïssinsky, *J. Chim. Phys.*, **34,** 321 (1937).
35. E. Rona and E. Schmidt, *Akad. Wiss. Wien, Abt. IIa,* **137,** 103 (1928).
36. E. Rona and E. Schmidt, *Z. Physik,* **48,** 784 (1938).
37. I. Curie and F. Joliot, *J. Chim. Phys.*, **28,** 201 (1931).
38. J. D. Gile, W. M. Garrison, and J. G. Hamilton, *J. Chem. Phys.*, **19,** 1426 (1951).
39. K. F. Chackett and F. Morgan, quoted by F. A. Paneth, *Quart. Revs.*, **2,** 93 (1948).
40. H. R. Haymond, K. H. Larson, R. D. Maxwell, W. M. Garrison, and J. G. Hamilton, *J. Chem. Phys.*, **18,** 391 (1950).
41. G. Wilkinson and W. E. Grummitt, *Nucleonics,* **9,** No. 3, 52 (1951).
42. D. Lee and G. B. Cook, *U.K.A.E.A. report AERE C/R 430,* 1949.
43. E. Broda and T. Schönfeld, *Radiochemische Methoden der Mikrochemie,* Springer, Vienna, 1955.
44. G. I. Cathers, *1955 Geneva Conference,* P. 743.
45. O. Erbacher and K. Philipp, *Angew. Chem.*, **48,** 409 (1935).
46. J. F. Flagg and E. O. Wiig, *Anal. Chem.*, **13,** 341 (1941).
47. F. Ferla, *Ann. Chimi. Applicata,* **28,** 331 (1938).
48. B. Cacciapuoti and F. Ferla, *Ann. Chimi. Applicata,* **29,** 166 (1939).
49. V. P. Shvedov, *J. Gen. Chem. Russ.*, **17,** 33 (1947).
50. V. P. Shvedov, *Zhur. Anal. Khim.*, **3,** 147 (1948).
51. J. E. Vance and R. E. Borup, *Anal. Chem.*, **25,** 610 (1953).
52. L. K. Bradacs, I. M. Ladenbauer, and F. Hecht, *Mikrochem. Acta,* **1953,** 229.
53. V. P. Shvedov, *Zhur. Anal. Khim.*, **3,** 147 (1948).
54. N. A. Rudnev, *Zhur. Anal. Khim.*, **8,** 3 (1953).
55. J. F. Flagg, *J. Am. Chem. Soc.*, **63,** 3150 (1941).
56. V. B. Miller, M. B. Neiman, and L. A. Sazonov, *Zhur. Anal. Khim.*, **7,** 269 (1952).
57. P. Daudel, R. Muxart, and R. Melet, *Bull. soc. chim. France,* **1953,** C 104.
58. G. Hevesy and L. Hahn, *Danske Videnskab. Selskab, Biol. Medd.*, **16,** 1 (1941).
59. C. Haenny and P. Mivelaz, *Helv. Chim. Acta,* **31,** 633 (1948).
60. F. G. Houtermans, D. H. Vincent, and G. Wagner, *Z. Elektrochem.*, **56,** 944 (1952).
61. G. Hevesy and F. A. Paneth, *Z. anorg. Chem.*, **82,** 322 (1913).
62. G. G. Joris and H. S. Taylor, *J. Chem. Phys.*, **16,** 45 (1948).
63. D. Dryssen and B. Hök, *Svensk. Kem. Tidsk.*, **64,** 80 (1952).
64. R. Ehrenberg, *Biochem. Z.*, **164,** 183 (1925); **172,** 10 (1926); **183,** 63, 68 (1927); **197,** 467 (1928).
65. J. Govaerts and C. Barcia-Goyanes, *Anal. Chim. Acta,* **6,** 121 (1952).
66. P. Süe, *Bull. soc. chim. France,* **1946,** 102.
67. T. Moeller and G. K. Schweitzer, *Anal. Chem.*, **20,** 1201 (1948).
68. A. Langer, *J. Phys. Chem.*, **45,** 639 (1941).
69. A. Langer, *Anal. Chem.*, **22,** 1288 (1950).

70. S. Blackburn and A. Robson, *Biochem. J.*, **54,** 295 (1953).
71. H. P. Kaufmann and J. Budvig, quoted in Ref. 43.
72. H. S. Isbell, *Science,* **113,** 532 (1951).
73. H. Gest, M. D. Kamen, and J. M. Reiner, *Arch. Biochem. Biophys.*, **12,** 273 (1947).
74. G. Hevesy and R. Hobbie, *Z. anal. Chem.*, **88,** 1 (1932).
75. P. Süe, *Bull. soc. chim. France,* **1947,** 405.
76. F. C. Henriques and C. Margnetti, *Anal. Chem.*, **18,** 476 (1946).
77. W. S. McDonald and H. S. Turner, *Chem. Ind.*, **1952,** 1001.
78. J. T. Craig, P. F. Tyron, and W. G. Brown, *Anal. Chem.*, **25,** 1661 (1953).
79. J. T. Craig, J. B. Tindall, and M. Senkus, *Anal. Chem.*, **23,** 332 (1951).
80. D. Rittenberg and G. L. Foster, *J. Biol. Chem.*, **133,** 737 (1940).
81. R. Schoenheimer, S. Ratner, and D. Rittenberg, *J. Biol. Chem.*, **130,** 703 (1939).
82. S. Graff, D. Rittenberg, and G. L. Foster, *J. Biol. Chem.*, **133,** 745 (1940).
83. M. G. Inghram, *Ann. Rev. Nuclear Sci.*, **4,** 81 (1953).
84. A. S. Keston, S. Udenfriend, and R. K. Cannan, *J. Am. Chem. Soc.*, **68,** 1390 (1946); **71,** 249 (1949).
85. K. Bloch and H. S. Anker, *Science,* **107,** 228 (1948).
86. H. Clark and R. Overman, *U.S.A.E.C. report MDDC-1329* (1949).
87. B. H. Ketelle and G. E. Boyd, *J. Am. Chem. Soc.*, **69,** 2800 (1947).
88. P. Albert, M. Caron, and G. Chaudron, *Compt. rend.*, **233,** 1108 (1951); **236,** 1030 (1953); **238,** 687 (1954).
89. E. D. Goldberg and H. Brown, *Anal. Chem.*, **22,** 308 (1950).
90. G. E. Boyd, *U.S.A.E.C. report AECD-2507,* 1949.
91. G. W. Winchester, *Progress in Inorganic Chemistry,* **2,** 1 (1960).
92. E. Picciotto and M. van Styvendael, *Compt. rend.*, **232,** 855 (1951).
93. H. Faraggi, A. Kohn, and J. Doumerc, *Compt. rend.*, **235,** 714 (1952).
94. J. V. Iakovlev, *1955 Geneva Conference,* P. 632.
95. A. A. Smales, *1955 Geneva Conference,* P. 770.
96. P. Lévêque and H. Goenvec, *Bull. soc. chim. France,* **1955,** 1213.
97. E. Oberlad, *Acta Radiol.*, **2,** 391 (1954).
98. P. Süe, *Compt. rend.*, **237,** 1696 (1953).
99. R. Basile, J. Huré, P. Lévèque, and C. Schuhl, *Compt. rend.*, **239,** 422 (1954).
100. D. O. Caldwell, *Rev. Sci. Instr.*, **23,** 501 (1952).
101. P. Süe, *Compt. rend.*, **240,** 88 (1955).
102. M. Ardenne and F. Bernhard, *Z. Physik,* **122,** 740 (1944).
103. G. E. Boyd, *Anal. Chem.*, **21,** 335 (1949).
104. I. Curie, *J. Phys. Radium,* **13,** 497 (1952).
105. P. Albert, G. Chaudron, and P. Süe, *Bull. soc. chim. France,* **1953,** C 97.
106. G. T. Seaborg and J. J. Livingood, *J. Am. Chem. Soc.*, **60,** 1784 (1938).
107. L. D. P. King and W. J. Henderson, *Phys. Rev.*, **56,** 1169 (1939).
108. T. I. Taylor, R. H. Anderson, and W. W. Havens, *Science,* **114,** 341 (1951).
109. L. Burger and L. Rainwater, *U.S.A.E.C. report AECD-2138,* 1948.
110. J. Martelly and P. Sue, *Bull. soc. chim. France,* **1946,** 103.

111. I. H. Ford and E. Picciotto, *Nuovo cimento,* **9,** 141 (1952).
112. T. I. Taylor and W. W. Havens, *Nucleonics,* **5,** No. 6, 4 (1949); **6,** No. 2, 66 (1950); **6,** No. 4, 54 (1950).
113. R. B. Jacobs and L. G. Lewis, *Oil Gas J.,* **52,** 128 (1953).
114. N. Bogdanov and V. Funke, quoted in Ref. 94.
115. S. Rubin and V. K. Rasmussen, *Phys. Rev.,* **78,** 83 (1950).

CHAPTER 23

TRACERS IN THE STUDY OF THE MECHANISM OF CHEMICAL REACTIONS

23–1 Applications in inorganic chemistry. The success of both radioactive and stable isotopic tracers in chemical kinetics is due to the fact that most of the other techniques used to establish reaction mechanisms are very indirect, and give (more or less) hypothetical information on the nature and sequential relationship of the unstable intermediate compounds. In only a few cases can spectroscopy or some other modern physicochemical method be used to identify the intermediate species unambiguously. The problems involved are virtually insoluble, especially with organic molecules containing a large number of identical atoms. Degradation of such compounds is often used in structural investigations, but this gives no information on the transition states involved in formation or decomposition reactions. By labeling compounds with D, T, C^{14}, N^{15}, P^{32}, etc., in well-defined positions, however, it is possible to distinguish radicals or identical groups of different origin, and in many cases, to choose between the various possible reaction mechanisms.

Before examining the applications of the method in organic chemistry, we will note some typical results obtained with inorganic compounds. For example, a long-standing controversy centered around the origin of the oxygen given off from aqueous solutions in reactions between H_2O_2 and strong oxidizing agents such as

$$PbO_2,\ MnO_4^-,\ Cr_2O_7^{2-},\ Ce(IV),\ HOCl,\ Cl_2,\ etc.$$

Some authors suggested that each reagent (or H_2O_2, and the solvent) provides an atom to the O_2 molecule

$$PbO\boxed{O + O}OH_2 \rightarrow PbO + H_2O + O_2, \qquad (23\text{–}1)$$

while others believed that both atoms came from hydrogen peroxide alone. The use of O^{18}-labeled hydrogen peroxide and mass-spectrometric isotopic analysis of the oxygen produced in the above reaction showed quite definitely [1–5] that all the gas comes from H_2O_2, and not from the anions or from the solvent. The same is true for the catalytic decomposition of hydrogen peroxide by the noble metals Pt, Pd, Au, Ag, by MnO_2, Br_2, I_2, Fe(III), and by catalase.

These measurements also revealed a relatively large isotope kinetic effect, of the order of 6 to 7%, in the oxidation of Fe^{2+}, Cr^{2+}, Sn^{2+}, and Cu^+ ions by hydrogen peroxide, whereas only a very small isotope effect is found in the oxidation of Ti^{3+}, in reactions with oxidizing agents, and in the decomposition by catalase. The absence of an isotope effect should correspond to a mechanism involving dissociation ($H \cdot O_2 \cdot H$) rather than the rupture of the O—O bond in hydrogen peroxide. For example, in the case of catalase, the mechanism proposed by Chance [6] does not involve —O—O bond rupture

$$>\text{FeOH} + \text{HOOH} \rightarrow >\text{FeOOH} + H_2O, \tag{23-2}$$

$$>\text{FeOOH} + \text{HOOH} \rightarrow >\text{FeOH} + H_2O + O_2. \tag{23-3}$$

The bond rupture occurs in the FeOOH group in which the two oxygen atoms are weakly bonded, since its oxygen appears in H_2O, or can exchange with H_2O; this process should cause no isotopic fractionation. Such a mechanism predicts no exchange of oxygen between H_2O_2 and H_2O, as has been confirmed experimentally.

The formation of Caro's acid, H_2SO_5, from $H_2O_2 + H_2SO_4$, and its subsequent hydrolysis, shows no isotope effect because neither process involves rupture of the —O—O bond [5]

$$\text{HOOH} + (\text{HO})_2\text{SO}_2 \rightleftharpoons (\text{HOO})(\text{HO})\text{SO}_2 + H_2O. \tag{23-4}$$

Measurements by Cahill and Taube [4] show that the fractionation factor in the catalytic decomposition of hydrogen peroxide by Fe(III) is the same as that in the oxidation of Fe(II) by hydrogen peroxide. This result, and other kinetic features of these reactions, lead these authors to suggest that chain propagation in the catalytic decomposition is by Fe^{2+} ions (with the intermediate formation of Fe(IV):

Chain initiation

$$Fe^{3+} + H_2O_2 \rightleftharpoons FeOOH^{2+} + H^+, \tag{23-5}$$

$$FeOOH^{2+} \rightarrow Fe^{2+} + HO_2, \tag{23-6}$$

$$Fe^{3+} + HO_2 \rightarrow Fe^{2+} + O_2 + H^+, \tag{23-7}$$

Propagation

$$Fe^{2+} + H_2O_2 \rightarrow Fe^{4+} + 2OH^-, \tag{23-8}$$

$$Fe^{4+} + H_2O_2 \rightleftharpoons FeOOH^{3+} + H^+, \tag{23-9}$$

$$FeOOH^{3+} \rightarrow Fe^{3+} + HO_2, \tag{23-10}$$

$$Fe^{3+} + HO_2 \rightarrow Fe^{2+} + H^+ + O_2, \tag{23-11}$$

Termination

$$Fe^{2+} + H_2O_2 \rightarrow Fe^{3+} + OH^- + OH, \tag{23-12}$$

$$Fe^{2+} + OH \rightarrow Fe^{3+} + OH^-. \tag{23-13}$$

This reaction scheme differs from that proposed by Haber and Weiss [7] for Fenton's reaction, for which it was suggested that propagation is by the HO_2 radical

$$Fe^{2+} + H_2O_2 \rightarrow Fe^{3+} + OH + OH^-, \qquad (23\text{–}12)$$
$$H_2O_2 + OH \rightarrow H_2O + HO_2, \qquad (23\text{–}14)$$
$$H_2O_2 + HO_2 \rightarrow O_2 + H_2O + OH, \qquad (23\text{–}15)$$
$$OH + Fe^{2+} \rightarrow Fe^{3+} + OH^-, \qquad (23\text{–}13)$$
$$HO_2 + Fe^{3+} \rightarrow Fe^{2+} + O_2 + H^+. \qquad (23\text{–}11)$$

The thermal decomposition of ammonium nitrate,

$$NH_4NO_3 \rightarrow N_2O + 2H_2O, \qquad (23\text{–}16)$$

has been studied [8, 9] by labeling the NH_3 nitrogen with N^{15}, and then analyzing the N_2O by mass spectrometry or infrared spectroscopy. All the heavy nitrogen is recovered as $N^{15}N^{14}O$, from which it follows that during the reaction the nitrogen of the NO_3^- ion remains bonded to one of the oxygens in the intermediate states, retaining a symmetrical position relative to the ammonia nitrogen. If this were not the case, $N^{14}N^{15}O$ and $N^{15}N^{15}O$ would be formed in equal quantities. Friedman and Bigeleisen [10] have re-examined this reaction by measuring the kinetic isotope effects with nitrate labeled with O^{18}. The conclusion drawn from these results is that the mechanism cannot be an oxidation-reduction process such as

$$NH_4^+ + NO_3^- \rightarrow NH_3OH^+ + NO_2^- \xrightarrow[-H_2O]{-2H^+} \begin{cases} 2NO^- + H_2O \rightarrow N_2O + 2OH^- \\ H_2N_2O_2 \rightarrow N_2 + H_2O, \end{cases} \qquad (23\text{–}17)$$

but is probably a series of successive dehydration reactions

$$NH_4NO_3 \xrightarrow{-H_2O} NH_2NO_2 \rightarrow HN = N\begin{matrix} \diagup\!\!\!\diagup O \\ \diagdown OH \end{matrix} \rightarrow N_2O + H_2O. \qquad (23\text{–}18)$$

Various interactions involving the different valency states of chlorine (oxidation, dismutation) have been studied by Taube and Dodgen with the aid of Cl^{38} [11].

By labeling the trithionate ion with S^{35} in two different positions

$$\begin{matrix} & SO_3^- \\ \diagup & \\ S^{35} & \\ \diagdown & \\ & SO_3^- \end{matrix} \quad \text{and} \quad \begin{matrix} & S^{35}O_3^- \\ \diagup & \\ S & \\ \diagdown & \\ & S^{35}O_3^- \end{matrix}$$

Fava and Divo [12] have shown that the decomposition of this ion at pH 8 occurs by way of a hydrolytic mechanism involving symmetrical rupture

$$\begin{array}{c} SO_3^- \\ | \\ S \\ ---|--- \\ SO_3^- \end{array} + \begin{array}{c} H^+ \\ -|-- \\ OH^- \end{array} \rightarrow \begin{array}{c} HS_2O_3 \\ + \\ HSO_4^- \end{array} \rightarrow S_2O_3^{2-} + SO_4^{2-} + 2H^+, \tag{23–19}$$

although in alkaline solution the distribution of the tracer does not agree with the mechanisms generally assumed. The labeling was carried out by reacting tagged thiosulfates $S^{35}SO_3^{2-}$ and $SS^{35}O_3^{2-}$ with iodine to give tetrathionates, which were then reacted with unlabeled sulfite. These authors also studied the decomposition of labeled tetrathionates. Brodsky and Eremenko [13] have used S^{35} to study the mechanism of various polythionate reactions, including the formation of tetrathionates and pentathionates from $S_2O_3^{2-}$, with As_2O_3 as the catalyst. It was shown that all the reactions studied occur by displacement of SO_3^{2-} or $S_2O_3^{2-}$ groups, a mechanism previously suggested by Fava [14] for isotope exchange reactions between polythionates.

Radiosulfur has also been used by various workers to investigate the removal of sulfur from cast iron by oxides (CaO, Al_2O_3, SiO_2), a problem of considerable metallurgical importance. According to Travin and Shvartsman [15], at relatively low temperatures the rate of the process obeys a first-order kinetic equation relative to the concentration of sulfur in the liquid metal. The order of the reaction increases with temperature, approaching a value of 2 in the neighborhood of 1700°C. These observations are interpreted as meaning that the rate is determined by the diffusion of sulfur ions in the slag, and that the change of order is due to turbulence and agitation produced by bubbles of carbon monoxide released in the reaction

$$FeS + CaO + C \rightarrow Fe + CaS + CO. \tag{23–20}$$

23–2 Acid-base catalysis. A large number of protolytic reactions, involving the intermolecular transfer of a hydrogen or deuterium ion, are catalyzed by acids and bases, where we use these words in their most general sense of species (either ions or molecules) which can release or accept a proton. Other reactions are catalyzed only by classical acids and bases, that is to say, by the ions H^+ or OH^- (specific catalysis). It is often (but not always) found that there is a relation between the type of catalysis and the isotope effects observed in H_2O (with the ions H^+ or OH^-) and in D_2O (with D^+ or OD^-). The isotope effects are normal (i.e., $k_{H_2O}/k_{D_2O} > 1$) for catalytic reactions of the first type, but the rate of reaction is generally greater in heavy water ($k_{D_2O}/k_{H_2O} > 1$) for specific catalysis (Section 9–5). Some examples of these isotope effects are given in Table 23–1, taken from Brodsky [16] and Wiberg [17], where the appropriate references will be found.

TABLE 23–1

ISOTOPE EFFECTS IN ACID-BASE CATALYSIS

Reaction	T, °C	Catalyst	k_{H_2O}/k_{D_2O}
(a) Acid catalysis			
Mutarotation of glucose	25	H_3O^+	1.2
Mutarotation of glucose	25	CH_3COOH	2.5
Bromination of acetone	25	H_3O^+	0.5
Bromination of acetone	25	CH_3COOH	1.4
Inversion of saccharose	25	H_3O^+	0.5
Hydrolysis of ethyl formate	18	H_3O^+	0.5
Hydrolysis of methyl acetate	15	H_3O^+	0.6
Hydrolysis of ethyl acetate	15	H_3O^+	0.5
Hydrolysis of acetamide	25	$H_3O^+(0.1\ N)$	0.48
Hydrolysis of acetamide	25	$H_3O^+(4\ N)$	1.2
Decomposition of dithionic acid	60	$H_3O^+(4\ N)$	0.4
Decomposition of oxalic acid	136	$H_3O^+(4\ N)$	0.8
Oxidation of halides by halates		$H_3O^+(4\ N)$	0.1–0.4
(b) Base catalysis			
Mutarotation of glucose	25	H_2O	3.8
Mutarotation of glucose	25	CH_3COO^-	2.4
Bromination of acetone	25	H_2O	1.9
Bromination of acetone	25	CH_3COO^-	1.1
Bromination of nitromethane	25	CH_3COO^-	1.15
Hydrolysis of ethyl acetate	15	OH^-	0.75
Hydrolysis of acetamide	25	OH^-	1.1
Hydrolysis of acetonitrile	35	OH^-	0.8
Decomposition of nitramide	35	H_2O	5.3
Neutralization of nitroethane	5	OH^-	0.7

The inverse isotope effect in specific catalysis is explained [18] by the two-stage mechanism of the reaction

$$RH + HA \underset{k_2}{\overset{k_1}{\rightleftharpoons}} RH_2^+ + A^-, \tag{23–21}$$

$$RH_2^+ \xrightarrow{k_3} \text{products}. \tag{23–22}$$

For this type of reaction, k_3 is often smaller than k_2 and so governs the overall rate, which is given by

$$v = k_3[RH_2^+] = k_3 \frac{K}{K_{HA}} [H_3O^+][RH], \tag{23–23}$$

where

$$K = \frac{[RH_2^+][A^-]}{[RH][HA]} \quad \text{and} \quad K_{HA} = \frac{[A^-][H_3O^+]}{[HA]}.$$

It will be seen that the rate is proportional to the hydrogen ion concentration. When D_2O is substituted for H_2O, k_3 decreases, but the ratio K/K_{DA} generally increases to a much greater extent, since D_2O is a weaker base than H_2O (see Table 9–3). It follows that in such cases, $k_{H_2O}/k_{D_2O} < 1$. This is not a general rule, however, and exceptions to it are known; the existence of such cases can be predicted from the mechanism described, but it is necessary to analyze each case separately [17].

As would be expected, the rate of protolytic reactions depends upon the solvent. Indene, acetophenone, fluorene, nitrobenzene, and other organic compounds which do not exchange, or which exchange very slowly, with D_2O, exchange hydrogen fairly quickly with heavy liquid ammonia (ND_3), which is more basic than D_2O [19, 20]. The rate of exchange increases considerably in the presence of KND_2, which is a very strong base in this solvent, dissociating into K^+ and ND_2^-; this anion has a strong deuteron affinity.

23–3 Hydrolysis and esterification. Measurements of the isotope effect in the hydrolysis of tri-organosilanes have helped in establishing the mechanism of this reaction [21]. In alkaline solution (water/piperidine or water/ethanol) the rate constant for the reaction in a solvent SH

$$R_3SiH + OH^- + SH_1 \rightarrow R_3SiOH + H_2 + S^-, \qquad (23\text{–}24)$$

decreases by a factor of 1.28 to 1.49 when T is substituted for H in the silane. When H is replaced by T in the solvent, k_H/k_T is 3.0 with piperidine and 7.0 with ethanol. These results show that the rate-determining process involves the rupture of the Si—H bond in silane and of the C—H bond in the solvent. Consideration of the zero-point energies suggests that the two atoms H (or T) are strongly bonded in the activated complex.

In the saponification of esters, as well as in the reverse process of esterification, two distinct mechanisms appear possible:

$$RCOO|R' + HO|H \rightleftharpoons RCOO|H + HO|R', \qquad (23\text{–}25)$$

or

$$RCO|OR' + H|OH \rightleftharpoons RCO|OH + H|OR'. \qquad (23\text{–}26)$$

This problem was investigated by hydrolyzing amyl acetate [22] and methy succinate [23] in O^{18}-labeled water. The heavy oxygen was found in the acid, so that reaction (23–26) is the correct one. Similarly, in the esterification of benzoic acid with heavy methanol ($CH_3O^{18}H$) the O^{18} was found in the ester and not in the water, which also favors this reaction mechanism [24]. The mechanism of the alkaline hydrolysis of methyl phosphate in D_2O is also similar to Eq. (23–26), but in acid media the heavy oxygen is distributed between the acid and the alcohol so that both mechanisms are possible [25].

Two mechanisms can also be postulated for the reaction between an acid anhydride and an alcohol

$$\mathrm{RCOO\boxed{COR + HO}R' \rightleftharpoons RCO\boxed{OH + R'}OOCR}, \qquad (23\text{–}27)$$

$$\mathrm{RCO\boxed{OCOR + H}OR' \rightleftharpoons RCOO\boxed{H + R'O}OCR}. \qquad (23\text{–}28)$$

Experiments with acetic anhydride and heavy ethanol favor the latter mechanism [26]. Similarly, the two possible reaction schemes for the hydrolysis of chloral are

$$\mathrm{O{=}\underset{}{\overset{H}{\overset{|}{C}}}{-}\boxed{CCl_3 + H}OH \rightleftharpoons HCCl_3 + HCOOH}, \qquad (23\text{–}29)$$

$$\mathrm{O{=}\underset{\boxed{H}}{C}{-}\boxed{CCl_3} + HOH \rightleftharpoons HCCl_3 + HCOOH}. \qquad (23\text{–}30)$$

The second of these equilibria predicts that if water enriched with D_2O is used, deuterated formic acid should be produced, but experiment shows that this is not the case, so that reaction (23–29) is the correct one [28] (see also Ref. 29).

In the hydrolysis of ethyl benzoate, isopropyl benzoate, or *t*-butyl benzoate, O^{18} from the carbonyl group exchanges with oxygen in the solvent. Bender [28] has concluded that this implies the reversible formation of a symmetrical intermediate, probably the un-ionized hydrate

$$\mathrm{H{-}O^{18}{-}\underset{OR}{\underset{|}{\overset{R}{\overset{|}{C}}}}{-}OH}.$$

23–4 Organic oxidation reactions. The oxidation of fatty acids in solution often results in the formation of an acid with a smaller number of carbon atoms, plus CO_2. For example, if propionic acid is oxidized by $KMnO_4$ in alkaline solution, oxalate and carbonate are produced

$$\mathrm{CH_3{\cdot}CH_2{\cdot}COO^- + 4MnO_4^-} \\ \rightarrow \mathrm{(COO)_2^{2-} + CO_3^{2-} + OH^- + 2H_2O + 4MnO_2}. \qquad (23\text{–}31)$$

The problem is to find out whether the carbonate anion comes from the carboxylic acid group of the initial acid, or whether it is the result of the oxidation of a carbon atom of the fatty acid chain. Labeling the carboxylic group with C^{11} or C^{14} gave the answer to this problem [30, 31, 32]; at the end of the reaction, 30% of the tracer was found in the carbonate, and 70%

in the oxalate. The probabilities of rupture of CH_2—COO and of CH_3—CH_2 in

$$\begin{array}{c} CH_3 \\ | \\ CH_2 \\ | \\ C^*OO^- \end{array} \rightarrow \begin{array}{c} COOH \\ | \\ COOH \\ \\ C^*O_2 \end{array} \quad \text{or} \quad \begin{array}{c} CH_3 \\ | \\ CH_2 \\ | \\ C^*OO^- \end{array} \rightarrow \begin{array}{c} CO_2 \\ \\ COOH \\ | \\ C^*OOH \end{array} \qquad (23\text{–}32)$$

are therefore in the ratio 3 : 7. This ratio decreases with increasing alkalinity, falling to 1 : 6.6 in 1 M caustic soda solution. Lactic acid and β-hydroxypropionic acid show qualitatively the same behavior.

When propionic acid is oxidized with dichromate in acid solution, however, inactive acetic acid is obtained, and all the activity is found in the carbon dioxide, so that in this case the rupture is exclusively of the C—C bond between CH_2 and COO^-. In the oxidation of fumaric acid by acid permanganate, all the C^{11} tracer was found as CO_2, while the formic acid produced simultaneously was inactive [33]. Similar results have been reported for the oxidation of malic, oxaloacetic, and α-ketoglutaric acids, so that in all these cases the carbon dioxide comes from the carboxylic group.

The oxidation of formaldehyde by hydrogen peroxide in alkaline media can be written stoichiometrically as

$$2HCHO + H_2O_2 \rightarrow 2HCOOH + H_2. \qquad (23\text{–}33)$$

The hydrogen produced may come from the organic compound, from the hydrogen peroxide, or from the solvent. Using water containing 50% D_2O, it was shown [34] that the gas given off contained no deuterium, even though D_2O exchanges with H_2O_2, so that the hydrogen comes from the formaldehyde, which probably forms a short-lived peroxy complex

$$\begin{array}{c} HO\cdot CH\cdot OO\cdot CH\cdot OH. \\ \quad\;\; | \qquad\quad\;\; | \\ \quad\;\; H \qquad\quad\;\; H \end{array}$$

The formation and decomposition of such peroxides in the reaction of secondary and tertiary alcohols with hydrogen peroxide has been studied with the aid of heavy oxygen. As in the case of inorganic reactions with hydrogen peroxide (Section 23–1), all the oxygen in the peroxy group comes from H_2O_2, and the oxygen of the H_2O formed in the decomposition comes from the alcohol [35]

$$RO^{18}H + HOOH \rightleftharpoons ROOH + H_2O^{18}. \qquad (23\text{–}34)$$

In the oxidation of ethanol to acetaldehyde by bromine, the rate of rupture of the C—H bond is seven times larger than that of the C—T bond [36]. It had been previously suggested that the slowest step in the reaction was the formation of ethyl hypobromite, but since this does not involve bond rupture, there would be no isotope effect; it is now believed that

TABLE 23–2

PROBABILITY (%) OF THE FORMATION OF HCHO FROM DIFFERENT CARBON ATOMS OF HYDROCARBON MOLECULES

Hydrocarbon	Position of C atom in chain				
	1	2	3	4	5
Propane	39	22	39	—	—
n-butane	22	28	28	22	—
n-pentane	17	26.5	13	26.5	17

direct proton transfer occurs

$$
\begin{array}{lllll}
CH_3CH_2OH + Br_2 \rightarrow & [CH_3CHOH]^+ & + & [HBr_2]^- & \\
& \downarrow & & \downarrow & \quad (23\text{–}35)\\
& CH_3CHO + H^+ & & H^+ + 2Br^-. &
\end{array}
$$

The well-known theory of destructive oxidation [37] assumes that the oxidation of a hydrocarbon molecule begins at the end of the hydrocarbon chain, with the formation of an aldehyde. This then reacts with oxygen, giving CO and H_2O, so that a series of aldehydes with gradually reducing hydrocarbon chain length is obtained. The reaction schemes deduced from this theory assume that formaldehyde can only form at the end of the molecule undergoing oxidation, and that acetaldehyde can only come from the two carbon atoms at the end of the chain. In order to investigate this theory, Neiman and his collaborators [38] synthesized a series of isotopic isomers of propane, butane, and pentane containing C^{14} in different positions in the molecule. After oxidation, HCHO and CH_3CHO were separated from the reaction products, and the specific activity of these compounds determined. In this way, the probability of the formation of HCHO and CH_3CHO from the different atoms of the hydrocarbons in question could be established. Some of the results are shown in Table 23–2. It will be seen that formaldehyde can be formed from all the carbon atoms of the hydrocarbon molecules; a similar result was obtained for acetaldehyde. The theory of destructive oxidation is not therefore borne out by the experimental facts, and must be replaced by a theory involving the oxidation of hydrocarbons via free radical chains.

23–5 The isotope kinetic method.* The identification of the precursors of stable intermediate products in complex reactions, and the measurement of their rates of formation and disappearance are difficult problems, and the general solution has only recently become possible by means of the isotope kinetic method [39, 40]. If a number of intermediate products are

* This section was specially written for the Russian translation of this book by the author of the method, Prof. M. B. Neiman.

formed by some process such as

$$\left.\begin{array}{r}\cdots \xrightarrow{w} \mathrm{A} \\ \cdots \rightarrow \mathrm{C}\end{array}\right\} \underset{w_2}{\overset{w_1}{\rightarrow}} \mathrm{B} \overset{w_3}{\rightarrow} \mathrm{D} \rightarrow \cdots, \tag{23–36}$$

one will have

$$\frac{d[\mathrm{B}]}{dt} = w_1 + w_2 - w_3. \tag{23–37}$$

Suppose that a small quantity of a labeled intermediate product A is introduced into the reaction mixture, thereby changing the specific activity β of the substance B; it can be shown that

$$\frac{d\beta}{dt} = \frac{w_1\left[\alpha - \beta\left(\frac{w_1 + w_2}{w_1}\right)\right]}{[\mathrm{B}]}, \tag{23–38}$$

in which α is the specific activity of A. In the case in which $w_2 = 0$, this can be simplified to

$$\frac{d\beta}{dt} = \frac{(\alpha - \beta)w_1}{[\mathrm{B}]}. \tag{23–39}$$

If a small quantity of unlabeled substance B is added to the reaction mixtures at the same time as A, then at $t = 0$, $\beta = 0$, and $d\beta/dt > 0$. The specific activity of B goes through a maximum when $\beta = \alpha$, and when this condition is verified, it can be concluded that A is the only precursor of B.

Neiman, *et al.*, [41] introduced small quantities of $HC^{14}HO$ and CO into the mixture $CH_4 + O_2 + NO$; the experimental specific activities of HCHO and CO changed in the way shown in Fig. 23–1. The maximum

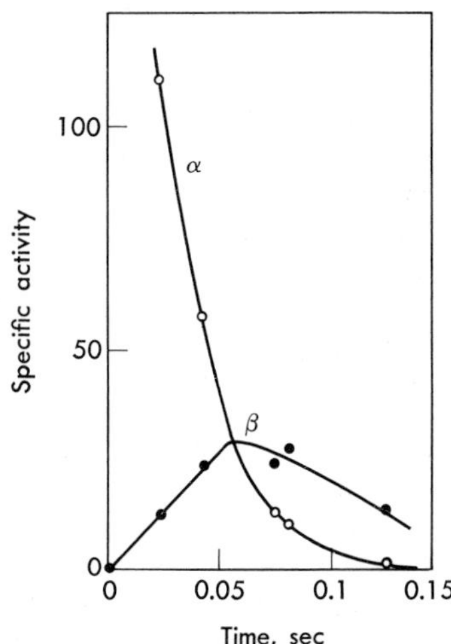

FIG. 23–1. Changes in the specific activities of formaldehyde (α) and CO (β) in the oxidation of methane: addition of $HC^{14}HO$ and CO (Ref. 41).

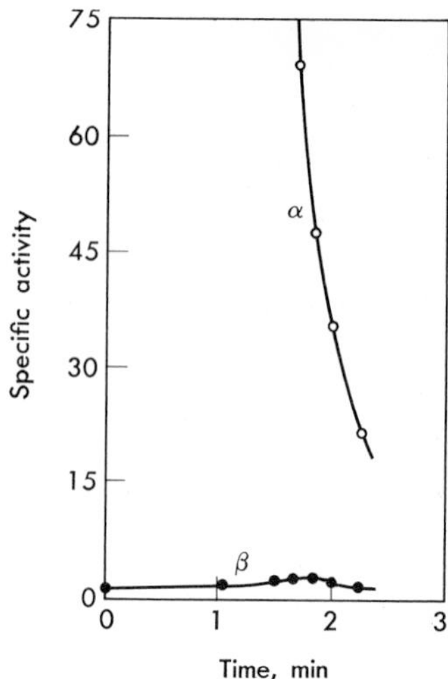

FIG. 23–2. Changes in the specific activities of CO (α) and CO_2 (β) in the oxidation of butane: addition of $C^{14}O$ and CO_2 (Ref. 41).

specific activity of CO is found at the point where the curve intercepts the corresponding curve for the specific activity of HCHO, so that CO is formed virtually completely from HCHO. The same technique was used to show that ethylene is the sole precursor of ethane in the cracking of propane to which C_2H_4 and C_2H_6 were added [42]. The results obtained by Lukovnikov and Neiman [43] on the oxidation of butane (with added $C^{14}O$ and CO_2) are shown in Fig. 23–2, which gives the specific activities of CO and CO_2. The curves obtained are in good agreement with Eq. (23–38). At the maximum value of β, one has

$$\frac{\alpha}{\beta} = \frac{w_1 + w_2}{w_1} \approx 40,$$

so that under the experimental conditions used, only 2.5% of the CO_2 is formed by the oxidation of CO.

The kinetic isotope method can be used to determine the rate of formation w of the intermediate product A (see above). For this purpose it is necessary to introduce small quantities of labeled A into the mixture; the specific activity α will then decrease according to the equation

$$-\frac{d\alpha}{dt} = \frac{\alpha w}{[\mathrm{A}]}, \qquad (23\text{–}40)$$

which can be used to calculate w. By determining $d\mathrm{A}/dt$, it is also possible to calculate w_1, the rate at which A is used up in further reaction. Neiman, *et al.*, have used this approach to measure the rate of formation and disappearance of acetaldehyde in the oxidation of both propylene and butane [44, 51].

If D is the final product, one has

$$w_3\beta\, dt = dI_{\mathrm{D}},$$

in which I_{D} is the total activity of the product D. Neiman and Serdyuk [45] were able to calculate the rates of formation of CO and CO_2 from the acetyl radical from this formula. They introduced $CH_3C^{14}HO$ into a mixture of propylene and oxygen at 300°C. The acetyl radical can react in the following ways:

$$CH_3C^{14}O \xrightarrow[k[O_2]]{k_1} \begin{cases} CH_3 + C^{14}O, \\ CH_3O + C^{14}O_2, \end{cases} \tag{23–41}$$

so that

$$k_1[CH_3C^{14}O]\alpha\, dt = dI_{\mathrm{CO}}, \tag{23–42}$$

$$k_2[CH_3C^{14}O][O_2]\alpha\, dt = dI_{\mathrm{CO_2}}, \tag{23–43}$$

from which it follows that

$$k_2 = k_1 \frac{dI_{\mathrm{CO_2}}}{dI_{\mathrm{CO}}} \cdot \frac{1}{[O_2]} \cdot \tag{23–44}$$

The constant for the monomolecular decomposition of the acetyl radical, $k_1 = 10^{13} \cdot e^{-2800/RT}$ [46], and the authors therefore calculate that at 300°C, $k_2 = 1.1 \times 10^{-12}$ cm^3/sec.

The isotope kinetic method has been applied in the study of the pyrolysis of propane and isobutylene [47, 48], the oxidation of methane, propylene, butane [49, 50, 51], and cyclohexane [52].

This method can also be used to determine the order of the reaction in which some intermediate species X is used up in a complex reaction [53]. By adding a small quantity of the labeled product X to the reaction mixture, and then determining the concentration of X and its total activity I at different times, the order of the reaction n can be determined from the equation

$$-\frac{d \log_e I}{dt} = k[A]^{n-1}. \tag{23–45}$$

If various labeled intermediates are added to the reaction mixture in several series of experiments (or better, the same product labeled in different positions), it is possible to establish the reaction route for the formation and decomposition of a series of intermediate products. Thus Neiman and his collaborators introduced $CH_3C^{14}HO$, $C^{14}H_3CHO$, $C^{14}H_3OH$, and $C^{14}H_3N{=}NC^{14}H_3$ into a mixture of propylene and oxygen at 315°C, and showed that about half of the methanol formed came from the methyl group of acetaldehyde, and the other half from methyl radicals. About 20% of the methanol formed was oxidized to HCHO, CO, and CO_2.

The isotope kinetic method has also been applied in research into the mechanism of catalytic processes. Balandin, *et al.*, [54] investigated the mechanism of the dehydrogenation of butane to divinyl. In a series of experiments, C^{14}-labeled C_4H_{10}, C_4H_8, and C_4H_6 were added to the reaction mixture, and it was found that the reaction scheme was

$$\begin{array}{ccc} C \leftarrow C_4H_{10} & \xrightarrow{w_1} & C_4H_8 \rightarrow C \\ & w_3 \searrow \quad \swarrow w_2 & \\ & C_4H_6 \rightarrow C. & \end{array} \tag{23–46}$$

These experiments showed that the rates of formation of carbon from divinyl, butene, and butane are in the proportions 60 : 4 : 1. Butene, formed from butane, is desorbed from the catalyst at a rate 30 times greater than its rate of reaction to give divinyl. This method was also used by Neiman and Popov [56] to show that in the oxidation of isopropyl alcohol on silver, the active particles leave the surfaces of the catalyst and pass into the gas phase, and that at low temperatures these particles initiate the back reaction (the hydrogenation of acetone to isopropyl alcohol). Finally, the isotope kinetic method would seem to have useful possibilities for studying the mechanism of biochemical reactions.

23–6 Atom transfer reactions and decompositions. Brodsky and his collaborators [57] have reported an interesting type of simple molecular migration in labeled phenol C_6H_5OD. When heated to 210°C, deuterium migrates from the OH group into the benzene nucleus, and after two days was found to be distributed in equivalent quantities between the four available positions

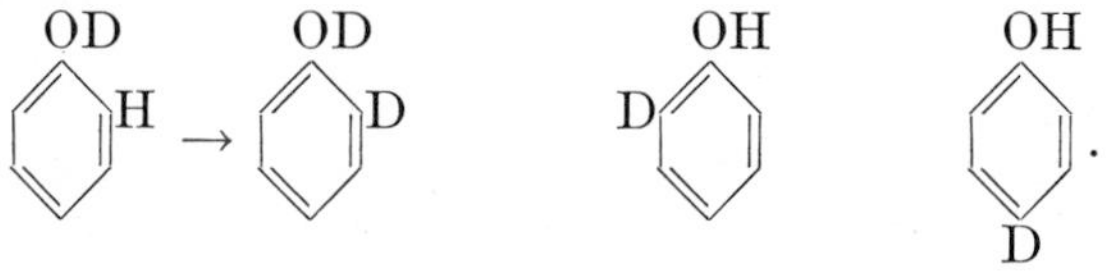

[Structural formulas: OD-substituted benzene ring with H (ortho) → OD-substituted ring with D (ortho); OH-substituted ring with D (ortho); OH-substituted ring with D (para).]

It was also shown that when anisole ($C_6H_5OCH_3$) or phenetol ($C_6H_5OC_2H_5$) are present, deuterium from C_6H_5OD can transfer to the nuclei of the two other compounds. This shows that the rearrangement is intermolecular, and not intramolecular, going by an electrophilic mechanism

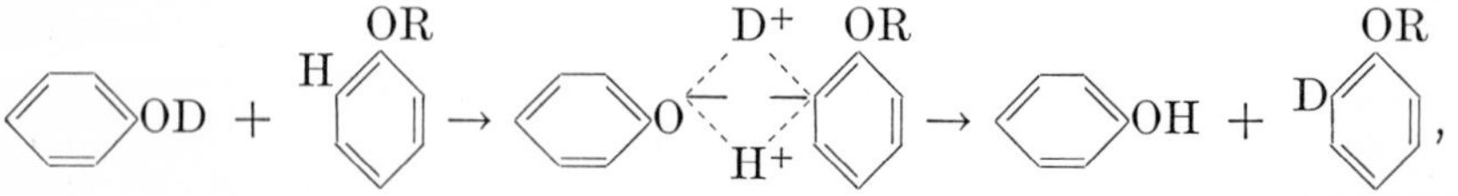

[Structural formulas: C_6H_5OD + H-substituted ring bearing OR → C_6H_5O complex with D⁺ and H⁺ bridging to ring bearing OR → C_6H_5OH + D-substituted ring bearing OR,]

(23–47)

in which R = H, CH_3, or C_2H_5. This rearrangement occurs in the absence of catalysts, because of the acidic nature of phenol, but it does not occur with aniline, which cannot form the necessary intermediate complex for electrophilic exchange.

Melander [58, 59] has studied electrophilic aromatic substitutions using tritiated benzene. This author found no isotope effect in the nitration of benzene and some of its derivatives, whereas the sulfonation of C_6H_6 and of C_6H_5Br does show such an effect. Theory distinguishes two possible mechanisms for these reactions. The first is a bimolecular electrophilic substitution S_E2, with the formation of an activated complex

$$\left[C_6H_6 \cdots \begin{matrix} H \\ X \end{matrix} \right]^+$$

which involves no perturbation of the conjugated π-electron system in the aromatic molecule; this mechanism implies an isotope effect with a lower velocity for the heavier molecules. Secondly, one may have covalent formation of intermediate addition quinoid compounds

$$C_6H_5 \begin{matrix} H \\ X \end{matrix}$$

of variable stability, using two π-electrons. The subsequent expulsion of a proton results in substitution. For this reaction path, there are two possible kinetic conclusions; in case (a), in which the decomposition of the intermediate determines the overall kinetics, there will be an isotope effect (dissociative mechanism), but in case (b), where the formation is the rate-determining process (addition mechanism) there will be no isotope effect. The experimental results therefore show that nitration goes by mechanism 2b, while sulfonation goes either by mechanism 1 or by mechanism 2a.

The mechanism of more complex rearrangements, such as the Claisen rearrangement [60, 61, 62]

$$C_6H_5(OR) \rightarrow C_6H_4(OH)(R),$$

or the Beckmann rearrangement [63]

$$\begin{matrix} R{-}C{-}R' \\ \| \\ NOH \end{matrix} \rightarrow \begin{matrix} R{-}C{=}O \\ | \\ NHR' \end{matrix}$$

have also been established by the use of labeled molecules.*

Brodsky and his collaborators used N^{15} in a study of the condensation of primary or secondary amines [38]

$$RNH_2 + R'NH_2 \rightarrow RNHR' + NH_3, \qquad (23\text{–}48)$$

and showed that the rupture of the C—N bond occurs in the less basic

* See Ref. 64 for a bibliography of this subject.

amine, which gives NH_3, and that the more basic amine is transformed into a secondary amine RNHR′. The bond energy therefore decreases in the order aniline > α-naphthylamine > benzamide, which is the order of the basicities. It was also concluded that the reaction occurs by nucleophilic addition of R′ to the nitrogen attached to R, and transfer of an amine proton from RNH_2 to the NH_2 radical from the other amine.

Differing mechanisms have been suggested to explain the disproportionation of aldehydes (the Cannizzaro reaction), and the choice between these was a difficult one. By condensing benzaldehyde in the presence of KOH in deuterated water, Fredenhagen and Bonhoeffer [66] were able to establish that the transfer of hydrogen atoms from one aldehyde molecule to the other occurs directly, and does not involve participation of the solvent. The reaction therefore proceeds via the formation of an intermediate compound

$$2RCHO + DO^- \rightarrow R{-}\underset{\displaystyle H}{\overset{\displaystyle OD}{\underset{|}{\overset{|}{C}}}}{-}O{-}\underset{\displaystyle H}{\overset{\displaystyle O^-}{\underset{|}{\overset{|}{C}}}}{-}R \tag{23–49}$$

$$\rightarrow RCOOD + RCH_2O^-.$$

The same authors used heavy water to establish the conditions in which D-glucose isomerizes to D-fructose and D-mannose by enolization, or through an intermediate compound.

Tracers have made an important contribution to an understanding of the Willgerodt reaction, which is the transformation of an aromatic ketone; for example, acetophenone heated in pyridine at 170° in the presence of ammonium polysulfide or $NH_3 + S$, gives phenylacetamide (80%) and phenylacetic acid (20%)

$$C_6H_5{\cdot}CO{\cdot}CH_3 \rightarrow \begin{cases} C_6H_5{\cdot}CH_2{\cdot}CO{\cdot}NH_2, \\ C_6H_5{\cdot}CH_2{\cdot}COOH. \end{cases} \tag{23–50}$$

In the amide, the CO group has moved relative to the phenyl group, and the question was whether this ketocarbon atom comes from the original ketone group or from the methyl group. To clarify this point, acetophenone was labeled with C^{14} in the carbonyl position and transformed into phenylacetic acid. Decarboxylation of the latter with copper chromite gave inactive CO_2, so that the amide carbonyl is not the same as that in the acetophenone [67]. On the other hand, it was also found that the carboxyl group of the phenylacetic acid formed directly in Eq. (23–50) was active, so that this compound must be formed by a different mechanism from the amide, and requires at least a partial rearrangement of the molecule. However, this latter point has not been confirmed by another group of authors, who used different degradation methods [68].

A similar problem [69] arises in the thermal decomposition of ethyl pyruvate

$$CH_3{\cdot}CO{\cdot}COOC_2H_5 \rightarrow CO + CH_3{\cdot}COOC_2H_5, \tag{23–51}$$

and here the problem is whether the carbon monoxide gas comes from the keto group or from the carboxyl group of the ester. Experiments with C^{14} favor the latter hypothesis.

In some cases, experiments with labeled molecules have led to the rejection of a mechanism suggested by the chemical study of certain organic reactions, without, however, giving sufficient evidence to establish any other mechanism. A typical example of this is the study of the Menschutkin reaction, which can be represented by the general equation

$$R_3N + RX \rightleftharpoons R_4N^+ + X^-. \tag{23–52}$$

A peculiar kinetic feature of this reaction is that the steric factor P in the Arrhenius equation

$$k = PZe^{-E/RT} \tag{23–53}$$

is very small. By definition, $P = 1$ if every collision between reacting molecules leads to reaction, with a rate constant k. In the Menschutkin reaction, the value of P, which depends strongly on the solvent, is only of the order of 10^{-5} to 10^{-8}. In order to explain this anomaly, it had been suggested that the reaction proceeded by the formation of an activated complex ($R_3N{\cdot}RX$), which had a very low probability of dissociation, so that the measured rate constant k refers not to the velocity of the bimolecular reaction $R_3N + RX$, but to the rate of decomposition of the complex. To check this hypothesis, tritiated CH_3I was prepared [70], and this was reacted with an excess of inactive $(CH_3)_3N$ in ethanol or benzene. The four methyl groups in the activated complex should be equivalent, and at the end of the reaction the trimethylamine should contain some of the tritium. In fact this compound was found to be inactive, and the same negative result was found with dimethylaniline and CH_3I. The reaction therefore does not involve the formation of an activated complex in which the R groups are equivalent, and the kinetic anomaly remains unexplained.

Tracer experiments did, however, confirm the mechanism for the decomposition of glucose by mineral acids [71]. Chemical arguments made it likely that 5-hydroxymethyl-2-furfural is formed as an intermediate product, which by hydration, fission, and reorganization gives levulinic and formic acids

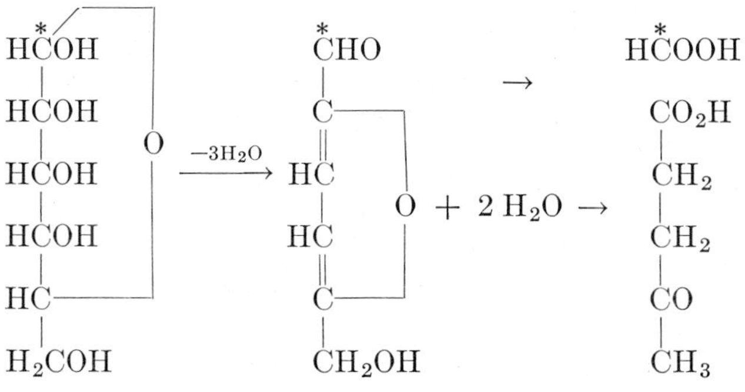

$$\begin{array}{l} H\overset{*}{C}OH \\ | \\ HCOH \\ | \\ HCOH \\ | \\ HCOH \\ | \\ HC \\ | \\ H_2COH \end{array} \text{(ring O from C-1 to C-5)} \xrightarrow{-3H_2O} \begin{array}{l} \overset{*}{C}HO \\ | \\ C \\ \| \\ HC \\ | \\ HC \\ \| \\ C \\ | \\ CH_2OH \end{array} \text{(ring O)} + 2\,H_2O \rightarrow \begin{array}{l} H\overset{*}{C}OOH \\ \\ CO_2H \\ | \\ CH_2 \\ | \\ CH_2 \\ | \\ CO \\ | \\ CH_3 \end{array} \tag{23–54}$$

The formic acid should therefore come from the terminal CHOH group; in agreement with this, labeling this group with C^{14} showed that the activity appeared quantitatively in HCOOH.

23–7 Heterogeneous catalysis and surface reactions. Mention was made at the end of Section 19–7 of isotope exchange experiments with H_2, D_2, N_2, and NH_3 on various metals, particularly iron. One of the objects of this work was to clarify the mechanism of the ammonia synthesis. A number of other catalytic reactions with important industrial applications, such as the Fischer-Tropsch synthesis (hydrogenation of CO to give hydrocarbons), the hydrogenation of unsaturated hydrocarbons, the oxidation of CO, etc., have also been studied with tracers. In the Fischer-Tropsch synthesis on Fe, Ni, Co, etc., it was generally believed that the real catalyst was a metal carbide formed on an intermediate. To check this hypothesis, the surface of the metal was covered with C^{14}-labeled carbide before reacting H_2 and inactive CO together [72]. The mixture of hydrocarbons produced contained virtually no C^{14}; in other experiments with active CO and unlabeled carbide, the carbide remained inactive after the reaction. Methane was also ruled out as a possible intermediate by working in the presence of labeled samples of this gas. If, however, small quantities of various labeled alcohols are added, all the hydrocarbons formed contain a significant fraction of the activity, so that during the synthesis the CO and H_2 gas pass through an activated complex which is identical with or similar to that which the alcohols form.

The oxidation of carbon monoxide by air on MnO_2, Co_2O_3, CuO, etc., was thought to proceed in two stages, such as

$$CO + MnO_2 \rightarrow CO_2 + MnO, \tag{23–55}$$

$$MnO + \tfrac{1}{2}O_2 \rightarrow MnO_2. \tag{23–56}$$

On this basis, if labeled dioxide is used (MnO_2^{18}), the carbon dioxide formed should be enriched in heavy oxygen, whereas in fact experiment showed that this was not the case [73].

The reduction of CO_2 on a graphite or carbon surface at temperatures above 700°C

$$CO_2 + C \rightarrow 2CO \tag{23–57}$$

has been studied using C^{14} [74, 75]. It was shown that the reaction proceeds in two stages. The CO_2 molecule first reacts rapidly with the surface, giving up an oxygen atom and liberating a molecule of CO, and this second molecule of CO is subsequently released in a slower process. In a very small number of cases (1 to 2%) the carbon atom of the sorbed molecule remains on the surface, and oxygen removes two other carbon atoms.

Roginski and his group [76] have used C^{14} as a tracer to study the secondary reactions which occur during the catalytic cracking of hydrocarbons. The experimental procedure was similar to that already discussed for the oxidation of butane (Section 23–5), and consisted in adding one of the cracking products labeled with C^{14} to the inactive hydrocarbon before the reaction, and subsequently determining the C^{14} distribution in the various products. For example, by adding $C_2^{14}H_6$ to n-hexane prior to cracking at 520°C on aluminum silicate, it was shown that for 12.4% decomposition of C_6H_{14}, 9% of the radioactive ethane had reacted. Ethylene was the only active unsaturated hydrocarbon formed; the saturated hydrocarbons, C_3H_8, C_4H_{10}, and C_5H_{12} contained about 1 to 3% of this activity, very probably due to reactions such as

$$n\text{-}C_6H_{14} + C_2H_6 \rightleftharpoons C_3H_8 + n\text{-}C_5H_{12}. \tag{23–58}$$

The coke formed in this case contained only 0.6% of the activity, but with labeled ethylene, and also in the cracking of iso-octane and labeled propylene, the activity of the coke was much greater, so that unsaturated hydrocarbons contribute more to the carbonization than does ethane. These experiments also showed that while the hydrogenation of C_2H_4 is relatively slow under the conditions used, that of C_3H_6 is very rapid, going by reactions such as

$$i\text{-}C_8H_{18} + C_3H_6 \rightleftharpoons n\text{-}C_4H_{10} + n\text{-}C_7H_{14}. \tag{23–59}$$

Margolis and Roginski [77] used this same technique to show that the catalytic oxidation of olefines on silver or V_2O_5 does not involve a series of successive reactions:

$$\text{ethylene} \rightarrow \text{ethylene oxide} \rightarrow \text{aldehyde} \rightarrow CO \rightarrow CO_2,$$

but that these products are formed in parallel processes which are independent of each other.

The isomerization of butane to isobutane above 100° in the presence of $AlCl_3 + HCl$ (on a support of earth or charcoal) has been examined by labeling either the hydrocarbon or the HCl with tritium [78]. After the reaction, tritium was found in both butanes, which suggests that the catalyst is effectively $HAlCl_4$, which forms an intermediate complex with butane; rearrangement followed by dissociation then gives isobutane

$$\underset{}{CH_3}\text{—}\underset{\underset{T}{\uparrow}}{CH_2}\text{—}\underset{\underset{AlCl_4}{\downarrow}}{HCH}\text{—}CH_3 \rightarrow CH_3\text{—}\underset{\underset{CTH_2}{|}}{CH}\text{—}CH_3 + HAlCl_4. \tag{23–60}$$

Later experiments using $AlBr_3 + DBr$ as catalyst showed, however, that the isomerization requires the presence of butene or some other olefine, which probably sets up a chain reaction via a series of equilibria involving the compound $CH_3{\cdot}CH_2{\cdot}CH{\cdot}CH_3$, initially formed by the addition of a proton to $CH_3{\cdot}CH{=}CH{\cdot}CH_3$ [79] (see also Ref. 80).

Turkevich and Smith [81, 82] used tritium to study the isomerization of butenes on various hydrogenated catalysts, and the isotope exchange between these and the hydrocarbons, and showed that the two processes go on together at comparable rates. The authors concluded from this that the isomerization involves hydrogen transfer from one molecule to another via the catalyst. The latter should therefore have both "donor" and "acceptor" sites, about 3.5 A apart. Aluminum silicate, phosphoric acid,

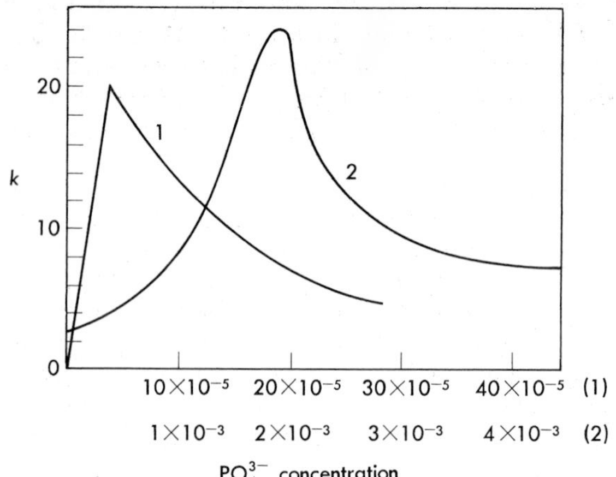

FIG. 23–3. Influence of PO_4^{3-} concentration on (1) catalytic decomposition of H_2O_2, (2) catalytic hydrogenation of C_2H_4.

copper pyrophosphate, and some other catalysts satisfy these conditions. However, the $AlCl_3$ catalyzed isomerization of α-bromonaphthalene to β-bromonaphthalene, and the reverse reaction, are much more rapid than the isotope exchange between $AlBr_3$ and each of the organic bromine compounds [83], so that the catalysis does not involve atom transfer.

The tracer technique has been used in research on the best conditions of using promoters for certain catalysts. For example, acetylene is oxidized by air at about 150° on silver nitrate deposited upon alumina. Johnson and Krieger used C^{14}-labeled acetylene to show that the catalytic activity varies with the nitrate concentration, reaching a maximum at 10% silver [84]. This is associated with a slight formation of metallic silver. Roginski and his co-workers [85] used P^{32} to investigate the action of phosphorus in promoting the catalytic activity of palladium in the decomposition of hydrogen peroxide, and the hydrogenation of ethylene. Labeled orthophosphate ion was added to a solution containing a palladium salt, which was then reduced by formate. Figure 23–3 shows the catalytic activity as a function of the relative concentration of phosphorus; it will be seen that this activity goes through a very sharp maximum, at 0.2% P for the hydrogenation, and $5 \times 10^{-3}\%$ for the decomposition of hydrogen peroxide. It would of course have been extremely difficult, if not impossible, to obtain this evidence by methods not involving tracer or radioactive techniques.

The poisoning of catalysts for the ammonia synthesis (Fe + 2.9% Al_2O_3 + 1.1% K_2O) by $C^{14}O$ and $C^{14}O_2$ has been studied at 450°C with mixtures of $N_2 + H_2$ at 30 atm pressure [86]. It was found that the effect of the oxides of carbon is not due to these covering the surface of the catalyst, but to the water vapor formed by hydrogenation

$$CO_2 + 4H_2 \rightarrow CH_4 + 2H_2O, \qquad (23\text{–}61)$$

$$CO + 3H_2 \rightarrow CH_4 + H_2O. \qquad (23\text{–}62)$$

References

1. E. R. S. Winter and H. V. A. Briscoe, *J. Am. Chem. Soc.*, **73,** 496 (1951).
2. P. Baertschi, *Experientia,* **7,** 215 (1951).
3. M. Dole, D. P. Rudd, G. R. Muchow, and C. Comte, *J. Chem. Phys.*, **20,** 961 (1952).
4. A. E. Cahill and H. Taube, *J. Am. Chem. Soc.*, **74,** 2312 (1952).
5. C. A. Bunton and D. R. Llewellyn, *Research,* **5,** 142 (1952).
6. B. Chance, *J. Biol. Chem.*, **179,** 1299 (1949); **180,** 947 (1949).
7. F. Haber and J. Weiss, *Proc. Roy. Soc. (London)*, **A147,** 332 (1934).
8. J. T. Kummer, *J. Am. Chem. Soc.*, **69,** 2559 (1947).
9. W. S. Richardson and E. B. Wilson, *J. Chem. Phys.*, **18,** 694 (1950).
10. L. Friedman and J. Bigeleisen, *J. Chem. Phys.*, **18,** 1325 (1950).
11. H. Taube and H. Dodgen, *J. Am. Chem. Soc.*, **71,** 3330 (1949).
12. A. Fava and D. Divo, *Gazz. Chim. Ital.*, **82,** 558, 564 (1952); **83,** 98 (1953).
13. A. I. Brodsky and R. K. Eremenko, *Doklady Akad. Nauk S.S.S.R.*, **95,** 539 (1954); **101,** 487 (1955).
14. A. Fava, *Gazz. Chim. Ital.*, **83,** 87 (1953).
15. O. V. Travin and L. A. Shvartsman, *Sess. Acad. Sci., U.S.S.R., Tech. Sect.*, July 1–5, 1955, p. 48.
16. A. I. Brodsky, *Isotope Chemistry,* Academy of Sciences, Moscow, 1957.
17. K. Wiberg, *Chem. Revs.*, **55,** 13 (1955).
18. E. A. Moelwyn-Hughes and K. F. Bonhoeffer, *Naturwiss.*, **22,** 174 (1934).
19. A. I. Shatenstein, *Doklady Akad. Nauk S.S.S.R.*, **70,** 1029 (1950).
20. A. I. Shatenstein, *Zhur. Fiz. Khim.*, **25,** 1206 (1951).
21. L. Kaplan and K. E. Wilzbach, *J. Am. Chem. Soc.*, **77,** 1297 (1955).
22. M. Polanyi and A. L. Szabo, *Trans. Faraday Soc.*, **30,** 508 (1934).
23. S. C. Datta, J. N. E. Day, and C. K. Ingold, *J. Chem. Soc.*, **1939,** 838.
24. I. Roberts and H. C. Urey, *J. Am. Chem. Soc.*, **60,** 2391 (1939).
25. E. Blumenthal and J. B. M. Herbert, *Trans. Faraday Soc.*, **41,** 611 (1945).
26. N. I. Dedusenko and A. I. Brodski, *J. Gen. Chem. Russ.*, **12,** 361 (1942).
27. I. Lauder and S. E. Wright, *Nature,* **158,** 381 (1946).
28. M. L. Bender, *J. Am. Chem. Soc.*, **73,** 1626 (1951).
29. I. Roberts and H. C. Urey, *J. Am. Chem. Soc.*, **61,** 2584 (1939).
30. P. Nahinsky and S. Ruben, *J. Am. Chem. Soc.*, **63,** 2275 (1941).
31. P. Nahinsky, C. N. Rice, S. Ruben, and M. D. Kamen, *J. Am. Chem. Soc.*, **64,** 2299 (1942).
32. H. R. Mahler and A. Roberts, *J. Am. Chem. Soc.*, **72,** 5095 (1950).
33. M. B. Allen and S. Ruben, *J. Am. Chem. Soc.*, **64,** 948 (1942).
34. K. Wirtz and K. F. Bonhoeffer, *Z. physik. Chem.*, **B32,** 108 (1936).
35. M. Bassey, C. A. Bunton, A. G. Davies, T. A. Lewis, and D. R. Llewellyn, *J. Chem. Soc.*, **1955,** 2471.
36. L. Kaplan, *J. Am. Chem. Soc.*, **76,** 4645 (1954).
37. J. C. Pope, F. J. Dykstra, and C. Edgar, *J. Am. Chem. Soc.*, **51,** 1875, 2203, 2213 (1929).
38. M. B. Neiman, A. F. Lukovnikov, and G. I. Feklisov, *Zhur. Obshchei Khim.*, **25,** 1317 (1955).

39. M. B. Neiman, *Zhur. Fiz. Khim.*, **28,** 1235 (1954).

40. M. B. Neiman, *J. Applied Radn. Isotopes,* **3,** 20 (1958).

41. I. N. Antonova, V. A. Kuzmin, R. I. Moshkina, A. B. Nalbandyan, M. B. Neiman, and G. I. Feklisov, *Izvest. Akad. Nauk, Otdel Khim.*, **1955,** 789.

42. N. I. Medvedeva, M. B. Neiman, and H. Torsueva, *Compt. rend.*, **243,** 1203 (1956).

43. A. F. Lukovnikov and M. B. Neiman, *Zhur. Fiz. Khim.*, **29,** 1410 (1955).

44. M. B. Neiman, N. K. Serdyuk, V. Y. Efremov, and A. F. Lukovnikov, *Izvest. Akad. Nauk, Otdel Khim.*, **1956,** 408.

45. M. B. Neiman and N. K. Serdyuk, *Problems in Kinetics and Catalysis,* Vol. 9, Moscow, 1958.

46. N. N. Semenov, *Problems in Chemical Kinetics,* Academy of Sciences, Moscow, 1958.

47. N. I. Medvedeva, M. B. Neiman, and H. Torsueva, *Doklady Akad. Nauk S.S.S.R.*, **115,** 347 (1957).

48. V. D. Moiseev, Y. I. Lyadova, V. I. Vedeneev, M. B. Neiman, and V. V. Voevodski, *Doklady Akad. Nauk S.S.S.R.*, **123,** 292 (1958).

49. R. I. Moshkina, A. B. Nalbandyan, M. B. Neiman, and G. I. Feklisov, *Izvest. Akad. Nauk, Otdel Khim.*, **1957,** 801.

50. A. B. Nalbandyan and N. A. Kleimenov, in press.

51. M. B. Neiman and G. I. Feklisov, *Zhur. Fiz. Khim.*, **30,** 1126 (1956).

52. A. B. Nalbandyan, M. B. Neiman, and I. M. Emanuel, *U.N.E.S.C.O. Conference on Radioisotopes*, Paris, 1957.

53. M. B. Neiman, *Izvest. Akad. Nauk, Otdel Khim.*, **1957,** 511.

54. A. A. Balandin, M. B. Neiman, O. K. Bogdanova, G. V. Isagulyants, A. P. Shcheglova, and E. I. Popov, *Izvest. Akad. Nauk, Otdel Khim.*, **1957,** 157, 270.

55. A. A. Balandin, M. B. Neiman, O. K. Bogdanova, G. V. Isagulyants, A. P. Shcheglova, and E. I. Popov, *U.N.E.S.C.O. Conference on Radioisotopes,* Paris, 1957.

56. M. B. Neiman and E. I. Popov, *Compt. rend.*, **245,** 1234 (1957).

57. A. I. Brodsky, G. P. Miklukhin, I. I. Kukhtenko, and I. P. Gragerov, *Doklady Akad. Nauk S.S.S.R.*, **57,** 463 (1947).

58. L. Melander, *Acta Chem. Scand.*, **3,** 95 (1949).

59. L. Melander, *Arkiv Kemi,* **2,** 213 (1950).

60. G. D. Kistiakowsky and R. I. Tichenor, *J. Am. Chem. Soc.*, **64,** 2302 (1942).

61. A. S. Fomenko, G. P. Miklukhin, and E. A. Sadovnikova, *Doklady Akad. Nauk S.S.S.R.*, **62,** 91 (1948).

62. H. Schmid and K. Schmid, *Helv. Chim. Acta,* **35,** 1879 (1952).

63. G. P. Miklukhin and A. I. Brodsky, *J. Gen. Chem. Russ.*, **12,** 351 (1942).

64. P. Bevillard, *Bull. soc. chim. France,* **1954,** D 55.

65. A. I. Brodsky, B. A. Geller, and R. Y. Sheinfain, *Doklady Akad. Nauk S.S.S.R.*, **95,** 273 (1954).

66. H. Fredenhagen and K. F. Bonhoeffer, *Z. physik. Chem.*, **A181,** 379, 392 (1939).

67. W. G. Dauben, J. C. Reid, P. E. Yankwich, and M. Calvin, *J. Am. Chem. Soc.*, **68,** 2117 (1946); **72,** 121 (1950).

68. E. V. Brown, E. Cerwonka, and R. C. Anderson, *J. Am. Chem. Soc.*, **73**, 3735 (1951).

69. M. Calvin and R. M. Lemmon, *J. Am. Chem. Soc.*, **69**, 1232 (1947).

70. D. Harman, T. D. Stewart, and S. Ruben, *J. Am. Chem. Soc.*, **64**, 2294 (1942).

71. J. C. Sowden, *J. Am. Chem. Soc.*, **71**, 3568 (1949).

72. J. T. Kummer and P. H. Emmett, *J. Am. Chem. Soc.*, **75**, 5177 (1953).

73. F. M. Vainshtein and G. Turovski, *Doklady Akad. Nauk S.S.S.R.*, **72**, 297 (1950).

74. F. Bonner and J. Turkevich, *J. Am. Chem. Soc.*, **73**, 561 (1951).

75. F. Brown, *Trans. Faraday Soc.*, **48**, 1005 (1952).

76. E. A. Andreev, T. J. Andrianova, B. V. Klimenok, O. V. Krylov, S. Z. Roginski, and M. M. Sakharov, *Doklady Akad. Nauk S.S.S.R.*, **96**, 681 (1954).

77. L. Y. Margolis and S. Z. Roginski, *Doklady Akad. Nauk S.S.S.R.*, **89**, 915 (1953); **90**, 311, 549 (1954).

78. T. M. Powell and E. B. Reid, *J. Am. Chem. Soc.*, **67**, 1020 (1945).

79. H. Pines and R. C. Wackher, *J. Am. Chem. Soc.*, **68**, 2518 (1946).

80. J. W. Otvos, D. P. Stevenson, C. D. Wagner, and O. Beeck, *J. Chem. Phys.*, **16**, 745 (1948); **17**, 418 (1949).

81. J. Turkevich and R. K. Smith, *J. Chem. Phys.*, **16**, 466 (1948).

82. J. Turkevich, *1955 Geneva Conference*, P. 163.

83. N. E. Brezhneva and S. Z. Roginski, *Uspekhi Khim.*, **7**, 1503 (1938).

84. W. T. M. Johnson and K. A. Krieger, quoted by R. R. Edwards, *Ann. Rev. Nuclear Sci.*, **1**, 301 (1952).

85. S. Z. Roginski, *Adsorption and Catalysis*, Academy of Sciences, Moscow, 1948.

86. C. Bokhoven, *Proc. 2nd Oxford Radioisotope Conf.*, Vol. 2, p. 53 (1954).

CHAPTER 24

THE BIOCHEMICAL, PHYSIOLOGICAL, AND MEDICAL APPLICATIONS OF ISOTOPIC TRACERS

The innumerable uses of tracers in biochemistry and physiology are among the most fruitful applications of the tracer method, since in many cases an immediate answer can be obtained to problems which are otherwise insoluble. Hevesy [1] has discussed the use of radioactive indicators in animal biochemistry, and gives over 1000 bibliographical references (up to 1948). Similarly, in 1949 Dougherty [2] gave 332 references to work using deuterium in biochemical problems, 395 for radioactive phosphorus, 188 for the carbon isotopes, 125 for radioactive iodine, and 72 for radioactive iron and a number of others. Since that time, the number of publications on the subject has continued to increase. It is also worth noting that the radioactive isotopes supplied by the atomic energy authorities of different countries for biological and medical purposes often outnumber those required for research in physics and chemistry, or for industrial use (see Tables 25–1 and 25–2).

Within the limits of the present work, it will not be possible to give even a superficial review of all these various applications. This will be restricted to a presentation of some typical results from the different fields in which these biochemical and physiological studies have been carried out.* As far as possible, these will be classified by the indicator used.

24–1 Radiocarbon labeling: photosynthesis. The use of radiocarbon to study the mechanism of photosynthesis is one of the most spectacular applications of radioactive tracers in biochemistry. The assimilation of carbon dioxide by green plants, with the formation of carbohydrates and the release of oxygen, is the result of a long chain of chemical changes, catalyzed by enzymes, and involving a large number of intermediate products, and the process is much more complex than is suggested by the overall stoichiometric equation

$$6CO_2 + 6H_2O \xrightarrow{h\nu} C_6H_{12}O_6 + 6O_2 - 112\text{ kcal.} \qquad (24\text{–}1)$$

This reaction, which is the reverse of the process of respiration, is endothermic, the energy being supplied by light absorbed by chlorophyll. This pigment ($C_{35}H_{72}N_4O_5Mg$), containing four pyrrole nuclei, is not only a physical photosensitizer, but must also take part in the chemical reactions, since it becomes radioactive if the photosynthesis is carried out in the presence of labeled CO_2. Some theories envisage chlorophyll as a hydrogen-transfer agent in a reversible oxidation-reduction cycle, but this transfer does not seem to be confirmed by experiments carried out in deuterated or

---

* For a further bibliography, see Refs. 3 and 4.

tritiated water, since the tracer is not incorporated into the pigment under these conditions [5, 6].

We saw earlier (Section 10–3) that oxygen produced in photosynthesis comes from water and not from carbon dioxide. This has been established by isotopic analysis of the oxygen given off in photosynthesis with the algae *Helodea* [7, 8] and *Chlorella* [9, 10] in the presence of labeled H_2O or CO_2. This result is confirmed indirectly by the fact that the natural carbohydrates have the same O^{18} content as atmospheric CO_2; this content is higher than that in atmospheric oxygen [7, 8]. In addition, chemical research had already shown that the primary action of the light does not involve CO_2, but rather that the latter is reduced by a hydrogen donor, RH_2, which is itself produced indirectly by the interaction of light with chlorophyll. This result has been confirmed by Benson and Calvin [11], who first exposed the algae *Chlorella* and *Scenedesmus* to light in the absence of CO_2, and then introduced labeled $C^{14}O_2$. The assimilation subsequently proceeded in darkness at a rate which was not very different from that found when the algae were exposed to light (within 90%). This aftereffect may last for about 10 min after cutting off the illumination. Schematically then, the reaction can be represented by an equation such as

$$CO_2 + (RH_2) \rightarrow A + B + \cdots \rightarrow A' + B' + \cdots \rightarrow \{CH_2O\} + H_2O. \qquad (24\text{–}2)$$

Most of the work with tracers such as T, P^{32}, and (especially) C^{14} has been aimed at identifying the intermediate products A, B, A′, B′, etc., and the way in which they are formed. In particular, this sort of work has been carried out at Berkeley by Calvin and his co-workers [12–16]; as the result of long, methodical, and laborious research, these workers have been able to give a complete schema for the reaction route followed by carbon in the process (24–2) [17]. In what follows, we shall be concerned with the results and interpretations given by Calvin.

One of the methods used consisted in exposing algae to light of variable intensity in the presence of labeled CO_2 (as $NaHC^{14}O_3$) with which the plant is contacted at a suitable moment. At the end of the exposure, which varied between several seconds and several minutes, the algae were rapidly treated with boiling ethanol to stop the enzymatic reactions, and then extracted with 80% and 20% aqueous alcohol respectively. The analysis of the soluble fraction, which for short periods of synthesis contained practically all the radiocarbon, was carried out by paper chromatography. The chromatogram was developed in two dimensions first with phenol-water in one direction and then with butanol-propionic acid-water in a direction normal to the first. Autoradiography, and subsequent measurements with a counter at various points of the chromatogram, gave the radiocarbon intensities and hence the relative activities of the corresponding compounds (see Fig. 24–1).

These compounds were identified by comparing the position of the spots obtained by autoradiography with the coloration given by known natural compounds on a chromatogram developed with the appropriate chemical reagents, such as ninhydrin for amino-acids, ammonium molybdate for

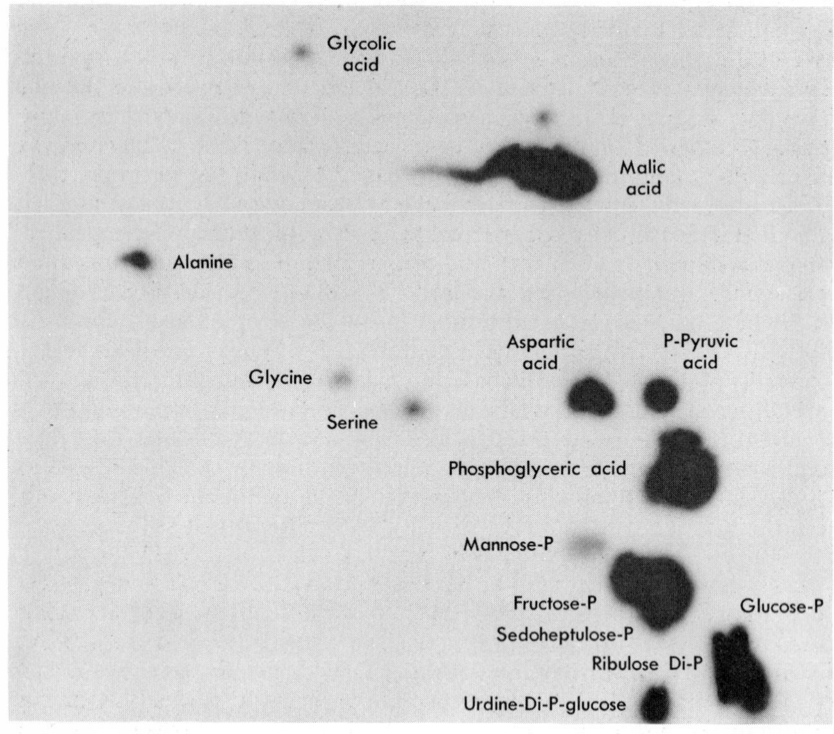

(a)

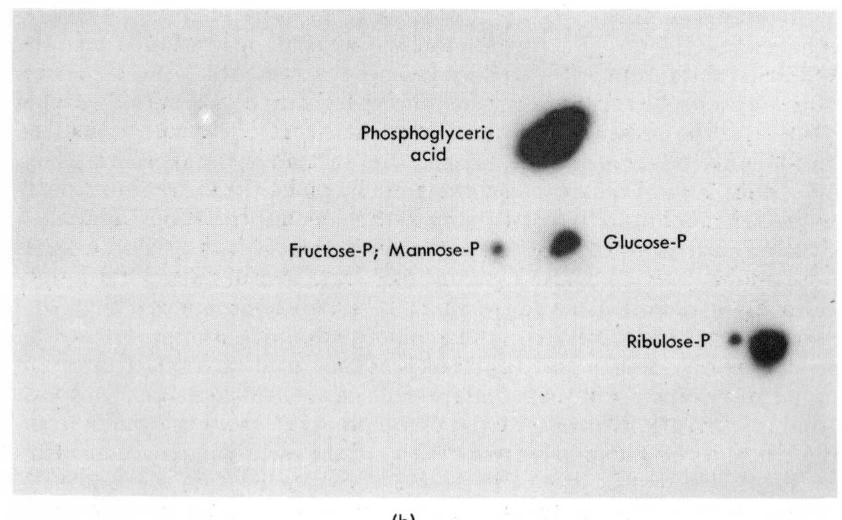

(b)

FIG. 24-1. Autoradiograph of chromatogram of products of photosynthesis after (a) 10 sec, and (b) 60 sec (Ref. 17).

phosphates, etc. The coincidence between the two types of spots for the same compound, including the edge details, is so perfect that Calvin regards this method of identification as being almost as certain as fingerprints. When the substances could be isolated on the chromatogram in sufficient quantity after photosynthesis, attempts were made to analyze them by chemical methods. In principle, these analyses of the products formed under different conditions can be used to work out the order in which they are formed, and to establish the probable chain of successive reactions.

The first conclusion from experiments carried out in this way is that for a very short exposure (about 10 sec), virtually all the radiocarbon is fixed in phosphorus compounds, with more than half as phosphoglyceric acid

$$(HO)_2P(=O)\text{—O—CH}_2\text{—CH(OH)—COOH} .$$

After 5 sec, 80% of the activity is incorporated in this acid. The quantity decreases as the illumination period is increased, so that phosphoglyceric acid is the primary product of the reduction of the CO_2 molecule, being formed by reaction with an appropriate "acceptor." Chemical degradation showed that 50% of the activity is fixed on the carboxylic acid group, and 25% on each of the other two carbon atoms. Pyruvic acid is also among the initial products of the photosynthesis, but this does not seem to be the precursor of phosphoglyceric acid, but rather a derivative of it. The chromatograms also show a fairly rapid formation of alanine, malic acid, and aspartic acid containing C^{14}, but the incorporation of the indicator into these compounds is thought not to be directly related to photosynthesis. More significant is the rapid appearance of the phosphates of hexoses (glucose and fructose), a pentose (ribulose), and a heptose (sedoheptulose). The chain length of these sugars has been confirmed by labeling with P^{32} and determining the C : P ratio. Degradation of the hexoses showed that 50% of their activity was in the 3 and 4 carbon positions, and that the remainder was uniformly distributed among the other four atoms.

This distribution corresponds to that which would be expected if each hexose molecule were formed by the condensation of two molecules of phosphoglyceric acid. The reduction of this acid to the aldehyde by the reducing agent formed by the action of light gives the hexoses, by a process which is the reverse of glycolysis, namely isomerization of the aldehyde to dihydroxy-acetone, and condensation to fructose and glucose. It was further established that the glucose phosphate reacts with uridine triphosphate to give uridine diphosphoglucose, which subsequently gives saccharose by reaction with fructose (probably as the phosphate). The genetic relationships between the trioses, hexoses, pentose, and heptose are more complex, but it appears that ribulose is formed by the action of the enzyme *transcetolase* on the triose and heptose phosphates (24–3), and that the heptose follows the product synthesized by aldolase from a C_3 molecule

and another C_4 molecule (24–4)

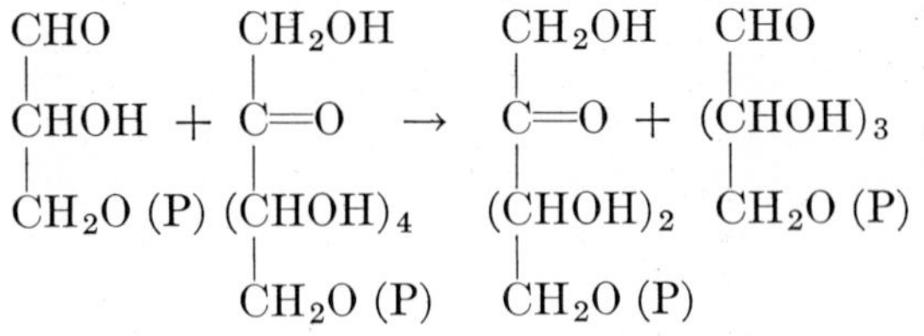

$$
\begin{array}{ccccccc}
\mathrm{CHO} & & \mathrm{CH_2OH} & & \mathrm{CH_2OH} & & \mathrm{CHO} \\
| & & | & & | & & | \\
\mathrm{CHOH} & + & \mathrm{C{=}O} & \rightarrow & \mathrm{C{=}O} & + & \mathrm{(CHOH)_3} \\
| & & | & & | & & | \\
\mathrm{CH_2O\,(P)} & & \mathrm{(CHOH)_4} & & \mathrm{(CHOH)_2} & & \mathrm{CH_2O\,(P)} \\
 & & | & & | & & \\
 & & \mathrm{CH_2O\,(P)} & & \mathrm{CH_2O\,(P)} & &
\end{array} , \qquad (24\text{–}3)
$$

$$
\begin{array}{ccccc}
\mathrm{H_2CO\,(P)} & & \mathrm{CHO} & & \mathrm{H_2CO\,(P)} \\
| & & | & & | \\
\mathrm{C{=}O} & + & \mathrm{(CHOH)_2} & \rightarrow & \mathrm{C{=}O} \\
| & & | & & | \\
\mathrm{H_2COH} & & \mathrm{H_2CO_2\,(P)} & & \mathrm{(CHOH)_4} \\
 & & & & | \\
 & & & & \mathrm{H_2CO\,(P)}
\end{array} \qquad (24\text{–}4)
$$

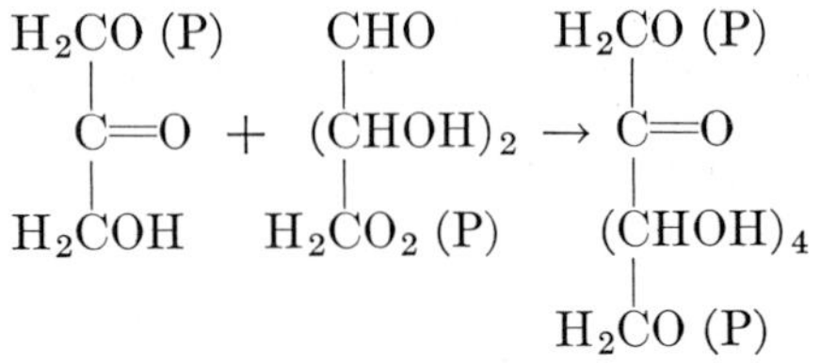

The C_4 molecule may be produced by enzymatic scission of fructose.

It was at one time suggested that the acceptor was a C_2 molecule, arising from the scission of pentose or heptose, but Calvin and his collaborators now believe [17] that ribulose diphosphate reacts enzymatically with CO_2 to give phosphoglyceric acid. This, as noted above, is reduced to the triose phosphate, a reaction which requires a takeup of photochemical energy. By the series of changes suggested above, the triose then gives saccharose and forms ribulose once again, as the monophosphate, which is transformed photochemically into the diphosphate, and the cycle begins again. The complete photosynthetic cycle proposed by Calvin is shown schematically in Fig. 24–2.

Photosynthetic investigations using tracers have also been carried out in a number of other laboratories; the results obtained are not always in agreement with the scheme just described [18, 19, 20]. Boitchenko and Zakharova [21] in particular have criticized Calvin and his group for using too high specific activities of C^{14}, whose radiation may affect the normal development of the photosynthetic process. These authors also report that special care is necessary to minimize alteration of the chloroplasts during the experiments. To this end, they transferred the green leaves of *Primula obconica* into an iso-osmotic solution of saccharose, held at 1 to 3°C, and separated the chloroplast by centrifuging; 60% acetone was then added to the solution, and the precipitate formed again separated by centrifuging. According to these authors, the phosphoglyceric acid is in the filtrate; the CO_2 acceptor, which is in the precipitate, contains 1% iron, which is essential for the assimilation of carbon dioxide.

The problem of the mechanisms of the biosynthesis of the nucleic acids, which are extremely complex macromolecules, has also been attacked by various authors by administering purines, pyrimidines, etc., labeled with C^{14} or other tracers to rats, and subsequently carrying out chemical degradations of the metabolic products.* Work with C^{14} on the biosyn-

---

* For a bibliography, see Refs. 22 and 23.

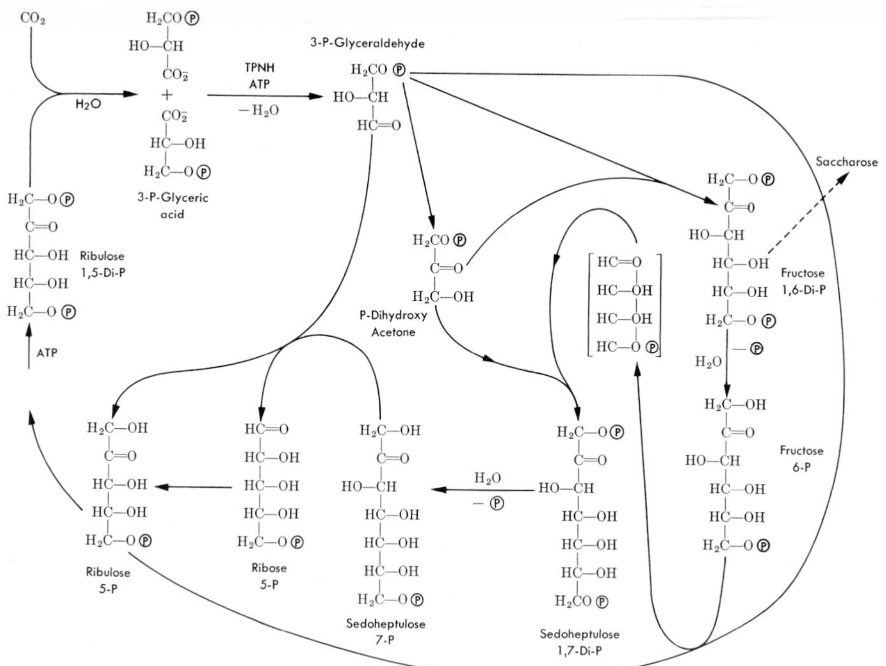

FIG. 24–2. The carbon cycle in photosynthesis (Ref. 17).

thesis of haemoglobin *in vitro* gave evidence for a mechanism involving the formation of the porphyrin from glycol and acetates, and identified the origin of the various carbon atoms in the molecule [24].

Despite its very short half-life (21 min) the isotope C^{11} was successfully used in a number of metabolic studies before C^{14} was available. Conant [25, 26], for example, used this tracer to follow the formation of glycogen in animals to which labeled lactate, bicarbonate, or fatty acids had been administered, and established the probable mechanism for the metabolism of this important compound. This isotope has also been used to examine the subsequent elimination by the human body of carbon monoxide inhaled in less than toxic quantities [27].

We shall also mention some results obtained with radiocarbon for enzymatic processes. We saw earlier (Section 23–5) that glucose is decomposed in the presence of mineral acids to give formic and levulinic acids. In the presence of *Lactobacillus casei*, however, lactic acid is formed. After establishing the distribution of C^{14} among the different positions of the labeled glucose, it was possible to identify the origin of each carbon atom in the acid formed [28, 29]

$$\begin{array}{c} \overset{1}{\text{HOCH}}\text{—}\overset{2}{\text{CHOH}}\text{—}\overset{3}{\text{CHOH}}\text{—}\overset{4}{\text{CHOH}}\text{—}\overset{5}{\text{CH}}\text{—}\overset{6}{\text{CH}_2\text{OH}} \\ \llcorner\_\_\_\_\_\_\_\_\_\_\text{O}\_\_\_\_\_\_\_\_\_\_\lrcorner \\ \rightarrow 2\,\underset{1,6}{\text{CH}_3}\text{—}\underset{2,5}{\text{CHOH}}\text{—}\underset{3,4}{\text{CO}_2\text{H}}. \end{array} \qquad (24\text{–}5)$$

The theory proposed by O. Meyerhof to explain the alcoholic fermentation of glucose, from which it follows that radiocarbon in position 1 should be found uniquely in the methyl group of CH_3CH_2OH, is also confirmed experimentally [30].

On fermentation with *Methanobacterium omelianskii*, methanol gives methane and carbon dioxide

$$4CH_3OH \rightarrow 3CH_4 + CO_2 + 2H_2O. \qquad (24\text{–}6)$$

When this process is carried out in the presence of bicarbonate labeled with C^{11}, the methane obtained is radioactive [31], which implies that the CO_2 is not only a product of the reaction, but that it takes part in the formation of CH_4. Similar experiments on the fermentation of acetic acid with CO_2 labeled with C^{14} showed that the methane formed contained only 0.5 to 2% of the activity, so that in this case the CH_4 is produced by a mechanism involving the decomposition of acetic acid itself [32, 33]. In contrast to this, the same technique applied to the fermentation of propionic acid showed that here the CO_2 and CH_4 can come from the three carbon atoms of the acid, and that CO_2 is at least a partial precursor in the formation of methane [34].

The formation of caproic acid from ethanol and butyric acid in the presence of *Clostridium kluyveri* has been studied by labeling the carboxylic acid group with C^{14} [35]. After the fermentation, only the carbon in the β-position of the caproic acid was found to be active. The acetic acid which had been added to the mixture before the reaction was inactive, proving the absence of exchange between the labeled carboxylic group and the intermediate C_2 fragments in equilibrium with acetic acid. It is concluded from this that the carboxyl group is reduced to CH_2, and that the CH_2OH group of the alcohol is oxidized to carboxyl

$$CH_3(CH_2)_2C^{14}OOH + CH_3CH_2OH \rightarrow CH_3(CH_2)_2C^{14}H_2CH_2COOH + H_2O. \qquad (24\text{–}7)$$

24–2 Metabolic studies with stable isotopes. The fundamental work of Schoenheimer [36, 37] on fatty acids, amino acids, and carbohydrates labeled with deuterium, N^{15}, or P^{32} in living organisms demonstrated quite clearly the essentially dynamic character of the synthetic processes and transformation in organs and tissues. Atoms and molecules which at any given moment may be localized in specific chemical forms in a cell or other organism pass at different rates into other forms in other cells or organs as a result of the continuous processes of renewal, formation, degradation, and reconstitution. Later experiments showed that these constant exchanges and dynamic equilibria extend to all tissue, including the bones and teeth, although in these latter cases the rates of renewal may be much smaller; such exchanges also involve the structural components of the body, as well as products introduced in food.

When a deuterated fatty acid is incorporated into food, the deuterium rapidly appears in the fatty acids in all the organs. If D_2O is injected into adult rats, which are subsequently given drinking water whose isotopic composition is such that the deuterium content of the body liquid remains constant, half the fatty acid molecules attain the average deuterium content of the body within a few days. If the food contains casein with ammonium citrate labeled with heavy nitrogen [38, 39], the latter is found in all the amino-acids of the body (with the exception of lysine), in the creatine in the muscles, in the hippuric acid in the urine, etc., in a few days. These processes are particularly rapid if the animal's diet is deficient in proteins, but even if the diet is balanced in nitrogen, the migration of the tracer still occurs. The same is true if the animal is fed with glycine, leucine, tyrosine, or other N^{15}-labeled amino-acids.

From the rate of assimilation of the tracer, it can be calculated that half the proteins are renewed in the liver of rats at the end of 5 to 6 days; in the blood plasma of the dog after 1 to 2 weeks; and much more slowly in the muscles. Different amino-acids behave differently in this respect; thus tyrosine gives up most of its N^{15} to liver proteins, and less to the plasma, but the reverse is found for leucine. Half the cholesterol in a mouse is renewed in 3 weeks. If deuterated acetate is added to the diet of rats and mice, the cholesterol extracted from these animals contains large quantities of deuterium, so that the organism is capable of synthesizing this compound from acetates [40].

The exceptional behavior of lysine, mentioned above, can be explained by the fact that this amino-acid is not synthesized by the organism. This has been proved [41] by double labeling the α-position with D and N^{15}, $NH_2(CH_2)_4CD(N^{15}H_2)COOH$; the D : N^{15} ratio did not change when the amino-acid passed through an organism. This result also shows that the deamination of this compound is irreversible, since substitution of $N^{14}H_2$ group for $N^{15}H_2$ would have caused an increase in the D : N^{15} ratio. Similar experiments established the reversible deamination of leucine, although the latter is not synthesized by the organism either.

With the help of these two indicators, Schoenheimer [42] has also showed that the formation of creatine

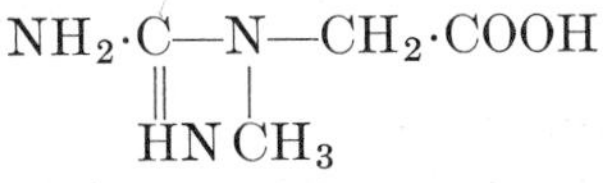

$$\begin{array}{l} NH_2\cdot C\!-\!N\!-\!CH_2\cdot COOH \\ \qquad\;\, \| \quad\; | \\ \qquad HN\;CH_3 \end{array}$$

in muscle requires the presence of three amino-acids: glycine ($NH_2\cdot CH_2\cdot COOH$), arginine which provides the

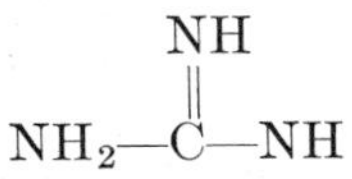

$$\begin{array}{c} NH \\ \| \\ NH_2\!-\!C\!-\!NH \end{array} \quad \text{group,}$$

and methionine which furnishes the methyl group. The mechanism of the transformation of creatine into creatinine

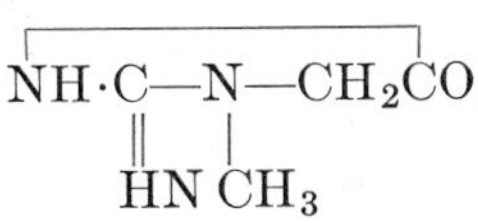

$$\begin{array}{l} \overline{NH\cdot C\!-\!N\!-\!CH_2CO} \\ \qquad \| \quad\; | \\ \quad\;\; HN\;CH_3 \end{array}$$

by irreversible dehydration has also been established by using N^{15}.

The metabolic rate of proteins in various tissues of the rat, measured by incorporating deuterium into the animal, decreases in the order liver, intestine, spleen, kidney, stomach, heart, lung, brain [43].

The natural fatty acids almost always contain an even number of carbon atoms. This has led to the suggestion that the synthesis and decomposition of these acids in organisms takes place by the addition and loss of C_2 groups, and that in oxidation, oxygen attacks the carbon in the β-position to the carboxyl group:

$$CH_3(CH_2)_n\overset{\beta}{C}H_2\overset{\alpha}{C}H_2COOH \rightarrow CH_3(CH_2)_{n-2}\overset{\beta}{C}H_2\overset{\alpha}{C}H_2COOH, \qquad (24\text{–}8)$$

$$CH_3(CH_2)_4\overset{\beta}{C}H_2\overset{\alpha}{C}H_2COOH \rightarrow CH_3CH_2CH_2COOH \rightarrow \begin{cases} CH_3COCH_2COOH, \\ 2CH_3COOH. \end{cases} \qquad (24\text{–}9)$$

This hypothesis was confirmed [44] by feeding rats with palmitic acid labeled with deuterium in the β-position. In the acids subsequently eliminated from the animal, 24% of the deuterium was found in palmitic acid itself (C_{16}), 10% in stearic acid (C_{18}), 6% in myristic acid (C_{14}) and lauric acid (C_{12}), and a little more than 1% in the unsaturated C_{18} acids, oleic and linoleic. Conversely, if the animal is fed with labeled stearic acid, deutero-palmitic acid is found, and on introducing labeled oleic acid, the deuterium appears in those saturated acids which contain an even number of carbon atoms. On adding acetic acid labeled with both D and C^{13} to the diet ($CD_3C^{13}OOH$), the two indicators are found to alternate in the liver fatty acids, that is,

$$CD_3 \cdot C^{13}H_2 \cdot CD_2 \cdot C^{13}H_2 \ldots C^{13}OOH.$$

Certain enzymatic reactions have been studied using O^{18} as tracer. For example, some condensations of carboxylic acids with other compounds which take place in the organisms require an input of energy, which comes from the enzymatic hydrolysis of adenosine triphosphate (ATP). In order to establish the route by which this transfer of energy occurred, the carboxyl group of glutamic acid was labeled with O^{18} and this compound was then made to react with unlabeled ATP in the presence of glutamine synthetase [45]. Isotopic analysis of the products, after the necessary chemical treatment, showed that the oxygen of the carboxyl group is directly transferred to the phosphate group $\rightarrow PO_3O^{18}$ of the ATP, despite the covalent character of the bonds involved.

This indicator has also been used to identify the points at which the rupture and formation of bonds occurs in enzymatic reactions [46]. For example, the formation of glucose by the hydrolysis of saccharose (written here as F—O—G) in the presence of invertase can take place by one of two routes. Experiments with H_2O^{18} showed that the glucose formed was free from O^{18}, so that the bond breaking occurs by the upper of the two following paths:

$$\text{G}\text{—O—}\text{F} + H_2O^{18} \begin{cases} \rightarrow \text{G}\text{OH} + \text{HO}^{18}\text{F} \\ \rightarrow \text{G}\text{O}^{18}\text{H} + \text{HO}\text{F} \end{cases} \qquad (24\text{–}10)$$

24–3 Tracer studies with tritium. Attention has already been drawn (Section 18–1) to the care which is necessary in interpreting quantitative experiments using isotopes of hydrogen as tracers, since in such cases the isotope effects are not negligible. Thus on administering water labeled with deuterium [47, 48] and tritium [48] to rats and subsequently determining the two isotopes in various organs, a decrease of up to 20% in the T : D ratio was demonstrated. Equally, differences of 8 and 18% were found in the incorporation of these two tracers into glycogen and the liver fatty acids of rats. By growing algae in a medium containing water labeled with D and T as the only source of hydrogen, Weinberg and Porter showed that H is incorporated twice as fast as D and the latter 1.1 times as fast as tritium. Furthermore, the isotope effects varied with the chemical nature of the fractions isolated from the algae [49, 50].

Since tritium became available rather later than deuterium, less use has so far been made of it in biochemical studies. There has been particular interest in the fate of T_2O in organisms. Irrespective of the way in which this liquid is administered, it distributes itself rapidly and uniformly throughout the various body fluids. The normal half-life for its residence in human beings varies between 9 and 14 days, so that traces ($\sim$ 1/1000) may be found even 3 to 5 months after its introduction into the organism. Tritium has been used to show that the passage of water through the skin into the interior of the organism takes place on exposure to water vapor (see Ref. 51; this review gives other applications of T).

The distribution and retention of T_2O, and of tritiated organic compounds in various animal tissues, and in algae, yeast, protozoa, etc., have also been studied by several authors. Glascock and Reinius [52, 53] administered tritiated stearic acid, dissolved in ground-nut oil, orally to a she-goat, and then analyzed the lipids in the milk, and so determined the contribution of this acid to the formation of volatile fatty acids combined with glycerol and lactose. These authors also studied the metabolism of hexoestrol labeled with very high specific activity tritium (more than 500 μc/mg). The transformation of phenylalanine into adrenalin

$$C_6H_5{\cdot}CH_2{\cdot}CH(NH_2)COOH \rightarrow C_6H_3(OH)_2{\cdot}CHOH{\cdot}CH_2{\cdot}NH_2$$

in the tissue of rats has been demonstrated by using tritium and C^{14} [54]. These two indicators were also used in studying the metabolism of cholesterol, the stimulation of the synthesis of fatty acids by insulin [55, 56], and the structure of the hormone aldosterone [57].

24–4 Radiophosphorus. The phosphorus isotope of mass 32 is a tracer favored as much by its own nuclear properties (half-life, radiation, ease of preparation) as by the chemical properties of the element itself. Moreover, since this element is particularly important in the metabolism of fats, proteins, carbohydrates, and nucleic acids, and in respiration, muscular contraction, and the circulation of the blood, etc., radiophosphorus occupies a unique position in modern biochemical research. Hevesy was the first pioneer in this field, and he and his co-workers have contributed some of the most striking results obtained so far [1].

Inorganic phosphates do not exchange phosphorus with the phosphate esters of the body, such as glycerophosphates, nucleic acids, phosphatides, casein, lecithin, etc. This means that it is possible to study the metabolism of phosphorus by injecting it or administering it in some other way, as the orthophosphate ion. Hevesy has shown in the early work that most of the inorganic phosphate penetrates into the liver; once the cells of this organ are reached, this phosphate participates very rapidly in various biochemical processes (by phosphorylation and dephosphorylation) and passes into the muscle, the plasma, the brain, the skeleton, and other tissues. Radiophosphorus has been used to determine the rate of renewal of the various organic forms of the element in tissue, and to localize the organs in which these are synthesized. Thus half the terminal phosphorus atoms in ATP are renewed in a few seconds, while the phosphorus of the desoxyribonucleic acid is renewed only very slightly after one month.

The assimilation of phosphorus into the liver is related to the activity of the respiratory enzymes; in the absence of oxygen, or in the presence of CO, H_2S, HCN, which inhibit respiration, the rate of assimilation is decreased by a factor of about 20. In the muscles, phosphorus exchanges rapidly into creatine-phosphoric acid, and into the adenosine- and hexose-phosphates, but more slowly into the phospholipids. Phosphorus is actively involved in the chemical transformations related to muscular effort, but even at rest it exchanges intensively into the muscles.

Phosphate penetrates slowly into brain tissue, the assimilation being accelerated in the presence of hexoses. It reaches the bones by the circulatory system, and deposits essentially in the form of tri-calcium phosphate (apatite). Because of the high phosphorus content of the skeleton, and the slow rate of phosphorus metabolism, a very large part of any radiophosphorus administered ends up in the bones.

By injecting Na_3PO_4 into gravid mice and determining the radiophosphorus in the tissue of the offspring, Hevesy showed that an adult animal retains about 40% of the phosphorus which it possessed at birth, and that about ten generations are necessary before this phosphorus disappears completely.

Molecules labeled with radiophosphorus or radiosulfur can be used to study the relationship between metabolism in the brain and the level of its functional development [58]. Results on the metabolism of phospholipids, nucleic acids, and nucleo-proteins, carbohydrates, etc., can be found in the specialized texts. Radiophosphorus has been widely used in such work by G. Hevesy, L. Hahn, I. L. Chaikoff, E. Chargaff, and several other authors. This indicator, and C^{14}, have also been used in research into vegetable metabolism, including the rate at which phosphorus passes from a culture solution into the germs of wheat, oats, and sunflowers; the exchange, absorption, and migration of phosphates from fertilizers into the soil (see Section 35–5); the way in which the roots of plants function; etc.

24–5 Radiosulfur and radioiodine. Unlike the metabolism of phosphorus, which can be studied by introducing inorganic phosphates into the organism, the study of sulfur metabolism requires the administration of certain organic compounds. Normal rats fed with labeled colloidal sulfur retained less than 0.3% of the tracer in the liver proteins and other internal organs after 48 hours [59, 60]. If sulfur is introduced into the stomach as Na_2S, most of it is eliminated in the urine as sulfate [61]; a very small fraction remains in the hair, liver, skin, and muscles, as cystine. On the other hand, after the administration of 1 mg of methionine

$$CH_3{\cdot}S^{35}{\cdot}(CH_2)_2{\cdot}CH(NH_2){\cdot}COOH$$

to starved rats, 56% of the S^{35} is found in the proteins in various organs, and 36% as sulfates [60]. The incorporation of radiosulfur introduced in this way into cystine is fairly rapid, and in general these results confirm the conclusions of Schoenheimer on the rapid scission and formation of peptide bonds.

It has been possible to show with radiosulfur that the enzymatic degradation of cystine and cysteine in the liver of a dog or a rat is reversible, whereas the *in vitro* degradation is irreversible [62].

Sulfur administered to plants as sulfite or sulfate is rapidly transformed into organic forms [63]; when it migrates from the leaves the roots or seeds, it goes transiently through the form of sulfate.

The radioisotopes of iodine, particularly the 8-day I^{131}, have been especially used in biochemistry in research on the thyroid, the endocrinal gland which secretes thyroxine,

$$HO{-}C_6H_2I_2{-}O{-}C_6H_2I_2{-}CH_2{-}CH(NH_2){-}COOH.$$

The thyroid contains other iodine compounds, such as tri-iodothyronine (with one iodine atom less than thyroxine) which has been recently identified in the gland by radioiodine studies, and the mono- and di-iodotyrosines.

When a labeled inorganic iodide is injected into an animal or a human being, the radioiodine rapidly concentrates in the thyroid as thyroxine and iodotyrosine [64, 65], but the capacity of the thyroid for uptake of iodine is limited. If the quantity of labeled iodine is of the order of a milligram, only a few percent pass into the gland, and the process is complete after about 10 min. If, however, the total dose of iodine is very small, the rate of uptake is slower, but virtually all of it is localized in the thyroid. The formation of di-iodotyrosine precedes that of thyroxine. This transformation is stimulated by another hormone which is produced by hypophysis pituitary, the destruction of which inhibits the synthesis of the labeled thyroxine but not of di-iodotyrosine [66]. By injecting labeled thyroxine into rabbits, it has been shown that this hormone penetrates directly from the thyroid into the cells of the pituitary [67, 68]. If a very strong dose of radioiodine is administered to a rat, the thyroid is destroyed [69], and thyroglobulin appears in the plasma, where it is rapidly destroyed, with the formation of radioactive thyroxine and radioactive iodide. The same decomposition is caused by administering labeled thyroglobulin [70].

Experiments with radioactive iodine have also shown that ablation of the thyroid does not completely stop the synthesis of thyroxine [71], although the process is considerably slowed down; the hormone, and di-iodothyronine, are then found in the small intestine, liver, plasma, and muscles. Compounds which inhibit the respiratory enzymes, such as CO, H_2S, HCN, etc., prevent the hormone synthesis in the thyroid. Fixation of radioiodine in the gland is also reduced by the effect of certain substances known as antithyroidyns, such as thiourea, aminothiazol, thiocyanates, etc. [72, 73].

The homologues of iodine, bromine [74], and astatine [75, 76], are also selectively fixed by the thyroid, but to a lesser extent than iodine.

Radioactive sulfur and iodine have been used in immunology in research on the mechanism of the reaction of antigens and antibodies, and on the localization of antibodies injected into the body [77, 78]. Finally, radioactive iodine has been used to follow the diffusion of labeled proteins and toxins in the central nervous system.

24–6 Radioactive iron. The absorption of labeled iron, its transformation in tissue, and its elimination have been extensively studied by P. F. Hahn and his co-workers [79, 80, 81]. Experiments on a dog rendered anaemic by bleeding and subsequently fed with an iron salt showed that the tracer is already detectable in the erythrocytes after 4 hours. After 4 to 7 days, all the iron is found as haemoglobin. The uptake depends on the iron content of the tissues. If the reservoir of iron is large, absorption is very small, or zero; thus the administration of a fraction of a milligram of labeled iron resulted in assimilation of 85%, but only 12% was absorbed if quantities of the order of 5 mg were administered. The renewal of the red blood cells takes place by utilizing the iron from the old erythrocytes, without recourse to the reserves of iron. Similarly, if the erythrocytes are destroyed with acetylphenyl-hydrazine, the iron from their hemoglobin is used to form new haemoglobin molecules. If the animal is made to absorb first unlabeled iron, and then labeled iron, the latter is not assimilated. The activity acquired by the haemoglobin remains for a long time, proof of the high stability of these molecules. In summary then, the organism tends to make the maximum use of the iron available, and does not have recourse to exchange with absorbed products unless necessary. Iron then differs in this respect from the other inorganic constituents of the tissue, which as we have seen are rapidly renewed by exchange both with the reserves and with ingested food.

On feeding young rats with Fe^{55}, 0.45% of this is found to pass into the cytochrome-C, and 80% into the hemoglobin [82]. A dog can absorb both divalent and trivalent iron, but a man absorbs divalent iron much more easily than trivalent [83]. On the other hand, it has been shown [84] that inorganic iron and that from haemoglobin, combine in the interstinal mucous with the protein apoferritin to give ferritin, a crystallizable compound containing 23% iron. This is also found in the liver, bone marrow, and other tissue. It is thought that trivalent iron introduced into the organism with foodstuffs is reduced to Fe(II), in which state it combines with apoferritin, and that the ferritin thus formed constitutes the reserve of iron. The absorption is controlled by the equilibrium established between the haemoglobin, the ferritin, and the free Fe^{2+} ions, the concentration of which in its turn depends on the redox conditions of the medium.

24–7 Circulation and permeability in organisms. Radioactive isotopes of those elements which are mainly found in the extracellular fluid such as Na^+, K^+ or Cl^-, have been particularly used to study the circulation of these liquids through the organism, and to investigate cell permeability. The rapidity of this circulation is simply demonstrated with deuterated or tritiated water; after one minute, the tritium distribution in the extravascular fluid corresponds to 95% of the equilibrium condition, and complete homogeneity is attained in 3 min [85]. Penetration into the intravascular fluid is slower. By introducing tritiated water intravenously into a man, and measuring the tritium content of blood samples removed periodically, it has been shown that virtually constant values are reached after half an hour [86]; the values correspond to a total weight of water equal to 65% of the body weight. Similar results have been obtained with deuterated water [87, 88]. The quantity of extracellular fluid in the human body, and in the bodies of rabbits and rats, has been determined by using Na^{24} or Cl^{38}. This fluid is of the order of 20% of the total body weight, and the volume of plasma in circulation corresponds to 7% of this weight [89].

Similar measurements have been carried out on the rate of circulation of other fluids, especially blood. By injecting $Na^{24}Cl$, it was shown that the time necessary for the blood to flow between the beginning of the femoral artery and the extremity of the tibial artery is 22 sec [90]. More precise measurements [91] have shown that the mixing of the salt into the blood is carried out in five successive stages, the first of which is complete in 30 sec, the second in two minutes, and the other three rather more slowly. Red blood cells removed from a human subject can be labeled with P^{32} by isotopic exchange with radiophosphate dissolved in isotonic solution (NaCl). If the labeled blood is then reinjected, the volume of blood and its rate of circulation can be determined by removing further blood samples. Three minutes are necessary to homogenize the mixture in normal subjects; violent muscular effort has no effect on the results [92]. By an improved technique, Govaerts [93] has found that the human body contains 73 to 75 ml of blood per kilogram. For dogs, an approximately linear relationship has been established between the volume of blood and the weight of the animal [94].

Radiophosphorus has also been used to measure the number of red cells circulating in various parts of the body, and to determine the life cycle of the erythrocytes. A time of 28 days has been found for the average life of red blood cells in hens. Shemin and Rittenberg have concluded from experiments involving the administration of N^{15}-labeled glycine that the life of the red cells in man is, on the average, 127 days, corresponding to the renewal of 0.85% per day [95].

The absorption of gas by an organism, and the dependence of this absorption on temperature and salt concentration, have been measured using radioactive krypton [96] and other labeled inert gases.

The permeability of the blood capilliaries (tiny channels whose diameter is of the same order of that of the red blood cells) to inorganic ions has been widely studied with tracers. For example, by injecting Na^{24} intravenously and measuring the rate at which the activity in the plasma decreased, it was possible to determine the permeability of the capillaries to these ions, since the rate of exchange between the blood plasma and the intercellular fluid depends on this permeability. The concentration in the plasma varies with time according to the equation [71]

$$c - c_{\text{eq}} = (c_0 - c_{\text{eq}})e^{-(k/q)t}, \tag{24–11}$$

where c_{eq} is the equilibrium concentration of Na^{24+} in the plasma, c_0 the initial concentration, and q the extravascular fraction of the total sodium. The exchange of radioactive sodium between blood and the cerebro-spinal fluid has recently been studied on 200 normal and abnormal subjects [98, 99].

The permeability is greater for Na^+ ions than for K^+, and still greater than for PO_4^{3-} and halide ions. The mechanism of the processes are also entirely different. The diffusion of K^+ or Cl^- ions across a membrane (for example, the skin of a frog in isotonic solution) obeys the equation [100, 101]

$$\frac{F_i}{F_e} = \frac{c_o f_o}{c_i f_i} e^{ET/RT}, \tag{24–12}$$

in which F_i and F_e are the flux of the ions to the interior and the exterior, $c_o f_o$ and $c_i f_i$ are the thermodynamic activities of the ions in the exterior and interior, E is the potential difference, and the other symbols have their usual meaning. This relation is not valid for the diffusion of sodium [74], which has been studied simultaneously in both directions using Na^{22} and Na^{24}. Moreover, if an external emf is applied to keep the concentration potential difference on the two sides of the membrane at zero, F_i becomes equal to F_e in the case of the K^+ or Cl^- ions, but the diffusion of Na^+ ions from the exterior is greatly in excess of that from the interior. The net flux of these ions is equivalent to the electric current transferred across the membrane. Finally, the transport is inhibited by poisons, such as cyanide, narcotics, dinitrophenol, etc. On the whole, these experiments show that the diffusion of Na^+ is a vital process, related to metabolic processes involving a free energy change.

The capilliary permeability for other ions, such as Rb^+, Sr^{2+}, Fe^{3+},

Zn^{2+}, Ra^{2+}, SO_4^{2-}, etc., has also been investigated with tracers, as has the rates of penetration of these various ions into cells. Other studies have been carried out on the metabolism of fluorine, calcium, manganese, cobalt, copper, zinc, and other minor constituents of organisms, using the appropriate tracers. The first of these metals, along with radiosodium, radiostrontium, and to a lesser degree radiofluorine and sulfur, have been particularly used in research on different metabolic processes in the bone skeleton.

24–8 Clinical and therapeutic applications. As in many other fields, the sensitivity of radioactive methods, and especially the activation method (Section 22–5), has proved extremely valuable in toxicology and pharmacology for research on trace elements, such as Mn, Co, Zn, As, Au, and many other elements normally or accidentally present in an organism. Thus gold concentrations of the order of 10^{-6} in the kidneys of invalids treated with colloidal gold can be detected by neutron activation and scintillation measurements [103]. The arsenic content of the skin can also be determined in patients with tumors caused by this element. The technique of searching for arsenic in the hair of suspected victims of arsenical poisoning has become normal practice in forensic medicine, although perhaps after insufficient prior investigation.

One of the most important of these applications is the study of metabolism, either in pathological conditions, or in the presence of medicine or toxic substances. Depending upon the particular problem, either these materials or the metabolized substances are labeled. It has been shown, for example, that the rate of elimination of an amino-acid labeled with C^{14} on the carboxyl group is different in a normal laboratory animal and in an animal with a tumor, but that these rates are the same if the methyl group is labeled [104]. A tumor in the mammary glands of a mouse stimulates the metabolism of P^{32}-labeled desoxyribonucleic acid in the normal tissue [105]. Such tests can therefore be used to detect neoplastic tissue.

Between 25 and 50% of radiophosphorus injected intravenously into a normal subject is eliminated in 4 to 6 days, principally in the urine, but in a case of leukemia, only 5 to 25% is eliminated over the same period [106]. It also seems that in some cases a malignant tumor (breast cancer) can be distinguished from a benign tumor from the fraction of radiophosphorus which is fixed, although the method is limited by the tendency of the radioelement to fix in certain rapidly growing normal tissues [107].

P. F. Hahn and his collaborators [108, 109] have reported that the total volume of blood in a dog is constant, and independent of the anaemic condition; when the volume of red cells diminishes, that of the plasma increases. The rate at which radioiron introduced as $Fe^{59}Cl_3$ is eliminated from the plasma has been measured under various pathological conditions. Even highly anaemic subjects are capable of producing the red cells at a normal rate, which suggests that anaemia is related to an insufficient average life for these cells [110].

Regeneration of the blood tissue of a rat after *in toto* irradiation with 450 roentgens of x-rays has been studied by Lamerton, *et al.*, using radioactive iron [111]. This tracer has also been used to prove that liver extract and folic acid accelerate the uptake of iron in the bone marrow of patients with pernicious anaemia [112]. Other clinical uses of radioiron are discussed in Ref. 113. The effects of adrenalin on the volume of blood in circulation has been examined with radiophosphorus [91]. Double labeling with P^{32} and Cr^{51} has been used to measure the volume of blood in a cat before and after bleeding [114].

Radiosodium [114] and radioactive krypton [115] have been used to follow the circulation of extracellular fluids through various regions of the organism of invalids. The dynamics of the circulation of blood through the heart has been examined [116] using an apparatus known as a "radiocardiograph"; this consists of two counters with appropriate screens which are placed above the heart of the invalid after the intravenous injection of Na^{24}. At suitable intervals, the register records waves corresponding to the passage of blood containing radioactive sodium through the two sides of the heart; in cardiac patients these waves are deformed, and half of them may even be missing completely.

Radioactive sodium has been used to demonstrate the effect of traumatic shock on the capilliary permeability [117]. Experiments with proteins labeled with radiosulfur or radioiodine show that the proteins disappear at the same rate in a normal dog and in a dog which has undergone a shock [118].

Administration of radioactive phosphorus [119], radioactive calcium, and radioactive strontium [120] into rachitic animals has been used to study the metabolism of these elements after injecting vitamin D. Radiophosphorus has also been used in work on the metabolism of phosphates in the blood, liver, and muscles after intravenous injections of insulin [121] or other compounds. The fate of insulin itself (labeled with radioactive iodine) injected into a rabbit has been studied in its relation with the concentration of blood sugar [122]. The distribution of radioactive nicotine in the tissue of rats and mice has been examined by various authors [123, 124]. The selective absorption of labeled elements by certain normal or abnormal tissues means that these radioelements have considerable application in the diagnosis of disease, and in therapy. Thus radioactive iodide has been particularly used in the diagnosis of disorders of the thyroid (hyperthyroidism and carcinoma). Since this tracer is rapidly concentrated in the thyroid by normal subjects, the tests are based on measurements of the rate of absorption of radioactive iodine by the thyroid, or of the activity combined with proteins in the plasma, or of the rate of elimination of the tracer by the thyroid. Since this latter process follows an exponential law [125], it is possible to define a "biological half-life" (T_b) which is related to the radioactive half-life T_r by the relation

$$\frac{1}{T_e} = \frac{1}{T_b} + \frac{1}{T_r},$$

where T_e is the half-life actually measured for the organism. With I^{131} ($T_r = 8$ days), Rotblat and Owen found $T_e = 62$ days for subjects with normal thyroids, $T_e = 11.5$ days for those with hyperthyroidism, and 7.2 days for cases of carcinoma.

References

1. G. Hevesy, *Radioactive Indicators: Application to Biochemistry, Animal Physiology and Pathology,* Interscience, New York, 1948.
2. E. C. Dougherty, in *Isotopic Tracers,* W. E. Siri, ed., McGraw-Hill, New York, 1949.
3. M. D. Kamen, *Radioactive Tracers in Biology,* Academic Press, New York, 1949.
4. M. Calvin, C. Heidelberger, J. C. Reid, B. M. Tolbert, and P. F. Yankwich, *Isotopic Carbon,* Wiley and Sons, New York, 1949.
5. T. H. Norris, S. Ruben, and M. B. Allen, *J. Am. Chem. Soc.,* **64,** 3037 (1942).
6. M. Calvin and S. Aronoff, *U.S.A.E.C. report UCRL-263* (1948).
7. A. P. Vinogradov and R. V. Teis, *Doklady Akad. Nauk S.S.S.R.,* **33,** 490 (1941); **56,** 59 (1947).
8. A. P. Vinogradov and E. I. Dontsova, *Doklady Akad. Nauk S.S.S.R.,* **56,** 391 (1947).
9. S. Ruben, M. Randall, M. D. Kamen, and J. L. Hyde, *J. Am. Chem. Soc.,* **63,** 877 (1941).
10. M. Dole and G. Jenks, *Science,* **100,** 409 (1944).
11. A. A. Benson and M. Calvin, *Science,* **105,** 648 (1947); **107,** 476 (1948).
12. M. Calvin, J. A. Bassham, and A. A. Benson, *Federation Proc.,* **9,** 524 (1940).
13. M. Calvin, J. A. Bassham, and A. A. Benson, *J. Chem. Educ.,* **30,** 274 (1953).
14. M. Calvin and P. Massini, *U.S.A.E.C. report UCRL-1950,* 1952.
15. M. Calvin, *Chem. Eng. News,* **31,** 1622, 1735 (1953); **32,** 3833 (1954).
16. M. Calvin, J. A. Bassham, A. A. Benson, and P. Massini, *Ann. Rev. Phys. Chem.,* **3,** 215 (1952).
17. M. Calvin and J. A. Bassham, *1955 Geneva Conference,* P. 259.
18. E. W. Fager, H. Gaffron, and J. L. Rosenberg, *Federation Proc.,* **9,** 535 (1950).
19. E. W. Fager, *Arch. Biochem. Biophys.,* **37,** 5 (1952); **41,** 383 (1952).
20. S. Aronoff and L. Vernon, *Arch. Biochem.,* **27,** 239 (1950); **28,** 424 (1950); **29,** 179 (1950).
21. E. A. Boichenko and N. I. Zakharova, *Sess. Acad. Sci., U.S.S.R., Biol. Sect.,* July 1–5, 1955, p. 184.
22. G. B. Brown, *1955 Geneva Conference,* P. 260.
23. C. A. Villee, *Ann. Rev. Nuclear Sci.,* **1,** 525 (1952).
24. D. Shemin and J. Wittenberg, *J. Biol. Chem.,* **192,** 315 (1951).
25. J. B. Conant, R. D. Cramer, A. B. Hastings, F. W. Klemperer, A. K. Solomon, and B. Vennesland, *J. Biol. Chem.,* **137,** 557 (1941).
26. A. K. Solomon, B. Vennesland, F. W. Klemperer, J. M. Buchanan, and A. B. Hastings, *J. Biol. Chem.,* **140,** 171 (1941).
27. C. A. Tobias, J. H. Lawrence, F. J. W. Roughton, W. S. Root, and M. I. Gregersen, *Am. J. Physiol.,* **145,** 263 (1945).
28. H. G. Wood, N. Lifson and V. Lorber, *J. Biol. Chem.,* **159,** 475 (1946).
29. S. Aronoff, H. A. Barker, and M. Calvin, *J. Biol. Chem.,* **169,** 459 (1947).

30. D. KOSHLAND and F. H. WESTHEIMER, *J. Am. Chem. Soc.*, **71,** 1139 (1949).

31. H. A. BARKER, S. RUBEN, and M. D. KAMEN, *Proc. Natl. Acad. Sci. U. S.*, **26,** 426 (1940).

32. A. M. BUSWELL and F. W. SOLLO, *J. Am. Chem. Soc.*, **70,** 1778 (1948).

33. T. C. STADTMAN and H. A. BARKER, *Arch. Biochem.*, **21,** 256 (1949).

34. A. M. BUSWELL, L. FINA, H. MUELLER, and A. YAHIRO, *J. Am. Chem. Soc.*, **73,** 1809 (1951).

35. H. A. BARKER, M. D. KAMEN, and B. T. BORNSTEIN, *Proc. Natl. Acad. Sci. U. S.*, **31,** 373 (1946).

36. R. SCHOENHEIMER, *Dynamic State of Body Constituents*, Harvard University Press, 1942.

37. R. SCHOENHEIMER and D. RITTENBERG, *J. Biol. Chem.*, **111,** 163, 169, 175 (1935); **113,** 505 (1936); **114,** 381 (1936); **117,** 485 (1937); **120,** 155 (1937).

38. R. SCHOENHEIMER, S. RATNER, and D. RITTENBERG, *Science*, **89,** 272 (1939).

39. R. SCHOENHEIMER, S. RATNER, and D. RITTENBERG, *J. Biol. Chem.*, **127,** 301, 333 (1939); **130,** 703 (1939).

40. K. BLOCH and D. RITTENBERG, *J. Biol. Chem.*, **143,** 297 (1942); **145,** 625 (1942).

41. N. WEISSMAN and R. SCHOENHEIMER, *J. Biol. Chem.*, **140,** 779 (1941).

42. K. BLOCH and R. SCHOENHEIMER, *J. Biol. Chem.*, **131,** 111 (1939).

43. S. Y. DAVYDOVA and A. S. KONIKOVA, *Doklady Akad. Nauk S.S.S.R.*, **73,** 349 (1950).

44. D. STETTEN and D. RITTENBERG, *J. Biol. Chem.*, **133,** 329 (1940).

45. D. E. KOSHLAND, *1955 Geneva Conference* P. 262.

46. D. E. KOSHLAND and S. S. STEIN *J. Biol. Chem.* **208,** 139 (1954).

47. R. F. GLASCOCK and W. G. DUNCOMBE *Biochem. J.*, **51,** 11 (1952).

48. M. L. EIDINOFF, G. C. PERRI, J. E. KNOLL, B. J. MARANO, and J. ARNHEIM, *J. Am. Chem. Soc.*, **75,** 248 (1953).

49. D. WEINBERG and J. W. PORTER, *Science*, **117,** 636 (1953).

50. D. WEINBERG and J. W. PORTER, *Arch. Biochem. Biophys.*, **50,** 160 (1954).

51. E. A. PINSON and E. ANDERSON, quoted by R. C. Thompson, *Nucleonics*, **12,** No. 9, 31 (1954).

52. R. F. GLASCOCK and L. R. REINIUS, *Proc. 2nd Oxford Radioisotope Conf.*, Vol. 1, p. 262 (1954).

53. R. F. GLASCOCK, *1955 Geneva Conference*, P. 456.

54. S. GURIN and A. M. DELLUVA, *J. Biol. Chem.*, **170,** 545 (1947).

55. M. BIGGS and D. KRITCHEVSKY, *Arch. Biochem. Biophys.*, **36,** 430 (1952).

56. J. H. BALMAIN, S. J. FOLLEY, and R. F. GLASCOCK, *Biochem. J.*, **53,** 26 (1953).

57. P. AVIVI, S. A. SIMPSON, J. F. TAIT, and J. K. WHITEHEAD, *Proc. 2nd Oxford Radioisotope Conf.*, Vol. 1, p. 313 (1954).

58. A. V. PALLADIN and G. E. VLADIMIROV, *1955 Geneva Conference*, P. 710.

59. H. TARVER and C. L. A. SCHMIDT, *J. Biol. Chem.*, **130,** 67 (1939); **146,** 69 (1942).

60. H. TARVER and W. O. REINHARDT, *J. Biol. Chem.*, **167,** 395 (1947).

61. D. D. DZIEWIATOWSKI, *J. Biol. Chem.*, **164,** 165 (1946).

62. C. V. SMYTHE and D. HALLIDAY, *J. Biol. Chem.*, **144,** 237 (1942).

63. M. D. Thomas, R. H. Hendricks, L. C. Bryner, and G. R. Hill, *Plant Physiology*, **19**, 227 (1944).

64. S. Hertz, A. Roberts, and R. D. Evans, *Proc. Soc. Exptl. Biol. Med.*, **38**, 510 (1938).

65. I. Perlman, M. E. Morton, and I. L. Chaikoff, *J. Biol. Chem.*, **139**, 433, 449 (1941).

66. M. E. Morton, I. Perlman, E. Anderson, and I. L. Chaikoff, *Endocrinology*, **30**, 495 (1942).

67. F. Joliot, R. Courrier, A. Horeau, and P. Süe, *Compt. rend.*, **218**, 769 (1944).

68. F. Joliot, R. Courrier, A. Horeau, and P. Süe, *Compt. rend. Soc. Biol.*, **139**, 278 (1945).

69. J. G. Hamilton and J. H. Lawrence, *J. Clin. Investigation*, **21**, 624 (1942).

70. F. Brown and H. Jackson, *Nature*, **175**, 472 (1955).

71. M. E. Morton, I. L. Chaikoff, W. O. Reinhardt, and E. Anderson, *J. Biol. Chem.*, **147**, 757 (1943).

72. R. W. Rawson, J. F. Tannheimer, and W. Peacock, *Endocrinology*, **34**, 245 (1944).

73. A. S. Keston, E. D. Goldsmith, A. S. Gordon, and H. A. Charipper, *J. Biol. Chem.*, **152**, 241 (1944).

74. I. Perlman, M. E. Morton, and I. L. Chaikoff, *Am. J. Physiol.*, **134**, 107 (1941).

75. J. G. Hamilton and M. H. Soley, *Proc. Nat. Acad. Sci. U. S.*, **26**, 483 (1940).

76. J. G. Hamilton, P. W. Durbin, and M. W. Parrott, *Proc. 2nd Oxford Radioisotope Conf.*, Vol. 1, p. 219 (1954).

77. D. Pressman, in *Advances Biol. Med. Physics*, **3**, 146 (1943).

78. F. J. Dixon, *1955 Geneva Conference*, P. 182.

79. P. F. Hahn, W. F. Bale, G. H. Whipple, et al., *J. Exptl. Med.* (1939–1944).

80. P. F. Hahn, W. F. Bale, G. H. Whipple, et al., *Am. J. Physiol.* (1942–1945).

81. P. F. Hahn, W. F. Bale, G. H. Whipple, et al., *J. Biol. Chem.* (1943–1946), etc.

82. H. Beinert and H. Maier-Leibnitz, *Science*, **108**, 634 (1948).

83. C. V. Moore, R. Dubach, V. Minnich, and H. K. Roberts, *J. Clin. Investigation*, **23**, 755 (1944).

84. P. F. Hahn, S. Granick, W. F. Bale, and L. Michaelis, *J. Biol. Chem.*, **150**, 407 (1943).

85. L. B. Flexner, A. Gellhorn, and M. Merrell, *J. Biol. Chem.*, **144**, 35 (1942).

86. W. E. Siri, *Federation Proc.*, **12**, 133 (1953).

87. G. Hevesy and E. Hofer, quoted in Ref. 1.

88. F. D. Moore, *Science*, **104**, 157 (1946).

89. F. Morel, *Helv. Physiol. Acta*, **8**, 146 (1950).

90. E. H. Quimby and B. C. Smith, *Helv. Physiol. Acta*, **100**, 175 (1944).

91. G. F. Warner, *et al.*, quoted by J. H. Lawrence, *Bull. N. Y. Acad. Med.*, **26**, 639 (1950).

92. G. NYLIN, *Arkiv Kemi,* **20,** No. 17, 1 (1947).
93. J. GOVAERTS, *Acta Biol. Belg.,* **4,** 425 (1942).
94. S. MUKHERJEE and S. ROWLANDS, *Lancet,* **11,** 89 (1951).
95. D. SHEMIN and D. RITTENBERG, *J. Biol. Chem.,* **166,** 627 (1946).
96. S. F. COOK and W. N. SEARS, *Am. J. Physiol.,* **144,** 164 (1945).
97. M. MERRELL, A. GELLHORN, and L. B. FLEXNER, *J. Biol. Chem.,* **153,** 83 (1944).
98. M. TUBIANA, P. BENDA, J. CONSTANS, M. DAVID, and T. PLANIOL, *Rev. Neurol.,* **85,** 17 (1951); **89,** 101 (1953).
99. P. BENDA, T. PLANIOL, M. TUBIANA, and J. CONSTANS, *Proc. 2nd Oxford Radioisotope Conf.,* Vol. 1, p. 161 (1954).
100. T. TEORELL, *Arch. Sci. Physiol.,* **3,** 205 (1949).
101. H. H. USSING, *Acta Physiol. Scand.,* **19,** 43 (1949).
102. H. H. USSING, *1955 Geneva Conference,* P. 908.
103. W. V. MAYNEORD, *1955 Geneva Conference,* P. 768.
104. H. B. JONES, quoted by Lawrence, Ref. 91.
105. L. S. KELLY and H. B. JONES, *Science,* **111,** 333 (1950).
106. W. V. MAYNEORD, *Reports on Progress in Physics,* **14,** 366 (1951).
107. B. V. A. LOW-BEER, H. G. BELL, H. G. MCCORKLE, R. S. STONE, H. L. STEINBACH, and W. B. HILL, *Radiology,* **47,** 492 (1946).
108. P. F. HAHN, W. F. BALE, and W. M. BALFOUR, *Am. J. Physiol.,* **135,** 600 (1941).
109. W. M. BALFOUR, P. F. HAHN, W. F. BALE, W. T. POMMERENKE, and G. H. WHIPPLE, *J. Exptl. Med.,* **76,** 15 (1942).
110. J. H. LAWRENCE, Ref. 91.
111. L. F. LAMERTON, E. H. BELCHER, and E. B. HARRIS, *Proc. 2nd Oxford Radioisotope Conf.,* Vol. 1, p. 210 (1954).
112. R. J. WALSH, E. D. THOMÁS, S. K. CHOW, R. G. FLUHARTY, and C. A. FINCH, *Science,* **110,** 396 (1949).
113. E. M. LEDLIE and C. F. BAXTER, *Proc. 2nd Oxford Radioisotope Conf.,* Vol. 1, p. 97 (1954).
114. S. ROWLANDS, T. FREEMAN, and P. C. FLEMING, *Proc. 2nd Oxford Radioisotope Conf.,* p. 193 (1954).
115. C. A. TOBIAS, H. B. JONES, J. H. LAWRENCE, and J. G. HAMILTON, *J. Clin. Investigation,* **28,** 1375 (1949).
116. M. PRINZMETAL, E. CORDAY, R. SPRITZLER, and W. FLEIG, *J. Am. Med. Assoc.,* **139,** 617 (1949).
117. A. GELLHORN, M. MERRELL, and R. M. RANKIN, *Am. J. Physiol.,* **142,** 27 (1944).
118. A. M. SELIGMAN and J. FINE, *J. Clin. Investigation,* **22,** 265, 284 (1943).
119. N. SHIMOTORI and A. F. MORGAN, *J. Biol. Chem.,* **147,** 201 (1943).
120. D. M. GREENBERG, *J. Biol. Chem.,* **157,** 99 (1945).
121. N. O. KAPLAN and D. M. GREENBERG, *Am. J. Physiol.,* **140,** 598 (1944).
122. L. REINER, E. S. KESTON, and M. GREEN, *Science,* **92,** 362 (1946).
123. A. GANZ, *Federation Proc.,* **8,** 294 (1949).
124. T. KIMURA and E. GEILING, *Federation Proc.,* **8,** 308 (1949).
125. J. ROTBLAT and G. M. OWEN, *Proc. 2nd Oxford Radioisotope Conf.,* Vol. 1, p. 68 (1954).

CHAPTER 25

TECHNOLOGICAL AND INDUSTRIAL APPLICATIONS

The previous chapters have given discussions of several of the applications of the tracer method, and of isotopic and radioactive techniques, to the study of the fundamental properties of matter, and of physico-chemical processes. Many of these are directly or indirectly related to problems which have arisen in the development of various industries, including, for example, diffusion and self-diffusion in metals, the structure of catalysts and the mechanism of catalytic action, adsorption on surfaces, electrolytic deposition, corrosion, polymerization, fermentation, aerosol formation, the problem of the latent image, analytical methods, etc. The present chapter is concerned with a number of applications of a more technological and applied nature carried out at either the laboratory or production level. We shall not be concerned in this chapter with the distinction between those techniques based on atomic properties of the isotopes (the tracer method) and those which make use of the emitted radiations.

25–1 Metallurgy. (a) *Inclusions.* Tammann [1, 2] in 1932 used the autoradiographic method to examine the distribution of a lead isotope (thorium-B) in various metals. He showed that tracer amounts of lead incorporated into tin, nickel, or bismuth by fusion concentrate at the surface of the crystals. More recently this technique has been used to show that the small quantities of labeled lead (0.004 to 0.04%) in rust-proof alloys are not distributed uniformly, but are found in the interdendritic sites [3, 4].

Chaudron and his collaborators [5] have shown by pile activation or tracer methods that even in 99.998% pure aluminum, the impurities accumulate at the grain boundaries. This has also been found by autoradiographs of radioactive gold, zinc, ruthenium, and other substances present in metals, either as trace impurities, or deliberately added. In refractory alloys containing 70% Ni, 25% Cr, and 5% W, labeled tungsten has also been shown to be localized in the interdendritic spaces, but in an alloy of this type containing Co, radiotungsten is precipitated in the axes of the dendrites, probably as intermetallic compounds [6].

Autoradiography has been used to examine [7] the distribution of small quantities of antimony in germanium ingots, in the hope of improving the semiconductor properties of the germanium. Here too, a considerable enrichment of antimony at the surface was found. Analogous studies have been carried out on the distribution of aluminum in silicon rectifiers.

From such distribution data, a very efficient procedure has been worked out for eliminating the last trace of impurities from a metal [8]. This consists in melting electrically successive layers of the metal ingot; as the molten zone advances, it carries with it the impurities, leaving behind a very pure solid. This *zone melting* method has been successfully applied to the purification of germanium [9], aluminum, and tin [10]; radioactive tracers can be used to follow the purification.

An interesting result has been reported by Robert, Robillard, and Lacombe [11] following an autoradiographic study of Al/Cu alloys containing 0.4% labeled copper. After heating to temperatures in the region of the melting point, it was found not only that there was an enrichment of copper at the grain boundaries, but also a migration from the joints towards the hottest zone of the alloy.

Finally, inclusions of phosphorus have been compared with those of arsenic in different steels by labeling and autoradiography [12, 13]. This study showed that the homogenization is achieved more rapidly for phosphorus than for arsenic, and is practically complete after annealing for 32 hours at 1200°C; the arsenic inclusions are only eliminated after annealing for at least 70 hours at 1275°C.

(b) *Equilibria and kinetics.* Winkler and Chipman [14] used P^{32}-labeled calcium phosphate to study the equilibria and the kinetics of the distribution of phosphorus between molten iron and basic slag at various temperatures and different compositions. At 1620 to 1660°C, equilibrium is established in 10 to 15 min. These experiments also helped in working out the conditions for removing phosphorus from iron; it was concluded that all the phosphorus is present as Fe_2P.

Kopecki [15] has measured the solubility of labeled calcium in liquid iron and in $Fe/Ca/O_2$ equilibrium mixtures. This radioelement has also been used to confirm that desulfuration of cast-iron or steel by basic slag occurs at the interface of the two phases, without any calcium compound being formed in the bulk of the liquid metal itself [16]. The kinetics of the transfer of sulfur across the metal-slag interface has also been studied by tracer techniques [17].

Iron sulfide labeled with S^{35} has been used to establish that the proportion of sulfur retained in the production of metallurgical coke, and consequently in the steel obtained, is independent of the origin of the sulfur (i.e., whether pyritic or organic), so that there is no point in choosing a coking coal which contains sulfur in one form rather than in another.

Radon has been utilized by Voice [19, 20] to determine the time taken for gases to pass through a blast furnace, that is to say the time between the blast entering through the blast pipes, and the moment at which the gas leaves through the furnace mouth. Under the experimental conditions used, this period was between 1 and 3 sec for samples collected near the walls, and between 6 and 9 sec in the center. This author has also suggested that the erosion of the bricks in a high temperature furnace could be followed by incorporating a small source of radiocobalt into the bricks, and then measuring the activity in the furnace periodically with a portable counter.

(c) *γ-radiography.* The radiography of metal castings by γ-rays can often advantageously replace x-ray radiography. The penetrating power of the γ-rays from Ra, Co^{60}, Ta^{182}, Eu^{154}, Cs^{137}, Ce^{144}, etc. (Section 18–2) is greater than that of the x-rays from the normal generators, and can therefore be used to examine greater thicknesses. Radioactive sources are in addition much less bulky than x-ray generators. On the other hand, unless a source of hundreds of curies of radiocobalt is used (which is, however, currently possible), a longer exposure time is needed to obtain a good image with γ-ray sources. The resolution obtained with high energy γ-rays is also lower than with x-rays, but the γ-radiation from Tm^{170} has an energy of only 84 kv, and its β-particles are easily absorbed, so that this source does not have this last drawback. For thin castings, the use of bremsstrahlung x-rays (Section 11–7) has been suggested [21, 22, 23] since the energies lie between 20 and 200 kv, depending on the β-spectrum. With the choice which is available with these different sources, γ-radiography is becoming a technique of increasing importance in industrial laboratories [24].

With a very thin source of Ir^{192}, a technique known as *radioscopy* has been developed; in this the image is projected onto a fluorescent screen [25].

(d) *Friction and wear.* It is very difficult to get evidence by normal chemical methods of the transfer of material which occurs when two metal surfaces rub against one another, especially if the two metals are the same, since the quantities of matter transported are extremely small. This difficulty can be avoided [26, 27, 28] by making one of the surfaces radioactive and then examining the other surface autoradiographically after friction has occurred. Such experiments have shown that transfer takes place even between very hard metals, such as chromium or hardened steel, and that although the presence of a lubricant between the two surfaces considerably reduces the quantity transported, it does not eliminate it completely. The quantities transported have been shown to be of the order of 10^{-8} to 10^{-10} gm. Rabinowicz and Tabor [29] have shown by autoradiography that the transfer between nonlubricated surfaces is nearly 40 times greater for two surfaces of the same metal (Cd/Cd, Ag/Ag, Zn/Zn, etc.) than for different metals, even though the coefficient of fraction is only slightly different (μ between 0.4 and 1). The transfer between well-lubricated surfaces is reduced by a factor of 20,000 or more, and μ is reduced at least 20-fold. Solid lubricant films cause least transfer of metal. With increasing temperature, the surfaces begin to behave like unlubricated surfaces, despite the visible presence of lubricant. These changes with temperature are reversible, and are probably due to changes in the state of the lubricating film.

Instead of studying the eroded surface by autoradiography, the lubricating oil itself can be circulated through a system containing a sensitive counter; the oil carries with it traces of radioactive material arising from the friction and wear of the surface, and the wear can therefore be continuously monitored over a given period of time. This procedure has found general application in the examination of metallic tools and castings. The wear of cutting tools has been determined by pile irradiation of the carbide tip before use [30]. Neutron activation produces radioactive isotopes of tungsten, tantalum, etc., and one can then subsequently measure the activity of the shavings.

To investigate the wear of steels in hot drawing, Jaoul [31] immersed small samples in a bath containing either $Fe^{59}Cl_3$ or $H_3P^{32}O_4$ for long enough to allow the metal to become radioactive either by isotopic exchange, diffusion, or penetration into micro-cracks. The activity picked up in this way falls off sharply from the surface towards the interior, and this depth distribution is established by removing successive layers by polishing. A graph of depth against activity, obtained by radiography, can then be used to measure the wear at any given point. By this method, Jaoul was able to show the effect of the profile of the die on the erosion phenomenon.

Wear and lubrication can also be studied by using a labeled oil (e.g., labeled with S^{32}). Worn or defective spots on the eroded surface are revealed by the activity due to oil residues which deposit at these points [32]. This procedure can also be applied to the detection of extremely fine cracks on the surface of a metal [33]. A radioactive grease is smeared onto the surface under pressure, and this is then cleaned and examined by autoradiography.

Labeled oils can also be used to follow the action of various detergents on metallic surfaces, and the efficiency of various cleaning techniques. For example, a layer of C^{14}-labeled oil is smeared onto the surface being studied; after cleaning the efficiency of the cleaning process is examined with a counter. Radioactive N-N-di-*n*-butylstearamide,

$$C_{17}H_{35}C^{14}ON(C_4H_9)_2$$

mixed with paraffin oil, has been suggested for this purpose [34].

25–2 Petroleum and mining industries. The use of labeled molecules has helped to give a better understanding of the elementary physico-chemical processes which are fundamental in *flotation*, a technique which is widely used in the concentration and separation of minerals. To make the mineral particles adherent, and to ensure that this adhesion shall be selective, reagents known as "collectors" are added to the flotation bath; these are organic molecules which often contain sulfur (as xanthates) or phosphorus (as dithiophosphates), and also "activators" which contain C, S, Ca, Cu, Ag, Ba, etc. By labeling these compounds with C^{14} or other suitable tracers, it is possible to determine the quantity of the various reactants which fix on the solid under various conditions, and also to study the rate of fixation, or the exchange equilibria between solid and solution, etc. [35, 36, 37]. In particular, evidence was found for the very important fact that a surface coverage of an appropriate reagent equivalent to 5% of a monomolecular layer is often sufficient to bring about complete flotation. The flotation is sensitive to changes in the coverage of the order of only 1%. Oxygen plays an important role in the flotation of certain sulfur minerals, such as pyrites.

In addition to the detection of radioactive strata, radiation can also be used to detect certain inactive minerals or elements, either because they are geochemically associated with the natural radioelements, or because they can be made artificially radioactive. Thus for example, diamond is localized in veins of kimberlite, a basaltic rock containing very small amounts of natural radioelements, and generally surrounded with quartz-bearing granitic rocks which is by contrast very active. The search for diamonds is therefore made easier by using sensitive detectors (usually scintillation counters) to chart sharp decreases in the radioactivity of the ground. This method of prospecting should however be confirmed by other suitable measurements.

The extraction of crystals of beryl which are distributed throughout a rocky mass is a very delicate operation, which requires the best possible localization in order to prevent breakages. The operation can be simplified by using a source of penetrating γ-rays, which interacts with the beryllium causing neutron emission, which can be easily detected with a neutron counter.

In prospecting for petroleum in particular, radioactive sounding methods have resulted in such a considerable improvement that they are now almost a normal technique [38]. The γ-ray signal gives information on the composition of the successive layers of the borehole, on the basis that shales are more radioactive than limestone, clay or coal, so that a curve of the activity as a function of the depth shows discontinuities on passing from one layer to the next. Neutrons can be used to reveal the possible presence of hydrogeneous liquids (water or hydrocarbons), because of the high slow-neutron absorption cross-section of hydrogen. In this technique, a Ra/Be neutron source is fixed at the end of the drilling tool or scraper; the γ-rays emitted in the reaction of neutrons with the various layers are then measured.

Tracers are widely used to detect leaks or obstructions in pipelines. For leak detection, a radioactive liquid is circulated through the pipes and its movement followed with a counter. In the second case, a γ-ray source is fixed to a ram, which is carried along by the pressure of the petroleum and stops at the point where the obstruction has occurred.

When the borehole of an oil well passes through an aqueous layer, the walls must be reinforced with cement. To ensure the soundness and strength of the construction, carnotite or some other radioactive mineral can be incorporated into the cement, and the thickness of the walls then measured with a counter.

A γ-emitter can also be used to mark the interface between two types of petroleum flowing down a pipe. A new and very rapid technique of injecting the indicator (a radioactive barium soap, or other metal-organic compounds labeled with active Se, Sb, etc.) can be used for continually monitoring the rate of mixing of two liquids.

A very important application of tracers in the petroleum industry is in the study of the flow of a three-phase mixture of petrol, water, and gas through various porous media, since the exhaustion of the reserves depends on processes of this type to a large extent. Tracers, in the form of some appropriate soluble compound, can be used to determine the permeability of the ground to fluids, their rate of flow, and their localization.

The water-tightness of reservoirs and of petrol pipes, and the quality of welding, all of which are difficult of access by x-ray radiography, are easily and simply examined by γ-radiography. Since the introduction of this technique in the petroleum industry, the number of accidents due to leakages has decreased considerably. Finally, technologists on the refining side of the industry hope to improve the quality of petrol, oils and lubricants by exposing petroleum to ionizing radiations, under conditions which have yet to be established.

In the catalytic cracking of petroleum, a coke is formed which reduces the catalytic activity of the silica-alumina catalyst. It is of some importance to find out [39] whether this formation is due to certain particular compounds in the petroleum, or to the carbon atoms in specific positions in a given hydrocarbon molecule. Labeling various hydrocarbons with C^{14} has shown that the specific activity of the coke produced is always the same, irrespective of the hydrocarbon or the position labeled.

In hydrology, tracers have been used to follow the flow of water and to establish possible relationships between underground rivers, lakes, etc. Despite the difficulties implicit in this method [40] it is sometimes preferable to labeling with a coloring matter, especially when the latter may be decolorized by dissolved reducing agents or adsorbed by solids. Investigations of this type have been carried out with radiorubidium in the underground waters around the Nile [41], and with radioactive bromine and iodine on the watershed of the river Durance [40].

25–3 Plastics and textiles. Although the production of plastics by the radiolytic polymerization of monomers (Section 14–4) has only recently begun to be usefully exploited on the industrial level, research in this field has made important contributions to the general physical chemistry of polymerization. Various monomers such as perfluoro-propylene, -butadiene, and -acrylonitrile have been polymerized for the first time by using ionizing radiations. An important aspect of these studies relates to the considerable changes produced in the properties of plastics by irradiation, or by grafting one polymer on another (Section 16–6). The use of labeled molecules has provided an efficient method of studying structures of polymers, mechanisms of polymerization, and effects of catalysts [42, 43].

A number of authors have used radiosulfur to study the mechanism of the vulcanization of rubber, either by incorporating S^{35} into the accelerators [44, 45, 46] (dibenzothiazol and tetramethylthiourea disulfides) and determining the distribution of the activity in the vulcanized product, or by measuring the rate of exchange between sulfur and organic polysulfides [47]. The rate of diffusion of plasticizers has been measured by introducing P^{32}-labeled triphenyl phosphate into plastics. This tracer has also been used to determine the wear of tires in relation to the road surface, temperature, the rate of movement, etc.; the radioactivity left on the surface after the passage of a vehicle is measured with a counter or by autogradiography. The wearing of plastic bearings or gears has been investigated by neutron activation of the sodium chloride which they contain and measurement of the activity carried into the lubricating oil by the eroded plastic [48]. The sensitivity of the method is such that measurements can be made after a few minutes wear. The best conditions for defrosting aircraft have been investigated using labeled silicone greases [49].

In preparing rayon, cellulose xanthate is dissolved in a solution of caustic soda. The concentration of the solution has been determined by measuring the scattering of the γ-rays emitted from a suitably placed source [50, 51], since the intensity of the scattered radiation depends on the thickness and density of the absorbent. This technique is a general one for the measurement of the density of fluids.

Cellulose xanthate is prepared by treated alkali cellulose with carbon disulfide which is eliminated at a later stage. The addition of radioactive sulfur allows these operations to be followed, and the complete removal of the sulfur checked [50, 51].

Rayon fibers are drawn from a very thin layer of an oil containing sodium oleate. By introducing radioactive sodium into this compound, the uniform surface coverage of the fiber was demonstrated; this is an important condition for the drawing technique [52].

The absorption and diffusion of anionic coloring matter plays an essential role in the dyeing of wool. Direct measurement on the fibers of the wool are rather difficult, but measurements have been carried out on membranes of keratin, which is chemically related to wool, using the acid coloring material Orange II labeled with S^{35} [53, 54]. Similar measurements have been made with Br^{82}.

In the stretching of wool, it is important to know the rate of dragging of the fibers by the cylinders ("feeders" and "deliverers") in order to be certain of the regularity of their movement. This has been studied by impregnating the fibers with labeled H_3PO_4 [55].

Rayon, nylon, and other synthetic and natural fibers are good insulators and acquire electrostatic charges by friction, and these cause serious inconveniences by collecting powders and dust from the atmosphere; these then fix on the material and alter its uniform appearance. Equally the charges cause repulsion between the fibers during the spinning and this causes faults in the weave. When organic solvents are being used, the vapors may catch fire and cause explosions. To avoid these dangers, the air in the immediate locality is made conductive by using radioactive sources such as Tl^{204} or Sr^{90}. This is however only sufficient when the machines are stationary or turning over slowly. The same technique is also used in the industrial handling of photographic and cinematographic films, paper, gramophone records, etc.

25-4 Electricity. (a) *Cells and batteries.* Even if that fraction of the energy of the fission process which is emitted as β-particles and γ-rays could be transformed completely into electricity, it would make a negligible contribution to the electrical power now available in different countries. This conversion would however be important if it could be used in portable sources of electricity such as cells or batteries. The different solutions which have been suggested to this problem are based on (1) collection of charge, (2) contact potential, (3) the production of charge in a semiconductor, and (4) the transformation of the heat given off into electricity by a thermocouple.

The first of these techniques was used as early as 1913 by Moseley [56], who obtained a potential difference of 150 kv and an initial current of 10^{-4} amp by collecting *in vacuo* the β-particles emitted by a 20 mc source of the radium active deposit. The source was placed in a very thin small quartz sphere, silvered on the outside, which was the anode; the cathode was another larger concentric quartz sphere, silvered on the inside. Lobanov and Beliakov have obtained currents 10 to 100 times greater by using artificial β-emitters [57]. Linder and Christian [58] set up an apparatus similar to that of Moseley, with 250 mc of $Sr^{90} + Y^{90}$, which gave a potential difference of 365 kv, but the current was only 10^{-9} amp and the impedance was 10^{14} ohms.

With a plastic insulator such as polystyrene placed between aluminum and lead electrodes, Coleman [59] found that a battery of 25 elements, each containing 10 mc of $Sr^{90} + Y^{90}$, gave a current of 4×10^{-12} amp, corresponding to a 33% collection yield. The power yield is probably very small. The maximum voltage of several thousand volts can be obtained in open circuit.

A low-voltage electrical cell based on the second of the procedures outlined above has been constructed by Ohmart [60], using the γ-rays from Ra, Co^{60}, or Ag^{110} to ionize a gas between two electrodes with different work functions. With gold and lead in air, the current flows from the first to the second electrode; the same holds when copper is substituted for gold, but the current intensity is much smaller, although it increases if the copper is oxidized. With the aluminum-lead couple, the current is reversed. The maximum potential difference of 1.34 v in open circuit was obtained with electrodes of Al_2O_3 and PbO_2. The current increases with the ionization density, and depends on the molecular weight of the filling gas, and probably on its ionization potential. The maximum yield (in watts) for this setup was about 0.02%. A battery working on the same principle, using tritium, gave voltages as high as 400 v at very small currents [61]; with 0.5 curies of tritium, current of 10^{-9} amp was obtained. In this case too the voltage varies with the characteristics of the surface of the electrodes. The power output is very small and increases with time (but not with the voltage). Such a battery would have an average life of the order of 18 years.

In connection with the cell developed by Ohmart, it is interesting to note some experiments by Westermark and Erwall [62] on the deposition of the active deposit from thoron on the surfaces of various metals in air. These authors perforated a lead disc at a number of points, and fixed sheets of Pt, Ag, Cu, Mo, W, and brass in the resultant holes. When the disc was negatively charged (50 v/cm), the deposit on a given metal was shown by autoradiography to depend on the work function; a reverse order was found with a positively charged disc. Positive ions from the gaseous phase consequently discharge preferentially on a metal which is negatively charged with respect to another metal.

Another way of constructing cells [63, 64, 65] consists in bombarding a *p-n* junction of a Ge or Si semiconductor with β-particles (Section 15–3); the secondary electrons produced by ionization in the *n*-region of the crystal are collected across the junction in the *p*-region (see Fig. 25–1). With 50 millicuries of $Sr^{90} + Y^{90}$, the maximum voltage for silicon is 0.25 v and the current 10^{-5} amp; the values for germanium are -0.03 v and 2×10^{-5} amp. The yield in watts for silicon is 0.4%, but this can be increased up to 2%; the yield for germanium is lower. Because of structural changes caused by the radiation, a semiconductor exposed to an intense source must be regenerated by heat treatment.

Finally, the heat given off by a radioelement has been transformed into electricity [66] by placing a strong source of polonium in a small closed capsule, the surface of which was in contact with the hot junction of

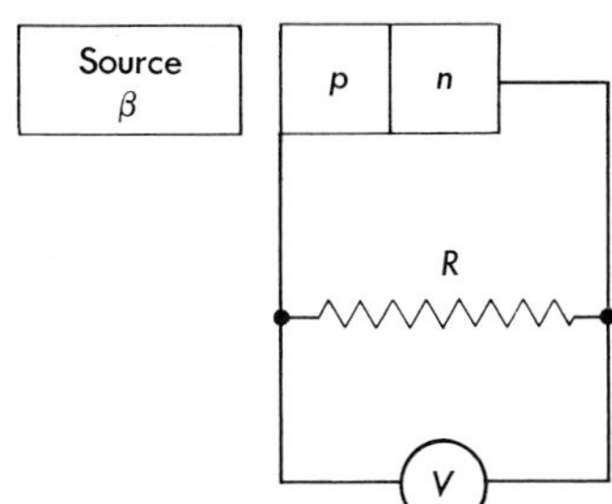

Fig. 25–1. Diagram of a cell involving bombardment of a semiconductor by β-particles.

40 thermocouples; the cold junctions were on the surface of a vessel surrounding the capsule and thermally insulated from it. The measured voltage was 0.75 v, and the current 25 ma. The maximum power with a source of 146 curies is only 9.4 milliwatts (0.2% of the thermal power). The life of such a device is limited by the half-life of the polonium. According to more recent information, successful attempts have been made in the United States to build a "portable generator" with 3000 curies of polonium; this would have an initial power of 58 watts and a yield of 8 to 10%. After one half-life the yield would have fallen to 3 watts, and the yield to 5 to 6%. The cost of the prototype was of the order of $30,000,000 (1959).

(b) *Electronics.* Certain defects in the working of electron tubes is caused by oxides (BaO + SrO) evaporating from the cathode and depositing at other parts of the valve [67]. By incorporating radioactive barium and strontium into the tube, it is possible to measure the loss from the cathode and the quantities deposited on the grid and the anode. It has further been shown that the evaporation occurs essentially during the construction and activation of the valves, and not during their working life. The vapor pressure of SrO between 1000 and 1375°C has been measured using radioactive strontium [68]. Other experiments with $C^{14}O_2$ demonstrated the absorption of residual gas in the tube by the oxide layer.

In certain radar installations, the gas discharge tubes must respond to the applied voltage within a fraction of a microsecond. In the complete absence of ions in the gas, the discharge can be considerably delayed, so that the working of the radar set is defective. If, however, a small quantity of radioactive material is introduced into the tube, the discharge can then take place at the necessary speed [52].

In the construction of high-frequency apparatus, and television sets, powdered iron, of extremely small particle size (of the order of a few microns) is used. The particle dimensions depend on the conditions in which the crystal germs are formed and allowed to grow. An American patent [70] outlines a possible way of increasing the number of germs, and hence decreasing the particle size, by suitable irradiation with β-particles or γ-rays.

(c) *Telephony.* Long-distance telephone cables are often placed beneath the surface of the ground (about 2 ft deep); a lead sheath protects the wire, from which it is insulated by paper. The smallest leakage may allow water to enter, and this results in damage of large lengths of cable. Leakage can be rapidly detected by injecting CH_3Br labeled with radiobromine into the sheath [71, 40].

Submarine transoceanic cables contain repeaters at various intervals, and water-tightness is of course essential in the operation of these devices. This has been checked by smearing the repeater with varnish, and then when it is dry, immersing it in a solution of sodium carbonate labeled with C^{14}. After dissolving off the varnish, the repeater showed no activity whatsoever [71].

25–5 Agriculture. Since the discovery of radioactivity many workers have set out to examine the possible stimulant effect of radiation from natural radioelements on the rate of growth of cultures and plants, and on the quality and yield of the harvest, but in general the results of these studies have been contradictory and inconclusive. (See Ref. 72 for a bibliography.) In recent years, these studies have been repeated in various countries [73–76]. It now appears that the effects are very sensitive to the conditions of the medium, and to the dose, and that for some plants at least, positive effects are found when the conditions are suitably chosen (Section 14–8). The techniques used include irradiating the grains, treating them with radioactive solutions before sowing, introducing radioelements into the soil, or continual irradiation of the plants with γ-rays from Co^{60} during growth. Radioactive isotopes of phosphorus, carbon, calcium, sulfur, sodium, iron, cobalt, zinc, molybdenum, and other inorganic constituents of vegetables have been widely used in research on the transport of these elements from the soil into plants, and their migration, exchange, and metabolism in the plants themselves (see Ref. 77).

Various P^{32}-labeled phosphates have been made, and the relative efficiencies of these as fertilizers have been studied. After placing the phosphate in the soil, the specific activity of the plant is measured periodically and compared with the initial activity of the soil. These measurements can be used to determine which part of the phosphorus assimilated comes from the fertilizer, and which from the soil itself. In this way, considerable differences between the behavior of wheat, potato, and soya beans have been established [78] (see also Refs. 79 and 80). These measurements also showed that for neutral or basic Canadian soils, $NH_4H_2PO_4$ is a much more efficient fertilizer than superphosphate or calcium phosphates [81, 82], although the order may be reversed in an acid soil [83, 77]. The action of phosphate fertilizers occurs particularly during the early stages of growth of the plant; in the later stages, most of the phosphorus comes from the soil. Analogous experiments have been carried out with Ca^{45} [84].

The humidity of the soil may be measured by measuring absorption of neutrons from a Ra/Be source, in a similar way to that described earlier for petroleum (Section 25–2). The density of the soil can be measured from the absorption of γ-rays, which is approximately proportional to the density.

Certain citrus fruit tree diseases are attributed to sulfur, but there was some doubt as to whether the sulfur came from sulfates added to the soil or from sulfur used as a fungicide. Labeling the latter with S^{35} showed that the depth of penetration into the fruit was practically equal to the depth of the lesions, which makes the second hypothesis more likely [85]. The mechanism in which various insecticides and fumigants act, and their effect on the organisms of large animals, have also been studied using labeled molecules [86]. By adding a labeled manganese compound to a solution of DDT, the distribution of DDT on land sprayed from aircraft has been determined. Other applications are discussed in Ref. 87.

In certain entomological and ecological research, whole populations of insects, flies, mosquitoes, etc., have been labeled with indicators. This labeling can be carried out either by feeding the larvae with radioactive phosphorus or strontium [88], by mechanical insertion of a very small source (for example, Co^{60}) into the insect, or by attaching a similar source externally [89, 90]. The aim of such work is to follow in particular the movement and disappearance of insects in natural conditions, under the effect of various factors such as time, wind, temperature, etc. For example, in Nigeria it was shown that the distance traveled by labeled mosquitoes which carry yellow fever depends more on the meteorological conditions than on their own flight. Analogous labeling experiments were carried out to examine the underground movement of worms.

25–6 Foodstuffs. Several attempts have been made to utilize the actions of radiations on microorganisms to "pasteurize" preserved foodstuffs and pharmaceutical products. Experiments by Proctor and Goldblith [91] with very strong doses of cathode rays, with energies of several Mev, have shown that if such a sterilization is possible, there are still problems to be solved concerning changes in the taste and color of food, the disappearance of vitamins, toxicity, etc. For example, the irradiation of milk with Co^{60} γ-rays resulted in the destruction of 31% of the vitamin A after 1 hour, and 70% after 6 hours [92]. Riboflavin is more resistant, but nevertheless 47% was destroyed in a 12-hour irradiation. More encouraging results have however been reported recently, provided that certain γ-ray doses are not exceeded [93].

The storage of potatoes is appreciably prolonged after irradiation with 5000 to 20,000 r of γ-rays; the growth of buds is inhibited and the external appearance is improved, without any change in the taste. After 18 months, the loss of weight in irradiated potatoes was 20%, compared with 55% for unirradiated roots. With stronger doses, however, there is the risk of deterioration of the nutritious elements, especially the vitamins. Similar effects have been observed with onions. The nutritive value of certain foodstuffs is sometimes increased by enrichment with iron, either as the metal or as a salt, but since the food often contains phytic acid, the question has been raised as to whether the formation of insoluble iron phytate would decrease the expected nutritive benefit [94]. By labeling the breakfast of human beings with radioactive iron, and subsequently measuring the radioactivity of samples of red blood cells removed from these subjects, it was shown that there was no direct relationship between the assimilation of iron and the natural phytic acid content of the food.

Traces of potassium iodate are sometimes added to flour to improve its quality. The fate of the iodate has been investigated by analyzing bread prepared from flour to which KIO_3 labeled with radioactive iodine had been added [95]. It was shown that most of the iodine is found as iodide, a small fraction remains as iodate, and that the amount of free iodine, and incorporated into fats and proteins, is negligible.

The best conditions under which cattle assimilate copper and iodine added to kitchen salt has been examined using copper carbonate labeled with Cu^{64} and dithymol iodide labeled with I^{131} [96, 97].

In flour milling, one of the factors which affects the quality of the bread is the fineness of the flour, so that it is necessary to be able to determine this fineness quickly. Spinks and Tollefson [98] have shown that this information can be obtained by measuring the adsorption of radioactive Ru^{3+} ions by the flour, since the adsorption decreases with the fineness.

In some food industries, such as cider making, special filters are used to eliminate the bacterial flora from the liquid, and it is necessary to check periodically that these filters have not been holed. This can be done either by growing the bacteria in a culture containing radiophosphorus, or by using small granules of plastic covered with radioactive gold [99]. The latter method appears to be the more suitable.

25–7 Miscellaneous industries and technologies. The permeability of filters used in other industries for fogs, smokes, and powders can also be examined using labeled molecules. Tricresyl phosphate is sometimes used, but radioactive aerosols (Section 21–6) can also be employed for this purpose. During World War I, the efficiency of gas masks was checked by measuring their permeability to radon [100].

The permeability of thin layers of varnish (for example applied to metals as protection against corrosion) has been examined by exposing them to tritiated water vapor [101]. Successive layers are then subsequently dissolved and their activity measured. The hygroscopic properties of varnishes have been studied by a similar technique after leaving them in a moist atmosphere. The permeability of the skin to various cosmetic products has been examined using C^{14}, P^{32}, S^{35}, I^{131}, etc. [95, 102].

In workshops in which toxic substances such as mercaptans, CS_2, H_2S, are being produced, the incorporation of radiosulfur into these products can be used for the rapid detection of any dangerous leakage.

The fabrication of certain types of lamps requires the sealing of a lateral tube containing a drop of mercury; this operation is carried out by blowing with the mouth, which could give rise to a health hazard because of the toxicity of mercury vapor. In order to be certain that the quantity inhaled in each operation was below the tolerance level, radiomercury was used to measure the contamination of the air, and it was shown [103] that 1 m^3 of the air contained approximately 0.1 mg of mercury, which is 10 times less than the tolerance limit.

To check the efficiency of a ventilation hood, a labeled inert gas such as radiokrypton or radioxenon is introduced, and the activity subsequently spread outside the hood measured. This same technique can be applied in investigating the renewal of air in a room.

In localities in which there is a fire hazard, small plates of metal carrying small α-particle sources can be installed. An appropriate electronic circuit activates an alarm bell when the absorption of the α-particles is increased by the presence of traces of smoke [99]. The use of P^{32}, Tl^{204}, Po^{210}, or other radioactive substances to ionize the air has been suggested for preventing fires in hospitals, theaters, or other places where there may be an accumulation of static charge [104].

We saw earlier that the elimination of charge by the use of radioactive sources is a common procedure in many different domains. The same is true of measurements of density and the circulation of fluids, examples of which have also been discussed. Still more widespread are radioactive measurements of the thickness of thin sheets, which finds wide industrial application because of the simplicity, precision, and economies which can be achieved by this method. For radiation of given initial intensity, and given properties, passing through a solid screen, the residual intensity depends on the thickness according to the relations established in Chapter 11. Measurement of the absorption with a counter or ionization chamber therefore gives the thickness directly. This method has been applied to rubber, plastics, artificial leather, linoleum, etc., for measuring extremely thin layers, down to a micron in thickness. Depending on the thickness to be measured, α-particles, β-particles of differing penetrating power, soft γ-rays or secondary radiations (back-scattering) are used. The sensitivity of the method has been considerably increased by using scintillation measuring techniques. The minimum dimensions which can be measured have been reduced, and it is now even possible to determine the thickness of curved surfaces.

The thickness of extremely thin layers can also be determined by other procedures. By introducing radioactive phosphorus pentachloride into printing ink, it was possible to evaluate the quantity of ink deposited on each page by measuring its activity [105]. This procedure allowed 10 γ/cm^2 of ink to be measured. It was also possible to establish the optimum quantity necessary for good printing, and to investigate the effect of the quality of the paper. The same technique has been applied in the impregnation of wood by introducing labeled $SrCl_2$ into the solutions used.

The measurement of the level of a liquid can also be based on the absorption of radiation; conveniently protected fixed γ-emitting sources are placed at various heights on the outside of a recipient containing liquid, or better still a beam of γ-rays from a movable source is directed at various levels. This procedure has been applied in measuring the level of molten cast iron in a furnace crucible, in locating the catalyst in cracking operations, in determining the height of molten glass in a vat, etc.

In the fabrication of glass, the components can be labeled with radioactive sodium, barium or phosphorus, or with both indicators, to establish the optimum length of flow of the liquid through the furnace, and the conditions for establishing uniform mixtures, etc. [49].

25-8 The distribution and uses of isotopes. The rapid development of the many applications of tracers in industry, medicine, and research is emphasized by the increasing demand for radioisotopes from the various production centers. Table 25-1 shows how the demand increased in France over the years 1950 to 1955 [106]. The production and use of radioelements

TABLE 25–1

USE OF RADIOISOTOPES PRODUCED BY THE C.E.A., FRANCE*

	1950	1951	1952	1953	1954	1955
Medicine	118	192	130	162	457	1280
Biology	3	33	60	67	116	176
Physics and chemistry	600	767	618	531	648	512
Industry	8	71	97	131	174	416
Miscellaneous	8	5	28	39	55	144
C.E.A.	198	382	209	564	669	672
Total	935	1450	1142	1494	2119	3200

* This does not include shipments overseas (264 in 1950, 678 in 1951, 965 in 1952, 1264 in 1953, and 1196 in 1954).

TABLE 25–2

DISTRIBUTION OF RADIOISOTOPES FROM O.R.N.L. IN THE UNITED STATES IN 1959, 1960, AND 1961

Radioactive isotope	1959		1960		1961	
	Activity, curies	Samples	Activity, curies	Samples	Activity, curies	Samples
C^{14}	15	255	23	300	40	310
Cs^{137}	42,906	188	29,626	202	48,535	199
Co^{60}	127,427	146	141,037	146	235,298	130
T	39,421	206	5203	115	43,642	216
I^{131}	593	2510	503	2327	177	1838
Ir^{192}	8216	135	8538	109	5808	90
Kr^{85}	3066	122	3290	116	4475	165
P^{32}	153	1998	141	1957	130	1934
Pm^{147}	487	66	2285	64	862	78
Sr^{90}	116	115	302	107	98,326	101
Others	303	6297	173	6330	912	6846
Total	222,703	12,028	191,121	11,773	438,205	11,907

has continued to increase since this period; the total numbers of samples supplied in France by the C.E.A. were 5449 in 1958, 6342 in 1959, and 8086 in 1960 [107]. The users in 1960 were distributed as follows: medicine 93, research and teaching 300, industry 588.

The rapid increase in the production and distribution of isotopes in the United States is even more striking. Table 25–2 shows the number of samples, and the activity for the main radioisotopes supplied by the Oak Ridge National Laboratory in the years 1959, 1960, and 1961 [108].

TABLE 25–3

DISTRIBUTION OF RADIOACTIVE ISOTOPES FOR THE YEARS 1946 TO 1961

Radioactive isotope	Activity, curies	Samples
C^{14}	149	3763
Cs^{137}	179,494	1729
Co^{60}	1,057,610	2331
T	144,592	1351
I^{131}	7294	48,359
Ir^{192}	45,767	968
Kr^{85}	14,550	581
P^{32}	1937	30,503
Pm^{147}	4539	481
Sr^{90}	99,225	960
Others	2627	65,210
Total	1,557,784	156,236

TABLE 25–4

NUMBER OF SAMPLES, AND ACTIVITIES, SUPPLIED BY OAK RIDGE NATIONAL LABORATORY

	Radioactive				Stable		
	1946–53		1954		Isotope	1946–53	1954
	samples	curies	samples	curies			
I^{131}	18,713	2026	5023	557	D and D_2O	1734	313
P^{32}	12,059	607	2405	153	$B^{10,11}$	106	64
C^{14}	1649	29	269	5	He^3	25	10
Na^{24}	1928	23	448	9	O^{18}	339	48
Au^{198}	1570	688	622	632	A^{38}	4	1
T	149	346	94	514	electromagnetically concentrated	1957	326
$Sr^{89,90}$	646	138	130	119			
Co^{60}	811	20,364	134	25,493			
Cs^{137}	411	52	104	327			
Ir^{192}	32	36	99	1200			
Po^{210}	56	312	57	819			
Others	13,593	379	3200	246			
Total	51,617	25,000	12,585	29,728		4165	762

This table takes no account of the millions of curies produced and distributed by such large organizations as the Mound Laboratory or the Brookhaven National Laboratory.

Table 25–3 shows the distribution of the same isotopes over the period August 2, 1946 to November 30, 1961 [108].

No statistics are available for the U.S.S.R., although the use of radioelements in that country has certainly developed at a rate comparable to that just described for the U.S.A.

The production centers in Great Britain distributed 135 samples in 1947, 1414 in 1948, and 9274 in 1953 [109]; in 1960, 40,000 samples, with activities varying between a few microcuries and 150,000 curies, were dispatched to 60 countries [110].

The range of activities shows that the distributed radioelements are used either as indicators or as sources of radiation. Taken as a whole, the data quoted, together with what is known about reactors, demonstrates quite clearly that nuclear phenomena are playing an essential role, not only in fundamental research, but also in widely varying applications in technology, biology and medicine, industry, and agriculture.

References

1. G. Tammann, *Z. Elektrochem.*, **38,** 530 (1932).
2. G. Tammann and G. Bandel, *Z. Metallkunde,* **25,** 153, 207 (1933).
3. L. G. Erwall and M. Hillert, *Research,* **4,** 242 (1951).
4. L. R. Standifer and M. G. Fontane, *Metal Progress,* **60,** 65 (1951).
5. F. Montariol, P. Albert, and G. Chaudron, *Compt. rend.*, **235,** 477 (1952).
6. W. Jones, quoted in Ref. 13.
7. G. L. Pearson, J. D. Struthers, and H. C. Theuerer, *Phys. Rev.*, **77,** 809 (1950).
8. W. G. Pfann and K. M. Olsen, *Phys. Rev.*, **89,** 322 (1953).
9. G. Morrison, *Nucleonics,* **11,** No. 1, 28 (1953).
10. F. Montariol, R. Reich, P. Albert, and G. Chaudron, *Compt. rend.*, **238,** 815 (1954).
11. M. Robert, A. Robillard, and P. Lacombe, *Compt. rend.*, **240,** 1089 (1955).
12. A. Kohn, *Compt. rend.*, **233,** 178, 1617 (1951).
13. A. Kohn, *Rev. Métal.*, **50,** 139 (1953).
14. T. B. Winkler and J. Chipman, *Trans. Am. Inst. Met. Eng.*, **167,** 111 (1946).
15. E. S. Kopecki, *Iron Age,* **160,** 60 (1947).
16. W. O. Philbrook, K. M. Goldman, and M. M. Helzel, *J. Metals,* **188,** 361 (1950).
17. L. Chang and K. M. Goldman, *Am. Inst. Mining Eng., Iron and Steel Div.*, Tech. Pub. 2367 (1948).
18. S. E. Eaton, R. W. Hyde, and M. H. Rood, *Anal. Chem.*, **21,** 1062 (1949).
19. E. W. Voice, *J. Iron Steel Inst.*, **163,** 312 (1949).
20. E. W. Voice, *Proc. 1st Oxford Radioisotope Conf.*, Vol. 1, p. 23 (1951).
21. L. Reiffel, *Nucleonics,* **13,** No. 3, 22 (1955).
22. J. G. Kereiakes and A. T. Krebs, *Nucleonics,* **13,** No. 4, 78 (1955).
23. P. Lévêque and P. Martinelli, *J. phys. radium,* **16,** 729 (1955).
24. See *Proc. 1st and 2nd Oxford Radioisotope Confs.*, 1951 and 1954.

25. C. Garriet and A. Morrison, *Nucleonics,* **9,** No. 3, 44 (1951).
26. J. N. Gregory, *Nature,* **157,** 443 (1946).
27. B. Sackman, J. T. Burwell, and J. W. Irvine, *J. Appl. Phys.,* **15,** 459 (1944).
28. J. T. Burwell, *Nucleonics,* **1,** No. 4, 38 (1947).
29. E. Rabinowicz and D. Tabor, *Proc. Roy. Soc.* (*London*), **A 208,** 455 (1951).
30. H. Colding and L. G. Erwall, *Proc. 2nd Oxford Radioisotope Conf.,* Vol. 2, p. 181 (1954).
31. B. Jaoul, *Compt. rend.,* **238,** 648 (1954).
32. G. L. Clark, S. G. Gallo, and B. H. Lincoln, *J. Appl. Phys.,* **14,** 428 (1943).
33. H. F. Kaiser, *Trans. Am. Soc. Metals,* **27,** 403 (1939).
34. J. C. Harris, R. E. Kamp, and W. H. Yanko, *ASTM Bull.,* No. 158, 49 (1949).
35. A. M. Gaudin, *Eng. Min. J.,* **149,** 53 (1948).
36. A. M. Gaudin, *Atomes,* **10,** 56 (1953).
37. A. M. Gaudin and P. L. de Bruyn, *Can. Min. Met. Bull.,* **42,** 331 (1949).
38. See *Atomics,* **2,** 329 (1951), and *Sess. Acad. Sci. U.S.S.R.,* July 1–5, 1955, Tech. Sect.
39. R. E. McMahon, *Ind. Eng. Chem.,* **47,** 844 (1955).
40. J. Guéron, *J. phys. radium.,* **15,** 65 A (1954).
41. K. Fearnside, *Proc. 1st Oxford Radioisotope Conf.,* Vol. 2, p. 14 (1951).
42. J. T. Kummer and P. H. Emmett, *J. Am. Chem. Soc.,* **75,** 5177 (1953).
43. J. C. Bevington and H. W. Melville, *Proc. 2nd Oxford Radioisotope Conf.,* Vol. 2, p. 3 (1954).
44. D. Craig, A. E. Juve, and W. L. Davidson, *J. Polymer Sci.,* **5,** 709 (1950); **6,** 7, 13, 117 (1951).
45. B. A. Dogadkin and Z. N. Tarasova, *Doklady Akad. Nauk S.S.S.R.,* **85,** 1869 (1952).
46. Z. N. Tarasova, M. Y. Kaplunov, and B. A. Dogadkin, *Doklady Akad. Nauk S.S.S.R.,* **99,** 819 (1954).
47. E. N. Guryanova, *Zhur. Fiz. Khim.,* **28,** 67 (1954).
48. M. Ezran, *Compt. rend.,* **234,** 1947 (1952).
49. S. E. Eaton, *1955 Geneva Conference,* P. 146.
50. A. P. Schreiber, *Nucleonics,* **2,** No. 1, 33 (1948).
51. A. P. Schreiber, *Electronics,* **22,** 90 (1949).
52. J. W. Irvine, *Anal. Chem.,* **21,** 364 (1949).
53. M. L. Wright, *Discussions Faraday Soc.,* **16,** 58 (1954).
54. M. L. Wright, *Trans. Faraday Soc.,* **49,** 95 (1953).
55. D. Taylor, *Proc. 2nd Oxford Radioisotope Conf.,* Vol. 2, p. 156 (1954).
56. H. G. J. Moseley, *Proc. Roy. Soc.* (*London*), **A 88,** 471 (1913).
57. I. A. Lobanov and A. P. Belyakov, *Doklady Akad. Nauk S.S.S.R.,* **47,** 332 (1945).
58. E. G. Linder and S. M. Christian, *J. Appl. Phys.,* **23,** 1213 (1952).
59. J. H. Coleman, *Nucleonics,* **11,** No. 12, 42 (1953).
60. P. E. Ohmart, *J. Appl. Phys.,* **22,** 1504 (1951).
61. A. Thomas, *Chem. Eng. News,* **32,** 1622 (1954).
62. T. Westermark and L. G. Erwall, *Nature,* **169,** 703 (1952).

63. P. RAPPAPORT, *Phys. Rev.*, **93,** 246 (1954).

64. P. RAPPAPORT and E. G. LINDER, *J. Appl. Phys.*, **24,** 1110 (1953).

65. W. G. PFANN and W. VAN ROOSEBROECK, *J. Appl. Phys.*, **25,** 1422 (1954).

66. K. JORDAN and J. BIRDEN, *Chem. Eng. News*, **32,** 4188 (1954).

67. J. BEYDON, L. BAUDOIN, J. CHALLANSONNET, and J. DEBIESSE, *Compt. rend.*, **229,** 353 (1949).

68. G. E. MOORE, H. W. ALLISON, and J. D. STRUTHERS, *J. Chem. Phys.*, **18,** 1572 (1950).

69. F. DE BOER and W. F. NIKLAS, *Brit. J. Appl. Phys.*, **5,** 341 (1954).

70. J. LAMBERT, U. S. Patent No. 2604442.

71. J. GUÉRON, *Nucleonics*, **9,** No. 5, 53 (1952).

72. A. M. KUZIN, *1955 Geneva Conference*, P. 699.

73. L. EHRENBERG, I. GRANHALL, and A. GUSTAFSSON, *1955 Geneva Conference*, P. 793.

74. K. MIKAELSEN, *1955 Geneva Conference*, P. 890.

75. A. SPARROW and R. SINGLETON, *Am. Nat.*, **87,** 29 (1953).

76. See the series of articles in *Acta Agric. Scand.*, **4,** No. 3 (1954).

77. A. L. KURSANOV, *1955 Geneva Conference*, P. 618, 696.

78. B. A. KRANTZ, W. L. NELSON, C. D. WELCH, and N. S. HALL, *Soil Sci.*, **68,** 171 (1949).

79. A. V. SOKOLOV, *1955 Geneva Conference*, P. 695.

80. V. M. KLECHKOVSKI, *1955 Geneva Conference*, P. 694.

81. J. W. T. SPINKS and H. G. DION, *J. Chem. Soc.*, **1949,** S 410.

82. J. W. T. SPINKS, H. G. DION, and J. E. DEHM, *Can. Chem. Ind.*, Nov. 1950.

83. L. E. ENSMINGER and J. T. COPE, *J. Am. Soc. Agron.*, **39,** 1 (1947).

84. H. C. HARRIS, W. H. MACINTIRE, C. L. COMAR, W. M. SHAW, S. H. WINTERBERG, and S. L. HOOD, *Science*, **113,** 328 (1951).

85. F. TURELL, *Plant. Physiology*, **25,** 13 (1950).

86. F. P. W. WINTERINGHAM, *J. Chem. Soc.*, **1949,** S 416.

87. S. B. HENDRICKS and L. A. DEAN, *Ann. Rev. Nuclear Sci.*, **1,** 597 (1952).

88. J. C. BUGHER and M. TAYLOR, *Science*, **110,** 146 (1949).

89. F. FREEDEN, J. W. T. SPINKS, J. ANDERSON, A. P. ARNASON, and J. REMPEL, *Can. J. Zoology*, **31,** 1 (1953).

90. R. A. FULLER, J. W. T. SPINKS, A. P. ARNASON, and H. McDONALD, *Rept. Entomol. Soc. Ontario*, **1950,** 7.

91. B. E. PROCTOR and S. A. GOLDBLITH, *U.S.A.E.C. report NYO-3337*, 1952.

92. *Atomics*, **4,** 256 (1953).

93. L. E. BROWNELL and J. V. NEHEMIAS, *Proc. 2nd Oxford Radioisotope Conf.*, Vol. 2, p. 213 (1954).

94. L. M. SHARPE, W. C. PEACOCK, R. COOKE, R. S. HARRIS, H. LOCKHART, H. YEE, and G. NIGHTINGALE, *J. Nutrition*, **41,** 433 (1950).

95. C. ROSENBLUM, in *Radioisotopes in Industry*, J. R. Bradford, ed., Reinhold, New York, 1953.

96. W. MAHIAN, quoted in Ref. 95.

97. R. R. BALDWIN, R. THIENSEN, and E. E. MCIHRAY, *Science*, **106,** 217 (1947).

98. J. W. T. SPINKS and C. I. TOLLEFSON, quoted by G. H. Guest, *Radioisotopes: Industrial Applications*, Pitman, London, 1951.

99. H. SELIGMAN, *Atomics*, **5,** 299 (1954).

100. F. A. Paneth, *Radioelements as Indicators,* McGraw-Hill, New York, 1928.

101. G. D. Calkins, M. Pobereskin, V. Young, and L. Novacki, *Nucleonics,* **13,** No. 2, 76 (1955).

102. G. H. Guest, Ref. 107.

103. C. Goodman, J. W. Irvine, and C. F. Horan, *J. Ind. Hyg. Toxic.,* **25,** 275 (1943).

104. A. Quinton, *Proc. 2nd Oxford Radioisotope Conf.,* Vol. 2, p. 188 (1954).

105. B. Buchdahl and M. F. Polglase, *Ind. Eng. Chem., Anal. Ed.,* **18,** 115 (1946).

106. C. Fischer, *1955 Geneva Conference,* P. 330, and personal communication.

107. L. Cassin, *Bull. Inform. Scient. Tech.,* No. 51, 105 (1961).

108. U.S.A.E.C., *Major Activities in the Atomic Energy Program,* 1959, 1960, 1961.

109. Data kindly provided by W. S. Eastwood and P. Onions, A.E.R.E., Harwell.

110. U.K.A.E.A. 7th Annual Report, 1961.

PROBLEMS

by

MLLE. C. FERRADINI, GLEN E. GORDON,
AND CHARLES D. CORYELL

CHAPTER 1

1–1. Natural uranium has isotopic abundances 99.28% U^{238} and 0.712% U^{235}. The half-life, $t_{1/2}$, of U^{238} is 4.51×10^9 yr and that of U^{235} is 7.13×10^8 yr. The disintegration constant, λ, is $0.6931/t_{1/2}$ and the rate of disintegration (i.e., the activity) of N atoms is λN. (a) The two half-lives are computed from the isotopic abundances measured by mass spectrometry and the specific activities for U^{238} and U^{235}. Show that the specific activities in disintegrations per second per gram of natural uranium are 1.22×10^4 and 556, respectively. (b) Note that uranium salts aged a few months will be in secular equilibrium with Th^{234}, Pa^{234}, U^{234}, and Th^{231}. Find from a suitable reference which radiations of this set are the ones that gave the Becquerel photographic effect. Which ones cause the high discharge rate that a thin film of uranium compound gives in an electroscope?

1–2. Calculate the specific activity of 1622-yr Ra^{226}; of 138.4-day Po^{210}; of natural neodymium, with 23.87% abundance of the alpha emitter 2×10^{15}-yr Nd^{144}.

1–3. All members in a decay chain in secular equilibrium with a primary member of very long half-life show the same activity: $\lambda_i N_i = \lambda_1 N_1$, where N is the number of atoms. (a) Calculate the grams of 1622-yr Ra^{226} in secular equilibrium with 10^6 gm of uranium. (b) Calculate the grams of 138.4-day Po^{210} in equilibrium with 1 gm of radium. (c) Calculate the isotopic abundance of 2.48×10^5-yr U^{234} in equilibrium with U^{238} in natural uranium.

1–4. Write a chemical equation for the radioactive transformation of ${}_{92}U^{238}$ to ${}_{82}Pb^{206}$ plus ${}_2He^4$. Taking the physical atomic weights ($O^{16} = 16$) as: $U^{238} = 238.12644$, $Pb^{206} = 206.03942$, and $He^4 = 4.003876$, calculate the energy release in atomic mass units and in Mev for this transformation (1 amu = 931.14 Mev).

1–5. Estimate the output in cc of ${}_2He^4$ (S.T.P.) per year of a body containing 10^6 gm of uranium. [*Ans:* 0.118 cc]

1–6. The law of decay of species 2 removed from a system in radioactive equilibrium, as shown in Fig. 1–3, is $A_2 = A_1^0 e^{-\lambda_2 t}$, and the law of growth in the fraction containing purified parent is $A_2 = A_1^0(1 - e^{-\lambda_2 t})$, where A_1^0 is the (constant) activity of primary radioactivity. Find the initial rate of growth of species 2, and show that if this growth were sustained, it would reach A_1^0 at $t_{1/2}/0.693$, where $t_{1/2}$ is the half-life of species 2. At what time (in half-lives) will A_2 reach $0.500\ A_1^0$?

CHAPTER 2

2–1. Calculate the maximum β^--particle energy for decay of the neutron (including the effect of nuclear recoil, if appreciable), given that $m_H = 1.008146$ and $m_n = 1.008986$.

2–2. Show that in the limit of $v \ll c$, the kinetic energy given by relativistic mechanics approaches that given by classical mechanics, $m_0 v^2/2$. [*Hint:* Involves an expansion of the term $[1 - (v/c)^2]^{1/2}$.]

2–3. The special theory of relativity gives the following law for transformation of time:

$$t' = \frac{t}{\sqrt{1 - (v/c)^2}},$$

where t' is time in the laboratory system, and t is time in the moving system. How far can muons having the following kinetic energies travel during their mean lifetimes: (a) 1 Mev; (b) 10^3 Mev; (c) 10^6 Mev? [*Ans:* (b) 6.6×10^5 cm]

2–4. For the following particles, at what kinetic energy is the relativistic mass of the particle 2% greater than the rest mass: e, p, He^4?

2–5. The positive pion decays at rest to give a muon and a neutrino. Equation (2–7) shows that the sum of the kinetic energies of the muon and neutrino is 34 Mev. From momentum conservation, show that the kinetic energy of the muon is 4.13 Mev. (See the useful relativistic equation given in Problem 6.)

2–6. Calculate the threshold (i.e., minimum kinetic energy of the bombarding proton) for production of the antiproton via the reaction

$$\mathrm{p} + \mathrm{p} \rightarrow \mathrm{p} + \mathrm{p} + \mathrm{p} + \bar{\mathrm{p}}.$$

Assume that the target proton is initially at rest. The following helpful equation is given:

$$W = \sqrt{(pc)^2 + (m_0 c^2)^2},$$

where W is the total energy of the particle (=kinetic energy + rest-mass energy), p is the momentum, and $m_0 c^2$ is the rest-mass energy. Express answer in units of $m_p c^2$.

2–7. In order to obtain information about the nuclear charge distribution, one can perform scattering experiments with high-energy projectiles. If it is required that the wavelength of the projectile be one tenth the nuclear radius, what energy (a) electrons, (b) muons, and (c) protons would be required for investigation of a nucleus having $A = 64$? [Assume $R = 1.2 \times 10^{-13} A^{1/3}$ cm.] [*Ans:* (b) 2.45×10^3 Mev]

2–8. One can obtain diffraction patterns by scattering particles having the appropriate energies from crystal lattices. What energies must the following particles have if their wavelengths λ are to be of the order of the distance between atoms of a crystal, say 1 A: (a) x-ray, (b) electron, (c) neutron? Express answer in ev or multiples thereof.

2–9. Calculate the average energy in ev, the wavelength λ, and the velocity of thermal neutrons (i.e., neutrons in equilibrium with material at a temperature of 25°C).

CHAPTER 3

3–1. (a) If a hydrogen atom in its ground electronic state ($^2S_{1/2}$) were placed in a magnetic field of 10^4 gauss, what would be the energy difference (in ergs) between states $M_J = \frac{1}{2}$ and $M_J = -\frac{1}{2}$? (b) What magnetic field would be required to create the same energy difference between states $M_J = \frac{1}{2}$ and $M_J = -\frac{1}{2}$ for a free proton? (c) What frequency of electromagnetic radiation would be required to induce the transition from the lower to upper magnetic substate of the free proton in a field of 10^5 gauss?

3–2. Calculate the expected mass of a π^0 meson assuming that it binds the proton and neutron together in the deuteron by exchange, i.e.,

(a) p n, normal proton and neutron,

(b) p $\rightarrow \pi^0 \rightarrow$ n, π^0 emitted by proton,

(c) p n, π^0 absorbed by neutron, followed by the inverse process.

This process would seem to violate the law of conservation of mass and energy, but by the uncertainty principle it is allowed if the transit time Δt is short enough that the uncertainty relationship $\Delta E\,\Delta t \approx \hbar$ is obeyed, where ΔE is the mass difference between structures (a) and (b). Assume that the π^0 travels with a velocity close to the speed of light, and that the distance traveled is approximately the radius of the deuteron as calculated according to the equation $R = 1.2 \times 10^{-13} A^{1/3}$ cm.

3–3. Calculate the potential energy in Mev of two protons 10^{-13} cm apart due to (a) gravitational forces, (b) coulombic forces, (c) magnetic forces, and (d) nuclear forces, using Eq. (3–15) with $g = 10^{-17}$ erg · cm.

3–4. In an atomic-beam experiment, transitions between magnetic substates of In^{113} were found to occur at a frequency of 3.74×10^6 sec^{-1} in a magnetic field of 4000 gauss. (a) Calculate the nuclear gyromagnetic ratio of In^{113}. (b) Using the known spin of In^{113} ($I = \frac{9}{2}+$) what is its nuclear magnetic dipole moment? (c) What value of the magnetic moment would one obtain by use of the Schmidt-model formula? Indicate the assumed shell-model level occupied by the 49th proton. [*Note:* The nuclear magneton = Bohr magneton/1836, see Table 2–1.] [*Ans:* (b) 5.53 nuclear magnetons]

3–5. Indicate whether or not the spins of the following nuclides can be explained on the basis of the independent particle model and, if so, the assumed orbital of the unpaired nucleon: Na^{23}, $I = \frac{3}{2}+$; Ca^{43}, $I = \frac{7}{2}-$; Ti^{47}, $I = \frac{5}{2}-$; Fe^{55}, $I = \frac{3}{2}-$; Kr^{83}, $I = \frac{9}{2}+$; Pd^{105}, $I = \frac{5}{2}+$; Ag^{107}, $I = \frac{1}{2}-$.

3–6. Explain why there are no observed nuclides having ground-state spins of $\frac{11}{2}-$, although an $h_{11/2}$ level is predicted to occur slightly below the closed shell of 82 nucleons and $\frac{11}{2}-$ excited states are observed in nuclides having an odd number of nucleons slightly less than 82.

3–7. For $Al^{26}(5+)$, $P^{32}(1+)$, $Cl^{34m}(3+)$, $K^{40}(4-)$, $V^{50}(6+)$, and $Ga^{68}(1+)$, determine the ground-state spins to be expected on the basis of Nordheim's rules. Note in each case whether or not the rule is obeyed. Also, for each odd proton and neutron, give the shell-model designation assumed by you in applying Nordheim's rule. A short table of nuclear spin values needed in this problem is given at the end of the problem set.

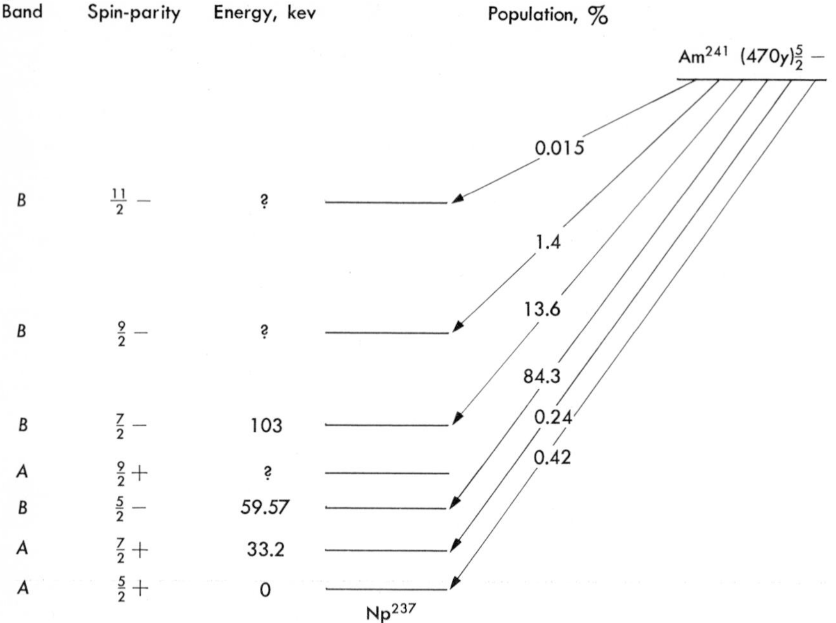

FIG. 1. Alpha decay of Am^{241} to levels of Np^{237}.

3–8. The first excited rotational level of Pu^{238} lies 44 kev above the ground state. Predict the energies of the next two higher members of the rotational band. The experimentally measured energies of these levels are 146 and 304 kev.

3–9. Alpha decay of Am^{241} populates members of at least two rotational bands (here designated A and B) in Np^{237} according to the partial decay scheme shown in Fig. 1. (a) According to the collective model, predict the energies of the $\frac{9}{2}+$, $\frac{9}{2}-$, and $\frac{11}{2}-$ levels. Experimentally they are found to be 76.1, 158.5, and 225 kev, respectively. (b) From the rotational energy constant $\hbar^2/2P$ obtained in fitting the B band, calculate the effective moment of inertia, P, of Np^{237}. Compare the result with the rigid-body moment of inertia, P_0, calculated under the assumption of a spherical nucleus of radius $R = 1.5 \times 10^{-13} A^{1/3}$ cm.

3–10. (a) Calculate the binding energy and binding energy per nucleon of Mg^{24} and C^{12}. (b) Determine whether the following reaction is endoergic or exoergic, and by what magnitude (in Mev):

$$C^{12} + C^{12} \rightarrow Mg^{24}.$$

3–11. Calculate the total binding energy, binding energy per nucleon, and the packing fraction of He^4, Fe^{56}, and U^{238}.

3–12. The mass of Sc^{41} is 5.95 Mev greater than that of Ca^{41}. Use this information along with the semiemperical mass equation and the ${}_0n^1 - {}_1H^1$ mass difference to calculate the nuclear radius constant r_0.

3–13. Calculate, according to the semiempirical mass equation, the hypothetical most stable charge, Z_A, for mass 125 (neglecting pairing energy terms). What would be the value of Z_A for $A = 125$ in the absence of the symmetry term $(N - Z)^2/A$?

NUCLEAR SPINS*

Mg^{25}	$\frac{5}{2}$	K^{39}	$\frac{3}{2}$
Al^{27}	$\frac{5}{2}$	K^{41}	$\frac{3}{2}$
Si^{27}	$(\frac{5}{2})$	Ca^{41}	$(\frac{7}{2})$
P^{31}	$\frac{1}{2}$	Ti^{49}	$\frac{7}{2}$
P^{33}	$(\frac{3}{2})$	V^{49}	$\frac{7}{2}$
S^{33}	$\frac{3}{2}$	V^{51}	$\frac{7}{2}$
S^{35}	$\frac{3}{2}$	Cr^{51}	$(\frac{7}{2})$
Cl^{34}	(0)	Zn^{65}	$(\frac{5}{2})$
Cl^{35}	$\frac{3}{2}$	Zn^{67}	$\frac{5}{2}$
Cl^{37}	$\frac{3}{2}$	Zn^{69}	$(\frac{1}{2})$
Ar^{35}	$(\frac{3}{2})$	Ga^{67}	$\frac{3}{2}$
Ar^{39}	$(\frac{7}{2})$	Ga^{69}	$\frac{3}{2}$
Ar^{41}	$(\frac{7}{2})$		

* Parentheses indicate probable, but not certain, values.

CHAPTER 4

4–1. The data given in the next table were obtained for the α-particle counting rate of a mixture of astatine activities. Plot the data on semilogarithmic paper and resolve the decay curve into its components. Give the half-life and the activity at time $t = 0$ for each component. [*Note:* These are actual experimental data, so do not be surprised if not all the points fall on smooth curves.]

4–2. At this time (1963) it is not known which of the pair Te^{123}-Sb^{123} is unstable with respect to the other. Suppose that by observation of antimony-K x-rays, one finds that Te^{123} decays by electron capture to Sb^{123} at a rate of 0.01 disintegrations per second per gram of natural tellurium. What would be the half-life of Te^{123}? [*Ans:* 9×10^{13} yrs]

4–3. Suppose that an active species of half-life $t_{1/2}$ is produced at a constant rate R (number of atoms formed per unit time). Derive an expression for the activity of the product as a function of length of production time. Use the expression obtained to calculate the activity of a species of 5-min half-life following 10 min of production at a rate of 10^9 atoms per second. Repeat the calculation assuming a 20-min period of production.

4–4. (a) Radiations from an activity of half-life $t_{1/2}$ are counted from time $t = 0$ to time $t = t_c$ comparable to the half-life of the activity. Derive a relationship between the average counting rate (i.e., number of counts observed/t_c)

Time after chemical separation, min	Activity, counts/min
12	756
17.2	725
23.1	683
30.0	600
37.7	545
47.5	494
59.5	435
73	380
87	341
102	288
121	256
140	215.5
161	178.5
184	150.7
211	127.3
243	101.9
276	84.9
308	68.2
340	55.0

and the true counting rate at $t = 0$. (b) A sample of a 5-min activity gave 1000 counts during a count from 12:10 to 12:20. What would the count rate of the sample have been at 12:00?

4–5. For a decay chain in which the daughter nuclide is also radioactive, i.e., $A \rightarrow B \rightarrow C$, the activity of the daughter, A_B is given by

$$A_B = \frac{-dN_B}{dt} = A_A^0 \frac{\lambda_B}{\lambda_B - \lambda_A} (e^{-\lambda_A t} - e^{-\lambda_B t}) + A_B^0 e^{-\lambda_B t},$$

where λ_A, λ_B are decay constants of species A and B, and A_A^0, A_B^0 are activities of species A and B at time $t = 0$. (a) Calculate and plot on semilogarithmic paper the activity of 12.8-day Ba^{140} and of its 40-hr La^{140} daughter. Assume an initially pure Ba^{140} sample having an activity of 1000 d/min. In order to show the features of the activity curves well, your points should be rather closely spaced (~5–10-hr intervals) near $t = 0$, but the spacing may increase to ~1 or 2 days after about one half-life of Ba^{140}. Extend your plot to cover about 2 or 3 half-lives of Ba^{140} decay. (b) From your plot of (a), to what apparent half-life does the slope of the La^{140} activity curve correspond at times $t \gg 40$ hr? This situation is commonly known as *transient equilibrium*. Extrapolate this linear part of the La^{140} decay back toward $t = 0$, subtract from the resulting curve (denoted A'_B) the actual activity of La^{140} at various times, and plot the resulting values as a function of time, denoting the curve A''_B. To what apparent half-life does the slope of the curve A''_B correspond? Obtain expressions for curves A'_B and A''_B from the equation for A_B and use them to show why the curves have the slopes which you have determined. (c) From the expression for

A_{B} (with $A_{\text{B}}^0 = 0$), derive an expression for the time t_m at which the activity of B is maximum. Calculate t_m for La^{140} and indicate its position on your graph of part (a). What is the relationship between A_{A} and A_{B} at time $t = t_m$?

4–6. (a) For Pu^{234} the partial half-life for a α-decay is 150 hr and that for electron-capture decay is 9.6 hr. If these are the only decay modes of Pu^{234}, what are the values of its overall half-life and α-branching ratio (α disintegrations/total disintegrations)? (b) A sample of Pu^{234} is observed to emit 100 α-particles per minute at 11:00 P.M. How may atoms of Pu^{234} were present in the sample at 9:30 A.M.? [*Ans:* (a) 9.0 hr, 6%]

4–7. The fission reaction is an excellent source of neutron-rich activities (β-emitters). Short-lived Br^{86} and Br^{87} are produced via the following paths in the fission of U^{235} with thermal neutrons:

(1) Fission yield 1.50%: 17-sec $Se^{86} \xrightarrow{\beta^-}$ 54-sec $Br^{86} \xrightarrow{\beta^-}$ stable Kr^{86}

(2) Fission yield 0.50%: 54-sec $Br^{86} \xrightarrow{\beta^-}$ stable Kr^{86}

(3) Fission yield 2.50%: 55-sec $Br^{87} \xrightarrow{\beta^-}$ 78-min $Kr^{87} \xrightarrow{\beta^-} Rb^{87}$

Give in appropriate units the following: (a) The activities of 17-sec Se^{86}, 54-sec Br^{86}, 55-sec Br^{87}, and 78-min Kr^{87} existing in a sample of U^{235} that has undergone fission at a rate of 10^6 per sec for 20 min. (b) The *ratio* of the activities of 17-sec Se^{86} to 55-sec Br^{87} formed in a very short burst of fission (less than 0.1 sec).

4–8. Derive the relationship

$$Q^{\beta}(Z, A) = B^{\text{p}}(Z + 1, A) - B^{\text{n}}(Z, A) + 0.78 \text{ Mev},$$

where $B^{\text{p}}(Z + 1, A)$ = proton separation energy in nucleus $(Z + 1, A)$, and $B^{\text{n}}(Z, A)$ = neutron separation energy in nucleus (Z, A).

4–9. Copper-64 decays with a 12.8-hr half-life, 38% by emission of 0.571-Mev β^--particles to give stable Zn^{64}, 19% by emission of 0.656-Mev β^+-particles, and 43% by electron capture to give stable Ni^{64}, and 0.43% by electron capture to give an excited state of Ni^{64} at 1.34 Mev. (a) From the values of Q^{EC} and Q^{β} for Cu^{64}, show that $Z_A = 28.8$ and $\delta = 1.2$ Mev if B_A is taken as 2.4 Mev. (b) Estimate the Q of the reaction Zn^{64}(n, p)Cu^{64}. (c) What is the partial half-life for the β^--decay of Cu^{64}?

4–10. Making use of the decay energy of Rn^{215} ($Q^{\alpha} = 8.78$ Mev) and the decay energy of Bi^{211}($Q^{\alpha} = 6.75$ Mev, $Q^{\beta} = 0.60$), calculate the β^--decay energy of At^{215}($Q^{\alpha} = 8.16$ Mev). Ignoring pairing effects at odd A, give Z_A for $A = 215$ if $B = 1.15$. [*Ans:* —0.02 Mev, 85.48]

4–11. In the long α-decay chains of Th^{232}, U^{235}, Np^{237}, and U^{238}, β-decay is interposed with α-decay. Explain and calculate the average number of β-decays per α-decay from the Z_A versus A function, whose slope in this region is 0.35.

4–12. Using the following data, predict whether Fm^{259} or Es^{259} is more stable with respect to β-decay, calculate the Q value for the decay process connecting these two nuclides, and calculate the mass of Fm^{259}.

Alpha-particle energies for ground-state transitions:

$_{97}Bk^{255}$: 5.00 Mev	$_{98}Cf^{255}$: 5.65 Mev
$_{100}Fm^{259}$: 6.36 Mev	$_{99}Es^{259}$: 5.64 Mev
Q^{β} of Bk^{255}: 2.67 Mev	
Mass of Bk^{255}: 255.17383	

4–13. Calculate the Q value for emission of C^{12} from Cm^{242}. Since the energy release in this process is considerably greater than in the case of α-decay, why has spontaneous C^{12} emission not been observed experimentally? Masses: Cm^{242}, 242.13575; Th^{230}, 230.10621; C^{12}, 12.003815.

4–14. (a) From the data given in Problem 3–9, calculate the partial α half-life for the transitions to the $\frac{5}{2}+$ and $\frac{5}{2}-$ levels of Np^{237}. (b) By interpolating between the curves for alpha transitions of neighboring even-even nuclides in Fig. 4–12, predict the half-lives that the transitions of part (a) would have if they occurred in even-even nuclides. (c) Calculate the hindrance factor for each of the transitions. The hindrance factor is the experimental partial α half-life over that predicted from even-even α-transitions. (d) Qualitatively interpret the hindrance factors for these transitions in terms of the individual levels occupied by the protons and neutrons that form the outgoing α-particle.

4–15. (a) Predict from Fig. 4–10 the α-decay energy Q_{α} of the unknown Cm^{236}. (b) By an extrapolation on Fig. 4–12, predict the partial α half-life of Cm^{236}. Note that for decay of even-even nuclides in this region, the population of the ground state of the daughter nucleus is $\sim$75% and that of the first excited state (at $\sim$44 kev) is $\sim$25%. The hindrance factor for decay to the excited state is normally about 1.7. (c) If the partial half-life for EC-decay (the only important decay mode in addition to α-decay) were 1 hr, what would be the half-life and α branching ratio (α-decays/total decays) of Cm^{236}?

4–16. A 64-day isomer of an even-Z, odd-A nuclide of mass $\sim$90 occurs at 105 kev above ground state and decays 10% by EC and 90% by isomeric transition. If the conversion coefficient $\alpha(=e/\gamma)$ is 50, what is the gamma-ray lifetime of the transition, and, using the relationships between energies and half-lives for various spin changes given in the text, what is the most likely spin change for this transition? If this is a magnetic transition and the metastable state has spin and parity $\frac{1}{2}-$, what are the spin and parity values of the ground state? In terms of the independent-particle model, what are the probable individual levels occupied by the odd proton in the upper and lower isomer?

4–17. An interesting set of isomers occurs for the odd-A isotopes of tellurium involving states of spin $\frac{11}{2}-$, $\frac{3}{2}+$, and $\frac{1}{2}+$. (a) Give the shell-model designations for protons and neutrons which give obvious explanation of these three levels. (b) In Table 1 are given the chief data for the isomeric transitions of this sequence. Explain the sudden disappearance of the $\frac{1}{2}+$ level after Te^{125}. Identify the multipolarity and nature (electric or magnetic) of the time-setting transition $\frac{11}{2}-$ to $\frac{3}{2}+$ and of the following γ for $\frac{3}{2}+$ to $\frac{1}{2}+$. (c) Calculate for each species the partial half-lives for the isomeric transition in seconds. (d) Make a plot of log $t_{1/2}$(I.T.) versus $E(\frac{11}{2}-) - E(\frac{3}{2}+)$ in kev. Also plot on this graph the Goldhaber-Sunyar half-lives expected for these transitions. Discuss any differences in trends between the experimental and Goldhaber-Sunyar curves. (e) Make also a plot of

$E(\frac{11}{2}-) - E(\frac{3}{2}+)$ and of $E(\frac{1}{2}+) - E(\frac{3}{2}+)$ versus A. Try to estimate the position of $\frac{1}{2}+$ in Te^{127}. Comment on the possibilities for isomerism in $Te.^{135}$

Table 1. Energy Levels in Odd-A Tellurium Isotopes

A	121	123	125	127	129	131	133
Energy $\frac{11}{2}-$	0.296	0.248	0.145	0.089	0.106	0.182	0.334
Energy $\frac{3}{2}+$	0.214	0.159	0.035	0	0	0	0
Energy $\frac{1}{2}+$	0	0	0	high	high	high	high
Fraction I.T.	100%	100%	100%	98%	~100%	22%	13%
Half-life ($\frac{11}{2}$—level)	154 day	104 day	58 day	105 day	33.5 day	30 hr	63 min

CHAPTER 5

5–1. (a) Derive an equation for the energy of a particle of mass M_1 and initial energy E elastically scattered at an angle θ from a target nucleus of mass M_2. [*Hint:* Use the cosine law applied to a momentum triangle made up $\mathbf{p}$, $\mathbf{p}_1$, and $\mathbf{p}_2$ and the law of conservation of energy.] (b) Use the equation derived in (a) to calculate the energy of He^4 ions of initial energy 40 Mev scattered from Au^{197} and Al^{27} at 30, 90, 120, 180°. What is your conclusion regarding the effectiveness of energy transfer to the target nucleus as a function of M_2/M_1 for constant M_1, E, and θ? (c) Consider the case of He^4-He^4 scattering. Derive a simpler relationship than that obtained in (a) for the special case of $M_1 = M_2$. What is the relationship between the energy of the projectile scattered at an angle θ and that of the target atom scattered to the same angle? Prove that the angle between the scattered projectile and target is always 90°. What is the maximum scattering angle for $He^4 + He^4$? (d) Calculate the maximum angle to which 40-Mev He^4 ions can be elastically scattered from hydrogen nuclei.

5–2. The center-of-mass (CM) system is defined as the moving frame of reference in which the vector sum of the linear momenta of the projectile and target nucleus is zero. This is equivalent to the statement that the CM system has mass equal to the sum of the masses of the target and projectile and moves forward along the beam axis with momentum equal to that of the projectile in the laboratory system (LS). (a) What is the velocity of the CM system, U_C, if a particle of mass M_1 and energy E_{1_L} strikes a target (at rest) of mass M_2? (b) What is the velocity, U_{1_C}, of the projectile in the CM system? (c) Derive an expression for the LS energy, E_{a_L}, of a particle of mass M_a and CM energy E_{a_C} emitted at a CM angle θ_{aC}. [*Hint:* A velocity vector diagram is most helpful in making this derivation. It is frequently convenient to use a parameter $\eta = U_C/U_{aC}$, where U_{aC} is the velocity of particle a in the CM system.] (d) Derive an expression giving the LS angle, θ_L, as a function of the CM angle and the quantity η defined in (c).

5–3. (a) What is the excitation energy of the compound nucleus Ga^{69} formed by bombardment of Cu^{65} with 40-Mev He^4 ions? Remember to correct for the energy taken up by CM motion! (b) What is the Q value for the reaction $Cu^{65}(\alpha, 2n)Ga^{67}$? (c) What is the threshold for the reaction of part (b)? (d) Assuming a radius constant of 1.5×10^{-13} cm, what is the value of the coulomb barrier against formation of a compound nucleus in the system $Cu^{65} + He^4$? Classically, what is the minimum bombarding energy at which compound-nucleus formation is possible? [*Ans:* (b) —14.1 Mev; (d) 10 Mev, 10.6 Mev]

5–4. (a) Classically, the minimum energy (in the *CM* system) of protons emitted from the Ga^{69} compound nucleus of Problem 3 is equal to the barrier height against formation of a compound nucleus via the inverse reaction, i.e., $Zn^{68} + H^1$. Calculate the minimum energy of protons emitted by Ga^{69}. (b) What will be the *LS* energy of the protons of part (a) at 0, 90, and 180° if the compound nucleus is formed by bombardment with 40-Mev He^4 ions? (c) What will be the excitation energy of the Zn^{68} residual nucleus formed in part (a) if the compound nucleus was formed by bombardment with 40-Mev He^4 ions?

5–5. Neutrons evaporated from a compound nucleus are emitted with an average kinetic energy of $\sim 2\tau$, where τ is the nuclear temperature of the residual nucleus. What is the optimum bombarding energy for the production of Ga^{66} via the reaction Cu^{65} (α, 3n) Ga^{66} if the average nuclear temperature is ~ 1.6 Mev? [*Ans:* 37.2 Mev]

5–6. If the cross section for the $Al^{27}(n, \gamma)$ Al^{28} reaction is 210 mb, what would be the rate of production of 2.3-min Al^{28} (number of atoms/sec) if 100 mg of Al^{27} is placed in a reactor of flux 10^{13} neutrons/cm^2-sec? What would be the Al^{28} disintegration rate following a 1-min irradiation under these conditions?

5–7. A sample of NaCl is placed in a thermal neutron flux of 10^{13} n/cm^2-sec for 5 hrs. What is the ratio of the activity of 15.1-hr Na^{24} to that of 37.3-min Cl^{38} at 1 hr after the end of the irradiation? [$\sigma_{Na^{23}}(n, \gamma) = 0.5$ b, $\sigma_{Cl^{37}}(n, \gamma) = 0.6$ b]

5–8. A target consisting of a uniform coating of 300 $\mu g/cm^2$ of natural CuO on gold backing foil is bombarded with He^4 ions of an energy below the Cu^{65} (α, 3n) threshold at which the cross section for the Cu^{63} (α, n) reaction is 200 mb. If the beam current of $He^{4(+2)}$ ions striking the target is 1 μamp, what will be the disintegration rate of the 9.4-hr Ga^{66} 5 hours after a 1-hr bombardment? [*Ans:* 9.6×10^3 disintegrations/min]

5–9. A BF_3 counter detects neutrons of 1-ev energy with 20% efficiency, i.e., 20% of the neutrons passing through the gas are absorbed. What will be its approximate efficiency for 10-ev neutrons? (Neglect effects of resonance capture phenomena.)

5–10. (a) Neutron binding energies and energies of excited states in a nucleus Z^{A+1} can be determined by measurement of the energies of proton groups emitted in the reaction,

$$Z^A + {}_1D^2 \rightarrow Z^{A+1} + {}_1H^1.$$

From the equations obtained in Problem 2, derive an expression for the energy of protons observed at 90° in *LS* as a function of the *LS* energy of the deuterons and the *Q* value for the reaction. (b) If the two highest energy proton groups observed at 90° from an isotopically pure Cu^{65} target bombarded with 5.00-Mev deuterons occur at 9.53 and 9.36 Mev, what is the *Q* value for the Cu^{65}(d, p)Cu^{66} reaction, what is the energy of the excited state formed in the emission of the lower energy proton group, and what is the binding energy of the 37th neutron in Cu^{66}?

5–11. What is the range of neutron energies obtainable by bombarding $_1T^3$ with 1.5-Mev deuterons? [*Ans:* 12.2 to 17.6 Mev]

5–12. Determine which of the following reactions can proceed via Yukawa (strong) or electromagnetic interactions. If they cannot, why not?

(a) $\Lambda^0 \rightarrow p + \pi^-$
(b) $\pi^- + p \rightarrow \Lambda^0 + K^0$
(c) $\Lambda^0 \rightarrow \overline{K}^0 + n$
(d) $n + n \rightarrow \Lambda^0 + \overline{\Lambda}^0$
(e) $\Sigma^0 \rightarrow \Lambda^0 + \gamma$
(f) $\gamma + n \rightarrow \overline{K}^0 + \Lambda^0$
(g) $\Theta^- \rightarrow \Lambda^0 + \pi^-$

5–13. Devise reactions in which the following particles can be made using the lowest possible bombarding energies:

$$\Lambda^0, \pi^-, \Sigma^+, K^+, \Theta^0.$$

Consider the initial reaction to be protons on protons or neutrons. You may use secondary reactions in which you initially form pions of high energy which are used as the bombarding particle in the secondary stage. Write out the equations for your proposed mechanisms and make certain that they are balanced. Do not worry about small energy differences, such as the differences in rest mass between protons and neutrons, or between variously charged mesons of a given type.

5–14. Calculate the classical radius of a muon in the *K*- and the *L*-orbitals of carbon. Calculate the frequency and energy of the x-ray emitted when the muon drops from the *L*- to the *K*-orbital. Assume a point nucleus, use the simple Bohr equations, and neglect the effect of the carbon electrons. Qualitatively, how would each of these quantities be affected by inclusion of the finite size of the nucleus?

5–15. Do the calculations of Problem 14 for a $\overline{K}^-$-particle instead of the muon.

5–16. For the spallation of O^{16} by 2.7-Bev protons

$$O^{16}(p, 3p)C^{14}.$$

(a) Establish the energy balance for the reaction. (b) Calculate the height of the energy barrier for the incident proton. (c) In order to determine the cross section for this reaction, water was bombarded with a beam of 2.7-Bev protons under the following conditions. The target was a glass vessel, in the form of a right cylinder, volume 12 cm, filled with water, and aligned so that the direction of the incident protons was parallel to the axis of the cylinder. The open end was covered with an aluminum sheet, of the same dimensions; this sheet, of constant thickness, weighed 6 mg. After 15 hrs bombardment, the total C^{14} activity in the water was 57.5 dis/min; 15 hrs after the end of the bombardment, the β^--activity of Na^{24} formed in the $Al^{27}(p, 3pn)Na^{24}$ reaction was 10^5 dis/min for the whole sheet. Calculate the cross section for $O^{16}(p, 3p)C^{14}$ reaction for the protons used. Radius of proton $= 1.15 \times 10^{-13}$ cm, radius of $O^{16} = 3.50 \times 10^{-13}$ cm, half-life of $C^{14} = 5570$ yr, half-life of $Na^{24} = 15$ hrs. Cross section of the $Al^{27}(p, 3pn)Na^{24}$ reaction for 2.7-Bev protons is 10.5×10^{-27}

cm^2. Neglect the presence of oxygen isotopes other than O^{16}. [*Ans:* (a) −22.3 Mev, (b) 2.47 Mev, (c) 2.42 millibarns]

CHAPTER 6

6–1. Calculate from the half-life for spontaneous fission of U^{238} the ratio of fission to α-emission.

6–2. From the masses of U^{235}, the neutron, Ba^{137}, and Mo^{97}, compute the total energy release for fission in this mode. [*Ans:* 209 Mev]

6–3. The total decay energy in fission products is about 12 Mev of maximum β-energy and 12 Mev of γ-energy, and about 8 Mev of prompt γ-energy is released. The total neutron kinetic energy is about 5 Mev, and the energy released on neutron capture in a typical large reactor is 6 Mev per neutron. The average kinetic energy of the fragments is 167 Mev. Assume that 90% of the radioactive decay energy, except neutrinos, is dissipated in a reactor; estimate the total measurable energy release in Mev per fission.

6–4. The kinetic energy in fission comes from the coulombic repulsion of the two fragments. Taking typical primary fragments as ${}_{53}I^{138}$ and ${}_{39}Y^{98}$ with kinetic energy of 167 Mev, estimate the internuclear distance at the time of separation (scission). How does this compare with the sum of the nuclear radii?

6–5. (a) From the semiempirical mass equation (see Chapter 3) derive an equation for the energy release in symmetric, bipartite fission of a nucleus as a function of Z^2/A and $E_s^{(0)}$ $(=4\pi r_0^2\sigma A^{2/3})$ of the nucleus (neglect pairing energy terms). Using the Green values for the constants of the mass equations, calculate the value of $(Z^2/A)_{\text{crit}}$ and find the nucleus along the line of beta stability at which bipartite, symmetric fission first becomes energetically possible. (b) Derive an equation for the energy release in fission of a nucleus into n fragments of equal mass and charge. Using the constants obtained in part (a), calculate the energy released when ${}_{100}Fm^{256}$ fissions into 2, 3, 4, and 5 fragments. [*Ans:* (a) $(Z^2/A)_{\text{crit}} = 50.1$; (b) $n = 2256$ Mev; $n = 4252$ Mev]

6–6. According to the Bohr-Wheeler treatment of fission, the condition for stability of a nucleus against fission, $Z^2/A < (Z^2/A)_{\text{crit}}$, is obtained from consideration of the change of coulomb and surface energies with small changes in deformation. Show that the same fissionability parameter, Z^2/A, is obtained by setting the energy release in fission (from mass equations) equal to the electrostatic potential energy of the two cotangental spheres of mass $A/2$ and charge $Z/2$, and having the normal radii of nuclei of that mass number. Using the constants of Problem 5(a), what is the critical value of Z^2/A calculated in this manner? [*Ans* $(Z^2/A)_{\text{crit}} = 60$]

6-7. How much does the loss of 12 neutrons change Z^2/A for ${}_{84}Po^{211}$ from 190-Mev deuterons acting on Bi^{209}? Roughly how much energy is required to emit these? How does Fig. 6–3 give evidence on the total number of nucleons emitted by the system undergoing fission?

6–8. The "activation energy" for fission (i.e., the excitation energy at which the mean life for fission is approximately equal to that for gamma emission), E_a, is given by Vandenbosch and Seaborg [R. Vandenbosch and G. T. Seaborg, *Phys.*

Rev. **110**, 507 (1958)] as

$$E_a = 18.1 - 0.36 \frac{Z^2}{A} + \epsilon \text{ Mev},$$

where $\epsilon = 0$ for even-even nuclides, $\epsilon = 0.4$ Mev for odd-A nuclides, and $\epsilon = 0.7$ Mev for odd-odd nuclides. Using this treatment, predict whether or not each of the following nuclides is fissionable with thermal neutrons: Th^{229}, Am^{242}, Cm^{238}, Cm^{247}, Cf^{252}.

6–9. By fitting an equation to the data on spallation-fission competition (see R. Vandenbosch and J. R. Huizenga, *1958 Geneva Conf.*, Vol. 15, p. 284), the neutron-emission-to-fission branching ratio, Γ_n/Γ_f, for plutonium isotopes at moderate excitation energy is approximately given by

$$\log (\Gamma_n/\Gamma_f) = 0.159A - 38.4.$$

If the peak cross section for the $Pb^{203}(\alpha, 4n)$ reaction is about 1.2 barns, predict the maximum cross section for the $U^{234}(\alpha, 4n)Pu^{234}$ reaction. The experimental value is 1 mb. [*Ans:* 0.8 mb]

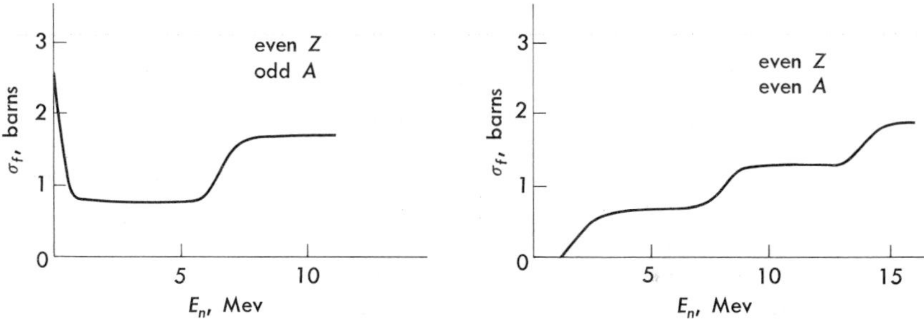

FIG. 2. Fission cross section as a function of neutron heavy energy for even Z, odd A and even-even nuclides.

6–10. Figure 2 shows typical excitation curves for fission induced by neutron bombardment of even-even and even-odd target nuclides. Explain (a) why the second rise occurs and (b) why the curves are different at low energies, particularly the sharp rise in cross section near zero energy in the case of the even-odd target. What can you conclude about the energy dependence of Γ_n/Γ_f from these data?

6–11. Consider a crude fission-fusion-fission bomb (1 megaton equivalent) with 5% of the energy release in the fission trigger, 70% in the fusion reaction (consider the main reaction to be $Li^7 + D^2 \rightarrow 2He^4 + {}_0n^1$), and 25% from fission in the natural U or pure U^{238} tamper. Estimate per megaton equivalent of explosive (1 MT = 50 kg of U fission) the number of curies of Sr^{90} and, within a factor of 2, the number of curies of C^{14} produced in the atmosphere by $N^{14}(n,p)C^{14}$.

Indicate what guesses have to be made about neutron escape, etc., and what errors of more than 10% might come from change of the mass yield curve with neutron energy or change in the fissile species, and from multiple neutron capture.

6–12. The most stable charge, Z_A, for mass 143 is 59.9 and for mass 91, is 40.2. If U^{236} emits ~2 prompt neutrons in fission, (a) assuming that charge divides according to the equal-charge-displacement (ECD) prescription what is the most probable charge, Z_p, of fragments of mass 91? (b) Assuming constant-charge ratio (CCR)? (c) Assuming the minimum-potential-energy (MPE) hypothesis suggested by Present, Way and Wigner, Swiatecki and Blann [see C. D. Coryell, M. Kaplan, and R. D. Fink, *Can. J. Chem.* **39,** 646 (1961)]? According to one version of this hypothesis, the fragments divide in such a way that the sum of nuclear potential energy, $PE[=M(A_L, Z_L) + M(A_H, Z_H)]$, and fragment kinetic energy KE given by the electrostatic potential energy of the fragments at the scission point, $kZ_LZ_He^2/(A_L{}^{1/3})r_0$, where k/r_0 is adjusted to give agreement with the experimentally determined fragment kinetic energy release is minimized. Using the average total kinetic energy release for U^{236} fission, 167 Mev, evaluate k/r_0. Using the values $B_{91} = 1.75$ and $B_{143} = 1.20$, calculate the most probable charge of fragments of mass 91 predicted by the MPE hypothesis. (d) Using the Z_p calculated according to the ECD prescription and the charge-dispersion relation,

$$f_i = 0.595 \exp\left[\frac{-(Z_i - Z_p)^2}{0.9}\right],$$

calculate the fractional chain yield, f_i, of Y^{91}.

6–13. Taking the nominal figure of 200 Mev per fission, calculate the number of fissions per second per watt.

6–14. Taking for U^{235}(n, f) the fission yields: 50.4-day Sr^{89}, 4.79%; 27.7-yr Sr^{90}, 5.77%; 67-hr Mo^{99}, 6.06%; 30.4-yr Cs^{137}, 6.15%; 12.8-day Ba^{140}, 6.35%; and 2.64-yr Pm^{147}, 2.4%, (a) estimate the grams of 2.1×10^5-yr Tc^{99} and of Pm^{147} formed per kg of U^{235} fissioned. (b) Estimate the curies of 12.8-day Ba^{140} and of its daughter 40.2-hr La^{140} in a reactor that has been operating for several months at a power level of 1000 kw (see Problem 13). (c) Show how the activity of Mo^{99} per gram of uranium undergoing fission for T can be used to measure the fission rate. (d) Calculate the ratio of activity of Sr^{89} to Sr^{90} in a reactor that has been operating at a constant rate for a short time (<1 day). Do the same for a reactor that has been operating 1 year. [*Ans:* (b) 5.36×10^4 curies; (d) 166, 33.6]

6–15. The yield in U^{235}(n, f) of 55.6-sec Br^{87} is estimated to be 2.5%. Estimate the fraction of its β-decays that are followed by neutron emission from excited states of Kr^{87}.

6–16. The 9.1-hr Xe^{135} is the most serious "pile poison" because of its large thermal-neutron capture cross section (3.5×10^6 b) and the high fission yield of the mass-135 chain. The growth (from 6.7-hr I^{135}) and disappearance [by (n, γ) reactions and radioactive decay] may be treated using the equation for activity of a radioactive daughter (see Problem 4–5) if λ_B is replaced by $\Lambda_B(=\lambda_B + \phi\sigma_B)$, where ϕ is the neutron flux and σ_B is the capture cross section. (a) If a reactor producing I^{135} at a rate R has been running for a time $t \ll 9$ hrs, what is the true radioactive decay rate of Xe^{135} if the flux is 10^{12} n/cm²-sec? (b) At what time following shutdown of the reactor will the amount of Xe^{135} present be maximum?

6–17. In a thermal neutron flux, Pu^{239} is produced from U^{238} and depleted by (n, γ) and (n, fission) reactions according to the following sequence of reactions:

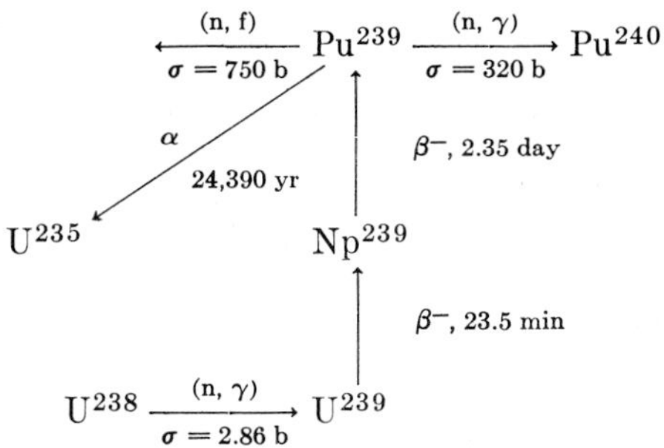

Suppose a 1-gm piece of natural uranium is placed in a reactor at a position where the thermal neutron flux is 10^{13} n/cm^2-sec. (a) Ignoring the depletion of U^{238}, how many atoms of each of the following species are present when the condition of secular equilibrium has been established up through Pu^{239}: U^{239}, Np^{239}, Pu^{239}? (b) How long must the sample be in the reactor before the amount of Pu^{239} has reached 90% of its secular-equilibrium value? (c) How large is the error made in assuming no depletion of U^{238} by the time Pu^{239} is 90% of the way to secular equilibrium? (i.e., by what fraction has the number of U^{238} atoms been reduced upon bombardment for the time calculated in part (b)?) (d) What is the fission rate of Pu^{239} at secular equilibrium? (e) What is the α-decay rate of Pu^{239} at secular equilibrium? [*Ans:* (a) Pu^{239}: 6.7×10^{18}; (b) 6.8 yrs; (e) 6.05×10^6/sec]

6–18. Suppose one wishes to determine by activation analysis the amount of barium impurity present in a 1-gm sample of $SrCl_2$. The sample is irradiated for 2 hrs in a flux of 10^{12} neutrons/cm^2-sec. At the end of irradiation the sample is dissolved in a solution with 10 mg of Ba^{2+} carrier. At the end of the chemical separation, the barium is precipitated and weighed as $BaCrO_4$. The precipitate weighs 15 mg. The β-particles from 83-min Ba^{139} are observed with a proportional counter that has an effective geometry of 30%. The counting rate observed 1 hr, 23 min after the end of irradiation is 1.05×10^4 counts per minute:

$$Ba^{138}(n, \gamma)Ba^{139}, \qquad \sigma = 0.55 \text{ b}.$$

Neglect products formed by neutron capture in barium isotopes other than Ba^{138}. (a) What is the chemical yield in the barium separation? (b) How many Ba^{139} atoms were present at the end of the irradiation? (c) How many Ba^{139} atoms were produced during the irradiation? (d) What is the ratio of barium atoms to strontium atoms in the original sample?

MASSES NEEDED FOR PROBLEM SET:

Cm^{238}: 238.12869	Cm^{248}: 248.15118
Cm^{239}: 239.13087	Cf^{252}: 252.16176
Cm^{247}: 247.14873	Cf^{253}: 253.16553

CHAPTER 7

7–1. If a given sample of water has 10 atoms of T per 10^{18} atoms of H, calculate the disintegrations per second of T per liter (S.T.P.) of H_2 derived from the water. What enrichment is required to bring the activity up to 10 dis/sec?

7–2. Show from the laws of radioactive equilibrium that a production rate of C^{14} in the atmosphere of 2.4 atoms/cm^2-sec and an active reservoir of 8.3 gm/cm^2 of carbon in dynamic equilibrium with the atmosphere leads to a specific activity of 17 dis/min/gm.

7–3. What is the specific activity of 5568-yr C^{14} per gram of carbon for a wooden artifact of 15,000 years age? What is the uncertainty in this age coming from 5% uncertainty in specific activity, ignoring uncertainty in the half-life of C^{14}? How does the uncertainty in age which comes from the uncertainty in specific activity depend upon the age?

7–4. Calculate the isotope abundance (atom percent) of 1.25×10^9-yr K^{40} for 5.0×10^9 years ago, and the heat output in cal/yr then occurring per gram of potassium. The present isotopic abundance is 0.0119%. [*Ans:* 0.0457%; 10.4×10^{-6} cal/yr]

7–5. If $Fe(OH)_3$ is used to separate thorium from 1 gm of uranium (carbonate complex), the decay curve of the thorium fraction will show what species in what intensities? Note that the U^{235}(actino-uranium) series has the specific activity of 563 dis/sec and the U^{238} series 12,223. If then MnO_2 precipitation is used to separate protactinum from thorium, after 6.7-hr Pa^{234}(UZ) has grown to equilibrium, the protactinium decay curve will show what species in what intensities?

7–6. The lead fraction from the thorium series Pb^{212} = ThB is often used as a radioactive source. Its daughter Bi^{212} = ThC decays 36.2% by α-emission to Tl^{208} = ThC″ and 63.8% by β-emission to Po^{212} = ThC′. Sketch the time dependence, over a period of 4 hrs of the following types of activity from a source initially pure of Th^{212}: the β-activity of Th^{212}, β-activity and α-activity of Bi^{212}, α-activity of Po^{212}, and β-activity of Tl^{208}.

7–7. If the 3.83-day Rn^{222} in equilibrium with 1 gm of 1622-yr Ra^{226} is collected in a needle and allowed to decay away, what will be the activity in dis/sec of 138.4-day Po^{210} in the needle? [*Ans:* 1.02×10^9 dis/sec]

7–8. Tetravalent polonium is carried efficiently in HCl solutions by Cs_2SnCl_6 and is considered to be $PoCl_6^{2-}$. Ferrous ion in 1 to 3 *M* HCl solution reduces $PoCl_6^{2-}$ slowly to a lower state not carried by Cs_2SnCl_6. At equilibrium the ratio of Po (carried) to Po (not carried) is proportional to $(Fe^{3+})^2/(Fe^{2+})^2$ and also proportional to the square of the Cl^- activity. Show how these data support the formula $PoCl_4^{2-}$ for the Po in lower valence state in HCl solution.

CHAPTER 8

8–1. The simple parabolic relation between energy and charge Z for odd A (Chapter 3) leads to the rule that Z_A, the most stable charge for given A, lies for odd A within 0.5 charge units of the Z for any β-stable species. Determine the Z for β-stability for odd-A values from 227 through 255, and establish the course of Z_A versus A graphically. Assuming that Z_A is linear with A, what is the slope dZ_A/dA in this region?

8–2. Identify the states of U, Np, Pu, Am, and Bk that would be produced in 1 N acid solution by the I_3^--I^- couple; by the Br_2-Br^- couple; by the Cl_2-Cl^- couple.

8–3. Taking electrode potentials from Table 8–4 for 1.0 M $HClO_4$, estimate the equilibrium concentration of UO_2^+ in an equimolal mixture of U^{4+} and UO_2^{2+}. Show how this concentration depends on H^+ ion for the pH range before hydrolysis of U^{4+} or UO_2^{2+} occurs.

8–4. The absence of any evidence for Np(VII) or Pu(VII) or Pu(VIII) leads to what conclusions about the electronic structure changes on going up the series UO_2^{2+}, NpO_2^{2+}, PuO_2^{2+}, and AmO_2^{2+}?

8–5. Predict the possibilities of obtaining oxidation states in acid solution other than the ions M^{3+} for the elements 102, 103(Lw), and 104. Should one expect the first post-actinide element to be more like Th^{4+} or Hf^{4+}?

CHAPTER 11

11–1. Particles emitted in nuclear reactions are often identified by the use of two detectors, one behind the other. The front detector is "thin," i.e., it absorbs only a fraction ΔE of the energy of the particles. The particles deposit their residual energy, $E - \Delta E$, in the back detector which is "thick." Electronically the product $\Delta E \times E$ is formed. Show from Eq. (11–2) that the quantity $\Delta E \times E$ is approximately constant for a given type of particle and proportional to MZ^2.

11–2. A 40-Mev He^4 ion passes through a 1-cm path length in an ionization chamber containing argon at 1 atm pressure. (a) Calculate the number of ion pairs formed if the average energy to form an ion pair is 30 ev. (b) Calculate the height of the voltage pulse produced upon collection of the ions formed if the capacity of the collecting electrode circuit is 10 $\mu\mu$farads, assuming the time constant, RC, to be sufficiently great that there is negligible decay of the pulse before complete collection.

11–3. Starting with the appropriate (relativistic) energy and momentum conservation relationships, derive the expression for the Compton effect in which the energy of the scattered photon is given in terms of the energy of the initial photon and the angle of the scattered photon.

11–4. Calculate the energy of the 180° Compton-scattered photon if the energy of the initial photon is: (a) 0.100 Mev, (b) 1 Mev, (c) 10 Mev, (d) ∞.

11–5. (a) If a collimated beam of 10^6 photons of 3-Mev energy strike a 0.5-cm thick Al foil, how many photons are transmitted without loss of energy? (b) Assuming all Compton-scattered photons escape from the foil without further interaction, and that all photoelectrons, Compton electrons, and positron-electron pairs deposit their energy within the foil, how much energy is deposited in the foil by passage of the 10^6 photons?

11–6. Repeat Problem 5 for 0.5-cm Pb foil.

11–7. Assuming that a γ-ray expends on ionization 3.5×10^{-5} of its energy per cm path length in air at S.T.P., calculate the dose rate in rads per hour produced by a 1-curie source of 0.20-Mev γ-rays at 1 meter.

11–8. Beta-particles from a nuclide having a single β-group of 1.5-Mev end-point energy are counted through a 100-mg/cm^2 lucite absorber. (a) By what factor does the observed counting rate have to be multiplied to correct for absorption in the lucite? (b) What is the approximate maximum range of the β-particles in lucite.

11–9. (a) A 100-mg sample of Ag is placed in a thermal neutron flux of 10^{12} n/cm^2-sec for 3 min. Calculate the activities of 2.3-min Ag^{108}, 253-day Ag^{110m}, and 24.2-sec Ag^{110} at the end of irradiation. (b) By what factor would these activities be reduced if the silver sample is surrounded by cadmium foil of thickness 250 mg/cm^2?

Thermal neutron cross sections:

$$Ag^{107}(n, \gamma)Ag^{108}, \sigma = 44 \text{ b}$$
$$Ag^{109}(n, \gamma)Ag^{110m}, \sigma = 2.8 \text{ b}$$
$$Ag^{109}(n, \gamma)Ag^{110}, \sigma = 110 \text{ b}$$
$$Cd(n, \gamma), \sigma = 2450 \text{ b}$$

11–10. In a proposed experiment, a Van de Graaff machine is to be used to produce a beam of monoenergetic electrons. (a) If these electrons have an extrapolated range of 0.8 mm in aluminum, what is their initial energy? (b) The electron beam passes through 10 cm of air (at 1 atm pressure) and then impinges vertically on a dilute aqueous solution. What depth of solution is actually irradiated? (c) What intensity (in μA) of the electron beam will be required to give an energy deposition of 10^{19} ev/ml/hr in 5 ml of solution? (d) Suppose that an accelerator produces protons with the same energy as the electrons referred to above; could the same experimental set-up be used for the irradiation of aqueous solutions? [Density of Al = 2.7; weight of 1 liter of air at NTP = 1.3 gm; 1 faraday = 96,500 coulombs.] [*Ans:* (a) Approx. 0.6 Mev, (b) 2 mm, (c) 3.9×10^{-3} μA, (d) No]

CHAPTER 12

12–1. The dissociation energy of water is 117.55 kcal/mole. Using the values given in the text for the appearance potentials of the OH^+ ion in water vapor and in hydrogen peroxide, calculate the dissociation energy of the latter. The kinetic and excitation energies of the the fragments can be neglected. [*Ans:* 55 kcal/mole]

12–2. The α-particles emitted by Po^{210} have an energy of 5.298 Mev and an average range in air at NTP of 3.842 cm. Calculate: (a) The average range in air at NTP of the α-particles from Cm^{242} (E_α = 6.105 Mev), and the number of ion pairs produced per α-particle. (b) The average range in air of 1.527-Mev protons. [*Ans:* (a) 4.752 cm, 1.75×10^5 ion pairs; (b) 4.585 cm]

12–3. (a) Calculate the number of ion pairs produced by a Po^{210} α-particle in high-purity helium and argon. (b) Draw a graph showing the number of ion pairs produced by a Po^{210} α-particle in helium-argon mixtures as a function of the partial pressures of the two components (assuming that the additivity law is valid). What is the form of the curve thus obtained? Compare this with the experimental results. [E_α for Po^{210} = 5.298 Mev; the stopping power of argon relative to air is 0.95, and of helium 0.17.] [*Ans:* (a) He 1.24×10^5 ion pairs, Ar 2.00×10^5 ion pairs; (b) hyperbolic]

CHAPTER 13

13–1. When a sulfuric acid solution of vanadium (IV) (VO^{2+}; concentration 10^{-3} *M*) is irradiated with Po^{210} α-particles in the presence of air, partial oxidation to vanadium (V) occurs, with an initial yield $G_i(VO_2^+) = 2.10$. When a solution of VO_2^+ is irradiated under the same conditions, one observes a partial reduction of VO_2^+, with an initial yield $G_i(VO^{2+}) = 1.20$, and the simultaneous production of the peroxy-cation VO_3^+; $G_i(VO_3^+) = 1.25$. If these irradiations are carried out in the absence of air, hydrogen is given off, with a yield which is the same in each case, namely $G(H_2) = 1.55$.

In these reactions, the OH radicals preferentially reduce VO_3^+, or in its absence oxidize VO^{2+} to VO_2^+; H and HO_2 radicals reduce VO_2^+; H_2O_2 forms the peroxy-compound with VO_2^+, or in its absence, oxidizes VO^{2+}.

(a) Calculate the radical and molecular yields in the decomposition of water by Po^{210} α-particles, assuming that the four primary products in the radiolysis are H, OH, H_2O_2, and H_2. (b) Show why a reaction scheme involving only these four products does not give a stoichiometric balance for the decomposition of water. [*Ans:* (a) $G_{OH} = 0.20$, $G_H = 1.0$, $G_{H_2O_2} = 1.45$, $G_{H_2} = 1.55$]

13–2. In order to study the chemical effects of the radiations from a nuclear reactor on aqueous solutions, it is necessary to know: (1) the thermal neutron flux at the point where the solution is to be placed; (2) the energy absorption per milliliter of solution due to high-ionization-density radiation (consisting essentially of protons "knocked-on" by fast neutrons); (3) the energy absorption per milliliter of solution due to γ-radiation. To measure these parameters, the following three solutions were irradiated in a neutron flux which was constant with respect to both time and volume: (i) A dilute solution of ferric orthophenanthroline; 3.3×10^{17} molecules/ml were found to have been reduced after a 1-hr irradiation. (ii) A dilute solution of ceric sulfate containing boric acid (concentration 10^{-3} *M*); 7×10^{17} molecules/ml of Ce(IV) were reduced in 1 hr. (iii) An identical solution of ceric sulfate containing no boric acid; 10^{17} molecules/ml were reduced in 1 hr.

From these results, calculate: (a) the neutron flux, (b) the γ-ray energy deposited per milliliter of solution per hour (i.e., the dose rate), (c) the energy deposition per milliliter per hour due to the high-ionization-density radiation. The cross-section for the $B^{10}(n, \alpha)Li^7$ reaction with thermal neutrons is 3740 barns. The sum of the kinetic energies of the α and Li^7 particles is 2.49 Mev.

The yields for the reduction of ferric orthophenanthroline by γ-rays are $G_\gamma = 9.3$, and by dense ionization radiation $G_d = 1.1$; the corresponding yields for the reduction of Ce(IV) are $G_\gamma = 2.45$ and $G_d = 2.8$. The chemical effects of the different radiations are known to be additive. [*Ans:* (a) 5.65×10^{12} n/cm^2-sec, (b) 3.47×10^{18} ev/ml-hr, (c) 0.53×10^{18} ev/ml-hr]

13–3. An approximately millimolar solution of ferrous sulfate in 0.8 *N* sulfuric acid was shown to contain no Fe(III) ions; after a 5-min irradiation with γ-rays from a Co^{60} source, the Fe(III) concentration was 2.15×10^{-4} *M*.

Five milliliters of a 10^{-3} *M* ceric sulfate solution in 0.8 *N* H_2SO_4 were then sealed in the presence of air at 1 atm pressure in a 10-ml ampoule, and irradiated with the same source and the same geometry for 1 hr. After this irradiation, the gas pressure in the ampoule was found to have increased by 0.48%. The Ce(IV) concentration was measured by titration with 10^{-3} *M* ferrous sulfate, using ferric orthophenanthroline as indicator; 5 ml of the irradiated solution required 2.07 ml less ferrous sulfate than the same volume of unirradiated solution.

(a) Write the chemical reactions involving the solute in the two irradiation systems. (b) Calculate the energy deposition in ev/ml-hr. (c) Calculate the yields (in molecules per 100 ev) for the reduction of ceric sulfate and for the production of gas. (d) Deduce the values for the radical yields G_H and G_{OH} and the molecular yields $G_{H_2O_2}$ and G_{H_2} in the decomposition of water in 0.8 N sulfuric acid by Co^{60} γ-rays.

The yield for the radiolytic oxidation of Fe^{2+} in 0.8 N H_2SO_4 is $G(Fe^{3+}) =$ 15.6 molecules per 100 ev. The solubility of the gas in the solution can be neglected. [*Ans:* (b) 10^{19} ev/ml-hr; (c) $G(Ce^{3+}) = 2.5$, $G(H_2) = 1.30$; (d) $G_{OH} = 2.87$, $G_H = 3.67$, $G_{H_2O_2} = 0.85$, $G_{H_2} = 0.45$]

13–4. The table below gives the reported values for the oxidation of Fe(II) in aerated dilute aqueous solution by various radiations, and for the corresponding yields of hydrogen gas. Calculate the initial rate of linear energy transfer (LET) for each radiation (in kev/μ) from the Bethe equation, and plot both yields as a function of the logarithm of the initial LET. For the complex radiation produced in the $B^{10}(n, \alpha)Li^7$ reaction, use the average of the initial LET's.

From the values given, draw a graph of the yield for the decomposition of water as a function of the initial LET of the radiation concerned. Discuss the curve obtained in terms of the theoretical treatment of the radiolysis of water.

Mean excitation potential of water = 66 ev.

Radiation	G_{H_2}	$G(Fe^{3+})$
160-Mev protons	0.45	15.6
Protons from the $N^{14}(n, p)C^{14}$ reaction induced by slow neutrons		7
16.8-Mev deuterons	0.7	10
35-Mev helium ions	1	8
5.3-Mev α-particles	1.55	5.6
3.4-Mev α-particles		4.9
α and Li^7 particles from the $B^{10}(n, \alpha)Li^7$ reaction with slow neutrons	2	4

CHAPTER 15

15–1. It is required to determine the number of defects created in a sample of copper by bombardment with an integral flux of 10^{16} deuterons (energy 12 Mev) at 12°K. The sample (0.1 mm^2 cross section, 1 cm long) has an electrical resistance 2×10^{-3} ohm greater than that of an unirradiated sample. Calculate the number of defects produced per cm^3 by the radiation, knowing that the resistivity of copper increases by 3×10^{-6} ohm · cm when the lattice contains 1% defects, on the assumption that the resistivity increases linearly with the number of defects. Is this hypothesis valid for very high integral fluxes? Density of copper 8.92.

15–2. When Pa^{233} is extracted from 6 M hydrochloric acid, in the presence of chromous chloride, by benzene solutions of TTA of differing concentrations, the following results are found. What is the formula of the extracted complex?

Molar conc. of TTA in organic phase	% Pa^{233} extracted
0.10	20
0.12	25
0.14	40
0.15	48
0.17	58
0.20	70
0.23	79
0.25	83

CHAPTER 17

17–1. When cacodylic acid, $(CH_3)_2AsOOH$, is bombarded with thermal neutrons, radioactive arsenic (As^{76}) is formed by an (n, γ) reaction. (a) Calculate the energy of the de-excitation photon, assuming that only one photon is emitted, and neglecting the recoil energy in the calculation. (b) Calculate this recoil energy making use of the photon energy calculated above. [*Ans:* (a) 7.057 Mev, (b) 351 ev]

CHAPTER 20

20–1. A 20-mg drop taken from a solution of ThC gave an activity of 10^4 α-particles/min over a 2π solid angle. Five hours after this measurement, the critical potential for the cathodic deposition of ThC was determined with this solution. What value would be found if the deposit obeys the Nernst electrochemical equation? The standard potential of the Bi/Bi^{3+} couple is 0.23 volt relative to the hydrogen electrode.

TABLE OF NUCLIDES

TABLE OF NUCLIDES*

Symbol	Z	A	Half-life	Decay mode and/or % natural abundance	Mass excess (C^{12} = 0) (kev)	Mass excess (C^{12} = 0) (μmu)	Principal method of formation
n	0	1	11.7 min	β^-	8071.34	8665.44	see Table 11–13, p. 345
H	1	1	—	99.98	7288.73	7825.22	—
		2	—	0.015	13135.36	14102.19	—
		3	12.262 yr	β^-	14949.07	16049.40	D^2(d, p); Li^6(n, α); Be^9(d, 2α)
He	2	3	—	1.3(10^{-4})	14930.94	16029.94	—
		4	—	100	2425.11	2603.61	—
		6	0.82 sec	β^-	17604	18900	Be^9(n, α); Li^6(n, p)
Li	3	6	—	7.5	14089.3	15126.3	—
		7	—	92.5	14908.0	16005.3	—
		8	0.84 sec	β^-	20946.6	22488.4	Li^7(n, γ)
		9	0.17 sec	β^-	—	—	Be^9(d, 2p)
Be	4	7	53.55 day	e	15768.7	16929.3	Li^7(p, n)
		9	—	100	11350.3	12185.8	—
		10	2.5(10^6) yr	β^-	12607.3	13535.3	Be^9(d, p); B^{10}(n, p)
		11	14.1 sec	β^-	—	—	B^{11}(n, p)
B	5	8	0.78 sec	β^+	22924.4	24611.7	B^{10}(p, t)
		9	0.75 sec	β^+	12420.5	13334.7	Be^9(p, n)
		10	—	18.8	12051.9	12938.9	—
		11	—	81.2	8667.14	9305.09	—
		12	0.022 sec	β^-	13368.9	14352.9	B^{11}(d, p)
		13	0.035 sec	β^-	16560	17780	B + p; Li + p
C	6	9	?	β^+	—	—	emulsion + p
		10	19.1 sec	β^+	15670	16830	B^{10}(p, n)
		11	20.4 min	β^+	10649.5	11433.4	B^{11}(p, n); C^{12}(n, 2n)
		12	—	98.892	0	0	—
		13	—	1.108	3124.3	3354.3	—

		14	5760 yr	β^-	3019.67	3241.93	N^{14}(n, p)
		15	2.25 sec	β^-	9873.3	10600.0	C^{14}(n, γ)
		16	0.74 sec	β^-	—	—	C^{14}(t, p)
N	7	12	0.013 sec	β^+	17600	18900	C^{12}(p, n); B^{10}(He^3, n)
		13	10.1 min	β^+	5345.5	5738.9	C^{12}(d, n)
		14	—	99.635	2863.60	3074.38	—
		15	—	0.365	100.7	108.1	—
		16	7.35 sec	β^-	5672	6089	N^{15}(n, γ); O^{16}(n, p)
		17	4.14 sec	β^-	7990	8580	C^{14}(α, p); O^{18}(γ, p); F^{19}(d, 3pn)
O	8	14	70.9 sec	β^+	8012	8601	N^{14}(p, n)
		15	2.1 min	β^+	2861.3	3071.9	N^{14}(d, n)
		16	—	99.759	−4736.43	−5085.06	—
		17	—	0.037	−807.2	−866.6	—
		18	—	0.204	−782.57	−840.17	—
		19	29.1 sec	β^-	3332.1	3577.3	F^{19}(n, p)
		20	?	β^-	—	—	O^{18}(t, p)
F	9	17	1.1 min	β^+	1954.5	2098.4	N^{14}(α, n); O^{16}(d, n)
		18	109.7 min	β^+e	884.8	949.9	O^{18}(p, n)
		19	—	100	−1486.1	−1595.4	—
		20	11.5 sec	β^-	−13.5	−14.5	F^{19}(n, γ)
		21	5 sec	β^-	−26	−28	F^{19}(t, p)
Ne	10	18	1.6 sec	β^+	5100	5480	F^{19}(p, 2n)
		19	18 sec	β^+	1762	1892	F^{19}(p, n)
		20	—	90.92	−7041.3	−7559.6	—
		21	—	0.257	−5729.1	−6150.8	—

* Reprinted by permission from Nouveau Traitè de Chemie Minèrale, **15,** Masson et Cie, Paris, 1962.

m: metastable; e: electron capture; γ: photon emission or electrons from internal conversion; f: fission; sf: spontaneous fission. When nuclides has several disintegration modes ($\alpha\beta^+$, $e\beta^+$, etc.), the order of listing does not reflect the relative intensities. Metastable states with life-times of less than a millisecond are not listed in this table.

The natural abundances are those listed in Table 3–3, p. 22.

Mass excesses are based on the atomic weight scale, C^{12} = 12, and are taken from F. Everling, L. A. König, J. H. E. Mattauch, and A. H. Wapstra, *Nuclear Physics*, **18,** 529 (1960).

For radiation energies and decay schemes, see Strominger, Hollander, and Seaborg, "Table of Isotopes," *Rev. Mod. Phys.*, **30,** 585 (1958).

(Continued)

TABLE OF NUCLIDES (*Continued*)

Symbol	Z	A	Half-life	Decay mode and/or % natural abundance	Mass excess (C^{12} = 0) (kev)	Mass excess (C^{12} = 0) (μmu)	Principal method of formation
		22	—	8.82	−8024.9	−8615.5	—
		23	38.0 sec	β^-	−5146	−5525	Na^{23}(n, p)
		24	3.4 min	β^-	−5964	−6403	Ne^{22}(t, p)
Na	11	20	0.38 sec	β^+	8280	8890	Ne^{20}(p, n)
		21	22 sec	β^+	−2207	−2370	Ne^{20}(p, γ); Ne^{21}(p, n)
		22	2.6 yr	β^+	−5183.3	−5565	F^{19}(α, n); Mg^{24}(d, α)
		23	—	100	−9526.2	−10227.4	—
		24	15.1 hr	β^-	−8413.8	−9033.1	Na^{23}(n, γ); Mg^{24}(n, p)
		24m	0.019 sec	$\beta^-\gamma$	—	—	Na^{23}(n, γ); Mg^{24}(n, p)
		25	60 sec	β^-	−9390	−10080	Mg^{25}(n, p)
		26	1.04 sec	β^-	—	—	Mg^{26}(n, p)
Mg	12	23	11.9 sec	β^+	−5467	−5869	Na^{23}(n, p)
		24	—	78.60	−13930.1	−14955.4	—
		25	—	10.11	−13189.4	−14160.3	—
		26	—	11.29	−16215.5	−17409.1	—
		27	9.45 min	β^-	−14581.2	−15654.5	Mg^{26}(n, γ); Al^{27}(n, p)
		28	21.3 hr	β^-	−15015	−16120	Mg^{26}(α, 2p); Si^{30}(p, 3p)
Al	13	24	2.1 sec	β^+	90	90	Mg^{24}(p, n)
		25	7.3 sec	β^+	−8928	−9586	Mg^{25}(p, n)
		26	7.4(10^5) yr	β^+e	−12201.5	−13100	Mg^{26}(d, 2n)
		26m	6.3 sec	β^+	—	—	Na^{23}(α, n); Mg^{26}(p, n)
		27	—	100	−17199.2	−18465.1	—
		28	2.27 min	β^-	−16851.5	−18091.9	Al^{27}(n, γ); P^{31}(n, α)
		29	6.56 min	β^-	−18140	−19470	Mg^{26}(α, p)
		30	3.3 sec	β^-	—	—	Si + n
Si	14	26	1.7 sec	β^+	—	—	Al^{27}(p, 2n); Mg^{24}(He^3, n)

		27	4.4 sec	β^+	−12384	−13295	Al^{27}(p, n)
		28	—	92.27	−21491.0	−23072.9	—
		29	—	4.68	−21897.4	−23509.2	—
		30	—	3.05	−24440.3	−26239.3	—
		31	2.62 hr	β^-	−22961.1	−24651	Si^{30}(n, γ); P^{31}(n, p)
		32	~710 yr	β^-	−24200	−25980	Si^{31}(n, γ)
P	15	28	0.28 sec	β^+	−7690	−8260	Si^{28}(p, n)
		29	4.4 sec	β^+	−16937	−18184	Si^{29}(p, n)
		30	2.52 min	β^+	−20193	−21680	Al^{27}(α, n); S^{32}(d, α)
		31	—	100	−24437.8	−26236.6	—
		32	14.3 day	β^-	−24303.2	−26092.1	P^{31}(n, γ); S^{32}(n, p); Cl^{35}(n, α)
		33	25.2 day	β^-	−26333.9	−28272.2	P^{32}(n, γ); Cl^{33}(n, p)
		34	12.4 sec	β^-	−24830	−26660	S^{34}(n, p); Cl^{37}(n, α)
S	16	30	1.35 sec	β^+	—	—	Si^{28}(He^3, n)
		31	2.8 sec	β^+	−19002	−20401	P^{31}(p, n)
		32	—	95.1	−26011.7	−27926.2	—
		33	—	0.74	−26582.9	−28539.5	—
		34	—	4.2	−29932.4	−32135.5	—
		35	87.16 day	β^-	−28842.9	−30965.8	S^{34}(n, γ); Cl^{35}(n, p)
		36	—	0.016	−30653	−32909	—
		37	5.04 min	β^-	−26980	−28960	Cl^{37}(n, p)
		38	172 min	β^-	−26800	−28780	Cl^{37}(α, 3p)
Cl	17	32	0.31 sec	β^+	−13010	−13970	S^{32}(p, n)
		33	2.5 sec	β^+	−21008	−22554	S^{32}(d, n)
		34	1.6 sec	β^+	−24512	−26317	S^{34}(p, n)
		34m	32.4 min	$\beta^+\gamma$	—	—	P^{31}(α, n); S^{34}(p, n)
		35	—	75.4	−29010.2	−31145.5	—
		36	$3.08(10^5)$ yr	β^-e	−29516	−31688	Cl^{35}(n, γ); K^{39}(n, α)
		37	—	24.6	−31765.9	−34104.1	—
		38	37.3 min	β^-	−29804	−31998	Cl^{37}(n, γ); K^{41}(n, α)
		38m	1.0 sec	γ	—	—	Cl^{37}(n, γ)
		39	55.5 min	β^-	−29803	−31997	Ar^{40}(γ, p)
		40	1.4 min	β^-	−27500	−29600	Ar^{40}(n, p)

(Continued)

TABLE OF NUCLIDES (*Continued*)

Symbol	Z	A	Half-life	Decay mode and/or % natural abundance	Mass excess (C^{12} = 0) (kev)	Mass excess (C^{12} = 0) (μmu)	Principal method of formation
Ar	18	35	1.83 sec	β^+	−23030	−24725	$S^{32}(\alpha, n)$; $Cl^{35}(p, n)$
		36	—	0.337	−30227.0	−32451.9	—
		37	35 day	e	−30949.9	−33228.0	$Cl^{37}(p, n)$; $Ca^{40}(n, \alpha)$
		38	—	0.063	−34719.9	−37275.5	—
		39	~265 yr	β^-	−33233	−35679	$K^{39}(n, p)$
		39	160 sec	β^-	—	—	$Ar^{38}(d, p)$
		40	—	99.60	−35037.3	−37616.2	—
		41	110 min	β^-	−33058	−35492	$Ar^{40}(n, \gamma)$; $K^{41}(n, p)$
		42	≥3.5 yr	β^-	—	—	$Ar^{40}(2n, \gamma)$
K	19	37	1.2 sec	β^+	−24830	−26660	$K^{40}(p, \alpha)$
		38	7.7 min	β^+	−28791	−30910	$Cl^{35}(\alpha, n)$; $Ca^{40}(d, \alpha)$
		38	0.95 sec	β^+	—	—	$K^{39}(\gamma, n)$
		38m	$1.1(10^9)$ yr	β^+e	—	—	natural (?)
		39	—	93.08	−33798.3	−36286.0	—
		40	$1.25(10^9)$ yr	β^-e 0.0119	−33524.5	−35992.1	natural
		41	—	6.91	−35548.3	−38164.9	—
		42	12.46 hr	β^-	−35006	−37583	$K^{41}(n, \gamma)$; $Sc^{45}(n, \alpha)$
		43	22.4 hr	β^-	−36577	−39269	$Ar^{40}(\alpha, p)$
		44	20 min	β^-	−35360	−37960	$Ca^{43}(n, p)$
		45?	34 min	β^-	—	—	V + p
Ca	20	38	0.66 sec	β^+	—	—	$Ca^{40}(\gamma, 2n)$
		39	0.88 sec	β^+	−27188	−29190	$K^{39}(p, n)$; $Ca^{40}(n, 2n)$
		40	—	96.97	−34846.0	−37410.8	—
		41	$1.1(10^5)$ yr	e	−35135	−37721	$Ca^{40}(n, \gamma)$
		42	—	0.64	−38535.9	−41372.3	—

		43	—	0.145	−38394.0	−41220.0	—
		44	—	2.06	−41458.7	−44510.3	—
		45	164 day	β^-	−40807.0	−43810.6	$Ca^{44}(n, \gamma)$; $Sc^{45}(n, p)$
		46	—	0.0033	−43136	−46311	—
		47	4.7 day	β^-	−42370	−45488	$Ca^{46}(d, p)$
		48	—	0.185	−44226	−47481	—
		49	8.8 min	β^-	−41298	−44338	$Ca^{48}(n, \gamma)$
Sc	21	40	0.18 sec	β^+	−20950	−22490	$Ca^{40}(p, n)$
		41	0.87 sec	β^+	−29185	−31333	$Ca^{40}(d, n)$
		42	0.62 sec	β^+	−32600	−35000	$Ca^{42}(p, n)$
		43	3.9 hr	β^+	−36174	−38837	$Ca^{40}(d, n)$; $Ca^{40}(\alpha, p)$
		44	4.0 hr	β^+e	−37811	−40594	$K^{41}(\alpha, n)$; $Sc^{45}(n, 2n)$
		44m	2.4 day	γ	—	—	$K^{41}(\alpha, n)$; $Sc^{45}(n, 2n)$
		45	—	100	−41058.9	−44081.1	—
		46	84.2 day	β^-	−41754	−44827	$Sc^{45}(n, \gamma)$; $Ti^{48}(d, \alpha)$
		46m	19.5 sec	γ	—	—	$Sc^{45}(n, \gamma)$
		47	3.43 day	β^-	−44335	−47598	$Ca^{44}(\alpha, p)$
		48	44 hr	β^-	−44494	−47769	$Ti^{48}(n, p)$; $V^{51}(n, \alpha)$
		49	57 min	β^-	−46490	−49910	$Ti^{49}(n, p)$
		50	1.5 min	β^-	−45100	−48400	$Ti^{50}(n, p)$
Ti	22	43	0.6 sec	?	—	—	$Ca^{40}(\alpha, n)$
		44	$\sim 10^3$ yr	e	−37656	−40427	$Sc^{45}(d, 3n)$
		45	3.09 hr	β^+e	−39001	−41871	$Sc^{45}(p, n)$
		46	—	7.95	−44119.2	−47366.6	—
		47	—	7.75	−44935	−48242	—
		48	—	73.45	−48483.6	−52052.2	—
		49	—	5.51	−48559.1	−52133.4	—
		50	—	5.34	−51425.7	−55210.9	—
		51	5.8 min	β^-	−49716	−53376	$Ti^{50}(n, \gamma)$; $V^{51}(n, p)$
V	23	46	0.4 sec	β^+	−36820	−39530	$Ti^{46}(p, n)$
		47	31 min	β^+	−42023	−45116	$Ti^{47}(p, n)$
		48	16.0 day	β^+e	−44467	−47740	$Ti^{48}(p, n)$; $Ti^{48}(d, 2n)$
		49	330 day	e	−47948	−51477	$Ti^{48}(d, n)$

(Continued)

TABLE OF NUCLIDES (*Continued*)

Symbol	Z	A	Half-life	Decay mode and/or % natural abundance	Mass excess (C^{12} = 0) (kev)	Mass excess (C^{12} = 0) (μmu)	Principal method of formation
		50	$\sim 10^{16}$ yr	e, β^- 0.24	—49213.0	—52835.4	natural
		51	—	99.76	—52181.3	—56022.1	—
		52	3.75 min	β^-	—51414	—55198	V^{51}(n, γ); Mn^{55}(n, α)
		53	2.0 min	β^-	—52750	—56630	Cr^{53}(n, p)
		54	55 sec	β^-	—	—	Cr^{54}(n, p)
Cr	24	46	1.1 sec	?	—	—	V + p
		48	23 hr	e	—43070	—46240	Ni + p
		49	41.9 min	β^+	—45388	—48729	Ti^{46}(α, n); Cr^{50}(n, 2n)
		50	—	4.31	—50250.6	—53949.3	—
		51	27.75 day	e	—51428.7	—55214.1	Cr^{50}(n, γ); V^{51}(p, n)
		52	—	83.76	—55407.9	—59486.3	—
		53	—	9.55	—55280.0	—59348.9	—
		54	—	2.38	—56930.3	—61120.6	—
		55	3.5 min	β^-	—54880	—58920	Cr^{54}(n, γ); Mn^{55}(n, p)
		56	5.94 min	β^-	—	—	$Mn^{56} \xrightarrow{\beta^-}$
Mn	25	50	0.28 sec	β^+	—42600	—45700	Cr + p
		50m	2 min	β^+	—48250	—51800	Cr + p
		51	45.2 min	β^+	—48250	—51800	Cr^{50}(d, n)
		52	5.7 day	β^+e	—50705	—54437	Cr^{52}(p, n); Cr^{54}(d, α)
		52m	21.3 min	β^+	—	—	Cr^{52}(p, n); Cr^{54}(d, α)
		53	$\sim 2(10^6)$ yr	e	—54683	—58707	Cr^{53}(p, n)
		54	290 day	e	—55551	—59640	Cr^{54}(p, n); Fe^{56}(d, α)
		54m	2.1 min	β^-	—	—	Fe^{54}(n, p)
		55	—	100	—57699.4	—61946.4	—
		56	2.58 hr	β^-	—56898	—61086	Mn^{55}(n, γ); Co^{59}(n, α)

		57	1.7 min	β^-	−57480	−61710	Fe^{57}(n, p)
		58	1.1 min	β^-	—	—	Fe^{58}(n, p)
Fe	26	52	8.3 hr	β^+e	−48322	−51879	Cr^{50}(α, 2n)
		53	8.9 min	β^+	−50691	−54422	Cr^{50}(α, n); Fe^{54}(n, 2n)
		54	—	5.84	−56239	−60379	—
		55	2.6 yr	e	−57467.7	−61697.6	Mn^{55}(p, n); Fe^{57}(d, γ)
		56	—	91.68	−60607	−65068	—
		57	—	2.17	−60177	−64606	—
		58	—	0.31	−62153	−66728	—
		59	44.3 day	β^-	−60667	−65133	Fe^{58}(n, γ); Co^{59}(n, p)
		60	~3(10^5) yr	β^-	—	—	Cu^{63}(p, 4p)
		61	5.5 min	β^-	—	—	Cu^{65}(n, αp)
Co	27	54	0.2 sec	β^+	−47400	−50900	Fe^{54}(p, n)
		54m	1.5 min	β^+	—	—	Fe^{54}(p, n)
		55	18.2 hr	β^+e	−54008	−57983	Fe^{54}(d, n); Ni^{58}(p, α)
		56	77.3 day	β^+e	−56007	−60130	Fe^{56}(p, n)
		57	270 day	e	−59607	−63994	Fe^{56}(d, n)
		58	71.3 day	β^+e	−59841	−64246	Fe^{57}(d, n); Ni^{58}(n, p)
		58m	9.1 hr	γ	—	—	Mn^{55}(α, n); Ni^{58}(n, p)
		59	—	100	−62230.4	−66810.9	—
		60	5.26 yr	β^-	−61656	−66194	Co^{59}(n, γ); Ni^{60}(n, p)
		60m	10.5 min	$\beta^-\gamma$	—	—	Co^{59}(n, γ); Ni^{60}(n, p)
		61	99 min	β^-	−62934	−67566	Ni^{61}(n, p)
		62	13.9 min	β^-	−61522	−66051	Ni^{62}(n, p)
		62m	1.9 min	β^-	—	—	Ni^{62}(n, p)
		63	1.4 hr	β^-	—	—	Ni^{64}(n, np)
		63	52 sec	β^-	—	—	Ni^{64}(γ, p)
		64	7.8 min	β^-	—	—	Ni^{64}(n, p)
		64m	2 min	β^-	—	—	Ni^{64}(n, p)
Ni	28	56	6.4 day	e	—	—	Fe^{54}(α, 2n)
		57	36 hr	β^+e	−56372	−60521	Ni^{58}(n, 2n); Fe^{54}(d, n)
		58	—	67.76	−60225	−64658	—
		59	8(10^4) yr	e	−61154.6	−65656	Ni^{58}(n, γ); Co^{59}(d,(2n)

(Continued)

TABLE OF NUCLIDES (*Continued*)

Symbol	Z	A	Half-life	Decay mode and/or % natural abundance	Mass excess ($C^{12} = 0$) (kev)	Mass excess ($C^{12} = 0$) (μmu)	Principal method of formation
		60	—	26.16	−64472	−69217	—
		61	—	1.25	−64224	−68951	—
		62	—	3.66	−66742	−71655	—
		63	92 yr	β^-	−65512	−70334	$Ni^{62}(n, \gamma)$; $Cu^{63}(n, p)$
		64	—	1.16	−67102	−72041	—
		65	2.25 hr	β^-	−65160	−69960	$Ni^{64}(n, \gamma)$; $Cu^{65}(n, p)$
		66	2.3 day	β^-	−66052	−70914	As + d; Bi + p
Cu	29	57?	0.18 sec	?	—	—	Ni + p
		58	9.5 min	β^+	−51710	−55510	$Ni^{58}(p, n)$
		59	81 sec	β^+	−56356	−60504	$Ni^{58}(d, n)$
		60	23.4 min	β^+e	−58325	−62618	$Ni^{60}(p, n)$
		61	3.33 hr	β^+e	−61993	−66556	$Ni^{60}(d, n)$
		62	9.8 min	β^+	−62812	−67436	$Co^{59}(\alpha, n)$; $Cu^{63}(n, 2n)$
		63	—	69.1	−65579	−70406	—
		64	12.8 hr	$\beta^-\beta^+e$	−65424	−70239	$Cu^{63}(n, \gamma)$; $Zn^{64}(n, p)$
		65	—	30.9	−67263	−72214	—
		66	5.1 min	β^-	−66252	−71129	$Cu^{65}(n, \gamma)$; $Zn^{66}(n, p)$
		67	58.5 hr	β^-	−67284	−72237	$Zn^{67}(n, p)$
		68	32 sec	β^-	—	—	$Zn^{68}(n, p)$
Zn	30	60	2.1 min	β^+e	—	—	$Ni^{58}(\alpha, 2n)$
		61	1.5 min	β^+	−56190	−60330	$Ni^{58}(\alpha, n)$
		62	9.3 hr	β^+e	−61122	−65621	$Cu^{63}(d, 2n)$
		63	38.3 min	β^+e	−62213	−66792	$Cu^{63}(p, n)$; $Zn^{64}(n, 2n)$
		64	—	48.89	−65997	−70855	—
		65	249.9 day	β^+e	−65915	−70766	$Zn^{64}(n, \gamma)$; $Cu^{65}(p, n)$
		66	—	27.81	−68882	−73952	—

		68	—	18.56	−69984	−75135	—
		69	52 min	β^-	−68318	−73347	$Zn^{68}(n, \gamma)$; $Ga^{71}(d, \alpha)$
		69m	13.8 hr	γ	—	—	$Zn^{68}(n, \gamma)$; $Ga^{71}(d, \alpha)$
		70	—	0.62	−69534	−74652	—
		71	2.2 min	β^-	−67100	−72030	$Zn^{70}(n, \gamma)$; $Ga^{71}(n, p)$
		71m	3 hr	β^-	—	—	$Zn^{70}(n, \gamma)$
		72	49 hr	β^-	−67300	−72260	Bi + d; Th + α
		73	<2 min	β^-	—	—	f
Ga	31	64	2.5 min	β^+	−58980	−63320	$Zn^{64}(p, n)$
		65	15 min	β^+e	−62656	−67267	$Zn^{64}(d, n)$
		66	9.45 hr	β^+e	−63712	−68401	$Cu^{63}(\alpha, n)$; $Zn^{66}(p, n)$
		67	77.9 hr	e	−66858	−71779	$Zn^{66}(d, n)$
		68	68 min	β^+e	−67066	−72003	$Cu^{65}(\alpha, n)$; $Zn^{68}(d, 2n)$
		69	—	60.5	−69223	−74318	—
		70	21.1 min	β^-	−68882	−73952	$Zn^{69}(n, \gamma)$; $Ge^{70}(n, p)$
		70m	0.01 sec	γ	—	—	$Ge^{70}(n, p)$
		71	—	39.5	−70005	−75160	—
		72	14.3 hr	β^-	−68902	−73970	$Ga^{71}(n, \gamma)$; $Ge^{72}(n, p)$; f
		72m	0.04 sec	γ	—	—	$Ga^{71}(n, \gamma)$
		73	5.0 hr	β^-	−69840	−74980	$Ge^{73}(n, p)$; f
		74	14.5 day	β^-	−67790	−72780	$Ge^{74}(n, p)$
		74m	7.5 min	γ	—	—	$Ge^{74}(n, p)$; f
		75	2.0 min	β^-	—	—	$Ge^{76}(\gamma, p)$
		75?	1.5 min	β^-	—	—	Ge + n
Ge	32	65	1.5 min	β^+	—	—	$Zn^{64}(\alpha, 3n)$
		66	~150 min	β^+?	—	—	$Ge^{70}(d, p5n)$
		67	21 min	β^+	−62460	−67060	$Ge^{70}(d, p4n)$
		68	280 day	e	−66400	−71300	$Zn^{66}(\alpha, 2n)$
		69	40 hr	β^+e	−66986	−71917	$Zn^{69}(d, 2n)$
		70	—	20.55	−70532	−75723	—
		71	11.4 day	e	−69772	−74910	$Ge^{70}(n, \gamma)$; $Ga^{71}(p, n)$
		71m	$20(10^{-3})$sec	γ	—	—	Ge^{72} (p, pn)
		72	—	27.37	−72890	−78260	—

(Continued)

TABLE OF NUCLIDES (*Continued*)

Symbol	Z	A	Half-life	Decay mode and/or % natural abundance	Mass excess (C^{12} = 0) (kev)	Mass excess (C^{12} = 0) (μmu)	Principal method of formation
		73	—	7.67	−71390	−76640	—
		73m	0.53 sec	γ	—	—	Ge^{73}(n, γ)
		74	—	36.74	−73440	−78850	—
		75	82 min	β^-	−71870	−77160	Ge^{74}(n, γ); As^{75}(n, p); f
		75m	48 sec	γ	—	—	Ge^{74}(n, γ)
		76	—	7.67	−73250	−78640	—
		77	11.3 hr	β^-	−71140	−76380	Ge^{76}(n, γ); f
		77m	57 sec	$\beta^-\gamma$	—	—	Ge^{76}(n, γ); f
		78	86 min	β^-	−71990	−77290	f
As	33	68?	7 min	?	—	—	Ge^{70}(p, 3n)
		69	15 min	β^+	−63090	−67730	Ge^{70}(p, 2n)
		70	52 min	β^+	−63990	−68700	As^{75}(d, p6n)
		71	62 hr	β^+e	−67763	−72750	Ge^{70}(d, n)
		72	26 hr	β^+e	−68530	−73570	Ga^{69}(α, n); Ge^{72}(p, n)
		73	76 day	e	−71020	−76240	Ge^{72}(d, n)
		74	17.5 day	$\beta^-\beta^+$e	−70880	−76090	Ga^{71}(α, n); Ge^{74}(p, n)
		75	—	100	−73045	−78420	—
		75m	$18(10^{-3})$ sec	γ	—	—	$Ge^{75} \xrightarrow{\beta^-}$; As(n, n′)
		76	26.4 hr	β^-	−72264	−77583	As^{75}(n, γ); Ge^{79}(p, n)
		77	39 hr	β^-	−73893	−79332	Ge^{76}(d, n); f
		78	90 min	β^-	−72890	−78250	Sc^{80}(d, α); Br^{81}(n, α); f
		79	9 min	β^-	−73590	−79010	f
		80	15.3 sec	β^-	−71760	−77050	Se^{80}(n, p)
		81	10 min	β^-	—	—	f
		81	33 sec	β^-	—	—	Se^{82}(γ, p); Se^{82}(n, np)
		85?	0.4 sec	β^-	—	—	f

Se	34	70	~44 min	β^+	—	—	$Ge^{70}(\alpha, 4n)$
		71	5 min	β^+	−63360	−68030	Ge + α; Cu + N^{14}
		72	8.4 day	e	—	—	As^{75}(d, 5n); $Ge^{70}(\alpha, 2n)$
		73	7.1 hr	β^+e	−68270	−73290	$Ge^{70}(\alpha, n)$
		73 or 75	44 min	β^+	—	—	Ge + α
		74	—	0.87	−72230	−77550	—
		75	119.9 day	e	−72179	−77490	$Se^{74}(n, \gamma)$; As^{75}(p, n)
		76	—	9.02	−75233	−80771	—
		77	—	7.58	−74577	−80066	—
		77m	18 sec	γ	—	—	f
		78	—	23.52	−76986	−82652	—
		79	$\leq 6.5(10^4)$ yr	β^-	−75893	−81479	$Se^{78}(n, \gamma)$; f
		79m	3.9 min	γ	—	—	$Se^{78}(n, \gamma)$
		80	—	49.82	−77764	−83488	—
		81	18 min	β^-	−76510	−82140	$Se^{80}(n, \gamma)$; Br^{81}(n, p); f
		81m	62 min	γ	—	—	$Se^{80}(n, \gamma)$; Br^{81}(n, p); f
		82	—	9.19	−77630	−83340	—
		83	25 min	β^-	−75530	−81090	$Se^{82}(n, \gamma)$; f
		83	70 sec	β^-	—	—	$Se^{82}(n, \gamma)$
		83m	25 min	β^-	—	—	$Se^{82}(n, \gamma)$
		84	3.3 min	β^-	—	—	f
		85	40 sec	β^-	—	—	f
		86 or 87	17 sec	β^-	—	—	f
Br	35	74	25.7 min	β^+e	—	—	Cu + C; Kr + p
		75	1.6 hr	β^+e	−69460	−74570	$Se^{74}(p, \gamma)$
		76	17.5 hr	β^+	−70643	−75843	Se^{76}(p, n)
		77	57 hr	β^+e	−73212	−78601	$As^{75}(\alpha, 2n)$; Se^{76}(d, n)
		77m	4.2 min	γ	—	—	$As^{75}(\alpha, 2n)$; Se^{76}(d, n)
		78	6.3 min	β^+	−73520	−78930	$Br^{79}(\gamma, n)$; Br^{79}(n, 2n)

(Continued)

TABLE OF NUCLIDES (*Continued*)

Symbol	Z	A	Half-life	Decay mode and/or % natural abundance	Mass excess (C^{12} = 0) (kev)	Mass excess (C^{12} = 0) (μmu)	Principal method of formation
		79	—	50.52	−76054	−81652	—
		79m	4.8 sec	γ	—	—	$Br^{79}(n, \gamma)$; $Se^{78}(p, \gamma)$
		80	18 min	$\beta^-\beta^+e$	−75875	−81459	$Br^{79}(n, \gamma)$
		80m	4.4 hr	γ	—	—	$Br^{79}(n, \gamma)$; $Se^{80}(p, n)$
		81	—	49.48	−77920	−83656	—
		82	35.85 hr	β^-	−77494	−83198	$Br^{81}(n, \gamma)$; $Se^{82}(d, 2n)$; $Rb^{85}(n, \alpha)$
		83	2.3 hr	β^-	−78982	−84795	$Se^{82}(d, n)$; f
		84	31.7 min	β^-	−77730	−83450	f
		84	6 min	β^-	—	—	f
		85	3.0 min	β^-	−78760	−84560	f
		86	54 sec	β^-	—	—	Kr^{86} (n, p)
		87	55.6 sec	β^-	−72690	−78040	f
		88	15.5 sec	β^-	—	—	f
		89	4.5 sec	β^-	—	—	f
		90	1.4 sec	β^-	—	—	f
Kr	36	74	12 min	β^+e	—	—	Sr + p; Br + p
		75	5.5 min	e	—	—	Br + p
		76	9.7 hr	β^+	—	—	Y + p
		77	1.2 hr	β^+e	−70332	−75510	$Se^{74}(\alpha, n)$
		78	—	0.354	−74172.2	−79632	—
		79	34 hr	β^+e	−74432	−79911	$Se^{76}(\alpha, n)$; $Br^{79}(p, n)$
		79m	55 sec	γ	—	—	$Se^{76}(\alpha, n)$; $Br^{79}(p, n)$
		80	—	2.27	−77880	−83612	—
		81	$2.1(10^5)$ yr	e	−77680	−83390	$Kr^{80}(n, \gamma)$
		81m	13 sec	γ	—	—	$Br^{81}(p, n)$
		82	—	11.56	−80586	−86517	—

		84	—	56.90	−82428.6	−88496	—
		85	10.3 yr	β^-	−81560	−87570	$Kr^{84}(n, \gamma)$; f
		85m	4.36 hr	$\beta^-\gamma$	—	—	$Kr^{84}(n, \gamma)$; f
		86	—	17.37	−83255	−89383	—
		87	78 min	β^-	−80689	−86630	$Kr^{86}(n, \gamma)$; f
		88	2.77 hr	β^-	−79920	−85800	f
		89	3.18 min	β^-	—	—	f
		90	33 sec	β^-	—	—	f
		91	9.8 sec	β^-	—	—	f
		92	3 sec	β^-	—	—	f
		93	2 sec	β^-	—	—	f
		94	1.4 sec	β^-	—	—	f
		95	short	β^-	—	—	f
		97	~1 sec	β^-	—	—	f
Rb	37	79	20.9 min	β^+	—	—	$Cu(O^{16}, xn)$; Br + α
		80	34 sec	e	—	—	Ga + N
		81	4.7 hr	β^+e	−75440	−80990	$Br^{79}(\alpha, 2n)$
		81m	31.5 min	$\beta^+\gamma$	—	—	$Br^{79}(\alpha, 2n)$
		82	1.25 min	β^+	−76416	−82041	$Br^{79}(\alpha, n)$
		82m	6.3 hr	β^+e	—	—	$Br^{79}(\alpha, n)$
		83	83 day	e	—	—	$Br^{79}(\alpha, 2n)$
		84	33 day	$\beta^-\beta^+e$	−79776	−85648	$Rb^{85}(n, 2n)$; $Sr^{86}(d, \alpha)$
		84m	23 min	eγ	—	—	$Br^{81}(\alpha, n)$
		85	—	72.15	−82240	−88290	—
		86	18.68 day	β^-	−82750	−88840	$Rb^{85}(n, \gamma)$; $Sr^{86}(n, p)$; f
		86m	1.02 min	γ	—	—	$Rb^{85}(n, \gamma)$
		87	4.7–58(10^{10}) yr	β^- 27.85	−84590	−90820	natural; f
		88	17.8 min	β^-	−82720	−88810	$Rb^{87}(n, \gamma)$; $Sr^{88}(n, p)$; f
		89	15.4 min	β^-	−82700	−88780	f
		90	2.74 min	β^-	—	—	f
		91	14 min	β^-	—	—	f
		91	1.67 min	β^-	—	—	f

(Continued)

TABLE OF NUCLIDES (*Continued*)

Symbol	Z	A	Half-life	Decay mode and/or % natural abundance	Mass excess (C^{12} = 0)		Principal method of formation
					(kev)	(μmu)	
		92	5.3 sec	β^-	—	—	f
		93	5.6 sec	β^-	—	—	f
		94	2.9 sec	β^-	—	—	f
		95	2.5 sec	β^-	—	—	f
		97	short	β^-	—	—	f
Sr	38	80	100 min	e	—	—	Ga + N
		81	29 min	β^+e	—	—	Rb^{85}(p, 5n)
		82	25.5 day	e	—	—	Ag + p
		83	1.4 day	β^+e	—	—	Ag + p
		84	—	0.56	−80685	−86624	—
		85	64.0 day	e	−81130	−87100	Sr^{84}(n, γ); Rb^{85}(p, n)
		85m	70 min	eγ	—	—	Rb^{85}(p, n)
		86	—	9.86	−84520	−90740	—
		87	—	7.02	−84870	−91110	—
		87m	2.8 hr	eγ	—	—	Sr^{86}(n, γ); Rb^{87}(p, n)
		88	—	82.56	−87920	−94390	—
		89	50.36 day	β^-	−86620	−92990	Sr^{88}(n, γ); f
		89m	~10 day	γ	—	—	f
		90	27.7 yr	β^-	−86330	−92680	f
		91	9.7 hr	β^-	−84040	−90220	Zr^{94}(n, α); f
		92	2.6 hr	β^-	−83350	−89480	f
		93	8.2 min	β^-	—	—	f
		94	1.3 min	β^-	—	—	f
		95	0.8 min	β^-	—	—	f
		97	short	β^-	—	—	f
Y	39	82	~10 min	e	—	—	Y + p; As + C

		84	39 min	β^+e	—	—	Sr^{84}(p, n)
		85	5 hr	e	—	—	Y + p
		86	14.6 hr	β^+	−78510	−84290	Sr^{88}(p, 3n)
		86m	49 min	γ	—	—	Rb^{85} (α, 3n)
		87	80 hr	β^+e	−83180	−89300	Sr^{86}(d, n); Sr^{87}(p, n)
		87m	14 hr	γ	—	—	Sr^{86}(d, n); Sr^{87}(p, n)
		88	104 day	β^+e	−84470	−90690	Sr^{88}(p, n); Y^{89}(n, 2n)
		88m	14.5 (10^{-3}) sec	γ	—	—	Sr^{88} (p, n)
		89	—	100	−88090	−94570	—
		89m	16.1 sec	γ	—	—	Y^{89}(n, n)
		90	64.4 hr	β^-	−86860	−93260	Y^{89}(n, γ); f
		90m	3.2 hr	γ	—	—	Rb + α; Sr + d
		91	57.5 day	β^-	−86710	−93090	Zr^{91}(n, p); f
		91m	50.3 min	γ	—	—	Zr^{91}(n, p); f
		92	3.6 hr	β^-	−85270	−91540	Zr^{92}(n, p); f
		93	10.1 hr	β^-	−84590	−90810	f
		94	20.35 min	β^-	−82430	−88490	Zr^{94}(n, p); f
		95	10.9 min	β^-	—	—	f
		96	2.3 min	β^-	—	—	Zr^{96}(n, p)
		97	short	β^-	—	—	f
Zr	40	85	6 min	e	—	—	Y + p
		86	17 hr	e	—	—	Nb^{93}(p, 8n)
		87	94 min	β^+e	−79670	−85530	Sr^{84}(α, n)
		88	85 day	e	—	—	Nb^{93}(p, 6n)
		89	79.3 hr	β^+e	−85240	−91520	Y^{89}(p, n); Mo^{92}(n, α)
		89m	4.4 min	β^+eγ	—	—	Y^{89}(p, n)
		90	—	51.46	−89120	−95680	—
		90m	0.83 sec	γ	—	—	Zr^{90}(n, n)
		91	—	11.23	−88260	−94750	—
		92	—	17.11	−88870	−95410	—
		93	9.5(10^5) yr	β^-	−87480	−93920	f
		94	—	17.40	−87430	−93860	—
		95	65 day	β^-	−85770	−92080	Zr^{94}(n, γ); f

(*Continued*)

TABLE OF NUCLIDES (*Continued*)

Symbol	Z	A	Half-life	Decay mode and/or % natural abundance	Mass excess ($C^{12} = 0$)		Principal method of formation
					(kev)	(μmu)	
		96	—	2.8	−85500	−91800	—
		97	17.0 hr	β^-	−83200	−89320	$Zr^{96}(n, \gamma)$; f
		98	~1 min	β^-	—	—	f
		99	35.5 sec	β^-	—	—	f
Nb	41	89	1.9 hr	β^+	−81360	−87350	$Zr^{90}(p, 2n)$
		89m	0.8 hr	β^+	—	—	$Zr^{90}(p, 2n)$
		90	14.6 hr	β^+	−83000	−89110	$Zr^{90}(d, 2n)$
		90m	24 sec	γ	—	—	$Mo^{90} \xrightarrow{\beta^+}$
		90m	6.5(10^{-3}) sec	γ	—	—	$Mo^{90} \xrightarrow{\beta^+}$; Zr + p
		91	long	e	−86660	−93040	$Zr^{90}(d, n)$
		91m	60 day	γ	—	—	$Zr^{90}(d, n)$
		92	10.1 day	e	−86790	−93180	$Zr^{92}(p, n)$; $Mo^{92}(n, p)$
		92m	121.6 min	γ	—	—	$Nb^{93}(n, 2n)$
		93	—	100	−87540	−93980	—
		93m	12 yr	γ	—	—	$Nb^{93}(n, n)$
		94	2.03(10^4) yr	$\beta^-\gamma$	−86660	−93040	$Nb^{93}(n, \gamma)$
		94m	6.6 min	$\beta^-\gamma$	—	—	$Nb^{93}(n, \gamma)$
		95	35 day	β^-	−86890	−93280	$Mo^{97}(d, \alpha)$; f
		95m	90 hr	γ	—	—	f
		96	23.35 hr	β^-	−85780	−92090	$Zr^{96}(p, n)$
		97	72.1 min	β^-	−85860	−92180	$Mo^{97}(n, p)$; f
		97m	60 sec	γ	—	—	f
		98	51.5 min	β^-	—	—	f
		99	2.4 min	β^-	—	—	f
		100	3.0 min	β^-	—	—	f
		101	~1.0 min	β^-	—	—	f

		91m	66 sec	$\beta^+ e\gamma$	—	—	$Mo^{92}(\gamma, n)$
		92	—	15.86	−87280	−93710	—
		93	>2 yr	e	−87060	−93470	$Mo^{92}(n, \gamma)$
		93m	6.95 hr	γ	—	—	$Mo^{92}(n, \gamma)$; $Mo^{94}(\gamma, n)$
		94	—	9.12	−88730	−95260	—
		95	—	15.70	−87820	−94280	—
		96	—	16.50	−88900	−95450	—
		97	—	9.45	−87790	−94250	—
		98	—	23.75	−88010	−94490	—
		99	67 hr	β^-	−85810	−92130	$Mo^{98}(n, \gamma)$; f
		100	—	9.62	−86090	−92430	—
		101	14.6 min	β^-	—	—	$Mo^{100}(n, \gamma)$; f
		102	11.5 min	β^-	—	—	f
		104	1.1 min	β^-	—	—	f
		105	<2 min	β^-	—	—	f
		107	40 sec	β^-	—	—	f
Tc	43	92	4.3 min	$\beta^+ e$	−80900	−86800	$Mo^{92}(d, 2n)$
		93	2.75 hr	$\beta^+ e$	−83900	−90070	$Mo^{92}(d, n)$
		93m	43.5 min	$e\gamma$	—	—	$Mo^{92}(d, n)$
		94	53 min	$\beta^+ e$	−84410	−90620	$Mo^{94}(p, n)$
		95	20 hr	e	−86160	−92500	$Mo^{95}(p, n)$
		95m	60 day	$\beta^+ e\gamma$	—	—	$Mo^{95}(p, n)$
		96	4.2 day	e	−85930	−92250	$Nb^{93}(\alpha, n)$; $Mo^{96}(p, n)$
		96m	51.5 min	$\beta^+\gamma$	—	—	$Mo^{96}(p, n)$
		97	~2.6(10^6) yr	e	—	—	$Mo^{97}(d, 2n)$
		97m	91 day	γ	—	—	$Mo^{97}(d, 2n)$
		98	1.5(10^6) yr	β^-	−86300	−92700	$Mo^{97}(d, n)$
		99	2.12(10^5) yr	β^-	−87190	−93610	$Ru^{99}(n, p)$; f
		99m	6.0 hr	γ	—	—	$Ru^{99}(n, p)$; f
		100	15.8 sec	β^-	—	—	$Mo^{100}(p, n)$
		101	14.3 min	β^-	—	—	f
		102	5 sec	β^-	−85580	−91880	f
		102	4.5 min	β^-	—	—	$Ru^{102}(n, p)$

(Continued)

TABLE OF NUCLIDES (*Continued*)

Symbol	Z	A	Half-life	Decay mode and/or % natural abundance	Mass excess (C^{12} = 0) (kev)	Mass excess (C^{12} = 0) (μmu)	Principal method of formation
		103	1.2 min	β^-	—	—	Ru + p
		104	3.8 min	β^-	—	—	Ru^{104}(n, p)
		104	18 min	β^-	—	—	Ru^{104}(n, p)
		105	7.5 min	β^-	—	—	f
		107	<1.5 min	β^-	—	—	f
		108	<1 min	β^-	—	—	f
Ru	44	93	50 sec	β^+?	—	—	Mo + α
		94	57 min	e	—	—	$Mo^{92}(\alpha, 2n)$
		95	1.65 hr	β^+e	−83960	−90140	$Mo^{92}(\alpha, n)$; Ru^{96}(n, 2n)
		96	—	5.68	−86100	−92400	—
		97	2.88 day	e	—	—	$Mo^{94}(\alpha, n)$; $Ru^{96}(n, \gamma)$
		98	—	1.91	−88000	−94500	—
		99	—	12.70	−87480	−93920	—
		100	—	12.69	—	—	—
		101	—	17.01	—	—	—
		102	—	31.52	−89680	−96280	—
		103	39.8 day	β^-	−87920	−94390	$Ru^{102}(n, \gamma)$; Rh^{103}(n, p); f
		104	—	18.67	−88000	−94470	—
		105	4.5 hr	β^-	−86350	−92710	$Ru^{104}(n, \gamma)$; f
		106	366.6 day	β^-	−86600	−92970	f
		107	4.8 min	β^-	—	—	$Pd^{110}(n, \alpha)$; f
		108	4.4 min	β^-	—	—	f
Rh	45	96	11 min	β^+	—	—	Ru^{96}(p, n)
		97	35 min	β^+	—	—	Ru + d
		98	8.7 min	β^+	−83800	−90000	Ru + α
		99	4.7 hr	β^+e	−85380	−91670	Ru^{96}(p, n)
		99	15 day	β^+	[illegible]	[illegible]	Ru + p

		101	4.7 day	e	—	—	Ru^{101}(p, n)
		101	5 yr	γ	—	—	Ru + p
		102	210 day	$\beta^-\beta^+e$	−87410	−93850	Ru^{102}(p, n); Pd^{104}(d, α)
		103	—	100	−88670	−95200	—
		103m	57 min	γ	—	—	Rh^{103}(n, n); f
		104	44 sec	β^-	−87390	−93820	Rh^{103}(n, γ); Ru^{104}(p, n)
		104m	4.4 min	$\beta^-\gamma$	—	—	Rh^{103}(n, γ); Ru^{104}(p, n)
		105	36.5 hr	β^-	−88260	−94750	Ru^{104}(d, n); Pd^{105}(n, p); f
		105m	45 sec	γ	—	—	f
		106	30 sec	β^-	−86630	−93010	Pd^{108}(d, α); f
		106	130 min	β^-	—	—	Pd^{106}(n, p)
		107	23 min	β^-	−86980	−93380	f
		107m	136 min	β^-	—	—	Ta + p
		107m	~30 sec	γ	—	—	f
		108	18 sec	β^-	—	—	f
		109	<1 hr	β^-	—	—	f
Pd	46	98	17.5 min	e	—	—	Ru^{96}(α, 2n)
		99	21.6 min	β^+	−81600	−87600	Ru^{96}(α, n)
		100	4 day	e	—	—	Rh^{103}(d, 5n)
		101	8.5 hr	β^+e	—	—	Ru^{98}(α, n)
		102	—	0.8	−88540	−95060	—
		103	17 day	e	−88110	−94590	Rh^{103}(p, n)
		104	—	9.3	−89830	−96440	—
		105	—	22.6	−88820	−95360	—
		105m	23 sec	γ	—	—	Pd^{105}(α, α)
		105m	2 sec	β^-	—	—	f
		106	—	27.2	−90160	−96800	—
		107	7.5(10^6) yr	β^-	−88480	−94990	Pd^{106}(n, γ); f
		107m	23 sec	β^-	—	—	Pd^{106}(n, γ); f
		108	—	26.8	−89490	−96080	—
		109	13.6 hr	β^-	−87650	−94100	Pd^{108}(n, γ); f
		109m	4.8 min	γ	—	—	Pd^{108}(n, γ); f
		110	—	13.5	−88950	−95500	—

(Continued)

TABLE OF NUCLIDES (*Continued*)

Symbol	Z	A	Half-life	Decay mode and/or % natural abundance	Mass excess ($C^{12} = 0$) (kev)	Mass excess ($C^{12} = 0$) (μmu)	Principal method of formation
		111	22 min	β^-	−86030	−92360	$Pd^{110}(n, \gamma)$; f
		111m	5.5 hr	$\beta^-\gamma$	—	—	$Pd^{110}(n, \gamma)$; f
		112	21 hr	β^-	−86160	−92510	f
		113	1.4 min	β^-	—	—	U + d; f
		114	2.4 min	β^-	—	—	f
		115	45 sec	β^-	—	—	f
		116	<30 sec	β^-	—	—	f
		117	<30 sec	β^-	—	—	f
Ag	47	102	16 min	β^+	—	—	$Pd^{102}(p, n)$
		103	66 min	β^+e	—	—	$Pd^{104}(p, 2n)$
		104	29.8 min	β^+	−85550	−91850	$Pd^{104}(p, n)$
		104	1.1 hr	β^+e	—	—	$Pd^{104}(p, n)$
		105	39 day	e	−86800	−93200	$Rh^{103}(\alpha, 2n)$; $Pd^{105}(p, n)$
		106	8.2 day	e	−87190	−93610	$Rh^{103}(\alpha, n)$; $Pd^{106}(p, n)$; $Ag^{107}(n, 2n)$
		106	24 min	β^+e	—	—	$Rh^{103}(\alpha, n)$; $Pd^{106}(p, n)$; $Ag^{107}(n, 2n)$
		107	—	51.35	−88510	−95030	—
		107m	44.3 sec	γ	—	—	f
		108	2.3 min	$\beta^-\beta^+$e	−87650	−94110	$Ag^{107}(n, \gamma)$; $Cd^{108}(n, p)$
		108m	≥5 yr	e	—	—	$Ag^{107}(n, \gamma)$
		109	—	48.65	−88760	−95300	—
		109m	39.2 sec	γ	—	—	f
		110	24.2 sec	β^-	−87510	−93950	$Ag^{109}(n, \gamma)$
		110m	249 day	$\beta^-\gamma$	—	—	$Ag^{109}(n, \gamma)$
		111	7.5 day	β^-	−88230	−94720	$Pd^{100}(d, n)$; $Cd^{111}(n, p)$; f
		111m	74 sec	γ	—	—	$Pd^{100}(d, n)$; f
		112	3.2 hr	β^-	−86460	−92830	$Cd^{112}(n, p)$; $In^{115}(n, \alpha)$; f
		113	5.3 hr	β^-	−86850	−93240	f

		113m	1.2 min	β^-	—	—	f
		114	4.5 sec	β^-	−85220	−91500	Cd + n; f
		114	2 min	β^-	—	—	f
		115	21.1 min	β^-	−85010	−91260	f
		115m	~20 sec	β^-	—	—	f
		116	2.5 min	β^-	—	—	f
		117	1.1 min	β^-	—	—	f
Cd	48	103	10.5 min	β^+	—	—	Mo + O^{16}
		104	59 min	e	—	—	Ag^{107}(p, 4n)
		105	55 min	β^+e	—	—	Ag^{107}(p, 3n)
		106	—	1.215	−87600	−94050	—
		107	6.7 hr	β^+e	−87070	−93480	$Cd^{106}(n, \gamma)$; Ag^{107}(p, n)
		108	—	0.875	−89420	−96000	—
		109	470 day	e	−88610	−95130	$Cd^{108}(n, \gamma)$; Ag^{109}(p, n)
		110	—	12.39	−90380	−97030	—
		111	—	12.75	−89280	−95850	—
		111m	48.6 min	γ	—	—	$Cd^{110}(n, \gamma)$; Cd^{111}(n, n); f
		112	—	24.07	−90500	−97160	—
		113	—	12.26	−88850	−95390	—
		113m	14 yr	β^-	—	—	$Cd^{112}(n, \gamma)$; f
		114	—	28.86	−89820	−96430	—
		115	53 hr	β^-	−87910	−94380	$Cd^{114}(n, \gamma)$; f
		115m	44.2 day	β^-	—	—	$Cd^{114}(n, \gamma)$; f
		116	—	7.58	−88480	−94990	—
		117	50 min	β^-	−86280	−92640	$Cd^{116}(n, \gamma)$; f
		117m	2.9 hr	γ	—	—	$Cd^{116}(n, \gamma)$; f
		118	50 min	β^-	—	—	f
		119	10 min	β^-	—	—	$Sn^{122}(d, \alpha p)$
		119	2.9 min	β^-	—	—	f
In	49	106	5.3 min	β^+	—	—	Cd^{106}(p, n)
		107	30 min	β^+	—	—	$Cd^{106}(p, \gamma)$
		108	40 min	β^+	−84320	−90530	$Cd^{108}(\alpha, 4n)$
		108m	55 min	$\beta^+\gamma$	—	—	Cd^{108}(d, 2n)
		109	4.3 hr	β^+e	−86590	−92960	$Ag^{107}(\alpha, 2n)$; Cd^{108}(d, n)

(Continued)

TABLE OF NUCLIDES (*Continued*)

Symbol	*Z*	*A*	Half-life	Decay mode and/or % natural abundance	Mass excess ($C^{12} = 0$) (kev)	Mass excess ($C^{12} = 0$) (μmu)	Principal method of formation
		109m	<2 min	γ	—	—	$Ag^{107}(\alpha, 2n)$; $Cd^{108}(d, n)$
		110	66 min	β^+e	−86420	−92780	$Ag^{107}(\alpha, n)$; $Cd^{110}(p, n)$
		110m	5.0 hr	$e\gamma$	—	—	$Ag^{107}(\alpha, n)$
		111	2.84 day	e	−88040	−94520	$Ag^{109}(\alpha, 2n)$; $Cd^{110}(d, n)$
		112	14.5 min	$\beta^-\beta^+e$	−87890	−94360	$Cd^{112}(p, n)$
		112m	21 min	γ	—	—	$Ag^{109}(\alpha, n)$; $Cd^{112}(p, n)$
		113	—	4.23	−89160	−95720	—
		113m	1.73 hr	γ	—	—	$Cd^{112}(d, n)$; $In^{113}(n, n)$
		114	72 sec	$\beta^-\beta^+e$	−88400	−94910	$In^{113}(n, \gamma)$
		114m	50.0 day	e	—	—	$In^{113}(n, \gamma)$; $Cd^{114}(p, n)$
		114m	2.5 sec	γ	—	—	$In^{115}(\gamma, n)$
		115	$6.9(10^{14})$ yr	β^-, 95.77	−89360	−95930	natural
		115m	4.50 hr	$\beta^-\gamma$	—	—	$Cd^{114}(d, n)$; $In^{115}(n, n)$; f
		116	14 sec	β^-	−87890	−94360	$In^{115}(n, \gamma)$; $Cd^{116}(p, n)$
		116m	54 min	β^-	—	—	$In^{115}(n, \gamma)$
		117	1.1 hr	β^-	−88820	−95360	$Cd^{115}(d, n)$; f
		117m	1.9 hr	$\beta^-\gamma$	—	—	$Cd^{117} \xrightarrow{\beta^-}$
		118	4.5 min	β^-	—	—	f
		118	5.5 sec	β^-	—	—	f
		119	17.5 min	β^-	—	—	f
		120	3.0 sec	β^-	—	—	$Sn^{120}(n, p)$
		120m	50 sec	β^-	—	—	$Sn^{120}(n, p)$
		122	7.5 sec	β^-	—	—	Sn + n
Sn	50	108	9 min	e	—	—	$Cd^{106}(\alpha, 2n)$
		109	18.1 min	β^+e	—	—	$Cd^{106}(\alpha, n)$
		110	4 hr	e	—	—	$Cd^{108}(\alpha, 2n)$
		111	35.0 min	β^+e	−85520	−91820	$Cd^{108}(\alpha, n)$

		112	—	0.95	−88540	−95060	—
		113	119 day	e	−88470	−94990	In^{113}(p, n)
		113m	24 min	β^+	—	—	Cd^{110}(α, n)
		114	—	0.65	−90390	−97040	—
		115	—	0.34	−89860	−96470	—
		116	—	14.24	−91180	−97890	—
		117	—	7.57	−90290	−96940	—
		117m	14 day	γ	—	—	f
		118	—	24.01	−91470	−98210	—
		119	—	8.58	−89990	−96610	—
		119m	~250 day	γ	—	—	Cd^{116}(α, n); Sb^{121}(d, α); f
		120	—	32.97	−91160	−97870	—
		121	27.5 hr	β^-	−89260	−95830	Sn^{120}(n, γ); Sb^{121}(n, p); f
		121m	>400 day	β^-	—	—	Sn^{120}(n, γ); f
		122	—	4.71	−89970	−96590	—
		123	39.5 min	β^-	−87860	−94330	Sn^{122}(n, γ); f
		123	130 day	β^-	—	—	f
		124	—	5.98	−88260	−94760	—
		125	9.4 day	β^-	−85930	−92250	Sn^{124}(n, γ); f
		125	9.5 min	$\beta^-\gamma$	—	—	Sn^{124}(n, γ); f
		126	~50 min	β^-	—	—	f
		126	~10^5 yr	β^-	—	—	f
		127	123 min	β^-	—	—	f
		128	57 min	β^-	—	—	f
		130	2.6 min	β^-	—	—	f
		131	3.4 min	β^-	—	—	f
		132	2.2 min	β^-	—	—	f
Sb	51	112?	0.9 min	e	—	—	Sn^{112}(p, n)
		113	7 min	β^+	—	—	Sn^{112}(d, n)
		114	3.4 min	e	—	—	Sn^{114}(p, n)
		115	31 min	β^+	—	—	Sn^{114}(d, n)
		116	15.5 min	β^+	−86480	−92840	Sn^{116}(p, n)
		116m	60 min	β^+e	—	—	In^{115}(α, 3n); Sn^{116}(p, n)
		117	2.8 hr	β^+e	−88470	−94990	Sn^{117}(p, n)

(Continued)

TABLE OF NUCLIDES (*Continued*)

Symbol	Z	A	Half-life	Decay mode and/or % natural abundance	Mass excess (C^{12} = 0) (kev)	Mass excess (C^{12} = 0) (μmu)	Principal method of formation
		118	5.1 hr	e	—	—	$In^{115}(\alpha, n)$; $Sn^{118}(p, n)$
		118m	3.5 min	β^+	—	—	$In^{115}(\alpha, n)$; $Te^{118} \xrightarrow{\beta^+ e}$
		119	38 hr	e	−89410	−95990	$Sn^{118}(d, n)$
		120	16.6 min	β^+e	−88430	−94940	$Sn^{120}(p, n)$; $Sb^{121}(d, t)$
		120	5.8 day	e	—	—	$Sn^{120}(p, n)$
		121	—	57.25	−89650	−96250	—
		122	2.8 day	β^-e	−88380	−94880	$Sb^{121}(n, \gamma)$
		122m	3.5 min	γ	—	—	$Sb^{121}(n, \gamma)$
		123	—	42.75	−89280	−95850	—
		124	60.9 day	β^-	−87660	−94110	$Sb^{123}(n, \gamma)$; $I^{127}(n, \alpha)$
		124m	1.3 min	$\beta^-\gamma$	—	—	$Sb^{123}(n, \gamma)$
		124m	21 min	$\beta^-\gamma$	—	—	$Sb^{123}(n, \gamma)$
		125	2.6 yr	β^-	−88270	−94770	f
		126	9 hr	β^-	—	—	f
		126	18.8 min	β^-	—	—	$Te^{126}(n, p)$; f
		126?	28 day	β^-	—	—	$Te^{128}(d, \alpha)$; f
		127	88 hr	β^-	−86800	−93190	f
		128	9.6 hr	β^-	—	—	f
		128m	10.3 min	β^-	—	—	$Te^{128}(d, 2n)$; f
		129	4.2 hr	β^-	—	—	f
		130	7.1 min	β^-	—	—	f
		130	33 min	β^-	—	—	f
		131	23.1 min	β^-	—	—	f
		132	2.1 min	β^-	—	—	f
		133	4.4 min	β^-	—	—	f
		134 or 135	~50 sec	β^-	—	—	f

Te	52	115	6 min	e	—	—	$Sn^{112}(\alpha, n)$
		116	2.5 hr	e	—	—	I + p; Sb + p
		117	1.7 hr	e	—	—	$Sb^{121}(d, 6n)$
		118	6.0 day	e	—	—	$Sb^{121}(d, 5n)$
		119	12 hr	—	—	—	I + p
		119	4.25 day	e	—	—	$Sb^{121}(d, 4n)$
		120	—	0.089	−88940	−95490	—
		121	17 day	e	—	—	$Sb^{121}(p, n)$
		121m	154 day	γ	—	—	$Sb^{121}(p, n)$
		122	—	2.46	−90350	−97000	—
		123	1.23 (10^{13}) yr?	e, 0.87	−89250	−95820	—
		123m	104 day	γ	—	—	$Te^{122}(n, \gamma)$
		124	—	4.61	−90580	−97240	—
		125	—	6.99	−89030	−95580	—
		125m	58 day	γ	—	—	f
		126	—	18.7	−90125	−96758	—
		127	9.4 hr	β^-	−88401	−94908	$Sb^{126}(n, \gamma)$; f
		127m	105 day	$\beta^-\gamma$	—	—	$Sb^{126}(n, \gamma)$; f
		128	—	31.79	−88760	−95290	—
		129	72 min	β^-	−87019	−93424	$Te^{128}(n, \gamma)$; f
		129m	33.5 day	γ	—	—	$Te^{128}(n, \gamma)$; f
		130	—	34.49	−86910	−93300	—
		131	24.8 min	β^-	−85156	−91424	$Te^{130}(n, \gamma)$; f
		131m	30 hr	$\beta^-\gamma$	—	—	$Te^{130}(n, \gamma)$; f
		132	77.7 hr	β^-	−85192	−91463	f
		133	2 min	β^-	—	—	f
		133m	63 min	$\beta^-\gamma$	—	—	f
		134	44 min	β^-	—	—	f
		135	1.5 min	β^-	—	—	f
I	53	117	~10 min	β^+	—	—	I + p
		118	17 min	β^+	—	—	Cs + p; I + p
		119	4 min	β^+	—	—	Cs + p
		120	1.4 hr	e	−83940	−90120	$Sb^{121}(\alpha, 5n)$; Cs + p

(Continued)

TABLE OF NUCLIDES (*Continued*)

Symbol	Z	A	Half-life	Decay mode and/or % natural abundance	Mass excess (C^{12} = 0) (kev)	Mass excess (C^{12} = 0) (μmu)	Principal method of formation
		121	2.1 hr	β^+	—	—	$Sb^{121}(\alpha, 4n)$
		122	3.4 min	β^+	−86210	−92550	$Sb^{121}(\alpha, 3n)$; $Te^{122}(p, n)$
		123	13 hr	e	—	—	$Sb^{121}(\alpha, 2n)$
		124	3.4 day	β^+e	−87390	−93820	$Sb^{121}(\alpha, n)$; $Te^{124}(p, n)$
		125	60 day	e	−88880	−95420	$Te^{125}(p, n)$
		126	13 day	$\beta^-\beta^+$e	−88010	−94488	$Te^{126}(p, n)$; $I^{127}(n, 2n)$
		126	2.6 hr	—	—	—	U + p
		127	—	100	−89090	−95648	—
		128	24.99 min	β^-e	−87725	−94182	$I^{127}(n, \gamma)$; $Te^{128}(p, n)$
		129	$1.72(10^7)$ yr	β^-	−88499	−95013	f
		130	12.6 hr	β^-	−86918	−93315	$Te^{130}(p, n)$; $Cs^{133}(n, \alpha)$
		131	8.08 day	β^-	−87436	−93872	$Te^{130}(d, n)$
		132	2.33 hr	β^-	−85697	−92005	f
		133	20.8 hr	β^-	−86080	−92410	f
		134	52.5 min	β^-	—	—	f
		135	6.7 hr	β^-	—	—	f
		136	86 sec	β^-	−79420	−85260	f
		137	22 sec	β^-	—	—	f
		138	5.9 sec	β^-	—	—	f
		139	2.7 sec	β^-	—	—	f
Xe	54	121	40 min	β^+	—	—	$I^{127}(p, 7n)$
		122	19.5 hr	e	—	—	$I^{127}(p, 6n)$
		123	1.85 hr	β^+e	—	—	$I^{127}(p, 5n)$
		124	—	0.096	−87440	−93880	—
		125	18 hr	e	—	—	$Te^{122}(\alpha, n)$
		125m	55 sec	γ	—	—	$Cs^{125} \xrightarrow{\beta^+}$

		126	—	0.09	−89261	−95831	—
		127	36.4 day	e	−88390	−94900	I^{127}(p, n)
		127m	75 sec	γ	—	—	I^{127}(p, n)
		128	—	1.92	−89849	−96462	—
		129	—	26.44	−88688	−95216	—
		129	8 day	γ	—	—	Xe^{128}(n, γ)
		130	—	4.08	−89875	−96490	—
		131	—	21.18	−88406	−94913	—
		131m	12 day	γ	—	—	f
		132	—	26.89	−89267	−95838	—
		133	5.3 day	β^-	−87980	−94450	Xe^{132}(n, γ); Cs^{133}(n, p); f
		133m	2.3 day	γ	—	—	f
		134	—	10.44	−88116	−94602	—
		135	9.1 hr	β^-	−86580	−92960	Xe^{134}(n, γ); f
		135m	15.6 min	γ	—	—	Xe^{134}(n, γ); f
		136	—	8.87	−86418	−92779	—
		137	3.9 min	β^-	—	—	Xe^{136}(n, γ); f
		138	17 min	β^-	—	—	f
		139	41 sec	β^-	—	—	f
		140	16 sec	β^-	—	—	f
		141	1.7 sec	β^-	—	—	f
		143	1 sec	β^-	—	—	f
		144	~1 sec	β^-	—	—	f
		145	0.8 sec	β^-	—	—	f
Cs	55	123	6 min	β^+	—	—	I + α
		125	45 min	β^+e	—	—	I + α
		126	1.6 min	β^+e	−84460	−90680	$Ba^{126} \xrightarrow{e}$
		127	6.1 hr	β^+e	−86310	−92660	I^{127}(α, 4n)
		128	3.8 min	β^+e	−85850	−92170	$Ba^{128} \xrightarrow{e}$
		129	31 hr	e	—	—	I^{127}(α, 2n)
		130	30 min	$\beta^-\beta^+$e	−86884	−93279	I^{127}(α, n)
		131	9.6 day	e	−88051	−94532	$Ba^{131} \xrightarrow{e}$
		132	6.2 day	e	−87450	−93890	Xe^{132}(p, n); Cs^{133}(n, 2n)

(Continued)

TABLE OF NUCLIDES (*Continued*)

Symbol	Z	A	Half-life	Decay mode and/or % natural abundance	Mass excess (C^{12} = 0) (kev)	Mass excess (C^{12} = 0) (μmu)	Principal method of formation
		133	—	100	−88400	−94910	—
		134	2.26 yr	β^-	−87070	−93480	Cs^{133}(n, γ); Xe^{134}(p, n); f
		134m	2.9 hr	$\beta^-\gamma$	—	—	Cs^{133}(n, γ); Xe^{134}(p, n); f
		135	$2.1(10^6)$ yr	β^-	−87740	−94200	f
		136	12.9 day	β^-	−86510	−92870	La^{139}(n, α); f
		137	29.7 yr	β^-	−86790	−93180	Ba^{137}(n, p); f
		138	32.2 min	β^-	−83640	−89800	Ba^{138}(n, p); f
		139	9.5 min	β^-	−80820	−86770	f
		140	66 sec	β^-	—	—	f
		141	short	β^-	—	—	f
		142	~1 min	β^-	—	—	f
		143	short	β^-	—	—	f
		144	short	β^-	—	—	f
		145	short	β^-	—	—	f
Ba	56	123	2 min	e	—	—	In + O; In + n
		125	0.5 min	e	—	—	Sn + O; Sn + C
		126	103 min	e	—	—	In + N
		127	10 min	β^+	—	—	Cs^{133}(p, 7n)
		128	2.4 day	e	—	—	Cs^{133}(p, 6n)
		129	2.45 hr	β^+	—	—	Cs^{133}(p, 5n)
		130	—	0.101	−87326	−93753	—
		131	11.5 day	e	—	—	Ba^{130}(n, γ)
		132	—	0.097	−88370	−94880	—
		133	7.2 yr	e	−87910	−94390	Ba^{132}(n, γ); Cs^{133}(p, n)
		133m	38.8 hr	γ	—	—	Ba^{132}(n, γ); Cs^{133}(p, n)
		134	—	2.42	−89130	−95690	—
		135	—	6.59	−87950	−94430	—

		135m	28.7 hr	γ	—	—	Ba^{134}(d, p)
		135m	0.33 sec	β^-	—	—	Ba^{135}(n, n′)
		136	—	7.81	−89090	−95640	—
		137	—	11.32	−87960	−94440	—
		137m	2.6 min	γ	—	—	f
		138	—	71.66	−88470	−94990	—
		139	82.9 min	β^-	−85120	−91390	Ba^{138}(n, γ); La^{139}(n, p); f
		140	12.8 day	β^-	−83400	−89540	f
		141	18 min	β^-	—	—	f
		142	11 min	β^-	—	—	f
		143	<0.5 min	β^-	—	—	f
		144	short	β^-	—	—	f
		145	short	β^-	—	—	f
La	57	129	~24 min	β^+	—	—	Sm + p
		131	58 min	β^+	—	—	Ba + p
		132	4.5 hr	β^+	—	—	Ba + p
		133	4.0 hr	β^+e	—	—	Cs^{133}(α, 4n)
		134	6.5 min	β^+e	—	—	Ba^{134}(d, 2n)
		135	19.8 hr	e	−85430	−91710	Cs^{133}(α, 2n); Ba^{134}(d, n)
		136	9.5 min	β^+e	—	—	Cs^{133}(α, n)
		137	6(10^4) yr	e	−86090	−92420	$Ce^{137} \xrightarrow{e}$
		138	1(10^{11}) yr	β^-e, 0.089	—	—	natural
		139	—	99.911	−86800	−93190	—
		140	40.2 hr	β^-	−87500	−93940	La^{139}(n, γ); f
		141	3.8 hr	β^-	−84450	−90670	f
		142	85 min	β^-	−83250	−89380	f
		143	~19 min	β^-	—	—	f
		144	short	β^-	—	—	f
		145	short	β^-	—	—	f
Ce	58	129?	13 min	β^+, e?	—	—	Sm + p
		131?	30 min	β^+	—	—	Ce + p
		132	4.2 hr	β^+	—	—	Ce + p
		133	6.3 hr	β^+e	—	—	La^{139}(p, 7n)
		134	72.0 hr	e	—	—	La^{139}(p, 6n)

(*Continued*)

TABLE OF NUCLIDES (*Continued*)

Symbol	Z	A	Half-life	Decay mode and/or % natural abundance	Mass excess (C^{12} = 0) (kev)	Mass excess (C^{12} = 0) (μmu)	Principal method of formation
		135	22 hr	e	—	—	La^{139}(p, 5n)
		136	—	0.193	−86550	−92900	—
		137	8.7 hr	e	—	—	La^{139}(d, 4n)
		137m	34.5 hr	eγ	—	—	La^{139}(d, 4n)
		138	—	0.250	−87810	−94280	—
		139	140 day	e	−87230	−93650	La^{139}(p, n); Ce^{140}(n, 2n)
		139m	55 sec	β^+	—	—	Ce^{140}(γ, n)
		140	—	88.48	−88223	−94720	—
		141	33.1 day	β^-	−85681	−91987	Ce^{140}(n, γ); Pr^{141}(n, p)
		142	~5(10^{15}) yr?	α, 11.07	−84730	−90960	natural
		143	33 hr	β^-	−81805	−87830	Ce^{142}(n, γ); f
		144	284.5 day	β^-	−80630	−86570	f
		145	3.0 min	β^-	−78010	−83760	f
		146	13.9 min	β^-	−76130	−81730	f
		147	1.2 min	β^-	—	—	f
		148	0.7 min	β^-	—	—	f
Pr	59	134	36 min	e or β^+	—	—	Sm + p
		135	22 min	β^+e	—	—	Ce^{136}(p, 2n)
		136	70 min	β^+	—	—	Ce^{140}(p, 4n)
		137	1.4 hr	β^+e	—	—	Ce^{138}(p, 2n)
		138	2 hr	β^+e	—	—	Ce^{140}(p, 3n)
		139	4.5 hr	β^+e	−85230	−91510	Ce^{140}(p, 2n)
		140	3.4 min	β^+e	−84964	−91218	Ce^{140}(p, n); Pr^{141}(n, 2n)
		141	—	100	−86261	−92610	—
		142	19.2 hr	β^-	−84025	−90210	Pr^{141}(n, γ); Ce^{142}(p, n)
		143	13.76 day	β^-	−83246	−89370	Ce^{142}(d, n); f

		144	17.5 min	β^-	−80942	−86900	$Ce^{144} \xrightarrow{\beta^-}$; f
		145	5.95 hr	β^-	−80010	−85900	f
		146	24.4 min	β^-	−77130	−82800	f
		147	120 min	β^-	—	—	f
		148	1.95 min	β^-	—	—	f
Nd	60	138	22 min	β^+	—	—	Pr^{141}(p, 4n)
		139	5.5 hr	β^+e	—	—	Pr^{141}(p, 3n)
		140	3.3 day	e	—	—	Pr^{141}(p, 2n)
		141	2.42 hr	β^+e	−84461	−90678	Pr^{141}(p, n); Nd^{142}(n, 2n)
		141m	63.7 sec	γ	—	—	Pr^{141}(p, n)
		142	—	27.13	−86179	−92522	—
		143	—	12.20	−84180	−90380	—
		144	$2(10^{15})$ yr	α, 23.87	−83922	−90100	natural
		145	—	8.30	−81820	−87840	—
		146	—	17.18	−81330	−87310	—
		147	11.06 day	β^-	−78400	−84170	$Nd^{146}(n, \gamma)$; f
		148	—	5.72	−77800	−83520	—
		149	2.0 hr	β^-	−74670	−80170	$Nd^{148}(n, \gamma)$; f
		150	—	5.60	−73850	−79290	—
		151	15 min	β^-	−70590	−75780	$Nd^{150}(n, \gamma)$
Pm	61	141	20 min	β^+	—	—	Nd^{142}(p, 2n)
		142	~30 sec	β^+e	—	—	$Sm^{142} \xrightarrow{\beta^+}$
		142	2.2 (10^{-3}) sec	γ	—	—	Nd + p
		143	270 day	e	−83080	−89200	$Pr^{141}(\alpha, n)$
		144	300 day	e	—	—	$Pr^{141}(\alpha, 2n)$
		145	18 yr	e	−81680	−87690	$Sm^{145} \xrightarrow{e}$
		145	16 day	β^+	—	—	Nd + p
		146	~1 yr	β^-	−80380	−86300	Nd^{146}(p, n)
		147	2.64 yr	β^-	−79302	−85140	f
		148	42 day	β^-	—	—	$Pm^{147}(n, \gamma)$; Nd^{148}(p, n)
		148	5.3 day	β^-	—	—	Nd^{148}(p, n)
		149	2.2 day	β^-	−76310	−81930	f
		150	2.7 hr	β^-	−73500	−78910	Nd^{150}(p, n)

(Continued)

TABLE OF NUCLIDES (*Continued*)

Symbol	Z	A	Half-life	Decay mode and/or % natural abundance	Mass excess (C^{12} = 0) (kev)	Mass excess (C^{12} = 0) (μmu)	Principal method of formation
		151	28.4 hr	β^-	−72990	−78360	Nd + n
		152	6.5 min	β^-	—	—	Sm^{152}(n, p)
		153	5.5 min	β^-	—	—	Sm^{154} (γ, p)
		154	2.5 min	β^-	—	—	Sm^{154}(n, p)
Sm	62	142	72 min	β^+e	—	—	Nd^{142}(α, 4n)
		143	9 min	β^+	−79580	−85440	Sm^{144}(γ, n)
		143m	65 sec	γ	—	—	Sm^{144}(p, pn)
		144	—	3.16	−82290	−88350	—
		145	340 day	e	−81030	−87000	Sm^{144}(n, γ)
		146	$5(10^7)$ yr	α	−81130	−87100	Nd + α
		147	$1.2(10^{11})$ yr	α, 15.07	−79527	−85380	natural; f
		148	—	11.27	−79580	−85440	—
		149	—	13.84	−77370	−83070	—
		150	—	7.47	−77300	−82990	—
		151	~93 yr	β^-	−74790	−80290	Sm^{150}(n, γ); Eu^{151}(n, p); f
		152	—	26.63	−75130	−80650	—
		153	47 hr	β^-	−73040	−78420	Sm^{152}(n, γ); Eu^{153}(n, p); f
		154	—	22.53	−72960	−78330	—
		155	23.5 min	β^-	−70630	−75830	Sm^{154}(n, γ); f
		156	9 hr	β^-	—	—	f
Eu	63	144?	18 min	β^+	—	—	Sm^{144}(p, n)
		146	4.3 day	e	—	—	Sm^{147}(d, 3n)
		147	24 day	αe	−77700	−83410	Sm^{147}(p, n)
		148	54 day	e	—	—	Sm^{148}(p, n)
		149	120 day	e	—	—	Sm^{149}(p, n)
		150	15 hr	β^-	−74880	−80390	Sm^{150}(p, n)

		151	—	47.77	−74860	−80370	—
		152	12.7 yr	β^-e	−73270	−78660	$Eu^{151}(n, \gamma)$; $Sm^{152}(p, n)$
		152	9.2 hr	β^-e	—	—	$Eu^{151}(n, \gamma)$
		153	—	52.23	−73850	−79280	—
		154	16 yr	β^-	−72330	−77650	$Eu^{153}(n, \gamma)$; $Sm^{154}(p, n)$
		155	1.7 yr	β^-	−72400	−77730	$Sm^{154}(d, n)$; f
		156	15.4 day	β^-	−69890	−75040	f
		157	15.4 hr	β^-	−69050	−74140	f
		158	60 min	β^-	—	—	f
		159	20 min	β^-	—	—	$Gd^{158}(p, \gamma)$
Gd	64	144 or 145	24 min	eβ^+	—	—	$Sm^{144}(\alpha, xn)$
		146	52 day	e	—	—	Ta + p
		147	29 hr	e	—	—	Ta + p
		148	~130 yr	α	−76620	−82260	$Sm^{147}(\alpha, 3n)$
		149	9.3 day	αe	−75520	−81080	$Sm^{147}(\alpha, 2n)$
		150	$>10^5$ yr	α	−75950	−81540	$Eu^{151}(d, 3n)$
		151	150 day	e	—	—	$Eu^{151}(d, 2n)$
		152?	$1.08(10^{14})$ yr	α ,0.20	−75080	−80600	natural
		153	236 day	e	−73640	−79060	$Eu^{153}(p, n)$
		154	—	2.15	−74300	−79770	—
		155	—	14.73	−72640	−77990	—
		156	—	20.47	−72430	−77760	—
		157	—	15.68	−70750	−75960	—
		158	—	24.87	−70610	−75810	—
		159	18 hr	β^-	−69600	−74700	f
		160	—	21.90	−67720	−72700	—
		161	3.7 min	β^-	−66500	−71400	$Gd^{160}(n, \gamma)$
Tb	65	147?	24 min	e	—	—	Pr^{141} + C*
		148	70 min	e	—	—	Pr^{141} + C
		149	4.1 hr	αe	—	—	$Eu^{151}(\alpha, 6n)$
		149m	4.3 min	α	—	—	Lu + O^{16}

* The identification of the light isotopes of terbium is still somewhat confused; it is very likely that the mass numbers and half-lives will undergo large changes. This is also true for light isotopes of certain other elements.

(Continued)

TABLE OF NUCLIDES (*Continued*)

Symbol	Z	A	Half-life	Decay mode and/or % natural abundance	Mass excess (C^{12} = 0) (kev)	Mass excess (C^{12} = 0) (μmu)	Principal method of formation
		150	3.1 hr	e	—	—	Gd + p
		151	17.5 hr	e	−71740	−77020	$Eu^{151}(\alpha, 4n)$
		152	17.4 hr	$\alpha\beta^{+}e$	—	—	$Eu^{151}(\alpha, 3n)$; $Gd^{152}(p, n)$
		153	2.3 day	e	—	—	$Eu^{153}(\alpha, 4n)$
		154	21 hr	$\beta^{+}e$	—	—	$Eu^{153}(\alpha, 3n)$
		154	8.5 hr	e	—	—	Gd + p
		155	5.4 day	$\beta^{-}e$	—	—	Ta + p
		156	5.1 hr	$\beta^{-}e$	—	—	$Gd^{156}(p, n)$
		157	<0.1 day; >10 yr	e	—	—	Dy + n
		158	<4 hr; >10 yr	e	−70400	−75600	Dy + n
		158m	10.5 sec	γ	—	—	$Tb^{159}(\gamma, n)$
		159	—	100	−70500	−75700	—
		160	72.3 day	β^{-}	−68900	−74000	$Tb^{159}(n, \gamma)$; $Gd^{160}(p, n)$
		161	6.9 day	β^{-}	−68500	−73600	$Gd^{161} \xrightarrow{\beta^{-}}$
		162	14 min	β^{-}	—	—	$Dy^{164}(\gamma, p)$
		163	6.5 hr	β^{-}	—	—	f
		164	23 hr	β^{-}	—	—	f
Dy	66	149	~8 min	e (or β^{+})	—	—	Gd + α; Pr + N
		150	7 min	α	—	—	Pr + N
		151	19 min	α	—	—	Tb + p
		152	2.3 hr	α	−70430	−75620	$Gd^{152}(\alpha, 4n)$
		153	5 hr	α	−69520	−74630	$Gd^{152}(\alpha, 3n)$
		154	13 hr	α	−70060	−75220	$Gd^{154}(\alpha, 4n)$
		154	~10^{6} yr	α	—	—	$Gd^{154} + \alpha$
		155	9 hr	e	—	—	$Gd^{155}(\alpha, 4n)$; $Dy^{156}(p, n)$
		156	—	0.052	—	—	—
		157	8.5 hr	e	—	—	Ta + p

		158	—	0.090	—	—	—
		159	134 day	e	−70100	−75300	$Dy^{158}(n, \gamma)$
		159	38 min	e	—	—	Dy + p
		160	—	2.29	−70800	−76000	—
		161	—	18.88	−69100	−74200	—
		162	—	25.53	−69200	−74300	—
		163	—	24.97	−67400	−72400	—
		164	—	28.18	−67000	−71900	—
		165	2.42 hr	β^-	−64400	−69100	$Dy^{164}(n, \gamma)$; $Ho^{165}(n, p)$
		165m	1.25 min	$\beta^-\gamma$	—	—	$Dy^{164}(n, \gamma)$
		166	82 hr	β^-	−63400	−68100	Dy + n
Ho	67	154	~4 min	α	—	—	Sm + C
		155	46 min	β^+	—	—	Ta + p
		156	~1 hr	e	—	—	Dy + p
		158	2.4 hr	e	—	—	Ta + p
		158	11.5 min	β^+	—	—	Tb^{159} $(\alpha, 5n)$
		158m	29 min	γ	—	—	Tb^{159} $(\alpha, 5n)$
		159	~33 min	e	—	—	Tb + α
		160	28 min	β^+e	—	—	$Tb^{159}(\alpha, 3n)$
		160m	5 hr	γ	—	—	Dy + p; Ta + p
		161	1.9 hr	e	—	—	$Tb^{159}(\alpha, n)$
		162	67 min	e	—	—	$Tb^{159}(\alpha, n)$
		163	>500 yr	e	−65900	−70700	Er + n
		163m	0.8 sec	γ	—	—	$Ho^{165}(\gamma, 2n)$
		164	36.7 min	β^-e	−65600	−70400	$Dy^{164}(p, n)$
		165	—	100	−65600	−70400	—
		166	34 yr	β^-	−63900	−68600	$Ho^{165}(n, \gamma)$
		166	27.3 hr	$\beta^-\gamma$	—	—	$Ho^{165}(n, \gamma)$; $Er^{166}(n, p)$
		167	3 hr	β^-	−63200	−67900	$Er^{167}(n, p)$; $Er^{170}(p, \alpha)$
		169	44 min	β^-	—	—	$Er^{170}(\gamma, p)$
Er	68	158	27 min	e	—	—	Ta + p
		159	~1hr	e	—	—	Ta + p
		160	1.2 day	e	—	—	Ta + p
		161	3.1 hr	e	—	—	Ta + p

(Continued)

TABLE OF NUCLIDES (*Continued*)

Symbol	Z	A	Half-life	Decay mode and/or % natural abundance	Mass excess ($C^{12} = 0$) (kev)	Mass excess ($C^{12} = 0$) (μmu)	Principal method of formation
		162	—	0.136	—	—	—
		163	1 hr	e	—	—	Ho^{165}(p, 3n)
		164	—	1.56	−66500	−71400	—
		165	10 hr	e	—	—	Ho^{165}(p, n)
		166	—	33.41	−65700	−70600	—
		167	—	22.94	−64200	−68900	—
		167m	2.5 sec	γ	—	—	$Tm^{167} \xrightarrow{e}$
		168	—	27.07	−63900	−68600	—
		169	9.4 day	β^-	—	—	Er^{168}(n, γ); Tm^{169}(n, p)
		170	—	14.88	—	—	—
		171	7.8 hr	β^-	—	—	Er^{170}(n, γ); Yb^{174}(n, α)
		172	49.8 hr	β^-	—	—	Er^{171}(n, γ)
Tm	69	161	32 min	e	—	—	Yb + p
		163	<45 min	e	—	—	Er + γ
		163	2.0 hr	e	—	—	Yb + p
		164	<45 min	β^+	—	—	Ta + p
		165	1.2 day	e	—	—	Er + p
		166	7.7 hr	β^+e	−62600	−67300	Ho^{165}(α, 3n); Er + p
		167	9.6 day	e	—	—	Ho^{165}(α, 2n); Er + p
		168	93 day	e	—	—	Ho^{165}(α, n)
		169	—	100	—	—	—
		170	125 day	β^-	—	—	Tm^{169}(n, γ); Er^{170}(d, 2n)
		171	680 day	β^-	—	—	$Er^{171} \xrightarrow{\beta^-}$
		172	63.6 hr	β^-	—	—	Tm^{171}(n, γ)
Yb	70	161	82 min	β^+	—	—	Ta + p
		164	85 min	β^+e	—	—	Yb + p; Ta + p
		166	54 hr	e	—	—	U + p

		167	17.7 min	e	—	—	Tm^{169}(p, 3n)
		167	74 min	β^+	—	—	Ta + p
		168	—	0.140	—	—	—
		169	31.8 day	e	—	—	Tm^{169}(p, n)
		170	—	3.03	—	—	—
		171	—	14.31	—	—	—
		171m	short	γ	—	—	$Lu^{171} \xrightarrow{e}$
		172	—	21.82	—	—	—
		173	—	16.13	—	—	—
		174	—	31.84	—	—	—
		175	101 hr	β^-	—	—	Yb^{174}(n, γ); Lu^{175}(n, p)
		175m	0.067 sec	γ	—	—	Yb^{174}(n, γ)
		176	—	12.73	—	—	—
		176m	21.7 sec	γ	—	—	Yb + n
		177	1.9 hr	β^-	−52220	−56060	Yb^{176}(n, γ)
		177m	6.5 sec	γ	—	—	Yb^{176}(n, γ)
Lu	71	167	54 min	e	—	—	Ta + p; Yb + p
		168	7.1 min	e	—	—	Yb + p
		168	2.0 hr	e	—	—	Ta + p
		169	1.5 day	e	—	—	Yb + p
		170	1.9 day	e	—	—	Tm^{169}(α, 3n); Yb^{170}(p, n)
		171	~600 day	e	—	—	Yb^{171}(p, n)
		171	8.0 day	e	—	—	Tm^{169}(α, 2n)
		172	6.7 day	e	—	—	Tm^{169}(α, n)
		173	499 day	e	—	—	Yb^{173}(p, n)
		174	40 day	β^-e	—	—	Lu^{175}(n, 2n)
		174m?	1300 day	γ	—	—	Ta + p
		175	—	97.4	—	—	—
		176	2.17(10^{10}) yr	β^-, 2.6	—	—	natural
		176m	3.7 hr	β^-	—	—	Lu^{175}(n, γ)
		177	6.75 day	β^-	−53600	−57550	Lu^{176}(n, γ)
		178	22 min	β^-	—	—	Hf^{179}(γ, p)
		179	8 hr	β^-	—	—	Hf^{180}(γ, p)
		178 or 180	4.5 min	β^-	—	—	Hf + n

(Continued)

TABLE OF NUCLIDES (*Continued*)

Symbol	Z	A	Half-life	Decay mode and/or % natural abundance	Mass excess (C^{12} = 0)		Principal method of formation
					(kev)	(μmu)	
Hf	72	168	22 min	β^+	—	—	Lu + p
		169	1.5 hr	β^+	—	—	Lu + p
		170	112 min	β^+	—	—	Lu^{175}(p, 6n)
		171	16 hr	e	—	—	Lu^{175}(p, 5n)
		172	~5 yr	e	—	—	Lu^{175}(p, 4n)
		173	23.6 hr	e	—	—	Lu^{175}(p, 3n)
		174?	2.0(10^{15}) yr	α, 0.2	—	—	natural
		175	70 day	e	—	—	Lu^{175}(p, n)
		176	—	5.23	−55570	−59660	—
		177	—	18.55	−54100	−58080	—
		178	—	27.23	−53570	−57510	—
		178m	4–5 sec	γ	—	—	$Ta^{178} \xrightarrow{e}$
		179	—	13.73	−51770	−55580	—
		179m	19 sec	γ	—	—	Hf^{178}(n, γ)
		180	—	35.07	−51120	−54880	—
		180m	5.5 hr	γ	—	—	Hf^{179}(n, γ)
		181	42.4 day	β^-	−49110	−52720	Hf^{180}(n, γ); Ta^{181}(n, p)
		182	8.5(10^6) yr	β^-	—	—	Hf^{180}(2n, γ)
		183	64 min	β^-	−44710	−48000	W^{186}(n, α)
Ta	73	173	3.7 hr	e	—	—	Ho + N^{14}
		174	1.3 hr	e	—	—	Ho + N^{14}
		175	11 hr	e	—	—	Lu^{175}(α, 4n)
		176	8.0 hr	e	—	—	Lu^{175}(α, 3n); Hf^{176}(p, n)
		177	53 hr	β^+e	−52950	−56840	Lu^{175}(α, 2n); Hf^{177}(p, n)
		178	2.5 hr	e	—	—	Lu^{175}(α, n); Hf^{178}(p, n); Ta^{181}(γ, 3n)
		178m	9.35 min	β^+e	—	—	Lu^{175}(α, n); Hf^{178}(p, n); Ta^{181}(γ, 3n)

		179	~600 day	e	—	—	$Lu^{176}(\alpha, n)$; $Hf^{179}(p, n)$
		180	$\geq 2(10^{13})$ yr	β^-e, 0.01	—50560	—54280	natural
		180m	8.1 hr	β^-e	—	—	$Hf^{180}(p, n)$; $Ta^{181}(n, 2n)$
		181	—	100	—50130	—53820	—
		182	115.05 day	β^-	—48130	—51670	$Ta^{181}(n, \gamma)$; $Ta^{182}(n, p)$
		182m	16.5 min	$\beta^-\gamma$	—	—	$Ta^{181}(n, \gamma)$
		183	5.2 day	β^-	—46910	—50360	$W^{184}(\gamma, p)$
		184	8.7 yr	β^-	—	—	$W^{184}(n, p)$
		185	50 min	β^-	—44400	—47600	$W^{186}(\gamma, p)$
		186	10.5 min	β^-	—	—	$W^{186}(n, p)$
W	74	176	80 min	β^+e	—	—	$Ta^{181}(p, 6n)$
		177	2.1 hr	β^+e	—	—	$Ta^{181}(p, 5n)$
		178?	$6(10^8)$ yr	α	—	—	natural
		178	21.5 day	e	—	—	$Ta^{181}(p, 4n)$
		179	30 min	e	—	—	$Ta^{181}(p, 3n)$
		179	5.2 min	γ	—	—	$Ta^{181}(p, 3n)$
		180	—	β, 0.135	—51260	—55030	—
		180m	$5.5(10^{-3})$ sec	γ	—	—	$Ta^{181}(p, 2n)$
		181	145 day	e	—49930	—53610	$Ta^{181}(p, n)$
		182	—	26.4	—49860	—53530	—
		183	—	14.4	—47980	—51510	—
		183m	5.5 sec	γ	—	—	$W^{182}(n, \gamma)$
		184	—	30.6	—47360	—50850	—
		185	73.2 day	β^-	—46100	—49500	$W^{184}(n, \gamma)$; $Re^{185}(n, p)$
		185m	1.75 min	γ	—	—	$W^{186}(\gamma, n)$
		186	—	28.4	—45300	—48600	—
		187	24.0 hr	β^-	—40620	—43610	$W^{186}(n, \gamma)$; $Re^{187}(n, p)$
		188	69.5 day	β^-	—	—	W + n
Re	75	177	17 min	β^+	—	—	Re + p; W + p
		178	15 min	β^+	—	—	Re + p; W + p
		180	20 hr	β^+	—	—	$W^{180}(p, n)$
		180	145 sec	β^+e	—	—	$W^{182}(p, 3n)$
		180	18 min	e	—	—	Re + p

(Continued)

TABLE OF NUCLIDES (*Continued*)

Symbol	Z	A	Half-life	Decay mode and/or % natural abundance	Mass excess ($C^{12} = 0$) (kev)	Mass excess ($C^{12} = 0$) (μmu)	Principal method of formation
		181	20 hr	e	—	—	$Ta^{181}(\alpha, 4n)$
		182	64 hr	e	—	—	$Ta^{181}(\alpha, 3n)$; $W^{182}(0, n)$
		182	12.7 hr	eγ	—	—	$W^{182}(d, 2n)$
		183	71 day	e	—	—	$W^{183}(d, 2n)$
		184	50 day	e	—	—	$Ta^{181}(\alpha, n)$; $W^{184}(p, n)$
		184	2.2 day	e or γ	—	—	$Ta^{181}(\alpha, n)$; $W^{184}(p, n)$
		185	—	37.07	−46500	−49900	—
		186	90 hr	β^-e	−42770	−45920	$Re^{185}(n, \gamma)$; $W^{186}(p, n)$
		187	$6.2(10^{10})$ yr	β^-, 62.93	−41940	−45020	natural
		188	18.7 min	γ	—	—	$Re^{187}(n, \gamma)$
		189	150 day	β^-	—	—	$W^{186}(\alpha, p)$
		189?	23 hr	β^-	—	—	Os + n
		190	2.8 hr	β^-	—	—	Os + d
Os	76	180	<2 min	e	—	—	$Re^{185}(p, 6n)$
		181	23 min	e	—	—	$Re^{185}(p, 5n)$
		182	21.9 hr	e	—	—	$Re^{185}(p, 4n)$
		183	15.4 hr	e	—	—	$Re^{185}(p, 3n)$
		183m	10 hr	eγ	—	—	$Re^{185}(p, 3n)$
		184	—	0.018	—	—	—
		185	93.4 day	e	−45500	−48900	$Re^{185}(p, n)$
		186	—	1.59	−43840	−47060	—
		187	—	1.64	−41940	−45030	—
		187m	39 hr	γ	—	—	$Re^{187}(\alpha, 4n)$
		188	—	13.3	−41930	−45020	—
		189	—	16.1	−39850	−42780	—
		189m	5.7 hr	γ	—	—	$Ir^{189} \xrightarrow{\beta^-}$

		190	—	26.4	−39660	−42580	—
		190m	10 min	γ	—	—	Os + N^{14}
		191	16 day	β^-	−37040	−39770	$Os^{190}(n, \gamma)$; $Ir^{191}(n, p)$
		191m	14 hr	γ	—	—	$Os^{190}(n, \gamma)$
		192	—	41.0	−36780	−39490	—
		193	30.6 hr	β^-	−33950	−36450	$Ir^{193}(n, p)$
		194	1.9 yr	β^-	—	—	Os + n
		195	6.5 min	β^-	—	—	$Pt^{198}(n, \alpha)$
Ir	77	182	15 min	e	—	—	$Tm^{169}(O^{16}, 3n)$
		183	1 hr	e	—	—	Au + p
		184	3.1 hr	e	—	—	Au + p
		185	15 hr	e	—	—	$Re^{185}(\alpha, 4n)$
		186	14 hr	e	—	—	$Re^{185}(\alpha, 3n)$
		186	2 hr	β^+	—	—	Au + p
		187	11.8 hr	β^+e	—	—	$Re^{185}(\alpha, 2n)$
		188	41 hr	β^+e	−38930	−41790	$Re^{185}(\alpha, n)$
		189	11 day	e	—	—	$Pt^{189} \xrightarrow{e}$
		190	11 day	e	—	—	$Ir^{191}(n, 2n)$; $Os^{190}(p, n)$
		190m	3.2 hr	β^+e	—	—	$Re^{187}(\alpha, n)$
		191	—	38.5	−37350	−40100	—
		191m	4.9 sec	γ	—	—	$Ir^{191}(p, p)$
		192	74.4 day	β^-e	−35370	−37970	$Ir^{191}(n, \gamma)$; $Os^{192}(p, n)$
		192m	1.45 min	γ	—	—	$Ir^{191}(n, \gamma)$
		192m	>5 yr	γ	—	—	$Ir^{191}(n, \gamma)$
		193	—	61.5	−35080	−37660	—
		193m	11.9 day	γ	—	—	$Ir^{191}(2n, \gamma)$
		194	19.0 hr	β^-	−32760	−35170	$Ir^{193}(n, \gamma)$
		194m?	47 sec	$\beta^-\gamma$	—	—	$Ir^{193}(n, \gamma)$
		194m	0.05 sec	γ	—	—	$Ir^{193}(n, \gamma)$
		195	140 min	β^-	—	—	$Pt^{196}(\gamma, p)$
		196	9.7 day	β^-	—	—	$Pt^{196}(n, p)$
		197	7 min	β^-	—	—	Pt + γ
		198	50 sec	β^-	—	—	Pt + n

(Continued)

TABLE OF NUCLIDES (*Continued*)

Symbol	Z	A	Half-life	Decay mode and/or % natural abundance	Mass excess (C^{12} = 0)		Principal method of formation
					(kev)	(μmu)	
		198 or 199	9.7 hr	β^-	—	—	Pt + n
Pt	78	185	1.2 hr	e	—	—	Au^{197}(p, 13n)
		186	2.9 hr	e	—	—	Ir + p; Au + p
		187	2.2 hr	e	—	—	Au^{197}(p, 11n)
		188	10.0 day	e	—38410	—41230	Ir + p; Au + p
		189	11.5 hr	e	—	—	Ir^{191}(p, 3n)
		190	$5.9(10^{11})$ yr	α, 0.012	—38030	—40830	natural
		191	3.0 day	e	—	—	Ir^{191}(p, n)
		192	$\sim 10^{15}$ yr	α, 0.78	—36820	—39530	natural
		193	<500 yr	e	—35030	—37610	Pt^{192}(n, γ)
		193m	4.3 day	γ	—	—	Pt^{192}(n, γ); Au^{197}(p, 5n)
		194	—	32.8	—34990	—37570	—
		195	—	33.7	—33100	—35540	—
		195m	4.1 day	γ	—	—	Pt^{195}(n, n′)
		196	—	25.4	—32950	—35380	—
		197	18 hr	β^-	—30405	—32643	Pt^{196}(n, γ); Au^{197}(n, p)
		197m	78 min	γ	—	—	Pt^{198}(γ, n)
		198	—	7.23	—30240	—32470	—
		199	31 min	β^-	—27330	—29340	Pt^{198}(n, γ)
		199m	14.1 sec	γ	—	—	Pt^{198}(n, γ)
		200	11.5 hr	β^-	—	—	Pt^{199}(n, γ)
Au	79	185	7 min	e	—	—	Au + p; Pt + p
		186	12 min	e	—	—	Pt + p
		187	8 min	e	—	—	Au + p

		188	3.7 min	e	—33230	—35670	Ta + C^{12}; Au + p
		189	30 min	e	—	—	Pt + p; Au + p
		190	38.8 min	e	—	—	Au + p
		191	3.2 hr	e	—	—	Pt^{192}(d, 3n); Ir^{191}(α, 4n)
		192	4.7 hr	β^+e	—33580	—36050	Ir^{191}(α, 3n)
		193	15.8 hr	e	—	—	Ir^{191}(α, 2n)
		193m	3.9 sec	e	—	—	Pt + p
		194	39.5 hr	β^+e	—32430	—34810	Ir^{191}(α, n); Pt^{194}(p, n)
		195	185 day	e	—32830	—35250	Pt^{195}(p, n)
		195m	31 sec	γ	—	—	$Hg^{195} \xrightarrow{e}$
		196	6.17 day	β^-e	—31159	—33453	Au^{197}(n, 2n); Pt^{195}(d, n)
		196m	9.7 hr	γ	—	—	Au^{197}(n, 2n)
		197	—	100	—31155	—33448	—
		197m	7.2 sec	γ	—	—	Au^{197}(n, n)
		198	2.69 day	β^-	—29581	—31758	Au^{197}(n, γ); Hg^{200}(d, α)
		199	3.14 day	β^-	—29112	—31255	$Pt^{199} \xrightarrow{\beta^-}$; Hg^{201}(d, α)
		200	48 min	β^-	—27190	—29190	Hg^{200}(n, p)
		201	26 min	β^-	—26150	—28070	Hg^{202}(γ, p)
		202 or 204	~25 sec	β^- or γ	—	—	Hg(n, p)
		203	55 sec	β^-	—	—	Hg^{204}(γ, p)
Hg	80	185	45 sec	αe	—	—	Au + p
		186	1.5 min	e	—	—	Au + p
		187	3 min	e	—	—	Au + p
		188	3.7 min	e	—	—	Au + p
		189	9 min	e	—	—	Ta^{181} + N^{14}; Au + p
		190	21 min	e	—	—	Au + p
		191	55 min	e	—	—	Au + p
		192	5.7 hr	β^+e	—	—	Au + p
		193	4 hr	e	—	—	Au + p
		193m	12 hr	eγ	—	—	Au + p
		194	0.4 sec	—	—	—	Au + p

(Continued)

TABLE OF NUCLIDES (*Continued*)

Symbol	Z	A	Half-life	Decay mode and/or % natural abundance	Mass excess (C^{12} = 0) (kev)	Mass excess (C^{12} = 0) (μmu)	Principal method of formation
		194	~130 day	e	—	—	Au + p
		195	9.5 hr	e	—	—	Au + p
		195m	40 hr	eγ	—	—	Au + p
		196	—	0.146	−31838	−34181	—
		197	65 hr	e	—	—	Au^{197}(p, n)
		197m	24 hr	eγ	—	—	Au^{197}(d, 2n)
		198	—	10.02	−30953	−33231	—
		199	—	16.84	−29567	−31744	—
		199m	42 min	γ	—	—	Hg^{198}(d, p)
		200	—	23.13	−29486	−31656	—
		201	—	13.22	−27650	−29685	—
		202	—	29.80	−27356	−29370	—
		203	46.9 day	β^-	−25286	−27147	Hg^{202}(n, γ); Tl^{203}(n, p)
		204	—	6.85	−24700	−26518	—
		205	5.5 min	β^-	−22140	−23770	Hg^{204}(n, γ); Tl^{205}(n, p)
		206	7.5 min	β^-	—	—	$Tl^{206} \xrightarrow{\beta^-}$
Tl	81	191	<10 min	e	—	—	$W^{182}(N^{14}$, 5n)
		192m	11.4 min	e	—	—	Hg + p
		193	22.6 min	e	—	—	$W^{184}(N^{14}$, 5n)
		195	1.2 hr	e	—	—	$Pb^{195} \xrightarrow{e}$
		195m	3.5 sec	γ	—	—	$Pb^{195m} \xrightarrow{e}$
		196	2.4 hr	e	—	—	$Pb^{196} \xrightarrow{e}$
		197	2.7 hr	e	—	—	$Pb^{197} \xrightarrow{e}$
		197m	0.54 sec	γ	—	—	$Pb^{197m} \xrightarrow{e}$
		198	5.3 hr	e	—	—	$Au^{197}(\alpha$, 3n)
		198m	1.8 hr	eγ	—	—	$Au^{197}(\alpha$, 3n)

		199	7.4 hr	e	—	—	$Au^{197}(\alpha, 2n)$
		200	26.1 hr	e	−27036	−29026	$Au^{197}(\alpha, n)$
		201	72 hr	eγ	−27240	−29240	$Hg^{201}(d, 2n)$
		202	12.5 day	e	−25960	−27870	$Hg^{202}(p, n)$
		203	—	29.50	−25772	−27669	—
		204	3.9 yr	β^-e	−24320	−26110	$Tl^{203}(n, \gamma)$
		205	—	70.50	−23787	−25538	—
RaE″		206	4.19 min	β^-	−22280	−23920	natural
AcC″		207	4.79 min	β^-	−21008	−22554	natural
ThC″		208	3.1 min	β^-	−16760	−17994	natural
		209	2.2 min	β^-	−13697	−14705	$Bi^{213} \xrightarrow{\alpha}$
RaC″		210	1.32 min	β^-	−9313	−9998	natural
Pb	82	195	17 min	e	—	—	Tl + p
		196	37 min	e	—	—	Tl + p
		197m	42 min	eγ	—	—	Tl + p
		198	2.4 hr	e	—	—	Tl + p
		198	25 min	e	—	—	$Bi^{198} \xrightarrow{e}$
		199	90 min	e	—	—	$Bi^{199} \xrightarrow{e}$
		199m	12.2 min	γ	—	—	Tl(p, xn)
		200	12.6 hr	e	—	—	$Bi^{200} \xrightarrow{e}$
		201	9.4 hr	e	—	—	$Tl^{203}(d, 4n)$
		201m	60 sec	γ	—	—	$Bi^{201} \xrightarrow{e}$
		202	~3(10^5) yr	e	−25910	−27810	$Tl^{203}(d, 3n)$
		202m	3.6 hr	eγ	—	—	$Tl^{203}(d, 3n)$
		203	52 hr	e	−24775	−26600	$Tl^{203}(d, 2n)$
		203m	6.5 sec	γ	—	—	$Bi^{203} \xrightarrow{e}$
		204?	1.4(10^{17}) yr	α, 1.48	−25085	−26931	natural
		204m	67.5 min	γ	—	—	$Tl^{203}(d, n)$; $Pb^{204}(n, n)$
		205	3(10^7) yr	e	−23737	−25484	$Pb^{206}(d, 3n)$; $Pb^{204}(n, \gamma)$
		205m	4.7(10^{-3}) sec	γ	—	—	$Pb^{206}(n, 2n)$
		206	—	23.6	−23790	−25541	—
		207	—	22.6	−22450	−24102	—
		207m	0.8 sec	γ	—	—	$Pb^{207}(n, n)$

(Continued)

TABLE OF NUCLIDES (*Continued*)

Symbol	Z	A	Half-life	Decay mode and/or % natural abundance	Mass excess (C^{12} = 0) (kev)	Mass excess (C^{12} = 0) (μmu)	Principal method of formation
		208	—	52.3	−21755	−23356	—
		209	3.3 hr	β^-	−17610	−18906	$Pb^{208}(n, \gamma)$; $Bi^{209}(n, p)$
RaD		210	20.4 yr	β^-	−14738	−15823	natural
AcB		211	36.1 min	β^-	−10429	−11197	natural
ThB		212	10.64 hr	β^-	−7548	−8104	natural
RaB		214	26.8 min	β^-	−220	−240	natural
Bi	83	197	1.7 min	α	—	—	Pb + d
		198	7 min	αe	—	—	Pb + p
		199	~25 min	αe	—	—	Pb + d
		200	35 min	e	—	—	Pb + d
		201	62 min	αe	—	—	Pb + d
		201m	1.9 hr	e	—	—	Pb + d
		202	95 min	e	—	—	$Po^{202} \xrightarrow{e}$
		203	12.3 hr	αe	−21580	−23170	Pb + p
		204	11.6 hr	e	−20800	−22300	$Tl^{203}(\alpha, 3n)$
		205	14.5 day	β^+e	−21090	−22640	$Po^{205} \xrightarrow{e}$
		206	6.4 day	e	−20190	−21680	$Po^{206}(p, n)$
		207	38 yr	e	−20050	−21526	$Pb^{208}(d, 3n)$
		208	~$3(10^{14})$ yr	e	−18879	−20269	$Bi^{209}(n, 2n)$
		208m	$2.5(10^{-3})$ sec	γ	—	—	$Bi^{209}(\gamma, n)$
		209	$2(10^{17})$ yr?	α, 100	−18240	−19583	natural
RaE		210	4.99 day	β^-	−14801	−15890	natural; $Bi^{209}(n, \gamma)$
		210m	$2.6(10^6)$ yr	$\alpha\beta^-$	—	—	$Bi^{209}(n, \gamma)$
AcC		211	2.16 min	$\alpha\beta^-$	−11835	−12706	natural
ThC		212	60.5 min	$\alpha\beta^-$	−8130	−8729	natural
		213	47 min	$\alpha\beta^-$	−5282	−5671	$At^{217} \xrightarrow{\alpha}$

RaC		214	19.7 min	$\alpha\beta^-$	−1273	−1366	natural
		215	8 min	β^-	1770	1900	$At^{219} \xrightarrow{\alpha}$
Po	84	192	0.5 sec	α	—	—	Bi^{209}(p, 18n)
		193	4 sec	α	—	—	Bi^{209}(p, 17n)
		194	13 sec	α	—	—	Bi^{209}(p, 16n)
		195	30 sec	α	—	—	Bi^{209}(p, 15n)
		196	1.9 min	α	—	—	W(Ne^{20}, n)
		197	~4 min	α	—	—	Bi^{209}(p, 13n)
		198	~6 min	α	—	—	Bi^{209}(p, 12n)
		199	11.2 min	α	—	—	Bi^{209}(p, 11n)
		200	11 min	αe	—	—	Bi^{209}(p, 10n)
		201	18 min	αe	—	—	Bi^{209}(p, 9n)
		202	44.5 min	αe	—	—	Bi^{209}(p, 8n)
		203	42 min	e	—	—	Bi^{209}(p, 7n)
		204	3.5 hr	αe	—	—	Bi^{209}(p, 6n)
		205	1.8 hr	αe	—	—	Pb^{204}(α, 3n)
		206	9.5 day	αe	−18160	−19500	Pb^{204}(α, 2n)
		207	5.7 hr	αe	−17144	−18406	Pb^{206}(α, 3n)
		208	2.93 yr	α	−17451	−18736	Pb^{206}(α, 2n); Bi^{209}(p, 2n)
		209	103 yr	αe	−16340	−17543	Bi^{209}(p, n)
RaF		210	138.4 day	α	−15959	−17134	natural; Bi^{209}(d, n)
AcC′		211	0.52 sec	α	−12436	−13351	Pb^{208}(α, n); natural
		211m	25 sec	α	—	—	Pb^{208}(α, n)
ThC′		212	$3(10^{-7})$ sec	α	−10377	−11141	natural
		212m	44.9 sec	α	—	—	Pb + C
		213	$4.2(10^{-6})$ sec	α	−6672	−7163	$Bi^{213} \xrightarrow{\beta^-}$; $Rn^{217} \xrightarrow{\alpha}$
RaC′		214	$1.59(10^{-4})$ sec	α	−4479	−4808	natural
AcA		215	$1.83(10^{-3})$ sec	$\alpha\beta^-$	−495	−531	natural
ThA		216	0.158 sec	α	1786	1917	natural
		217	<10 sec	α	—	—	$Rn^{221} \xrightarrow{\alpha}$
RaA		218	3.05 min	$\alpha\beta^-$	8320	8930	natural
At	85	200	43 sec	eα	—	—	Bi + α
		201	1.5 min	eα	—	—	Bi + α; Au + C

(*Continued*)

TABLE OF NUCLIDES (*Continued*)

Symbol	Z	A	Half-life	Decay mode and/or % natural abundance	Mass excess (C^{12} = 0) (kev)	Mass excess (C^{12} = 0) (μmu)	Principal method of formation
		202	3.0 min	α	—	—	Bi + α; Au + C
		203	7.4 min	eα	—	—	Bi + α; Au + C
		204	9.3 min	eα	—	—	Bi + α; Au + C
		205	26.2 min	eα	—	—	Bi + α; Au + C
		206	29.5 min	eα	—	—	Bi + α; Au + C
		207	1.8 hr	eα	−13300	−14280	Bi + α; Au + C
		208	6.3 hr	e	−12600	−13500	$Bi^{209}(\alpha, 5n)$
		208	1.6 hr	αe	—	—	$Fr^{212} \xrightarrow{\alpha}$
		209	5.5 hr	αe	−12910	−13860	$Bi^{209}(\alpha, 4n)$
		210	8.3 hr	αe	−12140	−13030	$Bi^{209}(\alpha, 3n)$
		211	7.214 hr	αe	−11647	−12504	$Bi^{209}(\alpha, 2n)$
		212	0.22 sec	α	—	—	$Bi^{209}(\alpha, n)$
		213	short	α	−6440	−6910	$Fr^{217} \xrightarrow{\alpha}$
		214	~2(10^{-6}) sec	α	−3420	−3670	$Fr^{218} \xrightarrow{\alpha}$
		215	~10^{-4} sec	α	−1250	−1342	natural
		216	~3(10^{-4}) sec	α	2240	2405	$Fr^{220} \xrightarrow{\alpha}$
		217	0.018 sec	α	4328	4647	$Fr^{221} \xrightarrow{\alpha}$
		218	2.0 sec	$\alpha\beta^-$	7968	8554	natural
		219	0.9 min	$\alpha\beta^-$	10580	11360	natural
Rn	86	204	3.1 min	α	—	—	Au + N^{14}
		206	6.5 min	αe	—	—	Au + N^{14}
		207	11 min	αe	—	—	Au + N^{14}
		208	23 min	αe	—	—	Au + N^{14}
		209	30 min	αe	—	—	$Ra^{213} \xrightarrow{\alpha}$
		210	2.7 hr	αe	−9580	−10280	Th + p; Pb + C
		211	16 hr	αe	−8756	−9400	$Fr^{212} \xrightarrow{\alpha}$

		212	23 min	α	−8638	−9274	$Fr^{212} \xrightarrow{\alpha}$
		215	$\sim 10^{-6}$ sec	α	−1240	−1330	$Ra^{219} \xrightarrow{\alpha}$
		216	$\sim 10^{-4}$ sec	α	218	234	$Ra^{220} \xrightarrow{\alpha}$
		217	$\sim 10^{-3}$ sec	α	3648	3917	$Ra^{221} \xrightarrow{\alpha}$
		218	0.019 sec	α	5209	5592	$Ra^{222} \xrightarrow{\alpha}$
An		219	3.92 sec	α	8870	9523	natural
Tn		220	51.5 sec	α	10615	11396	natural
		221	25.2 min	$\alpha\beta^-$	—	—	Th + p
		222	3.823 day	α	16320	17530	natural
		223	12 min	β^-	—	—	Th + p
		224	4.9 hr	β^-	—	—	Th + p
Fr	87	205?	~4 sec	α	—	—	—
		206	15.8 sec	α	—	—	—
		207	18.7 sec	α	—	—	—
		208	37.5 sec	α	—	—	—
		209	54.7 sec	α	—	—	—
		210	159 sec	α	—	—	—
		211	186 sec	αe	—	—	Th + p
		212	19.3 min	αe	−3600	−3900	Th + p
		213	34 sec	α	—	—	—
		214	$3.9\ (10^{-3})$ sec	α	—	—	—
		215	$\ll 10^{-3}$ sec	α	—	—	—
		217	short	α	4450	4780	$Ac^{221} \xrightarrow{\alpha}$
		218	$5(10^{-3})$ sec	α	7010	7520	$Ac^{222} \xrightarrow{\alpha}$
		219	~0.02 sec	α	8615	9249	$Ac^{223} \xrightarrow{\alpha}$
		220	27.5 sec	α	11485	12330	$Ac^{224} \xrightarrow{\alpha}$
		221	4.8 min	α	13204	14176	$Ac^{225} \xrightarrow{\alpha}$
		222	14.8 min	$\alpha\beta^-$	—	—	Th + p
AcK		223	22 min	$\alpha\beta^-$	18444	19802	natural
		224	2 min	β^-	—	—	—
Ra	88	213	2.7 min	α	—	—	Th + p; Pb + C^{6+}
		219	$\sim 10^{-3}$ sec	α	9340	10030	$Th^{223} \xrightarrow{\alpha}$
		220	$3(10^{-2})$ sec	α	10220	10972	$Th^{224} \xrightarrow{\alpha}$

TABLE OF NUCLIDES (*Continued*)

Symbol	Z	A	Half-life	Decay mode and/or % natural abundance	Mass excess ($C^{12} = 0$) (kev)	Mass excess ($C^{12} = 0$) (μmu)	Principal method of formation
		221	30 sec	α	12910	13860	$Th^{225} \xrightarrow{\alpha}$
		222	38 sec	α	14312	15365	$Th^{226} \xrightarrow{\alpha}$
AcX		223	11.412 day	α	17292	18565	natural
ThX		224	3.64 day	α	18830	20216	natural
		225	14.8 day	β^-	21906	23518	$Th^{229} \xrightarrow{\alpha}$
		226	1622 yr	α	23620	25360	natural
		227	41.2 min	β^-	27217	29220	$Ra^{226}(n, \gamma)$
MsTh1		228	6.7 yr	β^-	29087	31228	natural
		229	~1 min	β^-	—	—	$Th^{233} \xrightarrow{\alpha}$
		230	1 hr	β^-	—	—	Th + d
Ac	89	221	0.1 sec	α	14620	15690	$Pa^{225} \xrightarrow{\alpha}$
		222	5.5 sec	α	16530	17750	$Pa^{226} \xrightarrow{\alpha}$
		223	2.2 min	αe	17808	19119	$Pa^{227} \xrightarrow{\alpha}$
		224	2.9 hr	αe	20200	21690	$Pa^{228} \xrightarrow{\alpha}$
		225	10 day	α	21556	23143	$Pa^{229} \xrightarrow{\alpha}$
		226	29 hr	β^-e	24380	26180	spallation U, Th
		227	21.6 yr	$\alpha\beta^-$	25907	27814	natural; $Ra^{227} \xrightarrow{\beta^-}$
MsTh2		228	6.13 hr	β^-	29032	31169	natural
		229	66 min	β^-	—	—	$Ra^{229} \xrightarrow{\beta^-}$
		230	<1 min	β^-	—	—	$Th^{232}(d, \alpha)$
		231	15 min	β^-	—	—	$Th^{232}(\gamma, p)$
Th	90	223	0.9 sec	α	19460	20890	$U^{227} \xrightarrow{\alpha}$
		224	1.05 sec	α	19913	21379	$U^{228} \xrightarrow{\alpha}$
		225	8 min	αe	22030	23660	$U^{229} \xrightarrow{\alpha}$
		226	30.9 min	α	23184	24890	$U^{230} \xrightarrow{\alpha}$
RdAc		227	18.17 day	α	25864	27768	natural

RdTh		228	1.91 yr	α	26778	28749	natural
		229	7340 yr	α	29461	31629	$U^{233} \xrightarrow{\alpha}$
Io		230	$8.0(10^4)$ yr	α	30820	33080	natural
UY		231	25.52 hr	β^-	33858	36350	natural; $Th^{230}(n, \gamma)$
		232	$1.39(10^{10})$ yr	α, 100	35591	38211	natural
		233	22.1 min	β^-	28588	41428	$Th^{232}(n, \gamma)$
UX1		234	24.1 day	β^-	40590	43570	natural
		235	$\leq$10 min	β^-	—	—	$Th^{234}(n, \gamma)$
Pa	91	224	0.6 sec	α	—	—	$Th^{232}(p, 9n)$
		225	0.8 sec	α	—	—	$Th^{232}(d, 9n)$
		226	1.8 min	α	25890	27800	$Th^{232}(d, 8n)$
		227	38.3 min	αe	26815	28789	$Th^{232}(d, 7n)$
		228	22 hr	αe	28830	30950	$Th^{232}(d, 6n)$
		229	1.5 day	αe	29761	31952	$Io^{230}(d, 3n)$
		230	17.7 day	β^-e	32010	34366	$Th^{232}(d, 4n)$
		231	$3.43(10^4)$ yr	α	33472	35936	natural
		232	1.31 day	β^-	35869	38509	$Th^{232}(d, 2n)$
		233	26.95 day	β^-	37358	40108	$Th^{232}(d, n)$
		233m	$3.7(10^{-8})$ sec	γ	—	—	$Th^{232}(d, n)$
UZ		234	6.66 hr	β^-	40400	43370	natural
UX2		234m	1.17 min	$\beta^-\gamma$	—	—	natural
		234m	$1.8(10^{-9})$ sec	γ	—	—	natural
		235	23.7 min	β^-	42320	45440	$U^{238}(d, \alpha n)$
		237	39 min	β^-	—	—	$U^{238}(d, 2pn)$; $U^{238}(\gamma, p)$
U	92	227	1.3 min	α	28800	30920	$Th^{232}(\alpha, 9n)$
		228	9.3 min	αe	29134	31278	$Th^{232}(\alpha, 8n)$; $Pu^{232} \xrightarrow{\alpha}$
		229	58 min	αe	31000	33280	$Th^{232}(\alpha, 7n)$
		230	20.8 day	α	31600	33926	$Th^{232}(\alpha, 6n)$; $Pa^{230} \xrightarrow{\beta^-}$
		231	4.3 day	αe	33840	36330	$Pa^{231}(d, 2n)$
		232	73.6 yr	α	34619	37167	$Th^{232}(\alpha, 4n)$; $Pa^{232} \xrightarrow{\alpha}$
		233	$1.62(10^5)$ yr	α	36790	39498	$Pa^{233} \xrightarrow{\alpha}$
		234	$2.48(10^5)$ yr	α	38100	40900	natural
UII				0.006			

(*Continued*)

TABLE OF NUCLIDES (*Continued*)

Symbol	Z	A	Half-life	Decay mode and/or % natural abundance	Mass excess (C^{12} = 0) (kev)	Mass excess (C^{12} = 0) (μmu)	Principal method of formation
AcU		235	7.13(10^8) yr	α 0.712	40921	43933	natural
		235m	26.5 min	γ	—	—	$Pu^{239} \xrightarrow{\alpha}$
		236	2.39(10^7) yr	α	42598	45733	$U^{235}(n, \gamma)$
		237	6.75 day	β^-	45250	48581	$U^{238}(n, 2n)$
UI		238	4.5(10^9) yr	α 99.28	47280	50760	natural
		239	23.5 min	β^-	50590	54320	$U^{238}(n, \gamma)$
		240	14.1 hr	β^-	52680	56560	$U^{239}(n, \gamma)$
		241–255	—	β^-	—	—	thermonuclear debris*
Np	93	231	~50 min	α	35640	38260	$U^{238}(d, 9n)$; $U^{235}(d, 6n)$
		232	~13 min	e	—	—	$U^{233}(d, 3n)$
		233	35 min	αe	37820	40600	$U^{235}(d, 4n)$
		234	4.4 day	β^+e	39900	42830	$U^{235}(d, 3n)$
		235	410 day	αe	41048	44069	$U^{235}(d, 2n)$
		236	22 hr	β^-e	43428	46625	$U^{238}(d, 4n)$; $Np^{237}(n, 2n)$
		236	>5000 yr	?	—	—	$U^{238}(d, 4n)$
		237	2.20(10^6) yr	α	44737	48030	$U^{237} \xrightarrow{\beta^-}$
		238	2.10 day	β^-	47430	50930	$U^{238}(d, 2n)$; $Np^{237}(n, \gamma)$
		239	2.346 day	β^-	49309	52938	$U^{239} \xrightarrow{\beta^-}$
		240	63 min	β^-	52320	56180	$U^{238}(\alpha, pn)$
		240m	7.3 min	β^-	—	—	$U^{240} \xrightarrow{\beta^-}$
		241	16 min	β^-	54450	58460	$U^{238}(\alpha, p)$
		241m	3.4 hr	β^-	—	—	$U^{238}(\alpha, p)$
		242–255	—	β^-	—	—	thermonuclear debris
Pu	94	232	36 min	αe	38260	41080	$U^{235}(\alpha, 7n)$; $U^{233}(\alpha, 5n)$

		233	20 min	αe	39840	42770	$U^{233}(\alpha, 4n)$
		234	9 hr	αe	40330	43290	$U^{235}(\alpha, 5n)$; $U^{233}(\alpha, 3n)$; $Cm^{238} \xrightarrow{\alpha}$
		235	26 min	αe	42220	45330	$U^{235}(\alpha, 4n)$; $U^{233}(\alpha, 2n)$
		236	2.85 yr	α	42913	46072	$U^{238}(\alpha, 6n)$; $U^{235}(d, n)$; $Cm^{240} \xrightarrow{\alpha}$
		237	45.6 day	αe	44967	48277	$U^{238}(\alpha, 5n)$; $U^{235}(\alpha, 2n)$; $Np^{237}(p, n)$; $Cm^{241} \xrightarrow{\alpha}$
		237m	0.18 sec	γ	—	—	$Cm^{241} \xrightarrow{\alpha}$
		238	86.41 yr	α	46130	49520	$U^{238}(\alpha, 4n)$; $U^{235}(\alpha, n)$; $Np^{237}(d, n)$; $Cm^{242} \xrightarrow{\alpha}$
		239	24390 yr	α	48585	52161	$U^{238}(\alpha, 3n)$; $Np^{239} \xrightarrow{\beta^-}$; $Pu^{238}(n, \gamma)$
		240	6620 yr	α	50274	53974	$U^{238}(\alpha, 2n)$; $Np^{240} \xrightarrow{\beta^-}$; $Pu^{239}(n,\gamma)$; $Cm^{244} \xrightarrow{\alpha}$
		241	13.25 yr	$\beta^-\alpha$	52823	56711	$U^{238}(\alpha, n)$; $Np^{241} \xrightarrow{\beta^-}$; $Pu^{240}(n, \gamma)$
		242	$3.8(10^5)$ yr	α	54690	58710	$Pu^{241}(n, \gamma)$
		243	4.98 hr	β^-	57740	61990	$Pu^{242}(n, \gamma)$
		244	$\sim 7.6(10^7)$ yr	α	—	—	$Pu^{243}(n, \gamma)$
		245	10.1 hr	β^-	—	—	$Pu^{244}(n, \gamma)$
		246	10.85 day	β^-	65420	70230	$Pu^{245}(n, \gamma)$
		247–255	—	β^-	—	—	thermonuclear debris
Am	95	237	1.3 hr	αe	46370	49780	$Pu^{239}(d, 4n)$
		238	1.86 hr	e	—	—	$Pu^{239}(d, 3n)$; $Np^{237}(\alpha, 3n)$
		239	12.1 hr	αe	49340	52970	$Pu^{239}(d, 2n)$; $Np^{237}(\alpha, 2n)$
		240	50 hr	e	—	—	$Pu^{239}(d, n)$; $Np^{237}(\alpha, n)$; $Pu^{239}(\alpha, p2n)$
		241	457.7 yr	α	52802	56689	$Pu^{241} \xrightarrow{\beta^-}$
		242	16 hr	β^-e	55400	59480	$Am^{241}(n, \gamma)$; $Am^{242m} \xrightarrow{\gamma}$
		242m	152 yr	$\alpha\gamma$	—	—	$Am^{241}(n, \gamma)$
		243	7950 yr	α	57174	61382	$Am^{242}(n, \gamma)$; $Pu^{243} \xrightarrow{\beta^-}$
		244	26 min	β^-e	60100	64520	$Am^{243}(n, \gamma)$
		245	119 min	β^-	61860	66420	$Pu^{245} \xrightarrow{\beta^-}$
		246	25 min	β^-	65040	69830	$Pu^{246} \xrightarrow{\beta^-}$; thermonuclear debris
		247–255	—	β^-	—	—	thermonuclear debris
Cm	96	238	2.5 hr	αe	49380	53010	$Pu^{239}(\alpha, 5n)$
		239	2.9 hr	e	—	—	$Pu^{239}(\alpha, 4n)$
		240	26.8 day	α	51698	55503	$Pu^{239}(\alpha, 3n)$

* Products in uranium exposed to an intense neutron flux during the explosion of a thermonuclear bomb in 1952.

(*Continued*)

TABLE OF NUCLIDES (*Continued*)

Symbol	Z	A	Half-life	Decay mode and/or % natural abundance	Mass excess (C^{12} = 0) (kev)	Mass excess (C^{12} = 0) (μmu)	Principal method of formation
		241	35 day	αe	53570	57510	$Pu^{239}(\alpha, 2n)$
		242	162.7 day	α	54770	58800	$Pu^{239}(\alpha, n)$; $Am^{242} \xrightarrow{\beta^-}$
		243	35 yr	αe	57169	61377	$Cm^{242}(n, \gamma)$
		244	17.59 yr	α	58596	62910	$Cm^{243}(n, \gamma)$; $Am^{244} \xrightarrow{\beta^-}$; $Pu^{239} + n$
		245	9320 yr	α	60950	65430	thermonuclear debris
		246	5480 yr	α	62750	67370	$Cm^{245}(n, \gamma)$; Pu + n
		247	$>4(10^7)$ yr	α	—	—	thermonuclear debris
		248	$4.7(10^5)$ yr	α	—	—	thermonuclear debris
		249	64 min	β^-	—	—	$Cm^{248}(n, \gamma)$
		250	$1.7(10^4)$ yr	sf	—	—	thermonuclear debris
		251–255	—	β^-	—	—	thermonuclear debris
Bk	97	243	4.5 hr	αe	58600	62920	$Am^{241}(\alpha, 2n)$
		244	4.4 hr	αe	—	—	$Am^{241}(\alpha, n)$
		245	4.95 day	αe	61700	66240	$Am^{243}(\alpha, 2n)$
		246	1.9 day	e	—	—	$Am^{243}(\alpha, n)$; $Cm^{244}(\alpha, pn)$
		247	$7(10^3)$ yr	α	65370	70180	$Cf^{247} \xrightarrow{e}$
		248	16 hr	β^-e	—	—	$Bk^{247}(n, \gamma)$; $Cm^{245}(\alpha, p)$
		249	314 day	$\beta^-\alpha$	69790	74930	$Cm^{249} \xrightarrow{\beta^-}$
		250	3.13 hr	β^-	73110	78490	$Bk^{249}(n, \gamma)$
		251–255	—	β^-	—	—	thermonuclear debris
Cf	98	244	25 min	α	61413	65933	$U^{238}(C^{12}, 6n)$; $Pu^{239}(Be^9, 4n)$; $Cm^{242}(\alpha, 2n)$
		245	44 min	αe	63230	67890	$U^{238}(C^{12}, 5n)$; $Cm^{242}(\alpha, n)$; $Cm^{244}(\alpha, 3n)$; $Pu^{239}(Be^9, 3n)$
		246	35.7 hr	α	64060	68780	$U^{238}(C^{12}, 4n)$; $U^{238}(N^{14}, p5n)$; $Cm^{244}(\alpha, 2n)$
		247	2.4 hr	e	—	—	$U^{238}(N^{14}, p4n)$; $Cm^{244}(\alpha, n)$
		248	250 day	α	67391	72350	$U^{238}(N^{14}, p3n)$; $Cm^{245}(\alpha, n)$

		249	470 yr	α	69670	74800	$Bk^{249} \xrightarrow{\beta^-}$
		250	9.3 yr	α	71310	76550	$Bk^{250} \xrightarrow{\beta^-}$; $Cf^{250}(n, \gamma)$
		251	660 yr	α	—	—	$Cf^{250}(n, \gamma)$
		252	2.55 yr (α) 82 yr (sf)	α sf	—	—	$Cf^{251}(n, \gamma)$
		253	20 day	β^-	—	—	$Cf^{252}(n, \gamma)$
		254	56.2 day	sf	—	—	$Es^{254} \xrightarrow{e}$
		255	—	β^-	—	—	thermonuclear debris
Es	99	246	7.3 min	αe	—	—	$U^{238}(N^{14}, 6n)$
		248	25 min	αe	—	—	$Cf^{249}(d, 3n)$
		249	2 hr	αe	70990	76220	$Bk^{249}(\alpha, 4n)$; $Cf^{249}(d, 2n)$
		250	8 hr	e	—	—	$Bk^{249}(\alpha, 3n)$; $Cf^{249}(\alpha, p2n)$
		251	1.5 day	αe	74380	79850	$Bk^{249}(\alpha, 2n)$
		252	~140 day	α	—	—	$Bk^{249}(\alpha, n)$
		253	20.03 day	α	78960	84780	U + n; Pu + n
		254	480 day	α	82070	88110	$Es^{253}(n, \gamma)$; Pu + n
		254m	38.5 hr	β^-e	—	—	$Es^{253}(n, \gamma)$; Pu + n
		255	24 day	β^-	—	—	U + n; Pu + n
		256	1 hr	β^-	—	—	$Es^{255}(n, \gamma)$
Fm	100	248	0.6 min	α	—	—	$Pu^{242}(C^{12}, 6n)$
		249	2.5 min	α	—	—	$U + O^{16}$
		250	30 min	α	74040	79480	$U^{238}(O^{16}, 4n)$; $Cf^{249-252}(\alpha, xn)$
		251	7 hr	αe	—	—	$Cf^{249}(\alpha, 2n)$
		252	22.7 hr	α	76980	82650	$Cf^{249-252}(\alpha, xn)$; $Cf^{250}(Be^9, \alpha 3n)$
		253	4.5 day	αe	—	—	$Cf^{252}(\alpha, 3n)$
		254	3.24 hr (α) 246 day (sf)	α sf	81040	87000	$Cf^{252}(Be^9, \alpha 3n)$; $Es^{254m} \xrightarrow{\beta^-}$
		255	21.5 hr	α	—	—	$Cf^{252}(Be^9, \alpha 2n)$; thermonuclear debris
		256	160 min	sf	—	—	$Cf^{252}(Be^9, \alpha n)$; $Es^{253}(\alpha, p)$; $Es^{256} \xrightarrow{\beta^-}$
		257 or 258	11 day	sf	—	—	Cm + n
Md	101	255	~0.5 hr	e	—	—	$Es^{253}(d, 2n)$

(Continued)

TABLE OF NUCLIDES (*Continued*)

Symbol	*Z*	*A*	Half-life	Decay mode and/or % natural abundance	Mass excess (C^{12} = 0		Principal method of formation
					(kev)	μmn	
		256	~1.5 hr	e	—	—	$Es^{253}(\alpha, n)$
	102	251 or 253?	~10 min	α	—	—	$Cm^{244}(C^{13}$, 4 or 6n)?
		254?	3 sec	α	—	—	$Cm^{246}(C^{12}$, 6n); $Cm^{246}(C^{13}$, 7n)
		255?	?	α	—	—	Cf + C
Lw	103	257?	8 sec	α	—	—	Cf + B

AUTHOR INDEX

SUBJECT INDEX

ABCDE69876543